Ref
598.2

Ref
598.2

LIBRARY

W9-BRP-338

THE Birds
OF BRITISH COLUMBIA

VOLUME 1   **NONPASSERINES**

**INTRODUCTION
AND LOONS THROUGH WATERFOWL**

THE Birds
OF BRITISH COLUMBIA

VOLUME 1   **NONPASSERINES**

INTRODUCTION
AND LOONS THROUGH WATERFOWL

by
R. Wayne Campbell, Neil K. Dawe,
Ian McTaggart-Cowan, John M. Cooper,
Gary W. Kaiser, Michael C.E. McNall

ROYAL
BRITISH
COLUMBIA
MUSEUM

 Environment
Canada

Canadian Wildlife
Service

Copyright © 1990 by the Royal British Columbia Museum.

All rights reserved.

No part of this book may be reproduced or transmitted in any form by any means, electronic or mechanical, including photocopying, recording or any information storage system now known or to be invented, without permission in writing from the publisher, except by a reviewer who may quote brief passages in a review.

Published by the Royal British Columbia Museum in association with Environment Canada, Canadian Wildlife Service.

This book was prepared and printed with the generous assistance of the Friends of the Royal British Columbia Museum, Employment and Immigration Canada, and the British Columbia Ministry of Environment Wildlife Branch.

Canadian Cataloguing in Publication Data

Main entry under title:
The birds of British Columbia

　　Contents: v. 1. Nonpasserines, introduction, loons through waterfowl – v. 2. Nonpasserines, diurnal birds of prey through woodpeckers.

　　ISBN 0-7718-8872-4

　　1. Birds - British Columbia. I. Campbell, R. Wayne (Robert Wayne), 1942-　　. II. Royal British Columbia Museum. III. Canadian Wildlife Service.

　　QL685.5.B7B57 1989　　598.29711　　C89-092228-4

Book design by Chris Tyrrell.
Cover and dedication photographs by Jack A. Barrie.
Bird illustrations by Michael Hames.
Page composition and typesetting in Palatino on MacIntosh II and Linotype 300 systems by Alston Graphics in Victoria, B.C.
Printed by Mitchell Press, Vancouver, B.C.
Bound by Northwest Bookbinding Company, Surrey, B.C.
Dr. G.E. John Smith of the Canadian Wildlife Service developed a system of computer programs to produce the species distribution maps.
Dennis A. Demarchi of the British Columbia Wildlife Branch developed and coordinated the regional ecosystem classification used in the Environment section.
The Royal British Columbia Museum
675 Belleville Street
Victoria, British Columbia
V8V 1X4

And when the dawn-wind stirs through the
ancient cottonwoods, and the gray light steals
down from the hills over the old river sliding
softly past its wide brown sandbars – what if
there be no more goose music?

– Aldo Leopold

This book is dedicated to:

Robert D. Harris
Ernest W. Taylor
R. Thomas Sterling

biologists whose work in the marshes,
meadows, and mountains of British Columbia
has preserved wildlife habitat to ensure that
the goose music plays on.

CONTENTS

FOREWORD

More than forty years have passed since the publication of *A Review of the Bird Fauna of British Columbia* by James A. Munro and Ian McTaggart-Cowan. In its day it served us extremely well. Today an up-to-date treatment of the subject is overdue.

British Columbia is an ornithological delight. It is a land of magnificent ecological contrasts, correspondingly complex habitat patterns, and a consequent large and varied avifauna. Many of us easterners saw our first Black Oystercatcher on its coasts, or heard for the first time the eerie voice of a Varied Thrush deep in its mountain solitudes. I personally cherish one magic morning when I first heard the silvery notes of a Canyon Wren come cascading from a steep cliff wall somewhere in the southern Okanagan.

Mountains cover much of the province. Their bases are deeply shaded by vast coniferous forests and their loftier peaks capped by arctic alplands, home of the White-tailed Ptarmigan. Great and small rivers swirl down deep intermontane canyons, and chains of lakes attract thousands of migrating birds. Dripping rain forests contrast strikingly with sun-drenched semi-deserts, grasslands, and glades of the southern interior. Along its ocean shores are rugged fiords, thousands of islands, mudflats, and the famous Fraser River delta. With so much diversity, it is not surprising that British Columbia has more species of breeding birds than any one province of Canada—and many that are not found anywhere else in this country. Moreover, its gentle coastal climate provides wintering grounds for birds in great numbers and variety, the envy of many a Christmas Bird Census taker in frozen more easterly parts of the country.

The birds still come and go with seasonal regularity, much as they did when the Munro and Cowan book was new, but the intervening four decades have brought great changes that cannot be ignored. Interest in birds has burgeoned with a correspondingly rapid rise in the numbers of competent observers and, through their efforts, a greatly accelerated increase in ornithological knowledge. Attitudes towards wildlife conservation have much improved while at the same time bird habitats are being altered by the pressures of human expansion, mostly for the worse. Ornithological methods and systems have been modified and generally improved. In short, a vast body of new information has accumulated in a thousand places, needing to be harvested, processed, and made available in a completely new publication tailored for today's requirements.

The authors have ably taken on the task of preparing this three-volume set. They went through the notebooks of an army of competent amateurs, the literature, countless files and specimens in museums, universities, and government institutions, and they drew heavily on their own unique professional and field experience. They sought out, stored, and evaluated not only the obvious nuggets of information, but they retained as well the bits and pieces so necessary for a truly complete understanding of the subject.

These volumes are a sound assessment of the seasonal, ecological, numerical, and breeding status of the birds of British Columbia today. Excellent range maps show not only the breeding distributions, but the nonbreeding distributions throughout all four seasons as well. The text amply supports map details with data that are definite and documented. Accounts of the reproductive cycles derive much of their depth from the long-flourishing nest record system of the Royal British Columbia Museum.

Professionals in the field of ornithology, wildlife biology, and resource management, as well as the ever-growing body of serious amateurs, will welcome this unusually thorough, authoritative, and up-to-date inventory of the intriguing avifauna of British Columbia.

W. Earl Godfrey
Curator Emeritus of Ornithology
National Museum of Natural Sciences
Ottawa, Ontario.

PREFACE

Until now, the most comprehensive treatment of the birds of British Columbia was *A Review of the Bird Fauna of British Columbia* completed in 1947 by James A. Munro and Ian McTaggart-Cowan. In the 40 years since, habitat for birds in the province has been greatly altered to satisfy the demands of an expanding human population. Our provincial economy is based on resource-extraction and decisions are made every day that alter the environment of birds and other wildlife. Frequently, those decisions are made in the absence of data that would allow us to determine the scale of the impacts on the birds dependent on that environment. As timber cutting proceeds, as mines are developed and dispose of their mineral and chemical wastes, as rivers are impounded for hydro-electric development, as access roads, highways, or airstrips are constructed, and as wild land is converted to urban, industrial, and agricultural lands, the environment for birds is altered to the benefit of some species and the detriment of others.

In the past 40 years, there has also been a significant change in attitudes towards the protection, management, and serious study of birds. What was once a provincial Game Commission has evolved into a Ministry of Environment staffed with professional biologists, foresters, and agrologists. The Canadian Wildlife Service staff in British Columbia has increased from a single biologist to 34 biologists and technicians, with professional responsibilities to oversee the conservation of migratory birds. Provincial and national parks have added trained staff to protect and interpret park wildlife, including birds. Ducks Unlimited Canada has become active in the province, devoting itself to the improvement of aquatic habitats for waterfowl, and incidentally enhancing habitat for other wetland and riparian species. The universities, too, have contributed significantly to ornithological

knowledge through the research they have undertaken.

In addition, amateur students of ornithology have become increasingly prominent since 1947. In British Columbia, the number of naturalist's organizations increased from 2 in 1946 to 36 in 1987 with an increase in membership from less than 100 to more than 8,000 during the same period. Bird-watching has become the fastest-growing wildlife recreational activity in North America (Harrison, G.H. 1979). By the mid-1980s an estimated 30 million people on the continent participated in birding activities, collectively spending up to 20 billion dollars annually (Butler, J.R. and Fenton 1986; Kellert 1985; Lyons 1982; United States Department of the Interior 1982).

Many thousands of British Columbians carry binoculars and telescopes, maintain winter bird feeders, put up nest boxes, and enjoy birds in other ways. Enthusiasts journey long distances to find species of birds they have not seen before, and many keep extensive field notes and detailed records of their bird observations (Fig. 1). By doing so, they too have made major contributions to our understanding of the birds in the province.

From all those individuals and agencies a wealth of data gradually accumulated on the biology, ecology, and distribution of birds in British Columbia. However, that information was scattered throughout the literature, buried in government and corporate files, or hidden in naturalists' field diaries. Our goal was to consolidate and summarize the information on the distribution, abundance, and other aspects of the ecology of the bird fauna of British Columbia.

We have written this book with two groups of people in mind. Firstly, it is for the professionals working in the fields of ornithology, wildlife biology, and resource management in British Columbia. Like shopkeepers who operate a business, wildlife

Figure 1*. Birders from throughout North America visited Iona Island to catch a glimpse of and study the Spoonbill Sandpiper in late summer 1978 (Robert A. Cannings).*

managers have to know what is on the shelves. The book is a descriptive and complete inventory of the avifauna of British Columbia to the end of December 1987; significant information through to the publication of each volume has been incorporated in the book as postscripts and addenda. Secondly, we have written the book for the serious amateur students of birds in the province, a good many of whom have contributed much of the data in these volumes. For those who want to know more than they can find in field guides or regional publications, this book should meet their needs.

Due to the size of the data base, which includes nearly 2 million records, and a reference bibliography of nearly 4,700 articles from British Columbia (see Campbell et al. 1979b, 1988), we have divided the information into 3 volumes: 2 volumes containing nonpasserine birds — loons through waterfowl and diurnal birds of prey through woodpeckers, and a passerine or "perching" birds volume — flycatchers through Old World sparrows.

In the nonpasserine volumes, we report on the occurrence, or nonbreeding and breeding distribution, of the 223 species known to regularly occur in British Columbia and adjacent coastal waters to 60 km offshore. For all regularly occuring species, we describe nonbreeding habitat, migration routes and chronology, and wintering and staging areas so far as they are known. For those 155 nonpasserine species that have bred in the province, breeding habitat, chronology, major breeding concentrations and colonies, and significant aspects of their breeding biology are covered. We have excluded discussions of diet, identification features, and behaviour, except where they may have bearing on the conservation of the species; such information is usually well covered in field guides and technical literature.

Also included are discussions of 44 casual, accidental, extirpated or extinct species, bringing the total number of nonpasserine birds known to occur or have occurred in British Columbia to 266 through December 1987. In addition, we briefly report on 23 hypothetical species—species reported elsewhere in the literature as occurring in British Columbia but for which, in our opinion, the documentation is insufficient.

As well, between December 1987 and the date the manuscript went to press, 4 new species were added to the provincial list of nonpasserine birds. They are treated in the Addenda to each volume.

Similar information is presented in Volume 3 for the passerine birds of the province.

We shall be forever grateful to the army of volunteers who assisted with the transfer, entry, filing, and maintenance of data in our files or who reviewed various sections of the manuscript. All are individually acknowledged elsewhere. The Royal British Columbia Museum has provided support through the many years it has taken to complete these volumes. The Canadian Wildlife Service, Pacific and Yukon Region, has been a strong supporter of the project, providing the time of staff, computer resources and expertise, financial support, and encouragement. The Friends of the Royal British Columbia Museum, Employment and Immigration Canada, and the British Columbia Ministry of Environment, Wildlife Branch, also provided financial and logistical support.

Additional major financial support, important to the completion of the project, was received from the Victoria Natural History Society, Ducks Unlimited Canada, MacMillan Bloedel Limited, the Frank M. Chapman Memorial Fund (American Museum of Natural History), the Centennial Wildlife Society of British Columbia, James R. Slater, the Vancouver Natural History Society, the British Columbia Waterfowl Society, Shearwater Scaling and Grading Limited, the Federation of British Columbia Naturalists, and Bernice Smith.

Finally, these volumes would not be as complete were it not for the efforts and enthusiasm of those who generously took the time to contribute their observations or research results, much of which was not yet published, to this project. The value of those contributions cannot be overemphasized. As A.C. Bent (1932 p.xi) notes, in his *Life Histories of North American Gallinaceous Birds:*

The reader is reminded . . . that this is a cooperative work; if he fails to find in these volumes anything that he knows about the birds, he can blame himself for not having sent the information to . . .

R. Wayne Campbell
Neil K. Dawe
Ian McTaggart-Cowan
John M. Cooper
Gary W. Kaiser
Michael C.E. McNall

ACKNOWLEDGEMENTS

This book has truly been a cooperative effort. Many agencies and organizations, and over 4,600 individuals have contributed in various ways. Tens of thousands of hours of volunteer help have been spent during the past 10 years in amassing the data from which the book was prepared. Many people have given months of their own time transferring field notes and observations to standard data cards. Everyone has had an opportunity for direct input, and the information from those who took advantage of that opportunity was used in the preparation of introductory chapters, species accounts, and the appendices.

A project of this magnitude has depended on the cooperation of all those we approached for information or assistance, and only a few disappointed us. Thus, the many contributors to this work are not too numerous to mention and are listed under 10 general categories as follows:

1) Encouragement
2) Contributors to the Data Base
3) Museum Collections
4) Volunteers
5) Student Support
6) Financial Support
7) Manuscript Typing
8) Maps, Figures, and Photographs
9) Reviewers
10) Appendices

We sincerely thank everyone involved for their assistance, encouragement, understanding, patience, and belief that the project would be completed; it was that support which inspired us to go on.

Encouragement

In the early years, 81 individuals reviewed a species account prototype and provided encouragement and constructive criticism which shaped the format that we were to follow:

W. Sean Boyd, Robert M. Bradley, Fred L. Bunnell, Tom E. Burgess, Frank E. Camp, Eileen C. Campbell, Richard J. Cannings, Ken N. Child, Myke J. Chutter, Albert R. Davidson, Gary S. Davidson, Karen E. Dawe, Raymond A. Demarchi, Adrian Dorst, Donald S. Eastman, Michael C.R. Edgell, Alan Edie, R. Yorke Edwards, Rick Ellis, Anthony J. Erskine, J. Bristol Foster, Daniel D. Gibson, W. Earl Godfrey, J.E. Victor Goodwill, James Grant, Jude Grass, Patrick T. Gregory, Edward Hagmeier, D. Raymond Halladay, Larry Halverson, Alton S. Harestad, Fred E. Harper, David F. Hatler, Margo Hearne, Daryl Hebert, Ed Hennan, Werner Hesse, Hilde Hesse, Harold Hosford, C. Stuart Houston, Richard R. Howie, Douglas W. Janz, Brina Kessel, David G. King, Dave Low, David A. Manuwal, Peter B. McAllister, William E. McIntyre, Richard W. McKelvey, Ronald T. McLaughlin, Ed McMackin, William J. Merilees, William T. Munro, M. Timothy Myres, Henri Ouellet, Dennis R. Paulson, Brian J. Petrar, G. Allen Poynter, Laszlo Retfalvi, Ralph W. Ritcey, Anna Roberts, Michael S. Rodway, Glen R. Ryder, Spencer G. Sealy, Gary F. Searing, Michael G. Shepard, Chris R. Siddle, James N.M. Smith, R. Thomas Sterling, David Stirling, Geoff E. Stewart, Kenneth R. Summers, Miklos D.F. Udvardy, Ben van Drimmelin, Nicolaas A.M. Verbeek, Terrence R. Wahl, Wayne C. Weber, Stephen P. Wetmore, Douglas J. Wilson, Tom Wood, and Fred C. Zwickel.

As the project grew—and it did grow—we continued to receive feedback, encouragement, and constructive criticism from friends and colleagues. Through missed deadlines and many problems (a few of them real), the support and encouragement continued. It is important to us that these special people are known:

William D. Barkley, W. Sean Boyd, Eileen C. Campbell, Richard J. Cannings, Robert A. Cannings, Dianne L. Cooper, Karen E. Dawe, Dennis A. Demarchi, Donald S. Eastman, J. Bristol Foster, W. Earl Godfrey, Charles J. Guiguet, Alton S. Harestad, Harold Hosford, Arthur M. Martell, John D. McIntosh, Richard W. McKelvey, Faye L. McNall, Joyce McTaggart-Cowan, William T. Munro, Laszlo Retfalvi, G.E. John Smith, Geoff E. Stewart, Donald E.C. Trethewey, Wayne C. Weber, Stephen P. Wetmore, and Phillip Whitehead.

Contributors to the Data Base

In total, 4,629 people provided information on some aspect of the distribution, natural history, and ecology of birds in the province through contributions to the following data bases: British Columbia Nest Records Scheme, British Columbia Wildlife Records Scheme, British Columbia Photo-Records File, and the Bibliography of British Columbia Ornithology, Volumes 1 and 2. Their names appear in an Appendix to each volume.

Museum Collections

The following list includes curators and staff who either responded to requests for information on specimens of British Columbia birds housed in their collections or assisted the senior author during visits to their institutions:

Academy of Natural Sciences (Frank B. Gill), American Museum of Natural History (John Bull, Wesley E. Lanyon), Australian Museum, Carnegie Museum of Natural History (Kenneth C. Parkes), Colorado State University, Field Museum of Natural History (Robert K. Johnson), Delaware Museum of Natural History (David M. Niles), Florida State Museum (Tom Webber), Malaspina College Museum of Natural History (David C. Kerridge), Manitoba Museum of Man and Nature (Herb Copeland), Museum of Comparative Zoology (Raymond A. Paynter, Jr.), Museum of Vertebrate Zoology (Ned K. Johnson), National Museum of Canada (W. Earl Godfrey, Michel Gosselin, Henri Ouellet), North American Nest Record Card Program (James D. Lowe), Peabody Museum of Natural History (Charles G. Sibley), Provincial Museum of Alberta (Bruce W. McGillivray), Queen Charlotte Islands Museum (N. Gessler), Royal Ontario Museum (Jon C. Barlow, Ross D. James), United States National Museum (Richard C. Banks, Ralph M. Browning), University of Alaska Museum (Daniel D. Gibson), University of British Columbia Cowan Vertebrate Museum (Richard J. Cannings), University of Kansas Systematics Museums (Richard Johnston), University of Michigan Museum of Zoology (Robert B. Payne, Robert W. Storer), University of Victoria (Patrick T. Gregory), Washington State Museum, Burke Museum University of Washington (Dennis R. Paulson, Sievert A. Rohwer), and Western Foundation of Vertebrate Zoology (Lloyd F. Kiff).

Volunteers

The following people gave their valuable time to assist in transferring records from the literature and hand-written field diaries, filing, producing initial distribution maps from the raw data, counting records, and proofing various stages of the manuscript. While all gave what they could afford, a few spent an inordinate amount of time on the project and are so noted with an asterisk following their name.

Matt J. Amedro, Gerry Anderson, Gladys Anderson, Ernie Bates, Marjorie Bates, Mac Beedle, Alistair Bell, Eileen Bell, Bruce Bennett, Douglas F. Bertram, Elizabeth Brooke*, Valerie Brown, Eileen C. Campbell*, D. Sean Campbell, Tessa N. Campbell, Sharon Chapman, Vivian Clarke, Dianne L. Cooper, Muriel Craig, Noel Craig, James Currie, Gary Davidson, Lyndis Davis*, Jordan T. Dawe, Karen E. Dawe*, Jesse Dunning, John Elliott*, Alice Elston, David F. Fraser, Gerrie Fyall, L.A. (Violet) Gibbard*, Margaret E. Goodwill*, J.E. Victor Goodwill*, Jude F. Grass, Chris Gray, Tony Greenfield, Barbara Gustafson, Shannon Hackett, John Haegart, Larry Halverson*, John Hamilton, Charles Harper, Lori Hogg, Maureen Holms, Joan Hooper, Tracey D. Hooper*, Bill Huxley, Mae Huxley, Doug Innes, Kate Jones, W. Douglas Kragh*, Sonia Liboiron, Renate L. Liddell, Mary Lynott, Barbara McGrenere, John D. McIntosh, Faye L. McNall*, Maureen Mills*, May Mossey, Alice Mould, Frank Mould, Angela Muellers, Geri Nishi, June Nowosad, Bill Parker, Harold Pollock, Jeff Reeve, Karel Sars*, Ron Satterfield*, Kelly Sendall, Michael G. Shepard*, Christopher R. Siddle*, Bernice Smith*, Roger Smith, Terry Snye*, Win Speechly*, Doreen Sutherland, William Taylor, Howard A. Telosky*, Herbert Van Kampen*, Audrey Viken*, Margaret Wainwright*, Jodi Ann Waites, Alma Waller, Art Waller, Wayne C. Weber*, Lillian Weston*, Nell Whellams, Eldred Williams*, Mavis E. Willox, Seff E.Wilson, Mrs. J.M. Winterbottom, John G. Woods, and Ki Zroback.

Student Support

The following students were assigned to the Canadian Wildlife Service through the Career Oriented Summer Employment Program (COSEP) and other summer youth employment programs of Employment and Immigration Canada; they assisted with various aspects of the project. Student project leaders are indicated with an asterisk.

Angela Anderson, Alistair Bell, Julie Benyon, Douglas F. Bertram, Nancy Bose*, Tom Broadley, Valerie Brown, Alice L.E.V. Cassidy, Beth Cavers, Sharon Chapman, Holly Clermont, James Currie, Allan Dunlop, Barry Forer, Kim Gage, Mark Griffin, Shannon Hackett, Jennifer Hawkin, Lori Hogg, Robin Hood, Tracey D. Hooper*, Heather Jones*, John D. McIntosh, Christine McKim, Edward L. Nygren, Ron Parsons, Jeff Reeve, Pam Stacey, Jenny Stevens, Megan Stone, Andy Tzuetcoff, Louise Waterhouse and Michaela Waterhouse.

Financial Support

The following organizations and individuals provided financial support to the project, either directly or indirectly:

British Columbia Hydro and Power Authority; British Columbia Ministry of Environment, Wildlife Branch; British Columbia Ministry of Municipal Affairs, Recreation, and Culture, Royal British Columbia Museum; British Columbia Waterfowl Society; Centennial Wildlife Society of British Columbia; Ducks Unlimited Canada; Frank M. Chapman Memorial Fund (American Museum of Natural History); Custom Drafting Ltd. (Victoria); Employment and Immigration Canada; Environment Canada, Canadian Wildlife Service, Pacific and Yukon Region; Environment Canada, Parks; Federation of British Columbia Naturalists; Friends of the Royal British Columbia Museum; MacMillan Bloedel Limited; Northwest Wildlife Preservation Society; James R. Slater; Salt Spring Island Garden Club; Shearwater Scaling and Grading Limited; Bernice Smith; Win Speechley; William Taylor; Vancouver Natural History Society; Victoria Natural History Society.

Manuscript Typing

In a document such as this, with its many authors and their varied handwriting styles, the typing of accounts for review, and retyping them again following review and revision can be a trying and tiring exercise. That, coupled with changes in format over the years put our wordprocessors to the test. Susan J. Garnham (Canadian Wildlife Service) supervised the typing for the project, cheerfully retyped accounts due to format changes, and thoughtfully offered suggestions that expedited the completion of the manuscript. The fact that Susan is still talking to us is more a reflection of her abilities than of ours. Others involved in typing various sections of the manuscript were Shelly Lear (Canadian Wildlife Service), Barbara Kuluah (Royal British Columbia Museum), and Karen E. Dawe.

Maps, Figures and Photographs

A protoype distribution map was prepared by Custom Drafting Ltd., Victoria (G.A. Reimer). Proofing of the data in preparation for map production was completed by Herbert Van Kampen. G.E. John Smith (Canadian Wildlife Service) designed and wrote a series of computer programs to edit, reformat, and summarize the distributional data and to produce the species distribution maps. Rick P. Thomas (British Columbia Wildlife Branch) drafted the figures for the Environment section, and Pamela Whitehead (Canadian Wildlife Service) the figures in the species accounts. J. Mark Poiré (British Columbia Surveys and Resource Mapping Branch) provided aerial photographs of the physiographic features of the province.

We thank the many people throughout the province who submitted photographs to the British Columbia Photo-Records File (see Campbell and Stirling 1971); we have used a number of those throughout the volumes. The photographer is acknowledged in the caption for each figure. We would especially like to thank Ervio Sian, Tim Zurowski, and Mark Nyhof for their major contributions to the book and to Jack A. Barrie and Ervio Sian who supplied the cover photographs. Jack also provided the photograph for the Dedication.

Photographs were processed at the Royal British Columbia Museum by Andrew Niemann, Burton F. Storey, and Grant R. Hollands.

Reviewers

Gerald L. Truscott was publication coordinator for the book.

Richard J. Cannings served as the publication's editor and read the manuscript . . . several times.

R. Yorke Edwards reviewed the chapter on Ornithological History. Herbert Van Kampen commented on all introductory chapters.

Dennis A. Demarchi, Robert D. Marsh, Andrew P. Harcombe, and Edward C. Lea prepared the ecological description of the province in the Environment section and reviewed subsequent drafts.

Nonpasserine species accounts were reviewed from a regional perspective by the following:

Gary S. Davidson (west Kootenay), Adrian Dorst (Tofino-Ucluelet), J.E. Victor Goodwill (southern Vancouver Island), Richard R. Howie (Thompson-Nicola valleys), Anna Roberts (Chilcotin-Cariboo), Michael S. Rodway (marine birds), Chris R. Siddle (Peace River region), Michael G. Shepard (pelagic waters), David Stirling (British Columbia general), and Wayne C. Weber (Fraser Lowlands and British Columbia general). In addition, W. Earl Godfrey commented on each account from a national perspective.

The following 148 individuals reviewed at least one nonpasserine species account in their field of expertise:

David G. Ainley, Gordon D. Alcorn, David S. Aldcroft, Bertin W. Anderson, Winston E. Banko, Thomas W. Barry, James C. Bartonek, Frank L. Beebe, William H. Behle, Frank C. Bellrose, James F. Bendell, Lawrence C. Binford, Donald A. Blood, Carl E. Bock, William R.P. Bourne, Hugh Boyd, W. Sean Boyd, Clait E. Braun, Andre M. Breault, Richard G.B. Brown, Robert W. Butler, Harry R.

Carter, Charles T. Collins, Peter G. Conners, F. Graham Cooch, Rick G. Davies, Ralph A. Davis, Christian P. Dau, Raymond A. Demarchi, Ralph W. Dexter, Robert W. Dickerman, David L. Dunbar, James H. Enderson, Anthony J. Erskine, David L. Evans, William T. Everett, L. Scott Forbes, Eric D. Foresman, Leigh H. Frederickson, Ruth S. Gale, Lee Gass, Anthony J. Gaston, Bryan R. Gates, Daniel D. Gibson, Robert E. Gill, J.E. Victor Goodwill, J. Paul Goossen, Susan J. Hannon, Brian A. Harrington, Ross E. Harris, E. Brian Hartwick, David F. Hatler, Robert B. Hay, Helen Hays, Ed Hennan, Charles J. Henny, Joseph J. Hickey, Keith A. Hobson, Keith A. Hodson, E. Otto Hohn, Richard T. Holmes, Geoffrey L. Holroyd, C. Stuart Houston, Marshall A. Howe, Joseph R. Jehl, Jr., Paul A. Johnsgard, David W. Johnston, Robert D. Jones, Jr., Lawrence Kilham, Jini Kushlan, Charles F. Leck, Moira Lemon, Robert C. Lincoln, John T. Lokemoen, David A. Manuwal, Carl D. Marti, Patrick W. Martin, Judith W. McIntyre, Richard W. McKelvey, Martin K. McNicholl, M. Brooke Meanley, Rosa H. Meehan, Heinz Meng, E. Charles Meslow, Betty-Ann C. Mosher, David H. Mossop, William T. Munro, M. Timothy Myers, R. Wayne Nelson, Robert W. Nero, Ian Newton, Isabel Ohanjanian, Lewis W. Oring, Gary W. Page, Ralph S. Palmer, David F. Parmelee, Dennis R. Paulson, Wayne R. Petersen, Brian J. Petrar, Thomas H. Pogson, Helen M. Pratt, John T. Ratti, Roland L. Redmond, Austin Reed, E.M. Reilly, Tom E. Reimchen, James V. Remsen, Richard T. Reynolds, Morley E. Riske, Ralph W. Ritcey, Michael S. Rodway, John P. Ryder, Ronald A. Ryder, Jean-Pierre L. Savard, Ralph W. Schreiber, J. Michael Scott, Spencer G. Sealy, Stanley E. Senner, Theodore R. Simons, Neal G. Smith, William E. Southern, Alexander Sprunt IV, R. Thomas Sterling, Henry M. Stevenson, Andrew C. Stewart, Dave Stewart, Paul A. Stewart, Joseph G. Strauch, Jr., Paul I.V. Strong, Paul W. Sykes, Jr., Keith Taylor, Scott B. Terrill, Max C. Thompson, Theodore G. Tobish, Miklos D.F. Udvardy, Gerrard F. van Tets, Nicolaas A.M. Verbeek, Peter D. Vickery, Terrence R. Wahl, Lawrence H. Walkinshaw, J. Dan Webster, Robert B. Weeden, Milton W. Weller, Clayton M. White, Douglas J. Wilson, John G. Woods, Dale Zimmerman, and Fred C. Zwickel.

Reviewers of the passerine species accounts can be found in Volume 3.

Appendices

The regional species migration dates listed in Appendix 1 of each volume were completed by the following devoted birders:

J.E. Victor Goodwill (Victoria), W. Douglas Kragh and Wayne C. Weber (Vancouver), Margo Hearne (Masset), Richard J. Cannings (Okanagan), Gary S. Davidson (Nakusp), Larry R. Halverson (Radium Hot Springs), Richard R. Howie (Kamloops), Anna Roberts (Williams Lake), Don G. Wilson (Prince George), Chris R. Siddle (Fort St. John), and Jack Bowling (Fort Nelson).

Initial species summaries for the Christmas Bird Count Appendicies were prepared by Eileen C. Campbell.

INTRODUCTION

GENERAL INTRODUCTION

Figure 2. *Satellite image of British Columbia showing its varied topography. It is characterized by a mountainous topography ranked in a general northwest-southeast alignment, broad plateaus, prominent valleys, extensive areas of lowlands as well as deep fiords, exposed coasts, and sheltered waterways with numerous islands (National Air Photo Library, Ottawa).*

The Province

British Columbia is a vast province of some 900,000 km² of mainly mountainous terrain (Fig. 2). It extends from the 48°14'N latitude in the south to the 60th parallel in the north. The eastern boundary with the province of Alberta follows the crest of the Rocky Mountains to about the 54th parallel, and then the 120th meridian northward, thus adding to British Columbia a wedge of terrain lying east of the mountains, in which the biota is dominated by species of the boreal and northeastern forests. Except for the Alaska panhandle, the western edge of the province is bounded by the Pacific Ocean; for the purposes of this book we have extended the boundaries 60 km to sea.

As a habitat for birds, British Columbia is far more than an expanse of mountains with their bases clothed in dense coniferous forests and their craggy heights barren of vegetation. The arrangement of a sequence of mountain ranges interrupting the prevailing winds leads to great variation in vegetation ranging from coastal rain forests that receive some 7,500 mm of precipitation annually to semi-deserts where less than 300 mm of annual precipitation can occur. In the drier areas of the southern and central interior, plateaus of grassland and parkland glades are characteristic features. Between the mountain ranges, great rivers and glaciers have carved deep valleys, several with chains of lakes, that provide corridors and staging areas for thousands of migratory birds.

Almost 27,000 km of coastline features magnificent fiords, many with glaciers at their heads. Thousands of islands, varying in size from Vancouver Island, 450 km in length, to rocky pinnacles of a few square metres, shield much of the mainland coast from the open ocean.

Scattered along the coast are sheltered estuaries where each low tide exposes stretches of mud and fine silt with a rich invertebrate fauna attractive to migrating shorebirds. The estuary of the Fraser River, even though largely converted to urban use, is still one of the richest habitats for birds in the province and an impor-

3

tant international resource (Butler, R.W. and Campbell 1987). The influx of fresh water into the sea has a strong impact on the diversity and abundance of prey items for marine birds so that the nearshore habitats along the coast are as varied as the terrestrial.

Lastly, there is the sea itself: often harsh and dangerous but a rich source of plankton, other invertebrates, and fish for the millions of seabirds that come here to breed or overwinter.

The Bird Resource: Its National and International Significance

The diverse habitats of the province support an astounding array of nonpasserine and passerine species that breed, stage, and winter, or are resident in British Columbia. Of these many are of national or international significance. Passerine species are reviewed in Volume 3; a discussion of nonpasserine species follows.

British Columbia supports more species of breeding birds than any other province in Canada. Two hundred and ninety-seven species of nonpasserine and passerine birds are known to nest in the province, about 70% of all species known to breed in Canada (see Godfrey 1986). It is also rich in species that nest exclusively in a single province. There are 65 such species in Canada, and more than half occur only in British Columbia (Bunnell and Williams 1980). Of those, 25 are nonpasserine species:

Fork-tailed Storm-Petrel
Brandt's Cormorant (Fig. 3)
Pelagic Cormorant
Chukar
California Quail
Mountain Quail
Black Oystercatcher
Glaucous-winged Gull
Pigeon Guillemot
Marbled Murrelet
Ancient Murrelet
Cassin's Auklet
Rhinoceros Auklet
Tufted Puffin
Horned Puffin
Band-tailed Pigeon
Flammulated Owl

Figure 3. Brandt's Cormorant on nest at Sea Lion Rocks, 27 July 1969 (R. Wayne Campbell). This is one of 25 species of Canadian nonpasserine birds that breed exclusively in British Columbia.

Western Screech-Owl
Spotted Owl
White-throated Swift
Black-chinned Hummingbird
Anna's Hummingbird
Red-breasted Sapsucker
Williamson's Sapsucker
White-headed Woodpecker.

Figure 4. Adult male Harlequin Duck at Clover Point, Victoria, May 1979 (Ervio Sian). British Columbia is the centre of this species' breeding range in Canada.

For another 15 species of nonpasserines, British Columbia is the centre of their range and supports most of the Canadian breeding population:

Harlequin Duck (Fig. 4)
Barrow's Goldeneye
Bald Eagle
Peregrine Falcon
Blue Grouse
White-tailed Ptarmigan
Barn Owl
Northern Pygmy-Owl
Common Poorwill
Black Swift
Vaux's Swift
Calliope Hummingbird
Rufous Hummingbird
Lewis' Woodpecker
Red-naped Sapsucker.

Ten species are of international significance because much of the world's population breeds in British Columbia. Those species, with estimates of the proportion of their populations in British Columbia, are:

Barrow's Goldeneye (60-90%)
Bald Eagle (20-35%)
Blue Grouse (40-60%)
White-tailed Ptarmigan (50-70%)
Black Oystercatcher (30-35%)
Marbled Murrelet (20-30%)
Ancient Murrelet (74%)
Cassin's Auklet (80%; Fig. 5)
Rhinoceros Auklet (57%)
Rufous Hummingbird (40-60%)

Those estimates will be refined as habitat requirements, precise range, and the ecology of each species become better known.

General Introduction

Not only does British Columbia provide habitat for a remarkable variety of breeding birds, but the province is a major migration corridor and staging area for many nonpasserine species. For example, large proportions of the populations of Brant and Surf Scoters stage along the coast during their spring migrations, over half of the North American population of "Lesser" Sandhill Cranes pass through northeastern British Columbia moving to and from their Alaskan breeding grounds, and virtually all the world's population of Western Sandpipers depend on the coastal mudflats of southern British Columbia twice each year.

The moderate climate of the south coast creates a major wintering area for many species; Christmas Bird Counts there collectively tally more than 170 species in most years. For 11 species of nonpasserine birds, British Columbia has reported the highest numbers on Christmas Bird Counts in North America:

Western Grebe
Trumpeter Swan
Eurasian Wigeon
Barrow's Goldeneye
Surf Scoter
Black Turnstone
Glaucous-winged Gull
Thayer's Gull
Marbled Murrelet
Ancient Murrelet
Snowy Owl (Fig. 6)

For another 100 species of nonpasserine birds, British Columbia has reported the highest Christmas Bird Counts in Canada:

Red-throated Loon
Pacific Loon
Common Loon
Yellow-billed Loon
Pied-billed Grebe
Horned Grebe
Red-necked Grebe
Eared Grebe
Short-tailed Shearwater
Double-crested Cormorant
Brandt's Cormorant
Pelagic Cormorant
American Bittern
Great Blue Heron
Great Egret
Cattle Egret

Figure 6. Snowy Owl at Roberts Bank (Ervio Sian). The Snowy Owl is one of 11 species of nonpasserine birds for which British Columbia has the highest numbers reported from Christmas Bird Counts in North America.

Green-backed Heron
Mute Swan
Greater White-fronted Goose
Snow Goose
Brant
Green-winged Teal
Mallard
Northern Pintail
Cinnamon Teal
Northern Shoveler
American Wigeon
Ring-necked Duck
Harlequin Duck
Black Scoter
White-winged Scoter
Bufflehead
Hooded Merganser
Ruddy Duck
Turkey Vulture
Osprey
Bald Eagle
Northern Harrier
Sharp-shinned Hawk
Cooper's Hawk
Golden Eagle
Peregrine Falcon
Chukar
Ring-necked Pheasant
Blue Grouse
California Quail
Mountain Quail
Virginia Rail
Sora
American Coot
Sandhill Crane
Black-bellied Plover
Lesser Golden-Plover
Semipalmated Plover
Killdeer
Black Oystercatcher
Greater Yellowlegs
Lesser Yellowlegs
Willet
Wandering Tattler

Figure 5. Adult Cassin's Auklet, Cleland Island, July 1969 (R. Wayne Campbell). About 80% of the world's population breeds in British Columbia .

Figure 7. Black Turnstones at Tofino, March 1985 (Adrian Dorst). One of one hundred species of nonpasserine birds for which British Columbia has the highest numbers reported from Christmas Bird Counts in Canada.

Spotted Sandpiper
Whimbrel
Long-billed Curlew
Black Turnstone (Fig. 7)
Surfbird
Sanderling
Western Sandpiper
Least Sandpiper
Pectoral Sandpiper
Rock Sandpiper
Dunlin
Short-billed Dowitcher
Long-billed Dowitcher
Common Snipe
Red Phalarope
Parasitic Jaeger
Franklin's Gull
Heermann's Gull
Mew Gull
California Gull
Western Gull
Common Murre
Pigeon Guillemot
Cassin's Auklet
Rhinoceros Auklet
Tufted Puffin
Rock Dove
Band-tailed Pigeon
Barn Owl
Western Screech-Owl
Northern Pygmy-Owl
Burrowing Owl
Short-eared Owl
Boreal Owl
Anna's Hummingbird
Belted Kingfisher
Lewis' Woodpecker
Red-breasted Sapsucker
White-headed Woodpecker
Pileated Woodpecker.

We have a special responsibility to maintain the environment in good condition and in adequate amount for all those species.

There are also 387 recognized subspecies of birds in British Columbia of which 192 are nonpasserines (Campbell 1981a). Of those, 71 are restricted to British Columbia; they are found nowhere else in Canada although they may range into Alaska, Washington, Idaho, Montana, and other coastal states. Seven subspecies are endemic to British Columbia—they are found nowhere else in the world. Those races occur mainly or exclusively on the largest offshore islands of the province, and include:

Sharp-shinned Hawk (*Accipiter striatus perobscurus*) - known to breed only on the Queen Charlotte Islands.

Northern Goshawk (*Accipiter gentilis laingi*) - breeds and is probably resident only on Vancouver Island and the Queen Charlotte Islands.

White-tailed Ptarmigan (*Lagopus leucurus saxatilis*) - restricted to Vancouver Island

Ruffed Grouse (*Bonasa umbellus brunnescens*) - resident only on Vancouver Island and the adjoining mainland.

Northern Pygmy-Owl (*Glaucidium gnoma swarthi*) - restricted to Vancouver Island.

Figure 8. Northern Saw-whet Owl at Dadens, Langara Island, 5 April 1971 (Spencer G. Sealy). This race (Aegolius acadicus brooksi) is endemic to the Queen Charlotte Islands.

Northern Saw-whet Owl (*Aegolius acadicus brooksi*) - restricted to the Queen Charlotte Islands (Fig. 8).

Hairy Woodpecker (*Picoides villosus picoides*) - restricted to the Queen Charlotte Islands.

TABLE 1

Changes in total number of nonpasserine and passerine species recorded in British Columbia from 1890 through 1987*.

Year	Non-passerines	Passerines	Total	Source
1890	185	122	307	Fannin (1891)
1924	203	133	336	Brooks & Swarttz (1925)
1947	215	152	367	Munro & Cowan (1947)
1977	251	171	422	Campbell (1977a)
1987	266	179	445	Campbell (1988d)

*Since January 1988, 4 more species of nonpasserine birds have been added to the provincial list (see Addenda, Volumes 1 and 2).

Figure 9. *Double-crested Cormorants at nest, Mandarte Island, August 1970 (R. Wayne Campbell). The population of this cormorant in the province has increased from 3 pairs in 1927 to about 2,000 pairs some 60 years later.*

Changes in the Bird Resource

A review of previous inventories of the total avifauna of the province reveals a steady increase in the number of species known to occur in the province. Table 1 shows that during the 98 years since the first published avifaunal list, the provincial total increased by 138 species. The greatest increase has been in non-passerine species, a discussion of which follows; changes in passerine species are outlined in Volume 3.

The background to the increasing number of nonpasserine species is complicated. In large part, it is the result of more and better-equipped observers, and time has provided increased opportunity for rare vagrants to wander to the province. Some of the increase, however, reflects genuine changes in the numbers and distribution of species. Major changes since *A Review of the Bird Fauna of British Columbia* by J.A. Munro and I. McTaggart-Cowan (1947) follow.

Seven species, formerly rare in the province, are now classed as regular:
Yellow-billed Loon
Brown Pelican
Eurasian Wigeon
King Eider
Hudsonian Godwit
Sharp-tailed Sandpiper
Stilt Sandpiper.

Eight species that used to nest in small numbers at a few localities have extended their breeding ranges and numbers:
Double-crested Cormorant (Fig. 9)
Gadwall
Long-billed Curlew
Wilson's Phalarope
Mew Gull
Rhinoceros Auklet
Barn Owl
Calliope Hummingbird.

Twenty-two species unknown as part of the breeding avifauna at the time of J.A. Munro and Cowan (1947), are now known to breed:
Pacific Loon
Brandt's Cormorant
Trumpeter Swan
Green-backed Heron
Black-crowned Night-Heron

Figure 10. *Forster's Tern nest, Duck Lake (Creston), 26 June 1983 (Mark Nyhof). The Forster's Tern is one of 22 species new to the breeding avifauna of the province since 1947.*

Gyrfalcon
Rock Ptarmigan
Lesser Golden-Plover
Least Sandpiper
Short-billed Dowitcher
American Avocet
Hudsonian Godwit
California Gull
Ring-billed Gull
Caspian Tern
Forster's Tern (Fig. 10)
Thick-billed Murre
Horned Puffin
Flammulated Owl
Barred Owl
Anna's Hummingbird
White-headed Woodpecker.

Several long-time resident species have either greatly increased their numbers (e.g. Glaucous-winged Gull), or have expanded their range with unknown population changes (e.g. Common Goldeneye, Golden Eagle, Barred Owl, White-throated Swift). Others have successfully invaded the province seasonally and are now of regular occurrence:

Laysan Albatross
Buller's Shearwater
Great Egret
Cattle Egret
Tufted Duck
Broad-winged Hawk
Franklin's Gull

Following a century of occupation of the province by industrial man and the sweeping alterations he has imposed upon the original habitats occupied by birds, there are now 29 species or subspecies of birds that are endangered, threatened, or of special concern. Three species that used to breed in the province no longer do so: Sage Grouse, Burrowing Owl, and Yellow-billed Cuckoo. Attempts are being made to re-establish the owl (Lincoln 1986). Two of the three species were restricted to the habitats of the southern Okanagan valley where the original ecosystems are today most threatened. The Western Grebe, American White Pelican and Spotted Owl are now considered threatened with extirpation as nesting species. The former two are colonial and sensitive to disturbance. In addition, the Western Grebe winters along the coast in large concentrations and at that time is vulnerable to oil spills (Fig. 11). The Spotted Owl is dependent on a vanishing resource: old growth forests. It is also threatened by competition from an invading species: the Barred Owl. Two of the above species, American White Pelican and Burrowing Owl, are officially listed as endangered by the provincial government. One other species, the Marbled Murrelet, is of immediate concern. Observations indicate that a large, but unknown proportion (perhaps up to 30%) of the world population nests along our coast. Not one Marbled Murrelet nest has yet been found in the province, but all evidence points to its use of commercially valuable old-growth or mature forests as breeding habitat (Fig. 12). In some areas along the coast, heavy mortality of the Marbled Murrelet occurs through the gill-net fishery (Carter, H.R. and Sealy 1984). Also, because the Marbled Murrelet concentrates in nearshore regions it is vulnerable and would likely suffer high mortality were an oil spill to occur.

Figure 11. *Oiled Western Grebe washed ashore near Coal Harbour, Vancouver, 23 February 1969 (R. Wayne Campbell).*

Figure 12. We don't know what the impact of clearcut logging is to many wildlife species. For example, while evidence suggests that the Marbled Murrelet nests in mature forests, not a single nest has been found in the province despite the fact that nearly one third of the world's population of this species may breed here. It is imperative that industry and wildlife biologists work closely together to ensure that industrial activities do not impact negatively on wildlife populations (R. Wayne Campbell).

Another 22 species and subspecies of nonpasserines are considered threatened or of special concern for particular reasons, including Pacific Loon (small breeding populations), Brandt's Cormorant (small breeding population, major localized wintering concentrations), American Bittern (encroachment and draining of wetlands), Brant (small wintering populations), Sharp-shinned Hawk (Queen Charlotte Islands subspecies), Northern Goshawk (coastal breeding subspecies), Ferruginous Hawk (localized breeding), Peregrine Falcon (interior breeding populations), White-tailed Ptarmigan (Vancouver Island subspecies), Ruffed Grouse (Vancouver Island subspecies), Sharp-tailed Grouse (Thompson-Okanagan populations), Mountain Quail (declining numbers, may be extirpated), Ring-billed Gull (localized breeding), California Gull (localized breeding), Forster's Tern (localized breeding), Thick-billed Murre (localized breeding), Barn Owl (habitat loss), Northern Pygmy-Owl (Vancouver Island subspecies), Northern Saw-whet Owl (Queen Charlotte Islands subspecies), White-throated Swift (localized breeding), Lewis' Woodpecker (reduced coastal numbers, may be extirpated there), and Hairy Woodpecker (Queen Charlotte Islands subspecies).

To those who have concerns for our native birds, the above will sound alarming, and it should. Wildlife managers throughout British Columbia are charged with, and are constantly striving to achieve, the maintenance of our abundant, healthy, and diverse bird populations. However, those same wildlife managers have little control over the very thing that would allow them to carry out their mandate—the habitat. Land-use decisions are made each day with no regard for the wildlife that shares the land with us. If we cannot give birds a place to live there is nothing else we can do for them. Ironically, in most instances man and wild birds can co-exist. It may mean that more money must be spent by developers to mitigate impacts to bird habitat, it may

mean that some habitat types that are now in short supply such as our coastal and interior wetlands will have to remain "undeveloped", and it may mean that some vanishing habitats, such as our old-growth forests, will have to be set aside in adequate amounts. But, if we are to ensure that today's bird populations and species diversity are here for future generations, those kinds of actions must take place now.

History of the Project

The project was conceived in 1972 by Wayne Campbell and Ian McTaggart-Cowan at the University of British Columbia. At that time, only an atlas of the distribution of British Columbia birds was planned, and so the concept remained until 1981. It soon became apparent that, while the atlas would be the core of the work, much more information was available that could be included. As the concept grew, so did the body of work to be accomplished and the group of authors. Acquisition and transfer of data by Campbell began in 1972 before the advent of inexpensive, user-friendly computers. Over the next 14 years, a huge data base was amassed which included the transfer of all available specimen records, literature, notebooks and field diaries of collectors and naturalists, and hundreds of thousands of observations by birders to 3 by 5 inch cards (Fig. 13). Neil Dawe joined the project in 1978 and provided important avenues of communication between the Royal British Columbia Museum and the Canadian Wildlife Service. Gary Kaiser and Michael McNall joined the project in 1980, and John Cooper in 1981. Wayne Campbell served as chairman and coordinator of the entire project.

Figure 13. *Volunteers at work sorting, gridding, and filing data cards at the Royal British Columbia Museum (Grant Hollands). From left to right: John Elliot, Lillian Weston, Herbert Van Kampen, Terry Snye, Bernice Smith, Elizabeth Brooke, and Margaret Wainwright.*

The Book

While the starting point was *A Review of the Bird Fauna of British Columbia*, the present book is a new body of information. J.A. Munro and Cowan (1947) based their book on specimen data: for every species acknowledged as inhabiting part of the province there was a museum specimen as voucher. The known distribution was based on about 30,000 specimens amassed by museums and private collectors. The input of amateur naturalists was minimal. Only 17 names are acknowledged as contributors and only 9 of those are non-collectors. In the present project, about 97% of all records in the data base are from over 4,600 contributors, most of whom are non-collectors. The data base for the nonpasserines alone totals 1,064,069 records of which 909,662 are occurrence/nonbreeding records, and 154,407 are breeding records (Table 2). Nearly one-half of all records are from the months April through July.

The 3 volumes are divided into 4 main sections: **Introduction, Species Accounts, Appendices,** and **References Cited**. All sections were reviewed by experts; major emphasis was on the species accounts. In addition to comments from researchers familiar with a particular species, each account was carefully read by 10 regional reviewers with detailed knowledge of various parts of the province, and by W. Earl Godfrey, who reviewed the species accounts from a national perspective. A brief description of the content of those 4 sections follows.

Introduction

Following the **General Introduction**, a brief **Ornithological History** in British Columbia is discussed. The revolution in bird study, from the dependence on museum specimens to the study of living birds in their environment, is a notable change. An era has passed; the collector-naturalists who established the basic facts of distribution and aspects of the life histories of birds in British Columbia are, with one exception, gone. We considered it timely, therefore, to review the history of ornithology in the province. The task was undertaken by the survivor of that transition era: Ian McTaggart-Cowan.

The section on the **Environment** of British Columbia provides the framework for the habitat descriptions used in this book. It was prepared by Dennis A. Demarchi with information

TABLE 2
Total number of occurrence/nonbreeding and breeding records, by month, for regular species of nonpasserine birds through 31 December 1987.

Month	Occurrence/ Nonbreeding	Breeding	Total
January	65,506	6	65,512
February	59,858	29	59,887
March	68,317	501	68,818
April	99,750	2,733	102,483
May	107,755	10,309	118,064
June	80,362	82,433	162,795
July	77,858	47,137	124,995
August	77,616	10,808	88,424
September	76,944	407	77,351
October	72,233	31	72,264
November	56,296	7	56,303
December	67,167	6	67,173
Total	909,662	154,407	1,064,069

on climate provided by Robert D. Marsh, physiography by Holland (1964) and oceanography by R.E. Thomson (1981). Relevant vegetation information was prepared by Andrew P. Harcombe and Edward C. Lea with reference to the British Columbia Ministry of Forests (1988) biogeoclimatic map. The ecoregions concept (Demarchi, D.A. 1987, 1988b) is now in general use throughout the province. A description of modifications to the environment since 1947 is also included.

A discussion of the nomenclature and taxonomy we have followed can be found in **Taxonomy**.

Finally, completing the **Introduction**, are the **Methods, Terms, and Abbreviations**. There, we discuss our methodology and the resources we drew upon to complete the species accounts. A complete description of the species account headings, their content, and the terms and abbreviations we have used throughout the volumes is included.

Species Accounts

The section on species accounts begins with a phylogenetic checklist of the birds of British Columbia that are covered in each volume, followed by the species accounts. They are divided into 3 categories: **Regular Species**, each of which has an accompanying distribution map, **Casual, Accidental, Extirpated and Extinct Species** and **Hypothetical Species**. Accounts for Regular Species include descriptions of the North American and world range, British Columbia status and change in status since J.A. Munro and Cowan (1947), ecological aspects of distribution with selected records for different localities, migration chronology, population estimates when available, and summaries of significant Christmas Bird Counts. For breeding species, the text also includes information on breeding distribution, habitat preferences, dates of nests, eggs, and young, clutch and brood sizes, and incubation and fledging periods, if known. Special information such as taxonomic changes, identification, food habits, and endangered or threatened status is included in remarks at the end of each account. Seasonal distribution data for every regular species is presented for each map sheet of the National Topographic Grid System. Each map also includes a summary of data used for the account and a bar graph of occurrence or nonbreeding and breeding chronology.

That is followed by brief discussions of the **Casual, Accidental, Extirpated, and Extinct Species** and **Hypothetical Species** from the British Columbia perspective.

Appendices and References Cited

The Appendices include tables of **Migration Chronology** for 10 locations throughout the province, summary tables of official **Christmas Bird Counts** from 1957 through 1984 (1988 in Volume 3) for all count areas, and a detailed list acknowledging the many thousands of people who supported and contributed to this study. Volume 3 has an additional Appendix: **Breeding Bird Surveys**. The last major section, the **References Cited**, contains a list of all published and unpublished articles which have been cited in the text.

The Future

Despite numerous field studies, there is still some 20% of the province for which knowledge of the birds is inadequate (Figs. 14 to 18; Table 3). Those areas include 60% of the Boundary Ranges, between 25% and 50% of the Southern Rocky Mountains, Central Rocky Mountains, Skeena and Omineca mountains, Northern Rocky Mountains, Fort Nelson Lowlands, Liard Basin, and Northern Mountains and Plateaus, and between 10% and 25% of the Pacific and Cascade ranges, Columbia Mountains and Highlands, Southern Rocky Mountain Trench, Nass Basin and Alberta

Plateau. All other Ecoregions have observations from over 90% of their grids.

For many species, we lack basic information on reproductive biology, populations, habitat requirements, and the manner in which the habitat is used. We hope that the summary of data we have assembled in these volumes will provide the incentive for researchers to fill in the missing elements. Man's impact on the environment, and the changes he imposes will demand even more detailed and specific information on the biology and ecology of the birds of British Columbia if we are to maintain the numbers and diversity of the avifauna of the province. That is the challenge to the professionals working in the field of wildlife management and to the dedicated amateurs who will continue to make significant contributions to our knowledge and understanding of the birds of British Columbia.

	TABLE 3		
Gaps in observer coverage of the province based on the number of grids that lack data.			
Ecoregion	Total Grids (approx.)	Empty Grids	(%)
Northern Mountains and Plateaus	133	56	42
Skeena and Omenica Mountains	60	26	43
Boundary Ranges	40	24	60
Fort Nelson Lowland	55	23	42
Northern Rocky Mountains	52	20	38
Alberta Plateau	69	14	20
Central Rocky Mountains	45	12	27
Pacific and Cascade Ranges	70	10	14
Columbia Mountains and Highlands	100	10	10
Liard Basin	20	8	40
Coastal Gap	95	7	7
Southern Rocky Mountains	26	7	27
Fraser Basin	57	4	7
Fraser Plateau	100	3	3
Southern Rocky Mountain Trench	10	1	10
Nass Basin	8	1	13
Thompson-Okanagan Plateau	37	<1	1
Nass Ranges	12	0	0
Queen Charlotte Lowland	8	0	0
Queen Charlotte Ranges	21	0	0
Western Vancouver Island	34	0	0
Eastern Vancouver Island	14	0	0
Lower Mainland	6	0	0
Strait of Georgia	6	0	0
Okanagan Range	3	0	0
Chilcotin Ranges	20	0	0
Tatshenshini Basin	5	0	0
Total Province	1106	226	20

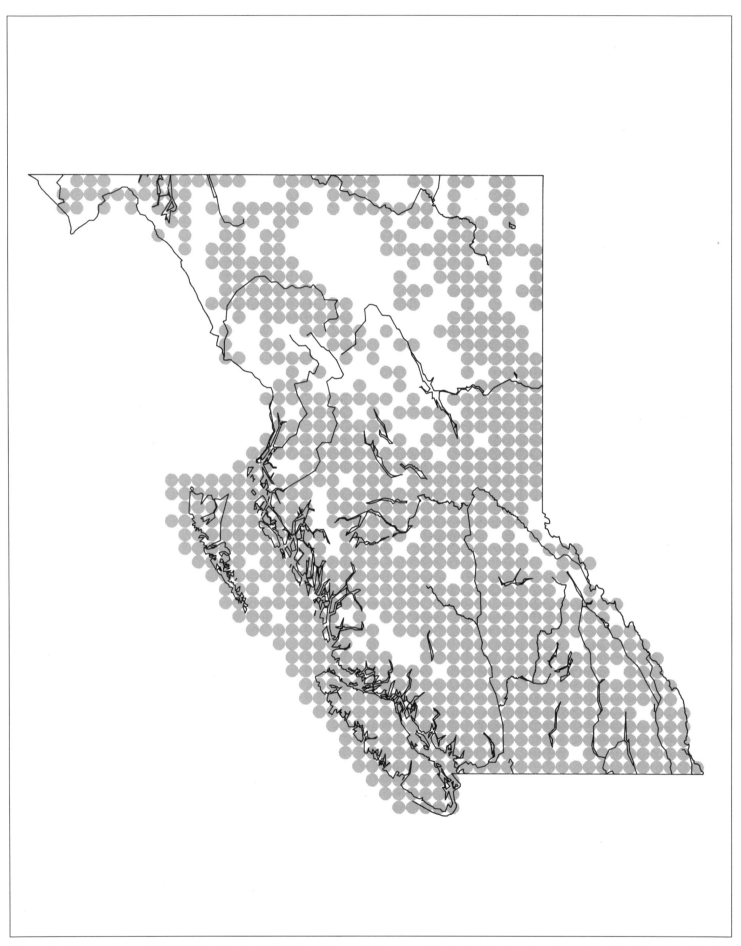

Figure 14. *Observer coverage in British Columbia. Each filled circle within a particular map grid indicates that at least one observer has visited that map grid during the period covered by this study.*

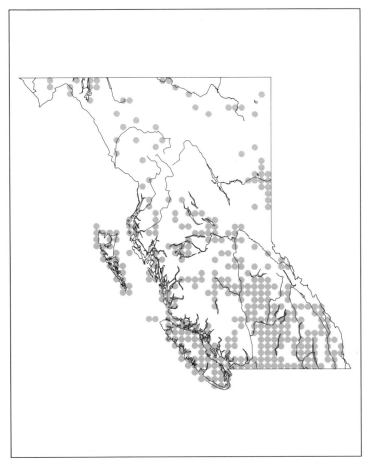

Figure 15. *Observer coverage for the spring season in British Columbia.*

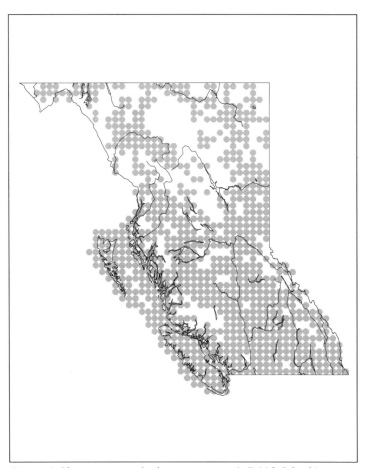

Figure 16. *Observer coverage for the summer season in British Columbia.*

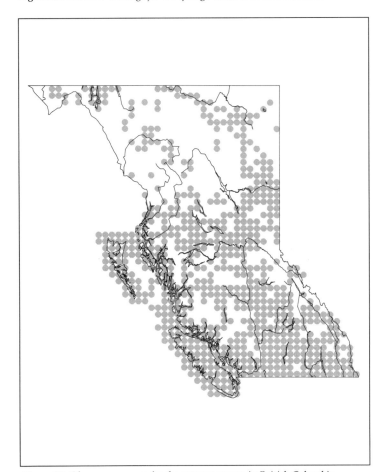

Figure 17. *Observer coverage for the autumn season in British Columbia.*

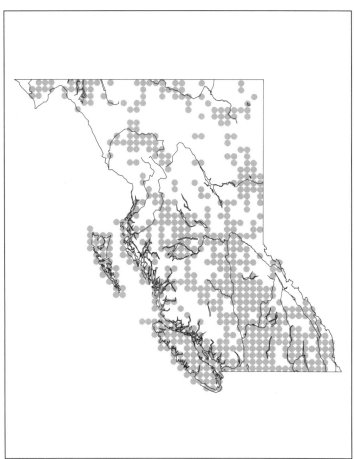

Figure 18. *Observer coverage for the winter season in British Columbia.*

ORNITHOLOGICAL HISTORY

The first questions asked by the explorer naturalist in a new land are "What organisms am I seeing and how do they relate to the creatures already known?" The answers to those questions require the collection of specimens; carefully prepared, and as carefully stored, they provide the reference point for all subsequent questions. The study of the specimens must result in the publication of descriptions sufficiently detailed that the creature can be recognized by other biologists, and the descriptions must be attached to names.

After the first two questions have been answered, it is logical to ask, "How is the organism distributed geographically, ecologically, and seasonally?" More precisely, we may also wish to know how the creature lives, what foods it eats, what are its predators, parasites, and diseases, what is its capacity to increase, how is it influenced by biological and non-biological forces, what is the structure of its population, how and what does it communicate, and on and on. Depending upon the precision required and the plasticity of the species in question, the answers to that family of questions may or may not require the collection of additional specimens.

In this chapter we review the history of ornithological investigations in British Columbia which can be conveniently considered in 6 sections: the contributions by the early European explorers, the bird and egg collectors active until about 1970, natural history societies, the contemporary observer-naturalists, university research, and the activities of conservation and management agencies.

The Explorers

The first specimens of birds collected for scientific study along the coast of what is now British Columbia were taken by the naturalists of the James Cook Expedition in the spring of 1778, in the vicinity of Nootka (referred to by Cook as King George Sound). William Anderson was the official naturalist and, although he became ill and died later in the expedition, it is probable that he was the one who made the first collections.

Fifteen species were represented and most were later given scientific names by J.G. Gmelin in the 13th edition of *Systema Naturae* and entered into the faunistic literature in Thomas Pennant's *Arctic Zoology* (1785). Those first species from our coast to be introduced to science include: Snow Goose, Bald Eagle, Wandering Tattler, Red Knot, Least Sandpiper, Dunlin, Rufous Hummingbird, Red-breasted Sapsucker, Northern Flicker, Steller's Jay, Varied Thrush, Golden-crowned Sparrow, Dark-eyed Junco, and a sandpiper of unknown species. So far as is known, none of those specimens is still in existence. If any do survive they are most likely in either the Vienna or the Berlin museums where they arrived after several changes in custody.

The next major expedition to British Columbia was that of George Vancouver; Archibald Menzies was official naturalist. Vancouver and his crew explored the coast in remarkable detail in the summers of 1792 and 1793, circumnavigating Vancouver Island and the Queen Charlotte Islands (Fig. 19). Menzies made extensive collections of the plants he saw, but, though many birds

Figure 19. The mist-shrouded Queen Charlotte Islands were visited in the summers of 1792 and 1793 by Captain George Vancouver (R. Wayne Campbell).

are mentioned by common name, no specimens from the expedition reached England. Vancouver's voyage therefore did not add significantly to the knowledge of the birds of British Columbia.

The only other definitive contribution by the early sea-borne explorers to our knowledge of the birds of the Pacific coast of Canada arose from the voyage of Captain A. J. Markham in *H.M.S. Triumph* between 1880 and 1892. Members of his crew collected 149 specimens of birds along the coasts of North and South America, a number of them from Esquimalt: Bufflehead, American Kestrel, Least Sandpiper, Belted Kingfisher, Northern Flicker, Pileated Woodpecker, Steller's Jay, Bohemian Waxwing, and White-crowned Sparrow. The specimens went to the British Museum of Natural History (Salvin 1883).

It is strange that, of all those who sailed to our coast from Russia, Spain, France, England, and the United States of America in the years between the mid 1700s and the mid 1800s, only Cook and his naturalist, Anderson, had the curiosity to collect and preserve birds for scientific study. The journals of others refer to many kinds of birds that, thanks to the work of later ornithologists and collectors, we can now identify. However, their contribution to knowledge of the rich avifauna that they were seeing daily, and indeed killing and eating, was essentially nil.

Biological exploration of the interior of British Columbia was a daunting task. Alexander Mackenzie crossed the province from the Peace River canyon to the Pacific shoreline at Bella Coola in 1793. David Thompson just entered the area from Alberta via Howse Pass in 1807; 4 years later he traversed Athabasca Pass and explored the Columbia River to its mouth. From 1806 to 1808, Simon Fraser followed Mackenzie's route through the Rocky Mountains via the Peace River, explored the lower Nechako and then followed the river now bearing his name to its mouth. All of those were explorers with a predominant interest in the fur industry and in extending economic authority over the land. The difficulties of their travels made biological collecting impossible and they added nothing to our knowledge of the fauna and flora except to record the scarcity of large mammals.

David Douglas, during his return from 4 years at Fort Vancouver (now in Washington state), used the well-established route opened by Thompson, ascending the Columbia and Canoe rivers to cross the Rockies via Athabasca Pass to the head of the Whirlpool River. At what is now the boundary between Alberta and British Columbia, he collected a small "partridge" which, in 1829, he named *Tetrao franklini* (Franklin's Grouse, now considered conspecific with the Spruce Grouse). That specimen is in the Royal Scottish Museum, and whether it was taken in Alberta or British Columbia, it was the first bird described from the Canadian Rockies. In the same publication, Douglas also described *Tetrao umbelloides* from the same region, now recognized as a subspecies of the Ruffed Grouse.

While almost no ornithological exploration was taking place north of the 49th parallel and west of the Rocky Mountains, there was much activity in adjacent American territory. The Lewis and Clark Expedition of 1804 to 1806 had traversed the entire region from the head of the Missouri River to the mouth of the Columbia River, and birds had been taken and sent to the American Museum of Natural History in New York. The American desire to consolidate holdings in Oregon Territory led, between 1853 and 1856, to a series of transects of the same region seeking the best route for a railroad. There were naturalists with each exploratory party and the hundreds of specimens of birds and mammals collected became part of the collections of the United States National Museum. One of the exploratory parties concentrated on the area between the 47th and 49th parallels and was sampling the same avifauna as that of southern British Columbia. The report on the birds taken during those expeditions, authored by Spencer F. Baird, was published in a volume of 1,005 pages (Baird 1858b). The original descriptions of some of the birds of British Columbia were based upon specimens taken by those railroad explorations.

In 1858, Lieutenant Thomas Wright Blakiston, then a 25-year old scientist with the John Palliser Expedition to the western plains of Canada, entered the Rocky Mountains via the Castle (Railway)

and Carbondale rivers, crossing the summit through North Kootenay Pass into the valley of the Flathead River in southeastern British Columbia. He followed the west fork of that river to its head and descended the Wigwam River to the Kootenay River which he followed south into Montana. He re-entered British Columbia up the Kishinena River (Haig 1980; Myres 1986) and crossed the summit of the Rockies again to enter what is now Waterton Lakes National Park where he discovered and named the lake.

Blakiston was keenly interested in birds and published 3 papers on the birds collected and observed on that first biological exploration of southeastern British Columbia. Species actually taken in the province were: Red-tailed Hawk, Spruce Grouse, Clark's Nutcracker, and Smith's Longspur. The last 2 were new records of occurrence for the province (Blakiston 1861-62, 1863).

The field work of the commission appointed to survey and mark the boundary between Canada and the United States of America marks the end of what we regard as the exploratory phase in British Columbian ornithology. The Commission began its work in the spring of 1860 and completed it in 1863. John Keast Lord was the official naturalist with the field parties in the west and did an extraordinary job of collecting a wide variety of natural history specimens, the majority of which were deposited with the British Museum of Natural History. There, the birds were identified by George Gray. The list of birds taken or recorded is given by Lord (1866) on pages 291 to 301 of the second volume of his rambling work *The Naturalist in Vancouver Island and British Columbia*: 226 species are listed. The notes on occurrence are very general and sometimes inaccurate, but this was the first attempt at listing the occurrence and distribution of the birds occupying a substantial part of British Columbia.

The Collectors
Early Expeditions

Among the fur-oriented employees of the Hudson's Bay Company, Roderick MacFarlane established a reputation as a naturalist. He appeared on the British Columbia scene in 1886 or 1887 when he was transferred to the New Caledonia district and stationed at Fort St. James on Stuart Lake (Preble 1922). His were the first specimens and notes taken of the birds of central British Columbia; they were sent to the United States National Museum.

Several little-known naturalists visited the coast of the province between the 1860s and 1880s, and each added a little bit to what was known. Brooks and Swarth (1925) mention Robert Brown and his paper of 1868, "Synopsis of the Birds of Vancouver Island." About the same time, J. Hepburn travelled by ship up the coast at least as far as Fort [Port] Simpson where he collected a specimen of the Rosy Finch (*Leucosticte arctoa*).

William E. Brooks and his son Allan arrived in Chilliwack in 1887 and began collecting local birds. For Allan it was the beginning of a lifetime devoted to the study of the birds of British Columbia, where he lived until his death in 1946.

About the time of Brooks' arrival, the American Museum of Natural History and the United States National Museum had developed an interest in the species and distribution of birds in British Columbia and began a series of collecting expeditions.

Clark P. Streator, a collector for the American Museum of Natural History, was in the province from 21 April to 15 November 1889, during which time he prepared about a thousand specimens from the Fraser River estuary, Ashcroft, Ducks (Monte Creek) and Duncan's Station (Duncan). That material was reported on by Chapman, F.M. (1890). Streator was in the province again in 1895 and 1896. At that time, he was collecting for the United States Bureau of Biological Survey in the Fraser River estuary and at Ashcroft, Kamloops, and Sicamous.

One of the most remarkable biological explorers was Edward A. Preble of the United States Bureau of Biological Survey. He began his work in our province at Port Moody and Langley in July 1897 and then proceeded north along the coast collecting at Gibson's Landing, Malaspina Inlet, Rivers Inlet, Port Simpson, and

Inverness on the Skeena River. It was 1910 before he returned and ascended the Stikine River to Telegraph Creek, then travelled overland to the Klappan Range and Thutade Lake - the first biologist to enter this remote mountainous area. He returned in 1913 and, starting at Hazelton, explored the Babine Range, Tacla [Takla] Lake, Bear Lake, and revisited Thutade Lake before reaching Tatletuey [Tatlatui] Lake and returning to Hazelton.

The year 1886 was a most important one as it saw the first interest by British Columbia in its own living resources by its earliest residents. That was the founding year of a Provincial Museum in British Columbia and of the appointment of a resident naturalist, John Fannin, as its first Director. There is no doubt that Fannin's (1891) publication—the first check-list of the birds of British Columbia—had something to do with the mounting of a most ambitious expedition in 1892 by the eminent ornithologist Samuel N. Rhoads of the Philadelphia Academy of Natural Sciences. That party, made up of Rhoads, G.S. Morris and J.W. Evans, landed at Victoria on 3 May 1892 and through the next 4 months collected at Lulu Island, Ashcroft, Bonaparte (Cache Creek), Clinton, Lac la Hache, Kamloops, Sicamous, Vernon, Nelson, Field, and then proceeded to Washington state. It is not clear whether Morris and Evans accompanied Rhoads during the entire summer in British Columbia.

As a result of the specimens collected on the expedition, Rhoads published a revised list of the birds known to occur in British Columbia and Washington. His list includes 20 species or subspecies not in the Fannin list, and he deleted 2 species Fannin had included: the Clark's Grebe, a look-alike of the Western Grebe, and a subspecies of the Yellow Warbler (*Dendroica petechia morcomi*). Both are now known to inhabit the province.

Most of Rhoads' additions to Fannin's list were newly detected or newly described subspecies. Genuine additions to the known species were the Bank Swallow, Hutton's Vireo, Nashville Warbler, Magnolia Warbler, Yellow-breasted Chat, and Harris' Sparrow (Rhoads 1893a). The planning of the Rhoads' expedition, and especially the localities visited, certainly rested upon Fannin's work and may have been decided upon with his advice.

The Canadian government was intensifying its geological explorations across Canada in the late 1800s. In 1886, John Macoun was appointed as naturalist to the geological survey and, in 1887, he first reached the Pacific coast of British Columbia. Intermittently, between that year and 1969, there were field parties from Ottawa collecting birds in the province and studying the distribution of the species there as part of the preparation of a sequence of books on the "Birds of Canada." Those years of exploration are treated later in the section on the National Museum of Natural Sciences.

One of the last expeditions from the United States Bureau of Biological Survey to study bird distribution in British Columbia was a 2-man field party consisting of Wilfred H. Osgood (Fig. 20) and Edmund Heller. They visited the Queen Charlotte Islands between 13 June and 18 July 1900 (Osgood 1901). Osgood's report was the first to describe the vertebrate fauna of the Islands in detail. Coming from the Biological Survey, where C. Hart Merriam of Life Zone fame was the Director, Osgood collected many plant specimens and described some plant associations. He identified 96 species of birds, described a new species of woodpecker (*Dryobates picoideus*, now regarded as a subspecies of Hairy Woodpecker), and named new subspecies of the Northern Saw-whet Owl, *Cryptoglaux acadica brooksi* and the Steller's Jay, *Cyanocitta stelleri carlottae* .

In 1906, the Museum of Vertebrate Zoology of the University of California turned its attention to the Pacific Northwest and began a series of field expeditions designed to produce the data required to examine the bird and mammal fauna of the little-known region. Under the direction of Joseph Grinnell, the leading student of avian ecology and evolution in North America, the museum began a sequence of yearly collecting expeditions to assemble specimens to illustrate the microevolutionary responses of birds to differing environments.

Most of the migratory species of land birds nesting in Alaska and British Columbia either winter in or pass through California.

To understand the diversity of form, colour, and behaviour the ornithologists were encountering in California during the winter, the answers had to be sought on the nesting grounds. Statistical solutions to the problems were needed, thus a large series of well-prepared specimens accompanied by insightful field notes was required.

Miss Annie M. Alexander (Fig. 21), herself an amateur bird enthusiast, offered to finance a series of expeditions to study the birds and mammals of various parts of the northwestern areas of North America. Harry S. Swarth (Fig. 22) was chosen to lead the expeditions and, from 1906 to 1909, he explored and collected in Alaska. In 1906, the expedition went to the Kenai Peninsula, in 1907 and 1909 to the Sitkan district, and in 1908 to Prince William Sound. In all of those areas Swarth was collecting and studying species known in British Columbia either as migrants or residents.

To obtain representative specimens of the breeding birds along the coast south of the Sitkan district, the museum sent an expedition to Vancouver Island during the summer of 1910. Miss Alexander herself, accompanied by her friend Louise Kellogg, arrived at Parksville on 24 April. Their camp was later moved to Little Qualicum River, French Creek, and Errington. Swarth joined the party in June and they collected at Beaver Creek near Alberni, Mount Arrowsmith, the Golden Eagle Basin (Port Alberni), Mount Douglas near Alberni, and Nootka Sound. The expedition completed its work on 30 September (Swarth 1912).

The material accumulated during those 3 years of field work was the source of many scientific papers by Swarth and Grinnell. Among the specimens collected on Vancouver Island by Swarth was a new subspecies of Northern Pygmy-Owl described by Grinnell (1913).

During his earlier research in Alaska Swarth became convinced that the Sitkan area of coastal southeastern Alaska had received its fauna in substantial part by migration from the interior rather than by diffusion along the coast. The Stikine valley met the criteria for such a migration route and, in 1919, Swarth, with Joseph Dixon of Berkeley, embarked upon a 3-month field study from Telegraph Creek down the river to Great Glacier and the sea. The results of that field work are reported in Swarth (1922).

Swarth had met Allan Brooks in 1910, and their long and fruitful professional collaboration resulted in a totally new review of the birds of British Columbia (Brooks and Swarth 1925). For the first time, life zones and faunal areas are treated and a life zone map of the province is provided; status and distribution are given for 409 species and subspecies, exclusive of introduced species.

Almost simultaneously with Swarth's expedition to Vancouver Island, the Alpine Club of Canada set out to climb Mount Robson. Arthur O. Wheeler, Director of the Club, approached the Smithsonian Institution to appoint a small group of biologists to accompany the expedition in order to investigate the biology of the region. Mr. J.H. Riley, of the Division of Birds of the United States National Museum, undertook the bird study. The party entered British Columbia from Jasper Park via Yellowhead Pass on 9 July 1911, and was collecting and observing in the province until 2 September. He collected 62 species of birds, and described new subspecies of Song Sparrow (*Melospiza melodia inexpectata*) and Fox Sparrow (*Passerella iliaca altivagans*) from the specimens he obtained (Riley 1912).

It is appropriate now to return to the founding of the British Columbia Provincial Museum and to follow the path of the contributions to knowledge of the birds of British Columbia made by residents of the province.

The Royal British Columbia Museum

The starting point for the systematic study in British Columbia of the birds inhabiting the province came with the establishment of a Provincial Museum of Natural History and Anthropology. The fledgling museum was fortunate in obtaining as its first curator John Fannin, an experienced naturalist and taxidermist with a keen interest in birds. He had begun collecting and studying the birds in the Burrard Inlet area about 1870, and

Figure 20. *Wilfred H. Osgood, 25 October 1922 (courtesy of Smithsonian Institution, Washington, D.C.). Osgood was the first collector to describe the vertebrate fauna of the Queen Charlotte Islands.*

Figure 21. *Annie M. Alexander, a bird enthusiast, financed early expeditions that studied birds and mammals in the Pacific Northwest (courtesy of Museum of Vertebrate Zoology, Berkeley).*

Figure 22. *Harry S. Swarth participated in field research on Vancouver Island in 1910 (courtesy of Museum of Vertebrate Zoology, Berkeley). He later became Curator of Ornithology at the California Academy of Sciences.*

his collection became the nucleus of the Provincial Museum. He immediately began organizing what was known about the birds of the province and, in 1891, published the first check-list of British Columbia birds.

In the introduction to that first "home grown" summary of existing knowledge of the birds in the farthest west and most faunistically complicated part of Canada the author states:

British Columbia is a country of magnificent distances - a country where modes of travel are slow and expensive . . . a country where "distribution" is a problem in itself; so much so that to obtain specimens of all our birds one must travel the entire length and breadth of the province. The Cascade Mountains form an absolute barrier to many species east and west. The Gulf of Georgia shuts off other species from Vancouver Island, the west coast of which is the habitat of others which are strangers to the waters separating the Island from the Mainland; and, throughout the Province, there occur other lines, purely imaginary, over which certain species never cross.

That is a remarkably perceptive statement of the main facts of avian distribution in the province.

Fannin acknowledges the assistance of many friends who helped assemble the data for his checklist: W.B. Anderson of Fort Simpson and Comox, James Porter of Dease Lake, Captain and Miss Cox of Cape Beale lighthouse, Allan C. Brooks of Chilliwack, R.V. Griffin of Similkameen (near Keremeos), George Hyde of Beaver Pass, and H.W. Harvey of Clinton. Even as early as 1890, there was a network of enthusiastic observers and collectors of birds widely scattered across the province.

Fannin's list includes 307 species with notes on their distribution and seasonal occurrence. For each, the accepted common and scientific names are given. The Fannin list is a remarkable achievement given the sparse population and the formidable barriers to travel and communication.

Fannin himself was an Associate of the American Ornithologists' Union and had already associated himself with the pioneers of American ornithology. He was in contact with the museum collections already developing in New York, Boston, Philadelphia, and Washington. He drew heavily on the experts there for the identification of specimens collected in British Columbia.

In 1898, Fannin revised the list with the addition of new discoveries, and published it within *A Preliminary Catalogue of the Collections of Natural History and Ethnology in the Provincial Museum, Victoria, B.C.* The new list contained 329 species.

The next landmark in the study of the birds of British Columbia was the publication by Francis Kermode, who had succeeded Fannin as curator, of a completely rewritten and updated *Catalogue of British Columbia Birds* (Kermode 1904). In the preface, he acknowledges the aid of Allan C. Brooks, Chilliwack, Okanagan and Cariboo; Rev. J.H. Keen, Queen Charlotte Islands and Metlakatla; Thomas Kermode, William Head Quarantine Station; E.P. Venables, Vernon; and Charles de Blois Green, Fairview and Keremeos. An almost entirely new cast of actors had appeared on the ornithological stage in the province since Fannin's last publication.

The Provincial Museum had meagre financial resources, but it was not inactive. In 1913, E.M. Anderson and C.D.B. Garrett spent from 5 April to the end of June on a general collecting expedition to the southern Okanagan. Anderson's report (Anderson, E.M. 1914) lists 130 species of birds, 92 of which were represented in their collections.

In September of the same year, Francis Kermode and E.M. Anderson visited Atlin on a short collecting trip during which they took specimens of 16 species out of 33 seen (Kermode and Anderson 1914).

Again in 1914, Anderson and Garrett were in the field, this time to Atlin from 5 June to 19 August. They had a successful 2 months extending the birds known in the area to 84 species, 3 of which were new to the province (Anderson, E.M. 1915).

In 1915, the museum spread its wings a bit further and had 3 collectors in the field during the summer: E.M. Anderson near

Duncan on Vancouver Island from May to July; C.D.B. Garrett in the area near Cranbrook from 5 May to the end of July; and a new name, J.A. Munro in the Okanagan from 1 May to 21 August. Each of them collected plants, insects, amphibians, reptiles, and mammals as well as birds. The total of bird specimens added to the collection was about 1,000.

That was the first appearance of J.A. Munro as a field naturalist in British Columbia. It was the beginning of a lifelong career associated with the study of birds.

Munro collected for the Provincial Museum again in 1916, in the north Okanagan and Shuswap districts (Munro, J.A. 1917). That summer was the end of organized biological field work by the museum for a period of 20 years. Canada had been involved for nearly 2 years in the First World War and the nation was reorganizing its financial priorities. In 1917, the museum's budget was seriously cut, all field work ceased, and a series of events led to the cessation of work on the birds and mammals of the province. What resources were available went into the archaeological and ethnological collections and even that activity ceased in the early 1930s.

In May of 1935, with a newly earned doctorate in Vertebrate Zoology from the University of California, Ian McTaggart-Cowan was appointed a biologist at the Provincial Museum. The museum had been so embroiled in conflict between the director and the former biologist, William Newcombe, that its reputation had suffered and its biological collections had been allowed to deteriorate.

Within a year, however, a good start had been made in bringing the curatorial work up to date, new catalogues had been opened, and a beginning had been made in bringing new techniques and philosophies to the refurbishing and extending of the museum display and educational efforts. McTaggart-Cowan also introduced to the museum the concept that the study of the living creature in its habitat was an appropriate museum activity that would contribute importantly to the educational and display functions as well as to science within the museum.

A decision was made also to reinstate field collecting by the museum. A second-hand Chevrolet panel van was purchased for use as a field vehicle and the necessary equipment bought or borrowed. In 1936, McTaggart-Cowan and his wife Joyce collected at Anarchist Mountain, 10 Mile Lake near Quesnel, at Ootsa and Eutsuk lakes, and Indianpoint Lake. The 1937 field trip was to Monashee Pass and Mount Revelstoke to obtain specimens of the birds and mammals of the Monashee and Selkirk mountain ranges.

The Peace River area of British Columbia was biologically unknown at the time and the museum's 1938 expedition was to spend 2 months between Tupper Creek and Charlie Lake. Patrick W. Martin accompanied McTaggart-Cowan on that trip. That expedition resulted in the addition of 14 species of birds to the known fauna of British Columbia. The results of the Peace River study were published as the first of a new museum publication series, the Occasional Papers (Cowan 1939).

In 1939, attention turned to the north coast of British Columbia, an area featuring a succession of deep fiords and many hundreds of islands large and small and with varying degrees of isolation, and almost unknown biologically.

Elinor and Tom McCabe had been exploring that coast since 1936, and in 1939 they chartered the *Sea Bird*, owned and skippered by Patrick W. Martin, to serve as floating laboratory and field home for the expedition. The McTaggart-Cowans were invited by the McCabes to join the field party and did so for June and July. Field camps were established at Kwakshua on Calvert Island, on the east side of Spider Island, and several adjacent islands were studied. The collaboration led to several publications, dealing especially with the evolution of the smaller mammals.

In 1940, McTaggart-Cowan accepted an assistant professorship at the University of British Columbia and resigned from the museum. At the same time Francis Kermode retired after 36 years as Director of the Museum and G. Clifford Carl was appointed to succeed him. That was a happy choice for the museum; Carl led the museum through 30 years of steady growth and improvement.

Carl's interests in the biological world were boundless. He became a talented motion picture photographer of nature sub-

Figure 23. G. Clifford Carl demonstrating specimen preparation at Victoria, 1952 (courtesy of Division of Visual Education, Victoria).

jects and used his films to promote a greater public understanding of wildlife, especially the sea birds which are so richly represented in British Columbia.

He fostered the research function of the museum along with displays and teaching (Fig. 23). He was held in respect by the political leaders of the day—a respect which led to new and much enlarged facilities for the museum. Important to our interest in the history of bird study, the research tower in the new museum provided greatly improved facilities for housing the bird collection along with offices for the increased staff and for the growing numbers of volunteer workers.

During his early years in office, Carl hired Frank L. Beebe (Fig. 24) as a biological assistant. He was an accomplished bird artist, and participated in the development of displays and in curating the bird and mammal collections from 1944 to 1946. He rejoined the museum as an illustrator and technical assistant for the period 1952 to 1974, published 9 papers, including the classic on marine peregrines of the Pacific Northwest (Beebe 1960).

By 1944, it was apparent that the increased knowledge of the avifauna of the province had rendered the Brooks and Swarth monograph of 1925 seriously out of date. J.A. Munro and I. McTaggart-Cowan began to assemble the data for a new review designed to bring together all available information and to update the nomenclature and faunistics. That work was published by the museum as *A Review of the Bird Fauna of British Columbia* (Munro, J.A. and Cowan 1947).

A vacancy occurred in the museum staff in 1948, and Carl took the opportunity to strengthen the ornithology and mammalogy at the museum by appointing Charles J. Guiguet to the staff. Guiguet, a knowledgeable and enthusiastic student of birds and mammals with a master's degree in vertebrate zoology from the University of British Columbia, had many years of experience as a field biologist with the National Museum of Canada, during which he undertook field work along the mainland coast from Powell River to the Bella Coola valley. Under Guiguet's curatorship the collection of bird specimens increased substantially.

Figure 24. Frank L. Beebe banding a Peregrine Falcon chick at an eyrie on Langara Island, Queen Charlotte Islands, June 1958 (G. Clifford Carl).

Figure 25. *Royal British Columbia Museum field party at Cleland Island, 29 June 1970 (R. Wayne Campbell). From left to right, J. Bristol Foster, Philip R. Nott, and Charles J. Guiguet.*

During that period, Guiguet's field work took him to some of the most remote and difficult-to-reach areas of the province. Significant collections added to our knowledge of the Cassiar, Spatsizi Plateau, and the Chilkat Pass areas, Wells Gray Park, the islands along the west coast of Vancouver Island (Fig. 25) and the Queen Charlotte Islands.

He published about 30 titles on the birds of British Columbia including a series of 10 important handbooks, each devoted to a group of related families of birds (Guiguet 1954, 1955a, 1955b, 1957, 1958, 1960b, 1964, 1972, 1978, 1983). He served the museum as curator of birds and mammals until his retirement in 1980 (Campbell 1980).

Carl was succeeded as Director by J. Bristol Foster, a graduate of the University of Toronto with a Ph.D. from the University of British Columbia, where he had studied the fauna of the Queen Charlotte Islands. He, too, was an expert movie photographer and had practised his art and science on 4 continents. Foster assembled a highly talented team of scientists and museologists and was able to expand the museum's area of expertise and begin the task of revolutionizing the displays as well. It was Bristol Foster and Charles Guiguet who provided the initial support and encouragement for the massive task of building the database upon which this book rests. Foster resigned in 1975 to become Director of Ecological Reserves in British Columbia.

During Foster's directorship, R. Wayne Campbell (Fig. 26) joined the museum staff in January 1973, bringing with him the British Columbia Nest Records Scheme and the British Columbia Photo-Records File from the University of British Columbia.

Campbell conceived the idea of reviewing and bringing up-to-date the huge mass of information that now existed on the distribution and the biology of the birds of the province and persuaded the present co-authors to join him in the task.

When R. Yorke Edwards succeeded Foster as Director of the museum in 1975, he brought to the task the training and experience gained from degrees in forestry and zoology from the University of Toronto and University of British Columbia respectively,

and years as a specialist in nature interpretation with the British Columbia Parks Branch and the Canadian Wildlife Service. He was successful in gaining the services of very skillful and talented people. The museum displays blossomed during his period in office. He continued to encourage scientific activity. Edwards retired from the museum in 1984. His successor, and present Director, is William D. Barkley who has supported the "Birds of British Columbia" project through to completion. E.H. Miller replaced Guiguet as Curator of the Vertebrate Zoology Division in 1980. Miller came with a Ph.D. in zoology from Dalhousie University where he studied the breeding biology of the Least Sandpiper. His research interests include studies of systematics of birds, especially shorebirds and woodpeckers. He is presently Assistant Director of Research and Interpretation at the museum and holds an adjunct position in biology at the University of Victoria.

In the late 1970s and early 1980s more exploration of the little known areas of the province was accomplished than had been done in the previous 40 years. Expeditions were made to the Haines Triangle, Kotcho Lake (Campbell and McNall 1982), Tatshenshini River and Alsek River (Campbell et al. 1983), Spatsizi Plateau, Manning Park, Cassiar, Peace River, as well as the Queen Charlotte Islands, Tofino, Okanagan valley, Wells Gray Park, and Ootsa Lake. A most ambitious program was undertaken to visit each of the many sea bird nesting islands along the entire coast making census counts of species present (see Campbell 1976a; Campbell and Garrioch 1979).

Two important developments in the study of the birds of British Columbia were born at the University of British Columbia, Department of Zoology, and transferred later to the Royal British Columbia Museum. In 1955, M. Timothy Myres (Fig. 27), then a graduate student in the Department, conceived the idea of adapting to western North America the nest records scheme organized in 1939 by the British Trust for Ornithology (see Erskine 1971a).

Early in 1955 the British Columbia Nest Records Scheme was developed (Myres et al. 1957), appropriate data cards were print-

Figure 26. *R. Wayne Campbell (left) and J. Bristol Foster during field work on Solander Island, 6 May 1976 (R. Wayne Campbell).*

Figure 27. *M. Timothy Myres, while a graduate student in zoology at the University of British Columbia, initiated the British Columbia Nest Records Scheme (courtesy of University of British Columbia, Vancouver).*

ed and a letter was sent to all possibly interested individuals. The idea was greeted with enthusiasm by many amateur students of birds and in the first year 578 cards were returned representing 899 nests of 64 species. In the second year, 60 observers from British Columbia, 3 from Alaska, and 4 from Washington state contributed 1,003 cards covering 1,606 nests of 139 species. In 1962 the name was changed to the Pacific Nest Records Scheme to recognize the growing contribution being made by observers outside British Columbia from Alaska to California. By 1966, 10 years after the scheme was launched, there were 21,243 nest record cards on file representing details of nest-building, egg-laying, clutch sizes, hatching success, and success in rearing young to fledging, for 148 species. Four substantial papers had been published analysing data drawn from the files on species of birds represented by large samples (Myres 1957; Drent 1961; Drent and Guiguet 1961; Drent et al. 1964).

Running the scheme was a labour born of the enthusiasm of a sequence of graduate students at the university. It was a large task maintaining contact with 60 or more observers each year, mailing cards, sorting and filing the incoming reports, and each year preparing a numerical analysis of the data to send to all those who had contributed observations. They were originally issued from the University of British Columbia as mimeographed reports and subsequently were published annually in the *Federation of British Columbia Naturalists Newsletter* (e.g. Drent et al. 1971, 1972; Campbell and Gibbard 1973) and its successor *B.C. Naturalist* (e.g. Campbell and Gibbard 1981, 1986). M. Timothy Myres managed the scheme from 1955 to 1958; Rudolph H. Drent 1959 to 1960; William J. Merilees 1961 to 1962; George M. McKay 1963 to 1965; R. Wayne Campbell 1966 to present.

In 1966, James F. Bendell of the University of British Columbia, the faculty member then overseeing the scheme with the assistance of Kay M. Smith, thought it would be a good idea to decentralize its operations. He asked naturalist Violet Gibbard (Fig. 28) of Penticton if she would assume responsibility of coordinating the scheme's activities. Gibbard agreed, little knowing what she was getting into. In those days, the scheme covered 11 states, including California, Oregon, Washington and Alaska, as well as British Columbia and the Yukon.

Fortunately, by 1968-69 regional nest records schemes were set up in the United States and soon thereafter Gibbard could concentrate her entire efforts towards maintaining and promoting the scheme in British Columbia. During the next 2 decades she never faltered, and her dedication was rewarded by organizing the largest regional nest card program in North America. She retired from this onerous task in 1986 after 20 years of service to ornithology in British Columbia (Campbell 1986b). She was succeeded by Margaret Harris.

At the end of the 1987 season, the nest records scheme had about 120 contributors each year, sending in about 3,000 cards. The total number of cards in the central file now numbers 150,000, covering nests of nearly 300 species. The file is available to anyone wishing to obtain reproductive data on any of the recorded species, and it has many users. It has been of extraordinary value as a data source for these volumes and has been the basis of many publications.

Major contributors to the nest record files, those represented by 1,000 or more record cards, include Winnifred and Fred Bennie, R. Wayne Campbell, Richard J. Cannings, Neil K. Dawe, Anthony J. Erskine, Violet and Les Gibbard, Ken Kennedy, William D. McLaren, Mark Nyhof, Mary and Trudy Pastrick, Michael G. Shepard, Chris R. Siddle, George P. Sirk, Gerrard F. van Tets, and the Williams Lake Field Naturalists Club.

The second innovation was the British Columbia Photo-Records File, which was conceived by Wayne Campbell. Within the museum at the University of British Columbia they were asking themselves what constituted an acceptable record of occurrence of a bird—did it have to be a specimen or an identifiable part of a bird, or could a photograph constitute such a record? The improvement in photographic equipment and the general availability of telephoto lenses was leading an increasing number of bird observers to document what they saw with good photographs.

Figure 28. *Violet Gibbard at Naramata, June 1989 (Robert R.T. Gibbard). She served as Regional Coordinator of the British Columbia Nest Records Scheme from 1966 to 1986.*

For most species of birds in our area, a good photograph with full data is as reliable a record of occurrence as a museum specimen. A decision was made in 1970 to establish and advertise a central photo-records file where the photographic records of the occurrence of unusual birds in British Columbia would be maintained with the same scrupulous attention to detail and care as is accorded specimens (see Campbell and Stirling 1971). It was popular with students of birds throughout the province as increasing numbers of them were unwilling to collect birds as evidence of their presence. In 1987 the photo-records file, now housed at the Royal British Columbia Museum, held about 1,200 prints or slides, most of them in colour. They represent 297 species of which 52 were previously not known to have occurred in the province.

Major contributors to the photo-records file have been R. Wayne Campbell, Richard J., Robert A., and Stephen R. Cannings, Gary S. Davidson, Neil K. Dawe, Adrian Dorst, Michael Force, James Grant, David F. Hatler, Robert E. Luscher, William J. Merilees, G. Allen Poynter, Ervio Sian, Chris R. Siddle, Kenneth R. Summers, and Tim Zurowski.

Other Canadian Museums

The **National Museum of Natural Sciences** was established in Ottawa in 1911 under the name Victoria Memorial Museum. In developing its mandate, it has undertaken many expeditions into various parts of British Columbia to study the avifauna and to collect the specimens essential to the development of its research collection. The first expedition of record was that of John M. Macoun, naturalist to the Geological Survey of Canada, who spent part of the summer of 1887 on Vancouver Island and collected a few bird specimens. He returned in 1889 and brought with him as field assistant, William Spreadborough, a man whose name was to be associated with ornithological field studies in British Columbia for the next 24 years.

In 1889, they collected at Burrard Inlet, Agassiz, Spences Bridge, and Kamloops. In subsequent years, Spreadborough collected specimens for the museum at Revelstoke, Deer Park, Vancouver Island, Chilliwack, Trail, Cascade, Penticton, Fernie, Elko, Midway, Osoyoos, Skagit River, Hope-Princeton trail, Similkameen River, Comox, Texada Island, Brackendale, Lillooet, Alert Bay, and Hazelton.

During those years, Spreadborough kept detailed field notes and the 1,530 specimens he took back to the museum were a major addition to knowledge of the birds of the province. His final expedition into British Columbia was with Percy A. Taverner (Fig. 29), the Curator of Ornithology at the National Museum (see Ouellet 1987). From 18 June until 30 August 1914, they collected and made observations at Hazelton and Alert Bay (Taverner 1918, 1919).

All the field studies from 1889 until 1918 were undertaken during the 3 summer months when breeding populations were present and birds were abundant and in maximum variety. In 1918, the museum introduced a new venture and awarded a contract covering the period 28 December 1918 to 26 March 1919 to James A. Munro.

In 1922, Taverner returned to British Columbia and brought with him as his assistant Hamilton M. Laing, an enthusiastic student of birds from Saskatchewan. He spent 5 months continuously in the field studying the birds in the south Okanagan and at Comox.

Laing took over where Spreadborough had left off and was the leader of all the museum's field parties into British Columbia from 1924 until 1938. During those years, the museum undertook first a systematic traverse across the province along the 49th parallel from Vancouver Island to Newgate, and then instituted a similar study northward along the coast from Powell River to the Bella Coola valley.

Thereafter, the National Museum's collecting expeditions were focused on localities presenting unusual problems. Austin Rand worked along the Alaska Highway in the summer of 1943. In 1953, W. Earl Godfrey, Curator of Ornithology, collected in the

Figure 29. Percy A. Taverner at Rideau Lake, summer 1948 (courtesy of National Museums of Canada, Ottawa).

Figure 30. W. Earl Godfrey examining 2 races of Great Horned Owl in the National Museums collection (courtesy of National Museums of Canada, Ottawa).

Figure 31. Major Allan Cyril Brooks at his private collection in 1942 (courtesy of A.C. Brooks Jr.).

east Kootenay and in the southwest corner. Later, S.D. MacDonald led an expedition to the Dease Lake area, accompanied by Ian Stirling as field assistant.

In 1964, MacDonald and Godfrey carried their studies to the Clinton, Ashcroft, and Lytton areas. The National Museum field expeditions ceased with a short stay by Godfrey at Prince George in 1969.

During the 80 years of field research in British Columbia, approximately 7,000 specimens from the province were added to the museum's collections and the information gained was incorporated in the museum's monographs on the birds of Canada published by John Macoun in 1900, J. and J.M. Macoun in 1909, P.A. Taverner in 1919a and 1926, and W.E. Godfrey in 1966 and 1986 (Fig. 30) .

The **Royal Ontario Museum**, Toronto, houses a large scientific collection of bird specimens for research purposes. The field explorations in British Columbia began in 1940 when T.M. Shortt collected along the Chilkat Pass area. Expeditions were directed to areas of special interest to them: Golden 1968; Haines Road, Vancouver Island, Okanagan 1973; Prince Rupert and Queen Charlotte Islands 1979; and, in 1980, the ocean off Vancouver Island. In 1970 and 1973, J.C. Barlow and R.D. James undertook some collecting along with song recording of vireos on Vancouver Island, Pine Pass, Garibaldi, and Saltspring Island.

Private Collectors in British Columbia

Even though the Provincial Museum became inactive in advancing the knowledge of birds and mammals in the province from 1916 until 1936, bird study in the province was thriving. A small group of ardent bird students took up the serious study of distribution in the province. The Canadian Migratory Bird Protection Office, provided the members of this group with permits to collect and retain specimens of birds after establishing their competence and seriousness of purpose.

The specimens assembled by that small group of private collectors of birds in British Columbia served the immediate purpose of increasing the knowledge of the collectors and providing them with the source material for their publications. More importantly, the specimens in their collections were available to others, were frequently used to illustrate talks to school classes and natural history society groups and eventually, with one exception, they were deposited in one of the major museums in Canada or the United States where they are now part of the data base for studies of the systematics and distribution of birds. Collectively, some 30,000 specimens along with accompanying field notes, representing about 50 man-years of labour, were donated to public museums by this small and dedicated group of ornithologists.

Allan Cyril Brooks was born in 1869 in Etawok, Uttar Pradesh, India, where his father was an engineer with the East Indian Railroad. Allan was sent to England for his schooling. In 1881 the family left India for Canada, settling first on a 200-acre farm near Milton, Ontario. The family moved to Chilliwack, British Columbia in 1887 and bought a farm in what is now Sardis (Laing 1979). Brooks was 18 then and already a talented ornithologist and expert in the preparation of bird specimens for scientific study with a respect for the meticulous detail that must accompany each specimen. He was even then developing the artistic skills which led him to make much of his living from painting birds. He became recognized as one of the leading bird artists and was called upon to illustrate many ornithological monographs. He studied birds and painted in many lands, but most of his life he spent in British Columbia, mainly at his two homes: Okanagan Landing and Comox. His travels in the province took him to Victoria, Cowichan, Masset, the length of the Okanagan valley, Midway, Newgate, Crow's Nest Pass, 150 Mile House and to Porcher Island and Port Simpson.

When Brooks died in 1946, he left a solid legacy to ornithology: 25 volumes of detailed notes on birds, largely his observations in British Columbia, a wealth of illustrations and paintings done in meticulous detail, a bibliography of 85 publications, and a collection of 9,000 beautifully prepared bird specimens (Fig. 31), now in the Museum of Vertebrate Zoology, Berkeley, California (Laing 1979).

Robert A. Cumming, a carpenter by trade, lived in South Vancouver. He collected from about 1923 to the late 1930s. Most of his specimens were taken in the Vancouver area, but he spent some time on the Queen Charlotte Islands and at Stewart. He published 14 articles on birds between 1924 and 1935. His collection, numbering 1,000 specimens, is now in the Royal British Columbia Museum.

Leo Jobin, according to his personal account, was born in a trap-line tent in arctic Quebec and grew up in the environment of a subsistence user of wildlife. Nothing is known of the middle part of his life, but he became a British Columbia game warden in 1929, stationed first at Kamloops, transferring to Merritt in 1930, and to Williams Lake in 1940. He retired to Kelowna in 1955.

He was an excellent field man with a keen eye. His work took him to remote areas where he made a number of significant discoveries, publishing 19 papers on birds between 1952 and 1955. Part of his collection (1,013 specimens) is now in the National Museum of Natural Sciences with the remainder (425 specimens) in the Royal British Columbia Museum. It is particularly useful as it comes from areas where little collecting has been done: the Douglas Plateau and the south Chilcotin-Cariboo region.

Walter B. Johnstone was born in Marden, England in 1883, and trained as a Civil Engineer. He emigrated to Canada in the early 1900s, going first to Ontario, and then worked in the United States for several years before arriving in Edgewood, British Columbia in 1910, a very small community on the shores of the Arrow Lakes. There he became the first registered big game guide in the province and ran a trapline to augment his income as a surveyor. From 1924 to 1929 he was a superintendent for L.H. Rawlings Construction Company on road building projects, including the first road from Edgewood to Vernon via Monashee Pass. In 1929, he joined the Provincial Department of Public Works as a road engineer and served there until retirement in 1948.

From childhood, he had an enthusiasm for nature, especially birds, and he soon met Allan Brooks, James Munro and J.E.H. Kelso, the keen naturalist resident in Edgewood. Kelso taught Johnstone the technique of preparing scientific specimens of birds and encouraged him to undertake serious observation backed up by written records.

He moved to Cranbrook in 1937, and lived there until his death. His notes and specimens from the west Kootenay are believed to have been destroyed in a fire, but at Cranbrook he began again and the results of his work on the birds of the east Kootenay were published by the Provincial Museum (Johnstone, W.B. 1949) as Occasional Papers Number 7. His collection of birds from the east Kootenay is in the Royal British Columbia Museum.

J.E.H. Kelso (Fig. 32) was born in Fort Bellary, Madras, India in 1860 and was educated in Edinburgh where he qualified as a doctor of medicine. He arrived in Canada in 1913 where he accepted the position of medical officer in Edgewood and surrounding district on the Arrow Lakes.

His hobby from early boyhood was ornithology and before coming to Canada he had joined the British Ornithologists' Union and had published papers on British birds. In his new home at Edgewood he found an entirely new avifauna and pursued his hobby with vigour, using collected specimens, photographs, and observations. He established contacts with the other ornithologists of the day, and published at least 9 papers on the birds in the province. It was fortuitous that W.B. Johnstone was posted to Edgewood; their shared hobby brought the 2 men together in friendship and Johnstone, in his diaries, acknowledges how much he learned from Kelso. Kelso died at Edgewood in 1932; his collection of bird skins is in the Royal Ontario Museum.

Hamilton Mack Laing (Fig. 33) was born in Ontario in 1883, but he grew up in Clearsprings, Manitoba where his family farmed. He had a natural aptitude and enthusiasm for natural history and hunting. With no obvious way of making a living from those interests, he entered school-teaching, which he practised for 14 years. He was a versatile and talented man and put his many talents to work for him during a long life; teacher, artist, author, field-naturalist, and farmer, he worked hard and successfully at each of them.

Figure 32. Dr. J.E.H. Kelso collected throughout the west Kootenay, mainly in the vicinity of Edgewood.

Figure 33. Hamilton Mack Laing with Great Horned Owl collected near Princeton, late 1928. (courtesy of Provincial Archives of British Columbia, Victoria).

His formal work on the birds of western Canada began in 1920, when he was a member of a 3-man expedition to Lake Athabasca for the American Museum of Natural History. Laing began his many years of field collecting in British Columbia in 1922, when he accompanied P.A. Taverner of the National Museum of Canada to collect birds in the Okanagan valley and at Comox. Laing fell in love with Comox, bought 5 acres of waterfront land there, and made it his home for the rest of his life.

He collected for the National Museum of Canada in 1925 on the Mount Logan Expedition and in 1929 began for the museum a 4-year traverse of the southern boundary of the province with base camps at Huntingdon, Hope, Princeton, the Ashnola River, Osoyoos, Anarchist Mountain, Midway, Yahk, Cranbrook, Elko, and Newgate.

When the depression cancelled museum field work between 1931 and 1933, Laing made his living writing, farming, and collecting bird and mammal specimens for sale to museums and private collectors. The Carnegie Museum of Natural History hired him as a field collector on Vancouver Island in 1934. Then in 1935, the National Museum of Canada began an ambitious and demanding study of the mammals of the British Columbia coast. The first year concentrated on the northern tip of Vancouver Island, with a field party consisting of Laing, Kenneth Racey, and Robert E. Luscher. Between 1936 and 1939 Laing worked from Powell River to the Bella Coola valley and the Rainbow Mountains with Charles Guiguet as his assistant. Although mammals were the primary focus of the expedition, Laing made significant bird collections as well.

The year 1940 again saw the cancellation of field work and Laing returned to the Bella Coola valley and the Rainbow Mountains on an expedition of his own, the last serious collecting he did.

His private collection of 2,000 specimens is in the Royal British Columbia Museum, and many other specimens collected by him are in the National Museum of Canada, the American Museum of Natural History, the Carnegie Museum of Natural History and elsewhere. He wrote 18 scientific articles on birds.

One of his least known contributions to zoology was his influence on the student scientists who served as his field assistants (Mackie 1985). He was a good teacher and his expertise as a field naturalist was extraordinary. Ian McTaggart-Cowan, George Holland, and Charles Guiguet not only were his students in the field, but remained his friends through the years that followed.

Robert E. Luscher, an architect born and educated in Switzerland, arrived in British Columbia in 1932. He was a keen fisherman and hunter and a knowledgeable student of birds. He particularly enjoyed the Thompson River valley both for its steelhead trout fishing and for its birds, and much of his collecting was done along that valley and in the Fraser River estuary. His field notes, consisting of annotations to a copy of J.A. Munro and Cowan (1947) covering 1949 to 1960, are in the private collection of Wayne Campbell. His collection of more than 300 specimens is in the Royal British Columbia Museum and Cowan Vertebrate Museum at the University of British Columbia.

A.C. Mackie for many years owned and operated a boys' school at Vernon. He collected birds between 1927 and 1939. His specimens are in the Cowan Vertebrate Museum at the University of British Columbia.

Patrick W. Martin (Fig. 34) was born in Droxford, England in 1915, where his father was on active service in the Canadian forces. He was educated in schools in Nova Scotia (Wolfville) and in British Columbia (Victoria). Following service in the Royal Canadian Navy Volunteer Reserve he attended the University of British Columbia, graduating with a B.A. in 1950.

Martin's interest in ornithology originated during his close friendship with W. Earl Godfrey and Robie Tufts in Wolfville in his early teens, and further interest was sparked by the Provincial Museum in Victoria. Martin's prime interest was in collecting specimens to further taxonomic and distributional studies. He made several collections from time to time, all of which are now deposited in public museums. Upon graduation from university he was employed as the regional game biologist in Kamloops by the British Columbia Game Department. Subsequently, he spent 2 years in Uganda as a consultant, and 2 years in Zambia working

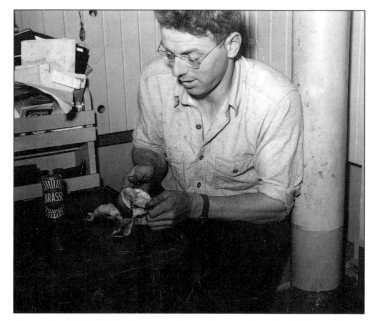

Figure 34. *Patrick W. Martin preparing specimens collected on the Goose Group in 1948.*

for the Food and Agriculture Organization of the United Nations. Upon his return from Zambia he did some consulting and returned to salmon trolling, his pre-war occupation. As an offshore fisherman he had many opportunities to observe and record data on pelagic birds and mammals. Martin kept extensive notes on the pelagic species which are on file in the Royal British Columbia Museum. He has now retired from fishing and resides in Sointula. He has published 2 important papers describing his observations of marine birds on the coast of British Columbia (Martin 1942; Martin and Myres 1969) and authored at least 20 in-house reports while a provincial biologist.

Thomas T. McCabe, born and educated in the United States, was a wilderness enthusiast before it became a popular avocation. While a university student, about 1900, he participated in an expedition to the Jasper National Park area and developed an affection for mountainous western Canada. He returned again when he and his bride undertook a canoe trip from Summit Lake down the Peace River, a trip which ended tragically when they capsized in the rapids and she drowned.

He came to Canada again in 1915 to enlist in the Canadian army for service in the war then raging in Europe. After the war he married **Elinor Bowles**, and in 1920, suffering from war-induced disabilities, he and his wife came to British Columbia. They took up residence at Bowron Lake near Barkerville, British Columbia.

By 1925, they had acquired property at Indianpoint Lake, 11 km by trail from the end of the nearest road, and there built a fine log house which was to be their home for the next 26 years. Inevitably Tom McCabe became interested in the abundant and diverse large mammals of the region, but it was Elinor who introduced him to the fascination of bird study. As with everything he did, Tom McCabe grasped the new area of interest with passion. He and Elinor began bird-banding, field observations, and collecting specimens.

Their interest in wildlife led to correspondence with Joseph Grinnell and Alden H. Miller of the Museum of Vertebrate Zoology, Berkeley, California, and thus to a visit there. The McCabes began sending specimens of birds and mammals to the museum in California and dividing their lives into summers spent collecting in various parts of British Columbia and winters at the museum. There they were provided with an office and space to store their collection.

Much of their collecting was done at Indianpoint Lake and at various points in the Cariboo district. The earliest specimens from Indianpoint Lake or Bowron Lake localities were collected in 1928. In 1932, the McCabes spent 4 months collecting birds and

Figure 35. *A series of Parasitic Jaegers collected by Thomas T. McCabe and Kenneth Racey at Spanish Banks and the Steveston Lightship, October 1937 (Kenneth Racey).*

Figure 36. *Ian McTaggart-Cowan on Mayne Island, summer 1976 (Joyce S. McTaggart-Cowan).*

mammals in the little known parts of the western Chilcotin, including Alexis Creek, Chezacut, Anahim Lake, Hotnarko River, and the Rainbow Mountains. They returned again in 1933.

The most adventurous and scientifically productive expeditions by Elinor and Tom McCabe were those along the coast of British Columbia from 1936 to 1939 (Fig. 35). Travelling by chartered power boat they collected birds and mammals on some 50 islands between Queen Charlotte Strait and Dixon Entrance and on the adjacent mainland. Collecting and preparing specimens of small mammals was the major preoccupation, but many bird specimens and much new information were obtained (see McCabe, T.T. and Cowan 1945).

The McCabe's enthusiasm then turned to the flora of the areas they were studying in British Columbia and many thousands of herbarium sheets of plants were deposited with the University of California, Department of Botany, but they made additions to the bird collection until 1941.

Tom McCabe died in 1948, his wife several years later. Their bird collection of 4,700 specimens from British Columbia was given to the Museum of Comparative Zoology at Harvard University (Dickinson 1953). Their publications on the birds of the province and adjacent regions include 19 titles.

Ian McTaggart-Cowan (Fig. 36) was born in Edinburgh, Scotland in 1910, and came to Vancouver with his parents in 1913. His parents encouraged a delight in, and curiosity for, natural history, and as a student in North Vancouver he met Kenneth Racey, who introduced him to the finer points of the study of birds and mammals.

Graduating in biology from the University of British Columbia in 1932, he proceeded to the University of California at Berkeley where he studied under the noted ecologist and ornithologist Joseph Grinnell. With his Ph.D. studies completed, he returned to British Columbia in May, 1935, as a biologist on the staff of the British Columbia Provincial Museum. In 1936, he and Joyce Stewart Racey were married, and from then on they worked in the field as a team whenever circumstances permitted. McTaggart-Cowan established close working relations with the British Columbia Game Commission and its field officers and began collaborative research on the black-tailed deer.

In 1940, he was appointed Assistant Professor of Zoology at the University of British Columbia and instituted courses in vertebrate zoology and wildlife biology which he taught for 36 years. His personal collection of birds and mammals became the nucleus of the Museum of Vertebrate Zoology (now the Cowan Vertebrate Museum) of the university, which he directed until 1963. During many years of field-work in British Columbia and

elsewhere he continued to add to the museum's collections for research and teaching.

Serving successively as Professor of Zoology, Head of the Department of Zoology, and Dean of the Faculty of Graduate Studies, McTaggart-Cowan also taught and continued his research. During 36 years at the university, approximately 100 graduate students studied under his direction. His bibliography includes 40 titles on the systematics, distribution, biology, and conservation of birds. He retired from the university in 1976, and he and his wife returned to Victoria where they maintain an active retirement heavily involved with conservation and the study of birds and mammals.

James Alexander Munro (Fig. 37) was born in Kildonan, Manitoba in 1883, but lived his childhood in the Toronto area, where he developed a life-long interest in birds. In 1910, he moved to Okanagan Landing where he built a home on the lakeshore and began his 48 years of association with the birds of British Columbia.

In the early years, he supported himself as an orchardist and professional field collector for the museums in Canada and the United States which eagerly sought his beautifully prepared specimens. In 1920, he was appointed Chief Federal Migratory Bird Officer for the western provinces—a position arising out of the Migratory Birds Convention Act of 1916. His responsibility for the next 13 years extended over the 4 western provinces. After 1933, Munro concentrated on the birds of British Columbia with special emphasis on the waterfowl.

He was a close associate of all the active ornithologists in the province and an important influence in the introduction of nature study in the schools as well as on the attitude of government and citizens to the conservation of wildlife. His more than 175 published papers included 16 monographs on species of waterfowl nesting in British Columbia, 6 regional faunistic studies and, in association with McTaggart-Cowan, the 1947 *A Review of the Bird Fauna of British Columbia.*

Munro's most intensive research was undertaken in the Okanagan valley, the Cariboo district, the Nechako River valley, Departure Bay on Vancouver Island, and the Creston area. He conceived the idea and was largely instrumental in the achievement of the Creston Valley Wildlife Management Area, the finest wildlife management area in British Columbia. A memorial to his honour stands by the refuge entrance at Summit Creek.

Munro retired in 1949, but continued studying birds until his death in 1959. His collection of about 8,500 specimens, along with his field notes, is in the Royal Ontario Museum (Carl 1959; Baillie 1969).

Figure 37. *James A. Munro , the first Chief Federal Migratory Bird Officer for western Canada.*

He was one of the founding members of the British Columbia Ornithologists' Union and the Burrard Field-Naturalist Club. Enthusiastic, knowledgeable, and friendly, he was on good terms with all his contemporaries and served to bridge some of the tensions concerning bird collecting that developed within the group of ornithologists and bird watchers.

He was a manufacturers' agent serving the mining and logging industries and built up a wide circle of friends among people in the hinterland. Racey was also a superb field naturalist and preparator of study specimens of birds and mammals, and his collection was of the highest quality.

Most of his collecting was done near his family's summer retreat on Alta Lake, and near their 20-acre farm at Huntingdon, but he also collected at Pavilion, Kamloops, the Okanagan valley and on Vancouver Island. In 1931, he carried out a 4-month collecting expedition with McTaggart-Cowan as his assistant. The month of May was devoted to the Tofino area, early June at Alberni and at Green Mountain on the Nanaimo River. July was spent at Osoyoos Lake and Anarchist Mountain and August at Chezacut Lake. He continued his collecting and study of birds until his death in May 1959.

His bibliography includes 29 titles, most of which are on the birds of British Columbia. His collection of 3,000 specimens of birds is part of the Cowan Vertebrate Museum at the University of British Columbia. His notebooks are in the McTaggart-Cowan library.

Theodora and **John F. Stanwell-Fletcher.** The Stanwell-Fletchers (Fig. 39) wrote to McTaggart-Cowan in the spring of 1936, seeking advice on a region in northern British Columbia that would offer them an outstanding wilderness experience. Their proposal was to reside in the region for at least 2 years, while they studied the wildlife and flora of the surrounding area.

Wilfred J. Plowden-Wardlaw lived in Vancouver from 1940 to 1945 and from 1960 to the present. He collected birds in British Columbia from 1940 to 1945 and from 1964 to 1969, primarily in the southwestern corner of the province and in the Okanagan valley. About 1,000 of his specimens are in the Cowan Vertebrate Museum at the University of British Columbia, and about 400 in the Australian Museum, Sydney, New South Wales. He has published 2 articles on birds in British Columbia.

Kenneth Racey (Fig. 38) was born on Isle d'Orleans, Quebec on 20 August 1882. He came to British Columbia in 1909, and established his home at Barnet on the shore of Burrard Inlet near where Port Moody now stands. He brought with him an interest in birds and mammals which he maintained throughout his life. The first entry into his diary making reference to bird collecting is in January, 1918.

Figure 38. *Kenneth Racey, a founding member of the British Columbia Ornithologists' Union, collected primarily throughout southwestern British Columbia.*

Figure 39. *Theodora Stanwell-Fletcher near Tetana (top) and John Stanwell-Fletcher in the Omineca Mountains collecting mammals, 1938. They are best known for their biological investigations of the Driftwood River area.*

The valley of the Driftwood River was decided upon, and in the summer of 1937, they built a cabin on Tetana Lake and used it as their base until 1941. Their collections of birds, mammals, and plants were given to the British Columbia Provincial Museum. A checklist for the region was published as an appendix to the book *Driftwood Valley* by Theodora Stanwell-Fletcher, 1946, and a detailed faunal study was produced as Occasional Paper No. 4 of the British Columbia Provincial Museum (Stanwell-Fletcher and Stanwell-Fletcher 1943).

Figure 40. Ronald McDonald Stewart made many additions to our knowledge of the birds of the Queen Charlotte Islands.

Ronald McDonald Stewart (Fig. 40) was born in England in 1881 and schooled there until the age of 16 when he left for Sydney, Australia to attend Agricultural College. He arrived in British Columbia in 1907, living first in the Okanagan where he met Allan Brooks and found in him a kindred spirit devoted to hunting, fishing, and the study of birds. It was Brooks' influence that started Stewart collecting bird specimens for serious study.

He arrived in Comox in late 1907, and after the First World War was employed first by the British Columbia Forest Service and later as a game warden by the Game Branch. When Hamilton Laing arrived in Comox in 1922, he and Stewart became good friends and field companions.

In 1926, Stewart transferred to Chilliwack where he was responsible for the McGillivray Creek Game Reserve. He moved to Atlin in 1931 where he found himself in an area where the bird life was little known. He was posted to Masset in 1936 and retired there in 1938. He loved the Queen Charlotte Islands and during his years of retirement made many significant additions to knowledge of birds there.

He died 3 May 1958 in Queen Charlotte City. His collection of 1,500 specimens of birds was left to the Royal British Columbia Museum where it provides a most useful addition because of its wealth of specimens from Atlin and the Queen Charlotte Islands.

J.W. Wynne was a farmer, orchardist and student of birds living at Enderby. We have no details as to his arrival there. The first entry in his bird notebooks, made 24 February 1926, refers to the sighting of the first robin of the year. From then until 1953, he recorded dates of spring arrival, nesting, and migratory passage of birds at Enderby. He gave his collection of birds and eggs to the Cowan Vertebrate Museum at the University of British Columbia.

Oologists

Through a period of about 90 years beginning in the 1880s, a small group of bird enthusiasts concentrated their attention on the nesting of birds in British Columbia. They built up small collections of nests and eggs to document their discoveries. Each of them was required by the Canadian Wildlife Service to maintain full data for each clutch of eggs collected. Most of the specimens and data are now in public museums.

Prior to the inception of the British Columbia Nest Records Scheme in the mid 1950s, much of what was known about the nesting of birds in the province arose from their collections. With the success of the nest records scheme, and changing attitudes towards collecting, the Canadian Wildlife Service ceased issuing permits to private individuals in 1971. Today permits are issued only to recognized museums and occasionally to researchers for scientific purposes. Major oologists included:

Robert Wayne Campbell was born in Edmonton, Alberta in 1942 and came to British Columbia with his parents in 1944. He lived in Burnaby from 1948 to 1969, and in Richmond from 1969 to 1973, then moved to Victoria where he presently resides. His early interest in wildlife was stimulated during fishing and hunting trips with his father, and bird-watching forays with his grandfather.

After graduating from high school, he worked at various jobs including, from 1964 to 1969, as a seasonal park naturalist with the British Columbia Parks Branch at Mitlenatch Island, Miracle Beach, Rathtrevor Beach, Alice Lake, and Long Beach. In 1969, he joined the staff at the University of British Columbia as Curator of the Vertebrate Museum in the Department of Zoology where he stayed through 1972. Also, during that period, he was consulting ornithologist with the Canadian Arctic Pipeline Studies. In 1973 he joined the Provincial Museum where he remains today as Curator of Ornithology.

In the late 1950s, he was introduced to oology by Arthur L. Meugens and John K. Cooper and during the next decade collected throughout the province. His collection (Fig. 41), much of which is in the Royal British Columbia Museum, included about 350 clutches of 162 species. Also, during this period, he banded nearly 75,000 birds, mostly colonial seabirds.

He earned a B.Sc. degree from the University of Victoria and his M.Sc. from the University of Washington. His research interests include the feeding ecology of raptors, distribution and migration of birds, and population dynamics of marine birds. He has written over 300 scientific papers, reports, popular articles, and books on British Columbia vertebrates and is a favourite public speaker on the birds in the province.

John Kennedy Cooper was born in Wingham, Ontario in 1909 and lived in Star City, Saskatchewan and Kamloops before moving to Surrey with his family in the 1920s. He spent his entire adult life building a successful real estate business based in New Westminster. He was an avid outdoorsman with a deep interest in nature. He collected butterflies in the 1920s and 1930s but turned to bird-watching and egg-collecting (Fig. 42; see Fig. 43) after meeting Walter S. Maguire. After collecting for Maguire and Arthur L. Meugens for a few years, he began his own egg collection in 1954. By 1971, when permits were no longer issued, he had amassed one of the largest private collections in British Columbia, totalling 400 clutches of 190 species.

Between 1954 and 1971, virtually every weekend from late April to early July, including annual vacation in June, was spent looking for and collecting birds' eggs. On every trip he was accompanied by his wife Louise and son John, who helped build the collection. Major collecting areas included the southern Okanagan valley, Chilcotin-Cariboo region, Fraser Lowlands, and extreme northwestern British Columbia.

Cooper collected with his good friends D.L. Frost and A.L. Meugens and also collaborated with G.R. Ryder and R.W. Campbell about oological matters. He published one paper providing details of the first known nesting of the White-headed Woodpecker in Canada (Cooper, J.K. 1969). He died in 1982; his collection is still held by the family.

Salomon John Darcus was a fruit grower at Penticton and an avid collector of birds' nests and eggs, but we have been unable to find biographical data. He was most active in the southern Okanagan in the 1920s and 1930s but made one trip to Langara Island, Queen Charlotte Islands, where he believed he had found nests of the Marbled Murrelet (Darcus 1927).

Figure 41. *R. Wayne Campbell showing the Kennedy brothers, Ken, Bruce, and Ian, part of his oological collection, April 1966 (Don Timbrell).*

Figure 42. *John K. Cooper collecting Redhead eggs at Blue Lake, Richter Pass, June 1960 (H. Shirley Parsons).*

Figure 43. *The last of the private oologists clearing eggs at Bridge Lake, June 1959 (Louise V. Cooper). Left to right: Arthur L. Meugens, David L. Frost, and John K. Cooper.*

His collection was dispersed to several museums, notable portions of which are in the Western Foundation of Vertebrate Zoology, the Delaware Museum of Natural History, the Royal British Columbia Museum (140 clutches) and the Cowan Vertebrate Museum (26 clutches). He published 13 papers regarding birds in the province.

David Lawrence Frost (Fig. 43) was born in Surrey, British Columbia in 1910 where he grew up on the family farm. He worked most of his adult life as a trapper and logger in remote areas at Adams Lake, north of Kamloops. He began serious birdwatching with his close friend J.K. Cooper in the 1950s. He collected eggs from 1956 to 1971 and donated his collection of 200 clutches representing 140 species to the Royal British Columbia Museum in 1980. Major collecting areas were the Fraser River valley, Keremeos, Richter Pass, Adams Lake, and the Cariboo/Chilcotin area. Some of his most exciting discoveries came from the forests of Adams Lake where he documented the rarely encountered nests of the Barred Owl and Northern Pygmy-Owl (Frost 1972).

Charles de Blois Green (Fig. 44) was born in England in 1863 and died in British Columbia in 1929. He came to the province in 1888 and lived at Fairview and Osoyoos where he became a rancher and land surveyor (Brooks 1930). He was a naturalist of broad interest and during his 40 years in the province he contributed much information on the biota, passing information to his close friend Allan Brooks and to Francis Kermode at the Provincial Museum.

He assembled a small collection of about 50 clutches, mostly from the southern Okanagan valley; they are now in the Royal British Columbia Mueseum. He was one of the earliest biologists to explore the Queen Charlotte Islands and lived at Masset for a year. While there he rowed a small boat from Masset to Langara Island and back, and documented the concentration of Peregrine Falcons nesting on that island. He was also one of the first naturalists to visit Triangle Island.

Walter S. Maguire was a long-time resident of New Westminster where he served as Director of the YMCA. He was active as an egg collector mostly in the 1940s and 1950s, mainly in southwestern areas of the province. He collected commercially for a short time, concentrating on Glaucous-winged Gulls and Pelagic Cormorants from Howe Sound. His collection of more than 500 clutches of 119 species is housed at the University of British Columbia. He published 5 papers, mostly referring to Christmas Bird Counts.

Arthur Lionel Meugens (Fig. 43) was born in India in 1881 and educated in England, coming to British Columbia about

Figure 44. *Pioneer bird and egg collectors photographed in the Okanagan valley, May 1922. Left to right: Percy A. Taverner, Allan C. Brooks, T.L. Thacker, and Charles de Blois Green.*

1900. He lived first in Kelowna where he helped initiate the Kelowna Regatta, moved to Victoria in 1915, and then to Burnaby. While in Victoria he was a co-founder of the Victoria Natural History Society. He began collecting eggs in the 1930s and continued until his death in 1967. His collecting areas included Vancouver Island, the Similkameen and Okanagan valleys, the Chilcotin-Cariboo region and the Fraser River delta. His collection, now in the Royal British Columbia Museum, includes 250 clutches representing 150 species. He prepared several reports summarizing his collecting trips, and co-authored a paper on the breeding birds of Richter Pass (Campbell and Meugens 1971).

Eric M. Tait was born in Summerland, British Columbia in 1910 and lived there all his life. As an orchardist, he lived close to nature and was in daily contact with the birds that were his hobby interest. He collected nests and eggs during the 1920s, 1930s, and 1940s primarily at Trout Creek near Summerland. His collection of 206 clutches representing about 100 species is housed in the Royal British Columbia Museum. He published 15 articles including the first provincial record of the Black-crowned Night-Heron (Tait 1932) and rare nesting records of the Harlequin Duck (Tait 1949).

Natural History Societies

Natural history societies have been important in British Columbia for almost a century. They have fostered the development of museums, campaigned for the protection of threatened species, stimulated an interest in the accurate observation and recording of the occurrences of bird species, the timing of migrations, nesting dates and details, organized annual Christmas Bird Counts, and involved themselves in the preservation of habitats suitable for the rich assemblage of birds and other creatures that comprise the biota of the province. Their primary purpose, however, was to bring together like-minded individuals to listen to interesting talks and discussions and so to increase their own knowledge of the wild species and human artifacts of the province.

Natural History Society of British Columbia. In 1890, the Natural History Society of British Columbia was founded with 40 "gentlemen" as its members. The first president was Ashdown Green, a salmon specialist. C.F. Newcombe, a medical doctor and anthropologist, was secretary and John Fannin, curator and librarian. The society met bi-weekly throughout the year in the museum, at each session listening to a well-prepared paper on some natural history topic delivered by one of the members.

From their first year they were making serious published contributions to the knowledge of the native people, the biota, and natural resources of British Columbia. In 1891, Volume 1 Number 1 of "Papers and Communications read before the Natural History Society of British Columbia" appeared. The paper was the "Salmonidae of British Columbia." The fourth paper was the "Birds of British Columbia" by Fannin.

We know of only a single volume under the above title. In 1893, the Bulletin of the Natural History Society of British Columbia was printed by the Queen's Printer and, so far as can be determined, just 2 volumes were published by the society. When Francis Kermode took over the direction of the museum in 1904, the close relationship of the museum and the Natural History Society ceased. Nothing seems to be recorded about the gradual demise of the society or when it held its last meeting.

Vancouver Natural History Society. Next on the scene was the Vancouver Natural History Society, organized in 1918, with the encouragement of the University of British Columbia. Professor John Davidson, botanist at the university, was the founding president and continued in that postion until 1938. At various times in its long history, the society has issued publications (e.g. Smith, K.M. et al. 1973), many of which have contained original observations on birds in the Vancouver area (see Campbell et al. 1972a, 1972b, 1974). The *Vancouver Natural History Society News* was published 2 to 4 times a year beginning in 1932 and continuing until 1970 when Number 147, the June to August issue, bore the new title *Vancouver Natural History Society Discovery*. That has

continued as a quarterly publication. In 1977, the birders group of the society began publishing the *Wandering Tattler*, a monthly newsletter which often contains summaries of noteworthy bird sightings. It has also been involved in many conservation activities (Fig. 45). For continuous survival, the Vancouver Natural History Society is in a class by itself being in its seventieth year in 1988.

In the mid 1920s, differences of opinion within the Vancouver Natural History Society led to the formation of a breakaway group, the **Burrard Field-Naturalists**. Its members were largely the serious students of birds, mammals and insects, all of whom collected specimens for their studies. They met monthly through the winter and spring at the Vancouver City Museum on the corner of Hastings and Main streets. Its date of demise appears to be unrecorded.

Figure 45. *Members of the Vancouver Natural History Society erecting Wood Duck nest boxes along the Vedder River, March 1963 (John G. Sarles). Between 1962 and 1965 more than 1,000 boxes were erected throughout the Fraser Lowlands.*

British Columbia Ornithologists' Union. On 29 August 1922, nine amateur and professional ornithologists met in Vancouver to form an association of like-minded individuals. Theed Pearse of Courtenay was in the chair and J.W. Winson of Huntingdon, the nature columnist for the Vancouver *Province* newspaper, was the pro-tem secretary. In preparation for that meeting, letters had been written to known bird enthusiasts and favourable replies had been received from 19 of them.

The membership list is interesting—a who's who of 1920s ornithologists: Dennis Ashby, Duncan; Allan Brooks, Okanagan Landing; W.F. Burton, Victoria; W.R. Carter, Victoria; R.A. Cumming, Vancouver; R. Glendenning, Agassiz; B.R. Harrison, Vancouver; W.B. Johnstone, Edgewood; Clement Kaufman, Victoria; J.E.H. Kelso, Edgewood; Francis Kermode, Victoria; J.A. Munro, Okanagan Landing; Theed Pearse, Courtenay; Kenneth Racey, Vancouver; G.D. Sprot, Cobble Hill; Mr. and Mrs. T.L. Thacker, Little Mountain, Hope; J.D. Turnbull, Vancouver; P.S. Walker, Vancouver; J.W. Winson, Huntingdon. Francis Kermode, Curator of the Provincial Museum, was elected the first President.

The society's objectives were the advancement of the study of ornithology and the conservation of bird life within the province. Its first recorded resolution was "that a protest be made against the provincial bounty on bald eagles."

The Union devised an interesting way of communicating between its far flung membership. A loose-leaf book circulated within the group, and as it did so each individual added his written contribution. They were immensely varied: suggestions for policy changes in the game laws and museum collecting, records of interesting observations, references to literature recently read, etc. That book, *The Migrant*, continued to circle the province for at least 10 years but, unfortunately only one volume, covering the period 1922 to 1925, is known to have survived. It is in the Royal British Columbia Museum and makes most interesting reading, made up of copies of each contribution that were filed at the museum. The original books have vanished.

Within the first 3 years of its life several other "birders" joined the Union: M.Y. Williams, Vancouver; W.H. Kelly, Vancouver; F.S. Mitchell, Millstream; M.W. Holdom, Surrey Centre; H.M. Laing, Comox; Mrs. R. Lloyd, Parksville; G.B. Simpson, Cowichan Lake; G.A. Hardy, Victoria; G.H. Corran, Victoria; W.P. Stark, Creston.

Victoria Natural History Society. After the demise of the Natural History Society of British Columbia in the early 1900s, Victoria was without such an organization until 1944, when the Victoria Natural History Society came into being. Its first president was Robert Connell who began immediately to publish a periodical, *The Victoria Naturalist* in April 1944. That publication has contained much ornithological information from the region it covers. The society has issued several books on the natural history of the Victoria region and Vancouver Island, and supported production of annual bird reports for southern Vancouver Island from 1969 to 1972.

Federation of British Columbia Naturalists. As population centres grew in the interior of the province and elsewhere along the coast, many more nature-oriented societies developed. The Federation of British Columbia Naturalists, founded in 1962, was an answer to the need to have a well-organized, well-informed body to represent the interests and concerns of naturalists in a socio-political environment where the natural environment was under increasing assault. In 1988, there were 31 such societies affiliated with the Federation. Their combined membership constitutes an effective observer corps covering a large part of the province. Its quarterly publication, the *Federation of British Columbia Naturalists Newsletter*, followed by the *B.C. Naturalist*, is now in its 25th year and is an indispensible source of news and specific information useful to the province's naturalists, including those whose chief delight is the birds.

The Observer-Naturalists

By 1960, the general collecting phase of bird study had passed. The emphasis required now was on concentrated studies of birds from areas of the province still largely unexplored, including the far northeast, the northwest corner traversed by the Alsek River, and the Flathead valley region of the southeast. More collecting was required only occasionally to support other more searching inquiries into aspects of the biology of birds. In 1971, the Canadian Wildlife Service ceased issuing permits to collect migratory birds and their nests and eggs apart from those made available to recognized museums and to scientists for limited purposes.

The improvement in optical equipment, telescopes, field glasses, cameras, and film, along with electronic sound recording and other technical developments facilitated a new approach to bird study. In most instances, species occurrence could now be documented by photographs as surely as by specimens and the level of general understanding flowing to the public from the university and museum research ornithologists changed the focus of the amateurs in the field.

British Columbia produced a new group of bird enthusiasts, who observed and recorded birds and their events, but shunned collecting. Among the many thousands of bird watchers and more serious students of birds in the province, a small group has made especially noteworthy contributions to ornithology as well as to the data upon which this book is based. Their prime passion is the documentation and study of birds. All have maintained records of their observations for a continuous period of 12 to 50 years or more and have made their records freely available to the Royal British Columbia Museum. In addition, some of those dedicated individuals have served as subregional coordinators for *Audubon Field Notes* and *American Birds* and have supplied detailed, quarterly summaries of significant records of birds in the province for a North American audience. Others have organized and compiled results for the annual Christmas Bird Counts. Eleven of them, considered local experts, have reviewed species accounts for regional accuracy and interpretation. Still others have spent countless hours writing up their observations and research for publication in scientific and natural history journals. In recognition of their contribution we have provided brief biographical sketches of their careers and contributions. The several thousand others, without whose help we could not have made this study as complete as it is, are acknowledged elsewhere.

Stephen R. Cannings was born in Penticton in 1914 and received his education there and at technical schools in Vancou-

Figure 46. *Stephen and Jean Cannings at Penticton, June 1989 (Sydney G. Cannings). Since 1946, they have been active field-naturalists in the Okanagan valley recording their observations, many of which have been used in this volume.*

Figure 47. *The Cannings brothers: Robert, Sydney, and Richard. As a group, they have contributed over 40 papers and reports on birds in the province including a major work on Birds of the Okanagan Valley, British Columbia.*

ver and California. He married **Jean Munn** of Summerland in 1943, and in 1947 they returned to the Okanagan where Steve began a 24-year career with the Agricultural Research Station at Summerland as technician and photographer.

Steve and Jean (Fig. 46) had 4 children, a girl Elizabeth (1946) and sons Robert (1948), Richard and Sydney (twins 1954). That is important to our history of ornithology as they have contributed much as a family, including about 50 papers and reports on birds in the province. Steve and Jean began their bird records in 1946; the children followed suit as soon as they could write.

Robert A. Cannings (Fig. 47) studied zoology at the University of British Columbia and received an M.Sc. in 1973. While in university, he worked as a seasonal park naturalist at Miracle Beach, Manning, Shuswap Lake, and Mt. Robson Provincial Parks. He subsequently worked as a park interpretation planner before becoming curator of the Spencer Entomological Museum at University of British Columbia in 1979. A year later he moved to the Royal British Columbia Museum as curator of Entomology, and is now Chief of Biology there.

Richard J. Cannings (Fig. 47) received a B.Sc. in zoology at the University of British Columbia in 1975, then studied the breeding biology of Horned Larks at the Memorial University of Newfoundland (M.Sc. 1977). He worked as a naturalist for 6 summers in British Columbia in Manning, Shuswap Lake, and Mt. Robson Provincial Parks, and did environmental consulting for Parks Canada and the Canadian Wildlife Service before returning to the University of British Columbia as curator of the Cowan Vertebrate Museum in 1981. He has been the Western Canada Regional Editor for Christmas Bird Counts published in *American Birds* since 1982.

Sydney G. Cannings (Fig. 47) worked as a seasonal naturalist in Mt. Robson and Okanagan Lake Provincial Parks while attending the University of British Columbia (B.Sc. 1975, M.Sc. 1978). He became curator of the Spencer Entomological Museum in 1980. He was president of the Vancouver Natural History Society from 1984 to 1986, and is now a director of the Federation of B.C. Naturalists.

The 3 brothers have recently (1987) completed *Birds of the Okanagan Valley, British Columbia* for the Royal British Columbia Museum, presenting a detailed look at the life history of the more than 300 species of birds recorded in that valley.

Albert R. Davidson (Fig. 48) was born in Hull, England in 1888 and had all his schooling in England. He moved to Canada in 1908, living in Toronto for 3 years before moving to New York in 1911. Two years there convinced him he should return to Canada, this time to Victoria. There he met J.W. Winson of Huntingdon, a

dedicated ornithologist and writer for the Vancouver *Province* newspaper. He moved from Victoria to Courtenay in 1936 and there met Theed Pearse. They became good friends and field companions for the next 11 years, until Davidson's return to Victoria.

Davidson has been very active in the Victoria Natural History Society, and has published over 130 articles on birds over the years. His field notes cover over 30 years of observation, mainly on Vancouver Island from Victoria to Oyster River.

Gary Steven Davidson (Fig. 49) was born in Birmingham, England in 1949 and came to Vancouver in 1958 where he com-

Figure 48. *Albert R. Davidson at Victoria. In his 100th year, he was still publishing articles on the bird life of the Victoria area.*

pleted his education. From 1973 to 1975 he lived in Fort Nelson before making his home in Nakusp. A casual interest in birds became a serious dedication as an outcome of his meeting Anthony J. Erskine in Fort Nelson (Erskine and Davidson 1976). His ornithology notebooks began in January 1975 and continue to this day, expanding to a computer file of 30,000 records of bird observations, mostly for the west Kootenay region. He was founder and first president of the Fort Nelson Naturalists Club, and president of the Arrow Lake Naturalists Club 1985 to 1986. He has published several articles on birds.

Figure 49. *Since 1975, Gary S. Davidson has contributed about 30,000 records of bird observations, from the Fort Nelson area and west Kootenay region, to this book.*

Figure 50. *Adrian Dorst's records from the Queen Charlotte Islands, Cortes Island, and the central west coast of Vancouver Island (over a 20-year period) have filled in knowledge of bird distribution for those little-known areas.*

Adrian Dorst (Fig. 50) came to Canada from his native Holland in 1952 at the age of 8, when his family left the Island of Flakee and settled in the Niagara Peninsula, Ontario. There he was introduced to the study of birds by his grade 5 teacher and whetted his interest on Fuertes' illustrations in *Birds of America*. He met Jacob Unger, a neighbour and museum collector, who taught him the skills of specimen preparation and taxidermy and introduced him to L.L. Snyder, curator of birds at the Royal Ontario Museum. He then spent 1968 and 1969 collecting and preparing birds for the University of Western Ontario.

In 1969, he decided against further collecting. He moved to British Columbia in 1970, spent a short time on the Queen Charlotte Islands and Cortes Island, and in 1972 moved to Tofino where he now lives. His observations have been incorporated into *Birds of Pacific Rim National Park* by Hatler et al. (1978). His detailed and continuous field notes and documentary photographs have been useful in the present study. He is actively involved in conservation activities, especially those related to habitat preservation in British Columbia.

Roger Yorke Edwards (Fig. 51) was born in Toronto in 1924 and received his education there, culminating in a forestry degree from the University of Toronto. He arrived in British Columbia in the spring of 1948 to work on waterfowl in the Chilcotin-Cariboo region and to undertake study towards a Master of Science degree with McTaggart-Cowan.

Yorke Edwards has had a busy and varied professional career associated with birds and the natural environment. For 16 years with the British Columbia Parks Branch, and then for 5 with the Canadian Wildlife Service, he specialized in nature interpretation, after which he was Director of the Royal British Columbia Museum for 12 years. He has published about 50 papers and articles on birds in British Columbia and 2 books on more general environmental topics.

In his park years, he influenced the establishment and enlargement of several provincial parks, and was also able to

Figure 51. *R. Yorke Edwards at Willows Beach, August 1982 (Gwynnath Hansen). Yorke, past director of the Royal British Columbia Museum, remains an active field-naturalist and continues to promote the conservation of birds.*

influence many young naturalists in ornithology who were hired to interpret in parks in the summer. He is now in active retirement and continues to contribute to the many aspects of conservation that have been central to his philosophy. His bird notebooks, begun in 1937, continue to grow.

Anthony John Erskine (Fig. 52) was born in Whinfield, England in 1931 and came to Canada when in his school years, growing up in Wolfville, Nova Scotia. His first training was in Chemistry (B.Sc., Acadia; M.A. and Ph.D., Queens) but he changed fields and in 1960 received an M.A. in Zoology (University of British Columbia).

He undertook field work on the birds of most major habitats in British Columbia every year from 1954 to 1975, and periodically since then. He was responsible for establishing the breeding bird surveys organized by the Canadian Wildlife Service and conducted by volunteers in British Columbia. He has published about 45 papers on the birds of British Columbia; his book *Buffleheads* (Erskine 1972) was an expansion of his M.A. thesis and is a major contribution to the literature on waterfowl. He has been employed by the Canadian Wildlife Service since 1960, where he is now a divisional chief in Sackville, New Brunswick responsible for migratory bird program management.

J.E. Victor Goodwill was born in Toronto in 1916 and educated there. He received a B.A.Sc. in Mining Engineering from the University of Toronto in 1938 and a D.B.A. from the University of Western Ontario in 1939.

He joined the Canadian Hydrographic Service in 1941 and worked as a hydrographer on charting operations on the Atlantic coast and the Eastern arctic. Incidental to his survey duties, he regularly contributed his observations on birds to *Audubon Field Notes* and *American Birds* as well as to W. Earl Godfrey for use in *Birds of Prince Edward Island* (Godfrey 1954), *Birds of Cape Breton Island, Nova Scotia* (Godfrey 1958), and *Birds of Canada* (Godfrey 1966, 1986). He was transferred to the Victoria hydrographic office in the spring of 1966 and continued in his profession on British Columbia coastal waters until his retirement in 1972. His meticulously detailed notes provided the only information available on the birds for several British Columbia coastal areas.

Vic Goodwill married **Margaret E. Pickford** in 1972. They (Fig. 53) collaborated on many ornithological projects, including the compilation of the quarterly bird report for Southern Vancouver Island for *American Birds* from 1 December 1972 until 30 November 1986, and operation of the rare bird alert for the Victoria Natural History Society from April 1977 to May 1987. Many observations that would have otherwise been lost were preserved for the record through their efforts. They were recipients of the Federation of British Columbia Naturalists "Club Service Award" in 1984. First confirmed records for Canada of Slaty-backed Gull, Thick-billed Kingbird, Rustic Bunting, and Terek Sandpiper resulted from their field trips.

They were consulted regularly by museum staff during the preparation of this volume.

James Grant (Fig. 54) was born in Trinity Valley near Lumby on 25 May 1920. He went to school in the north Okanagan and became a farmer and logger before enlisting in the Canadian army in 1941. He served in the Signal Corps in Europe until 1946. On return to Canada, he was employed by the Federal Forest Entomology Laboratory in Vernon. His work took him throughout the province and enabled him to increase his expertise in ornithology, entomology, and botany. In 1970, he was appointed field studies coordinator for the Vernon school district and remained there until retirement in 1978. His dedication and extensive knowledge of natural history made him a mentor and inspiration to many naturalists in the Okanagan area until his death in 1986.

He was a founding member of the North Okanagan Naturalists Club, published at least 30 articles on birds and their biology in various parts of the province, and maintained accurate written records of his observations, mainly from the north Okanagan valley and the Prince George area.

Hilde and Werner Hesse (Fig. 55) were born in Germany in

Figure 52. *Anthony J. Erskine, October 1964. He established North American Breeding Bird Surveys in British Columbia.*

Figure 53. *Margaret E. and J.E. Victor Goodwill at Race Rocks, February 1979. The Goodwills have been instrumental in thoroughly documenting and screening bird records from southern Vancouver Island since 1972.*

Figure 54. *James Grant , holding an immature Swainson's Hawk at Lavington, August 1984 (Tom Collins). He was a professional entomologist, and an experienced botanist. His observations and field notes, mainly from the Prince George and north Okanagan valley areas, were major sources of data for this book.*

Figure 55. Hilda and Werner Hesse's comprehensive and detailed field notes from throughout the province were a major contribution in the preparation of this volume.

1918 and 1926 respectively, and came to Canada in 1952. Their shared passion for birds makes it logical to recognize them as an inseparable team for biographical purposes.

Their interest in birds was aroused by a spectacular migration of American Kestrels in the Chilcotin-Cariboo in 1956. That interest led them to enroll in a night class in ornithology at the university given by Miklos D.F. Udvardy. Joining the Vancouver Natural History Society they met William M. Hughes who completed their introduction to rich birding areas near Vancouver, and Anthony J. Erskine and Rudolf H. Drent encouraged the Hesses to maintain a daily record of their field trips. Today their notes encompass 12 large volumes, cross referenced by species and geographical area. Their careful observations and meticulous records have been contributed to *Audubon Field Notes, American Birds*, and to the Christmas Bird Counts for Vancouver and Ladner, which they organized and compiled for many years.

Now retired, they live in Metchosin, near Victoria, continuing to follow their interest in birds and to maintain their records of observations. They have published several papers on occurrences of unusual birds in the province.

Canon Martin W. Holdom of White Rock, was probably the most faithful bird diarist in British Columbia from 1940 to 1966. Twelve volumes of his detailed daily notes are in the library of Wayne Campbell, and have been extensively used in this study. Unfortunately, we have been unable to find biographical data. He published about 40 articles on his observations.

Robert Richard Howie (Fig. 56), was born in 1946 at Vancouver where he lived until 1971. His early interest in birds focused on their identification and distribution

He completed a B.Sc. in agriculture at the University of British Columbia in 1970. In 1971 he joined the staff of Parks Canada, where he worked as Chief Park Naturalist at various locations across the country until 1977. The following year, he moved to Kamloops where he has been employed since as a Visitor Services Officer with the provincial Ministry of Parks.

He has been very active in ornithological activities wherever he has worked. His most intensive observations have covered the Rocky Mountain Trench from Field to Radium and the Kamloops-Merritt area where he has amassed a personal data base of 24,000 observations. In addition, he has served as subregional coordinator for *American Birds* since 1969, compiler for local Christmas Bird Counts and the Breeding Bird Survey since 1976, and he initiated and has conducted the annual swan census in the southern interior since 1978 (see Fig. 247). His bibliography contains 20 articles on birds in the province, among which are significant contributions to the natural history of the Flammulated Owl and migration of raptors in the Kamloops region.

William Douglas Kragh (Fig. 57) was born in 1951 in Ontario, but moved to Vancouver in 1978, already an experienced student of birds. He has been keeping a daily journal of bird observations for 12 years. He has been an active participant in the Vancouver Natural History Society (president from 1986 to 1988), the annual Christmas Bird Count and operated the Vancouver rare bird alert from 1980 to 1984. He has authored several articles on birds and has prepared seasonal reports for *American Birds* since 1981. In addition, he maintains a data base for the Vancouver checklist area of some 50,000 records.

Tex Lyon (Fig. 58) was born in Port Hardy in 1911, and was educated there in the one-room school. He had a natural love of birds which was fostered by his father. His first contact with serious bird study did not occur until 1930, when Kenneth Racey introduced him to collecting and preparing bird specimens. Soon after, he met another bird enthusiast, Arthur Peake, who was appointed to teach at Quatsino, northern Vancouver Island.

Lyon did not build a bird specimen collection himself but from time to time obtained specimens needed by J.A. Munro, A. C. Brooks, and T.T. McCabe. He was a keen observer, knowledgeable

Figure 56. Richard R. Howie is personally responsible for most of our knowledge of the Flammulated Owl in the province.

Figure 57. W. Douglas Kragh has spent thousands of hours over the past decade in maintaining an ornithology data base for the Vancouver checklist area.

Figure 58. *Tex Lyon at Port Hardy, 1987. Since 1930, Tex has been the major contributor of bird records for northern Vancouver Island.*

about birds and their local distribution, and made many useful contributions of specimens to these specialists. For some 15 years he maintained records of migration dates and occurrences of significance, mainly in the Port Hardy region, all of which have been made available to the Royal British Columbia Museum and the Cowan Vertebrate Museum at the University of British Columbia.

Lyon was wharfinger at Port Hardy for most of his working life. He retired in the mid 1970's.

William Adrian Beviss Paul (Fig. 59) was born in 1891 at Chard, England and completed his education there before moving to Canada in 1910. He had a life long interest in birds but did not begin his organized note-taking until 1946, at which time he lived in Kleena Kleene—a little known area in the western Chilcotin. He maintained his records of ornithological events there until 1976 and published about 20 articles on his observations. He was an active bird bander, contributor to the British Columbia Nest Records Scheme, and organizer of Christmas Bird Counts. He died in 1982 at Tatla Lake.

Theed Pearse (Fig. 60) was born in Bedford, England and studied law there before emigrating to Canada in 1914. He lived first in Vancouver but by 1919 he is listed as a barrister in Courte-

Figure 59. *Adrian Paul at Kleena Kleene, 1929. His many publications from the western Chilcotin added to our knowledge of the bird fauna of this little-known region.*

nay. He loved the area and remained there for the remainder of a very long life. He was active in civic politics in Courtenay and served as Mayor of the city for a short period.

His love of birds developed in his childhood and by 1905 he was a member of the British Ornithologists' Union. Ornithology was a lifelong passion, leading to a long series of notebooks recording his observations. Many of his more significant records were published in the *Murrelet, Condor,* and *Auk*—103 titles in all. He was recognized for his contributions to ornithology by receiving honorary memberships in both the Pacific Northwest Bird and Mammal Society and the Cooper Ornithological Society.

He was not by temperament a collector of birds, though he understood those whose studies required more detailed examination of the creatures than observation could provide. He was the first of the non-collecting but meticulous recorders of observations of birds in the province.

In 1967, after 14 years of research, he completed his most significant work *Birds of the Early Explorers in the Northern Pacific* (Pearse 1968).

Figure 60. *Theed Pearse at Comox in the late 1950s preparing his manuscript for* Birds of the Early Explorers in the Northern Pacific. *His daily field notes over the years were used by A.C. Bent in his famous life-history series, and provided the information in this volume that allowed the discussion of some historical trends.*

George Allen Poynter (Fig. 61) was born in 1929 in Northumberland, England and emigrated to British Columbia in 1956. His interest in birds developed in his early teens on the moorlands of Northumberland where birds in great variety were ever present. His arrival in British Columbia was preceded by 4 years at sea, with 4 circumnavigations of the world, when he developed a special interest in sea birds.

Though birds have been his major interest, he has broader concerns for the natural environment and its misuse, and has used his knowledge of birds and their environmental needs to promote better land use practices in the province. He has been most active in the Vancouver and Victoria natural history societies and is a past president and chairman of the ornithology section (1958 to 1960) of the latter. He served a term as a director of the Canadian Nature Federation and has helped organize the Victoria and Vancouver Christmas Bird Counts. He still contributes in many ways to local ornithology, and continues to encourage young naturalists in the fun of bird-watching.

He has published 30 contributions to the knowledge of birds in British Columbia, including the first regional, annual, bird report (Poynter 1960).

Ralph W. Ritcey (Fig. 62) was born in Halifax, Nova Scotia. In 1948, at 23 years of age, he arrived in British Columbia. Two

Figure 61. *G. Allen Poynter's bird reports for southern Vancouver Island were the models followed by compilers of similar annual reports from other regions of the province.*

Figure 62. *Ralph W. Ritcey was active for 35 years, especially in the Wells Grey Park and Kamloops areas, documenting the occurrence and numbers of birds.*

years later, he graduated from a wildlife biology program at the University of British Columbia where he carried on post-graduate studies until 1952.

He was employed by the Provincial Fish and Game Department in the Kamloops region, where he worked on the life history and population dynamics of moose and upland game birds for 35 years; 11 years in Wells Gray Park and 24 years in the Kamloops area. His reports and field notes, maintained from 1951 to 1987, contributed much to our knowledge of the birds of that

area. Prior to his retirement in March 1988, he directed the program to reintroduce Burrowing Owls into the southern interior.

Anna L. Roberts (Fig. 63) grew up on a farm near Stanstead, Quebec where she was born in 1929. Twenty-four years later, as a member of the Ottawa Field-Naturalists Club, she participated in field trips led by W. Earl Godfrey and caught the fascination of bird-watching. Another member of the Club, D.B.O. Saville, introduced her to orderly note-taking.

After her marriage, Roberts moved to Williams Lake in 1958

Figure 63. Anna L. Roberts has been active for over 30 years throughout the Fraser Plateau recording the distribution and abundance of birds and encouraging others to become involved.

where she instructed adult education classes in ornithology that led to the organization of a local group of bird watchers, and then to the first Christmas Bird Count for Williams Lake.

She has compiled an annotated check-list of birds of the Cariboo, and has participated in the Canadian Breeding Bird Survey for 15 years. Anna Roberts was instrumental in establishing the Scout Island Nature Center and coordinates the monitoring of 1,000 nest boxes situated in the Chilcotin grasslands.

Michael Stephen Rodway (Fig. 64) is another native of Vancouver, where he was born in 1951. He and his wife Joy Ann established a wilderness homestead at Port Neville, an area rich in marine birds and shorebirds, and there his interest in birds developed. It became focused in 1975 when he met Wayne Campbell and experienced the great scope of bird study.

Figure 64. *Over the past decade, Michael S. Rodway has conducted a complete inventory of all seabird nesting islands in the province (R. Wayne Campbell).*

During the next few years he participated in an inventory of seabird colonies along the British Columbia coast with staff at the then British Columbia Provincial Museum. By 1979 he had completed a Bachelor's degree and obtained a Teacher's Certificate at Simon Fraser University. In 1980 he joined the Canadian Wildlife Service seasonal inventory team devoting itself specifically to nesting sea birds. He has authored about 20 reports on nesting marine birds, has visited more coastal islands in British Columbia than any other biologist, and has freely contributed his detailed field records, from 1975 to 1988, to this book.

Glen R. Ryder (Fig. 65) was born in Vancouver in 1938 but spent his childhood in Kelowna, Salmon Arm, and Celista. He returned to the coast in 1954 and from there, through pleasure and work as an artist, travelled widely in British Columbia. During the 1960s he collected birds' eggs; his collection of about 100 clutches of 60 species was donated to the Royal British Columbia Museum. From 1971 to 1974 he was the first warden at the American White Pelican colony at Stum Lake (Ryder 1972, 1973).

Figure 65. *Glen R. Ryder as a seasonal naturalist with British Columbia Parks Branch. Only a handful of naturalists in the province are disciplined enough to record their field observations daily; Glen's notebooks include 19 large volumes.*

His very detailed, daily notes on bird observations span 19 years; a copy is in the library of Wayne Campbell. He wrote a bird column for 3 years in the *Surrey Leader* newspaper, and has been a regular participant in the nest record program and Christmas Bird Counts.

Michael Gary Shepard (Fig. 66), born in Toronto in 1951, was brought by his parents to Nanaimo a year later, and has lived in the province ever since.

Figure 66. *Michael G. Shepard helped develop the data base on which this book is built.*

His interest in birds developed with the encouragement of his parents out of an intrinsic attraction. Serious interest began with organized note-taking in 1961. In 1975, he completed a B.Sc. degree in Zoology at the University of British Columbia. He worked for the Royal British Columbia Museum from 1975 to 1979 and, during this time, helped establish the data base on which this volume is based.

He has served as coordinator for Christmas Bird Counts in Victoria (1977 to present) and Sooke (1983 to present), has organized pelagic birding trips off the west coast of Vancouver Island since 1970 and co-authored 3 annual bird reports (1970 to 1972) for the Vancouver area which were based on nearly 300,000 records.

He has published 35 articles on British Columbia birds and presently operates Swiftsure Tours in Victoria, specializing in natural history touring experiences.

Chris R. Siddle (Fig. 67) was born in Mission, British Columbia in 1950, with, as seems to be the rule, a passion for bird-watching. He began recording bird observations when he was 11 years old.

Figure 67. Chris R. Siddle birding at Fort St. John (R. Wayne Campbell). For nearly 15 years, Chris carefully documented the avifauna of the Peace River region by keeping daily records.

After completing a B.A. degree at the University of British Columbia he began a teaching career at Fort St. John in the Peace River district of British Columbia. Here he was strategically placed to observe and record ornithological events in one of the least known parts of the province. Since 1975, he has added thousands of observations to the museum's record files and made important contributions to the knowledge of the birds of the Peace River district. He has published 12 articles on birds and has written a major report on the status of birds in the Peace River area (Siddle 1982). Since 1980, he has served as regional coordinator for the Peace River region for *American Birds* and has organized annual Christmas Bird Counts since 1975. He is currently involved in conservation issues as they relate to habitat protection (Siddle 1981).

David Stirling (Fig. 68) was born in Athabasca, Alberta, in 1920 and grew up in a wilderness environment with his outdoorsman father. He learned to identify birds from postcard paintings by Allan Brooks and, when 12 years old, started a bird diary which he maintains today. In 1954, he moved to British Columbia and worked with the provincial Parks Branch as a nature interpreter from 1959 until his retirement in 1985. He assisted Yorke Edwards in developing a successful nature interpretation program, including permanent nature centres, throughout the province.

Figure 68. David Stirling, an experienced field-observer, continues to be active in the conservation and protection of birds. He also encouraged and assisted many young birders, including two of the authors of this book, in the techniques of field-observation.

From the late 1950s to the late 1970s he served long terms as a subregional coordinator for *Audubon Field Notes/American Birds*, including annual Christmas Bird Counts, and provincial coordinator for the continental breeding bird survey. In addition, he held executive positions with the American Birding Association, the Canadian Nature Federation, the Federation of British Columbia Naturalists, the Pacific Northwest Bird and Mammal Society, and the Victoria Natural History Society.

He has published about 80 scientific and popular articles on birds in British Columbia, presently leads international nature and bird-watching tours, and remains active in preservation of habitat and bird protection through the International Council for Bird Preservation and other conservation organizations.

Jeremy B. Tatum was born and raised in the United Kingdom and, in 1962, moved to Victoria. In 1969, he joined the faculty at the University of Victoria where he is presently a professor at the Department of Physics and Astronomy.

As long as he can remember, he has had a deep appreciation and respect for living things. In 1969, he established a bird records committee for southern Vancouver Island, whose function was to scrutinize the evidence upon which sight records would be accepted and reliably documented. He chaired that committee until 1972 during which time he also produced 4 annual bird reports and compiled Christmas Bird Counts for the Victoria area. In 1972, he recommended that consideration be given to establishing a Canadian Ornithological Records Committee (Tatum 1972a).

He has served as president of the Victoria Natural History Society and vice-president of the Canadian branch of the International Council for Bird Preservation. He has published about 20 scientific and popular articles on birds, the most significant paper relating to the effect of the Coriolis force on the flight of birds (Tatum 1980).

Wayne C. Weber (Fig. 69) was born in North Vancouver in 1947 and credits Stephen Cannings with fostering his early interest in birds during his teenage years in Penticton. He has studied birds since 1959 in most parts of the province, but mainly in the Vancouver area, Vancouver Island, and the southern interior.

He earned B.Sc. and M.Sc. degrees in zoology from the University of British Columbia, and a Ph.D. in biological sciences at Mississippi State University. He has published about 50 articles on British Columbia birds.

He compiled Vancouver Christmas Bird Counts in 1973 and 1974 and from 1979 to the present, served as *American Birds* sub-

Figure 69. Wayne C. Weber has been a major force in developing careful documentation and encouraging the participation of amateur ornithologists in the province.

Ornithology at British Columbia Universities

The University of British Columbia established its first undergraduate course in vertebrate zoology in 1941, followed 2 years later by graduate level courses. Both were organized and taught by Ian McTaggart-Cowan. The university steadily increased its reputation as a centre of teaching and research in ornithology and mammalogy and additional faculty appointments were made as student numbers increased. Miklos Udvardy joined the Department in 1952 and served until 1968, undertaking research in avian biogeography. James Bendell, who had been a graduate student at the university from 1952 to 1954, was appointed as assistant professor in 1956, and along with his general teaching duties, continued his studies of the biology of the Blue Grouse on Vancouver Island. A succession of graduate students studied for advanced degrees under his direction. He left the University of British Columbia in 1972, to join the Faculty of Forestry at the University of Toronto.

Rudolph Drent (Fig. 70) was born in California in 1937 and came to the University of British Columbia in 1954, where he achieved B.A. and M.A. degrees in ornithological topics, followed by a D.Sc. from the University of Gröningen, Netherlands in 1967. He returned to the University of British Columbia in 1968 as an assistant professor where he served until 1973 when he returned to Gröningen to take up a senior appointment. He initiated research at the University of British Columbia on seabirds breeding in the province while guiding the studies of several graduate students.

John Krebs came to the University of British Columbia from Oxford in 1970, teaching and undertaking research in avian behaviour until 1973. He then moved to the University of Wales at Bangor and then onto Oxford a year later.

Fred Bunnell joined the Faculty of Forestry of the University of British Columbia in 1971. His major research and that of most

regional editor for the northern Pacific coast region from 1970 to 1975 and 1979 to 1982, chaired the Vancouver Bird Records Committee from 1981 to the present, and served as Christmas Bird Count editor for western Canada for *American Birds* from 1980 to 1984. He is presently employed as a wildlife damage specialist with the Crop Protection Branch, British Columbia Ministry of Agriculture and Fisheries.

Figure 70. Rudolph H. Drent checking Rhinoceros Auklet burrows on Lucy Island, 7 June 1970 (R. Wayne Campbell).

of his graduate students have been devoted to mammals, but he has guided 6 graduate students in ornithology, involving the biology of forest birds, the breeding biology of the Gyrfalcon, and population dynamics of the American White Pelican.

Jamie Smith (Fig. 71) came to the Department of Zoology from Oxford in 1973, and continued the pioneering work of Frank Tompa on the behavioural ecology of a Song Sparrow population on Mandarte Island. His graduate students have studied such diverse topics as singing behaviour of Varied Thrushes, population ecology of ptarmigan, behavioural ecology of waterfowl, and the biology of Great Blue Herons.

Lee Gass arrived in the Department from Oregon in 1974. He and his students have studied the behavioural ecology of Rufous and Calliope hummingbirds.

Figure 71. *Jamie Smith watching Song Sparrows on Mandarte Island.*

In addition, at least 17 other University of British Columbia faculty members have supervised graduate students in ornithology. They include Jim Adams, Bob Blake, Kim Cheng, Dennis Chitty, C.S. "Buzz" Holling, Maryanne Hughes, David Jones, Charles Krebs, Peter Larkin, Robin Lyley, Bill Milsom, Dave Shackleton, Tony Sinclair, Dolph Schluter, Mary Taylor, Carl Walters, and Conrad Wehrhahn.

During the 42 years since the first degrees were granted in which ornithological topics were the focus, birds have been the research subjects of theses submitted by nearly 100 graduate students, about half of which were master of science candidates. The titles of all theses submitted to the University of British Columbia, Simon Fraser University, and the University of Victoria are included in the bibliographies of British Columbia ornithology (see Campbell et al. 1979b; Campbell et al. 1988).

An important facility for the study of birds at the University of British Columbia has been the Museum of Vertebrate Zoology, founded in 1952 by the acquisition of the collections of Kenneth Racey and Ian McTaggart-Cowan. Later it received major contributions of specimens from J.W. Wynne and Walter S. Maguire. Lewis Witt, formerly a professor of wildlife management in Hungary, was the first curator-preparator. He was succeeded in 1971 by Wayne Campbell who moved to the Royal British Columbia Museum in 1973. Subsequently, Nasar Din maintained the collections until 1981. From then until the present, Richard Cannings has been curator-preparator of the collections that now include over 14,000 specimens of bird skins and skeletons, and 2,000 clutches of eggs. In 1976, the museum was designated the Cowan Vertebrate Museum to commemorate Ian McTaggart-Cowan's role as founder, and for many years as director of the museum's activities.

Ornithology was introduced at Simon Fraser University with the appointment in 1977 of Nicholaas Verbeek (Fig. 72) to the Department of Biological Sciences. He has mainly studied aspects of the biology of the Glaucous-winged Gull and the Northwestern Crow. His students have studied the ecology and behaviour of Red-necked Grebe, Trumpeter Swan, Black Tern, Pigeon Guillemot, Northwestern Crow, as well as chickadees, kingbirds, and swallows. Alton Harestad took a faculty position at Simon Fraser in 1981, and has directed 5 graduate students in studies involving the management of birds as a natural resource. Ron Ydenberg has recently joined the Department, and is doing research and supervising graduate students in topics concerning the life history and behavioural ecology of birds, focusing on the Osprey and Rhinoceros Auklet.

The University of Victoria has never had a full-time faculty member whose field of expertise included ornithology. However, A.T. Bergerud, as an adjunct faculty member in the Department of Biology, has directed graduate students in research on grouse and quail. In addition, Michael Edgell of the Department of Geography has supervised several graduate students in avian biogeography topics.

Figure 72. *Nicholas Verbeek (foreground) and field assistant Peter McConnell at Mitlenatch Island observing the clam storage behaviour of the Northwestern Crow, summer 1988.*

Ornithology at Other Universities

Ornithologists at universities outside British Columbia have found exciting research opportunities relating to the avifauna of the province. Several developed their interest in studying birds in British Columbia and today continue noteable contributions to the knowledge of birds in the province, mainly through graduate students. The contributions of 3 are especially noteworthy.

Spencer G. Sealy, Professor of Zoology at the University of Manitoba, was born in Saskatchewan in 1943 and attended the University of Alberta, University of British Columbia, and University of Michigan (Ph.D., 1972). While in British Columbia he became interested in the breeding biology of the Alcidae and pursued research on Ancient and Marbled murrelets on the Queen Charlotte Islands. Other ornithological work has centred on studies of mixed-species feeding flocks of marine birds off Vancouver Island, natural history of the endemic Northern Saw-whet Owl on the Queen Charlotte Islands (see Fig. 8), and biology of the Northern Oriole in the Okanagan valley.

Fred C. Zwickel (Fig. 73), Professor Emeritus of Zoology at the University of Alberta, was born in Washington in 1926. He attended Washington State University where he obtained an M.Sc. degree in wildlife biology and in 1965 obtained his Ph.D. in zoology at the University of British Columbia on the population ecology of Blue Grouse on Vancouver Island. Nine graduate students worked nearly continuously on this species until 1984. Zwickel retired from the university in 1985 and is presently working with James F. Bendell on a 2-volume monograph on the Blue Grouse.

M. Timothy Myres was born in London, England in 1931. He obtained an M.A. and Ph.D. from the University of British Columbia on the behaviour of sea ducks. He joined the faculty at the University of Calgary in the Department of Biology in 1963 and retired in 1987. During that period he maintained his interest in research opportunities in British Columbia with radar studies of birds at sea and through the interior. He convinced Department of Transport personnel to have regular observations recorded at Ocean Station "Papa" from 1955 to 1983, when offshore weather ships were discontinued. His graduate students studied the behaviour and population ecology of Peregrine Falcons on the Queen Charlotte Islands and the distribution and movements of pelagic birds. For additional biographical information refer to Weseloh (1981) and Ealey (1986).

Conservation and Management of Birds in British Columbia

Federal Government

Canadian Wildlife Service

When Great Britain (on behalf of Canada) signed the Migratory Birds Convention with the United States in 1916, both parties hoped to end market hunting and embark on a broad policy of "insuring the preservation of such migratory birds as are either useful to man or are harmless." The subsequent endorsement of the convention by the parliament of Canada created the need for an enforcement agency with a strong scientific base. Today we know that agency as the Canadian Wildlife Service, but it was originally called the Migratory Birds Protection Office—a unit of the National Parks Service, headed by J.B. Harkin.

In 1920, James A. Munro was appointed as sole Migratory Bird Officer for the 4 western provinces. The addition of J. Dewey Soper in 1928, and Robie Tufts in 1933, allowed the division of the country into regions, and Munro was able to concentrate on British Columbia until his retirement in 1949. The decision to devote a large portion of the Migratory Bird Office's resources to British Columbia reflects the widespread unpopularity of the above mentioned legislation. It was not approved by the provincial government until special privileges, particularly the spring hunting of Brant, were guaranteed.

After World War II, the sudden expansion of Canada's population and the interest in developing the north led to the newly named Canadian Wildlife Service (CWS) being given the mandate for the conservation of wildlife on all federal lands, including the two northern territories and the national parks. CWS underwent a period of rapid expansion until the territorial governments established their own game branches. It was during that period that many nationally important researchers and wildlife managers were employed such as David A. Munro, John S. Tener, A.W. Frank Banfield, W.A. Fuller, John P. Kelsall, Anthony J. Erskine, Louis Lemieux, and F. Graham Cooch. Farley Mowat was also employed at that time and captures some of the pioneering spirit of the period in his stories.

CWS has come to represent Canada in inter-governmental and international matters involving wildlife, particularly those involving animals that migrate between Canada and the United

Figure 73. Fred Zwickel recording data on Blue Grouse population studies at the Comox burn, May 1972 (Jerome Mahrt).

States. CWS is also responsible for national programs involving threatened and endangered species and international trade in endangered species. Representatives are regularly sent to meetings of the International Ornithological Congress, International Waterfowl Research Bureau, and other important non-governmental agencies. Each year staff from British Columbia meet with other members of the Pacific Flyway Technical Committee, the Pacific Seabird Group, the Trumpeter Swan Society, the Wader Study Group, and the Society for Northwestern Vertebrate Biology. Those meetings help ensure that research and international management is coordinated and has the most up-to-date approach possible.

In British Columbia, CWS has both a research and administrative role in the conservation of migratory birds. CWS staff has inventoried seabird nesting colonies (Fig. 74) and made detailed studies of key species. Shorebird migration through the Fraser River estuary has been followed by banding thousands of birds on passage and studying their food requirements. However, the major effort has always involved waterfowl and their habitats. CWS has focused on the rich wintering grounds provided by coastal estuaries such as the Cowichan, Squamish, Chemainus, Little Qualicum, Nanoose/Bonell, and especially the Fraser River estuary. The Fraser estuary makes, by far, the greatest contribution in western Canada to the well-being of migrant waterfowl, shorebirds, gulls, herons, and many other species (see Butler, R.W. and Campbell 1987).

Throughout his career, James A. Munro was much concerned by the rate at which environment essential to the survival of many species was being destroyed. During the 1920s, he developed an understanding of the bird fauna of the province through the reports of a cadre of volunteers: the "Dominion Migratory Bird Officers," such as R.M. Stewart of Tlell, and officers of the Northwest Mounted Police (now Royal Canadian Mounted Police) who carried out mid-winter snowshoe and dogsled patrols to look for Trumpeter Swans in the Tweedsmuir Park area. He identified the most important areas under threat and established 5 Migratory Bird Sanctuaries between 1931 and 1944. Among those was Vaseux Lake, which today remains a spectacular patch of waterfowl habitat in the intensely developed southern Okanagan River valley.

David A. Munro joined the CWS in 1948 and opened an office at the University of British Columbia. His father, J.A. Munro, retired in 1949 and was replaced by Ronald H. Mackay who joined David at the university. They began conducting mid-

winter censuses of waterfowl along the coast and monitoring the harvest of ducks and geese during the annual hunting season. Mackay began his first studies of Trumpeter Swans that were to dominate his career for nearly 30 years.

In 1954, Munro left for duties elsewhere in Canada and was followed by Mackay in 1959. They were replaced by Robert D. Harris and W. Arthur Benson who continued and refined the waterfowl surveys. They also continued a program of providing winter feed for the Trumpeter Swans, at that time considered a vulnerable species. Inevitably, problems involving migratory birds increased as people extended their invasion of migratory bird habitats. An early problem was bird hazard to aircraft, especially at Vancouver International Airport. Harris undertook the problem study and was successful in devising ways of reducing the dangers to both aircraft and birds.

The expansion of agriculture in the small areas of flat land along river valleys introduced other hazards to birds. J.A. Munro had begun work on a particularly important flood plain of the Kootenay River at Creston. His impetus was continued by R.D. Harris, who gained the cooperation of Ducks Unlimited Canada, the United States Fish and Wildlife Service, and British Columbia Hydro and Power Authority to establish the Creston Valley Wildlife Management Area in 1968.

In 1965, the federal government embarked on an ambitous program to evaluate the production capability of the southern half of the country. Known as the Canada Lands Inventory (CLI), it was conceived as a tool for creating major land-use policies. The major categories of use were agriculture, forestry, recreation, game animals, and waterfowl. Ernest W. Taylor and Jose Carreiro joined the Vancouver office to survey waterfowl and wetlands in British Columbia. At about the same time, serious efforts were being made to understand British Columbia's role as a migration corridor. William A. Morris and Malcolm D. Noble travelled the interior banding ducks on breeding ponds and geese on migration stops.

An important development for CWS in British Columbia was the purchase, in 1972, of the Reifel farm in Delta. While the buildings provide a permanent home for research and administration, the surrounding land has become the Alaksen National Wildlife Area and is intensely managed for wintering waterfowl. It includes the George C. Reifel Bird Sanctuary (Fig. 75) which provides recreation and information to thousands of visitors every year.

The CWS staff in British Columbia, which consisted of a single energetic individual from 1923 to 1948, has grown to 34 members. The Alaksen office is the headquarters for CWS's Pacific and

Figure 74. *Triangle Island, August 1973 (R. Wayne Campbell). Canadian Wildlife Service staff have monitored populations and studied the biology of the birds that breed on this island—the largest seabird colony in the province.*

Figure 75. *George C. Reifel Bird Sanctuary and Alaksen National Wildlife Area on the Fraser River delta (R. Wayne Campbell). Through the cooperative efforts of the Canadian Wildlife Service, British Columbia Wildlife Branch, Ducks Unlimited Canada, and the British Columbia Waterfowl Society, these important lands are managed for the benefit of all wildlife and the people who enjoy viewing them.*

Figure 76. *Vaseux Lake Bird Sanctuary showing McIntyre Bluff, breeding site for White-throated Swifts (and formerly Peregrine Falcon), and Hatfield Island, breeding site for Canada Geese, 31 May 1978 (Robert A. Cannings).*

Yukon Region and supports branch offices at Qualicum Beach, Creston, and Whitehorse, Yukon.

Migratory Bird Sanctuaries

At present, 3,090 ha of land and water are protected in 7 Migratory Bird Sanctuaries:

1. **Christie Islet** (Howe Sound)
2. **Esquimalt Lagoon** (southern Vancouver Island)
3. **George C. Reifel** (Westham Island, Delta)
4. **Nechako River** (Vanderhoof)
5. **Shoal Harbour** (Sidney)
6. **Vaseux Lake** (Okanagan Falls; Fig. 76)
7. **Victoria Harbour** (Victoria)

National Wildlife Areas

There are 5 National Wildlife Areas (NWA) in British Columbia created under the Canada Wildlife Act of 1973. They comprise a total of 2,301 ha of land and water in the province:

1. **Alaksen** NWA (300 ha of upland and 283 ha of intertidal marsh, Westham Island)
2. **Columbia** NWA (1,000 ha, Columbia valley)
3. **Qualicum** NWA (83 ha, Vancouver Island)
4. **Vaseux Bighorn** NWA (792.3 ha, Okanagan valley)
5. **Widgeon Valley** NWA (125 ha, Pitt Lake)

As a result of the hearings on the reactivation of Boundary Bay Airport, a National Wildlife Area unit of 23 ha is being established along the edge of the bay.

Canada Land Inventory

In the multi-disciplined Canada Land Inventory of 1965 to 1970, CWS was responsible for the assessment and classification of wetlands' capability for waterfowl production and migration. During the 5-year term of the program, CWS personnel carried out ground and aerial assessments of all that portion of British Columbia lying south of 56°N latitude, and for that additional portion north from 56° to 59°N latitude between 120°W and 124°W longitude. The field data were used to draw capability maps and make synoptic descriptions of the environment and its use by waterfowl.

Environmental Assessment

Proposals for industrial development of habitats used by wildlife have been a constant and important part of the CWS operation. Among the major environmental impacts studied were the Vancouver International Airport expansion, the Roberts Bank Superport development, Boundary Bay wildlife and recreation plans and the Boundary Bay Airport reactivation, the northeast British Columbia coal development and its impact on marine birds because of the port expansion near Prince Rupert, and off-shore petroleum exploration. The key CWS staff in that activity have been E.W. Taylor, M.D. Noble, Laszlo Retfalvi, and Donald E.C. Trethewey.

Estuaries Working Group

Problems caused by the competition between man and wildlife for estuarine habitat have been a dominant subject of CWS activities. That competition extends to other groups of animals besides birds and has led to greater co-operation among the agencies responsible for their management. The interagency "estuaries working group" compiled a series of reports on the status of environmental knowledge for 10 major sites. They were used to develop federal-provincial management plans on the Cowichan (1972), Fraser (1977), and Squamish (1979) rivers that continue to guide development in those areas.

Research and Field Studies

Research has always played a major role in making reliable management decisions. The list of CWS projects over the past few years may seem piecemeal, but that only reflects the increased

Figure 77. *Barry Booth (left) and Stephen P. Wetmore studying the effects of logging on forest bird communities near Princeton, June 1983 (Stephen P. Wetmore).*

integration with supporting research carried out by provincial and American agencies and the universities. CWS research is given high priority and is directed to the solution of conservation problems brought on by human interference with the environment.

Since 1976, when the last major increase in staff took place in British Columbia, John P. Kelsall has studied the colonial activity of Great Blue Herons (Forbes et al. 1985a, 1985b); Kees Vermeer has looked at the breeding biology of colonial seabirds, their pelagic distribution, and the effectiveness of eagles in limiting gull populations (e.g. Vermeer 1978, 1979, 1981; Vermeer and Cullen 1982; Vermeer and Lemon 1986); Eoin McEwan investigated the winter habitat of Dunlin (McEwen, E.H. and Fry 1984); Richard W. McKelvey (1981b) looked at the carrying capacity of estuarine marshes used by Trumpeter Swans; Jean-Pierre L. Savard (1982, 1986) completed an exhaustive study of territoriality and its effect on breeding in Barrow's Goldeneye; Gary W. Kaiser monitored geographic variation in growth rates of nestling Rhinoceros Auklets (Bertram and Kaiser 1988); Stephen P. Wetmore (Fig. 77) looked at the impact of logging on forest birds (Wetmore et al. 1985); and Neil K. Dawe investigated the feasibility of creating or restoring estuarine marshes (Dawe and Jones 1986; Dawe and MacIntosh 1987; Dawe et al. 1987). Under the direction of Arthur M. Martell, research continues with W. Sean Boyd's study of the impact of Snow Geese on the Fraser River estuary marshes, Anthony J. Gaston's analysis of the breeding biology of the Ancient Murrelet; Austin Reed and Jim Hawkings' study of migratory Brant populations, and Robert W. Butler and Phillip E. Whitehead's investigation of the accumulation of dioxins in herons. None of these projects stands alone. All have involved university students as employees or as fellow researchers, and most functioned as part of a federal-provincial or inter-departmental team seeking the solution to a more general problem.

Provincial Government

Wildlife Branch

Since 1894, British Columbia has had a government office that administers laws and regulations to protect and manage wildlife, including birds. The office has had many names since it began under the Provincial Game and Forest Warden, including the Game Commission, Game Department, Fish and Game Branch, Fish and Wildlife Branch, and its present name of the Wildlife Branch. The responsibilities of this public service agency have greatly enlarged and diversified since the 1800s; what began as a harvest protection function now embraces population management, habitat protection and enhancement, conservation of endangered species, research, information and education, as well as administration and enforcement of the Wildlife Act. The history of wildlife management in British Columbia during the past 100 years is summarized by the Centennial Wildlife Society of British Columbia (1987).

The original concern for wildlife was about unrestricted and excessive harvests of the huntable or game species. In response to those concerns, the first efforts in 1895 dealt with harvest restrictions by prohibiting the buying and selling of any kind of deer as well as ducks, geese, woodcock, snipe, quail and grouse during stated periods between January and September (Cowan 1987). By the 1930s, the agency continued with its focus on huntable species by setting seasons and bag limits, and embarking on other methods of game management considered acceptable —controlling predators and introducing exotic species of game birds. For example, California and Mountain quail were released in the latter half of the 1800s, and the former was released again several times until at least 1910. Gray Partridges were introduced in several parts of the province in 1904 and 1909. Chukars were released several times up to 1956 and eventually established self-sustaining numbers. Ring-necked Pheasants were also released many times from the 1800s to the 1950s. From 1910 to 1933, government-funded pheasant farms reared birds for later release to hunters. Other attempted introductions included Wild Turkey, Northern Bobwhite, Crested Myna, and European species such as Black Grouse, Linnet,

Chaffinch, Skylark, Starling, and Capercaillie. Few of these were successful. In the 1920s and 1930s, the then Game Branch encouraged and participated in the control of hawks, owls, eagles, jays, crows, and ravens. Between 1922 and 1930, bounties were paid on 69,430 crows, 8,230 Black-billed Magpies, 7,204 eagles, and 20,625 hawks and owls. It was an unfortunate period, but with the enlightened concepts of wildlife biology during the 1940s, broad-scale, indiscriminate predator control was abandoned.

Beginning in the 1950s, the government wildlife agency underwent major changes in the scope of its activities and in the broadening of its philosophical basis of management. With the hiring of the first wildlife biologists in the late 1940s and 1950s, there was a progressive evolution to the Wildlife Branch of today, with its many activities on a wide, conservation-oriented front. With respect to birds, the Wildlife Branch now addresses the protection of all wild bird species (except the Rock Dove, crows, Black-billed Magpie, European Starling, and House Sparrow) and manages selected groups for a variety of reasons. The following offers a brief summary of activities conducted by Wildlife Branch staff in the management of British Columbia's bird fauna.

Population Management

The Wildlife Branch sets seasons and bag limits for game species. It also determines the levels of harvests through hunter questionnaires and by road checks. Productivity surveys are conducted for some species, such as drumming counts for Ruffed Grouse, and lek counts for Sharp-tailed Grouse. The Wildlife Branch conducts inventories of breeding populations of birds, particularly those whose numbers are low or otherwise of concern. In the interior, the province's only endangered species of birds, American White Pelican (Fig. 78) and Burrowing Owl, are censused regularly. Elsewhere in the province, Wildlife Branch staff have conducted surveys of Peregrine Falcons on the Queen Charlotte Islands at 5-year intervals, Gyrfalcons in the north, Bald Eagles along the coast in cooperation with the United States, Ospreys and Long-billed Curlews in the east Kootenay, and Spotted Owls in the old growth forests of southwestern mainland British Columbia.

The Wildlife Branch's primary goal is to ensure sustainable viable wildlife populations in the province. Staff have written, commissioned, and cooperated in the production of status reports for the Committee on the Status of Endangered Wildlife in Canada (COSEWIC) on the American White Pelican, Cooper's Hawk, Peregrine Falcon, Barn Owl, Flammulated Owl, and Spotted Owl. These species are of national as well as provincial interest. The Wildlife Branch has also participated in population enhancement activities for birds in British Columbia and in neighbouring jurisdictions. For example, Bald Eagles were transferred from Vancouver Island to California to re-establish wild populations there and Sharp-tailed Grouse from the Thompson area were sent to Montana to help rehabilitate their numbers. As well as those "exports", the Wildlife Branch has "imported" Burrowing Owls from Washington to the southern interior of the province to re-establish breeding populations in their former range. In addition to these "hands on" activities related to birds of immediate concern, Wildlife Branch staff participate in many inter-agency committees that address the conservation of birds.

Habitat Inventory

In 1985, the Wildlife Branch acquired the biophysical inventory activity that had originated with the Canada Land Inventory Program in 1965. Through the integration of diverse disciplines such as surficial geology, pedology, and plant and animal ecology, habitat elements critical to the management and protection of wildlife are identified and mapped. Similar mapping procedures have been used elsewhere in Canada, but in British Columbia professionals from various disciplines work for a common agency with unified project objectives. Inventory activities range from broad-scale ecoregion classification to critical area assessments. While this inventory activity was not established for birds (except in estuaries and shore-zones), the identification of specific habitat parameters from wetlands to old-growth forests is useful for any wildlife species. Several big game habitat inventory projects, however, have been concerned with bird habitat assessment as well. These include the Sheep Mountain Wildlife Area project in the East Kootenay Trench Ecosection, the Dewdrop Range project in the Thompson Basin, and the Skagit River project in the Cascade Range.

Figure 78. *American White Pelicans and Herring Gulls at Stum Lake breeding colony, 20 July 1971 (Ervio Sian).*

Habitat Management

Wildlife Branch staff spend considerable time and energy on habitat management, that is, on protecting and enhancing wildlife habitat. That is done via inter-agency planning activities and environmental impact assessments. About 18,000 referrals on land-use proposals are sent annually to regional and Victoria staff, and they deal with such widely differing activities as forest harvesting plans, mines, linear development, hydroelectric projects, pesticide applications, and wetland drainage proposals. Through referrals and inter-agency planning processes, the Wildlife Branch tries to reduce the adverse impacts of proposed activities on wildlife and their habitat via recommendations and guidelines. Those processes provide a general level of protection for all wildlife species, including birds.

Where it is not possible to protect birds and other wildlife by influencing other land use practices, the Wildlife Branch attempts to secure control over critical wildlife habitat. Several types of control are used. Map reserves are notations placed on maps held by the Ministry of Crown Lands that ensure Wildlife Branch staff are notified before an area is alienated. More than 200 map reserves exist, many of which are important to birds. For more critical habitats, a variety of more secure tenures are used, such as acquisition of private land, long-term lease, and transfer of administrative authority of certain crown lands. Often, private lands are acquired with the financial help of nongovernment organizations such as the Nature Trust of British Columbia, Nature Conservancy of Canada, Wildlife Habitat Canada, Ducks Unlimited Canada, as well as the province's Habitat Conservation Fund. The Wildlife Branch also enters into special partnerships for sensitive habitats (see Fig. 75), such as the Pacific Estuary Conservation Program, which is dedicated to preserving valuable estuarine habitats along the Pacific coast. To date, 125 areas consisting of 400,000 ha are under some kind of control. Many of those areas are important to birds, especially waterbirds, including Alkali Lake in the Chilcotin-Cariboo region, Englishman River estuary on Vancouver Island, Bummer's Flats in the east Kootenay, and McQueen's Slough in the Peace Lowlands.

The Branch has also designated Wildlife Management Areas (WMAs) for the management of important wildlife habitat. Of the 7 that currently exist, most are valuable for birds. For example, The Pitt WMA in the Fraser Lowlands is a popular wetland area for viewing birds; the Chilanko Marsh WMA in the Chilcotin-Cariboo region is an important marsh area for many bird species; the Reef Island WMA in the Queen Charlotte Islands is an important nesting area for colonial seabirds; and the Tranquille WMA near Kamloops is another significant wetland area.

As well, the Wildlife Branch is involved in other activities designed to protect habitat for birds including the placement of "Wildlife Tree" signs on trees that have special importance to birds and other wildlife, such as snags and eagle nest trees. Staff are developing policies and procedures for other government agencies and industry related to issues such as wildlife trees, old growth forests, and wetlands, that play key roles in maintaining habitat for birds.

In addition to the protection and acquisition of habitat, the Wildlife Branch is involved in enhancing habitat, both to rehabilitate degraded sites and to enhance an area's suitability to produce wildlife. A growing number of those activities are conducted specifically for birds, and, even those in which birds are not the target species, birds benefit. Some examples of projects for birds include the installation of nest boxes for bluebirds and American Kestrels in the Peace, Chilcotin-Cariboo, and Kootenay regions; the manipulation of vegetation and water in places such as the Pitt Wildlife Management Area to improve the production of food and cover through the creation of islands for nesting, clearing of waterways, and conversion of shrubby areas to productive plant communities; reclaiming damaged habitat through the burning of accumulated logs at Boundary Bay; removing invading trees in Long-billed Curlew habitat in the east Kootenay; installing artificial burrows for Burrowing Owls (Fig. 79); and cutting forests selectively in the Kamloops area to retain and provide trees suitable for cavity-nesting birds.

Figure 79. British Columbia Ministry of Environment staff and volunteers installing artificial burrows and holding pens for a Burrowing Owl transplant near Osoyoos Lake, May 1988 (Robert C. Lincoln).

Research

Traditionally, research has been a small part of the Wildlife Branch's efforts. However, staff have been involved in many research projects on birds, through direct financial support, logisitic services, publications, and administrative support. Some examples of projects include long-term studies on the population ecology of Vancouver Island Blue Grouse, breeding biology of American White Pelicans, tree selection of cavity nesting birds, Queen Charlotte Island Peregrine Falcon studies, Willow Ptarmigan in the northwest, Eared Grebes in the central interior, Ospreys in the west Kootenay, the Royal British Columbia Museum's vertebrate project, problem analysis on the effects of forest practices on Vancouver Island forest-dwelling birds, and Bald Eagles on the Fraser Lowlands. Also, the Branch was involved in a series of projects conducted mainly by graduate students at the University of British Columbia on the Fraser River estuary—bioenergetics of Snow Geese, primary productivity of foreshore vegetation, eelgrass ecology, decomposition of detritus, plant community structure, and habitat use by waterfowl. The Branch's role has been one of a cooperator and supporter of those studies.

Enforcement

Throughout its history, enforcement was a major function of the provincial wildlife agency. In fact, until the 1950s, regulation and enforcement were the primary activities of the agency as early regulations and laws demonstrate. Even though Conservation Officers were established as a separate Service in the Ministry of Environment in 1980, officers continue to enforce wildlife regulations (Fig. 80). They also play an important role in managing commercially valuable species such as raptors.

Figure 81. J. Bristol Foster on Solander Island, 5 May 1976 (R. Wayne Campbell). The first coordinator of the Ecological Reserves Unit, Foster was instrumental in establishing nearly 100 such reserves throughout the province.

Figure 80. Veterinarian Ken Langelier (left) and Conservation Officer Graham Turnbull releasing a rehabilitated Barred Owl near Nanaimo, January 1989. Many records for this volume have been obtained from these sources.

Ecological Reserves

One of the most significant developments for the protection of birds in British Columbia, particularly seabirds, came with the establishment of ecological reserves (Fig. 81).

In the mid 1960s, biologists in British Columbia became involved with the International Biological Programme, a cooperative project between the International Council of Scientific Unions and participating nations. Initially supported by the Canadian government, those scientists, under the leadership of Vladimir J. Krajina of the Department of Botany at the University of British Columbia, later convinced the provincial government to participate in efforts to survey and set aside areas of ecological significance. In 1968, a committee was formed for this purpose, composed of provincial civil servants and members of the academic community, and on 2 April 1971, the *Ecological Reserves Act* was passed by the British Columbia Legislature.

The *Ecological Reserves Act* allows setting aside areas of crown land for research and educational purposes and to protect representative examples of natural ecosystems, rare or endangered native species, and unique natural phenomena.

Marine bird colonies were recognized early as prime candidates for ecological reserve status and one of them, Cleland Island, became the first ecological reserve, established 4 May 1971. Since then, many of the important seabird colonies in the province have received ecological reserve status. At present, at least 20 ecological reserves hold bird nesting colonies. Included is Triangle Island (see Fig. 74), which encompasses the largest concentration of marine birds on the Pacific coast of Canada. Named Anne Vallee Ecological Reserve, to commemorate a young researcher who fell to her death from one of the island's towering cliffs, it holds about 622,000 breeding pairs of seabirds (M.S. Rodway pers. comm.). It is home to the world's largest Cassin's Auklet colony, the largest colony of Tufted Puffins south of Alaska, and the largest Common Murre colony in the province. It is the only breeding locality for Thick-billed Murres in British Columbia. Also, nesting Peregrine Falcons occur there.

Significant breeding populations, sometimes the largest in the province, occur in many of the remaining reserves, for example: Glaucous-winged Gull on **Chain Islets**, part of the Oak Bay Islands Ecological Reserve near Victoria; Pelagic Cormorant on the **Solander Island** reserve off Cape Cook, west Vancouver Island, and on the **Anthony Islands** reserve southwest of Moresby Island; Leach's Storm-Petrel in central eastern **Moresby Island**, in the **Anthony Islands** reserve and in the **Lepas Bay** reserve of northwest Graham Island; Fork-tailed Storm-Petrel in the **East Copper** and **Lepas Bay** reserves; Pigeon Guillemot on **Solander Island** and many other reserves; Ancient Murrelets in the **East Copper/Jeffrey/Rankine** reserve and on **Hippa Island**, part of the large **Vladimir J. Krajina Ecological Reserve** on the west coast of Graham Island.

There are 7 reserves where Peregrine Falcons are known to nest, 2 hold the uncommon Horned Puffin, and 1 is the suspected breeding habitat of the elusive Marbled Murrelet.

Several reserves with ornithological significance are still in the application stage at the time of writing, such as **Pine, Storm,** and **Tree islands** near Port Hardy, with large Fork-tailed and Leach's storm-petrel and Rhinoceros Auklet populations, and **Limestone Island** and **Dodge Point**, both in the Queen Charlotte Islands, with important Ancient Murrelet colonies.

Most seabird ecological reserves are closed to the public because of their vulnerability, but research under permit from the British Columbia Ministry of Parks is encouraged.

Inland ecological reserves focusing on bird life are less common. Red-throated Loons nest in the **Drizzle Lake** reserve in the interior of Graham Island and inland on the **Dewdney Island** reserve, located 150 km south of Prince Rupert. Both **Dewdney Island** and the **Mara Meadows** reserve near Enderby hold nesting Sandhill Cranes. Eared Grebe colonies occur in both an existing and a proposed ecological reserve near Williams Lake. The **Narcosli Lake** reserve northwest of Quesnel and the proposed **Boudreau Lake** reserve near Fort St. John are both prime interior waterfowl areas. Boudreau Lake is also important as a large Eared Grebe colony and as a Trumpeter Swan nesting locality.

Several upland bird species are protected in reserves established for other features, particularly vegetation.

Nongovernment Agencies

The Nature Trust of British Columbia

In July, 1971, the Right Honourable Pierre Elliot Trudeau, Prime Minister of Canada, in an address in Victoria stated:

> It is with great pleasure that I can announce this morning the disposition of the seven million dollars remaining of the ten million dollar centennial gift from the people of Canada to British Columbia . . .
>
> Four and one-half million will be placed in a special fund to be called the National Second Century Fund of British Columbia. The proceeds of this fund will be used to establish and develop nature conservation areas in every region of this province. I have asked Mr. Bertram Hoffmeister to become Chairman of the fund and I am pleased to announce that he has accepted.

Thus began one of the most imaginative and productive ventures in wildlife conservation anywhere in Canada. The Board of Directors of the National Second Century Fund, assisted by a small staff, has sought out and acquired conservation properties with a total area of 3,500 ha up to the end of 1986. These include 26 areas for which a most important purpose is the provision of habitat for birds. Many of the properties are marshes or estuaries where the interplay of biological and geomorphic forces leads to an especially rich fauna.

In 1984, the name of the National Second Century Fund was changed to The Nature Trust of British Columbia—a title that better describes the role of the fund. The lands purchased or received by gift are leased on a pro forma basis to the Provincial Ministry of the Environment, the Canadian Wildlife Service, or some other appropriate management body to operate under terms of reference established by the Trust.

Examples of areas now set aside in perpetuity for the protection of birds and other wildlife and for our enjoyment of the creatures that use them include: **Buttertubs Marsh** at Nanaimo, **Scout Island Nature Centre** at Williams Lake, **Swan Lake Christmas Hill Nature Centre** in Victoria, **Salmon River estuary, Qualicum National Wildlife Area** (Nanoose Unit), **Vaseux Wildlife Area** (Okanagan), **Duncan Flats** in the west Kootenay, **Kingcome River estuary** on the mainland coast, **Englishman River estuary** on Vancouver Island, **Coldfish Lake** on the Stikine River drainage, **Chilanko Marsh** and **Chilcotin Lake** in the Chilcotin, and **McQueen's Slough** and **Boundary Lake** in the Peace River district.

Ducks Unlimited Canada in British Columbia

Ducks Unlimited Inc. and Ducks Unlimited Canada (DU) are international, private, non-profit conservation organizations dedicated to maintaining and increasing North America's waterfowl populations through the preservation and enhancement of habitat.

Given the high quality and vulnerability of waterfowl habitat in British Columbia it was natural for DU Canada to play a role in the maintenance of British Columbia's waterfowl resource. Some "preliminary surveys" were carried out in 1940, but it wasn't until 1953 when DU Canada, as their first British Columbia project, assisted the Kelowna Sportsmen's Club in the development of Reisivig Slough. In 1954, DU Canada was registered as a company in British Columbia (and re-registered in 1968). Interest really developed almost 10 years later when the Creston valley, Becher's Prairie (Riske Creek), and the Fraser River delta were more closely appraised. Between 1964 and 1969, DU Canada assisted the British Columbia Waterfowl Society in the development of the marshes at the George C. Reifel Bird Sanctuary. The Serpentine Fen project in Surrey, built in 1973, was also being planned in the late 1960s. That project became the "nursery" for the establishment of the lower Fraser River valley Canada Goose flock.

Similarly, events in the Creston valley were leading up to the development of the largest complex of managed waterfowl habitat in the province (Fig. 82). In 1968, DU Canada assumed the task of designing and building the dykes, water controls, and islands, and installing pumps necessary to effect appropriate habitat management for the newly created Creston Valley Wildlife Management Area. Across the valley, complementary developments were carried out in cooperation with the Kootenay Indian Band. Over the 20 years since those wetland developments began, DU Canada has invested $1.8 million in the construction and maintenance of wetland management facilities in the Creston valley.

Between 1967 and 1969, DU Canada biologist, R.T. (Tom) Sterling and engineer, A.G.E. (Gunnar) Campbell investigated the potential for an extensive program throughout British Columbia. What they found was sufficient to establish a provincial office in Victoria and an area office in Creston in 1969. Campbell and Sterling became Provincial Engineer and Provincial Biologist respectively. The Creston office was managed by William E. (Bill) Hooey from its opening until his death in 1984. It was Hooey who promoted, negotiated, and supervised most of the DU Canada's work in the Creston valley.

During the 1970s, an area office was opened at Williams Lake (1972), and the provincial office was moved to Kamloops (1973). Annual aerial and ground reconnaissance provided an ever-expanding inventory of wetlands and potential project sites. Some of the more notable projects from that decade include the Chilko Ranch west pasture near Chilko Lake, Chilcotin Lake, Bald Mountain marshes, 108 Mile Lake marshes, and 148 Mile House marshes in the Chilcotin-Cariboo region; Cecil Lake in the Peace Lowlands; Swan Lake at Vernon; Moberly Marsh, Bummer's Flats, and Elizabeth Lake in the east Kootenay; and Pitt Marsh in the Fraser Lowlands.

Waterfowl habitat is generally secured through free easements with landowners coupled with construction of licensed water control structures designed to provide optimum water level management for waterfowl production. In the case of coastal and estuarine habitat, where water management as such is inappropriate, security is obtained through agreements tied to conservation legislation, or through support of fee simple ownership by appropriate land purchasing agencies such as The Nature Trust of British Columbia or Wildlife Habitat Canada.

In the 1980s, a significant increase in DU Canada's membership and revenues resulted in considerable growth in staff and the opening of 3 more area offices: Surrey, Kamloops, and Prince George. Sites such as Addington Point, Buttertubs Marsh, Cowichan Bay, Wolf Creek, Big Bar, Lac du Bois, Alixton Creek, Paxton valley, Chilanko Forks, Boundary Lake (Goodlow), Cranberry Lake, and Tatalaska Lakes were added to the list of projects. By December 1988, DU Canada had secured and developed 470

Figure 82. *Aerial view of the Corn Creek marshes and interpretive centre of the Creston Valley Wildlife Management Authority, 12 May 1988 (Ed Hennan). About 20 km of dykes, 30 water control structures, and 26 nesting islands have been built in this area by Ducks Unlimited Canada since the early 1970s.*

wetlands comprising about 20,000 ha of waterfowl breeding, migration, and wintering habitat in the province.

In the interior, the expanding programs of the 1980s meant that DU Canada was able to secure some of the more obvious, accessible, and threatened wetlands and press beyond that to habitats which would likely be in danger of loss or alteration in the near future. That was especially true in the Prince George, Nechako, and Peace River regions where a pioneering aspect of land-use was still in practice. Thus, numerous smaller wetlands were secured and developed during the decade. Hundreds more were investigated and reconnaissance reports filed.

Two major agreements were made during the 1980s to facilitate the process for securing waterfowl habitat. The first was a 5-year, automatically renewable Protocol Agreement with the British Columbia Ministry of Environment, signed in 1983. That agreement established a cooperative framework for securing and developing crown land wetlands and it provided a list of those habitats considered essential to the waterfowl resources of British Columbia.

The second agreement, signed in 1986, established a 3-year cooperative program between DU Canada, The Nature Trust of British Columbia, Wildlife Habitat Canada, and the British Columbia Ministry of Environment. The Pacific Estuary Conservation Program, in which the Canadian Wildlife Service, Fisheries and Oceans Canada, and the Ministry of Crown Lands are now participants, is designed to provide for the acquisition of important estuarine properties by nongovernment organizations, and the reservation of complementary crown foreshore habitat by the Ministry of Environment via the Ministry of Crown Lands. Ducks Unlimited Canada and the Ministry of Environment share the task of habitat rehabilitation and enhancement where appropriate. In the first 2 years of the program, 273 ha of strategic estuarine habitat were acquired and the administration of 300 ha of intertidal crown land was transferred to the Ministry of Environment.

In 1986, DU Canada also joined the Wildlife Branch and Canadian Wildlife Service on a permanent Waterfowl Technical Committee whose function it is to ensure efficient coordination of waterfowl and waterfowl habitat-oriented activities within the province.

British Columbia Waterfowl Society

On 15 December 1960, a group of sportsmen and game biologists of the Canadian Wildlife Service and the Provinical Fish and Game Branch met in the boardroom of the Vancouver *Province* newspaper, for a meeting chaired by Barry A. Leach. The purpose of the meeting was to discuss the formation of a society dedicated to the welfare of waterfowl and their habitat throughout British Columbia. At subsequent meetings in 1961, the formalities of organization were eventually concluded, and on 16 August 1961, the British Columbia Waterfowl Society was registered under the Societies Act.

The aims of the Society were:

1. To pursue the conservation of waterfowl and waterfowl habitat in British Columbia; 2. To establish and maintain waterfowl refuges in British Columbia; 3. To promote waterfowl study and research; 4. To promote public interest in waterfowl; 5. To improve the opportunities for public enjoyment of waterfowl.

As an initial focus for the Society's activities, an examination was made of wetlands of the Fraser lowlands and, in particular, those of the Fraser River estuary. The importance of the estuarine marshes to waterfowl, and the threat of industrial encroachment upon them, resulted in the selection of a portion of the foreshore lands of Westham Island as a site for the Society's operations (Leach 1970). Negotiations with the provincial Department of Lands and with Mr. George H. Reifel resulted in a reserve of 290 ha of Crown foreshore lands for sanctuary purposes under Order In Council 2595 effective 10 Oct. 1963, and a lease of approximately 40 ha of the adjoining Reifel farmland in March 1963. The combined area of those lands was named the George C. Reifel Waterfowl Refuge (see Fig. 75) in memory of Mr. Reifel's father whose interest in wildlife and conservation was long standing.

Funds for the development and operation of the Sanctuary were provided by donations from businessmen and, in 1964, through a Federal grant of $35,000 and $10,000 from Ducks Unlimited Canada. Those funds enabled the Society to construct a dyke enclosing some 40 ha of foreshore adjoining the upland dyke, to form an area which, through flooding or draining, would be of seasonal use to waterfowl. At the same time roads, a parking lot and observation tower were constructed.

In June 1967, a Federal Migratory Bird Sanctuary was established encompassing the provincial reserve and adjacent dyked lands leased to the Society. The total area of the sanctuary is 648 ha.

With the completion of major development in 1969, the number of visitors grew steadily and reached an estimated 80,000 persons annually from 1972 to 1976.

In 1972, the Canadian Wildlife Service purchased the Reifel farm and established the Alaksen National Wildlife Area. In so doing, they brought portions of the Sanctuary within the National Wildlife Area. Unfortunately the Refuge encountered financial problems between 1978 and 1983, and in 1983, the British Columbia Waterfowl Society was forced to turn to the Canadian Wildlife Service for help in keeping the Sanctuary operating. The Canadian Wildlife Service responded favourably to the appeal and agreed to take over the management and development aspects of the Sanctuary; budget restrictions and staff reductions, however, forced abandonment of further work and the plan was terminated in November, 1984. Since then, the Sanctuary operation has been maintained mainly through the support of Ducks Unlimited Canada.

The British Columbia Waterfowl Society has ensured the preservation of a substantial unit of estuarine wildlife habitat; it has stimulated public interest in avian wildlife and has provided an area for public enjoyment of this resource; and it has been of immeasurable benefit to an increasing number of migratory birds and other wildlife. Its avian use, particularly during winter months, embraces thousands of ducks of many species (Fig. 83), thousands of Snow Geese, many Canada Geese, shorebirds, gulls, raptors, passerines, and others. On occasion, it has been visited by species of birds rare to this part of the world whose appearance has attracted many bird-watchers and ornithologists from beyond the province.

Cooperative Wildlife Habitat Conservation

Today, perhaps more than ever, there is a need for cooperative efforts in the conservation of birds in the province, regardless of who has the legal mandate. Past efforts have resulted in 3 major projects that secure important habitat for birds.

1. Creston Valley Wildlife Management Area (6,477 ha) was established by the provincial government in 1968 as mitigation for the loss of waterfowl habitat brought on by the hydroelectric developments of the Columbia River Treaty. It is funded jointly by the Provincial and Federal governments with Ducks Unlimited Canada contributing most of the engineering development. It was the venue for a Canadian Wildlife Service Conservation Interpretive Program that attracted 35,000 visitors annually from 1973 until 1984 when the program became a function of the Creston Valley Wildlife Management Authority. The preservation of the area together with the habitat enhancement program has significantly increased bird diversity (Butler, R.W. et al. 1986).

2. Sturgeon Banks Cooperative Wildlife Area (130 ha) is based on a federal-provincial agreement signed in 1978. It sets aside the land from Gary Point near Steveston to Blundell Road in Richmond (about half of the front of Lulu Island) and acquisition of the remaining foreshore is being considered. The area is heavily used by Snow Geese and dabbling ducks but is also useful because it protects the high marsh for Short-eared and Snowy owls whose habitat is becoming very scarce in the lower mainland.

3. Ladner Marsh Cooperative Wildlife Area (78.6 ha) was established in 1980 and when complete should include the islands in the mouth of the Fraser River. It will provide a solid block of protected habitat on the south arm of the river contiguous with Alaksen National Wildlife Area and Sturgeon Banks Cooperative Wildlife Area.

Figure 83. Wintering and breeding waterfowl on the FraserRiver delta are becoming more dependent on areas such as the George C. Reifel Bird Sanctuary because of dwindling habitat (Ervio Sian).

THE ENVIRONMENT*

An Overview

British Columbia has many ecosystems due to its varied physiography and climates. It is located at mid- to northerly latitudes and is bounded on the west by oceanic influences of the northern Pacific Ocean and on the east by continental climates of the Interior Plains and Rocky Mountains. Its varied geological history has resulted in a complex topography. In addition, the province has had a complex climatic history. Current climatic patterns are varied but, most typically, the province is dominated by moist, cool to cold, temperate climates in a mountainous setting, most of which is higher than 1,000 m above sea level. The plants and animals of the province are affected by that environment and also by historic factors such as position of glacial refugia or barriers to dispersal and migration.

The combined influence of differential heating of land and ocean masses and the spin of the earth has created a general circulation in the earth's atmosphere (Thomson, R.E. 1981). That circulation is separated into a number of latitudinal belts, one being the prevailing westerly winds that influence British Columbia and most of southern Canada and the northern contiguous United States (Marsh 1988). Because of the prevailing winds, the general movement of the upper air is from west to east. Low and high pressure areas move across north-central North America embedded in the westerlies stream. Their movement is also associated with an interaction between southward flowing cold air

and northward flowing warm air. In winter, cold, high pressure areas dominate the interior of the continent and relatively warm, low pressure areas dominate the coastal areas. In summer the pattern is reversed with a large semi-permanent high pressure area over the northeastern Pacific dominating the general circulation in western Canada. These circulating patterns create 14 distinct regional climates (Fig. 84).

The rugged relief of the western cordillera has a great effect on the climate of western Canada, northern Washington, and the panhandle of Alaska. The Coast Mountains limit the mild, humid Pacific air to a narrow band along the coast. As the prevailing eastward-moving air is forced to rise over successive mountain ranges, precipitation occurs on windward slopes. The Rocky Mountains commonly block westward-moving outbreaks of cold Arctic air. Southward-moving Arctic air from the Yukon and northern British Columbia is impeded by the Coast Mountains and so flows into the interior of the province. During warm months, hot, dry air from the Great Basin of the United States occasionally moves into the southern interior plateau area from the southeast, bringing clear skies and hot temperatures.

Most of British Columbia is comprised of a series of land masses (terranes) that have collided with western North America during the past 190 million years (McMillan et al. 1987). The 2 major accretion events that have occurred have caused uplift and distortion of the original continental margin. These events are still happening as the last portion of the ocean plate disappears under the continent. By using these geological events, the province can be subdivided into several major physiographic units (Fig. 85). The oldest portion of the North American continent in the province, the northeastern plain, is a relatively flat plateau—the remnant of a great inland sea. West and southward,

---

* Prepared by D.A. Demarchi, R.D. Marsh, A.P. Harcombe, and E.C. Lea.

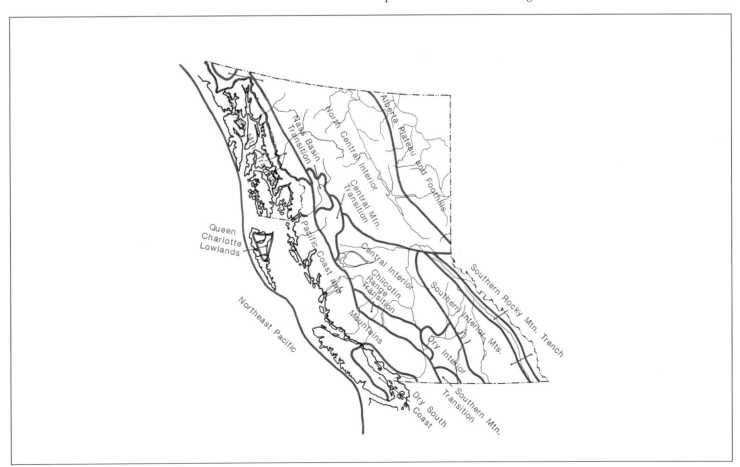

Figure 84. Macroclimatic regions of British Columbia (modified from Marsh 1988).

the former continental margin has been uplifted and distorted to form the Rocky and eastern Columbia mountains. In the centre of the province, the interior mountains and plateaus are composed of 4 large terranes and several smaller ones that form a superterrane that docked against the continent distorting the continental margin into the Rocky and Columbia mountains. The coastal mountains, islands, and continental shelf are composed of 2 large terranes and several smaller ones that docked as a second superterrane against the first. Intensive heating of basement rocks has resulted in a belt of extensive granitic intrusion. The westernmost portion of British Columbia is a deep-water, oceanic sea—the continental rise. That physiographic area consists of gentle slopes overlain by an apron of thick sediments.

Within the past 2 million years, 5 successive periods of continental glaciation, followed by warm periods, have occurred over British Columbia. The result has been a reshaping of the landforms and deposition of surface materials. Since the waning of the continental ice sheets 12,000 to 15,000 years ago, there have been several climatic fluctuations in the province (Clague 1981). As recently as a few hundred years ago, there was a short period of cordilleran ice build-up; however, the current climatic trend in British Columbia as we enter an era of global warming caused by the build up of "green house" gases possibly is for warmer and widely fluctuating climates.

The vegetation of British Columbia reflects the climatic and physiographic differences both provincially and regionally. Marked vegetation belts are a striking feature of regional vegetation. On the coast, the natural vegetation is needle-leaf forests of Douglas-fir, western redcedar, western hemlock, Sitka spruce, amabilis fir and yellow-cedar. They are some of the densest of all coniferous forests and hold some of the world's largest trees. On the upper mountain slopes lies a narrow subalpine belt of mountain hemlock and amabilis fir forests. Rugged, moist alpine is common at the higher elevations and relict glaciers dominate much of the high Pacific and Boundary ranges. In the Southern Interior, steppe vegetation dominates the major valleys and basins. Sagebrush, ponderosa pine, or Douglas-fir are common throughout. However, an increase in elevation prolongs the winter season enabling Douglas-fir, lodgepole pine, Engelmann spruce, and subalpine fir forests to become established. In the central interior and southeastern mountains at the lower levels is a montane belt of Douglas-fir and lodgepole pine forests, whereas western hemlock and western redcedar are characteristic where moisture is greatly increased. Above is the subalpine belt, dominated in most places by Engelmann spruce and subalpine fir or lodgepole pine forests. The uppermost vegetation belt is the alpine; quite often relict glaciers are present on the highest portions. In the Sub-Boreal Interior, the Sub-Boreal Pine - Spruce zone has forests of lodgepole pine with some white spruce, which are characteristic in the southern portion. In the northern portions, the Sub-Boreal Spruce zone forests of lodgepole pine, hybrid spruce, and subalpine fir are common. In the cold northern mountains, vertical vegetation is characterized by muskeg and black spruce in the low lying, poorly drained areas, or willow - birch shrublands in the low valleys where cold air frequently pools. White spruce, lodgepole pine, subalpine fir, and occasionally trembling aspen occur on the midslopes. Alpine grasslands dominate most rounded summits while barren rock or mat-vegetation occur on the highest summits. On the Alberta Plateau, white and black spruce and lodgepole pine forests are dominant. Some poorly drained areas have muskeg with black spruce and tamarack and the lower basins and riverbreak areas have shrub-rich grasslands intermixed with aspen. In the Fort Nelson Lowlands, extensive wetlands and muskeg occur over much of the area because it is so poorly drained, although the better drained upland areas have well developed boreal forests.

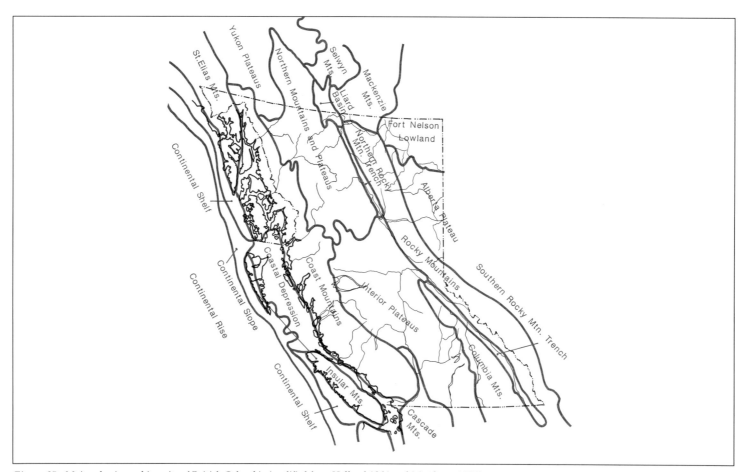

Figure 85. *Major physiographic units of British Columbia (modified from Holland 1964 and Matthews 1986).*

Ecoregions of British Columbia

The understanding of British Columbia's complex environment is essential for the management, utilization, and conservation of the province's natural resources. Like a map, the purpose of a regional ecosystem classification scheme is to organize the ecological mosaic into simple patterns and to provide a practical framework for managing natural resources (Bailey, R.G. and Hogg 1986). Several regional classification schemes exist for the stratification of parts of North America into ecosystem units. Each has its positive attributes, but each also has shortcomings for delineating regional ecosystems in a mountainous area such as British Columbia (see Munro, J.A. and Cowan 1947; Krajina 1965; Bailey, R.G. 1980, 1983; Wiken 1986).

Recently, an Ecoregion classification was developed for British Columbia to provide a systematic view of the small scale ecological relationships in the province (Demarchi, D.A. 1987, 1988a. This classification is based on macroclimatic processes (Marsh 1988), and physiography (Holland 1964), and it brings into focus the extent of critical habitats and their relationship with adjacent areas. Through time, each Ecoregion unit will be more clearly identified with additional animal observations, population evaluations, and habitat inventory.

Our mountainous province has also caused another level of complexity, that of topo-climatic zonation. Within each terrestrial region bounded by climatic processes and landform parameters, there are climatic zones that are reflected by the plant and animal communities present. This level is best pursued through the Biogeoclimatic Ecosystem Classification (Krajina 1965; Pojar et al. 1987; British Columbia Ministry of Forests 1988).

At the biogeoclimatic subzone level, the climate interacts with land surface materials to create particular environments suitable for the development of specific plant and animal communities (Rowe 1984; Demarchi, D.A. and Lea 1987). Oceanic environments, however, are the products of temperature, salinity, sea-bed configuration, and water depth (Thomson, R.E. 1981).

Ecoregion Classification

The Ecoregion classification of British Columbia divides the province into 119 units (Fig. 89; Table 4). However, arranging them into a hierarchical classification simplifies the result and makes them a useful tool for managing the natural resources of the province. The hierarchical levels have been defined as follows:

1. Ecodomain - an area of broad climatic uniformity,
2. Ecodivision - an area of broad climatic and physiographic uniformity,
3. Ecoprovince - an area with consistent climate or oceanography, relief, and plate tectonics,
4. Ecoregion - an area with major physiographic and minor macroclimatic or oceanographic variation,
5. Ecosection - an area with minor physiographic and macroclimatic or oceanographic variation.

The Ecodomains and Ecodivisions are very broad and place British Columbia in a global context (Figs. 86 and 87). Ecoprovinces, Ecoregions, and Ecosections are progressively more detailed and narrow in their scope and relate the province to other parts of North America or the Pacific Ocean, or segments of the province to each other (Fig. 88 and 89; Table 4). These lower 3 classes describe areas of similar climate, physiography, vegetation, and wildlife potential. Each Ecoregion or Ecosection class can be further subdivided by biogeoclimatic criteria to provide a basis for detailed interpretation of climate, topography, soil, and vegetation in the context of habitat and wildlife management.

Ecodomains

There are only 4 Ecodomains in North America (Bailey, R.G. 1980, 1983), and 3 in the surrounding oceans. British Columbia has 4 Ecodomains: **Cool Oceanic, Humid Temperate, Dry,** and **Polar** (Fig. 86).

The **Cool Oceanic Ecodomain** extends from the eastern Asian shore to western North America, north of the North Pacific Current (latitude 40°N). It is characterized by counterclockwise rotating oceanic gyres and a slow-moving westerly sub-Arctic current. In British Columbia it occurs from the 200-mile (300 km) limit to the continental shelf.

The **Humid Temperate Ecodomain** covers most of the mid-latitudes of North America from the east coast to the west. In British Columbia it occurs in the coastal islands and mountains, the central interior plateau, and the southern interior mountains. The climate is characterized by strong seasonal cycles of temperature and precipitation with a distinct winter.

The **Dry Ecodomain** covers the southern interior plateau and is an extension of the dry climate regime that occupies the interior of northern Mexico and the northwestern United States. Its 2 most commonly recognized climates are arid desert and semiarid steppe.

The **Polar Ecodomain** covers the northern latitudes. In British Columbia, it occupies the northern plains, mountains, and plateaus. Its climate is characterized by generally low temperatures, a severe winter, and only small amounts of precipitation.

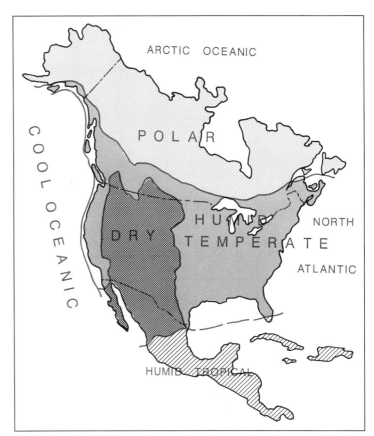

Figure 86. *Ecodomains of North America and the adjacent oceans.*

Ecodivisions

Continental or Oceanic resource planning occurs at the Ecodivision level. It is similar to the Ecozone classification of Wiken (1986). British Columbia contains components of 7 Ecodivisions (Fig. 87).

The **Sub-Arctic Pacific Ecodivision** occurs within the cool Oceanic Domain (Table 4) in the oceanic portion of the province. It contains the continental rise portion of the margin of the continent. The Sub-Arctic Current has a broad, slow, easterly drift. Near the coast of North America a divergence in the prevailing wind pattern causes the current to split; a northern branch to the northeast into the Gulf of Alaska (Alaska Current) and a southern branch to the southeast (California Current). The coast of British Columbia is at the point of this split with the Alaskan Current reaching west of Queen Charlotte Sound in the winter and the northern Queen Charlotte Islands in the summer. The California Current reaches south of British Columbia in the winter and northern Vancouver Island in the summer.

The **Humid Maritime and Highlands Ecodivision** is 1 of 2 in the province that are assigned to the Humid Temperate Ecodomain (Table 4). It occurs along the coast from sea level to the height of land on the Coast Mountains. It includes the Nass Basin and Nass Ranges. Its climate is temperate and rainy with warm summers. Precipitation is abundant throughout the year but is markedly reduced in summer. There is much cloud cover. The natural vegetation is usually a coniferous forest of Douglas-fir, western redcedar, western hemlock, Sitka spruce, amabilis fir, and yellowcedar. It contains some of the world's largest trees and some of the densest coniferous forests. In drier parts of the extreme south of the province, it contains arbutus and Garry oak communities.

The **Humid Continental Highlands Ecodivision** is the second part of the Humid Temperate Ecodomain in British Columbia. It occurs in the southeastern mountains and central plateau but does not cover the southern plateau area. It has a cold snowy winter with a warm summer. Precipitation is ample all year. The natural vegetation is a coniferous forest arranged in striking belts. At the lower levels there is a montane belt of Douglas-fir, and in the south, western larch. Grasslands are exceptional. The subalpine belt is usually dominated by Engelmann spruce and subalpine fir but western hemlock and western redcedar occur where moisture is increased. The uppermost belt is alpine where trees are absent.

The **Semi-Arid Steppe Highlands Ecodivision** occurs within the Dry Ecodomain (Table 4) in southern British Columbia and includes the leeward ranges of the Coast Mountains, the Thompson Plateau, the Clear Range, the Okanagan Range, and the western side of the Okanagan and Shuswap highlands. Winters are cold and the summers are warm to hot. Vegetation in the valleys and basins is typically steppe or bunchgrass prairie that may contain sagebrush or occasional ponderosa pine or Douglas-fir. At higher altitudes, coniferous forests can become established.

The **Boreal Ecodivision** is 1 of 3 parts of the Polar Ecodomain in British Columbia. It occurs east of the Hart and Muskwa ranges, in their foothills and in the Alberta Plateau, on plateau, uplands, and in the Peace River Lowlands. There is typically a cold winter and a moderately warm summer. There is little precipitation. In the lowland areas, moist grasslands mixed with trembling aspen develop. White and black spruce, and lodgepole pine dominate the uplands.

The **Sub-Arctic Ecodivision** lies north of the Boreal Ecodivision and is the second part of the Polar Ecodomain in the province. It extends from the Fort Nelson River Basin to the border of the Northwest Territories. It is semiarid and cold. Winters are long and summers brief but plants gain some advantage from the longer hours of daylight. There are some areas of permafrost. The riparian areas are dominated by balsam poplar. Better drained upland sites have white and black spruce, lodgepole pine, and tamarack. Extensive wetlands and muskeg occur throughout the area because of poor drainage.

The **Sub-Arctic Highlands Ecodivision** is the third part of the Polar Ecodomain in British Columbia (Table 4). It includes the mountains, high plateaus, and intermontane lowlands that extend from the northern part of the province into the Yukon, Northwest Territories, and Alaska. The area has severe and long winters with short summers. Precipitation does not vary greatly through the year but mountains in the east are generally drier than those in the west. Vegetation is characterized by muskeg and black spruce in low-lying areas with poor drainage. Low valleys often have willow-birch shrublands. White spruce and subalpine fir, and occasionally aspen, occur on the middle slopes. Alpine grasslands dominate most rounded summits, while barren rock, and mat-vegetation occurs on the highest peaks.

Ecoprovinces, Ecoregions, and Ecosections

There are 10 Ecoprovinces in British Columbia (Fig. 88; Table 4) that delimit areas of similar climate or oceanography, topography, and geological history. Their size and broad internal uniformity make them ideal units for the implementation of natural resource policies. They form the framework for the discussion that follows. The Ecoprovinces are divided into 30 Ecoregions and 68 Ecosections which are at a scale and detail suitable for local resource management (Fig. 89). Together, the 3 lower levels of classification put the avifauna of British Columbia in a subcontinental, provincial, or regional perspective.

What follows is an overview of the macroclimatic processes, landforms and their evolution, oceanography, vegetation, and representative wildlife species for each of the 10 Ecoprovinces that occur in British Columbia. Each account also includes either a biogeoclimatic or an oceanographic zone map and concludes with a brief description of the Ecoregion and Ecosection levels.

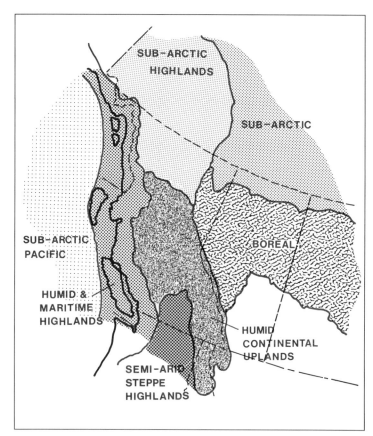

Figure 87. *Ecodivisions of British Columbia and surrounding areas.*

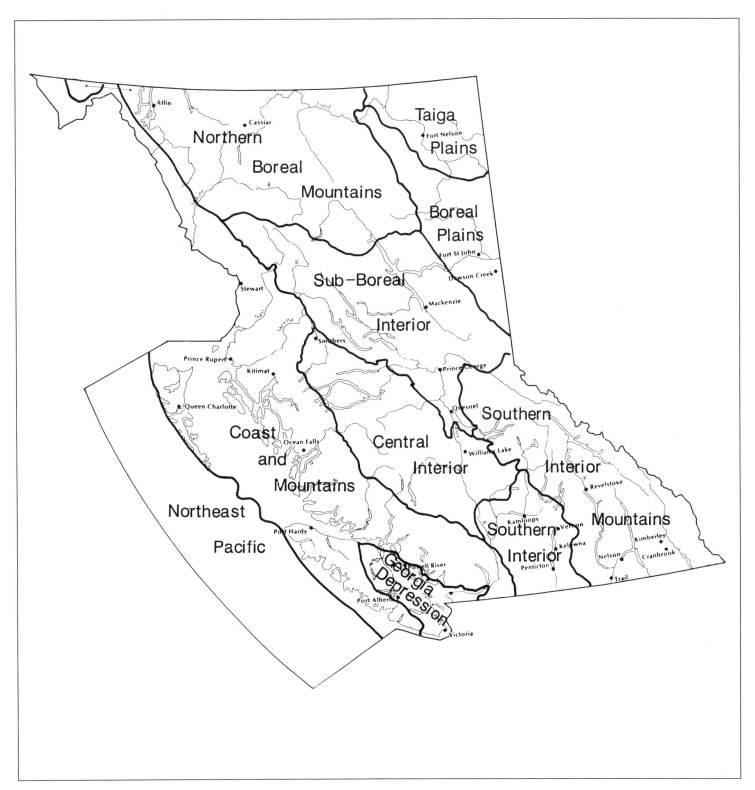

Figure 88. *Ecoprovinces of British Columbia.*

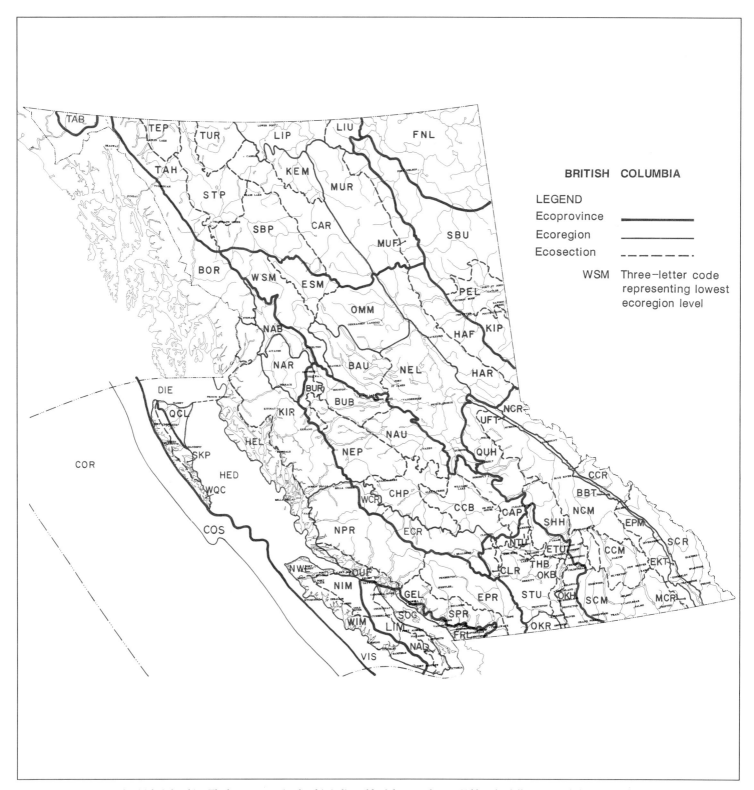

Figure 89. *Ecoregions of British Columbia. The lowest ecoregion level is indicated by 3-letter codes; see Table 4 for full names and classification level.*

			TABLE 4		
			Levels of Ecoregion delineation in British Columbia.		
Ecodomain	Ecodivision	Ecoprovince	Ecoregion	Ecosection	Code*
Cool Oceanic	Sub-Arctic Pacific	Northeast Pacific	Continental Rise	–	COR
			Continental Slope	–	COS
Humid Temperate	Humid Maritime and Highlands	Coast and Mountains	Boundary Ranges	–	BOR
			Coastal Gap	Hecate Lowland	HEL
				Kitimat Ranges	KIR
			Continental Shelf	Dixon Entrance	DIE
				Hecate Depression	HED
				Vancouver Island Shelf	VIS
			Nass Basin	–	NAB
			Nass Ranges	–	NAR
			Pacific and Cascade Ranges	Eastern Pacific Ranges	EPR
				Northern Pacific Ranges	NPR
				Outer Fiordland	OUF
				Southern Pacific Ranges	SPR
			Queen Charlotte Lowland	–	QCL
			Queen Charlotte Ranges	Skidegate Plateau	SKP
				Windward Queen Charlotte Mtns.	WQC
			Western Vancouver Island	Northern Island Mountains	NIM
				Nahwitti Lowland	NWL
				Windward Island Mountains	WIM
		Georgia Depression	Eastern Vancouver Island	Leeward Island Mountains	LIM
				Nanaimo Lowland	NAL
			Lower Mainland	Fraser Lowland	FRL
				Georgia Lowland	GEL
			Strait of Georgia	–	SOG
	Humid Continental Highlands	Central Interior	Chilcotin Ranges	Eastern Chilcotin Ranges	ECR
				Western Chilcotin Ranges	WCR
			Fraser Plateau	Bulkley Basin	BUB
				Bulkley Ranges	BUR
				Cariboo Plateau	CAP
				Chilcotin-Cariboo Basin	CCB
				Chilcotin Plateau	CHP
				Nazko Upland	NAU
				Nechako Plateau	NEP
		Sub-Boreal Interior	Central Rocky Mountains	Hart Foothills	HAF
				Hart Ranges	HAR
			Fraser Basin	Babine Upland	BAU
				Nechako Lowland	NEL
			Skeena and Omineca Mountains	Eastern Skeena Mountains	ESM
				Omineca Mountains	OMM
				Western Skeena Mountains	WSM

* Three-letter code representing lowest Ecoregion level (see Fig. 89).

(continued on next page)

| | | | | TABLE 4 (Continued) | |
| | | | | Levels of ecoregion delineation in British Columbia. | |
Ecodomain	Ecodivision	Ecoprovince	Ecoregion	Ecosection	Code*
		Southern Interior Mountains	Columbia Mountains and Highlands	Central Columbia Mountains	CCM
				Eastern Purcell Mountains	EPM
				McGillivary Range	MCR
				Northern Columbia Mountains	NCM
				Quesnel Highland	QUH
				Southern Columbia Mountains	SCM
				Shuswap Highland	SHH
			Southern Rocky Mountains	Central Continental Ranges	CCR
				Northern Continental Ranges	NCR
				Southern Continental Ranges	SCR
			Southern Rocky Mountain Trench	Big Bend Trench	BBT
				East Kootenay Trench	EKT
				Upper Fraser Trench	UFT
Dry	Semi-Arid Steppe Highlands	Southern Interior	Okanagan Range	–	OKR
			Thompson-Okanagan Plateau	Clear Range	CLR
				Eastern Thompson Upland	ETU
				Northern Thompson Upland	NTU
				Okanagan Basin	OKB
				Okanagan Highland	OKH
				Southern Thompson Upland	STU
				Thompson Basin	THB
Polar	Boreal	Boreal Plains	Alberta Plateau	Kiskatinaw Plateau	KIP
				Peace Lowland	PEL
				Sikanni-Beatton Plateau	SBU
	Sub-Arctic	Taiga Plains	Fort Nelson Lowland	–	FNL
	Sub-Arctic Highlands	Northern Boreal Mountains	Tatshenshini Basin	–	TAB
			Liard Basin	Liard Plain	LIP
				Liard Upland	LIU
			Northern Mountains and Plateaus	Cassiar Ranges	CAR
				Kechika Mountains	KEM
				Southern Boreal Plateau	SBP
				Stikine Plateau	STP
				Tahltan Highland	TAH
				Teslin Plateau	TEP
				Tuya Range	TUR
			Northern Rocky Mountains	Muskwa Foothills	MUF
				Muskwa Ranges	MUR

* Three-letter code representing lowest Ecoregion level (see Fig. 89).

Northeast Pacific Ecoprovince

> ECODOMAIN - COOL OCEANIC
>
> ECODIVISION - SUB-ARCTIC PACIFIC
>
> **ECOPROVINCE - NORTHEAST PACIFIC**
>
> Ecoregions - Continental Rise
>   - Continental Slope

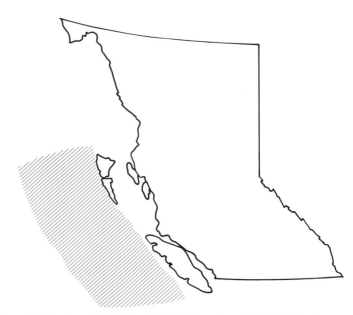

Figure 90. *Location of the Northeast Pacific Ecoprovince in British Columbia.*

Location

The Northeast Pacific Ecoprovince is the oceanic portion of British Columbia west of the Continental Slope—the 200-mile (300 km) Economic Expansion Zone (Fig. 90). It consists of the Continental Slope and Rise. Commercial fishing (Fig. 91) is the most important industry in the area.

Climate

The prevailing winds in the northeast sector of the Pacific Ocean are determined by 2 major pressure cells, the Aleutian Low and the North Pacific High. Those pressure systems influence the movement of winds and frontal systems. Storm tracks are commonly directed eastward and northeastward toward the coast. The Aleutian Low gradually increases in intensity from August to December as its centre shifts southeastward from the northern Bering Sea to the Gulf of Alaska. Maximum intensity of the low pressure cell and its associated counterclockwise winds occur in January. That is followed by a progressive weakening until July when the system is no longer evident. Generally light and variable winds occur in the Gulf of Alaska in July. The North Pacific High, which centres around 30°N to 40°N off the California coast, is pre-

sent year-round, and reaches maximum intensity from June to August, when it almost encompasses the entire Northeast Pacific Ocean. The combined pressure pattern produced by these 2 systems means that from late autumn to early spring, winds will be predominantly from southeast to southwest along the British Columbia and Washington coasts as the air circles counter clockwise around the dominant Aleutian Low, while from late spring to early autumn, the combined effect of a greatly weakened Aleutian Low and intensified North Pacific High results in a clockwise flow of air over the ocean. Coastal winds at that time are predominantly from the northwest. Hence, winds that are from directions other than northwest and southwest to southeast are only incidental to traditional weather systems.

Figure 91. *California Gulls and Sooty Shearwaters following a packing ship on the Continental Slope Ecoregion, October 1987 (Michael Force). Along the northeast margin of the Pacific Ocean, upwelling currents provide nutrients for the growth of plankton which supports large populations of fish.*

Physiography

The Ecoprovince consists of only 2 major physiographic systems (Fig. 92). The Continental Rise includes the more gentle slopes of the seaward edge of the continental margin. It is covered by an apron-thick sediment that has been deposited by sediment-laden water that flows downward along the sea floor from the adjacent Continental Slope. The bottom is characterized by broad underwater ridges, with peaks and valleys reminiscent of rift mountains on the continent. Those submarine ridges mark regions of active seafloor spreading off the coast of British Columbia. The Continental Slope is a steep oceanic region that marks the seaward extent of North America. The outer edge is delineated by the 1,800 m contour, while the inner edge rises to 180 m. In British Columbia, the Continental Slope has a highly rugged terrain of bumps, knobs, and deep-faced canyons.

Oceanography

The Northeast Pacific Ecoprovince in British Columbia (Fig. 93) lies almost entirely in the dilute salinity domain, where fresh water discharge from the coast has diluted the upper layer of the ocean. Because west coast rivers discharge considerably more water in warm months than cold, the maximum influence of coastal runoff influence lies farther west in summer and autumn than in winter and spring. Adjacent to the coast, offshore from central Vancouver Island to southern California, lies the upwelling salinity domain, where northwest winds cause deeper cold water to rise to the surface. In addition, there are 3 distinct vertical salinity layers. The upper layer extends to a depth of approximately 100 m and has the greatest seasonal variability with respect to temperature, salinity, plankton distribution, and nutrients. Beneath that layer to about 200 m is a stable layer of water. In the lower layer of water, salinity and temperature change more gradually to the bottom and undergo very minor alteration over periods of years or centuries.

Fauna

At least 158 nonpasserines have been reported from the Ecoprovince (Table 5). Characteristic species include Laysan Albatross, Northern Fulmar, Pink-footed Shearwater, Buller's Shearwater, Short-tailed Shearwater, Red Phalarope, the jaegers, South Polar Skua, Black-legged Kittiwake, and Sabine's Gull. Many passerine species occur at sea but only as migrants. Undoubtedly, thousands perish before reaching land. Marine mammals include northern fur seal, sperm whale, pacific white-sided dolphin, and Dall's porpoise.

Ecoprovince Subdivisions

The Northeast Pacific Ecoprovince contains 2 Ecoregions; no Ecosections have been recognized (see Figs. 89 and 93; Table 4).

The **Continental Rise Ecoregion** is the deep sea portion of British Columbia.

The **Continental Slope Ecoregion** is a relatively steep-floored oceanic area. Upwelling currents are common along its length.

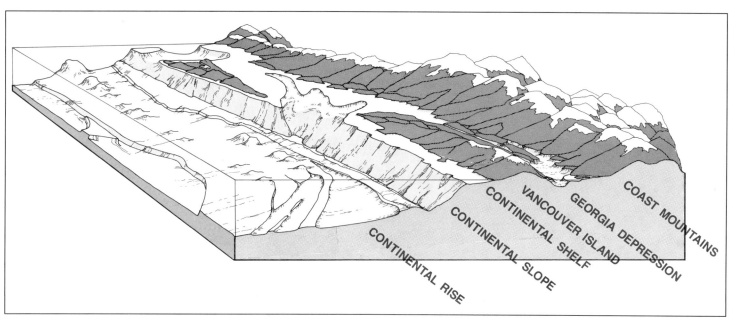

Figure 92. Profile of the oceanic margin of British Columbia.

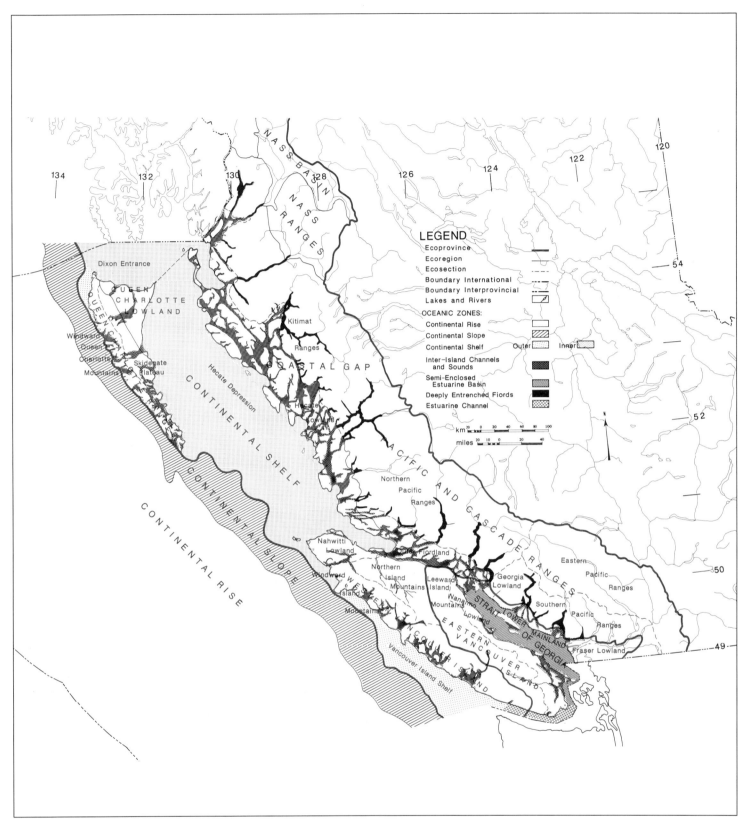

Figure 93. *Oceanic zones and Ecoregion units in the Northeast Pacific, Coast and Mountains, and Georgia Depression ecoprovinces.*

TABLE 5
Total number and percent of nonpasserine and passerine species known to occur and breed
in the 10 Ecoprovinces of British Columbia through December 1987.

Ecoprovince		Total species	% a	Breeding species	%b
Northeast Pacific	Nonpasserines	158	59	0	
	Passerines	c		0	
Coast and Mountains	Nonpasserines	213	80	86	55
	Passerines	137	77	83	58
Georgia Depression	Nonpasserines	239	90	88	57
	Passerines	163	91	90	63
Central Interior	Nonpasserines	161	61	91	59
	Passerines	129	72	91	64
Sub-Boreal Interior	Nonpasserines	135	51	67	43
	Passerines	119	66	69	49
Southern Interior Mountains	Nonpasserines	174	65	87	56
	Passerines	138	77	97	68
Southern Interior	Nonpasserines	187	70	104	67
	Passerines	143	80	103	73
Boreal Plains	Nonpasserines	145	55	64	41
	Passerines	125	70	73	51
Taiga Plains	Nonpasserines	101	38	43	28
	Passerines	89	50	62	44
Northern Boreal Mountains	Nonpasserines	131	49	71	46
	Passerines	103	58	55	39
Provincial Total	Nonpasserines	266	100	155	100
	Passerines	179	100	142	100

a. Expressed as a percent of the total species reported from the province.

b. Expressed as a percent of the total breeding species reported from the province.

c. Many passerines occur at sea but normally only as migrants.

Coast and Mountains Ecoprovince

ECODOMAIN - HUMID TEMPERATE

ECODIVISION - HUMID MARITIME AND
HIGHLANDS

ECOPROVINCE - COAST AND MOUNTAINS

Ecoregion - Boundary Ranges

Ecoregion - Coastal Gap

Ecosections - Hecate Lowland
- Kitimat Ranges

Ecoregion - Continental Shelf

Ecosections - Dixon Entrance
- Hecate Depression
- Vancouver Island Shelf

Ecoregion - Nass Basin

Ecoregion - Nass Ranges

Ecoregion - Pacific and Cascade Ranges

Ecosections - Eastern Pacific Ranges
- Northern Pacific Ranges
- Outer Fiordland
- Southern Pacific Ranges

Ecoregion - Queen Charlotte Lowland

Ecoregion - Queen Charlotte Ranges

Ecosections - Skidegate Plateau
- Windward Queen Charlotte
Mountains

Ecoregion - Western Vancouver Island

Ecosections - Northern Island Mountains
- Nahwitti Lowland
- Windward Island Mountains

Figure 94. *Location of the Coast and Mountains Ecoprovince in British Columbia.*

Climate

The major climatic processes involve the arrival of frontal systems from the Pacific Ocean and the subsequent lifting of those systems over the coastal mountains. In winter, oceanic low pressure systems dominate the area and pump moist, mild air onto the south and central coast. In summer, high pressure systems occur over the north Pacific Ocean and frontal systems become less frequent and tend to strike the coast farther north.

Various climatic subregions can be distinguished by the frequency of arriving fronts, the height of the mountains, the importance of rainshadow effects, and the frequency of Arctic air outbreaks. The southern coastal areas of Vancouver Island and the Pacific Ranges, are subjected to less frequent frontal systems. Where the coastal mountains are very high, they impede the passage of moist air into the interior. The central coast, Hecate Lowlands, and Kitimat Ranges are subjected to the greatest frequency of frontal systems. However, the central coast mountains are the lowest on the coast and the moist, oceanic air can move into the interior easily. The north coast, the Boundary Ranges, and the Alaska Panhandle are subjected to less frequent frontal systems. The mountains are very high and block the passage of moist, oceanic air into the interior. Rainshadow effects occur on the lee of Queen Charlotte Islands, in the Queen Charlotte Lowlands and in the Nass Basin. Those areas have drier conditions than other areas on the coast. The Nass Basin in addition, is subjected to frequent outbreaks of cold, dense Arctic air in the winter.

Physiography

The Coast and Mountains Ecoprovince consists of the large coastal mountains, a broad coastal trough and the associated lowlands, islands (Figs. 95 and 96), and Continental Shelf, as well as the insular mountains on Vancouver Island and the Queen Charlotte Islands archipelago.

Although glacial scouring modified the topography by sharpening the high peaks and rounding the lower ones while widening and deepening the valleys and fiords, the topographic framework was present before the coming of the ice. Great volumes of glacial materials were deposited in a widespread mantle of drift in valleys, as outwash plains and as end moraines when the ice waned. The great load of glacial ice, with a thickness of as much as 2,400 m depressed the land. With the melting of the ice the land has rebounded. Streams have been rejuvenated because of the rise, with the result that box canyons have been cut in many of the lower courses of drift.

Location

This Ecoprovince extends from coastal Alaska to coastal Oregon (Fig. 94). In British Columbia it includes the windward side of the Coast Mountains and Vancouver Island, all of the Queen Charlotte Islands, and the Continental Shelf including Dixon Entrance, Hecate Strait, Queen Charlotte Strait and the Vancouver Island Shelf (Fig. 97).

The forest industry dominates the landscape and clearcut logging has changed the habitats over large portions of the Ecoprovince (Fig. 108). Commercial fishing is also important but has less of an environmental impact. Mariculture, on the other hand, does have a significant impact on shoreline habitats and is in a period of rapid growth and development. There is no significant agricultural development in the area. All of the resource extraction industries are coming into more frequent conflict with the needs of a rapidly expanding tourism and recreation industry.

Figure 95. *Solander Island, west of Cape Cook on the Brooks Peninsula, Vancouver Island, August 1978 (R. Wayne Campbell). Exposed islands and islets, with stunted shrubs, grassy knolls, and rocky cliffs, are important seabird nesting colony sites along the outer coastline.*

Figure 96. *Reef Island, east of Moresby Island, Skidegate Plateau Ecosection, 11 July 1977 (R. Wayne Campbell). Coastal islands often have steep, rocky sides and forested crowns.*

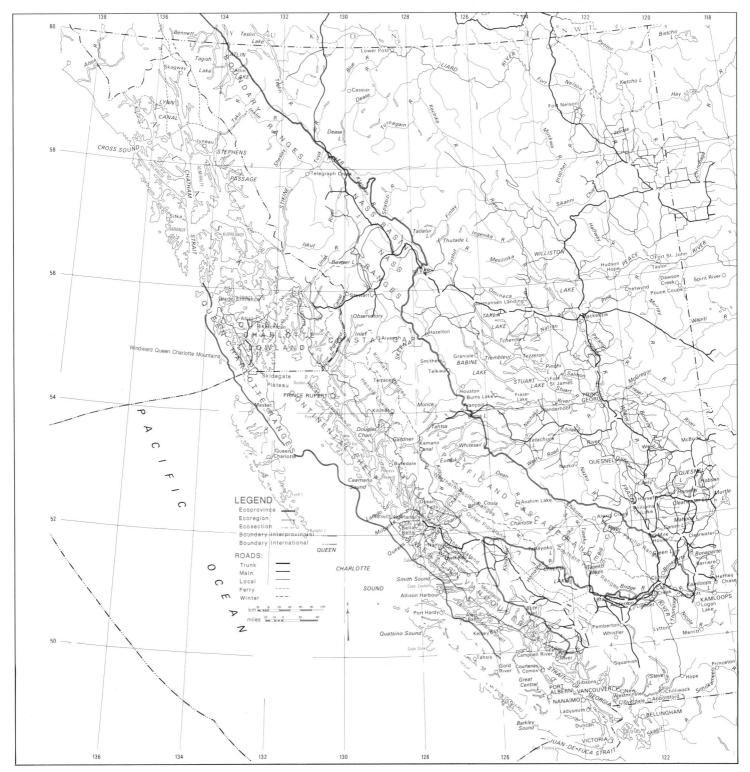

Figure 97. *Geographic location, major roads, and ferry routes of the Ecoregion units in the Coast and Mountains Ecoprovince in British Columbia.*

The Insular Mountains on Vancouver Island and the Queen Charlotte Islands rise abruptly from the coast and crest in low but rugged, serrated peaks. There is a coastal plain on the northeastern portion of Queen Charlotte Islands and a long, narrow coastal plain on the west side of Vancouver Island. The mountains on Vancouver Island are more massive, with deeper valleys and longer streams, and both island groups have numerous small and large estuaries.

The Continental Shelf consists of the outer continental shelf (Vancouver Island Shelf), the inner Continental Shelf (Hecate Depression), and several troughs (Dixon, Moresby, Reed, Goose Island, and Cook; see Fig. 93). The shelf is a shallow, gently ascending area. It is nearly non-existent off the western shores of the Queen Charlotte Islands; however, between the Queen Charlotte Islands and the mainland it is a broad submerged platform of sands and gravels that is less than 100 m deep.

The Coastal Trough consists of the Continental Shelf in Hecate and Queen Charlotte straits that is flanked by several lowlands (Queen Charlotte, Hecate, and Nahwitti). It has a width of 120 km between Graham Island and Porcher Island and is constricted to a width of 16 km at Sayward in Johnstone Strait. The lower areas have deep glacial deposits that rose above sea level as the land rebounded. Wetlands dominate most of the low areas, but rugged bedrock is occasionally exposed.

The Coastal Mountains consist of several mountain ranges with similar tectonic histories and rocks. The St. Elias Mountains and Boundary Ranges form one ecological unit of very high, rugged, ice-capped mountains. There are only a few large rivers that dissect them: the Alsek, Taku, and Stikine. They have large floodplains, but their estuaries lie within Alaska. The Kitimat Ranges are round-topped, dome-like granitic mountains that are much lower than the Boundary Ranges to the north or the Pacific Ranges to the south. Major rivers such as the Nass, Skeena, and Dean cross them in valleys that are only a few hundred metres above sea-level. Many fiords penetrate the heart of the ranges (Fig. 98). Inland from the Kitimat Ranges are 2 smaller physiographic features: the Nass Ranges, an area of serrated peaks and rounded summits, and the Nass Basin, a large flat-lying area of low relief that is surrounded by high mountains (Fig. 99). South of the Kitimat Ranges are the Pacific Ranges, a group of high, rugged granitic mountains that are capped with large glaciers (Fig. 100). They are drained by several large rivers such as the Kingcome, Klinaklini, Homathko, Southgate, Toba, Squamish, and Lillooet. The rivers have cut major valleys through the mountains, dividing them into blocks. All but the Lillooet River terminate in large estuaries. The Cascade Ranges are high mountains that are the southern-most of British Columbia's Coastal Range.

Oceanography

There are 6 oceanic zones in the Coast and Mountains Ecoprovince (see Fig. 93). The Outer Continental Shelf, west of Vancouver Island, has the greatest salinity of any shelf area in the province, being exposed to the open Pacific Ocean. Upwelling from the adjacent continental slope enhances the productivity of nutrients and plankton. The inner continental shelf in the Hecate Depression is a semi-enclosed estuarine environment. Fresh water from river and stream discharge is poorly mixed and the surface layer is merely brackish. The area is rich in nutrients, providing an abundance of prey species for diving birds and large fish. The nearshore zone or the zone at which point waves begin to break, has a variety of microhabitats. Perhaps the most important is the intertidal zone—that area between the highest and lowest tides. The exposed parts of the beaches are the least used nearshore habitat; the pounding surf is too harsh for most birds.

Figure 98. *The Kitimat Ranges Ecosection looking north northeast across Sheep Passage and up Mussel Inlet, 17 September 1947 (courtesy of British Columbia Ministry of Crown Lands, Survey and Resource Mapping Branch, Victoria). Roderick Island is on the right. Deep fiords are common throughout the Ecoprovince. The mountain summits are rounded and lower than the major mountain ranges to the south and north. These mountains have Coastal Western Hemlock forests with Mountain Hemlock and moist Alpine Tundra on the summits .*

Figure 99. *The Nass Basin Ecoregion looking northeast across Swan Lake towards the Western Skeena Mountains Ecosection, 18 September 1947 (courtesy of British Columbia Ministry of Crown Lands, Survey and Resource Mapping Branch, Victoria). A glacially eroded landscape is cloaked with Interior Cedar-Hemlock forests and depressions are filled by wetlands .*

Figure 100. *The Northern Pacific Ranges Ecosection looking southwest past the junction of Radiant and Scimitar glaciers to the peak of Mount Waddington, 25 September 1947 (courtesy of British Columbia Ministry of Crown Lands, Survey and Resource Mapping Branch, Victoria). Large glaciers, snowfields, and exposed bedrock dominate the upper slopes in the Ecosection.*

The sandy subtidal areas provide spawning habitat for the Pacific sand lance and Pacific herring, which are important prey species for alcids, gulls, and cormorants. Much of the constantly washed area of the rocky intertidal zone is occupied by mussels, which provide an excellent food source for many waterbird species. The inner-island channels and sounds provide protected habitat for many birds. Most of that shoreline is rocky and steep but with the influx of nutrients from rivers and creeks it is ideal habitat for mussels. The steep-sided fiords are usually quite barren. A shelf at their mouths, pushed up by glaciers, inhibits circulation and encourages the formation of a thick layer of fresh water on the surface. That layer does not seem to offer any abundant prey in any season. Only in the estuaries at the heads of the inlets does the freshwater create habitat for a variety of species. With the exception of the Nass and Skeena rivers, most estuaries in the Ecoprovince are medium to small in size. Estuaries provide 3 basic habitats: mudflats, marshes, and eelgrass beds. All 3 contain invertebrates that are exposed at low tides and attract flocks of migrant and wintering waterfowl and shorebirds.

Vegetation

The Coast and Mountains Ecoprovince encompasses the entire outer coastal portion of British Columbia (Figs. 102, 103, and 104), and the stabilizing influence of the ocean decreases the climatic variation which helps to reduce vegetation diversity. However, several important topographic events occur along the coast and between the mainland and major islands that create distinct communities. There are 6 different vegetation zones but generally only 3 occur in a single vertical transect.

Three lowland habitats that may be used by marine birds are of special interest. Rocky islets and shoreline cliffs, usually with herbaceous or shrubby vegetative cover, are important bird nesting and roosting habitats. Estuarine habitats, with tufted hairgrass, sedges, rushes, glasswort, and silverweed are found at the mouths of the many streams and rivers. On low relief areas of the coastal plains and lowlands, wetland vegetation may be extensive. Those wetlands range from open bogs to scrubby muskeg forests of shore pine (Fig. 106), western redcedar, and yellow-cedar. There is usually extensive development of sedges, Labrador tea, crowberry, deer-grass, and thick mats of sphagnum.

Vancouver Island

The lowest vegetation zone is dominated by western hemlock (Fig. 107). Except in the drier Nimpkish valley, where Douglas-fir is a common seral species, amabilis fir is also common. Sitka spruce forms a narrow belt adjacent to the ocean (Fig. 105). Other trees include western redcedar (lower elevations), yellow-cedar (higher elevations), shore pine, and red alder. Understories are dominated by woody shrubs such as blueberries, salal, huckleberries, and false azalea, with bunchberry, deer fern, sword fern, and a carpet of mosses. Floodplains are composed of Sitka spruce, red alder, salmonberry, and ferns. Soils are strongly weathered, reddish in colour, strongly acidic, and are rich in iron, aluminum, and organic matter. Wetter soils are common.

The subalpine vegetation zone has a mixed climax of mountain hemlock and amabilis fir, with seral yellow-cedar on richer sites. A dense shrub layer occurs. Common plants include blueberries, false azalea, copperbush, white-flowered rhododendron, twistedstalks, queen's cup, and dense mosses. At higher elevations, the forest cover becomes discontinuous and may be mixed with meadows (Fig. 101). Soils are even more weathered than at lower elevations. Poorly drained sites are uncommon.

The alpine tundra vegetation zone is very limited and is usually dominated by rock outcropping or mountain-heathers and meadows where soil occurs.

Figure 101. *Wetter seepage areas in the upper elevations of the coastal subalpine forest creat a variety of edge habitats within a coniferous forest landscape, September, 1978 (Dennis A. Demarchi). Note the characteristic shape of the trees, resulting from the heavy snow accumulation.*

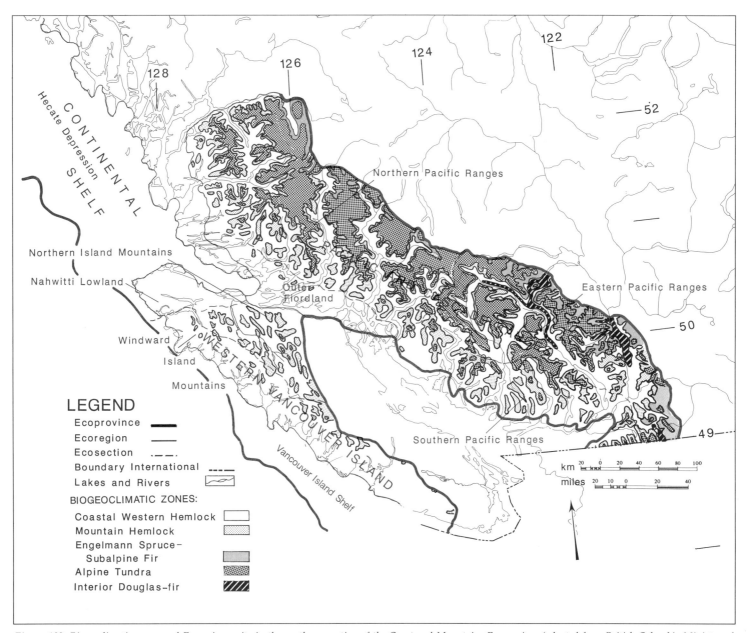

Figure 102. *Biogeoclimatic zones and Ecoregion units in the southern portion of the Coast and Mountains Ecoprovince (adapted from British Columbia Ministry of Forests 1988; Demarchi, D.A. 1988b).*

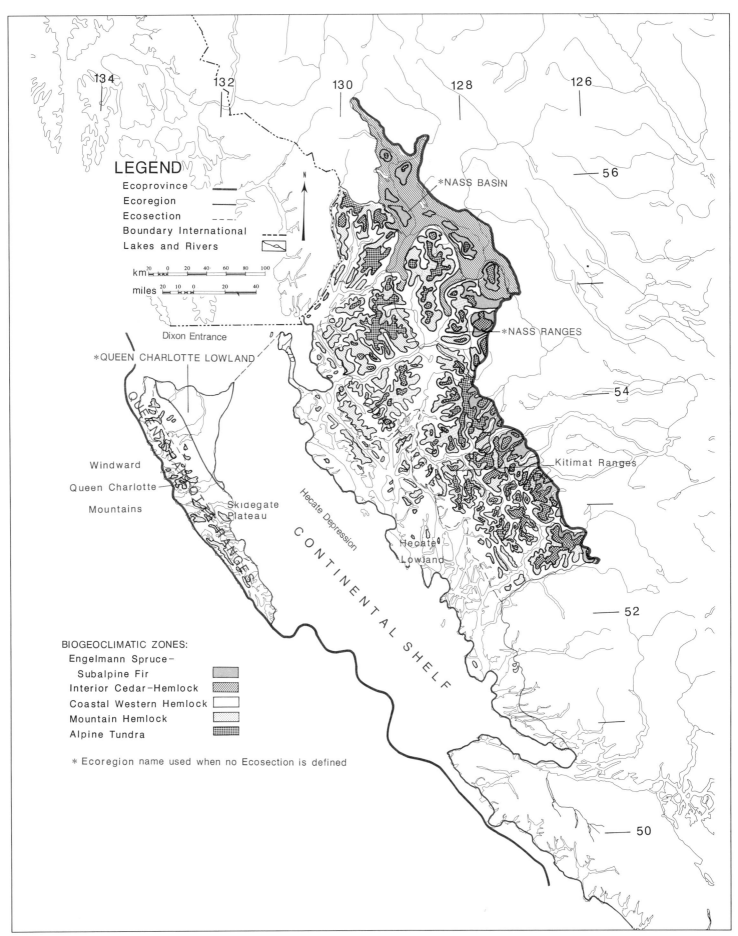

Figure 103. *Biogeoclimatic zones and Ecoregion units in the central portion of the Coast and Mountains Ecoprovince (adapted from British Columbia Ministry of Forests 1988; Demarchi, D.A. 1988b).*

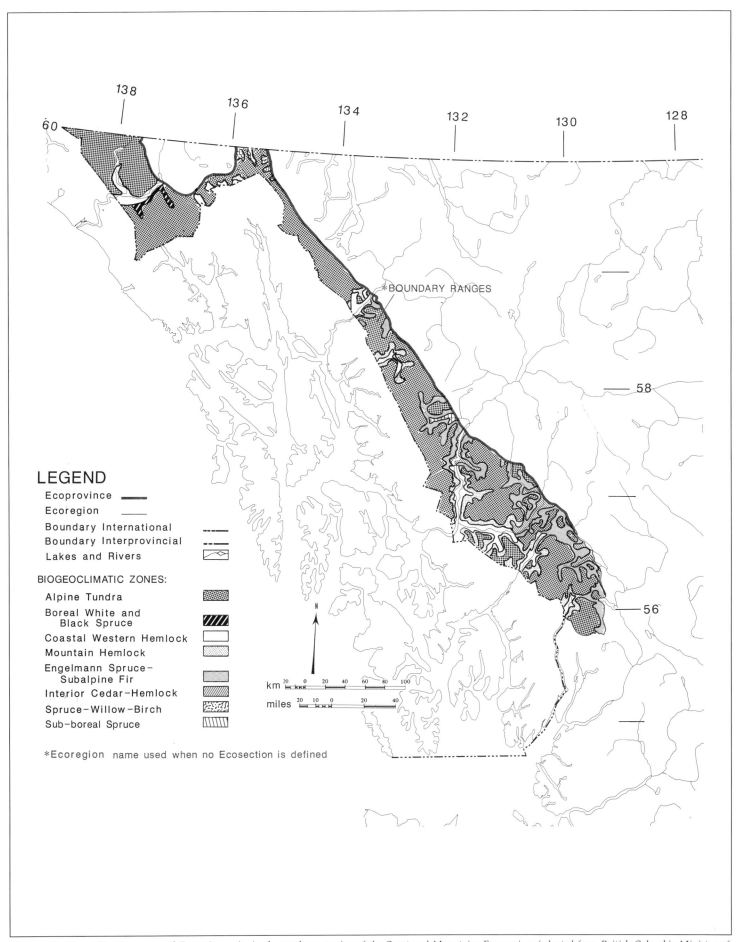

LEGEND

- Ecoprovince
- Ecoregion
- Boundary International
- Boundary Interprovincial
- Lakes and Rivers

BIOGEOCLIMATIC ZONES:

- Alpine Tundra
- Boreal White and Black Spruce
- Coastal Western Hemlock
- Mountain Hemlock
- Engelmann Spruce– Subalpine Fir
- Interior Cedar–Hemlock
- Spruce–Willow–Birch
- Sub-boreal Spruce

*Ecoregion name used when no Ecosection is defined

*BOUNDARY RANGES

Figure 104. *Biogeoclimatic zones and Ecoregion units in the northern portion of the Coast and Mountains Ecoprovince (adapted from British Columbia Ministry of Forests 1988; Demarchi, D.A. 1988b).*

Southern Coast Mountains

Three vegetation zones occur. The lower zone is dominated by western hemlock. In southern areas, Douglas-fir is the common seral species, with dense, shrub-dominated understories of salal, falsebox, false azalea, huckleberry, vanilla-leaf, sword fern, and dense mosses. In either higher elevations or more northern areas, amabilis fir is the common codominant climax species with western hemlock. Western redcedar (lower elevations) and yellow-cedar (higher elevations) are common seral species, with red alder pioneering on heavily disturbed sites. Understories are dense with salal, huckleberries, devil's club, ferns, foamflowers, and a thick moss layer. Floodplains may have Sitka spruce, black cottonwood, bigleaf maple, red alder, and a lush shrub cover of red-osier dogwood, salmonberry, and ferns. Avalanche chutes are densely covered with Sitka alder and moisture-loving herbs. Soils are strongly weathered, very acidic, reddish in colour, and rich in aluminum, iron, and organic matter.

The subalpine vegetation zone is densely forested with mountain hemlock and amabilis fir, often with yellow-cedar. Subalpine fir becomes common in eastern areas. Understories include white-flowered rhododendron, false azalea, blueberries, and thick mosses. Again, forests become discontinuous at upper elevations and are intermixed with wet and dry meadow vegetation (Fig. 101). Soils are strongly weathered and acidic.

The alpine tundra vegetation zone is dominated by rock and glaciers, with only scattered pockets of mountain-heather or meadow vegetation.

Central and Northern Coast Mountains

In the southern area, the lower forest zone is dominated by western hemlock and amabilis fir, except in low relief landscapes where muskeg-type forests become common. In inland valleys, subalpine fir may grow with the hemlock on valley bottoms that accumulate cold air. Farther north, Sitka spruce becomes codominant with western hemlock and amabilis fir is not found. Other common trees include western redcedar, lodgepole pine, red alder, and yellow-cedar. Understories are shrub-dominated, with blueberries, false azalea, salal, and devil's club. Common herbs are ferns, bunchberry, foamflowers, and queen's cup. Floodplains have dense forests of spruce, black cottonwood, and red alder, and a dense shrub cover of red-osier dogwood, red elderberry, salmonberry, horsetails, and ferns. Soils are strongly weathered, reddish in colour, acidic, and often have accumulations of organic matter, especially in areas that are flatter or that have higher precipitation.

The subalpine vegetation zone is dominated by forests of mountain hemlock, amabilis fir (coastal), and subalpine fir (inland). Common plants include red alder, yellow-cedar, blueberries, five-leaved bramble, and dense mosses. In mountainous areas, avalanche chutes with Sitka alder are common.

At higher elevations, forests open up, and become stunted and intermixed with heath vegetation. Soils are strongly weathered, acidic, and high in organic matter.

The alpine tundra vegetation zone is rock and glacier dominated, with pockets of drier alpine vegetation.

Queen Charlotte Islands

The lower vegetation zone has forests of western hemlock, Sitka spruce, and western redcedar whenever relief allows adequate drainage. Common plants in these forests include red alder, shore pine, blueberries, false azalea, salal, ferns, twisted-stalks, and mosses. In the lowland areas, with low relief, poor drainage results in extensive open to forested bogs and fens. Swamps are also common, with western redcedar, skunk cabbage, and a continuous moss cover. Floodplains are dominated by Sitka spruce and red alder. Upland soils are deeply weathered and leached, and are seldom dry. Lowland soils are often organic, and saturated for most of the year.

Figure 105. *Carmanah Creek, in the Windward Island Mountains Ecosection, southwestern Vancouver Island, September 1988 (Adrian Dorst). Many species of wildlife are dependent on old-growth forests, but as logging progresses, fewer of these ancient forests remain.*

Figure 106. *Open sphagnum bogs with stunted shore pine, sedges, and deep peat moss substrate, are common in flat, poorly drained areas along much of the Coast and Mountains Ecoprovince's coastal plains, February 1972 (Andrew P. Harcombe). This bog is near Long Beach in Pacific Rim National Park.*

The subalpine zone is uncommon, and is composed of yellow-cedar and mountain hemlock, with blueberries and dense moss. Wet meadows are frequently found as part of the subalpine mosaic, with Indian hellebore, ragwort, hairgrass, and sedges. There is an unusually high frequency of endemic and rare species (see Calder and Taylor 1968).

The alpine vegetation zone is rare, with heaths formed by mountain-heathers.

Fauna

The Coast and Mountains Ecoprovince holds the second highest number of birds in British Columbia (see Table 5), supporting 79% of all species known to occur in the province and 57% of those species known to breed. Waterbirds make extensive use of the coastal wetlands as well as nearshore and offshore habitats, including islands, islets, and cliffs. The colonial breeding seabirds are of note, and many of those species breed nowhere else in Canada. Offshore habitats provide feeding sites for pelagic birds like the Black-footed Albatross, Sooty Shearwater, jaegers, Northern Fulmar, gulls, and some shorebirds. Breeding Red-throated Loons and Spotted Owls are mostly restricted to this Ecoprovince. Some resident species, including the Bald Eagle, Peregrine Falcon, and Black Oystercatcher, contain significant portions of their world populations here. In winter, the estuaries and shores support most of the world's population of Trumpeter Swans and Barrow's Goldeneyes. The coast is also an important corridor for millions of migrating birds, especially shorebirds and waterfowl. The Townsend's Warbler is a high density breeder on Vancouver Island and The Queen Charlotte Islands. The Western Flycatcher is a high density breeder on the Queen Charlotte Islands.

The mule deer ("black-tailed") is the only common large terrestrial ungulate. Mountain goats are widespread but restricted to rugged areas in the Coast Mountains. Black bears occur throughout this Ecoprovince, wolves are absent from the Queen Charlotte Islands, cougars are absent from the Boundary Ranges and Queen Charlotte Islands, while grizzly bears occur only on the mainland except in the south where they have been extirpated. The sea otter was once one of the most abundant shellfish predators, and the river otter is still numerous and very widespread. Northern sea lions and harbor seals occur along the coastal areas and the killer whale is a common inhabitant.

Characteristic small mammals include the Keen's myotis, Vancouver Island marmot, and mink. There are many distinct island races of Townsend's vole and white-footed mouse.

The centre of abundance of the northwestern garter snake occurs here. The rough-skinned newt, northwestern salamander, western red-backed salamander, ensatina, clouded salamander, and red-legged frog are amphibians whose range is mostly restricted to the Coast and Mountains Ecoprovince.

Ecoprovince Subdivisions

The Coast and Mountains Ecoprovince is divided into 9 Ecoregions containing 14 Ecosections (see Figs. 89 and 97; Table 4).

The **Boundary Ranges Ecoregion** is a high, rugged, often ice-capped range of mountains, located on the northwestern margin of British Columbia. Much of the windward portion of these mountains is located within Alaska. There are no Ecosection subdivisions.

The **Coastal Gap Ecoregion** contains somewhat rounded mountains with lower relief than mountain ranges to either the north or south. Valley sides are rugged and steep. Because of their lower relief, they allow considerable moisture to enter the interior of the province. The Ecoregion contains 2 Ecosections.

The **Hecate Lowland Ecosection** is an area of low relief, consisting of islands, channels, rocks, and lowlands adjacent to Hecate Strait and Queen Charlotte Sound.

The **Kitimat Ranges Ecosection** is an area of subdued, yet steep-sided mountains, west of the Hecate Lowlands Ecosection.

The **Continental Shelf Ecoregion** is a shallow oceanic area located from the continental slope to Vancouver Island and the mainland coast. It has been subdivided into 3 Ecosections.

The **Dixon Entrance Ecosection** is located between northern Graham Island and Prince of Wales and Dall islands in southeastern Alaska.

The **Hecate Depression Ecosection** is a broad semi-enclosed estuarine waterway located between the mainland coast, the Queen Charlotte Islands and northern Vancouver Island.

The **Vancouver Island Shelf Ecosection** is a shallow oceanic area located west of Vancouver Island.

The **Nass Basin Ecoregion** is an area of low relief located within the Coast Mountains (see Fig. 99). It is influenced by both the mild, coastal and colder, Arctic weather systems. There are no Ecosection subdivisions.

The **Nass Ranges Ecoregion** is a mountainous area west of the Kitimat Ranges. Its climate is somewhat transitional between coastal and interior regimes. There are no Ecosection subdivisions.

The **Pacific and Cascade Ranges Ecoregion** is the southernmost mountain range of the Coast Mountains in British Columbia. It includes the coastal islands, channels, and fiords east of Queen Charlotte Sound, otherwise it lies east of the Georgia Depression Ecoprovince. The mountains are charcteristically high and rugged. It contains 4 Ecosections.

The **Eastern Pacific Ranges Ecosection** is a rugged inland area that has transitional climates including some rainshadow. It lies west of the Southern Interior Ecoprovince.

The **Northern Pacific Ranges Ecosection** is an area of steep, rugged, often ice-capped, mountains located in the northern portion of this Ecoregion (Fig. 100).

The **Outer Fiordland Ecosection** is an area of rugged, low relief, consisting of inlets, sounds, islands and peninsulas, east of Johnstone Strait and Seymour Narrows.

The **Southern Pacific Ranges Ecosection** is an area of high rainfall on steep, rugged mountains located east of the Georgia Depression Ecoprovince.

The **Queen Charlotte Lowland Ecoregion** is an area of low relief, poor drainage and extensive muskegs and wetlands in the northeastern part of the Queen Charlotte Islands. There are no Ecosection subdivisions.

The **Queen Charlotte Ranges Ecoregion** includes the fiords and mountains of the Queen Charlotte Islands and the Skidegate Plateau. It is subdivided into 2 Ecosections.

The **Skidegate Plateau Ecosecton** is a plateau in the lee of the Queen Charlotte Mountains. Precipitation is somewhat reduced here.

The **Windward Queen Charlotte Mountains Ecosection** is the very wet, rugged western side of the Queen Charlotte archipelago.

Figure 107. *The western hemlock - western redcedar forest with shrub-dominated understory of salal, false azalea, and huckleberry, is characterized by large redcedars with candelabrum branching and vigorous multi-aged regenerating hemlock. This forest, near Long Beach – July 1972, is common in the lower Coastal Western Hemlock vegetation zone on better drained sites (Andrew P. Harcombe).*

The **Western Vancouver Island Ecoregion** includes western lowlands, islands and mountains of Vancouver Island. It contains 3 Ecosections.

The **Northern Island Mountains Ecosection** is a partial rainshadow area of wide valleys and mountains located in the northern portion of Vancouver Island.

The **Nahwitti Lowland Ecosection** is an area of low to rolling topography, with high precipitation located at the north end of Vancouver Island.

The **Windward Island Mountains Ecosection** is the area of lowlands, islands (Fig. 95), and mountains on the western margin of Vancouver Island.

Figure 108. *Northern Moresby Island, June 1976 (R. Wayne Campbell). Clearcut logging and slash burning have been the main logging method and silvicultural practice throughout the coastal forests.*

Georgia Depression Ecoprovince

ECODOMAIN - HUMID TEMPERATE

ECODIVISION - HUMID MARITIME AND HIGHLANDS

ECOPROVINCE - GEORGIA DEPRESSION

Ecoregion - Eastern Vancouver Island

Ecosections - Leeward Island Mountains
- Nanaimo Lowland

Ecoregion - Lower Mainland

Ecosections - Fraser Lowland
- Georgia Lowland

Ecoregion - Strait of Georgia

Figure 109. *Location of the Georgia Depression Ecoprovince in British Columbia.*

Location

The Georgia Depression Ecoprovince lies between the Vancouver Island Mountains and the southern Coast Mountains (Fig. 109). It is a large basin containing the Strait of Georgia and Puget Sound. In British Columbia, it extends from the southern portion of Quadra Island and Desolation Sound to the southern tip of Vancouver Island and the lower Fraser valley (Fig. 110).

Most of the human population of British Columbia occurs in this Ecoprovince and the environment has been greatly modified. Large portions have been converted to exclusive urban and industrial use (Fig. 112). Agriculture is intense and includes dairy production, food crops, and cereals. Some lower quality areas have been planted with berry crops. Logging remains important on the periphery of the settled area but is coming into serious conflict with recreational use of the few remaining natural areas.

Climate

This Ecoprovince is characterized by a particularly effective rainshadow in the lee of the Vancouver Island Range of the Insular Mountains and the Olympic Peninsula of the Coast Mountains. After moving over these barriers, surface air flow is level or subsiding and creates clearer skies and drier conditions than in coastal areas adjacent to the Pacific Ocean. The southern parts of this Ecoprovince have the greatest annual amounts of sunshine in British Columbia. Temperatures througout the area are moderated by the ocean.

Except where prevailing winds and topography have combined to create rainshadow effects, such as on the Saanich Peninsula and Gulf Islands, the Vancouver Island side is wetter and cloudier than the Lower Mainland side because of increased exposure to moist air from the sea. On the Lower Mainland side, there is not sufficient relief to force moist air to cooler elevations, and as a result the area is fairly dry. Part of it is known locally as the Sunshine Coast.

Physiography

In British Columbia, the Georgia Depression Ecoprovince is a large basin that encompasses the southeastern Vancouver Island Mountains, the Nanaimo Lowlands, and the Gulf Islands in the west, the Strait of Georgia, in the middle, and the Georgia Lowlands and the Fraser Lowlands in the east.

The whole area was covered by ice during the glacial periods of the past one million years. Ice pouring westward from the Coast Mountains and eastward from Vancouver Island Ranges coalesced in the strait to form a glacier that flowed southeastward and southward and escaped to the sea westward through Juan de Fuca Strait. Much of the lowland area was flooded after being pushed below sea level by the weight of ice. Fine soils settled out over those areas. At some sites fast-moving water deposited coarse materials, and there are moraines of mixed rocks and soil.

The western portion of the Ecoprovince consists of high rugged mountains that have been deeply eroded, leaving some mountains isolated above the general land surface. East of these mountains are the Nanaimo Lowlands, an area with low relief and undulating topography mixed with areas of sharp crests and narrow valleys. Several medium-sized rivers (Cowichan, Chemainus, Nanaimo, Puntledge, and Campbell rivers) flow from the mountains through the coastal lowlands and terminate with well-developed estuaries (Fig. 113).

Within the Strait of Georgia are many small islands. Most are composed of bedrock, although a few are composed of glacial deposits. Savary Island is a particularly large end-moraine. The eastern portion of the Ecoprovince consists of a large delta that has filled in around low hills (Fraser Lowlands) and a narrow coastal plain of glacial deposits (Georgia Lowlands). The Fraser River dominates the area but there are several small rivers and streams that cross the valley from the mountains.

Oceanography

There are 4 distinct marine environments in the Georgia Depression Ecoprovince (see Fig. 93). The Strait of Georgia is a semi-enclosed estuarine environment. It is rich in a variety of foods at depths that many different diving birds can attain. Most of the shoreline is rocky and steep. Inter-island channels (Fig. 115) and sounds provide a variety of habitat quality. Most are steep-sided with fast tidal currents. Extensive shallow areas such as Baynes Sound provide a nutrient-rich environment. Estuaries trap nutrients carried down by rivers and create extremely diverse and rich ecosystems that attract thousands of migrant and wintering waterfowl and shorebirds. Several estuaries occur in the Ecoprovince, including the Fraser River estuary which is by far the largest in the province (Fig. 118).

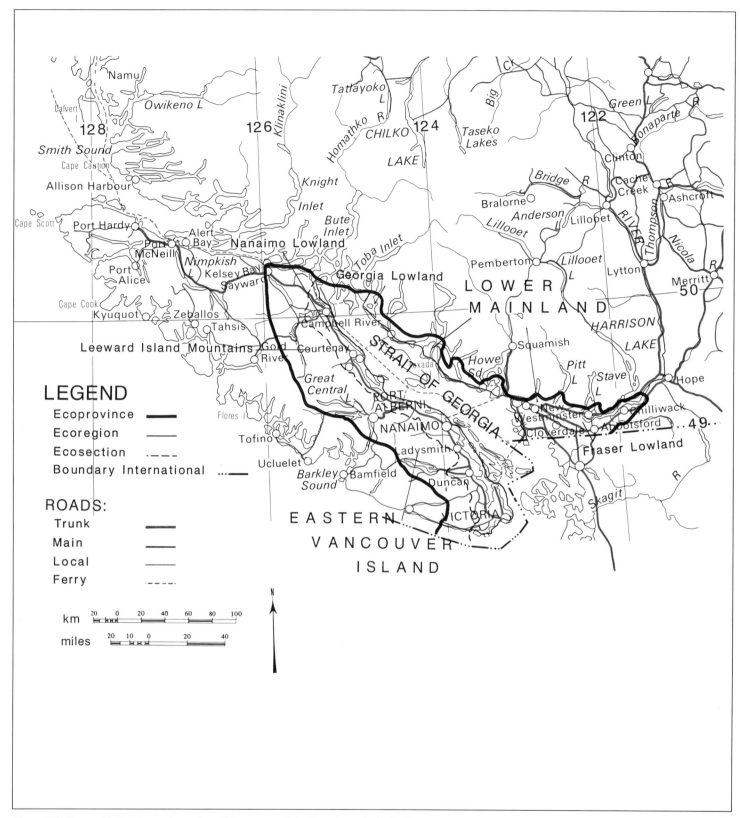

Figure 110. *Geographic location, major roads, and ferry routes of the Ecoregion units in the Georgia Depression Ecoprovince in British Columbia.*

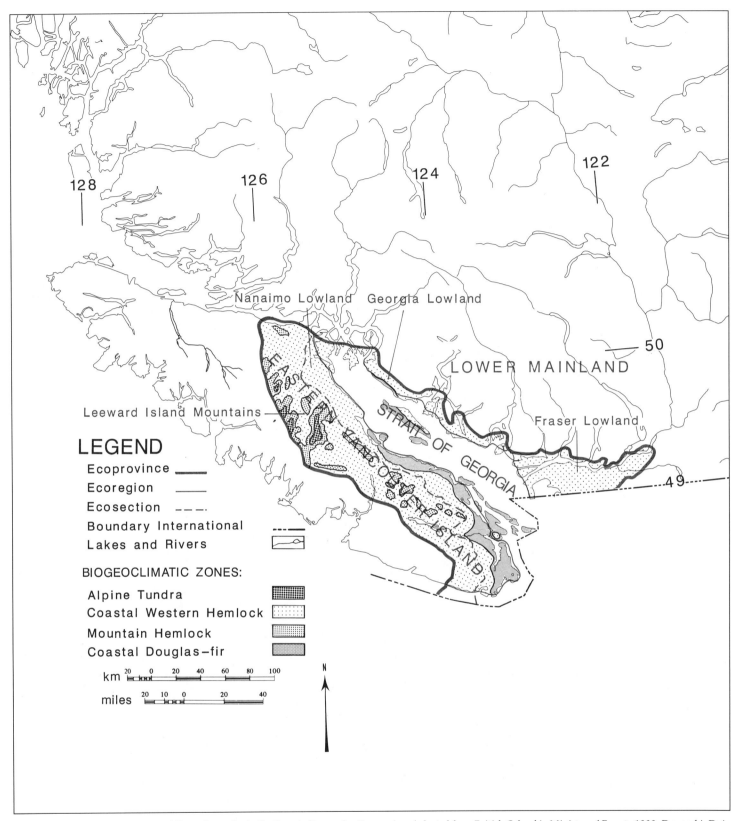

Figure 111. *Biogeoclimatic zones and Ecoregion units in the Georgia Depression Ecoprovince (adapted from British Columbia Ministry of Forests 1988; Demarchi, D.A. 1988b).*

Figure 112. *The Fraser Lowland Ecosection looking downstream over the Fraser River; Seabird Island is at the lower right and Harrison River is at the middle right, 29 June 1945 (courtesy of British Columbia Ministry of Crown Lands, Survey and Resource Mapping Branch, Victoria). Early in the province's history these lands were offered to railway companies for the construction of railroads throughout the province and for settlement.*

Figure 113. *The Cowichan River estuary looking southwest towards Cowichan Bay, June 1988 (Dennis A. Demarchi). Estuaries are very important for wintering water-birds and rearing salmon. However, industrial developments such as log booming grounds, dryland sorts, sawmills, pulp mills and farming have reduced the wildlife capabilities of these habitats. Fortunately, many estuaries are now being preserved for wildlife and fish through habitat purchases, land transfers, and rehabilitation techniques.*

Figure 114. *The Georgia Depression Ecoprovince includes British Columbia's largest urban residential areas where native vegetation is rapidly being replaced by houses, asphalt, and landscaped gardens. This historical view of Deer Lake and Burnaby Lake, near Vancouver, shows an intermediate stage between forest and complete urbanization: a mix of residential, park, and agricultural land uses, April 1965 (R. Wayne Campbell).*

Vegetation

The Georgia Depression Ecoprovince supports vegetation with the longest growing season in British Columbia. Four vegetation belts and two important local habitats have developed (Fig. 111). Estuarine habitats form where fresh water rivers enter the marine straits. From the high tide ridges to subtidal mudflats, there are bands of vegetation that include tufted hairgrass, fescues, rushes, seaside arrow-grass, silverweed, and sedges. Further inland, creeks and rivers support riparian forests dominated by black cottonwood, red alder, and bigleaf maple. Agricultural and residential development on most of the lowland areas has resulted in the loss of much of both habitats (Figs. 113 and 114).

At lower elevations, a vegetation zone dominated by Douglas-fir occurs (Fig. 116). The common trees include grand fir, western redcedar, and western flowering dogwood. Understory plants include a dense shrub cover of salal, dull Oregon-grape, red huckleberry, roses, salmonberry, Indian-plum, vanilla-leaf, sword fern, starflower, and mosses. Soils are moderately weathered, and become dry in summer. In the Fraser valley, fluvial soils are now extensively altered by agriculture. Of special interest, particularly on Vancouver Island and the Gulf Islands, are rocky sites with arbutus and Garry oak forests (Fig. 117), with understories dominated by spring wildflowers such as camas, sea blush, shootingstar, and blue-eyed Mary, and by shrubs such as oceanspray and common snowberry. This unique habitat has suffered from urban development.

Above the low elevation forests and farther inland, where climatic moisture increases, lies an extensive vegetation belt dominated by western hemlock, Douglas-fir and western redcedar are the common seral species in this moist zone. Understories are generally shrub-dominated, primarily with salal and dull Oregon-grape. Red alder, salmonberry, sword fern, bracken, fireweed, and dense mosses are characteristic. Logging history is extensive. At higher elevations, amabilis fir may be mixed with western hemlock.

The subalpine vegetation belt is dominated by dense forests of mountain hemlock and amabilis fir. Yellow-cedar may also be present, and understories are shrub-dominated with white-flowered rhododendron, false azalea, blueberries, queen's cup, bunchberry, twayblades, and five-leaved bramble. Soils are heavily leached and acidic, with thick forest floor accumulation. At upper elevations, the forest cover becomes discontinuous and dominated by mountain hemlock. Extensive dry areas between the tree clumps may be covered with mountain-heathers, crowberry, and partridgefoot. In wetter areas with delayed snow melt, moisture-requiring species such as Sitka valerian, Indian hellebore, white marsh-marigold, leatherleaf saxifrage, and black alpine sedge occur.

The upper alpine tundra vegetation belt is limited in extent to a few mountain peaks on Vancouver Island. Mountain-heathers, saxifrages, and lichens predominate and rock outcropping is extensive.

Fauna

This Ecoprovince supports the highest diversity of birds in British Columbia—90% of all species known to occur in the province (see Table 5). It also has 60% of the species that are known to breed in British Columbia. Many of these species are casual and accidental—spotted by the many birdwatchers in the area.

The wetlands of the Fraser River delta make up the largest single unit of wetland habitat in British Columbia. In addition, the mild climate enables it to be the most important migratory and wintering area for waterbirds in the province. Waterfowl are abundant, including Snow Geese during the winter months. The delta supports the largest wintering population of raptors in Canada. Notable among these are the Northern Harrier, Red-

Figure 115. *Areas of upwelling in the Strait of Georgia Ecoregion, such as here at Active Pass, are important foraging habitats and protective refuges for many migrating and wintering waterbirds (Richard J. Cannings).*

Figure 116. *The common coniferous forest of the Georgia Depression Ecoprovince is dominated by Douglas-fir (Hans Roemer).*

tailed Hawk, Rough-legged Hawk, and Short-eared Owl. The delta is also important to migrating shorebirds: most of the world's Western Sandpipers stage, rest, and feed there. In winter, Dunlin is the most numerous shorebird.

Large numbers of waterbirds winter in bays, surge narrows, and estuaries throughout the Georgia Depression Ecoprovince. Notable among these are the Pacific Loon, Western Grebe, Brandt's Cormorant, Common and Barrow's goldeneyes, Surf, White-winged and Black scoters, Greater and Lesser scaup, Thayer's and Glaucous-winged gulls, Common Murre, and Marbled and Ancient murrelets. The area is also important to wintering shorebirds such as Black Turnstone and Surfbird.

The only resident populations of Barn Owl and Anna's Hummingbird occur in this Ecoprovince. The Gulf Islands support the only breeding colonies of Double-crested Cormorants, and most of the colonies of Glaucous-winged Gulls in the province. Three species of passerines breed only in the Georgia Depression Ecoprovince: Purple Martin, Bushtit, and Hutton's Vireo. The Eurasian Skylark, introduced to the Victoria area, and the Crested Myna, introduced to the Vancouver area, maintain the only North American breeding populations in this Ecoprovince.

Mule deer ("black-tailed") are very abundant in the rural and natural areas throughout the Ecoprovince. Other large mammals include cougar, "Roosevelt" elk (Vancouver Island), and coyote (Lower Mainland). The extensive marine/land interface provides haul-out areas for harbour seals and northern and California sea lions. Off-shore, killer whales and harbor porpoises are common marine mammals. On-shore, in the estuaries, along river banks and lake shores, river otters, mink and raccoons are common predators.

Small mammals almost restricted to the Ecoprovince, include the Virginia opossum, marsh shrew, Trowbridge's shrew, shrew-mole, Townsend's and coast mole, Douglas' squirrel, eastern cottontail (introduced), gray squirrel (introduced), and creeping vole. Reptiles include the western pond turtle (introduced), and sharptail snake. Characteristic amphibians include the Pacific giant salamander, ensatina, bullfrog (introduced), and green frog (introduced).

Ecoprovince Subdivisions

The Georgia Depression Ecoprovince in British Columbia is subdivided into 3 Ecoregions containing 4 Ecosections (see Figs. 89 and 110; Table 4).

The **Eastern Vancouver Island Ecoregion** is an area of reduced rainfall leeward of the Vancouver Island Ranges. It is comprised of 2 Ecosections that correspond to physiographic differences.

The **Leeward Island Mountains Ecosection** is a mountainous area from the crest of the Vancouver Island Ranges to the Nanaimo Lowlands.

The **Nanaimo Lowland Ecosection** is a coastal plain that is situated on the southeastern margin of Vancouver Island. It has a mild climate with low snow depths.

The **Lower Mainland Ecoregion** is an area of reduced rainfall, but precipitation increases towards the Coast Ranges and the rainshadow is most distinct on the lowlands, and Fraser River delta. There are 2 Ecosections that correspond to physiographic differences.

The **Fraser Lowland Ecosection** consists of the Fraser River delta, estuary, lowlands, and associated uplands (Fig. 118).

The **Georgia Lowland Ecosection** consists of areas of low relief at the base of the Coast Ranges. Patches of rocky outcrop are connected by deposits of glacial gravel and debris.

The **Strait of Georgia Ecoregion** is a semi-enclosed estuarine basin that separates southern Vancouver Island from the mainland. It holds several islands that have very dry and mild climates (Fig. 117). In British Columbia, it has not been further subdivided into Ecosections.

Figure 117. *The driest habitat of the mild, inner coastal climate is dominated by Garry oak. These open, rocky habitats also support a diversity of spring wildflowers, such as blue camas, sea blush, and blue-eyed Mary (Hans Roemer).*

Figure 118. *Satellite image of the Fraser River delta and surrounding region, 21 September 1987. This estuary is the largest in the province and it supports the highest densities of wintering waterbirds, shorebirds, and raptors in Canada. Unfortunately for wildlife, the Fraser Lowland Ecosection also supports the densest human population and industrial base in British Columbia.*

Central Interior Ecoprovince

ECODOMAIN - HUMID TEMPERATE

ECODIVISION - HUMID CONTINENTAL
HIGHLANDS

ECOPROVINCE - CENTRAL INTERIOR

Ecoregion - Chilcotin Ranges

Ecosections - Eastern Chilcotin Ranges
- Western Chilcotin Ranges

Ecoregion - Fraser Plateau

Ecosections - Bulkley Basin
- Bulkley Ranges
- Cariboo Plateau
- Chilcotin-Cariboo Basin
- Chilcotin Plateau
- Nazko Upland
- Nechako Plateau

Figure 119. *Location of the Central Interior Ecoprovince in British Columbia.*

Location

The Central Interior Ecoprovince lies to the east of the Coast Mountains, between the Fraser Basin and the Thompson Plateau (Figs. 119 and 121). Some of the mountain ranges on the east side of the coastal mountains are included because they are much drier than the windward side and therefore have a more interior type of climate.

Agriculture is limited to grazing and small production of forage crops. Logging is the most extensive industry based on renewable resources and there are many mines.

Figure 120. *The forested/grassland mosaic of Becher's Prairie, August 1978 (Robert A. Cannings). The Chilcotin-Cariboo Basin Ecosection is dotted with pothole lakes—important breeding areas for waterfowl. The forest is a mixture of trembling aspen, Douglas-fir, and lodgepole pine, and the heavily-grazed grasslands are dominated by Richardson's needlegrass and goatsbeard.*

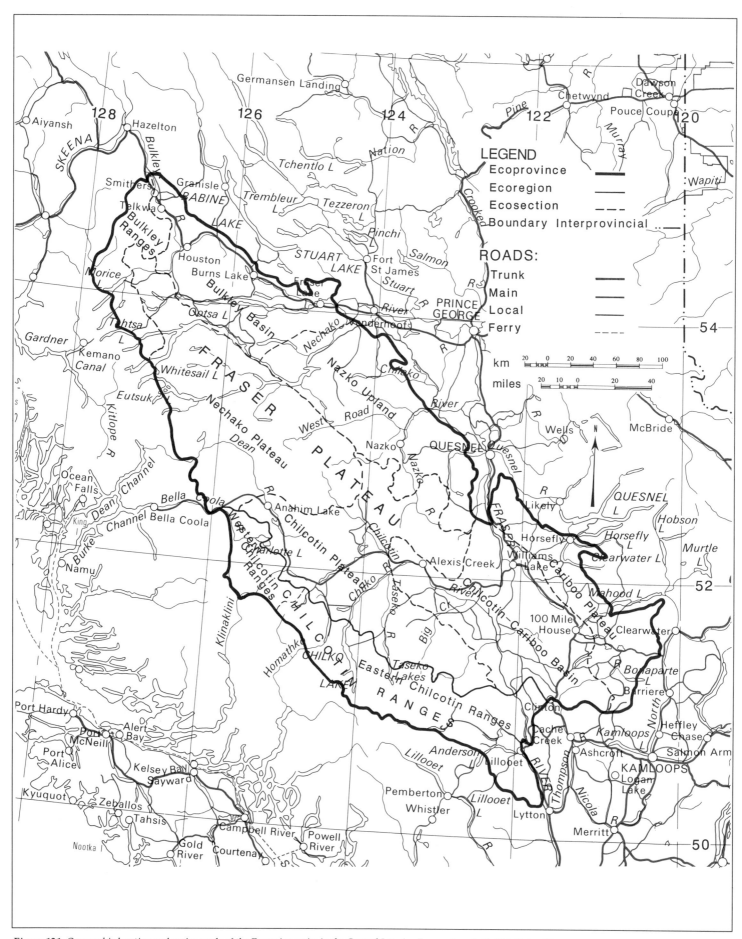

Figure 121. *Geographic location and major roads of the Ecoregion units in the Central Interior Ecoprovince in British Columbia.*

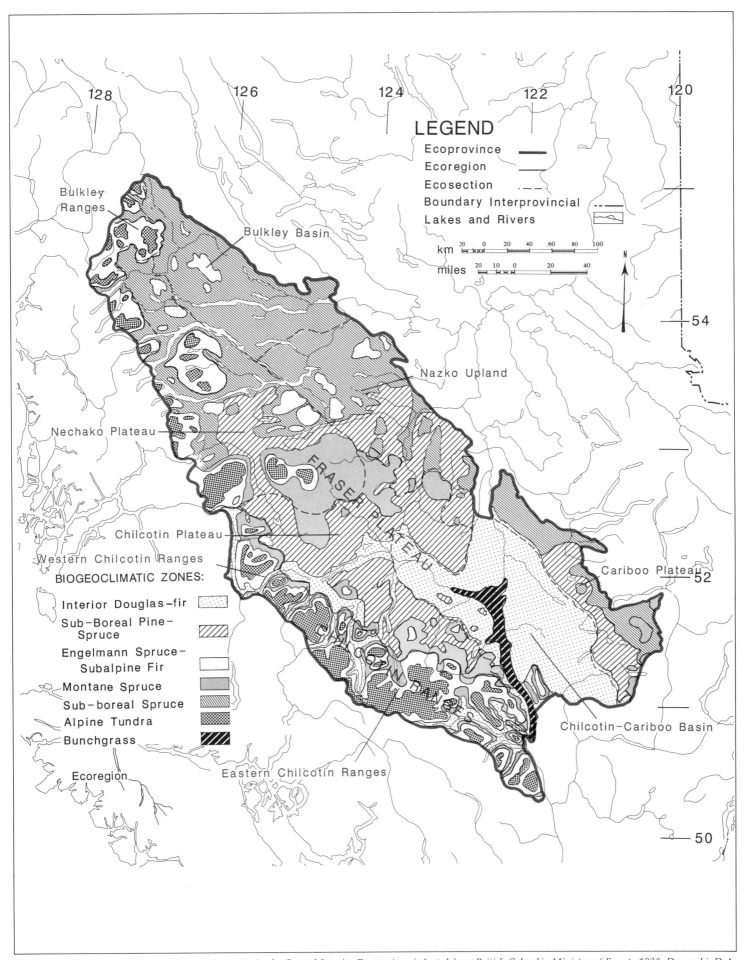

Figure 122. *Biogeoclimatic zones and Ecoregion units in the Central Interior Ecoprovince (adapted from British Columbia Ministry of Forests 1988; Demarchi, D.A. 1988b).*

Climate

The area has a typical continental climate: cold winters, warm summers, and a precipitation maximum in late spring or early summer. However, the moderating influences of Pacific air occur throughout the year, as is the case for most of the province south of 57°N. The area lies in a rainshadow leeward of the Coast Mountains. In summer there is intense surface heating and convective showers, and in the winter there are frequent outbreaks of Arctic air. They are less frequent than in areas to the north.

Along the leeside of the Coast Mountains, especially the Chilcotin, Bulkley, and Tahtsa ranges, there is an interplay of several climatic processes. Generally this is an area of rainshadow and is dry, but extreme western areas receive more rainfall. Local areas are subjected to higher precipitation where moist coastal air pushes through the lower mountain passes. During the winter and early spring, Arctic air frequently stalls on the eastern edge of these ranges.

The northern portion of the Fraser Plateau surface exhibits little rainshadow effect, because it lies east of the low Kitimat Ranges. There is a greater influence of Pacific air through increased rainfall and a smaller east-west precipitation gradient. The southern portion of the Fraser Plateau marks a better defined rainshadow region and is less affected by the low Kitimat Ranges to the northwest.

Physiography

The Central Interior Ecoprovince contains the Chilcotin and Cariboo plateaus, the southern two-thirds of the Nechako Plateau, and the Bulkley, Tahtsa, and Chilcotin ranges.

The Chilcotin, Cariboo, and Nechako plateaus are flat or gently rolling, and have large areas of undissected upland lying between 1,200 m and 1,500 m elevation. Much of the upland plateau is covered with glacial drift. Meandering streams and low depressions have created many wetlands and lakes (Fig. 123). The Fraser River and lower Chilcotin River have cut below the plateau surface forming a deep badlands area and dividing the plateau into the western Chilcotin Plateau and the eastern Cariboo Plateau (Fig. 124). To the southeast the upland surface rises gradually to 1,800 m. Most of the plateau surface is underlain by flat-lying lava flows. Those flows have steep escarpments along the rivers and creeks but almost horizontal upper surfaces (Fig. 127). In the vicinity of Anahim Lake, 3 shield volcanoes rise above the plateau surface. In the Whitesail Lake and West Road River area, isolated mountains of erosion-resistant granite also stand above the general level of the plateau.

The Chilcotin Ranges lie along the east side of the Pacific Ranges. They rise progressively higher in approaching the granite ranges to the west. For the most part, they display a combination of high, serrated peaks rising above lower rounded summits and gently sloping areas of undissected upland. The Bulkely and Tahtsa ranges are outliers of the Kitimat Ranges and consist of softer rocks than the hard granitic rocks of the Coast Mountains.

Figure 123. *The Cariboo Plateau looking southwest across Green Lake in the centre of the photo, 22 July 1947 (courtesy of British Columbia Ministry of Crown Lands, Survey and Resource Mapping Branch, Victoria). Watch Lake is on the lower right. Interior Douglas-fir forests that are interspersed with trembling aspen stands, meadows, wetlands, and shallow ponds and lakes dominate the upland portion of the Chilcotin-Cariboo Basin Ecosection.*

Figure 124. *Looking south below Watson Bar Creek where the Fraser River dissects the Eastern Chilcotin Ranges Ecosection, the Edge Hills are on the left, 19 June 1950 (courtesy of British Columbia Ministry of Crown Lands, Survey and Resource Mapping Branch, Victoria). At this lower elevation, Sagebrish-Steppe and Steppe dominate the highly eroded lower slopes, while sparse Interior Douglas-fir forests occur on the upper slopes.*

Figure 125. *The Eastern Chilcotin Ranges Ecosection is on the left and the Chilcotin Plateau Ecosection is on the right, 30 June 1948 (courtesy of British Columbia Ministry of Crown Lands, Survey and Resource Mapping Branch, Victoria). The steep, exposed slopes and rolling alpine of these mountains are contrasted with the Englemann Spruce - Subalpine Fir forest and wetlands on the plateau surface. The lighter tone on the plateau portion of the figure indicates an area that was burned by extensive forest fires.*

Vegetation

The area is intermediate in vegetation between the wet forests of the coast and interior mountains, the dry southern interior forests, and the cold northern boreal forests. Moisture increases from west to east and from south to north; increasing finer soil texture follows the same trend. Vegetation is relatively diverse and deciduous forests increase towards the northeast. Seven vegetation zones occur (Fig. 122).

In southern areas, the lowest vegetation zone along the major rivers is grassland. Common plants include big sagebrush, rabbit-brush, bluebunch wheatgrass, needlegrasses, pasture sage, and sand dropseed. Soils have a high organic content, with dark brown surface horizons.

The shrub-grassland habitats intergrade into a zone whose climax is Douglas-fir. At lower elevations, the open forest is dominated by Douglas-fir, with bluebunch wheatgrass understories. At higher elevations, the more closed forests proceed through a succession of lodgepole pine and pinegrass stages. Other tree species are trembling aspen, white spruce (moist sites), paper birch, and Rocky Mountain juniper. Common understory species include common juniper, prickly rose, soopolallie, willows, kinnikinnick, and aster. Floodplains are dominated by black cottonwood. Soils are moderately weathered and often calcareous.

Most of the upland area is covered by 2 sub-boreal vegetation zones. In the southern and western portion, where the climate is severe and dry, extensive even-aged stands of lodgepole pine dominate the rolling landscape. White spruce may only be present in the understory, except where increased moisture in depressions allows for better growth. Fires are frequent and succession extremely slow. Understories are sparsely vegetated, often with ground lichens and scattered common juniper, soopolallie, birch-leaved spirea, grouseberry, kinnikinnick, or pinegrass. Of special interest are the numerous, scattered wetlands that are characteristic of the central plateau (Figs. 120 and 123). Sedge fens, shrub fens, and marshes are widespread. Slight increases in climatic moisture in the east, allow greater vegetation diversity. White spruce becomes more common, often with transition stands of trembling aspen, lodgepole pine, or Douglas-fir. Understory shrub density increases to include thimbleberry, falsebox, Douglas maple, velvet-leaved blueberry, asters, and grouseberry. Soils often have clay accumulation and better moisture retention.

In moister and more northern areas, the second sub-boreal zone has a climax of white spruce, often with subalpine fir. Transitional forests of lodgepole pine are common, but stands of trembling aspen and paper birch may be more characteristic of the finer soil materials. Shrub and herb diversity is high, with prickly rose, highbush-cranberry, thimbleberry, creamy peavine, pinegrass, and blue wildrye occurring along with a moderately-developed moss layer. Wetlands are still common, but are often covered by shrubs or trees. Many are black spruce and sphagnum bogs.

In the southwestern area, bordering the coastal systems, there is a montane vegetation zone dominated by hybrid spruce, with scattered subalpine fir and extensive lodgepole pine forests. It has a sparse understory.

The subalpine vegetation zone is very limited. Its climax forest is Engelmann spruce and subalpine fir. Lodgepole pine is the common transitional species. Understories are dominated by shrubs and grasses. Whitebark pine may be present at higher elevations. Common plants include common juniper, soopolallie, grouseberry, lupines, arnicas, and lichens.

The alpine tundra zone is restricted to western areas (Fig. 126). In the Chilcotin Ranges, that zone is dominated by rock and glaciers. However, on some of the more rounded peaks in Tweedsmuir Park and Ichuz-Ilgachez ranges, alpine tundra vegetation is distinctive. Dense bunchgrasses, sedges, and hardy forbs predominate.

Fauna

This Ecoprovince supports 65% of all bird species known to occur in British Columbia and 61% of all species known to breed in the province (see Table 5). The only breeding colony of the American White Pelican in the province is found in the Chilcotin Plateau. Excellent habitat for waterfowl and other waterbird (e.g. grebes) production exists throughout the plateau. The world centre of breeding abundance for Barrow's Goldeneye occurs here. It is also the centre of breeding abundance for Greater Yellowlegs and the Yellow-headed Blackbird, and is one of two important breeding areas for Long-billed Curlew and Ring-billed Gull. High breeding concentrations of Eared Grebe, Sandhill Crane, Herring Gull, and Black Tern have also been found here.

Moose are the most widespread wild ungulate, while mule deer occur in large populations in the southern plateau and Fraser River badlands area. Several large populations of "California" Bighorn Sheep occur in the Fraser River badlands and alpine areas. Cougars, black bears, coyotes, and wolves are also common throughout the Ecoprovince.

Widespread small mammals include the western jumping mouse, muskrat and long-tailed weasel. Two species of bat, big brown and Townsend's big-eared, hibernate in the Ecoprovince. The western terrestrial garter snake is the most common reptile, while the western toad and spotted frog occur throughout the area.

Ecoprovince subdivisions

The Central Interior Ecoprovince contains 2 Ecoregions and 9 Ecosections (see Figs. 89 and 122; Table 4).

The **Chilcotin Ranges Ecoregion** is an area of high, somewhat rounded mountains, located in the rainshadow of the Pacific Ranges. Precipitation is greatest in the northwest portion and least in the southeastern portion. There are 2 Ecosection subdivisions.

The **Eastern Chilcotin Ranges Ecosection** is a dry, rounded mountain area located leeward of the Pacific Ranges in the Southeast. (Fig. 125).

The **Western Chilcotin Ranges Ecosection** is a rugged, moist mountainous area located just south of the low Kitimat Ranges.

The **Fraser Plateau Ecoregion** is a broad, rolling plateau that includes several shield volcanoes and a small portion of the leeward side of the Kitimat Ranges (Fig. 127). The climate is somewhat continental, although sufficient moisture reaches the area by way of the low Kitimat Ranges. It contains 7 Ecosections.

The **Bulkley Basin Ecosection** is a broad lowland area, with a rainshadow climate in the north.

The **Bulkley Ranges Ecosection** is a narrow, mountain area located leeward of the Kitimat Ranges in the northwest.

The **Cariboo Plateau Ecosection** is an upland area with increased moisture and moderate temperatures in the southeast.

The **Chilcotin-Cariboo Basin Ecosection** is the dissected portion of the Chilcotin and Cariboo plateaus and the Fraser Badland that lies between them (Figs. 123 and 124). It has the warmest and driest climate in the Ecoregion.

The **Chilcotin Plateau Ecosection** is a flat upland area, with a rainshadow climate located in the central west area (Fig. 125).

The **Nazko Upland Ecosection** is a flat upland area, with increased precipitation located in the north-northeast.

The **Nechako Plateau Ecosection** is a rolling upland area that has several high shield volcanoes with well developed alpine areas. It is located in the north-northwest.

Figure 126. *At higher elevations, such as this area near Kluskus, conifer forests become patchy near timberline. The harsh climate results in stunted "krummholz" growth in the scattered coniferous survivors, intermixed with a variety of alpine communities (Andrew P. Harcombe).*

Figure 127. *Extensive flat basaltic lava-flows occur across much of the Fraser Plateau Ecoregion. Here, a river has cut through this material to form cliffs and talus slopes, July 1978 (Horst Baender). Except for wetlands, soils are often shallow, and dry lodgepole pine forests dominate.*

Sub-Boreal Interior Ecoprovince

ECODOMAIN - HUMID TEMPERATE

ECODIVISION - HUMID CONTINENTAL HIGHLANDS

ECOPROVINCE - SUB-BOREAL INTERIOR

Ecoregion - Central Rocky Mountains

Ecosections - Hart Foothills
- Hart Ranges

Ecoregion - Fraser Basin

Ecosections - Babine Upland
- Nechako Lowland

Ecoregion - Skeena and Omineca Mountains

Ecosections - Eastern Skeena Mountains
- Omineca Mountains
- Western Skeena Mountains

Figure 128. *Location of the Sub-boreal Interior Ecoprovince in British Columbia.*

Location

The Sub-Boreal Interior Ecoprovince lies to the east of the Coast Mountains and to the west of the Interior Plains, in the north-central part of the province (Fig. 128). It consists of the large Fraser Basin, the southern portion of the Skeena, Omineca, and Muskwa ranges and the Hart Ranges (Fig. 130).

In this Ecoprovince, logging is the most extensive industry based on renewable resources; there are many mines. Agriculture is restricted to the area of finer textured soils in the Fraser Basin; it is limited to grazing and production of some forage crops.

Figure 129. *Johannesen Lake, in the Omineca Mountains Ecosection, showing edaphic grassy areas on the lower slopes, September 1988 (Mike Fenger). Extensive spruce forests cover the mountain sides, grading into rocky alpine at higher elevations.*

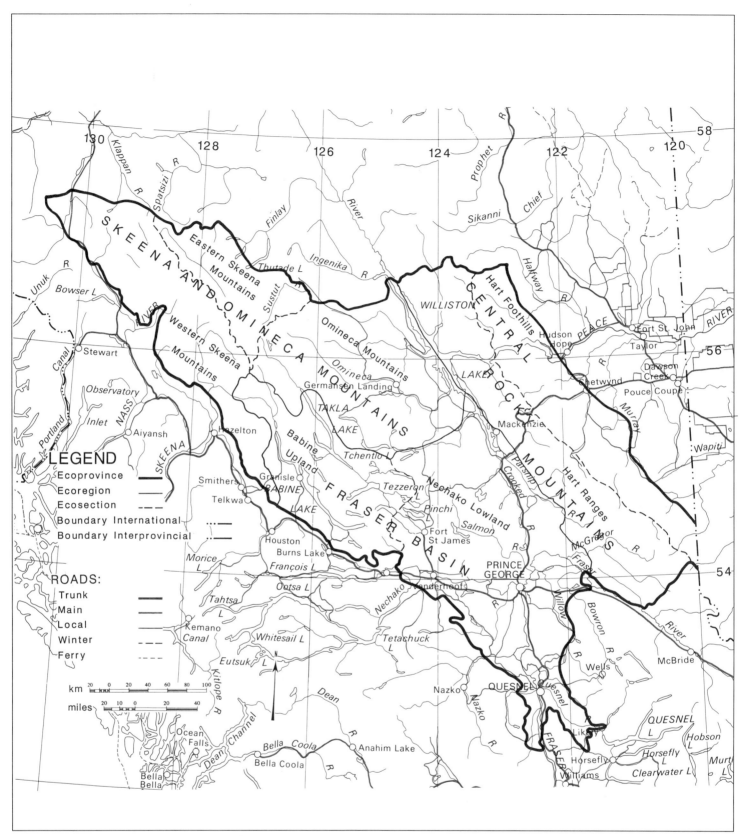

***Figure 130.** Geographic location and major roads of the Ecoregion units in the Sub-Boreal Interior Ecoprovince in British Columbia.*

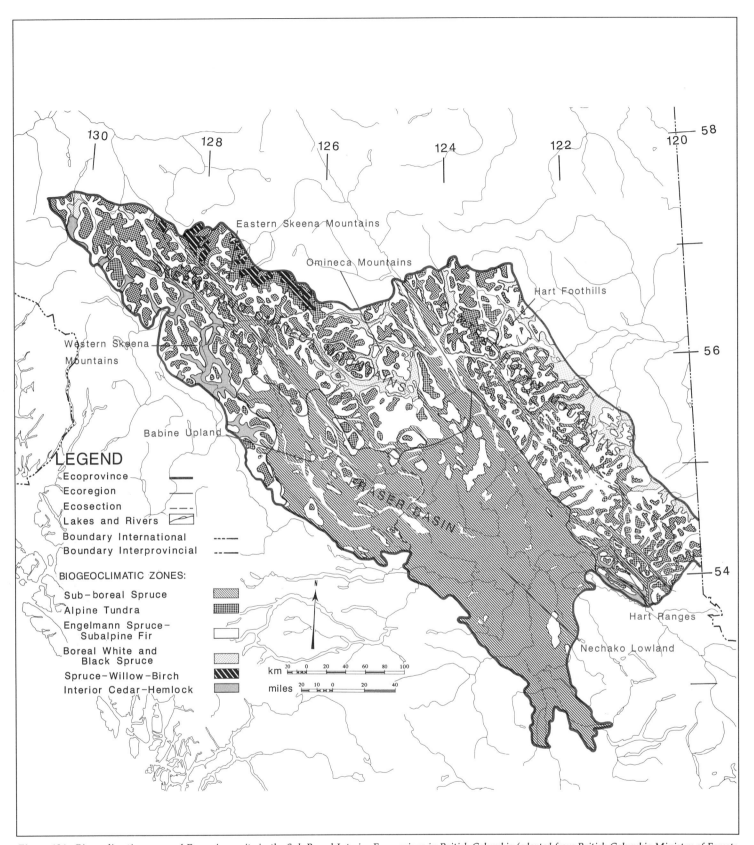

Figure 131. *Biogeoclimatic zones and Ecoregion units in the Sub-Boreal Interior Ecoprovince in British Columbia (adapted from British Columbia Ministry of Forests 1988; Demarchi, D.A. 1988b).*

Climate

Prevailing westerly winds bring Pacific air to the area over the Coast Mountains by way of the low Kitimat Ranges or the higher Boundary Ranges. Much of the region is in a rainshadow. Coastal air has low moisture content when it reaches the Ecoprovince. Moisture does enter the area when there is southwest flow over the low Kitimat Ranges. Summer surface heating, which leads to convective showers, and winter frontal systems result in precipitation that is evenly distributed throughout the year.

Outbreaks of Arctic air are frequent during the winter and early spring, the cold air moving unhindered from the north to the south. The southern edge of the Ecoprovince is near the typical southern extent of the Arctic air mass in January. The mountains are an area of relatively high snowfall.

Physiography

This Ecoprovince consists of several physiographic systems. The low lying plateau area is comprised of the Nechako Lowlands (Fig. 132), the northern portion of the Nechako Plateau, and the southern portion of the Northern Rocky Mountain Trench. The mountains to the north and west include the southern Skeena and Omineca Mountains (Fig. 129), while the mountains in the east are comprised of the Hart Ranges (Fig. 133) and associated foothills, the southern Muskwa Ranges and foothills, and the MacGregor Plateau.

The Interior Plateau portion is a broad area of low relief, with expanses of flat or gently rolling country. In places it is almost completely undissected, but elsewhere it is incised to the level of the Fraser, Nechako and other rivers. The Fraser Basin is of lower relief than the Nechako Plateau. Much of its drainage is poorly organized, and there are numerous lakes and wetlands. The Nechako Plateau is of higher relief with long low ridges. In the

Interior Plateau area, the Rocky Mountain Trench is similar in appearance to the Fraser Basin. During the past ice-age, large glaciers moved across the region leaving various deposits and 3 larger areas of fine textured lake-bottom silts.

The southern Skeena and Omineca mountains are a complex series of mountain ranges that occur north of the Interior Plateau and east of the coastal mountains. These mountains appear to rise from the plateau surface in long, rounded ridges and eventually to peaks and high ridges with the serrated and jagged profile created by intense alpine glaciation. The zigzag course of the Skeena river, downstream from Kludo Creek, which cuts across the northern Babine Range in 3 places, was determined by ice barriers in adjoining valleys. The present drainage of Babine Lake northward into the Skeena River below Atna Range rather than through the old portage route across to Stuart Lake must also be the result of damming by ice or moraines. The Omineca Mountains are composed of harder, erosion-resistant granite rocks; their lateral boundaries are a series of depressions and valleys. Drainage is generally to the east, while drainage in the Skeena Mountains is to the south and to the west.

The lower elevation central Rocky Mountains are comprised of the Hart Ranges (Fig. 133) and the southern portion of the Muskwa Ranges and adjacent foothills. They contrast sharply with the majestic mountain groups to the south and north. They are a narrow range that separates the Interior Plateau of central British Columbia from the Interior Plains. The Peace River dissects those mountains with a deep gorge; otherwise rivers generally are short and flow westward into the Parsnip and Fraser rivers or eastward into the Peace River. The upper surface of the continental ice-sheet once lay 1,800 m to 2,100 m thick on the mountains. Some of the rounded summits were overridden, and some were little affected by alpine and valley glaciation. The combination of greatly lessened elevation and relief, of different bedrocks and structure, and of reduced alpine and valley glacia-

Figure 132. The Nechako Lowland Ecosection looking southwest near Vanderhoof to Tachick and Nulki lakes, 29 August 1947 (courtesy of British Columbia Ministry of Crown Lands, Survey and Resource Mapping Branch, Victoria). Trembling aspen and lodgepole pine stands dominate much of the foreground while lodgepole pine and white spruce forests occur on the higher land in the background.

Figure 133. *The Hart Ranges Ecosection looking eastward up the Hominka River, 26 September 1948 (courtesy of British Columbia Ministry of Crown Lands, Survey and Mapping Branch, Victoria). A level gradient and cold air ponding have combined with the meandering river to create extensive wetlands on the valley floor; dense Engelmann Spruce – Subalpine Fir forests occur on the mountain slopes, while poorly developed Alpine Tundra communities occur only on the summits of the highest mountains.*

tion has resulted in a subdued topography. The Rocky Mountain Foothills in the area are similar to the adjacent Rocky Mountains except that their height diminishes towards the Interior Plains and they have a trellis pattern of drainage. In the foothills, the valleys have eroded along belts of soft rock and fault zones and are generally wide and flaring.

Vegetation

Vegetation of the Sub-Boreal Interior Ecoprovince reflects increased coolness and moisture with an increase in latitude when compared to the Central Interior Ecoprovince. The dominant vegetation is dense coniferous forests, from valley bottom to timberline, with increased shrub and tree cover on the scattered wetlands. Deciduous forests are more common here than in southern Ecoprovinces.

Three primary vegetation zones occur (Fig. 131). The lower zone that has a potential climax of white (hybrid) spruce and subalpine fir covers the greatest portion of the Ecoprovince. The predominance of fine-textured landforms results in moist soils and diverse understories. The transitional vegetation is sensitive to changes in both summer warmth and soil material. In lower, southern areas, Douglas-fir is the dominant conifer. Soils are less weathered than in the higher elevation or more northern areas, where lodgepole pine is common. On finer soils, where clay accumulation impedes moisture movement, trembling aspen and paper birch may form extensive deciduous forests before climax species can become established. Common plants of the understory include prickly rose, soopalallie, willows, black twinberry, thimbleberry, devil's club, bunchberry, arnicas, twinflower, fireweed, trailing raspberry, oak fern, creamy peavine, and asters. Wetlands are extensive in lower relief areas. Sedge fens are common (Fig. 135), as well as organics dominated by scrub birch, willows, and sedges. Of special interest are sphagnum bogs with black spruce, Labrador tea, and sedges that are more typical of areas farther north. Floodplain areas have black cottonwood and white spruce, with a lush understory of red-osier dogwood, highbush-cranberry, black gooseberry, horsetails, and bluejoint.

The middle vegetation zone is dominated by subalpine forests of Engelmann spruce and subalpine fir. Lodgepole pine is usually dominant (Fig. 134). Common species are white-flowered rhododendron, black huckleberry, mountain-ash, black gooseberry, bunchberry, arnica, twistedstalks, and a carpet of moss. In steeper terrain with high snowfall, there are avalanche areas marked by stands of Sitka alder. At higher elevations where the forest opens, the landscape may be intermixed with tree clumps and meadows of valerian, Indian hellebore, ragwort, and sedges. Subalpine soils are strongly acidic but well drained. They have a medium texture and a greater surface accumulation of litter than lower forests.

An extensive alpine tundra belt occurs at higher elevations of the northern mountains, where flatter topography results in a variety of alpine communities. The alpine is composed of a moist meadows of herbs such as Indian hellebore, ragwort, Indian paintbrush, and sedge, moist heath of mountain-heathers, and drier areas of Altai fescue, other grasses, sedges, dwarf willows, and lichens. In the eastern mountain area, the alpine has a greater component of exposed rock, with drier communities composed of dwarf willows, grasses, woodrushes, moss campion, louseworts, and white mountain-avens. Soils are strongly acidic, often with turfy topsoils, and frequently disturbed by frost churning and heaving.

Figure 134. *Coarser materials and extensive fire history in the Sub-Boreal Interior Ecoprovince usually result in even-aged successional stages dominated by lodgepole pine. Spruce regeneration is sparse; ground lichens and club mosses are common (Andrew P. Harcombe).*

Figure 135. *Tatlatui Park in the Eastern Skeena Mountains Ecosection has a mosaic of climax spruce forests and open wetlands, September 1988 (Mike Fenger). Note the string fen in the middle foreground, where the wetland is composed of a number of ridges and wetter low areas.*

Fauna

This Ecoprovince supports 57% of all bird species known to occur in British Columbia and 46% of all species known to breed in the province (see Table 5). The Boreal Owl is a typical resident species. Highest breeding numbers of Herring Gull and Black Tern occur here. Two passerine species of note are the Rusty Blackbird and Magnolia Warbler.

Moose is the most abundant and widely distributed ungulate, while the black bear and wolf are common throughout and grizzly bear is abundant in the wet forests of the mountains. Lynx, fisher and muskrat are widely distributed throughout this region.

The only reptile is the rare common garter snake. Western toad, wood frog, and spotted frog occur througout the Ecoprovince.

Ecoprovince Subdivisions

The **Sub-Boreal Interior Ecoprovince** is divided into 3 Ecoregions containing 7 Ecosections (see Figs. 89 and 130; Table 4).

The **Central Rocky Mountains Ecoregion** consists of steep-sided, but round-topped mountains and foothills that are lower than ranges of the Rockies to either the south or north. It contains 2 Ecosections.

The **Hart Foothills Ecosection** is an area of low, rounded mountains and wide valleys, on the east side of the Rocky Mountains. Cold Arctic air often stalls along the eastern margin or in the valleys.

The **Hart Ranges Ecosection** is a mountainous area that forms a low barrier to eastward moving Pacific air or southwestward moving Arctic air (Fig. 133).

The **Fraser Basin Ecoregion** consists of a broad, flat lowland and a rolling upland, located in the central plateau area of the interior of British Columbia. It has been divided into 2 Ecosections.

The **Babine Upland Ecosection** is a rolling upland with low ridges and several large lakes in the depressions.

The **Nechako Lowland Ecosection** (Fig. 132) is a broad, flat lowland with some dissection by the Fraser and Nechako rivers. Although the climate is sub-boreal, this Ecosection has a milder climate than its neighbour.

The **Skeena and Omineca Mountains Ecoregion** consists of several mountain groups that vary from high rugged ranges in the west to rounded, isolated ranges in the east. This Ecoregion is divided into 3 Ecosections.

The **Eastern Skeena Mountains Ecosection** is an area of high, isolated mountain groups located in the rainshadow of the Western Skeena Mountains Ecosection (Fig. 135).

The **Omineca Mountains Ecosection** is an area on the east side containing rounded mountains and ridges with wide valleys. It has the driest climate in the Ecoregion.

The **Western Skeena Mountains Ecosection** is an area on the west side containing rugged mountains and moist climate.

Southern Interior Mountains Ecoprovince

ECODOMAIN - HUMID TEMPERATE

ECODIVISION - HUMID CONTINENTAL
HIGHLANDS

**ECOPROVINCE - SOUTHERN INTERIOR
MOUNTAINS**

Ecoregion - Columbia Mountains and
Highlands

Ecosections - Central Columbia Mountains
- Eastern Purcell Mountains
- McGillivary Range
- Northern Columbia Mountains
- Quesnel Highland
- Southern Columbia Mountains
- Shuswap Highland

Ecoregion - Southern Rocky Mountains

Ecosections - Central Continental Ranges
- Northern Continental Ranges
- Southern Continental Ranges

Ecoregion - Southern Rocky Mountain Trench

Ecosections - Big Bend Trench
- East Kootenay Trench
- Upper Fraser Trench

Figure 136. *Location of the Southern Interior Mountains Ecoprovince in British Columbia.*

Location

The Southern Interior Mountains Ecoprovince consists of the Columbia Mountains and associated highlands, the southern Mountain Trench and the Continental Ranges of the Rocky Mountains (Figs. 136 and 138). It lies east of the interior plateaus in the southeastern portion of the province.

Agriculture is restricted to the Rocky Mountain Trench and wide southerly valleys. It is largely based on grazing and forage crops except in the extreme south where lowlands have been developed for cereal crops and orchards. Forest-based industries are important and include a rapidly expanding tourism and recreation element. Coal mining occurs in the Elk River valley and metal mining occurs in the lowlands and mountains. Extensive reservoir impoundments on the Columbia and Kootenay rivers have occurred throughout this Ecoprovince.

Figure 137. *The Columbia River marshes near Radium in the East Kootenay Trench Ecosection are important nesting and staging areas for waterfowl (Gary W. Kaiser).*

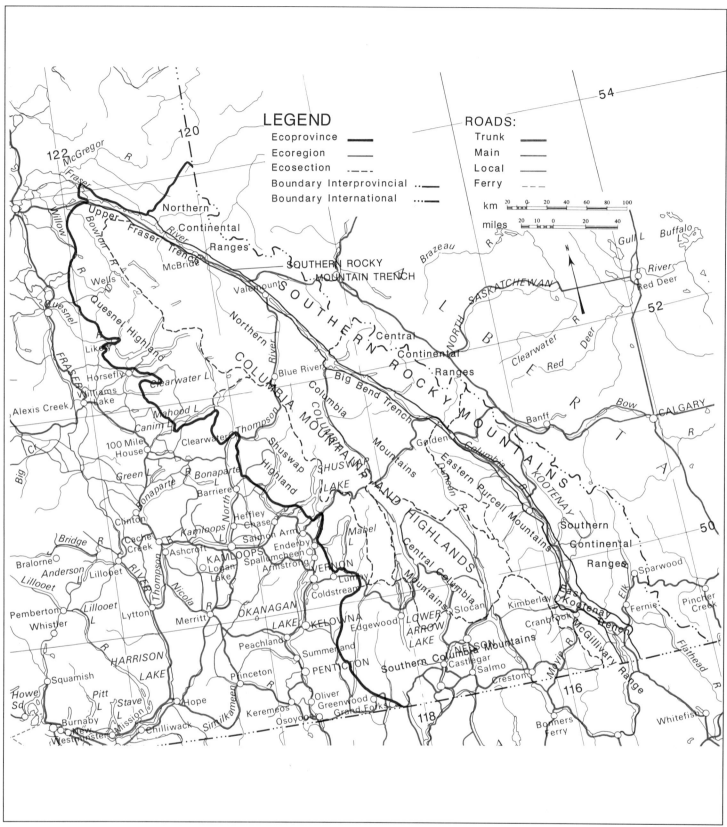

Figure 138. *Geographic location and major roads of the Ecoregion units in the Southern Interior Mountains Ecoprovince in British Columbia.*

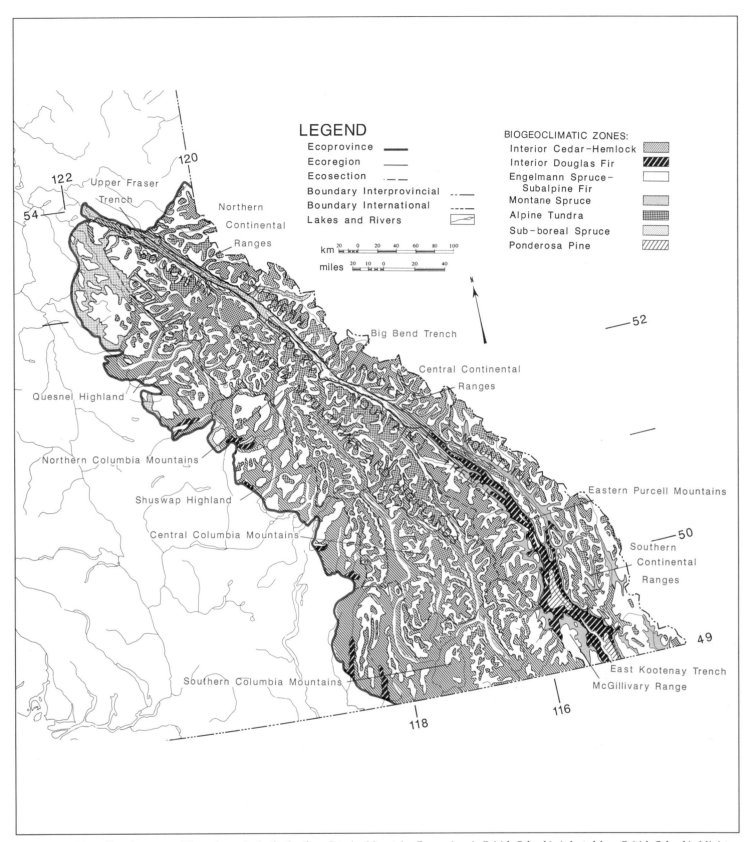

Figure 139. *Biogeoclimatic zones and Ecoregion units in the Southern Interior Mountains Ecoprovince in British Columbia (adapted from British Columbia Ministry of Forests 1988; Demarchi, D.A. 1988b).*

Climate

There are 2 distinct climate regimes—one in the mountains and the other in the Rocky Mountain Trench. Although there are strong temperature and precipitation gradients over the area, the climate regimes of the mountains are largely the same. Air masses approach from the west and lose moisture first, as they pass over the western Columbia Mountains and again as they pass over the Rocky Mountains. The rainfall in the Ecoprovince is obtained from three main sources: by way of the lower passes of the southern Coastal Mountains, by way of the low Kitimat Ranges, and through evaporation from surface waters on the interior plateaus. Surface water within the Rocky Mountain Trench is a minor contributor to precipitation in the Rocky Mountains.

The Rocky Mountain Trench bisects two large mountain blocks with significantly different physiography and macroclimatic processes. A strong rainshadow effect exists leeward of the Columbia Mountains. During the summer, intense surface heating creates strong updrafts in the hills. The resulting downdraft over the centre of the valley clears the sky and enhances the sunny conditions that characterize the trench's summer climate.

During the winter and early spring months, the Rocky Mountain Trench serves as an access route for outbreaks of cold, dense Arctic air. During minor outbreaks, the cold air remains in the trench, but during severe outbreaks, it passes into the valleys of the Columbia, lower Columbia, Elk, and Kootenay rivers.

Physiography

The Southern Interior Mountains Ecoprovince consists of several mountain ranges, valleys, trenches, and highlands. There are 4 main physiographic systems; the highlands on the western flank, the Columbia Mountains, the Southern Rocky Mountain Trench, and the Continental Ranges of the Rocky Mountains (Fig. 140).

The highlands consist of the Quesnel Highlands and the higher, eastern portion of the Okanagan and Shuswap highlands. The highlands represent a transition between plateaus and mountains and occur where the amount of dissection is fairly high and where the flat and gently sloping upland surfaces of higher elevations are small. Glacial ice covered most of the high areas during the past ice ages and consequently most summits are rounded. Cirques which developed on the northern and northeastern sides have sharpened the profiles of the highest peaks, whereas the valley sides were steepened and the valley bottoms broadened.

The Columbia Mountains consist of a series of ranges and alternating trenches of a complex geological origin. The mountain ranges get progressively higher from the southwestern Selkirks to the northern Cariboo Mountains. The high mountains, especially in the northern ranges, are mostly massive and have bold, sharp peaks separated by deep, steep-sided valleys. Lower summits were covered by glacial ice and subsequently have been sculptured by cirque and valley glaciers to sharp peaks and sawtooth ridges. It is only in the southern ranges at elevations below 2,100 m that rounded and moderately pointed summits prevail. The profiles of many valleys have been strongly modified by glaciation and its after effects. The retreating ice left moraines and other debris. Ice dams created large glacial lakes that disappeared as the melting progressed but have left extensive terraces of silts and compact gravels along the sides of the valleys.

The Southern Rocky Mountain Trench is a large, faulted valley that lies between the Columbia and Rocky mountains (Figs. 140 and 141). It is open to the Nechako Lowlands to the

Figure 140. The Southern Interior Mountains Ecoprovince looking southward from the junction of the Torpy and Fraser rivers, with the Northern Continental Ranges Ecosection on the middle left, the Upper Fraser Trench Ecosection in the middle, and the Northern Columbia Mountains in the right background, 26 September 1948 (courtesy of British Columbia Ministry of Crown Lands, Survey and Resource Mapping Branch, Victoria). In winter, the wide Southern Rocky Mountain Trench funnels cold Arctic air from the central interior south to the East Kootenay. In this area, Interior Cedar-Hemlock forests dominate the Trench and lower valleys, Engelmann Spruce - Subalpine Fir forests dominate the middle and upper mountain slopes, and Alpine Tundra occurs on the summits.

Figure 141. *The East Kootenay Trench Ecosection looking east across the Kootenay River to the Southern Continental Ranges Ecosection, 7 June 1948 (courtesy of British Columbia Ministry of Crown Lands, Survey and Resource Mapping Branch, Victoria). The Lussier River flows into the Kootenay and Premier Ridge is the low, burned-over ridge in the centre of the figure. The close proximity of low elevation winter ranges to the high elevation summer ranges has enabled the East Kootenay area to support the largest populations and most diverse species of big game in Canada.*

north and terminates in the Salish Mountains in Montana. Since it has been eroded and in-filled by glacial debris, it resembles a long, narrow plain with few bedrock outcrops. Several large rivers (Fraser, Canoe, Columbia, and Kootenay) meander along the valley floor, forming large floodplains and wetlands. Much of the middle portion has been flooded by the McNaughton Lake reservoir and the Koocanusa Lake resevoir fills the floodplain of the southernmost portion of the trench.

The Continental Ranges of the Rocky Mountains are comprised of a series of longitudinal ridges and deeply dissected valleys (Fig. 141). These mountains are highest and most rugged in the north portion that is drained by the upper Fraser and Canoe rivers. Here, short, steep rivers and streams flow down into the Rocky Mountain Trench. Southward the mountains become open with isolated ridges, and the valleys become wider. The rivers often flow for long distances before draining into the trench.

Vegetation

The Southern Interior Mountains Ecoprovince encompasses great habitat diversity because of combinations of very wet mountains and very dry rainshadow valleys. There are 7 vegetation zones present, but they are best described in 3 parts: the dry southeastern area on either side of the East Kootenay Trench and surrounding mountains, the area including the main portion of the Columbia Mountains and Highlands Ecoregion, and the rest of the Rocky Mountain Trench and surrounding mountains (Fig. 139).

East Kootenay Trench

In the lowest vegetation zone the climax forest is Douglas-fir. However, widespread fires and an extensive grazing history have created many transitional woodlands and open areas. In the valley bottom, ponderosa pine is the main seral species (Fig. 142), giving way at higher elevation and increasing moisture to western larch and lodgepole pine. Persistent shrub-grasslands have saskatoon, redstem ceanothus, antelope-brush, and grasses, including Idaho fescue, junegrass, Kentucky bluegrass, needlegrasses, and cheatgrass. In the forest, common shrubs include rose, saskatoon, soopolallie, and birch-leaved spirea. Pinegrass and kinnikinnick are common. Soils have dark surface horizons and are moderately weathered. Floodplains may have black cottonwood, spruce, red-osier dogwood, false Solomon's-seal, and horsetails. Of special note are the extensive marshes along the upper reaches of the Columbia River (Fig. 137), intermixed with riparian forests, that are important to waterfowl.

Southern Continental Ranges

The climax forest in the montane vegetation zone consists of Engelmann spruce, and subalpine fir. The zone is relatively dry, with Douglas-fir, western larch, and lodgepole pine as important seral species. Understories are shrubby, with Utah honeysuckle, soopolallie, saskatoon, birch-leaved spirea, false azalea, pinegrass, bunchberry, and mosses. Soils have clay layers that improve moisture retention. Widespread fires have been common, creating extensive stands of lodgepole pine.

The subalpine vegetation zone has open to closed Engelmann spruce and subalpine fir forests, although seral lodgepole pine predominates. Understories support white-flowered rhododendron, grouseberry, false azalea, thimbleberry, queen's cup, bunchberry, pinegrass, and mosses. Soils are strongly weathered and acidic. Moisture sites may have horsetails and meadowrue. Avalanche areas with dense Sitka alder and herbaceous cover are common throughout the zone. At the higher elevations, forest cover becomes discontinuous and in the Fording River valley

Figure 142. *Open ponderosa pine stand, with antelope-brush as the shrub understory, is found in the southern portion of the East Kootenay Trench Ecosection, August 1970 (Dennis A. Demarchi). This habitat, is an important winter feeding area for many big game species; it is also grazed in the summer by cattle.*

Figure 143. *In the higher snowfall areas of the Columbia Mountains and Highlands Ecoregion, such as this area in the Toby Creek valley, avalanche tracks are common, September 1988 (Dennis A. Demarchi). Dominated by alder and other moisture-loving plants, they provide a strong contrast to the subalpine coniferous forests.*

rough fescue grasslands occupy southerly-facing slopes and ridge tops. Whitebark pine and alpine larch may be found at timberline. Meadows may be intermixed with the forest.

The alpine tundra vegetation zone is mainly rock-dominated, with pockets of grass-sedge meadows and heath vegetation.

Columbia Mountains and Highlands

For most of the Ecoprovince, the climax forest of the lower vegetation zone is western hemlock and western redcedar. Seral forests are common in the drier areas, with Douglas-fir, western larch, grand fir, western white pine, lodgepole pine, paper birch, or trembling aspen. Common plants include blueberries, false box, devil's club, Utah honeysuckle, oak fern, twinflower, queen's cup, ferns, and mosses. However, in the wetter valleys, forests succeed directly to the climax species. Soils are usually deeply weathered, reddish in colour, and very acidic. Large valley lakes and reservoirs are characteristic of the area. Of special note are the extensive wetland complexes associated with the Creston valley.

The subalpine vegetation zone is dominated by subalpine fir and Engelmann spruce, sometimes with mountain hemlock at higher elevations. Seral forests are uncommon. Understory plants include white-flowered rhododendron, black gooseberry, false azalea, twistedstalk, Sitka valerian, bunchberry, and dense moss. Avalanche chutes, dominated by Sitka alder and herbs, occur frequently (Fig. 143). At higher elevations, the forest cover is mixed with lush herbaceous meadows. In southern areas, whitebark pine and alpine larch may occur at timberline.

The alpine tundra vegetation zone is rock and glacier dominated, with patches of heath vegetation and grass-sedge meadows.

Fauna

This Ecoprovince supports 70% of the bird species known to occur in British Columbia and 62% of the breeding avifauna of the province—the second highest diversity of breeding species (see Table 5). It contains the only breeding location of Forster's Tern and one of the highest breeding concentrations of Ospreys in the world. It is also one of the few areas in British Columbia where the Western Grebe and Long-billed Curlew breed. The Black-billed Cuckoo occurs regularly. Significant autumn and winter populations of waterbirds, especially American Coots, are found on large ice-free lakes. The extensive waterbodies are important migration staging areas for Tundra Swans, Canada Geese, and dabbling and diving ducks, particularly Redhead. The area is the centre of breeding abundance for the White-breasted Nuthatch. Large flocks of Clark's Nutcracker appear in the valley bottoms during autumn and winter.

Mountain goats are perhaps the most widely distributed wild ungulate in the Ecoprovince but mule and white-tailed deer are also widely distributed. Elk ("Rocky Mountain") are very abundant throughout the mountains and valleys adjacent to the southern portion of the Trench. Small, relict populations of caribou occur in old-growth spruce forests in the Northern Continental Ranges Ecosection and the Columbia Mountains and Highlands Ecoregion; the "Selkirk Herd" is the southern most population of caribou in the province. Grizzly and black bears are common throughout the area. Bighorn sheep are common in the Southern Continental Ranges Ecosection and adjacent trench.

Small mammals include the long-eared myotis, pika, hoary marmot, Columbian ground squirrel, golden-mantled ground squirrel, and water vole. The painted turtle, and common and western terrestrial garter snakes are typical reptiles. The long-toed salamander, western toad, and spotted and northern leopard frogs are the characteristic amphibians.

Ecoprovince Subdivisions

The Southern Interior Mountains Ecoprovince is divided into 3 Ecoregions containing 13 Ecosections (see Figs. 89 and 138; Table 4).

The **Columbia Mountains and Highlands Ecoregion** is a mountainous area that rises from highlands and isolated ridges on the west and south to culminate in high, rugged, often ice-capped, mountains along the north and northeastern margin. This block of mountains intercepts eastward flowing precipitation, making these the wettest mountains in the interior of the province. This Ecoregion contains 7 Ecosections in British Columbia.

The **Central Columbia Mountains Ecosection** is an area of high ridges and mountains, but the valleys and trenches are narrow. Precipitation is high from the valley bottoms to the upper slopes.

The **Eastern Purcell Mountains Ecosection** is a mountainous area with high valleys. It is located leeward of the Purcell Ranges and is within a distinct rainshadow.

The **McGillvary Range Ecosection** is an area of subdued ridges located in the southeast. It is relatively dry.

The **Northern Columbia Mountains Ecosection** is an area of high, rugged mountains, many of which are ice-capped. It has the highest precipitation and coldest temperatures.

The **Quesnel Highland Ecosection** is a highland area intermediate between the plateaus to the west and the high, rugged mountains to the east. Precipitation is higher here than in the Shuswap Highland Ecosection to the south.

The **Southern Columbia Mountains Ecosection** is an area of high ridges and mountains interspersed with wide valleys and trenches. The mountains become more prominant eastward. Precipitation is high on the mountain slopes but rainshadows are common in the southern valleys.

The **Shuswap Highland Ecosection** is a highland area intermediate between the plateaus to the west and the mountains to the east. The climate here is warmer and winters are milder than the Quesnel Highland Ecosection to the north.

The **Southern Rocky Mountains Ecoregion** has high, rugged mountains, usually with deep, narrow valleys. The climate here is continental. It contains 3 Ecosections.

The **Central Continental Ranges Ecosection** is an area of high, rugged mountains many of which are ice-capped; valleys are often short and steep-sided. The climate is cool and moderately dry.

The **Northern Continental Ranges Ecosection** is an area of high, rugged mountains, with many ice-capped and moderately wide valleys (Fig. 140). The climate is cool and moderately moist.

The **Southern Continental Ranges Ecosection** (see Fig. 141) is a dry mountainous area with many wide valleys and isolated ridges. The climate is warm in summer and cold in winter.

The **Southern Rocky Mountain Trench Ecoregion** is a long, wide, flat-bottomed valley that dissects the Southern Interior Mountains Ecoprovince. Cold Arctic air from the sub-boreal part of the province is able to move down the Trench easily, while in the summer months the southern part of the Trench is the driest part of the Ecoprovince. It contains 3 Ecosections.

The **Big Bend Trench Ecosection** is the narrow section in the central part of the Rocky Mounatin Trench. Most of the lowland has been flooded by a reservoir. This Ecosection has high precipitation.

The **East Kootenay Trench Ecosection** (Fig. 141) is a broad, flat glacial plain with a distinctive rainshadow that lies in the southern portion of the Rocky Mountain Trench.

The **Upper Fraser Trench Ecosection** is a broad, flat glacial plain (Fig. 140). The climate is moderately moist and cool, however there is an area with an increasingly distinct rainshadow upvalley from McBride to Valemount. This Ecosection is the northern portion of the Southern Rocky Mountain Trench.

Southern Interior Ecoprovince

ECODOMAIN - DRY

ECODIVISION - SEMI-ARID STEPPE HIGHLANDS

ECOPROVINCE - SOUTHERN INTERIOR

Ecoregion - Okanagan Range

Ecoregion - Thompson-Okanagan Plateau

Ecosections - Clear Range
- Eastern Thompson Upland
- Northern Thompson Upland
- Okanagan Basin
- Okanagan Highland
- Southern Thompson Upland
- Thompson Basin

Figure 144. Location of the Southern Interior Ecoprovince in British Columbia.

Location

The Southern Interior Ecoprovince lies east of the Coast and Cascade mountains and west of the Columbia Mountains (Figs. 144 and 146). It is the southernmost part of the Interior Plateau system. The leeward portion of the coastal mountains and the drier portion of the highlands are included because they share much the same climate as the main plateau.

The largest human population in the interior of British Columbia occurs in this Ecoprovince. Agriculture is largely based on grazing and forage crops (Fig. 150) but orchards and vineyards are integrated with a large and successful tourist industry in the valleys. The dry climate slows tree growth and logging is less widespread than in other southern areas of the province.

Figure 145. Kilpoola Lake near Richter Pass, 1 July 1964 (R. Wayne Campbell). Shrub-Steppe and grasslands dominate much of the Thompson Basin and Okanagan Basin ecosections. Here the effects of excessive cattle grazing are obvious: native grass species have been replaced by sagebrush.

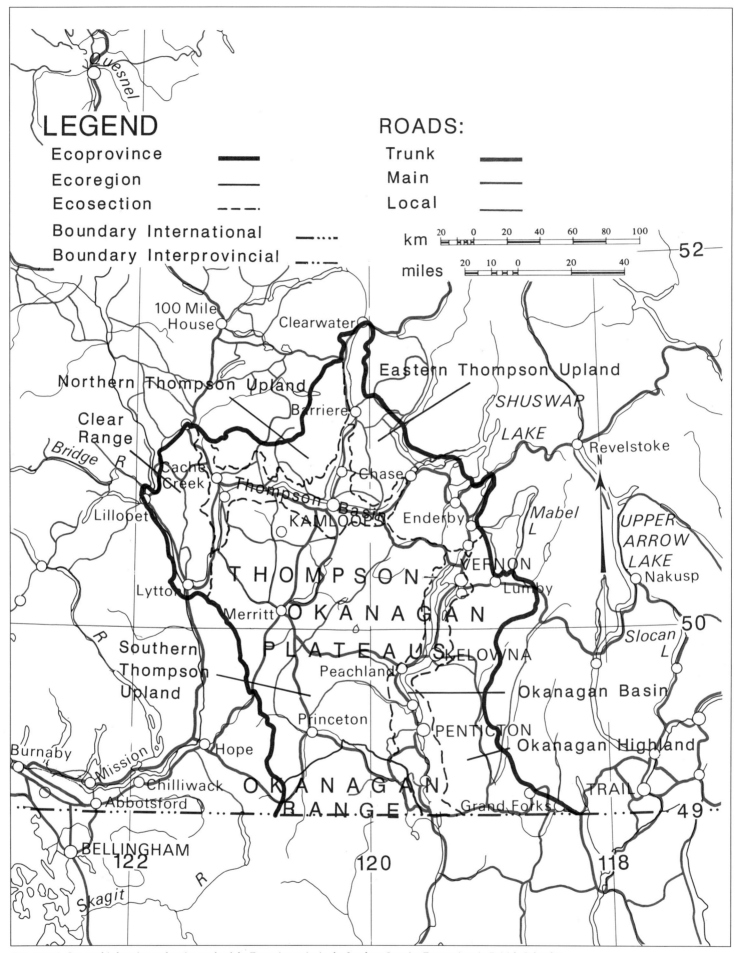

Figure 146. *Geographic location and major roads of the Ecoregion units in the Southern Interior Ecoprovince in British Columbia.*

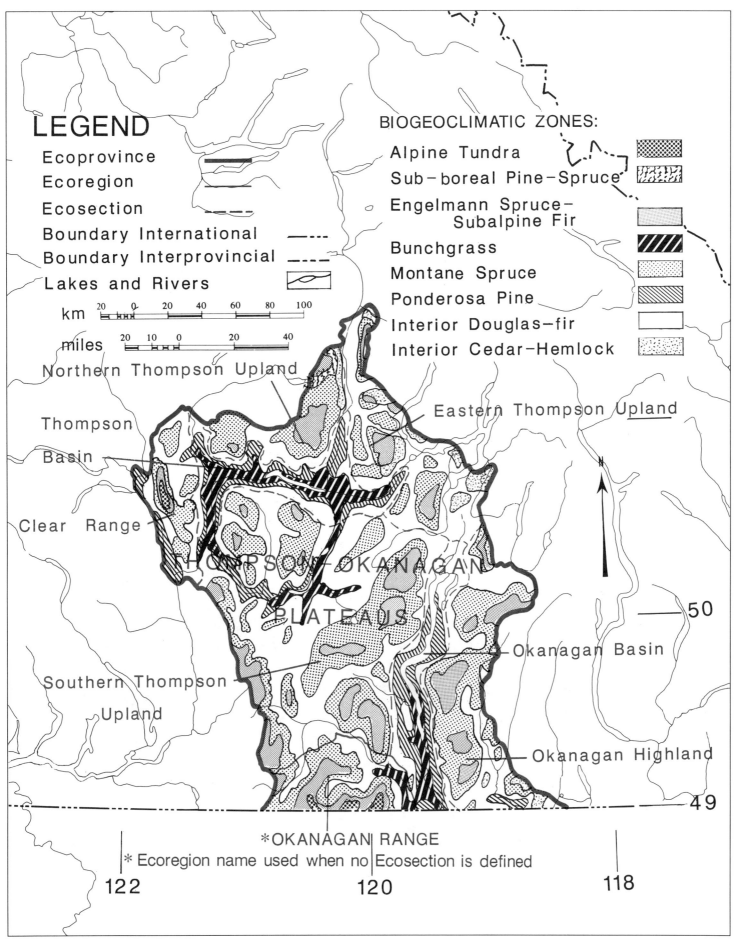

Figure 147. Biogeoclimatic zones and Ecoregion units in the Southern Interior Ecoprovince in British Columbia (adapted from British Columbia Ministry of Forests 1988; Demarchi, D.A. 1988b).

Climate

Because this Ecoprovince lies in the rainshadow of the Coast and Cascade mountains it contains some of the warmest and driest areas in summer. Air moving into the area has already lost most of its moisture on the west facing slopes of the Coast Mountains, reducing precipitation and contributing to clear skies, particularly in the summer.

In winter and early spring, there are frequent outbreaks of cold, dense Arctic air because there is no effective barrier in the north. However, such events are less frequent than on the plateaus farther north. When the cold air fills a valley and is capped with warmer moister air, deep inversions and prolonged periods of cold weather at middle and low altitudes result. At the same time, milder weather will occur at higher altitudes and in areas away from the valleys. There are occasional irruptions of hot, dry air from the Great Basin in the summer. They bring clear skies and very warm temperatures.

Annual distribution of precipitation is similar to other plateaus. Surface heating in summer results in characteristic convective showers. The river valleys have high temperatures and strong convection currents and, with their local sources of moisture, contribute to showers on the surrounding hills. Skies over the valleys are often free of clouds.

Physiography

This Ecoprovince includes the Thompson Plateau, the eastern portion of the Pavilion Ranges, the southeastern portion of the Cascade Ranges, and the western margin of the Shuswap and Okanagan highlands.

The whole area was glaciated during the Pleistocene and there are many surface features such as moraines, glacial lake and river beds, terraces, and ice-contact deposits. Most of the valley floors contain more recent floodplain deposits.

The Thompson Plateau is a gently rolling upland of low relief that is transitional with adjoining mountains (Fig. 149). The rise of the plateau towards the mountains is gradual, with greater dissection of the surface as the slope increases. Lava beds obscure large areas of the older rocks. The surface has been divided into two large basins by the Thompson and Okanagan rivers and into two smaller basins by the Nicola and Similkameen rivers.

The Marble and Clear ranges of the Pavilion Range form a high transitional zone in the northeast. It has a steep front along the Fraser River to the west and a somewhat more gentle slope into the Hat Creek valley on the east.

The Okanagan and Hozameen ranges of the Cascade Mountains are composed of folded and metamorphosed sedementary and volcanic rocks that have been intruded by granitic batholiths. The peaks and high ridges are serrated and show the effects of intense alpine glaciation. Cirque basins are particularly noticeable on north and northeast slopes. At lower elevations there are rounded ridges and dome-shaped mountains which were overridden by ice. To the east, the mountains become lower and grade into the plateau surface. The ranges are deeply dissected by the Similkameen and Ashnola rivers.

The western portions of the Okanagan and Shuswap highlands form the eastern boundary of the Ecoprovince. It is a gently sloping plateau with several large rounded ridges separated by deep streams and eventually gives way to the South Interior Mountains Ecoprovince.

Vegetation

This Ecoprovince supports a diverse set of upland and aquatic habitats that vary from open grasslands to dense coniferous forests and from small alkaline ponds to large, deep lakes.

There are 8 distinct vegetation zones (Fig. 147). A grassland of bluebunch wheatgrass occurs at the lowest elevations in the 4 river basins. It has largely been reduced by excessive livestock

Figure 148. *An open ponderosa pine forest with bluebunch wheatgrass forming the predominant understory. This habitat is common on the better drained sites on the slopes of the large, dry basins such as the Thompson Basin and Okanagan Basin ecosections (Ian McTaggart-Cowan).*

Figure 149. *The Southern Thompson Upland Ecosection looking northeast across Merritt and the Nicola valley to Douglas Lake, 29 June 1948 (courtesy of British Columbia Ministry of Crown Lands, Survey and Resource Mapping Branch, Victoria). Before the current period of urban development, most of the low elevation basins in the Southern Interior Ecoprovince were similar to this photograph. Note the riparian vegetation in the valley bottom, steppe vegetation on the lower slopes, and Interior Douglas-fir forests on the northerly and upper slopes.*

grazing and is frequently replaced by sagebrush (Fig. 145). The rate of succession in the vegetation communities is very slow because of severe summer drought. In the very dry valley bottoms of the southern Okanagan, antelope-brush and prickly-pear cactus dominate lower sites. Grassland soils are dominant, having developed on sites varying from coarse gravel to silts. Those soils are often calcareous, with dark brown to black surface layers, and are rich in organic matter.

In most other valleys, the vegetation forms an open parkland zone with ponderosa pine and Douglas-fir intermixed with shrub-grassland communities (Fig. 148). The common plants include saskatoon, big sagebrush, bluebunch wheatgrass, Idaho fescue, rough fescue, pinegrass, needlegrasses, and lupines. Floodplains have stands of black cottonwood, spruces, and trembling aspen, and a dense shrub growth of red-osier dogwood and black gooseberry. Horsetails are abundant at the edges. Soils vary from grassland soils to moderately weathered forest soils.

A lower montane vegetation zone occurs at slightly higher elevations. The climax is normally the Douglas-fir forest that covers much of the Ecoprovince (Fig. 151). The common plants include saskatoon, soopolallie, birch-leaved spirea, roses, pinegrass, twinflower, balsamroot, and kinnikinnick. Lower elevations within the zone support open, successional ponderosa pine and bunchgrass habitats. The communities at higher elevations are typically closed lodgepole pine and pinegrass. Although forest regeneration is fairly fast, grassland communities of Idaho fescue, bluebunch wheatgrass, and various forbs are persistent on southern exposures and rolling plains. The soils are generally weathered and calcareous.

The climax forest in the upper montane zone is a dense growth of white, Engelmann, or hybrid spruce. It is frequently mixed with subalpine fir. Transitional forests are dominated by lodgepole pine and Douglas-fir. The common understory plants include trapper's tea, grouseberry, falsebox, pinegrass, arnicas, kinnikinnick, and lupines. Fireweed communities occur in disturbed areas.

In the subalpine zone, the climax is a dense forest of Engelmann spruce and subalpine fir but frequent fires have allowed the development of lodgepole pine forests. Many of those forests have now matured and are vulnerable to insects. Common understory plants include black huckleberry, white-flowered rhododendron, grouseberry, arnica, and Sitka valerian. Alpine larch and whitebark pine may occur near the timberline. The open forests at higher elevations are intermixed with sedge-grass meadows. Soils change in the forested vegetation zones with increasing elevation and the associated cooler and moister climatic conditions. Soils at lower levels tend to be calcareous but with increasing elevation there is a gradient from weakly leached, moderately acid to increasingly leached and strongly acid types. Forest litter accumulation also increases.

The alpine tundra vegetation zone is dominated by low sedge-grass communities with pockets of heath. Common plants include sedges, alpine timothy, trisetum, alpine fescue, mountain-avens, dwarf willows, and lupines. The soils are often a shallow layer over bedrock. They are strongly acidic, coarse in texture, and have turfy, dark-coloured surfaces underlain by reddish or brownish layers. Outcrops of bedrock are common.

Figure 150. *Where irrigation water is available agriculture, especially production of hay crops, is a common land use in the valley bottoms of the major rivers south of Clearwater. In the North Thompson valley, much of the riparian and ponderosa pine forests have been converted to farmland (John Thompson).*

Figure 151. *Multi-aged Douglas-fir forests are common on the lower montane vegetation zone of the Southern Interior Ecoprovince (John Thompson). Snags and their cavities are important habitat elements and are used by a wide variety of birds for nesting, roosting, and perching. Unfortunately, loggers must remove them for safety reasons, and they are also sought after by firewood cutters.*

Fauna

This Ecoprovince has the greatest diversity of birds in the interior of British Columbia and the most breeding species of all the Ecoprovinces (see Table 5); it holds 74% of all bird species known to occur and 70% of those species know to breed in British Columbia (see Table 5), more breeding bird species than any other Ecoprovince. It is the centre of breeding abundance in the province for Swainson's Hawk, California Quail, Mourning Dove, Burrowing Owl, Long-eared Owl, White-throated Swift, Lewis' Woodpecker, Williamson's Sapsucker, Pygmy Nuthatch, Western Kingbird, Yellow-breasted Chat, and Lark Sparrow. Some species breed nowhere else in British Columbia: Ferruginous Hawk, Prairie Falcon, Gray Partridge (introduced), Chukar (introduced), California Gull, Flammulated Owl, Common Poorwill, Black-chinned Hummingbird, and White-headed Woodpecker; others breed nowhere else in Canada: Canyon Wren, Sage Thrasher, and Gray Flycatcher. It contains the only site in Canada that supports a major winter population of Tundra Swans.

Mule deer is the most abundant large ungulate although the white-tailed deer has been extending its range westward from the Okanagan Basin and the Okanagan and Shuswap highlands. Bighorn sheep occur on the rugged grasslands throughout the Thompson and Okanagan valleys and in the Clear Ranges.

Characteristic small mammals include spotted bats, pallid bats, Nuttall's cottontails, white-tailed jack rabbits, Great Basin pocket mice, and western harvest mice. The racer and western rattlesnake are characteristic reptiles. Tiger salamanders and Great Basin spadefoot toads are found nowhere else in the province.

Ecoprovince Subdivisions

The Southern Interior Ecoprovince is divided into 2 Ecoregions containing 7 Ecosections (see Figs. 89 and 146; Table 4).

The **Okanagan Range Ecoregion** lies in the strong rainshadow created by the Cascade Mountains and is very dry. It is the northern limit of an Ecoregion that extends along the east slope of the Cascade Ranges to the Columbia River in Washington. In British Columbia, it is not divided into Ecosections.

The **Thompson-Okanagan Plateau Ecoregion** is a broad plateau area with low elevation basins. It has the driest and warmest climates in the province and contains 7 Ecosections:

The **Clear Range Ecosection** is a mountainous upland area that is transitional with the Coast Ranges to the west and the plateau surface to the east. The Fraser and Thompson rivers have dissected the upland surface.

The **Eastern Thompson Upland Ecosection** is an area with dissected uplands. It has warm, dry summers and mild winters with relatively high snowfall.

The **Northern Thompson Upland Ecosection** is a broad flat plateau with extensive wetlands and small lakes. The climate is transitional between the drier and warmer climates farther south and moister and cooler climates to the north.

The **Okanagan Basin Ecosection** is a warm and exceptionally dry area with a high diversity and abundance of wildlife.

The **Okanagan Highland Ecosection** is an area with long, rounded ridges and wide deep valleys that is transitional in height between the Thompson Plateau to the west and the higher Columbia Mountains to the east. It has a moist climate.

The **Southern Thompson Upland Ecosection** (Fig. 149) is an area with flat plateau uplands, steep sided plateau walls, and 2 large lowlands. It has the driest climate of any plateau upland in this Ecoregion and it has 2 large grassland areas.

The **Thompson Basin Ecosection** is a warm and exceptionally dry, low elevation area with a high diversity and abundance of wildlife.

Boreal Plains Ecoprovince

ECODOMAIN - POLAR

ECODIVISION - BOREAL

ECOPROVINCE - BOREAL PLAINS

Ecoregion - Alberta Plateau

Ecosections - Kiskatinaw Plateau
- Peace Lowland
- Sikanni-Beatton Plateau

Location

A small portion of the Boreal Plains Ecoprovince lies in the northeast portion of British Columbia, east of the Rocky Mountains (Figs. 152 and 154). Eastward, it extends across Alberta and Saskatchewan to Manitoba.

Agriculture is limited to grazing with some cereal and forage crop production in the Peace Lowlands Ecosection (Fig. 156). Natural gas production and mining occurs throughout the hinterland and many seismic lines criss-cross the area. Recently, logging of trembling aspen has been promoted.

Figure 152. Location of the Boreal Plains Ecoprovince in British Columbia.

Climate

The climate is typically continental since most of the moist Pacific air has dried crossing successive ranges of mountains before it reaches the area. Air descends from the Rocky Mountains leading to generally dry conditions and sunny skies. In warmer months rain is largely due to surface heating, which leads to convective showers. Winters are cold because there are no barriers to irruptions of Arctic Air.

Figure 153. Trembling aspen, with its characteristic white and black bark, forms extensive forests in the Peace Lowland Ecosection. Understories are rich and diverse with both shrubs and herbaceous plants (Andrew P. Harcombe).

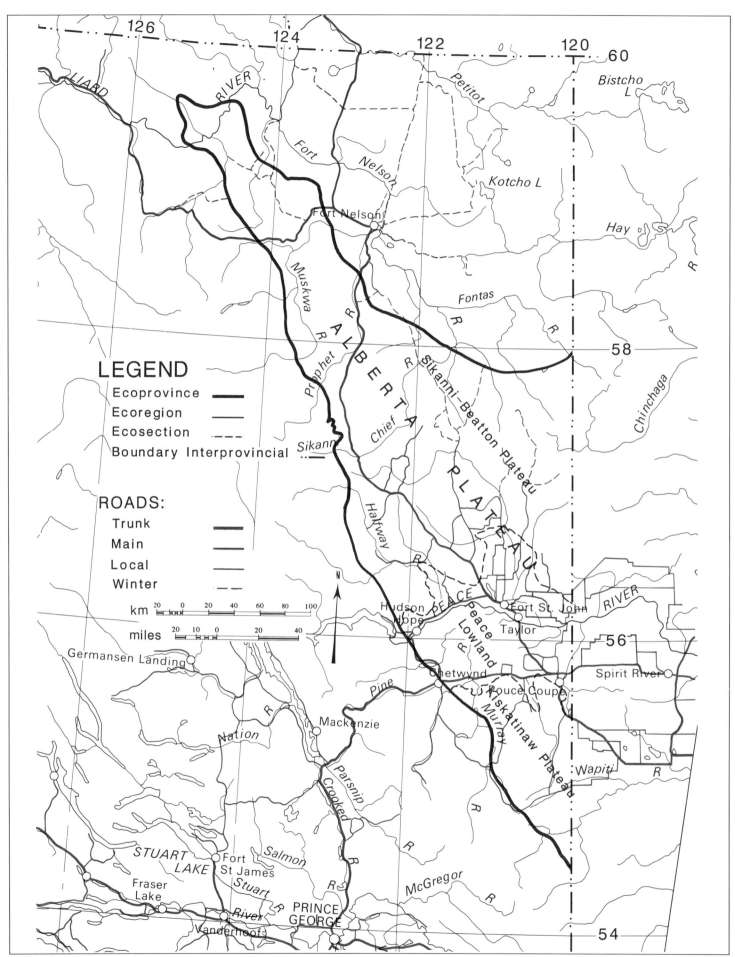

Figure 154. *Geographic location and major roads of the Ecoregion units in the Boreal Plains Ecoprovince in British Columbia.*

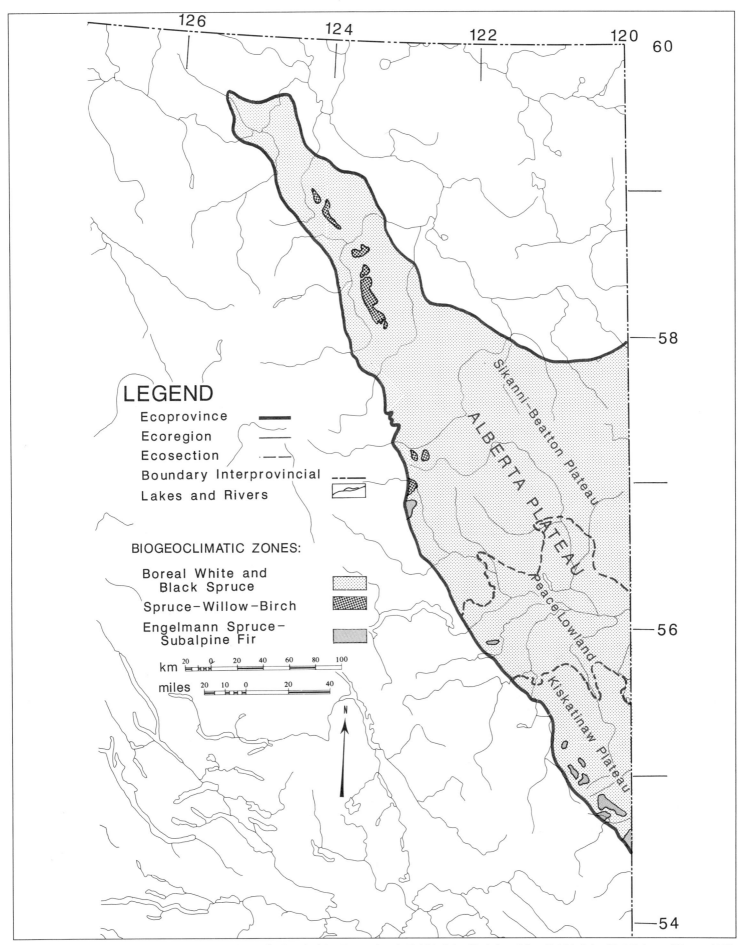

Figure 155. *Biogeoclimatic zones and Ecoregion units in the Boreal Plains Ecoprovince in British Columbia (adapted from British Columbia Ministry of Forests 1988; Demarchi, D.A. 1988b).*

Physiography

In British Columbia, the Boreal Plains Ecoprovince occurs on the Alberta Plateau. That area consists of plateaus, plains, prairies, and lowlands and is generally an area of low relief away from the deeply incised river beds. The plateau is dissected by the Peace River and its tributaries (Fig. 157). The upland surface lies between 900 m and 1,200 m above sea level rising to 1,500 m on the crest between the Muskwa and Beatton rivers. Drainage over part of the upland surface is poorly organized. There are large areas of muskeg, and streams meander across the surface. Several rivers, such as the Kiskatinaw, Halfway, Beatton, Sikanni Chief, Muskwa and Fort Nelson, have cut through the upland surface into the soft shale bedrock (Fig. 158).

The plateau was glaciated during the past ice age. Ice from the Keewatin centre of accumulation moved southwestward across the Alberta Plateau to the foothills, leaving a veneer of glacial till. As the ice waned, the Peace River valley was occupied by a temporary lake that left fine silt sediment to a depth of 30 m.

Vegetation

Most of the Boreal Plains Ecoprovince is covered in lowland forests. Fires have been common and seral forests predominate. Three vegetation zones occur (Fig. 155). The Ecoprovince is similar to larger areas in Alberta, where domination by deciduous trees and open shrub-grassland habitats are commonly referred to as the "aspen parklands".

The climax in the lower vegetation zone is white or black spruce, though the latter is more common on coarse textured materials. Trembling aspen (Fig. 153) and balsam poplar are dominant seral species on the widespread fine-textured soils (generally lower elevations), whereas lodgepole pine predominates in seral forests on coarser textured soils (generally higher elevations). Other common species are paper birches, highbush-cranberry, prickly rose, soopolallie, willows, fireweed, bunchberry, asters, creamy peavine, and mosses. Floodplains are composed of balsam poplar and white spruce, with red-osier dogwood and horsetails. The scattered wetlands may be covered with a scrubby forest of black spruce and tamarack, with Labrador tea, horsetails, and sphagnum (Fig. 159). A distinctive habitat occurs on steep, south-facing slopes or on dry river breaks, where saskatoon, trembling aspen, roses, wheatgrass, and needlegrass form an open shrub-grassland. Extensive marshes and shallow lakes create habitats important to aquatic birds.

Two subalpine zones, neither very extensive in area, occur along the western fringe of the Ecoprovince. South of about 57°N latitude, subalpine forests are dominated by Engelmann spruce and subalpine fir, commonly with seral lodgepole pine. Understories are composed of white-flowered rhododendron, black huckleberry, bunchberry, and mosses. Farther north, forests are more open, with white spruce and subalpine fir. At the upper elevations of the zone, forests are replaced by shrub-dominated vegetation, primarily willows and scrub birch.

The alpine tundra zone is rare, found only on a few of the western hills.

Figure 156. *The Peace Lowland Ecosection looking west up the Pouce Coupe River across the Alberta Plateau, 2 September 1950 (courtesy of British Columbia Ministry of Crown Lands, Survey and Resource Mapping Branch, Victoria). The Kiskatinaw and Peace rivers dissect the upland in the right background of the figure. Even in the early 1950s, farmland dominated much of the area. Trembling aspen and grassland remain only in the gullies.*

Figure 157. *The Peace Lowland Ecosection looking eastward down the Peace River from the mouth of the Halfway River 23, October 1954 (courtesy of British Columbia Ministry of Crown Lands, Survey and Resource Mapping Branch, Victoria). The Moberly and Pine rivers dissect the upland surface from the upper right to the upper left in the figure. Trembling aspen stands and grassland occur on the south-facing exposures at the left of the figure, while muskeg, wetlands, trembling aspen and lodgepole pine occur on the upland surface at the right.*

Figure 158. *The Sikanni-Beaton Plateau Ecosection (foreground) looking westward to the Northern Mountains Ecoregion, 6 September 1950 (courtesy of British Columbia Ministry of Crown Lands, Survey and Resource Mapping Branch, Victoria). The Muskwa Foothills Ecosection is in the middle-background. Balsam poplar stands occur along the riparian areas of Minaker River in the foreground; large forest fires have enabled trembling aspen and willow-birch communities to occur over much of the Boreal White and Black Spruce forests in the area. Rolling Alpine Tundra occurs on the summits of the Rocky Mountain Foothills.*

Fauna

This Ecoprovince supports 61% of all bird species known to occur in British Columbia, and 46% of all species known to breed in the province—the fourth lowest total in British Columbia (see Table 5). The many wetlands, ponds, and slow-moving streams on the upland surface provide excellent habitat for breeding and migrating waterbirds. Some of the largest breeding concentrations of Eared Grebe occur in this Ecoprovince. Some of the rarest shorebirds in British Columbia regularly migrate through the Peace Lowland Ecosection. They include the Hudsonian Godwit, White-rumped Sandpiper, and Stilt Sandpiper. The area is the centre of abundance in the province for Broad-winged Hawk, Sharp-tailed Grouse, Upland Sandpiper, Franklin's Gull, Common Grackle, and Eastern Phoebe. It is the only breeding area in the province for Philadelphia Vireo, Chestnut-sided Warbler, Black-throated Green Warbler, and Connecticut Warbler. The Boreal Plains Ecoprovince is also the major migratory corridor in British Columbia for Lapland Longspur.

The most abundant large mammal is the moose. Both mule deer and white-tailed deer are common in the Peace Lowland Ecosection. Large carnivores include wolves, and black bears.

The only small mammal restricted to this region is the Arctic shrew. The only reptile, the common garter snake, is rare. Only one salamander, the long-toed salamander, and four species of toads and frogs occur here. One species, the northern chorus frog, has its centre of distribution in this Ecoprovince.

Ecoprovince Subdivisions

In British Columbia, the Boreal Plains Ecoprovince has only one Ecoregion containing three Ecosections (Figs. 89 and 154; Table 4).

The **Alberta Plateau Ecoregion** is a large flat or rolling plateau that is incised by the Peace River and its tributaries. It contains three Ecosections in British Columbia.

The **Kiskatinaw Plateau Ecosection** is a flat upland with some dissection by the Murray, Kiskatinaw and Wapiti rivers. Numerous wetlands occur on the upland surface. It is located in the southern portion of the Ecoregion adjacent to the Hart Foothills Ecosection.

The **Peace Lowland Ecosection** is a large lowland that is deeply dissected by the Peace River and its tributaries (Figs. 156 and 157). This Ecosection has the mildest climate with the lowest snowfall in this Ecoregion.

The **Sikanni-Beatton Plateau Ecosection** (Fig. 158) is a rolling upland with some higher ridges, wide valleys and some dissection by the Sikanni Chief River. Numerous wetlands and slow-moving streams occur on the upland surface.

Figure 159. *Muskeg forests of black and white spruce and sometimes tamarack are found in depressional areas over most of the Boreal Plains Ecoprovince. The increased sunlight and moisture result in a diverse understory (Andrew P. Harcombe).*

Taiga Plains Ecoprovince

ECODOMAIN - POLAR

ECODIVISION - SUB-ARCTIC

ECOPROVINCE - TAIGA PLAINS

Ecoregion - Fort Nelson Lowland

Figure 160. *Location of the Taiga Plains Ecoprovince in British Columbia.*

Location

The Taiga Plains Ecoprovince lies to the east of the north Rocky Mountains and north of the Boreal Plains Ecoprovince in northeastern British Columbia (Figs. 160 and 162). It extends into the Mackenzie Basin in the Northwest Territory.

Limited forage crops are produced in the area and some logging also occurs. Guiding and fur trapping remain the most important industries based on renewable resources. Prospecting for natural gas has been extensive and numerous seismic lines criss-cross the area.

Climate

The climate is continental. Cold dense Arctic air is unimpeded from the north and may easily blanket the area in the winter and spring months. The long sub-arctic winters are generally dark with little heating by solar radiation. In summer, its location between the Arctic and Pacific air masses gives it long periods of cloud cover and unstable weather. In years of colder temperatures or more moisture, some soils remain frozen. Precipitation is light and in the warmer months is largely due to surface heating which leads to convective showers.

Figure 161. *Black spruce, with its distinctive bushy top, is commonly found associated with the very wet muskeg areas of the Taiga Plain Ecoprovince. (R. Wayne Campbell).*

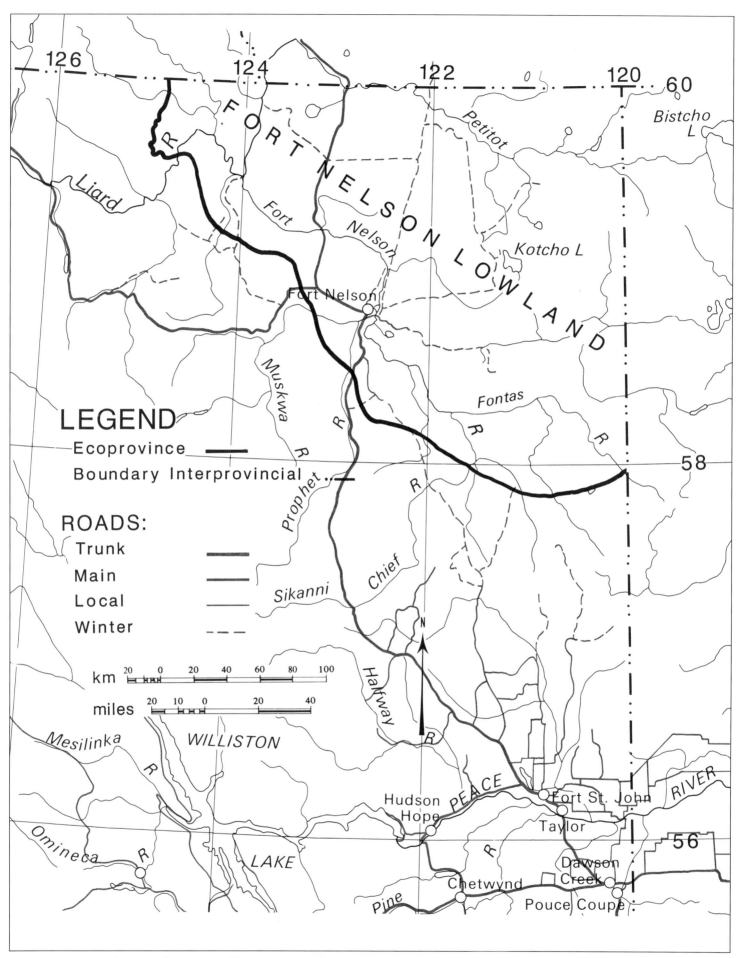

Figure 162. *Geographic location and major roads of the Fort Nelson Lowland Ecoregion and Taiga Plains Ecoprovince in British Columbia.*

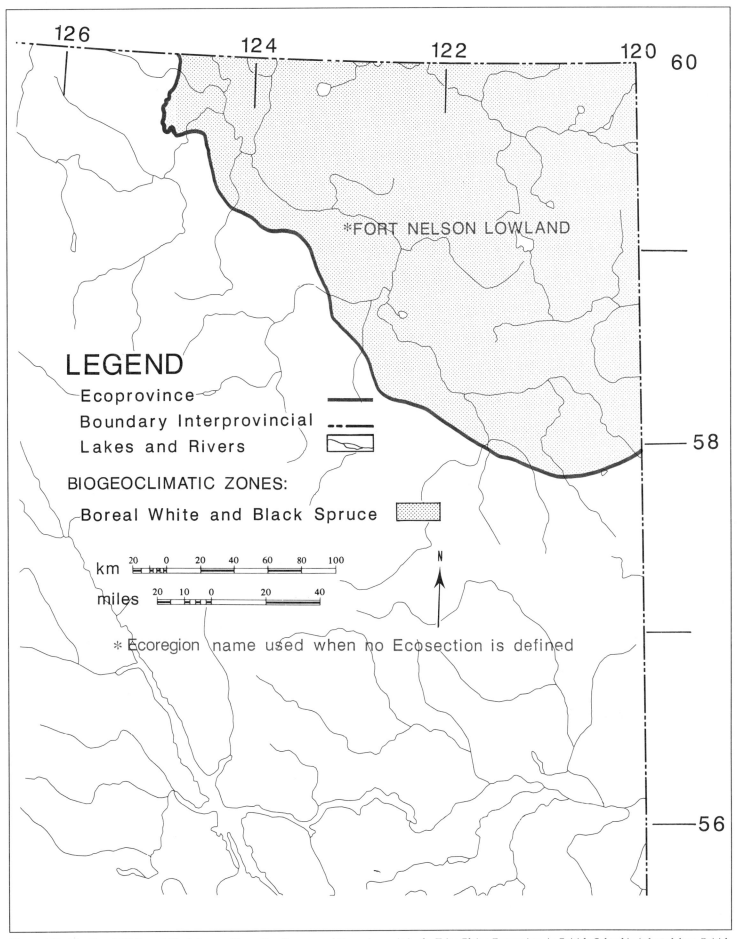

Figure 163. *The Boreal White and Black Spruce Biogeoclimatic zone and Ecoregion unit in the Taiga Plains Ecoprovince in British Columbia (adapted from British Columbia Ministry of Forests 1988; Demarchi, D.A. 1988b).*

Physiography

The British Columbia portion of the Ecoprovince is characterized as a large lowland area that has been dissected below the Alberta Plateau surface by the Liard River and its tributaries, namely the Fort Nelson and Petitiot rivers. The softer shales were eroded prior to the ice-age glacial advance. The Fort Nelson and Petitiot rivers are incised as much as 150 m below the general level terrain of the lowland, which lies near 450 m elevation. Elsewhere streams, muskeg, and small lakes dominate a surface which has remained unmodified since its emergence from the covering of ice (Fig. 165).

Vegetation

The Taiga Plains Ecoprovince has the least diversity of any of the Ecoprovinces (Fig. 163). Extensive fire history has resulted in dominance by deciduous seral forests, with numerous wetland areas.

There is a single vegetation zone whose climax should be white and black spruce (Fig. 161). Seral trembling aspen forests are common, often with balsam poplar and paper birch. Lodgepole pine is an uncommon seral tree; jack pine does occur on dry sites in the northeastern part of the area. Understories include prickly rose, soopolallie, highbush-cranberry, willows, twinflower, asters, and mosses. Floodplains are dominated by white spruce and balsam poplar, with alder, willows, red-osier dogwood, and horsetails. Wetlands are extensive (Fig. 164), mainly black spruce bogs with understories of Labrador tea, cloudberry, and sphagnum (peat) mosses, and tamarack fens (Fig. 166) with scrub birch, leatherleaf, sweet gale, buckbean, and fen mosses. Soils are usually fine textured, moist to very wet, and calcareous, with shallow to deep accumulations of organic material. Intermittent areas of permafrost occur.

Fauna

This Ecoprovince supports the lowest diversity of birds of any terrestrial Ecoprovince in British Columbia with only 43% of all species known to occur in the province having been reported (see Table 5); the area holds only 35% of all species known to breed. Part of the reason for that low diversity may simply be a reflection of the very low level of observer effort in the region. It is the centre of abundance for breeding Lesser Yellowlegs and Solitary Sandpipers. Spruce Grouse are abundant in the extensive boreal forests. It is the only breeding area in the province for Bay-breasted Warbler and is the centre of abundance for the swamp sparrow. Le Conte's Sparrow is locally abundant. Other breeding species of note include Cape May Warbler, Canada Warbler, Black and White Warbler, and Rose-breasted Grosbeak.

Moose are the most abundant ungulate, and black bear, and lynx the common carnivores. Scattered herds of caribou spend the winter months in all the upland, muskeg, and boreal forests.

The muskrat, meadow vole, northern red-backed vole, and meadow jumping mouse are widely distributed small mammals. No reptiles are known from the area and the only amphibians known to occur include the western toad, northern chorus frog, and wood frog.

Ecoprovince Subdivisions

In British Columbia, the Taiga Plains Ecoprovince has only one Ecoregion and it is not divided into Ecosections (see Figs. 89 and 162; Table 4).

The **Fort Nelson Lowland Ecoregion** (Fig. 165) is a large lowland area with wide valleys and only minor upland ridges. The climate is very cold in the winter and the summer daylight hours are long.

Figure 164. *Wetlands are common in the Taiga Plains Ecoprovince because of the low relief of the landscape and poor drainage capacity of the soil materials. The shrubby margins between forest and wetland create extensive edge habitat for bird nesting and moose browse (Michael C.E. McNall).*

Figure 165. *The Fort Nelson Lowland Ecoregion looking eastward across the junction of the Kahntah and Fontas rivers, 30 August 1950 (courtesy of British Columbia Ministry of Crown Lands, Survey and Resource Mapping Branch, Victoria). Extensive riparian communities develop along the floodplains while muskeg and stunted black spruce stands occurs on the upland surface.*

Figure 166. *Tamarack, a deciduous conifer, dominates the open forested wetlands of the Taiga Plains Ecoprovince. August 1988 (Mike Fenger).*

Northern Boreal Mountains Ecoprovince

ECODOMAIN - POLAR

ECODIVISION - SUB-ARCTIC HIGHLANDS

ECOPROVINCE - NORTHERN BOREAL MOUNTAINS

Ecoregion - Tatshenshini Basin

Ecoregion - Liard Basin

Ecosections - Liard Plain
- Liard Upland

Ecoregion - Northern Mountains and Plateaus

Ecosections - Cassiar Ranges
- Kechika Mountains
- Southern Boreal Mountains
- Stikine Plateau
- Tahltan Highland
- Teslin Plateau
- Tuya Range

Ecoregion - Northern Rocky Mountains

Ecosections - Muskwa Foothills
- Muskwa Ranges

Figure 167. *Location of the Northern Boreal Mountains Ecoprovince in British Columbia.*

Location

The Northern Boreal Mountains Ecoprovince lies east of the Boundary Ranges of the Coast Mountains, west of the Interior Plains in the northeastern part of British Columbia and south of the Yukon Territory (Figs. 167 and 169). It consists of mountains, plateaus, and lowlands that are strongly influenced by Arctic air.

There has been little obvious effect of human activity in the area. Mineral exploration, open-pit mining and placer mining, have had the most serious habitat impacts (see Fig. 173). Guiding remains the most important industry based on renewable resources.

Figure 168. *There are 2 treelines in many of the mid-elevation valleys in the Ecoprovince such as here in the Jennings River valley, August 1988 (Mike Fenger). The lower treeline has resulted from extensive cold air ponding in the valley bottom, the upper treeline is at the subalpine/alpine border. Willow-dominated shrublands are common in the valley bottom while fescue grasslands are common in the Alpine Tundra zone.*

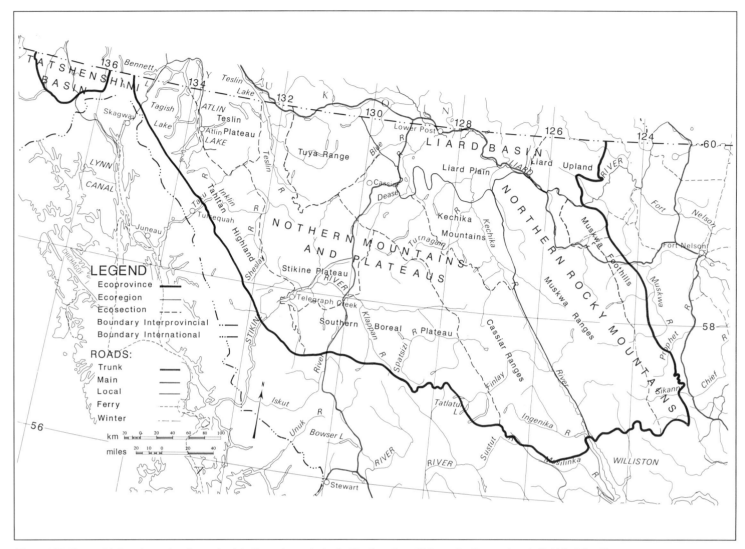

Figure 169. *Geographic location and major roads of the Ecoregion units in the Northern Boreal Mountains Ecoprovince in British Columbia.*

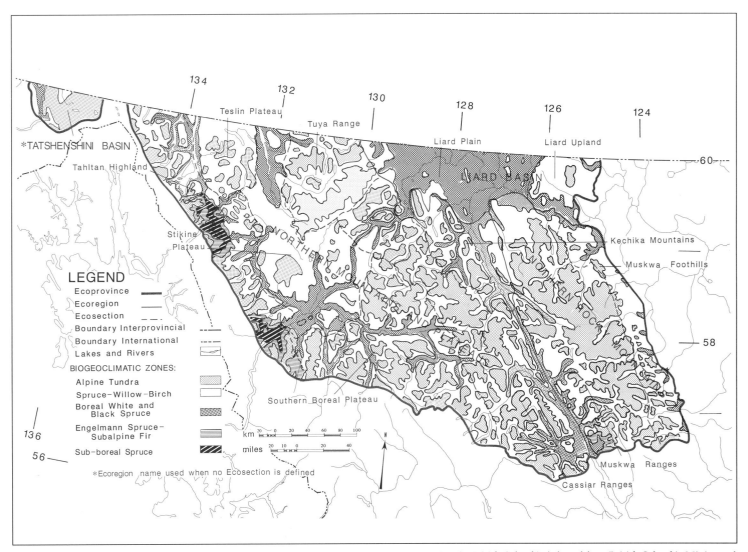

Figure 170. *Biogeoclimatic zones and Ecoregion units in the Northern Boreal Mountains Ecoprovince in British Columbia (adapted from British Columbia Ministry of Forests 1988; Demarchi, D.A. 1988b).*

Climate

Prevailing westerly winds bring Pacific air to the area over the high St. Elias Mountains and Boundary Ranges. Coastal air is greatly reduced in moisture when it reaches the area, and this Ecoprovince is characterized by rainshadow effects that can cause some areas to be very dry. Summertime surface heating leads to convective showers and together with winter frontal systems results in precipitation amounts that are evenly distributed throughout the year. Outbreaks of Arctic air are frequent during the winter and spring. The rugged relief leads to a complex pattern of surface heating and cold air drainage in the valleys.

Physiography

This Ecoprovince encompasses several mountain ranges and lowlands: the Alsek Ranges, the Teslin, Taku, Tanzilla and Stikine plateaus, the Cassiar Mountains, the Liard Plain, Liard Ranges, the northern portion of the Skeena and Omineca mountains, the Northern Rocky Mountain Trench, the Muskwa Ranges, and associated foothills.

The general character of the Ecoprovince is one of mountains and plateaus separated by wide valleys and lowlands (Fig. 171). Each has a different geological origin or structure. Glaciation in the northern mountains was uneven in intensity. The high areas were centres of accumulation from which valley glaciers moved outward across major lowlands. Late glaciation eroded the mountains further. Some areas, such as the foothills, show little or no evidence of glacial erosion and there may have been an ice-free corridor between the continental ice-sheets. Drainage of this area is through the coastal mountains by the Stikine, Taku, and Alsek rivers, north across the Yukon Territory and Alaska by the Yukon River or through the gorge between the Mackenzie and Rocky Mountains by the Liard River. The mountains show a variety of alpine conditions from rugged, serrated rock to rounded, rolling alpine. Lowland areas are often occupied with wetlands, small lakes, and meandering streams (Fig. 168), while valley bottoms in the mountains are often filled with glacial debris.

Figure 171. *The Southern Boreal Plateau Ecosection looking to Eddontenajon Lake from the Stikine valley, 24 September 1947 (courtesy of British Columbia of Crown Lands, Survey and Resource Mapping Branch, Victoria). Wetlands and alpine vegetation dominate much of the upland surface of the Northern Mountains and Plateaus Ecoregion; forests are restricted to the middle slopes above valleys with cold air ponding and below the Alpine Tundra zone.*

Figure 172. *The Tahltan Highland Ecosection looking southeastward down the Sloko River, 20 August 1949 (courtesy of British Columbia Ministry of Crown Lands, Survey and Resource Mapping Branch, Victoria). The Coast and Mountains Ecoprovince is in the right background. Moister Pacific air flowing into this continental area has enabled Sub-Boreal Spruce and Engelmann Spruce - Subalpine Fir forests to develop as well as the Boreal White and Black Spruce forests and the extensive Alpine Tundra zone.*

Vegetation

The Northern Boreal Mountains Ecoprovince is very large but, except for some transitional vegetation from coastal to boreal, is not very diverse. There are 5 vegetation zones (Fig. 170). The distinctive feature of the Ecoprovince is the extensive high subalpine and alpine habitats (Fig. 173).

In the northeastern area, in the Liard Basin, extensive fire history and fine-textured soil materials have resulted in domination by trembling aspen. The lowest vegetation zone has a climax of white and black spruce. Other common tree species are paper birches and balsam poplar. Understories are diverse, with green alder, highbush-cranberry, soopolallie, prickly rose, twinflower, Altai fescue, wild sarsaparilla, and mosses. On floodplains, young balsam poplar stands give way to white spruce, with alder, red-osier dogwood, and horsetails. Low nutrient black spruce bogs have Labrador tea, cloudberry, leatherleaf, lingonberry, and sphagnum. Rich tamarack fens have understories of sweet gale, willows, buckbean, sedges, and fen mosses.

In most of the Ecoprovince, the lowest vegetation zone is dominated by white spruce forests, with little black spruce. Lodgepole pine (coarser soils), trembling aspen (finer soils), and subalpine fir are encountered. This montane zone is highly fragmented in linear strips in lower valley bottoms. Understories are moss dominated. Wetlands tend to be richer in minerals, with both black and white spruce cover.

The subalpine vegetation zone is extensive except in the Liard Basin. Wildfires are less frequent than in lower areas. Trembling aspen and lodgepole pine are common on drier sites. The lower elevations are usually forested with white spruce and subalpine fir, which dominates on higher slopes. Understories include willows, soopolallie, crowberry, twinflower, Altai fescue, fireweed, and a well-developed moss layer. Permafrost may be found in some valleys, and massive cold air pooling leads to a mosaic of shrubfields, fens, and open grassland complexes (Fig. 168). The upper elevations of this zone are essentially a scrub/parkland, dominated by scrub birch and several willow species. Wetlands are usually rich, with white spruce, tall willows, scrub birch, and sedges. Subalpine grasslands are frequent, either on steep south-facing slopes, or on flat to gently rolling uplands. Altai fescue is the common grass.

The alpine tundra vegetation zone is widespread, dominated by shrubs such as dwarf arctic-alpine willows, mountain-heathers, moss campion, mountain-avens, Altai fescue, blackish locoweed, mosses, and lichens. Habitats range from dwarf scrub of prostrate woody plants to alpine grasslands to wet herb meadows (Fig. 173) to barren rock at the highest elevation.

Figure 173. *Alpine Tundra areas are extensive in the Northern Boreal Mountains Ecoprovince. Unfortunately, disturbances such as those caused by mining exploration can have long-term impacts on the fragile communities as can be seen on Black Fox Mountain, September 1988 (Mike Fenger).*

Figure 174. *The Liard Plain Ecosection looking southwest across the Liard River, 15 km east of Lower Post, 21 August 1949 (courtesy of British Columbia Ministry of Crown Lands, Survey and Resource Mapping Branch, Victoria). Boreal White and Black Spruce forests with muskeg occur throughout the Ecosection; wetlands, small ponds and lakes occupy depressions created during the past glaciations.*

141

Fauna

This Ecoprovince supports only 52% of all bird species known to occur in the province and 42% of all species known to breed (see Table 5). However, many species breed nowhere else in British Columbia including the Pacific Loon, Gyrfalcon, Lesser Golden-Plover, Wandering Tattler, Hudsonian Godwit, Red-necked Phalarope, Arctic Tern, Northern Shrike, Smith's Longspur, Snow Bunting, and Common Redpoll. It is the centre of abundance for Willow and Rock ptarmigan, Bohemian Waxwing, and American Tree Sparrow, and it supports the only breeding population of the dark race *(harlani)* of the Red-tailed Hawk. It is the only breeding area other than the Okanagan Basin Ecosection for Brewer's Sparrow.

Moose are the most numerous and widely distributed ungulate, but the thinhorn sheep (both the pure white Dall's and Stone's) and caribou best characterize the fauna. Mountain goats are an abundant species in rugged alpine areas. Grizzly bears, and black bears, and wolves are common throughout the valleys.

Characteristic small mammals include the collared pika, Arctic ground squirrel, tundra vole, and brown lemming. Wolverines and lynx are common.

Ecoprovince Subdivisions

The **Northern Boreal Mountains Ecoprovince** is subdivided into 4 Ecoregions containing 11 Ecosections (see Figs. 89 and 169; Table 4).

The **Tatshenshini Basin Ecoregion** is an area with rounded, subdued mountains and wide valleys leeward of the rugged Boundary and St. Elias ranges. In spite of its close proximity to the Pacific Ocean this area has a typically sub-arctic climate. This Ecoregion is not divided into Ecosections.

The **Liard Basin Ecoregion** is an extensive area of lowland to rolling upland that extends from northern British Columbia into the Yukon and Northwest Territories. In British Columbia this Ecoregion contains 2 Ecosections.

The **Liard Plain Ecosection** (Fig. 174) is a broad, rolling lowland area with a cold sub-arctic climate.

The **Liard Upland Ecosection** is an area of higher, upland relief. Its southern boundary is marked by the deeply incised Liard River Canyon.

The **Northern Mountains and Plateaus Ecoregion** is a large area with a complex of lowlands, rolling and high plateaus and rugged mountains. It has a dry sub-arctic climate. In British Columbia this Ecoregion contains 7 Ecosections.

The **Cassiar Ranges Ecosection** is the area with the highest and most rugged mountains in the Ecoregion. It has a broad band of mountains extending from the southeast corner of the Ecoregion to the northeast corner.

The **Kechika Mountains Ecosection** is an area with high mountains, but low, wide valleys in the rainshadow of the Cassiar Ranges to the west.

The **Southern Boreal Plateau Ecosection** (Fig. 171) consists of several deeply incised plateaus. Extensive rolling alpine and willow/birch habitat occurs. This Ecosection is located in the south-central part of the Ecoregion.

The **Stikine Plateau Ecosection** is a plateau area with variable relief, from lowland to rolling alpine. Low elevations along the Stikine, Nahlin, and Klastline river valleys are the driest in the Ecoregion.

The **Tahltan Highland Ecosection** (Fig. 172) is a rugged mountainous area leeward of the Boundary Ranges and is transitional with them and the plateaus to the east.

The **Teslin Plateau Ecosection** is a rolling plateau area. It lies in a distinct rainshadow.

The **Tuya Range Ecosection** is the area with the most extensive rolling alpine landscape in the province.

The **Northern Rocky Mountains Ecoregion** is an area of high, rugged mountains, several of which have large glaciers and rounded isolated foothills separated by wide valleys. This Ecoregion contains 2 Ecosections.

The **Muskwa Foothills Ecosection** is an area of more subdued mountains which are isolated by wide valleys (see Fig. 158). This area is in the rainshadow of the Rocky Mountains to the west; it is also more commonly under the influence of cold Arctic air in the winter.

The **Muskwa Ranges Ecosection** is the area with the highest, most rugged mountains in the Ecoprovince. It has more snowfall than the foothills to the east.

Changes In The Environment

For most of the last 10,000 years, man has had little effect on the environment of British Columbia. Until 100 years ago, modifications were limited to localized activities near villages and minor changes in river edges to help the harvest of salmon. In less than 100 years, however, large valleys have been cleared for agriculture, cities and ports built on estuaries, and roads pushed into many wilderness areas.

Except for 3 special cases, all of which occurred before World War II, the province has been developed at the expense of the forests. Trees have been cut for building space, for cash, and for agricultural land. The 3 special cases also involve the creation of agricultural areas:

a) The Fraser (Winter 1968), Nanaimo, Cowichan (Dawe and Jones 1986), Courtney, and other smaller river estuaries were dyked, destroying nearly all the foreshore marshes and changing the salinity of intertidal areas.

b) Sumas Lake, one of the largest aquatic wetlands west of the Rocky Mountains, was drained to create Sumas Prairie (Siemens 1968).

c) The dry bunchgrass ranges in the south Okanagan valley were ploughed and eventually converted to orchards and vineyards. Only a tiny remnant survives today (Scudder 1980).

In 1921, when J. A. Munro was beginning his career, there were already 1.2 million ha of farmland in the province. By the time he retired, in 1948, there were 1.8 million ha. For most of that period, commercial logging was confined to accessible stands on Vancouver Island, the Lower Mainland, and near Prince George, but 24.4 million cubic metres of timber were being cut per year between 1949 and 1953.

The post war influx of immigrants, elementary changes in technology, and a rapidly growing economy accelerated environmental changes through 1970. By 1971, the population had doubled to 2.2 million. Agricultural land expanded to 2.4 million ha in spite of the negative effects of urban sprawl (see Warren, C.L. and Rump 1981), highway construction, and the flooding of valley bottoms for hydroelectric projects. Much of that additional land came from forested areas in the Bulkley, Skeena, and Nechako valleys and the Peace River area. In the same period, new lightweight chain saws and reliable heavy-duty trucks helped increase timber production to 60 million cubic metres per year.

Commercial exploitation and fire have removed 22 million ha from the original forest; 5 million ha of that is not growing back with coniferous trees. The giant old-growth forests of Douglas-fir, Sitka spruce, and western redcedar that grew in the valley bottoms are almost extirpated. Today threatened or endangered ecosystems include Garry oak savanna and woodland, 3 coastal wet lowland forests, 6 interior dry forests, 8 Douglas-fir forests, 3 yellow-cedar forests, and 5 alluvial spruce forests (Pojar 1980).

The impact of large scale forest destruction is too large a subject for this book but, ironically, little is known about its impact on birds. Species such as the Spotted Owl and Ancient and Marbled murrelet are already the subject of grave concern because they appear to be dependent on the old growth forests that are rapidly becoming our rarest resource. Many other species such as Bald Eagle, Osprey, Bufflehead, Barrow's and Common goldeneye, and Pileated Woodpecker also need large trees as nesting sites. Wetmore et al. (1985) found that populations of birds in the spruce-fir forests declined in direct proportion to the amount of habitat lost, and that individual displaced birds were lost to the population.

There have also been important changes in the amount and quality of bird habitat provided by agricultural lands since 1948. Not the least of those is the conversion of farmland to urban environments and tightly managed business ventures. In the first case, 62% of the land converted to urban use between 1966 and 1976 had high capability for agriculture (Warren, C.L. and Rump 1981). This occurred at a rate of 0.5 ha per new resident in Vancouver. The second case developed as a response to demand for more production from the remaining land; hedgerows and ditches were cleared of all extraneous vegetation, and damage by insects or competition from plants was reduced by the application of chemicals. The possibility that such chemicals could harm the environment and needed to be controlled was not widely recognized until the mid-1960s, 20 years after their introduction. By that time, the interior race of Peregrine Falcon, the most notorious victim of accumulating pesticides, was on the verge of extinction in North America.

The production of power for export and to meet the needs of a rapidly expanding population is a late twentieth century phenomenon that has led to the construction of hydroelectric dams that have taken both forests and agricultural land out of the supply of bird habitats: 102,000 ha of the Columbia River valley, 175,000 ha of the Peace River, 91,000 ha of the Nechako River, and in 1983, parts of the Pend d'Oreille River valley. There are also plans for additional dams on the Peace River and the diversion of the Kootenay River.

The past 20 years has seen more change in the quality of new development rather than the quantity. The concentration of human populations in cities has increased the intensity of local impacts and changed the distribution and focus of these impacts. The population has risen to a little more than 2.9 million but farmland remains close to the 2.4 million ha total recorded in 1971. Lumber production has levelled off near the 1986 figure of 77 million cubic metres. Governments have established formal review processes for large industrial projects with potential environmental impact, and non-government groups have organized to ensure that their views are taken into consideration. The period of frontier development appears to be over.

Future changes will bring pressure on all sorts of environments. Urban environments contain mostly trouble for birds. If the birds do well by adapting to man, as have Rock Doves, European Starlings, House Sparrows, Cliff Swallows, gulls, and Canada Geese, their burgeoning populations cause health and safety concerns, noise problems, or reduce the aesthetic value of parks and the life span of buildings. If they are cute and readily attracted to bird houses, bird feeders, and gardens, they become easy prey for animals such as cats. If they are secretive and standoffish, the loss of their habitat raises little public sympathy.

In spite of the problems, urban wildlife remains a valuable recreation resource for many city residents who work hard to establish artificial bird habitats. Canada Geese are still fed and nurtured in Stanley Park, Vancouver, and suburban grasslands despite being considered a pest species. Thousands of tons of seed mixtures are imported annually to stock winter bird feeders throughout the province, and hundreds of people put up nest boxes in their gardens. Anna's Hummingbird capitalized on feeders and horticultural plants to extend its range and now winters in southwestern British Columbia; nest boxes have played a major role in maintaining numbers of Wood Duck and Western Bluebird.

The overall impact of environmental modification on birds has been incremental and poorly documented except where pockets of interesting birds have been lost. The Short-eared Owl has lost nearly all of its old-field habitat in the Fraser Lowlands, and the Sandhill Crane is disappearing from the Pitt River area. Red-necked Grebe, Eared Grebe, Pied-billed Grebe, Swainson's Hawk (Fig. 175), Sharp-tailed Grouse, Sage Grouse, Sandhill Crane, Long-billed Curlew, Wilson's Phalarope, Burrowing Owl, and several passerines associated with orchards and gardens have all been greatly reduced by changes in the Okanagan valley (Cannings, R.A. et al. 1987).

An objective observer could justifiably conclude that all conservationists and ecologists consider man-made change to be damaging. In part that is because ecologists are profoundly aware of how complex and fragile all ecosystems are and because human activities have two main impacts: they simplify the ecosystems by removing niches, and they fragment habitats with physical structures varying in size from footpaths and freeways to cities and agricultural landscapes.

The world is full of outrageous examples of simplified habitat but it is less dramatic situations such as the threat to many different forest ecosystems that should be raising more alarm (Pojar 1980). Simplification is most easily demonstrated by the scale of the efforts required to mitigate its effects. No agency has been more active in that area than Ducks Unlimited Canada. Each year they raise nearly 3 million dollars from sportsmen, spending it to create, restore, and secure wetlands. Their objective is to support the continental duck population in the face of agriculture's demand for more dry land. Their dams and reclaimed wetlands can be seen in areas such as the Columbia Valley, Chilcotin-Cariboo Basin, Fraser and Peace lowlands, and Vancouver Island. A single wetland supports dozens of birds along with hundreds of species of invertebrates and plants.

Fragmentation is the most insidious form of change because it occurs in subtle incremental steps. Often it affects some small creature, important only to its ecosystem, that cannot cross a road to new habitat. However, fragmentation is occurring on a regional scale. Consider the western edge of the Fraser River delta from the point of view of a forest bird trying to migrate south. From the remaining wooded slopes of North Vancouver, it must hop along a string of isolated woodlands in Stanley Park (Vancouver), the University of British Columbia Endowment Lands, and the Alasken National Wildlife Area, to Point Roberts, Washington. On the way, it risks injury at Vancouver International Airport and the maze of wires leading to Roberts Bank Superport. These hurdles could get much bigger in the near future as the airport consumes the rural farmland of Iona Island and the superport expands again. The islands of habitat are not so secure. Suburbs threaten Point Roberts and the endowment lands. Tourism and sports developments, traffic congestion, and security problems may reduce the forest in Stanley Park; and even the Alasken National Wildlife Area may have to concentrate its limited land resources on waterfowl management at the expense of tree-dwelling species.

In the next 40 years, large patches of important habitat are going to be exploited or developed solely for human use: the remaining old growth forest, wetlands, Site C on the Peace River, Burns Bog in Delta, and parts of the ocean floor. Conservation agencies, environmental impact review panels, and development proponents will all try to find innovative and effective ways of mitigating the most serious impacts but they cannot work alone. The vigilance of conservation groups and action by a concerned public will go a long way towards ensuring that the 2029 version of this publication is not significantly slimmer.

Figure 175. *Adult Swainson's Hawk on its nest near Osoyoos, June, 1976 (Ervio Sian). During the past 80 years this species' range has become more restricted and its population much reduced, mainly due to shooting and loss of prey, such as grasshoppers and crickets.*

TAXONOMY

In these volumes, the taxonomy and common English names for birds follow the most recent *Check-list of North American birds*, 6th edition (American Ornithologists' Union 1983) and its supplements (see American Ornithologists' Union 1984, 1985, 1987, 1989). Reference to subspecies follows the *Check-list of North American birds*, 5th edition (American Ornithologists' Union 1957) and Godfrey (1986), as well as recent studies such as White (1968) for Peregrine Falcon, Temple (1972) for Merlin, and D.H. Johnson et al. (1979) for Canada Goose.

The standardized names used here can promote communication about birds among people, which is the main purpose of this book. There is another function of ornithological nomenclature, however, and that is to provide a sequence of names that indicates evolutionary relationships among birds. This is a hotly-debated topic, and will probably remain so for a long time. Attendant with that topic go changes in species' common names and even their technical names as new research suggests different relationships among different groups of birds. There are several recognized publications that deal with general and specific aspects of taxonomy and nomenclature for North American birds. They can be consulted to sort out problems. General works include J.L. Peters et al. (1931-1979), Mayr and Short (1970) and Voous (1973). References for select groups include Jehl (1968) for shorebirds, Johnsgard (1968) for waterfowl and Payne and Risley (1976) for herons.

A standardized 4-letter code has been developed for all species of birds in British Columbia (Campbell and Harcombe 1985). Those codes are widely used throughout the province in field recording as well as in various wildlife data base systems. For convenience, they have been included with each species account.

The arrangement and use of common and scientific names for non-native North American species follows J.L. Peters (1931, 1934). Common plant names follow R.L. Taylor and MacBryde (1977), and Meidinger (1987). Common and scientific names for fishes follow J.L. Hart (1973), amphibians follow Green and Campbell (1984), reptiles follow Gregory and Campbell (1984), and mammal names follow J.K. Jones et al. (1986) and Honacki et al. (1982).

METHODS, TERMS, AND ABBREVIATIONS

Data Sources and Limitations

The Data

Information to complete the species accounts has come from the British Columbia Wildlife Records Scheme database housed at the Royal British Columbia Museum.

This database includes:
- specimen data gathered from other museums throughout the world
- transcribed field notes from naturalists and ornithologists and documented observations from naturalists and birders
- the published and unpublished ornithological literature
- British Columbia Nest Records Scheme
- British Columbia Photo-Records File

The species accounts in Volumes 1 and 2 are based on data from historical times to 31 December 1987 inclusive*. However, most data have come from the past two decades and the species accounts reflect the present condition of the species in the province. We have depended on early information for regions of the province that observers seldom visit, for comments on habitat changes, and for discussions of changes in status for species.

Coverage has not been even throughout the province. Unlike most 'atlases,' the data presented here have not been gathered systematically and tend to be weighted towards centres of human population. Thus, when an area of a distribution map is blank, suggesting that a particular species does not occur there, the species may not be absent; it may have been missed for one reason or another, or the area in question may not have been visited by an observer. The seasonal observer visitation for each map grid in the province is shown in Figures 14 to 18. Each quarter-filled circle within a map grid could be the result of one person visiting the area once, or 1,000 people visiting the area many times. An examination of the distribution maps for species with a widespread distribution will give an idea of the coverage we have attained (e.g. Mallard, Spotted Sandpiper).

Most of the information included in the breeding section came from cards contributed to the British Columbia Nest Records Scheme since 1955 (see Myres et al. 1957). However, records were also transferred from the technical literature, field notes, manuscripts, government and corporate reports, and diaries. Criteria for inclusion as a breeding species, unless otherwise noted, were restricted to observations of a nest with eggs, a nest with young, flightless young of precocial species, or recently fledged young incapable of sustained flight. We did not accept as evidence of breeding, observations of singing males, defense of territory, courtship behaviour or copulation, excavation of holes by woodpeckers, adults carrying nesting materials, adults sitting on nests (see Brandt's Cormorant), adults carrying food, distraction displays, or young capable of sustained flight. The kind and quality of information recorded on each card varied from record to record but every record meeting the criteria contains usable material and was used in our analyses. For example, although the contents of a woodpecker nest may not have been observed for all records, useful descriptions of habitat, tree species, or nest height were often reported. This is why sample sizes are not constant for the various analyses of egg and young dates, clutch and brood size, nest materials, and habitat.

The Christmas Bird Count summaries in the nonpasserine species accounts and Appendix 2 (Volumes 1 and 2) include only-

official counts published in *Audubon Field Notes* and *American Birds* for the 28-year period from 1957 to 1984. In total, data from 47 localities (Fig. 177), involving 388 individual counts, were analysed. Counts were divided, for convenience and interpretation, into coastal (28 localities with 294 total counts) and interior (19 localities with 94 total counts). All count localities with accompanying total number of counts are given in Table 6.

Christmas Bird Count summaries for passerine species are included in Volume 3.

Acceptance of Records

In the case of species that are difficult to identify, or those considered very rare, casual, or accidental, only records with:
1) documentation by more than one competant observer
2) photographs where the species is clearly identifiable, or
3) specimens were accepted for inclusion.

In recent years, improved optical equipment has made it possible for observers of living birds to make a detailed record of their sightings and to document them with colour photographs. At the earliest stage of planning, we decided that evidence of occurrence provided by photographs that permitted unequivocal identification of a species and accompanied by full details was as acceptable as a museum specimen. All such photographs (see Campbell and Stirling 1971), with their data, are housed at the

TABLE 6			
Localities holding official Christmas Bird Counts in British Columbia from 1957 through 1984.			
COASTAL		INTERIOR	
Bella Coola	- 1	Cranbrook	- 1
Campbell River	- 13	Fauquier	- 1
Chilliwack	- 11	Fort St. John	- 4
Comox	- 23	Kamloops	- 1
Deep Bay	- 10	Kelowna	- 1
Dewdney	- 1	Lake Windermere	- 6
Duncan	- 15	Mackenzie	- 1
Hecate Strait	- 1	Nakusp	- 6
Kitimat	- 7	North Pine	- 2
Ladner	- 26	Oliver-Osoyoos	- 6
Masset	- 3	Penticton	- 9
Nanaimo	- 19	Quesnel	- 4
North Saanich	- 1	Revelstoke	- 4
Pender Islands	- 19	Shuswap Lake	- 13
Pitt Meadows	- 13	Smithers	- 8
Port Alberni	- 1	Vaseux Lake	- 11
Port Clements	- 1	Vernon	- 10
Prince Rupert	- 5	Wells Gray	- 1
Sayward	- 12	Yoho National Park	- 5
Skidegate Inlet	- 3		
Sooke	- 2	TOTAL	94 counts
Squamish	- 5		
Sunshine Coast	- 6		
Surrey	- 7		
Terrace	- 20		
Vancouver	- 28		
Victoria	- 27		
White Rock	- 14		
TOTAL	294 counts		

---

* Significant records up to the date of publication have been included as postscripts or addenda.

Royal British Columbia Museum. Many have been included as components of the Casual, Accidental, Extirpated, and Extinct species accounts. We have included as hypothetical, those species reported in the literature but for which, in our opinion, inadequate documentation exists.

The Study Area

In the accounts, coastal refers to the land and ocean west of the crest of the Cascade and Coast Mountains, interior includes all land to the east (Fig. 176). Coastal records extend only about 60 km west of the nearest point of land except in inshore waters (e.g. Hecate Strait) where the entire area is included. True pelagic waters are not considered in any detail. Place names mentioned in the text conform to those in *Gazetteer of Canada – British Columbia* (see Anonymous 1985). Where 2 or more localities share the same name, (e.g. Boundary Lake occurs in the Kootenays and in the Peace Lowlands) a qualifier is normally added in parentheses, usually the nearest locality or prominant geographic feature [e.g. Boundary Lake (Goodlow)].

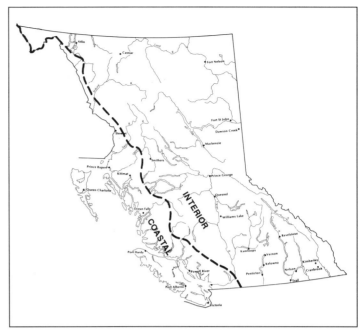

Figure 176. *British Columbia, showing the coastal/interior boundary as used in the Regular Species accounts.*

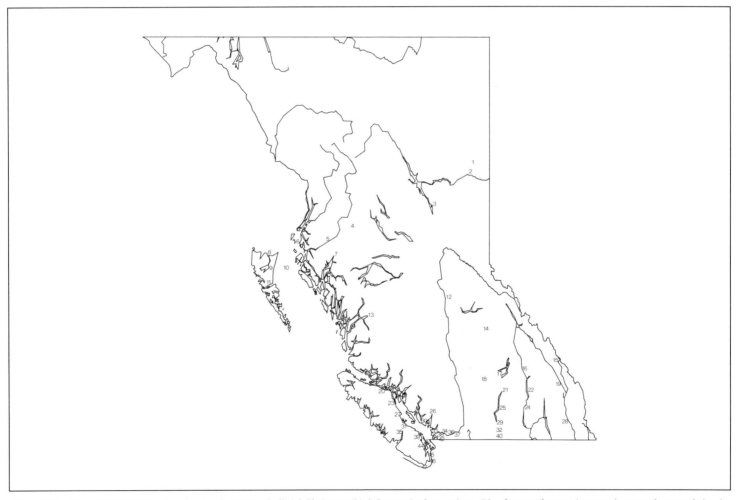

Figure 177. *Map of British Columbia showing locations of official Christmas Bird Counts in the province. Numbers on the map increase from north to south for the following locations:* Bella Coola - 13, Campbell River - 23, Chilliwack - 37, Comox - 27, Cranbrook - 28, Deep Bay - 31, Dewdney - 36, Duncan - 44, Fauquier - 24, Fort St. John - 2, Hecate Strait - 10, Kamloops - 18, Kelowna - 25, Kitimat - 7, Ladner - 41, Lake Windermere - 19, Mackenzie - 3, Masset - 8, Nakusp - 22, Nanaimo - 39, North Pine - 1, North Saanich - 45, Oliver-Osoyoos - 40, Pender Islands - 43, Penticton - 29, Pitt Meadows - 34, Port Alberni - 35, Port Clements - 9, Prince Rupert - 6, Quesnel - 12, Revelstoke - 16, Sayward - 20, Shuswap Lake - 17, Skidegate Inlet - 11, Smithers - 4, Sooke - 47, Squamish - 26, Sunshine Coast - 30, Surrey - 38, Terrace - 5, Vancouver - 33, Vaseux Lake - 32, Vernon - 21, Victoria - 46, Wells Gray - 14, White Rock - 42, Yoho National Park - 15.

Form and Content

The main body of these books lies in the **Species Accounts** which are divided into 4 sections: **Checklist of British Columbia Birds; Regular Species; Casual, Accidental, Extirpated, and Extinct Species;** and **Hypothetical Species.** The general outline for each type of account is shown in Table 7. An early decision was made to omit full accounts of subspecies from our consideration. That decision introduced some complications, especially where subspecies are so distinctive as to be easily identified in the field, and in the case of the many species for which migration dates and breeding chronology differ markedly among the subspecies. However, we decided that the most important objective of our study could be achieved at the species level, and important taxonomic or biological information for subspecies could be best handled in the Remarks section of each account. Only one subspecies has an accompanying map (see Canada Goose). See Taxonomy for further particulars on nomenclature.

The **Regular Species** section includes an account for each species accompanied by a seasonal distribution map. In some cases, species of infrequent occurrence are included because of the number of records (see Status below).

The **Casual, Accidental, Extirpated, and Extinct Species** section includes species for which there are only one to six records or species that have been extirpated from the province. Full details are included, frequently with photo-documentation, but without maps.

The format for the species accounts was developed from the comments of 82 ornithologists, wildlife biologists, wildlife managers, and naturalists in British Columbia and elsewhere who responded to a questionnaire sent out by us in 1981. The initial outline was based on two major sources. We followed the basic outline used by Bull (1974); the presentation of the breeding information, however, was modified from Peck and James (1983).

The Species Accounts

In the species accounts, statements made without citations are our conclusions based on analyses of data on file at the Royal British Columbia Museum. Each account begins with the species' common name as described by the American Ornithologists' Union (1983) and recent supplements (1984, 1985, 1987, 1989; see Taxonomy). Beside it is the species' 4-letter code that is widely used by ornithologists and wildlife managers who store their data on computer files and by many observers who want to save space in notebooks. We encourage use of the species codes when submitting records assuming they are used as outlined in Campbell and Harcombe (1985). The species' scientific name is presented next along with the name of the author who first described the species. This is followed by the major information headings within the account:

RANGE: A brief statement of the species' world range, and more specifically, its range in western North America, is included. The following general references were used: American Ornithologists' Union (1983), Godfrey (1986), P. Harrison (1983), National Audubon Society (1983) and R.S. Palmer (1962, 1976a, 1988a, 1988b).

STATUS: A brief summary is given of the species' frequency and relative abundance in British Columbia.

Abundance designations of the birds follow those used by Bull (1974). He divides species into those of "regular" or "irregular" occurrence and defines his categories by the number of individuals seen per day per locality. The categories are:

Regular Occurrence (usually reported annually)

Very abundant	- over 1,000 individuals per day per locality (often in large flocks)
Abundant	- 200 to 1,000 individuals per day per locality.
Very common	- 50 to 200 individuals per day per locality.
Common	- 20 to 50 individuals per day per locality.
Fairly common	- 7 to 20 individuals per day per locality.
Uncommon	- 1 to 6 individuals per day per locality.
Rare	- 1 to 6 individuals per season.

Irregular Occurrence (not reported annually)

Very rare	- over 6 records, but of very infrequent occurrence.
Casual	- 2 to 6 records, all time.
Accidental	- only 1 record.

Status definitions of birds are modified from A.L. Thomson (1964) and Terres (1980):

Resident	- A species that remains throughout the year in the area under reference (e.g. Blue Grouse).
Migrant	- A species that migrates to the area under reference and winters or breeds. Does not remain in the area under reference throughout the year (e.g. Trumpeter Swan). Does not include a species that wanders in the nonbreeding season (e.g. Heermann's Gull).

TABLE 7
Format for Species Accounts

Breeding Species (e.g. Canada Goose)	Nonbreeding Species (e.g. Sooty Shearwater)	Casual, Accidental Extirpated, or Extinct Species (e.g. Common Moorhen)
COMMON NAME	COMMON NAME	COMMON NAME
SCIENTIFIC NAME	SCIENTIFIC NAME	SCIENTIFIC NAME
SPECIES CODE	SPECIES CODE	SPECIES CODE
RANGE	RANGE	RANGE
STATUS	STATUS	STATUS
CHANGE IN STATUS	CHANGE IN STATUS	CHANGE IN STATUS
NONBREEDING	OCCURRENCE	OCCURRENCE
Distribution	Distribution	REMARKS
Habitat	Habitat	POSTSCRIPT
Migration/Summer/ Winter	Migration/Summer/ Winter	
Populations	Populations	
BREEDING	REMARKS	
Distribution	POSTSCRIPT	
Habitat	Noteworthy Records	
Populations	Spring	
Nests	Summer	
Eggs	Autumn	
Young	Winter	
REMARKS	Christmas Counts	
POSTSCRIPT	Extralimital Records	
Noteworthy Records		
Spring		
Summer		
Autumn		
Winter		
Christmas Counts		
Extralimital Records		

Transient — A species that appears on migration in the area under reference but neither breeds nor overwinters there (e.g. Western Sandpiper).

Visitant — A species that is present in the area under reference only at certain times of the year. Breeding or wintering status for a migrant (e.g. Snowy Owl).

Vagrant —A wanderer outside the normal migration range of the species (e.g. Willet).

CHANGE IN STATUS: Increases or decreases in distribution or numbers are summarized for those species of birds whose status has changed significantly during the 40 years since J.A. Munro and Cowan (1947) was published.

OCCURRENCE or **NONBREEDING:** These sections contain essentially the same information, the latter being part of the account of a breeding species. A summary is presented of the known distribution of the species in the province, including comments on altitudinal distribution. Because the province is so ecologically diverse, distribution statements were simplified by referring to the Ecoregion Classification for British Columbia (see Table 4; Demarchi, D.A. 1987, 1988a).

General habitats used by the species are discussed in decreasing order of frequency, based on observations from the British Columbia Wildlife Records Scheme and the literature. Spring and autumn migrations, with notes on chronology, corridors, peak movements, and numbers, as well as the winter and nonbreeding summer periods are also described. Major wintering, moulting, or staging areas are included when they are known. Noteworthy records, which support earlier statements, are highlighted at the end of each species account. These include a combination of maximum numbers, early arrivals, late departures, counts, and censuses to show trends, significant specimen or photographic records, and other noteworthy records to provide geographical coverage throughout the province. Thus, these records may not necessarily reflect the status, as they are only a very small proportion of the total number of records used to determine the status (see **Data Base** below each distribution map).

The seasons and order in which records are listed tend to follow the species' seasonal movements and are as follows:

Spring
(March to May) — south to north from coastal to interior

Summer
(June to August) — south to north from coastal to interior

Autumn
(September to November) — north to south from interior to coastal

Winter
(December to February) — north to south from interior to coastal

Following the seasonal records is a summary statement of the highest numbers reported on official **Christmas Bird Counts** from 3 count areas for both coastal and interior localities. Occasionally, more counts are listed when maxima for 2 or more localities are the same. Where a particular maximum is an all-time North American or Canadian high count, this is also noted. Complete species summaries for all Christmas Bird Counts are included in an Appendix to each volume.

Extralimital Records includes details of isolated records of the species that are far from their normal British Columbia range. This completes the records section.

BREEDING: The breeding section begins with a specific statement about the known breeding range within the province.

In many cases distribution has an altitudinal dimension. This is followed by a description of the general breeding habitat preferences as in the **NONBREEDING** or **OCCURRENCE** sections, and when possible, an estimate of the size of the breeding population. For colonial species or species that tend to nest in loose concentrations, a summary table of major colonies in British Columbia is included.

The next 3 subsections, **Nests, Eggs,** and **Young,** are summaries of the breeding data we analysed. The parameters discussed are listed in the same sequence for each species to facilitate comparison, and include site-specific nest habitats, nest position, nest substrate, nest heights, nest materials, nest dimensions, egg dates, clutch sizes, incubation periods, young dates, brood sizes, and fledging periods. Frequencies of observations are presented as a percentage of the number of observations that have information on a particular parameter. When data sets were sufficiently large, items such as nest heights, nest sizes, egg and brood dates, and clutch and brood sizes are given as a range occupying the middle percentiles. This avoids the anomoly of presenting information on parts of indivisible objects, i.e. 3.25 eggs (see Peck and James 1983). The average-clutch-range then, includes the commonest clutch sizes, that is, those that together represent at least 50% of the total number of nests. The total in the range may exceed 50%; therefore, in each statement the percentage and the total clutches are both listed. Data are presented, however, that will allow the calculation of the actual mean if that summary statistic is required. All clutch and brood sizes given on nest record cards are listed in each appropriate subsection. They include some incomplete clutch and brood sizes as well as small, or unusually large clutches and broods. However, the use of the interquartile range method eliminates extremes, except for some species with precocial young (e.g. American Coot). Dates for eggs and young are the earliest and latest dates reported for the species; also included is the range in dates for the middle 50+% to indicate the height of the laying and hatching seasons. Occasionally, extreme dates were calculated from known or estimated stages of incubation, or from young of known or estimated ages. Incubation and fledging periods not available from the British Columbia Nest Records Scheme were taken from the literature.

REMARKS: Miscellaneous topics not covered in the species accounts are discussed in this section. Depending on available space they include subspecies, taxonomic changes, diets, banding, competition, threatened status (Blue List), and research needs, particularly where they may be relevant to management or conservation of the species in British Columbia.

POSTSCRIPT: Although the cutoff date for the book was 31 December 1987, significant information for a particular species gathered through to the publication of each volume has been added to the end of that account as a Postscript. We have not included these data within the account or on the distribution map. We have, however, included 1988 census data in Tables for all breeding seabirds.

The Distribution Maps

The maps were originally prepared by hand; seasonal distribution data from the British Columbia Nest Records Scheme and the British Columbia Wildlife Records Scheme were drawn on a large copy of the Index to Numbering of Map Sheets, National Topographic Series map 1JNT. This summary of the data was then entered directly to computer files and the data were verified to the hand-drawn map. The final maps were subsequently produced by a computer-driven Hewlett-Packard Plotter. Each regularly occurring species is accompanied by a map that includes 4 components:

1. **Map Index** - each map contains an index to seasonal occurrence (black) and breeding (red). Breeding ranks in priority over occurrence.

2. Nonbreeding, Occurrence, and Breeding Chronology - occurrence chronology or nonbreeding chronology (both black) and breeding chronology, both for eggs and/or young (red), are displayed in the upper right-hand corner by a set of bars. A solid bar indicates the species was recorded continuously throughout each weekly period within the limits of the bar. To some extent it is biased for those species occurring throughout the year in the vicinity of mild coastal areas (e.g. Western Sandpiper). Extreme dates of occurrence for particular geographical areas of the province are often included in the body of the species account. Where reports on the occurrence of a species were missing for more than one continuous week, the occurrence bar was broken.

3. Map - seasonal occurrence (black) and breeding occurrence (red) are plotted as quarter-circles for each map grid, as follows: Spring - northwest quarter; Summer - northeast quarter; Autumn - southeast quarter; Winter - southwest quarter. Each major map grid of the National Topographic Series encompasses 1º latitude by 2º longitude. This grid is further divided into 16 smaller grids—the scale used on the species distribution map—and represents 15 minutes latitude by 30 minutes longitude (Fig. 178). We chose an artificial projection that allows the same size circle on all parts of the map. This causes some distortion, but allows the reader to use a ruler to identify any grid of interest. Each shaded seasonal segment (quarter-circle) represents at least one record. Also, the maps show only what has been documented; we have not extrapolated.

4. Data Base - includes a tally by month of the records on which each species account is based. There is a nonbreeding and breeding component for each breeding species and an occurrence component for all other species. A record consists of an observation of a single species per day per locality. For a species whose status is *rare* or *very rare*, the total number of records may be deceptive since a single bird could have had many observations reported over an extended stay.

Abbreviations

Our abbreviations follow those outlined in the *CBE Style Manual* Council of Biology Editors, Committee on Form and Style (1972), with the exception of lower case directions in the Noteworthy Records section (e.g. n = north of, sw = southwest of) and months in the same section, which are abbreviated to 3 letters only (e.g. Jan, Jul, Sep).

Museum specimens or photographs are listed by an abbreviation of the museum name and the specimen or photograph catalogue number, as follows:

AMNH	- American Museum of Natural History (New York)
ANS	- Academy of Natural Science (Philadelphia)
AUMU	- Australian Museum of Natural History (Sydney)
CM	- Centennial Museum (Vancouver, British Columbia)
CMNH	- Carnegie Museum of Natural History (Pittsburg)
CSUM	- Colorado State University Museum (Fort Collins)
DMNH	- Delaware Museum of Natural History (Greenville)
FMNH	- Field Museum of Natural History (Chicago)
FSM	- Florida State Museum (Gainesville)
MC	- Malaspina College Museum of Natural History (Nanaimo, British Columbia)
MCZ	- Museum of Comparative Zoology (Cambridge, Massachusetts)
MMMN	- Manitoba Museum of Man and Nature (Winnipeg)
MVZ	- Museum of Vertebrate Zoology (Berkeley)
NMC	- National Museum of Canada (Ottawa)

PMA	- Provincial Museum of Alberta (Edmonton)
PMNH	- Peabody Museum of Natural History (New Haven)
QCIM	- Queen Charlotte Island Museum (Queen Charlotte City, British Columbia)
RBCM	- Royal British Columbia Museum (Victoria)
RBCM Photo	- Royal British Columbia Museum Photo
ROM	- Royal Ontario Museum (Toronto)
UAM	- University of Alaska Museum (Fairbanks)
UBC	- University of British Columbia Cowan Vertebrate Museum (Vancouver)
UKMU	- University of Kansas Systematics Museum (Lawrence)
UMMZ	- University of Michigan Museum of Zoology (Ann Arbor)
USNM	- United States National Museum (Washington, D.C.)
UVIC	- University of Victoria (Victoria, British Columbia)
WFVZ	- Western Foundation of Vertebrate Zoology (Los Angeles)
WSM	- Washington State Museum (Seattle)

Addenda

Complete accounts for species added to the provincial list after 31 December 1987 are included in this section.

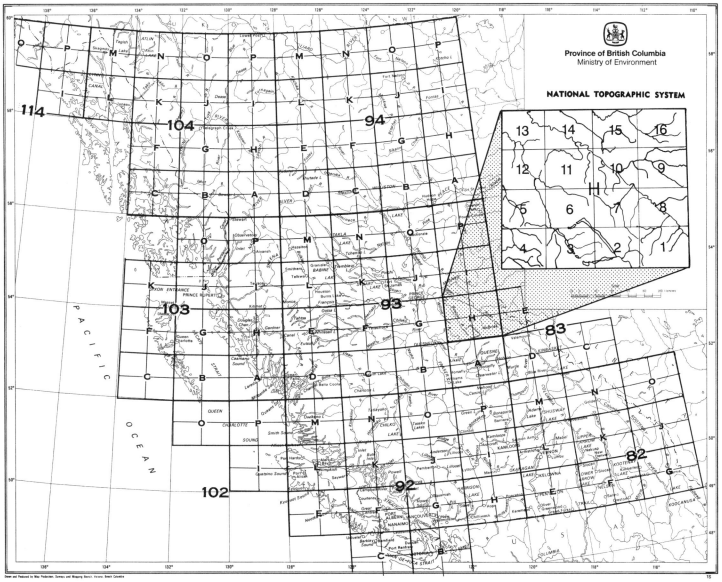

Figure 178. *Major and minor map grids of the National Topographic Series 1JNT map for British Columbia used in the preparation of the species distribution maps.*

SPECIES ACCOUNTS

Checklist of British Columbia Birds

Nonpasserines: Loons through Waterfowl

This phylogenetic list includes 85 species of birds, loons through waterfowl, that have been documented in British Columbia through 31 December 1987*.

Order GAVIIFORMES: Loons
Family GAVIIDAE: Loons

Red-throated Loon
Pacific Loon
Common Loon
Yellow-billed Loon

Order PODICIPEDIFORMES: Grebes
Family PODICIPEDIDAE: Grebes

Pied-billed Grebe
Horned Grebe
Red-necked Grebe
Eared Grebe
Western Grebe
Clark's Grebe

Order PROCELLARIIFORMES: Tube-nosed Swimmers
Family DIOMEDEIDAE: Albatrosses

Short-tailed Albatross
Black-footed Albatross
Laysan Albatross

Family PROCELLARIIDAE: Fulmars and Shearwaters

Northern Fulmar
Mottled Petrel
Pink-footed Shearwater
Flesh-footed Shearwater
Buller's Shearwater
Sooty Shearwater
Short-tailed Shearwater
Black-vented Shearwater

Family HYDROBATIDAE: Storm-Petrels

Fork-tailed Storm-Petrel
Leach's Storm-Petrel

Order PELECANIFORMES: Totipalmate Swimmers
Family PELICANIDAE: Pelicans

American White Pelican
Brown Pelican

Family PHALACROCORACIDAE: Cormorants

Double-crested Cormorant
Brandt's Cormorant
Pelagic Cormorant

Family FREGATIDAE: Frigatebirds

Magnificent Frigatebird

Order CICONIIFORMES: Bitterns, Herons, Egrets, and Allies
Family ARDEIDAE: Bitterns and Herons

American Bittern
Least Bittern
Great Blue Heron
Great Egret
Snowy Egret
Little Blue Heron
Cattle Egret
Green-backed Heron
Black-crowned Night-Heron

Family THRESKIORNITHIDAE: Ibises

White-faced Ibis

Family CICONIIDAE: Storks

Wood Stork

Order ANSERIFORMES: Swans, Geese, and Ducks
Family ANATIDAE: Swans, Geese, and Ducks

Fulvous Whistling-Duck
Tundra Swan
Trumpeter Swan
Mute Swan
Greater White-fronted Goose
Snow Goose
Ross' Goose
Emperor Goose
Brant
Canada Goose
Wood Duck
Green-winged Teal
Baikal Teal
American Black Duck
Mallard
Northern Pintail
Garganey
Blue-winged Teal
Cinnamon Teal
Northern Shoveler
Gadwall
Eurasian Wigeon
American Wigeon
Canvasback
Redhead
Ring-necked Duck
Tufted Duck
Greater Scaup
Lesser Scaup
Common Eider
King Eider
Steller's Eider
Harlequin Duck
Oldsquaw
Black Scoter
Surf Scoter
White-winged Scoter
Common Goldeneye
Barrow's Goldeneye
Bufflehead
Smew
Hooded Merganser
Common Merganser
Red-breasted Merganser
Ruddy Duck

* From January 1988 through to the publication of this volume, one new nonpasserine species has been added to the provincial list (see Addenda).

Regular Species

Red-throated Loon
Gavia stellata (Pontoppidan)

RTLO

RANGE: Breeds in North America from northern Alaska across northern Canada and Greenland, south on the Pacific coast to southern British Columbia, and on the Atlantic coast to Newfoundland and Anticosti Island; also across northern Europe and Asia. Winters on Pacific from Aleutian Islands south to Baja California, and on Atlantic from Newfoundland to Florida, rarely along Gulf coast. Also in Eurasia.

STATUS: *Common* to *very common* coastal migrant; locally *very abundant* in spring. *Very rare* to *rare* spring and autumn transient in the interior. In winter *uncommon* to *very common* on the south coast, including the Strait of Georgia; generally *uncommon* on the north coast; *casual* in the interior. Breeds along the coast and in the Chilkat Pass area.

NONBREEDING: The Red-throated Loon is widely distributed along the coast and scattered throughout the interior. It prefers more inshore and protected shallower waters, including bays, inlets, harbours, lagoons, and estuaries. In the interior, larger lakes and slow moving rivers are used. Immatures remain on the sea throughout the year but are rare in summer in most wintering areas. It occurs from sea level to 1,280 m.

The Red-throated Loon is rarely found in flocks larger than 50 birds. Spring and autumn migration is coastal and protracted. In spring, small flocks are evident in southern areas by late March and by early April single birds are moving north. The main movement occurs in late April and early May. Individuals occasionally linger to mid-June on the north coast. The autumn movement begins in late August and continues through early November. The main movement occurs in late September and October.

In summer, small numbers of nonbreeding individuals are scattered along coastal areas, while flocks of less than 20 birds may also occur locally on some coastal lakes (Reimchen and Douglas 1980). In winter, most birds are found throughout the Strait of Georgia and Juan de Fuca Strait, particularly in the vicinity of White Rock, Vancouver, Ladner, and Victoria. A few individuals also winter regularly on the lower reaches of the Fraser River, Pitt River, and Pitt Lake.

BREEDING: The Red-throated Loon breeds from Nitinat Lake on southern Vancouver Island north along the coast to Kitsault and the Queen Charlotte Islands and in the vicinity of Chilkat Pass. It breeds from near sea level to 1,070 m elevation.

On the coast, breeding areas are small freshwater lakes often surrounded by forests in close proximity to the sea, where the loon feeds. Douglas, S.D. and Reimchen (1988a) estimate the population of breeding Red-throated Loons on the Queen Charlotte Islands at between 784 and 892 pairs. The majority of the loons nest in the Lowlands, a broad expanse of bog terrain on

northeastern Graham Island. The number of loons nesting in a region is primarily a function of the number of lakes in the region and is unrelated to the water chemistry and geography, or the presence of resident fish in the lakes. In the Chilkat Pass area, habitat includes large ponds and small lakes in alpine tundra. There, loons feed on large lakes (e.g. Kelsall Lake).

Nests: Most nests (94%; n=54) were on small coastal lakes, the remainder on shallow ponds. Twenty-five nests were situated on the shore close to the water's edge, 6 on small vegetated islets, 3 anchored to submerged logs, and 8 on man-made structures. On the Queen Charlotte Islands, 2 pairs nested on a 112 ha lake, while another pair used a 1 ha tarn (Reimchen and Douglas 1984). In the Chilkat Pass area, one pond measured 61 m in diameter and 0.7 m in depth.

Nest structures ranged from small mounds of mosses, sedges, grasses, reeds, and weeds in shallow water to shallow depressions in vegetation (e.g. Sphagnum) in drier sites. Outside diameters ranged from 43 to 58 cm.

Eggs: Dates for 34 clutches ranged from 8 May to 24 July, with 54% recorded between 30 May and 15 June. Clutch size ranged from 1 to 2 eggs (1E-4, 2E-30), with 88% having 2 eggs. Incubation periods for 11 eggs from British Columbia were between 24.5 and 31 days, with a mean of 27 days (Douglas, S.D. and Reimchen 1988b).

Young: Dates for 37 broods ranged from 28 May to 14 September with 50% recorded between 5 and 27 July. Young could be found only rarely in late August. The September broods probably represented renestings. Brood sizes ranged from 1 to 2 young (1Y-11, 2Y-26), with 70% having 2 young. In British Columbia fledging period is 48 days (range 46 to 50 days) (Reimchen and Douglas 1984; Douglas, S.D. and Reimchen 1988b).

REMARKS: Unlike other breeding loons in British Columbia, the Red-throated Loon breeds mostly on freshwater and forages on the ocean. In the Chilkat Pass area, it does not feed on nesting lakes, but may feed on larger, nearby lakes (e.g. Kelsall Lake). According to Reimchen and Douglas (1984), herring/smelt (Clupeidae/Osmeridae), seaperch (Embiotocidae), sand lance (Ammodytidae), and cod (Gadidae) were the most common prey fed to chicks on the Queen Charlotte Islands.

All 4 species of loons exhibit little size dimorphism, males being 10 to 15% larger. Differentiation of the sexes in the field, however, is difficult. Reimchen and Douglas (1985) note that Red-throated Loons at Drizzle Lake may be sexed by a difference in the number and spacing of vertical white lines on the back of the neck, the females having 6 or 7 and the male 10 lines. That field mark is probably carried throughout adult life.

The Red-throated Loon appears on the "Blue List" from 1973 to 1976 (Tate 1981).

NOTEWORTHY RECORDS

Spring: Coastal - Esquimalt Lagoon 20 Mar 1971-23 (Tatum 1972), 2 Apr 1983-55, 12 May 1975-9; Tsawwassen 13 Apr 1975-9 off jetty; Reifel Island 28 Apr 1985-350 off Fraser River mouth; Qualicum Beach 11 Mar 1975-34; Comox 7 Mar 1948-large numbers, a decided movement (Pearse 1948); Port Hardy 26 May 1951-75; Brooks Bay to Quatsino Sound 26 May 1978-54; Goose Group 31 May 1948-60 passing northward (Guiguet 1953a); Rose Spit 23 Apr 1979-98, 25 Apr 1979-177, 29 Apr 1979-2,376, 30 Apr 1979-2,270, 4 May 1979-1,331; Lumme Lake 26 May 1979-36. **Interior** - Sorrento 25 Apr 1971-1; Charlie Lake 23 May 1983-3.

Summer: Coastal - Long Beach 19 Jun 1977-14, 20 Jul 1973-5; Port Hardy 16 Jun 1976-12; Tar Islands 10 Jul 1977-14; Drizzle Lake 18 Jul 1977-

17; Kumara Lake 19 Aug 1974-17; Rose Spit 19 Aug 1974-35, 20 Aug 1974-68, 21 Aug 1974-100. **Interior** - Wells Gray Park 10 Jun 1959-1 (Edwards and Ritcey 1967); Charlie Lake 21 Aug 1986-1 (McEwan, C. and Johnston 1987).

Autumn: Interior - Fern Lake (Kwadacha Wilderness Park) 3 and 4 Sep 1979-20 arrived with 8 Pacific Loons (Cooper, J.M. and Cooper 1983); Charlie Lake 20 Oct 1983-1; Smithers, last week Sep to first week Oct, migrating; Morice Lake 30 Sep 1974-33; Williams Lake 12 Sep 1982-2; Quilchena 27 Sep 1983-1; Okanagan Landing 18 Oct 1935-1. **Coastal** - Comox Harbour to Deep Bay 25 Oct 1980-193 on census; Reifel Island 7 Oct 1986-1,000 unusually large aggregation (Mattocks and Harrington-Tweit 1987a); Crescent Beach 3 Oct 1956-50;

Tsawwassen 24 Sep 1971-53 off jetty (Campbell et al. 1972b); Esquimalt Lagoon 26 Oct 1978-6, 25 Nov 1978-21; Port Renfrew 5 Oct 1974-25.

Winter: Interior - Okanagan Landing 26 Dec 1970-2 (Rogers, T.H. 1971b), 26 and 30 Jan 1963-1; Okanagan Lake 15 Feb 1964-1 with 2 Common Loons. **Coastal** - Iona Island 10 Feb 1973-27; Westham Island 22 Dec 1973-35; Lemmens Inlet 7 to 12 Jan 1982-33; Active Pass 17 Feb 1972-12 (Tatum 1973); Esquimalt Lagoon 30 Jan 1981-56.

Christmas Counts: Interior - Not recorded. **Coastal** - Recorded from 21 of 28 localities and on 69% of all counts. Maxima: White Rock 30 Dec 1973-**241**, all-time Canadian high count (Anderson, R.R. 1976); Vancouver 16 Dec 1984-205; Victoria 22 Dec 1962-147.

Red-throated Loon

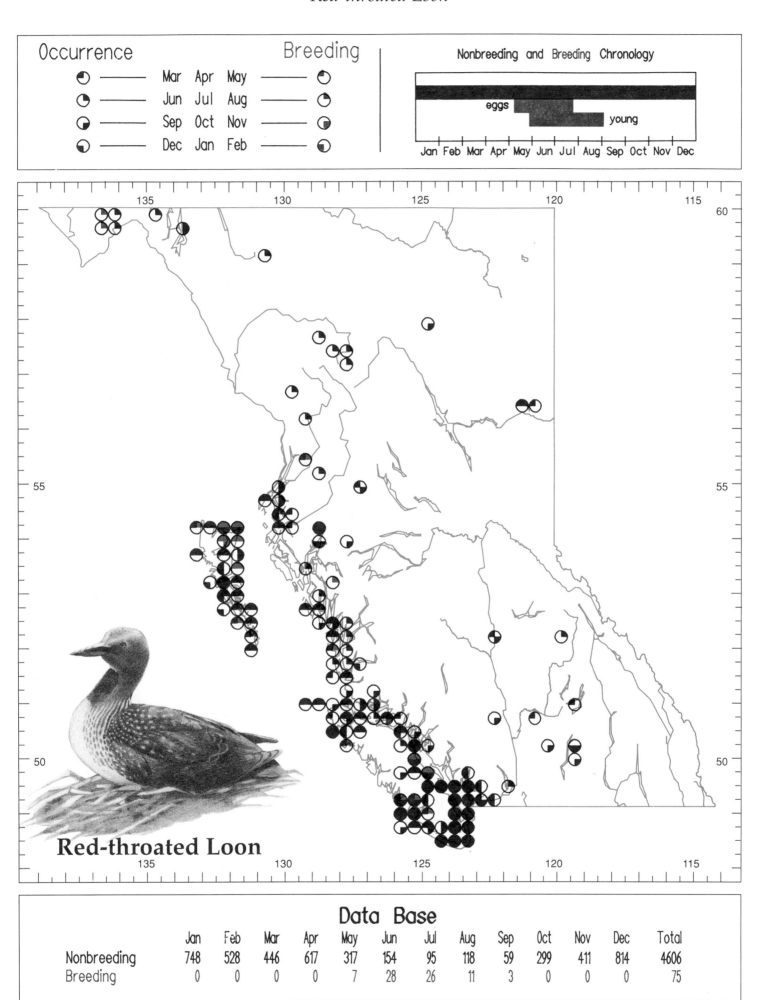

Occurrence

					Breeding
◐	—	Mar	Apr	May	— ◑
◐	—	Jun	Jul	Aug	— ◕
◔	—	Sep	Oct	Nov	— ◔
◖	—	Dec	Jan	Feb	— ◑

Nonbreeding and Breeding Chronology

eggs

young

Jan Feb Mar Apr May Jun Jul Aug Sep Oct Nov Dec

Red-throated Loon

Data Base

	Jan	Feb	Mar	Apr	May	Jun	Jul	Aug	Sep	Oct	Nov	Dec	Total
Nonbreeding	748	528	446	617	317	154	95	118	59	299	411	814	4606
Breeding	0	0	0	0	7	28	26	11	3	0	0	0	75

Pacific Loon

Gavia pacifica (Lawrence)

PALO

RANGE: Breeds in eastern Siberia and in North America from the Arctic coast of Alaska and the northern part of Canada east to Baffin Island and Hudson Bay. Winters south to Japan and along the Pacific coast of North America south to Baja California.

STATUS: *Abundant* spring and autumn migrant along the coast; *very rare* in the interior. *Uncommon* in summer along coastline, *casual* in southern interior. In winter, *fairly common* along the outer coast, including the Queen Charlotte Islands, and locally *abundant* to *very abundant* in the Strait of Georgia and Juan de Fuca Strait. *Casual* in the southern interior in winter. Breeds in northernmost British Columbia.

NONBREEDING: The Pacific Loon is widely distributed along the coast and scattered throughout the interior. It is the most gregarious of the loons and may be found in flocks of several thousand individuals in areas of upwelling in protected southern coastal areas. It prefers deeper waters than other loons, but also frequents coastal habitats such as bays, estuaries, surge narrows, channels, coves, and, less commonly, inlets and lagoons. All interior records are from larger lakes and rivers.

Spring migration is coastal and may begin as early as February and March in southern areas, but it is difficult to separate foraging movement into Pacific herring spawning areas from general northward movement. Concentrations of up to several thousand loons may be found in spring in areas where Pacific herring spawn and other small fish congregate in shallow waters along the coast (see Canada Department of Fisheries and Environment 1978). The northward movement is evident by late April, increases in intensity throughout May, and subsides in early June. Daily migration watches from Brooks Peninsula (northwestern Vancouver Island), from 14 May to 27 June 1973, produced an estimated northward movement in May of 153,900 birds and in June of 25,800 birds. The day of heaviest migration was 21 May (Campbell and Summers In press).

In summer, small flocks of nonbreeding birds, usually composed of less than 50 individuals, are scattered along the coast. Autumn migration begins in late August and carries through November; the main southward movement is in late September and October.

In winter, flocks of up to several hundred birds are distributed locally along the coast. The centre of abundance is in the Strait of Georgia where nutrient-rich areas of tidal turbulence (e.g. Active Pass) support thousands of birds. At times, there are noticeable movements of large numbers of loons throughout the Strait of Georgia which may be flights to and from foraging areas.

BREEDING: The Pacific Loon breeds on the Teslin Plateau in the vicinity of Atlin and throughout the Liard Basin from the Yukon boundary southward to latitude 59°23'N between longitudes 129°25'W and 125°32'W, an east-west stretch of about 260 km that lies east of Atlin. There is one isolated record from near Kitsault (Campbell et al. 1985). The Pacific Loon breeds from 720 to 1,200 m elevation.

It breeds on freshwater lakes and ponds from 3.6 to 41.4 ha in size, usually surrounded by forests.

Nests:: Eight nests have been reported from British Columbia; all were near the water's edge. Three nests were situated on small grassy islands, 2 on damp or drying islands, 2 on the shore and 1 on a beaver lodge. Two nests were composed of sparse collections of sedges, mosses, and aquatic plants; the other 6 lacked nesting material. Water depths at 3 nests measured 15, 28, and 85 cm.

Eggs: Dates for 5 clutches ranged from 1 June to 2 July; calculated dates indicate eggs could be found as early as 24 May. Clutch size ranged from 1 to 2 eggs (1E-2, 2E-3). Incubation period is 23.5 to 24.5 days (Jehl and Smith 1970).

Young: Dates for 9 broods ranged from 24 June to 12 August. Brood sizes ranged from 1 to 2 young (1Y-6, 2Y-3). Fledging period is about 60 days (Witherby et al. 1943).

REMARKS: The Pacific Loon was formerly considered a subspecies of the Arctic Loon (*Gavia arctica*; American Ornithologists' Union 1957, 1985).

Godfrey (1986) lists 2 specimen records of the Arctic Loon for British Columbia: Comox, November 1891 (RBCM 1440) and Victoria, March 1906 (RBCM 20). Both specimens have been re-examined following criteria discussed by Walsh (1988) and were determined to be Pacific Loons.

NOTEWORTHY RECORDS

Spring: Coastal - Cordova Bay 27 Apr 1979-200; Active Pass 14 Mar 1975-1,200, 14 Apr 1972-10,000, 19 Apr 1972-3,000, 29 Apr 1972-1,100, 14 May 1972-30 (Tatum 1973); Long Beach 7 May 1981-2,200; Tsawwassen 29 Apr 1981-250 off jetty; Cowichan Bay 18 Apr 1966-175; Comox 16 May 1969-2,000; Heriot Bay 20 Apr 1978-105; Lawn Point (Tlell) 20 Mar 1981-1,700 feeding on spawning Pacific sandlance; Masset Sound 16 May 1983-1,000+. **Interior** - Douglas Lake 18 May 1987-2; Emerald Lake 19 May 1977-1 (Wade 1977); Parker Lake (Fort Nelson) 7 May 1978-2.

Summer: Coastal - Cordova Bay 26 Jul 1976-25; Florencia Bay 8 Aug 1974-35+; Qualicum Beach 25 Jul 1975-46; Sutil Point 12 Jun 1975-200; Skedans Island 15 Jun 1985-150; Masset Sound 7 Jul 1983-14; Rose Spit 21 Aug 1974-300+; Masset Inlet 2 Aug 1986-1,100+. **Interior** - Lightning Lake 5 Jul 1986-1 adult; Botanie Lake 2-3 Jun 1973-2; Prince George 12 Jul 1986-1 adult; Babine Lake 3 Jun 1977-3; Swan Lake (Tupper) 21 Jun 1938-2

(Cowan 1939); Charlie Lake 6 Jun 1984-67.

Autumn: Interior - Fern Lake (Kwadacha Wilderness Park) 3 and 4 Sep 1979-8 arrived with 20 Red-throated Loons (Cooper, J.M. and Cooper 1983); Charlie Lake 16 Sep 1986-162 adults (Campbell 1986d), 27 Oct 1985-1 juvenile; Prince George 15 Oct 1986-1; Sorrento 28 Sep 1970-36, 31 Oct 1971-8; D'Arcy 26 Sep 1970-2; Okanagan Landing 23 Nov 1984-3; Trail 18 and 24 Oct 1979-2; Wasa 29 Oct 1912-1 (MVZ 99010). **Coastal** - Rose Spit 10 Oct 1982-70, 13 Oct 1982-100+, 22 Oct 1982-300; Quathiaski Cove 19 Nov 1978-350; Oyster Bay 10 Oct 1975-68; Qualicum Beach 11 Oct 1979-42; Chesterman Beach 5 Sep 1974-200+; Active Pass 23 Oct 1983-200+, 22 Nov 1984-500; Mandarte Island 2 Oct 1982-350; Island View Beach 12 Nov 1962-150; Clover Point 13 Nov 1984-586 passed in one hour.

Winter: Interior - Mabel Lake (Vernon) 15 Jan 1984-1; Okanagan Landing 1 to 31 Dec 1983-1 or 2;

Kelowna 22 Dec 1973-1; Summerland 23 Dec 1928-1 (Tait 1929). **Coastal** - Queen Charlotte City 16 Feb 1972-150; Quadra Island 31 Dec 1977-1,239 counted in 2.5 hour period; Comox Harbour to Deep Bay 21 Feb 1981-1,005 on census; Qualicum Beach 4 Feb 1976-55; Nanoose Harbour 28 Feb 1974-185; Vancouver 11 Feb 1980-37; Active Pass 24 Dec 1977-2,400, 8 Jan 1974-3,000, 15 Feb 1973-4,000+; Swartz Bay 24 Feb 1973-40; Cordova Channel 1 Dec 1973-89; Madrona Bay (North Saanich) 21 Jan 1984-1,340 (Campbell 1984a); Crescent Beach 3 Dec 1955-50+.

Christmas Counts: Interior - Recorded from 1 of 19 localities and on 2% of all counts. Maxima: Oliver/Osoyoos 28 Dec 1980-1, 28 Dec 1981-1. **Coastal** - Recorded from 22 of 28 localities and on 72% of all counts. Maxima: Pender Islands 23 Dec 1978-**1,626**, all-time Canadian high count (Anderson, R.R. 1979); Comox 18 Dec 1977-1,585; Campbell River 31 Dec 1978-515.

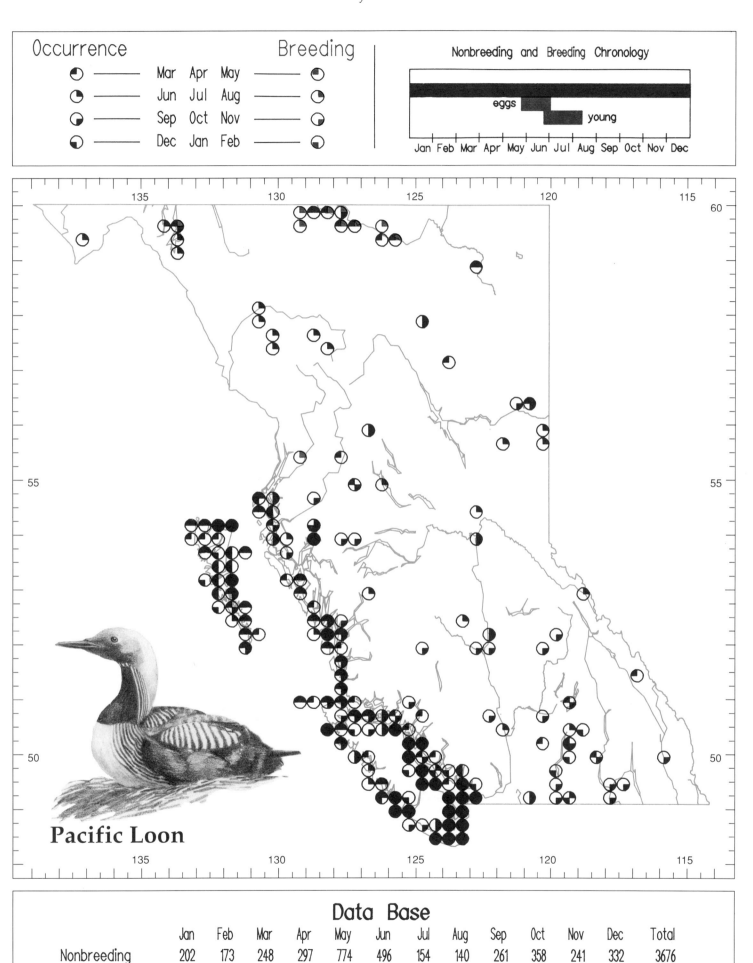

Occurrence

◐ —————	Mar Apr May
◔ —————	Jun Jul Aug
◵ —————	Sep Oct Nov
◕ —————	Dec Jan Feb

Breeding

————— ◐	Mar Apr May
————— ◔	Jun Jul Aug
————— ◵	Sep Oct Nov
————— ◕	Dec Jan Feb

Nonbreeding and Breeding Chronology

eggs young

Jan Feb Mar Apr May Jun Jul Aug Sep Oct Nov Dec

Pacific Loon

Data Base

	Jan	Feb	Mar	Apr	May	Jun	Jul	Aug	Sep	Oct	Nov	Dec	Total
Nonbreeding	202	173	248	297	774	496	154	140	261	358	241	332	3676
Breeding	0	0	0	0	0	10	6	1	0	0	0	0	17

Common Loon
Gavia immer (Brünnich)

COLO

RANGE: Breeds in North America from Alaska and Canada south to the northern United States; also in Greenland and Iceland. Migrates throughout most of North America. Winters primarily along the Pacific, Atlantic, and Gulf coasts of North America; also on the European coast.

STATUS: *Fairly common* to *very common* migrant and *uncommon* to *fairly common* summer visitant throughout the province. In winter *uncommon* to *common* along the coast, *casual* in the northern interior, *rare* to *uncommon* in the southern interior. Widespread breeder.

NONBREEDING: The Common Loon occurs throughout British Columbia from sea level to at least 2,290 m elevation. It frequents a variety of marine and freshwater habitats, including inshore sea coasts such as inlets, bays, coves, harbours, lagoons, and estuaries as well as small and large lakes and rivers.

Migration occurs throughout the province and a noticeable movement is also evident at sea during both passages. Spring migration begins in mid-to-late March in the south, generally carrying through into June. The peak of the migration occurs from late April to early May. Flocks are seen on larger lakes in the interior and on protected bays, inlets, and harbours on the coast during the relatively fast passage. In summer, flocks of usually less than 50 birds are found in bays and coves, and on lakes. Autumn migration begins in late August and is still evident in southern areas in late November. Peak movement occurs in the first half of October.

In winter, birds along the coast are generally more widely distributed and flocks are rarely larger than 20 birds. Major wintering areas occur at the northern end of the Strait of Georgia, off the Fraser River delta, and at the east end of the Juan de Fuca Strait.

BREEDING: The Common Loon breeds throughout the province, including the Queen Charlotte Lowlands and islands north of Queen Charlotte Sound (Munro, J.A. and Cowan 1947), from 49 to 1,520 m elevation. The Thompson-Okanagan and Fraser plateaus and the Fraser Basin region appear to be the centre of abundance. It breeds on large and small fresh water lakes (94%; n=512), in forested and open regions, and occasionally on sloughs, marshes, lagoons, and rivers.

Nests: Most nests (43%; n=194) were positioned on main shores (including peninsulas) of water bodies, 35% were on

islands, and the remainder were built on partially submerged logs and trees, muskrat pushups, or amongst emergent marsh vegetation. Three nests (all successful) were free-floating. Nests were up to 8 m from the water's edge but most (91%) were within 1 m of water. Fluctuating water levels result in some nests being far from the water by the end of incubation.

Nests consisted of heaped masses of aquatic vegetation which included grasses, reeds, rushes, cattail, weeds, mosses, twigs, leaves, and submerged aquatic plants. They ranged in size from 30 to 74 cm in diameter, and were up to 10 cm in height. Twenty-three clutches were found on bare ground without nesting materials. One nest site was used for 4 consecutive years.

Eggs: Dates for 211 clutches ranged from 21 April to 23 July, with 54% recorded between 27 May and 16 June. Calculated dates indicate that eggs could be found as early as 1 April. Sizes for 192 clutches ranged from 1 to 3 eggs (1E-55, 2E-136, 3E-1), with 71% having 2 eggs. Apparently, 1 female was responsible for the nest with 3 eggs (Bennie 1979). Incubation periods for 3 clutches in British Columbia were 29, 29, and 29.5 days.

Young: Dates for 334 broods ranged from 2 May to 27 September with 57% of all broods recorded between 22 June and 17 July. The late date was probably due to renesting. Sizes for 319 broods ranged from 1 to 4 young (1Y-111, 2Y-205, 3Y-2, 4Y-1), with 64% having 2 young. A brood of 4 small young (Lac la Hache, 10 July 1985) may have been a case of brood mixing (see Strong et al. 1986). Fledging period is 70 to 80 days (Olson and Marshall 1952).

REMARKS: In the Chilcotin-Cariboo Basin, Munro, J.A. (1945c) indicates that the same lakes are occupied each year despite the fact that nearby lakes, which appear to afford suitable nesting sites and food, are avoided.

Corkran (1988) discusses the status of the Common Loon in the Pacific Northwest and notes that, except in British Columbia, it has been all but extirpated from the region as a breeding species.

The Common Loon appears on the "Blue List" for 1980 and 1981 (Tate 1981). In 1982, it was delisted but maintained as a species of "special concern" owing to continuing powerboat effects on nesting success and the unknown potential of acid rain (Tate and Tate 1982). See McNicholl (1988) for a discussion of conservation problems in Canada.

The Common Loon, known as the Great Northern Diver in the Old World, and the closely related Yellow-billed Loon constitute a superspecies. A few authors consider them conspecific.

NOTEWORTHY RECORDS

Spring: Coastal - Whiffin Spit 2 Apr 1972-44; Lennard Island 15 May 1977-100+; Tsawwassen 13 Mar 1975-80 off jetty, 10 May 1979-21; Iona Island 30 Apr 1972-40 (Campbell et al. 1974); Comox Harbour 18 Apr to 14 May 1969-30+ (Crowell and Nehls 1969b); Port Neville 19 Mar 1977-24; Broughton Island 18 Apr 1966-31; Shingle Bay (Sandspit) 18 Apr 1982-56; Naden Harbour 1 Apr 1976-50. **Interior** - Okanagan Lake 18 Apr 1978-58; Okanagan Landing 19 Apr 1925-65, 22 Apr 1945-40; Wasa Lake 30 Apr 1975-8; Nicola Lake 16 Apr 1979-15; Kleena Kleene 11 May 1954-11 (Paul 1959); Williams Lake 10 Apr 1985-3, 18 Apr 1985-45, 21 Apr 1979-60; McLeese Lake 26 Apr 1985-17; Charlie Lake 6 May 1986-17 adults.

Summer: Coastal - Lemmens Inlet 6 Jun 1971-36 (Hatler et al. 1978); Vargas Island 21 Aug 1969-14; Comox Harbour to Deep Bay 22 Aug 1981-29 on census; Elma Bay 22 Jul 1939-50+; Upper Campbell Lake 18 Aug 1921-15; Security Cove 20 Jun 1977-111; Drizzle Lake 8 Jul 1977-58. **Interior** - Premier Lake 26 Jul 1948-7 (Johnstone, W.B.

1949); Pennask Lake 9 Jun 1976-16; Crooked Lake (Hendrix Lake) 30 Jul 1978-15; Williams Lake 1 Jul 1955-27; Bowron Lake early Jun 1975-30 adults; Tyhee Lake 13 Jul 1976-7; Charlie Lake 21 Aug 1985-10 adults.

Autumn: Interior - Kathlyn Lake 30 Nov 1987-1, lake open; Round Lake (Quick) 29 Nov 1987-1, lake open; Morice Lake 30 Sep 1974-18; Salmon Arm 15 Sep 1970-10+; Nicola Lake 13 Sep 1981-15; Okanagan Lake 10 Oct 1921-25, 10 Oct 1972-12; Lightning Lake 29 Oct 1985-5. **Coastal** - Masset Sound 20 Oct 1982-75; Cumshewa Inlet 30 Sep 1971-100+; Port Neville 13 Oct 1975-28; Comox Harbour to Deep Bay 19 Sep 1981-154 on census; Qualicum Beach 19 Sep 1980-25; Boundary Bay 11 Sep 1983-100; Tsawwassen 16 Sep 1982-150 off jetty, 28 Sep 1984-130; Vargas Island 24 Sep 1970-30 (Hatler et al. 1978); Esquimalt Lagoon 30 Sep 1984-30.

Winter: Interior - Atlin 30 Dec 1982-1 found on ice; Kathlyn Lake 1 Dec 1987-1, lake open; Eaglet

Lake 1 Dec 1987-2; Williams Lake 26 to 31 Dec 1974-1 on thin ice; Kamloops Lake 7 Feb 1987-4; Okanagan Lake 2 Jan 1977-3; Wasa Lake 13 Dec 1977-2; Nelson 5 Dec 1981-1. **Coastal** - Queen Charlotte City 15 Dec 1972-35, 20 Jan 1973-43; Comox Harbour to Deep Bay 17 Jan 1981-134 on census; Nanoose Harbour 19 Feb 1974-40; Crescent Beach 23 Dec 1961-15, 28 Dec 1944-15, 27 Feb 1975-15; Active Pass 19 Feb 1973-50; Royal Roads 24 Feb 1975-27.

Christmas Counts: Interior - Recorded from 10 of 19 localities and on 41% of all counts. Maxima: Oliver/Osoyoos 28 Dec 1981-10; Vernon 27 Dec 1981-8; Kelowna 20 Dec 1981-4; Penticton 27 Dec 1976-4, 27 Dec 1982-4. **Coastal** - Recorded from 24 of 28 localities and on 72% of all counts. Maxima: Comox 20 Dec 1981-**136**, all-time Canadian high count (Anderson, R.R. 1982); Ladner 28 Dec 1980-119; Deep Bay 30 Dec 1980-113.

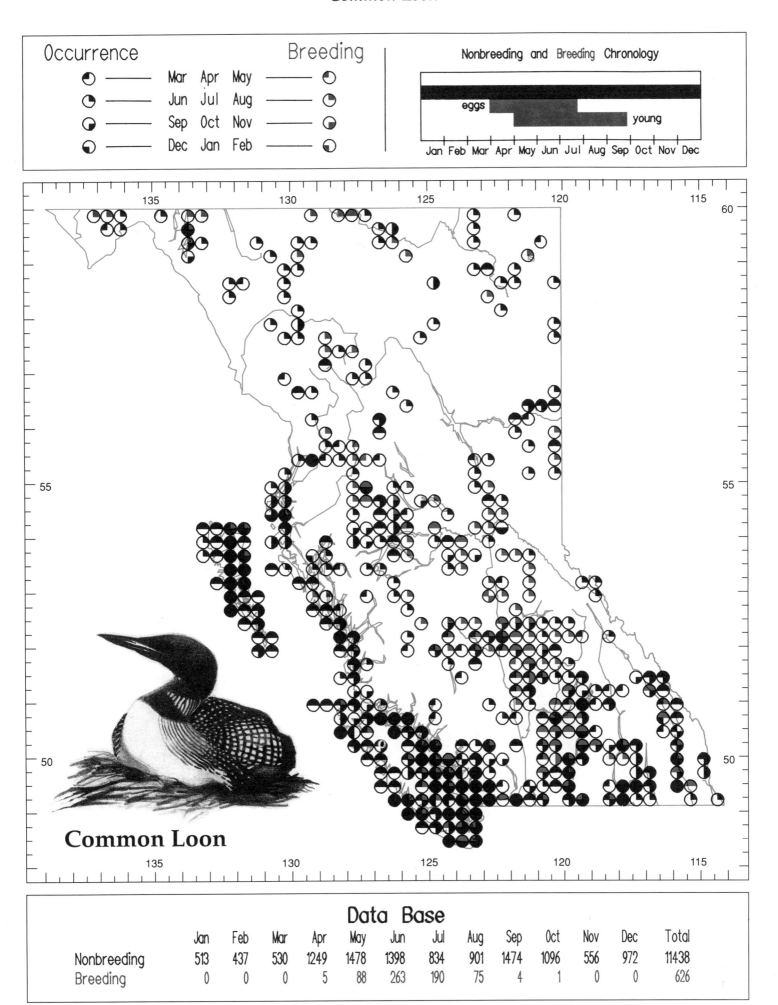

Common Loon

Yellow-billed Loon

YBLO

Gavia adamsii (Gray)

RANGE: Breeds in North America along Arctic coastal areas north of the tree-line from western and northern Alaska east to northern Keewatin and south to the latitude of Great Slave Lake. Winters along the Pacific coast south to Baja California, but primarily in Alaska. Also in Eurasia.

STATUS: *Uncommon* migrant; *rare* summer visitant and *rare* winter visitant along the coast. *Very rare* in the interior.

CHANGE IN STATUS: During the past century, the Yellow-billed Loon has gradually extended its nonbreeding range southward throughout the northern hemisphere (Burn and Mather 1974). In western North America, that southward expansion has occurred mostly during the last 2 decades. The species is now seen fairly regularly south to California (Remsen and Binford 1975). Since 1967 this large loon has been reported annually along the coast of Washington between 5 October and 22 April (Schultz 1970; Mattocks et al. 1976).

The same trend has been noted in British Columbia. Prior to 1924, the Yellow-billed Loon was on the hypothetical list (Brooks and Swarth 1925). By the mid-1940s, it was considered a "scarce winter visitant to coast littoral waters" (Munro, J.A. and Cowan 1947), and by the mid-1960s was listed as "casual in northwestern British Columbia; winters in small numbers in coastal British Columbia" (Godfrey 1966). At present, the Yellow-billed Loon occurs in small numbers along the coast throughout the year. Since 1979, it has been found occasionally in the southern interior of the province.

OCCURRENCE: The Yellow-billed Loon is found at all seasons along the outer and inner coasts and scattered throughout the interior. It has been reported more frequently in summer along the north coast and in late autumn and winter along the south coast. In the interior, the Yellow-billed Loon has been found mostly from October through January.

The Yellow-billed Loon prefers sheltered coastal waters. Habitat utilization, modified from Remsen and Binford (1975), shows the following preferences: moderately sheltered waters (e.g. exposed bays, shorelines, inlets) - 45% of records; very sheltered waters (e.g. unexposed bays, harbours, lagoons) - 33%; exposed open coast - 11%; offshore waters - 7%; lakes - 4%.

Spring migrants are difficult to distinguish from wintering birds, but most of the northward movement probably occurs from late March through May. Autumn migration is more pronounced. Birds move through waters of southeastern Alaska from late September through mid-November (Isleib and Kessel 1973) and arrive in British Columbia waters in late September and October. The main influx occurs in November and early December.

Yellow-billed Loons occur in small numbers and are widely distributed. Seven birds is the largest group reported from a single location. About 6% of all records for which age was recorded were of birds in breeding plumage.

Of 5 specimens taken in British Columbia, 3 were females, 1 was a male, and 1 was of undetermined sex. Although the sample is small, the preponderance of females is similar to results of specimens examined in California (Remsen and Binford 1975).

REMARKS: Known in the Old World as White-billed Diver. Burn and Mather (1974) and Binford and Remsen (1974) thoroughly discuss problems concerning the identification of this species during all plumage stages.

Figure 179. *Yellow-billed Loon near Tofino, 19 December 1987 (RBCM Photo 1237; Adrian Dorst).*

NOTEWORTHY RECORDS

Spring: Coastal - Sooke Harbour 13 May 1979-1; Boatswain Bank 8 May 1981-1 in breeding plumage; Parry Bay 3 Apr 1971-1 (Tatum 1972); Tsawwassen 13 Apr 1983-1 off jetty; Spanish Bank 13 Apr 1974-2 (Shepard, M.G. 1975a); Denman Island 1 May 1983-1 feeding with two Common Loons; Port Hardy 14 Apr 1936-1 (MVZ 99008); Guise Bay 19 May 1974-1 with Common Loon (Shepard, M.G. 1975a); Reef Island 12 and 31 May 1985-1; 44 km e Cumshewa Head 13 May 1983-7 adults; Alliford Bay 15 May 1985-1; 65 km ne Cape Ball River 10 May 1983-2 adults; 27 km e Rose Spit 14 Apr 1984-2 adults. **Interior** - Osoyoos Lake 14 May 1983-1 (Cannings, R.A. et al. 1987); Skaha Lake 21 May 1984-1 (RBCM Photo 915).

Summer: Coastal - 25 km w Tofino 3 Jun 1970-1 adult (Hatler et al. 1978); Grice Bay 6 Jul 1974-1; Lemmens Inlet 1 Jun 1982-1; Semiahmoo Bay 24 Aug 1983-1; Brant Point 7 Jun 1983-1; Friendly Cove 24 Aug 1974-2; Carpenter Bay 8 Jun 1985-5; Moore Island Jun 1977-1; Pip Islets 22 Jul 1977-1; Peril Bay 24 Jul 1977-1 (RBCM 17178); Murchison Island 12 Jul 1980-1 (RBCM Photo 725); Reef Island 13 Jun 1985-1; Masset Sound 10 Jun 1982-2; Naden Harbour 21 Jun 1947-1 (UBC 1443); Langara Island 26 Jul 1977-1 in breeding plumage. **Interior** - Peachland 12 Jun 1984-1; Stum Lake 14 Jun 1973-1 (Ryder 1973); Moose Lake 18 Jun 1975-1; Coldfish Lake 1 and 20 Jun 1976-1 (Osmond-Jones et al. 1977); Summit Lake (Fort Nelson) 31 Aug 1986-1 in breeding plumage (RBCM Photo 1146).

Autumn: Interior - Atlin Lake Oct 1930-1 (Brooks 1942); Adams River 25 Oct 1982-1 adult at mouth; Okanagan Landing 21 to 22 Nov 1983-1 (Cannings, R.A. et al. 1987); Okanagan Lake 22 Sep 1986-1. **Coastal** - Hunt Inlet 4 Nov 1977-3; Masset Sound 20 Oct 1982-1; Queen Charlotte City 26 Oct 1971-1; Skidegate Inlet 21 Sep 1987-2l; Smelt Bay 11 Sep 1982-1; Oyster Bay 15 Sep 1974-1; North Vancouver 11 Nov 1982-1 (RBCM Photo 832); Vancouver 14 Nov 1931-1 (RBCM 14506); Spanish Bank 1 Oct 1984-1; Ogden Point 25 Oct 1972-1; Royal Roads 29 Sep 1984-1; Port Renfrew 5 Oct 1974-1.

Winter: Interior - Shuswap Lake Dec 1971-1 (Jacobson 1974); Salmon Arm 3 Jan 1971-1; Okanagan Landing 4 Dec 1983-2 (Cannings, R.A. et al. 1987); Osoyoos Lake 29 Dec 1982-2; Nicola Lake 29 Dec 1986-1. **Coastal** - Prince Rupert 27 Jan 1979-2; Masset Sound 3 Feb 1983-1; Alliford Bay 12 Feb 1973-1; Comox 9 Jan 1929-1 (MVZ 99009); Tofino 19 Dec 1987-1 (RBCM Photo 1237; Fig. 179); Nanaimo Harbour 21 Jan 1985-1; Iona Island 16 Feb 1974-3 off jetty (Shepard, M.G. 1974); Ten Mile Point (Victoria) 14 Feb 1971-1 (Tatum 1972); Victoria Harbour 16 Jan 1972-1 (Tatum 1973).

Christmas Counts: Interior - Recorded from 3 of 19 localities and on 6% of all counts. Maxima: Oliver/Osoyoos 28 Dec 1982-1, 29 Dec 1983-1; Vaseux Lake 23 Dec 1979-1, 23 Dec 1982-1; Vernon 18 Dec 1983-1, 16 Dec 1984-1. **Coastal** - Recorded from 12 of 28 localities and on 8% of all counts. Maxima: Masset 18 Dec 1982-3, all-time Canadian high count (Anderson, R.R. 1983); Pender Island 21 Dec 1979-2; Prince Rupert 27 Dec 1983-2; Vancouver 18 Dec 1983-2.

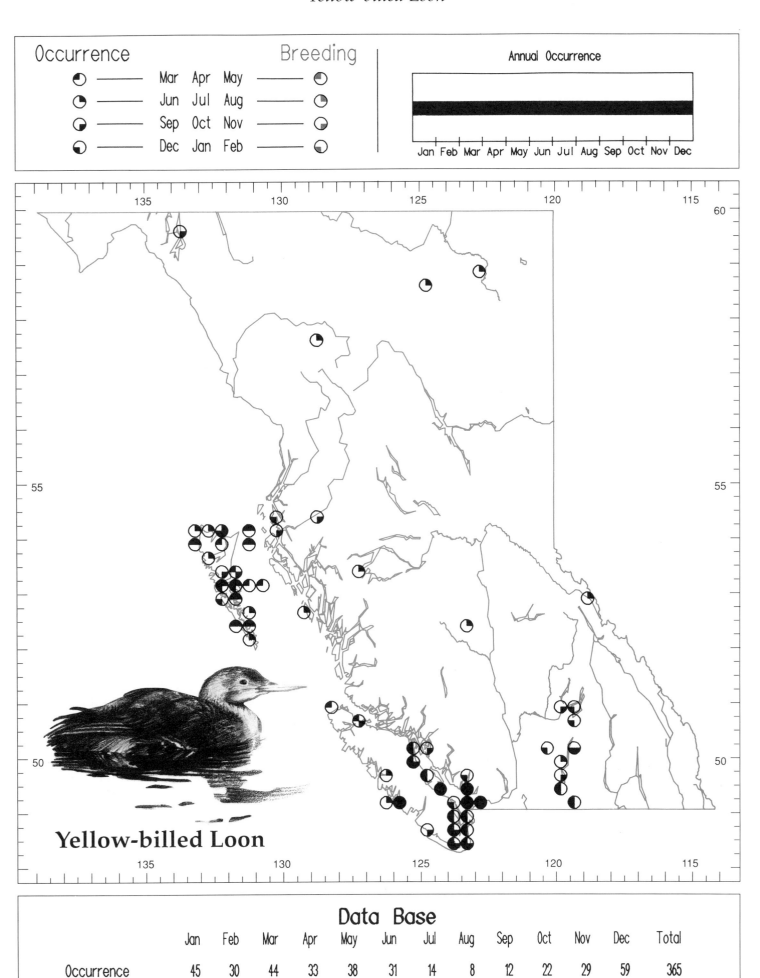

Yellow-billed Loon

	Mar	Apr	May	
	Jun	Jul	Aug	
	Sep	Oct	Nov	
	Dec	Jan	Feb	

Data Base

	Jan	Feb	Mar	Apr	May	Jun	Jul	Aug	Sep	Oct	Nov	Dec	Total
Occurrence	45	30	44	33	38	31	14	8	12	22	29	59	365

Pied-billed Grebe

Podilymbus podiceps (Linnaeus)

PBGR

RANGE: Breeds from central Canada south throughout most of North, Central, and South America. Winters on open water from southwestern British Columbia and the Great Lakes southward.

STATUS: *Uncommon* resident on the south coast including southeastern Vancouver Island, the Strait of Georgia, and adjacent mainland west of the Cascade Ranges.*Very rare* north of Vancouver Island including the Queen Charlotte Islands. *Fairly common* to *common* migrant in the south central interior north to at least the Chilcotin-Cariboo, where it is also a *fairly common* summer visitant and *uncommon* to *fairly common* in winter. *Uncommon* summer visitant in the northeast. Breeds.

NONBREEDING: The Pied-billed Grebe is widely distributed across the southern third of the province; it is localized seasonally in the Peace and Fort Nelson lowlands and is absent from the northwest. It occurs along the coast in quiet waters of bays, coves, inlets, estuaries, lagoons, and slow-moving rivers, but prefers fresh water. In the interior, it prefers permanent ponds and lakes usually at lower elevations but it has been found up to 1,310 m.

Migration is most pronounced in the interior. In spring, ice-free lakes can attract migrants as early as mid-March, which makes this species the earliest migrant of the grebes (Munro, J.A. 1941b). In most years, however, the earliest birds arrive in late March; the peak movement in southern areas is about mid-April. Flocks generally have fewer than 20 birds, although historical records document flocks of up to 150 birds. The onset of autumn migration is influenced by weather. In the Peace Lowlands, migration may start as early as late August and continue into September. In the south, depending on weather and temperature, passage may continue from late August (coast) to early September (interior) through October.

In summer, small flocks of nonbreeding birds frequent favourite shallow lakes or marshes (e.g. Quamichan Lake and Swan Lake, Vernon). Main wintering populations are found on calm marine and fresh waters in the vicinity of Ladner, Victoria, and Vancouver, and each year a few overwinter on larger ice-free lakes in some of the southern interior valleys.

BREEDING: The Pied-billed Grebe breeds on Vancouver Island north to the Campbell River area and on the mainland coast north to Malaspina Inlet. In the interior, it breeds from extreme southern British Columbia north to the vicnity of Quesnel, the Peace Lowlands, and rarely in the Fort Nelson Lowlands. It breeds from sea level to 1,280 m elevation.

Nesting habitat includes wetlands with shoreline vegetation of reeds, rushes, sedges, and grasses, or patches of such vegetation (including waterlilies) offshore. Freshwater marshes and ponds (57%) and shallow lakes (39%) are preferred nesting sites. Other sites include sloughs, sewage lagoons, bogs, backwaters of rivers, and large irrigation ditches.

Nests: Most nests were built on water and attached to stands of emergent vegetation, especially bulrush (51%), often in sparsely vegetated areas surrounded by denser vegetation around the perimeter of the wetland. Occasionally nests were built among waterlilies, on shores, or among drowned shrubs. Nests were sometimes free-floating. Water depths ranged from 20 cm to more than 2 m. Nests have been found up to 18 m from shore.

Nests were wet mounds of decayed and living vegetation including bulrushes, sedges, cattail, mosses, waterlilies, grasses, and mud. Nest mounds were up to 22 cm high and from 26 to 50 cm in diameter. Incubating adults leave the nests unattended, but covered, for prolonged periods. That behaviour may be related to the maintenance of a viable egg temperature by the moist, warm nest material (Davis et al. 1984).

Eggs: Dates for 153 clutches ranged from 20 April to 11 August (incubating adult) with 58% recorded between 16 May and 10 June. However, a downy chick found near Vancouver on 30 April indicates egg-laying begins on 1 April on the south coast where the breeding season can extend from March to September. Sizes for 176 clutches ranged from 1 to 10 eggs (1E-11, 2E-6, 3E-17, 4E-16, 5E-24, 6E-43, 7E-28, 8E-26, 9E-3, 10E-2), with 54% having 5 to 7 eggs. Incubation period is 23 days, with some variation (Deusing 1939). Four dump nests involving incubating Pied-billed Grebes and 4 other species have been reported: Swan Lake (Vernon), 26 May 1932-7 eggs of which 2 were Redhead (Munro, J.A. 1941b); near Wilkes Lake, 18 May 1978-9 eggs of which 1 was an American Coot; Westwick Lake, 10 June 1978-7 eggs, of which 2 were Mallard; Stump Lake (Quilchena), 19 June 1984-11 eggs of which 2 were Red-necked Grebe and 1 an American Coot (RBCM Photo 1083).

Young: Dates for 280 broods ranged from 30 April to 7 October (half-grown); the latter date probably represents a second brood (Palmer, R.S. 1962). Over half (57%) of all broods were recorded from 18 June to 20 July. Sizes for 291 broods ranged from 1 to 10 young (1Y-48, 2Y-52, 3Y-69, 4Y-38, 5Y-49, 6Y-26, 7Y-3, 8Y-4, 9Y-1, 10Y-1), with 55% having 2 to 4 young. The fledging period is unknown.

REMARKS: The centre of breeding abundance appears to be in the southern interior and the Chilcotin-Cariboo area. Populations in some major wetlands, however, are disappearing. For example, the Swan Lake (Vernon) population decreased from 60 birds in 1932 to 4 in 1965, and none was seen during a spring census in 1978 (Cannings, R.A. et al. 1987).

NOTEWORTHY RECORDS

Spring: Coastal - Elk Lake (Victoria) 5 Mar 1977-7; Swan Lake (Victoria) 25 Mar 1982-9; Pitt Lake marsh 1 Mar 1976-1; Drizzle Lake 11 to 17 May 1980-1. **Interior** - Vaseux Lake 23 Mar 1978 -13; West Arm (Kootenay Lake) 3 Mar 1985-4; Swan Lake (Vernon) 15 Apr 1932-150, 16 May 1932-60 (Munro, J.A. 1941b), 28 May 1940-24; Revelstoke 27 Mar 1983-1 first of year; Williams Lake 21 Mar 1978-2, 12 Apr 1978-7; Charlie Lake 6 May 1981-1, first of year.

Summer: Coastal - Quamichan Lake 20 Jun 1970-26; Nanaimo 20 Jul 1983-7, 30 Aug 1983-21; Iona Island 13 Jul 1969-10. **Interior** - Swan Lake (Vernon) 11 Jun 1930-20 (Munro, J.A. 1941b); Revelstoke 8 Jul to 26 Aug 1977-9 (Bonar 1978a); Forest Lake (Soda Creek) 2 Jun 1979-10;

Boundary Lake (Goodlow) 10 Jun 1984-5.

Autumn: Interior - Charlie Lake 26 Sep 1982-1, late record; Stump Lake (Quilchena) 5 Oct 1975-12; Vaseux Lake 24 Sep 1975-28, 22 Oct 1975-36, 6 Nov 1975-32; Creston 14 Sep 1985-25+. **Coastal** - Judson Lake 3 Nov 1974-50; Burnaby Lake 7 Nov 1979-35; Iona Island 29 Sep 1984-19; Nanaimo 15 Oct 1983-12, 22 Oct 1983-25; Portage Inlet 28 Sep 1979-24, 2 Oct 1979-28; Swan Lake (Victoria) 1 Sep 1982-16.

Winter: Interior - Williams Lake 24 and 27 Dec 1969-3; Athalmer 19 to 31 Jan 1982-1; Nakusp 2 Jan 1978-1; Thrums 22 Jan 1977-2; Okanagan Landing 9 Jan 1960-6. **Coastal** - Pallant Creek 9 to 18 Jan 1979-1; Chilliwack 15 Jan 1946-6 (Munro,

J.A. and Cowan 1947); Burnaby Lake 10 Dec 1979-20; Reifel Island 14 Dec 1974-11; Elk Lake (Victoria) 1 Jan 1965-120 (other lakes frozen), 9 Jan 1982-18 (other lakes frozen); Langford Lake 18 Dec 1982-18.

Christmas Counts: Interior - Recorded from 8 of 19 localities and on 45% of all counts. Maxima: Oliver/Osoyoos 28 Dec 1981-65; Vaseux Lake 23 Dec 1983-41; Penticton 27 Dec 1983-31. **Coastal** - Recorded from 18 of 28 localities and on 61% of all counts. Maxima: Ladner 23 Dec 1978-**101**, all-time Canadian high count (Anderson, R.R. 1979); Victoria 17 Dec 1983-84; Vancouver 18 Dec 1983-35.

Pied-billed Grebe

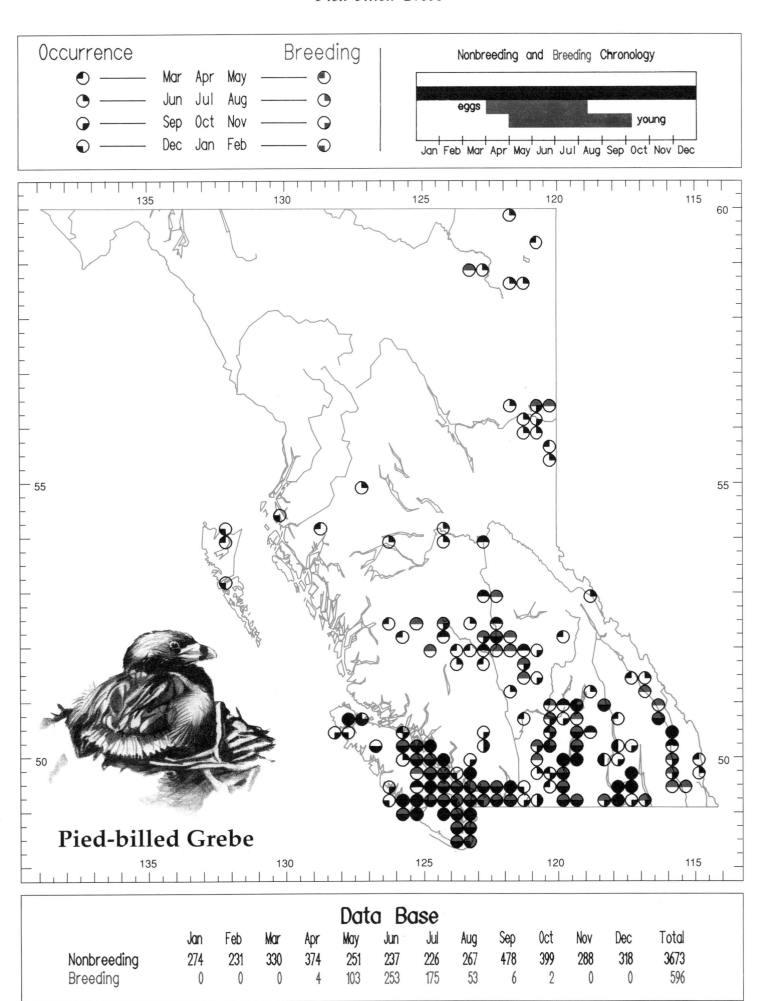

Occurrence

Mar Apr May
Jun Jul Aug
Sep Oct Nov
Dec Jan Feb

Breeding

Nonbreeding and Breeding Chronology

eggs

young

Jan Feb Mar Apr May Jun Jul Aug Sep Oct Nov Dec

Pied-billed Grebe

Data Base

	Jan	Feb	Mar	Apr	May	Jun	Jul	Aug	Sep	Oct	Nov	Dec	Total
Nonbreeding	274	231	330	374	251	237	226	267	478	399	288	318	3673
Breeding	0	0	0	4	103	253	175	53	6	2	0	0	596

Horned Grebe
Podiceps auritus (Linnaeus)

HOGR

RANGE: Breeds from central Alaska and northwestern Canada south to eastern Washington and east to Wisconsin. Winters on Pacific coast from southeastern Alaska to California, on Atlantic coast from Nova Scotia to Texas. Also in Eurasia.

STATUS: *Common* to *very common* migrant throughout the province. *Rare* summer visitant along the coast, *uncommon* to *fairly common* in the interior east of the Coast Ranges. In winter, *common* to *very common* along the coast; *fairly common* to *common* in the southern interior. Widespread breeder east of the Coast Ranges.

NONBREEDING: The Horned Grebe is widely distributed throughout the year along the coast and across the southern interior. It is most conspicuous during migration and winter when considerable numbers flock together in favoured areas. Along the coast, those include inshore marine waters such as bays, inlets, harbours, coves, and estuaries. Occasionally, small numbers are seen well offshore during migration. In the interior, sheltered areas of larger lakes are preferred.

On the coast, spring migration is mostly evident in April and early May. In some years, most birds have dispersed by mid-April, but in others the movement carries on into the first week of May. In the southern interior, early migrants appear during the latter half of March, their numbers build in April, and significant numbers are still present in the first week of May. In the Chilcotin-Cariboo and Peace and Fort Nelson lowlands, the spring movement is evident in late April, but most of the movement occurs during the first half of May. Autumn migration throughout the province generally begins in August, peaks in late September and October, and may carry over in some years to early November. Important wintering areas include Clayoquot Sound (Robertson 1974), western (see Fig. 180) and southern Strait of Georgia, Fraser River estuary, and Haro Strait on the coast, and Okanagan Lake, Kootenay Lake, Lower Arrow Lake, and Columbia River in the southern interior.

BREEDING: The Horned Grebe breeds throughout the interior valleys and tablelands including central-southern areas, the Peace Lowlands, and across the northern portion of the province. The centre of abundance is the Chilcotin-Cariboo Basin and Thompson-Okanagan Plateau regions. It prefers to nest on small freshwater lakes (46%; n=214) and marshes (32%), usually where vegetation is present. Other sites include ponds, sloughs, beaver ponds, and back-waters of calm rivers and streams. Nesting sites were observed in both open and forested country.

The Horned Grebe is primarily a solitary breeder, but loose colonies (3 to 20 pairs) have been observed on the Chilcotin-Cariboo Basin between Stum Lake and Green Lake with the largest colony (20 pairs) occurring in a slough near 70 Mile House. It breeds at elevations between 380 and 1,230 m.

Nests: Nests were built in shallow water and most (76%; n=84) were anchored among emergent vegetation. Bulrushes were preferred but cattail, sedges, rushes, and horsetails were also used. Other nest sites included open water (16%) as well as the edge of emergents, among floating algae, grass hummocks, submerged logs, floating branches, and man-made platforms. Water depths (n=8) ranged from 15 cm to 2 m. Most nests (91%; n=35) were situated within 8 m of shore, but some were up to 30 m from shore.

Nests were small pads of decayed and fresh aquatic vegetation with bulrush (41%; n=91) the preferred material. Other nesting materials included algae (18%) as well as northern spiked water-milfoil, cattail, fennel-leaved pondweed, bladderworts, horsetails, *Chara* sp., mosses, and occasionally twigs. Four nests ranged from 21 to 40 cm in diameter. The cup of one of these had an inside diameter of 22 cm. One nest was built to a height of 20 cm.

Eggs: Dates for 109 clutches ranged from 20 May to 10 August (Munro, J.A. 1941b) with 53% recorded between 12 June and 4 July. Calculated dates indicate that eggs could be found as early as 9 May. Clutch size ranged from 1 to 8 eggs (1E-7, 2E-7, 3E-19, 4E-38, 5E-26, 6E-9, 7E-1, 8E-2), with 59% having 4 or 5 eggs. Incubation period for 4 nests in British Columbia was 23 to 25 days.

Young: Dates for 146 broods ranged from 6 June to 5 September, with 53% recorded between 8 and 28 July. Sizes for 141 broods ranged from 1 to 7 young (1Y-41, 2Y-55, 3Y-19, 4Y-13, 5Y-9, 6Y-3, 7Y-1), with 68% having 1 or 2 young. Fledging period is unknown.

REMARKS: Consult Munro, J.A. (1941b) for information on moults and plumages, behaviour (also McAllister 1963), nesting habitat, nesting, and food and feeding habits.

The Horned Grebe appears on the "Blue List" for the first time in 1986 (Tate 1986) because it was greatly down in migrant and wintering numbers in northeastern North America.

Known as Slavonian Grebe in the Old World.

NOTEWORTHY RECORDS

Spring: Coastal - Saltspring Island 21 Apr 1962-30; Iona Island 4 Apr 1979-100+, 24 Apr 1971-100+, 30 Apr 1972-100+ (Campbell et al. 1974); Vancouver 2 May 1976-54; Port Neville 16 Apr 1977-44; Kagan Bay 11 May 1977-52; White Creek (Tow Hill) 7 May 1987-33. **Interior** - Okanagan Lake 10 Mar 1979-10, 21 Apr 1940-150; West Arm (Kootenay Lake) 3 Mar 1985-32, 11 Mar 1979-50; Nakusp 24 Apr 1979-98; Arrow Lake 29 Apr 1920-200+ (Kelso 1926); Emerald Lake (Field) 15 May 1976-85 (Wade 1977); Puntchesakut Lake 11 May 1944-17 (Munro, J.A. and Cowan 1947); Charlie Lake 25 Apr 1981-4, 7 May 1983-142+; Parker Lake (Fort Nelson) 5 May 1980-10; Atlin 9 May 1936-22 (Munro, J.A. 1941b).

Summer: Coastal - Esquimalt Lagoon 7 Jul 1973-4; Iona Island 30 Jul 1972-8 (Campbell et al. 1974).

Interior - Okanagan Lake 8 Aug 1973-10; 103 Mile Lake 6 Jul 1938-12 nonbreeders (Munro, J.A. 1941b); Big Lake (Lac la Hache) 18 Aug 1978-20; Nulki Lake 1 Jul 1974-10; Parker Lake (Fort Nelson) 8 Jun 1980-14.

Autumn: Interior - Charlie Lake 25 Sep 1983-34, 4 Nov 1986-1; Yoho National Park 7 Sep 1976-40+; Separation Lake 17 Sep 1978-30; Swan Lake (Vernon) 21 Sep 1977-16, 25 Oct 1977-28, 10 Nov 1977-60; West Arm (Kootenay Lake) 27 Oct 1979-50, 23 Nov 1982-67; Elkview 26 Sep 1984-22, 16 Oct 1984-26. **Coastal** - Rose Spit 24 Oct 1982-60; Oyster Bay 27 Sep 1973-250+; Mud Bay (Crescent Beach) 12 Sep 1971-30 (Campbell et al. 1972b); Esquimalt Lagoon 29 Sep 1984-50, 2 Oct 1984-105.

Winter: Interior - Okanagan Lake (near Penticton) 4 Dec 1973-29, 3 Feb 1974-75; Columbia River (Hugh Keenleyside Dam) 23 Jan 1977-42; West Arm (Kootenay Lake) 2 Dec 1978-93, 8 Feb 1981-150; Burton 12 Jan 1986-85. **Coastal** - Port Neville 22 Jan 1977-53; Comox 20 Jan 1932-50; Squamish River 19 Feb 1980-37 on estuary; Vancouver 6 Jan 1973-80; Roberts Bank 31 Jan 1982-50+; Esquimalt Lagoon 19 Dec 1973-71.

Christmas Counts: Interior - Recorded from 8 of 19 localities and on 53% of all counts. Maxima: Vernon 21 Dec 1980-163; Penticton 27 Dec 1976-90; Vaseux Lake 23 Dec 1979-77. **Coastal** - Recorded from 24 of 28 localities and on 85% of all counts. Maxima: Victoria 30 Dec 1967-**1,153**, all-time Canadian high count (Anderson, R.R. 1976); Duncan 17 Dec 1977-823; White Rock 22 Dec 1974-458.

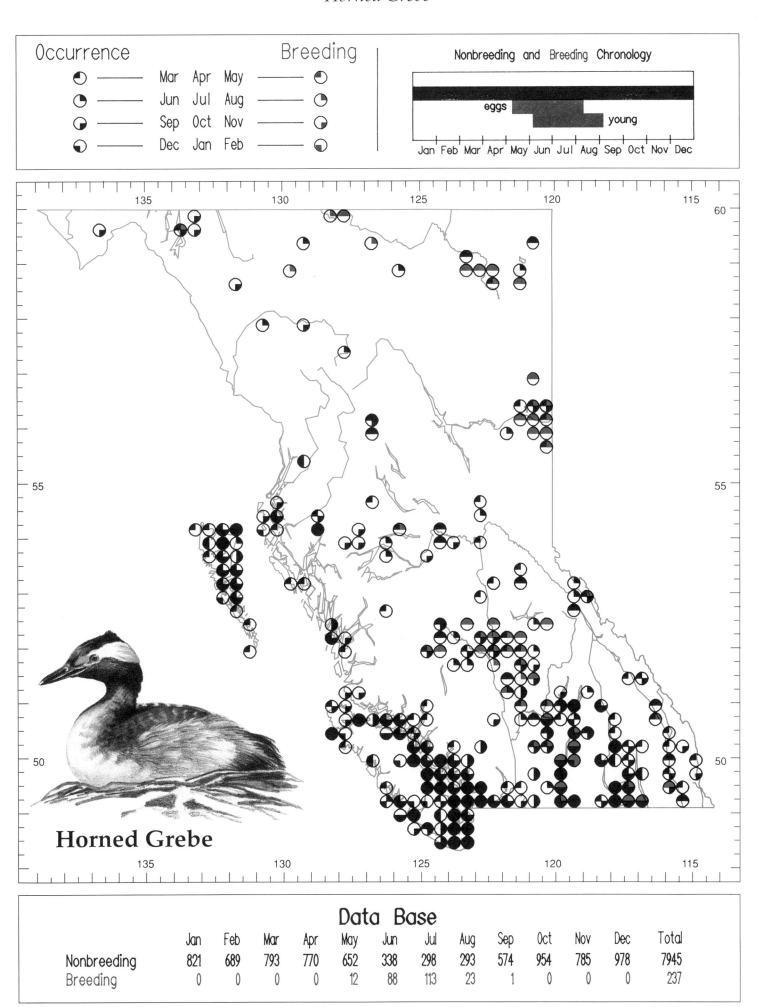

Horned Grebe

Occurrence   **Breeding**

Mar Apr May
Jun Jul Aug
Sep Oct Nov
Dec Jan Feb

Nonbreeding and Breeding Chronology

eggs
young

Jan Feb Mar Apr May Jun Jul Aug Sep Oct Nov Dec

Data Base

	Jan	Feb	Mar	Apr	May	Jun	Jul	Aug	Sep	Oct	Nov	Dec	Total
Nonbreeding	821	689	793	770	652	338	298	293	574	954	785	978	7945
Breeding	0	0	0	0	12	88	113	23	1	0	0	0	237

Red-necked Grebe

RNGR

Podiceps grisegena (Boddaert)

RANGE: Breeds from western Alaska across central Canada to Ontario, south to Washington and southern Wisconsin. Winters on both coasts from southern Alaska to central California and from Newfoundland south to central Florida. Also in Europe and northern Asia.

STATUS: *Very common* to *abundant* migrant, especially along the coast. *Uncommon* to *very common* summer visitant to the interior, becoming *uncommon* in the north half of the province; *rare* to *fairly common* along the coast. In winter, *fairly common* to *very common* along the coast, especially the south coast; *uncommon* in the southern interior. Widespread breeder in the interior; *accidental* on Vancouver Island.

NONBREEDING: The Red-necked Grebe is widely distributed throughout the province. It is gregarious but rarely associates with other species of grebes. Larger lakes and occasionally slow-moving rivers are preferred inland habitats while along the coast, bays, inlets, estuaries, and narrows are used. Large flocks (100+ birds) are common on the coast in autumn and winter, and may be seen occasionally throughout the province in spring migration.

Spring migration may begin as early as late February and early March in southern areas (Fig. 180), depending on open water in the interior, but peaks in the latter half of April. The main movement through the Chilcotin-Cariboo occurs during the second and third weeks of April and in the Peace Lowlands during the first half of May. Small numbers of nonbreeders are scattered along the coast in the summer. The return movement begins in late August but occurs mostly from late September to early October. Migrating birds have been found from sea level to 1,585 m elevation.

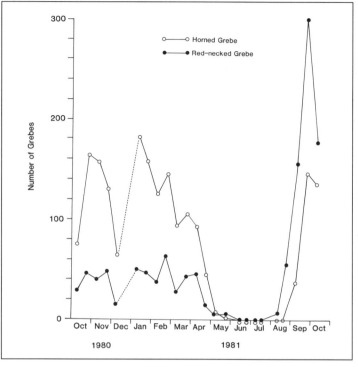

Figure 180. *Biweekly counts (averages) of Horned and Red-necked grebes, Comox Harbour to Deep Bay, Vancouver Island, 11 October 1980 to 10 October 1981 (Canadian Wildlife Service unpublished data). The dashed line indicates a period when counts were not made.*

Figure 181. *Location of Red-necked Grebe breeding site, Stump Lake (Quilchena), 4 July 1983 (Mark Nyhof).*

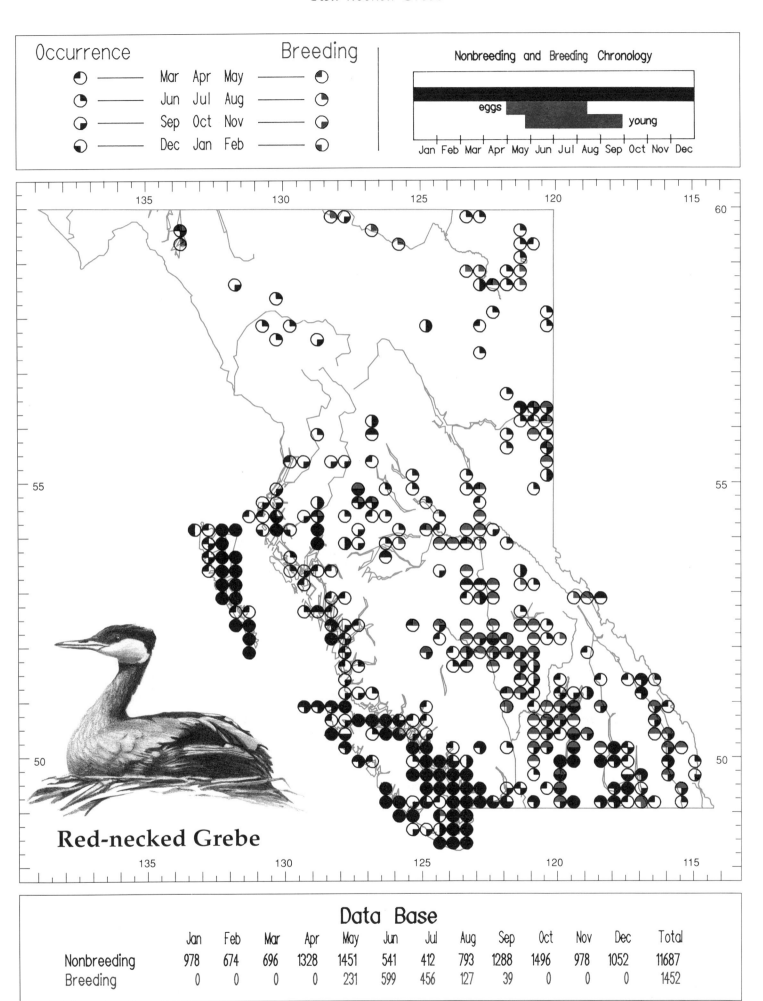

Red-necked Grebe

Occurrence		Breeding
Mar Apr May		
Jun Jul Aug		
Sep Oct Nov		
Dec Jan Feb		

Nonbreeding and Breeding Chronology

eggs   young

Jan Feb Mar Apr May Jun Jul Aug Sep Oct Nov Dec

Data Base

	Jan	Feb	Mar	Apr	May	Jun	Jul	Aug	Sep	Oct	Nov	Dec	Total
Nonbreeding	978	674	696	1328	1451	541	412	793	1288	1496	978	1052	11687
Breeding	0	0	0	0	231	599	456	127	39	0	0	0	1452

Table 8
Red-necked Grebe: location, history, and size of major breeding concentrations in British Columbia.

Location	First Record	Low Survey Results[1] Year		High Survey Results[1] Year		Recent Survey Results[1] Year		Source[2]
Interior - Colonies > 50 nests or pairs								
Charlie Lake	1938	Many N	1938	62 Ap	1962	C	1987	1,2
Duck Lake (Creston)	1956	5 N	1956	55 P	1982	C	1987	3, 4
Stump Lake (Quilchena)	1959	25 P	1964	64 Nc	1983		1983	1
Swan Lake (Vernon)	1916	3 N	1980	55 P	1939		1980	1,5,6

[1] A - active nests; C - nesting confirmed but no count or estimate made; N - nests; P - pairs. All data are estimates unless noted as follows: c - complete count; p - partial count.

[2] 1 - British Columbia Nest Records Scheme; 2 - Cowan 1939; 3 - Anonymous 1987; 4 - Munro, J.A. 1958a; 5 - Munro, J.A. 1941b; 6 - Munro, J.A. 1939f.

Main coastal wintering areas include the Strait of Georgia and sheltered waters of Juan de Fuca Strait. In the interior, the largest aggregations occur in the Okanagan valley.

BREEDING: The Red-necked Grebe breeds throughout much of the interior of the province east of the Coast Ranges, except the north-central portion.There is one, isolated coastal record: Cowichan Lake 14 August 1935-2 half-grown young (Munro, J.A. 1941b). It is usually a solitary nesting species but under certain conditions will form loose colonies. Colonies in British Columbia occur in widely separate locations, the largest being 64 pairs (Table 8). The centre of abundance is the southern interior from the Kootenays to the Chilcotin-Cariboo. At Duck Lake, Creston, densities have ranged from 0.4 ha per pair on a nearby marsh to 72.2 ha per pair on the lake itself (Ohanjanian 1986a).

The Red-necked Grebe breeds on sheltered, usually shallow, freshwater lakes (91%; n=823) with emergent and submergent vegetation, in both open and forested regions (Fig. 181). Sloughs, alkaline lakes, slow river channels, large open irrigation ditches, bogs, and ponds are used occasionally for nesting. Optimum habitat requirements usually include a combination of vegetation composition and density, anchorage for nests (emergents and submergents), protection from wind and wave action, and depth and size of breeding site (Munro, J.A. 1941b; Riske 1976; De Smet 1983). At least 50 to 60 m of open water are required by grebes for takeoff (Ohanjanian 1986a).

Nests have been located from 150 to 1,370 m elevation; most were reported between 760 and 910 m.

Nests: Most nests (81%; n=674) were positioned among or at the edge of emergent vegetation including bulrush (57%), cattail (35%), and sedges (8%). Other nests were built in open areas, usually on submerged aquatics such as northern spiked water-milfoil, bladderwort, and pondweed, among waterlillies, or occasionally on floating logs or anchored tree branches. Seven nests were free-floating. Nests were positioned from 0.6 to 91 m from shore. Recorded water depths at nests ranged from 0.2 to 3.6 m.

Nests were low accumulations of nearly submerged, usually decaying, aquatic vegetation (Fig. 182) including pondweeds, water-milfoils, and filamentous algae, sometimes mixed with mud and invariably lined with living or dead bulrush, cattail, sedges, mosses, waterlilies, rootlets, twigs, horsetails, or leaves. Outside diameters of 26 nests ranged from 33 to 122 cm, inside diameters from 18 to 28 cm, and heights from 8 to 25 cm.

Eggs: Dates for 703 clutches ranged from 2 May to 15 August. Ohanjanian (1986a) shows that although clutch initiation

Figure 182. Red-necked Grebe incubating, Paul Lake (Kamloops), 22 June 1988 (Mark Nyhof).

dates in exposed sites and sites protected from wind and waves were similar, hatching varies as much as 5 weeks between areas. Throughout the province most clutches (58%) were found between 2 and 20 June. Clutch size ranged from 1 to 25 eggs (1E-86, 2E-127, 3E-154, 4E-168, 5E-94, 6E-42, 7E-12, 8E-16, 9E-1, 10E-1, 11E-1, 25E-1) with 63% having 2 to 4 eggs. Munro, J.A. (1941b), Kevan (1970) and Riske (1976) note a seasonal decline in clutch size. Cringan (1957), Palmer, R.S. (1962) and Riske (1976) suggest that clutches containing more than 6 eggs are laid by more than 1 female while Kevan (1970) and De Smet (1983) indicate that nests containing 7 to 9 eggs were not joint layings. Ohanjanian (1986a), however, indicates that clutches of 11 and 25 eggs found at Creston were joint layings. Incubation periods for 12 nests from British Columbia were between 22 and 23 days.

Young: Dates for 577 broods ranged from 26 May to 30 September, with 54% recorded between 26 June and 29 July. Brood sizes ranged from 1 to 8 young (1Y-181, 2Y-262, 3Y-90, 4Y-25, 5Y-13, 6Y-4, 8Y-2), with 77% having 1 or 2 young. Fledging period is 56 to 70 days (Harrison, C. 1978).

REMARKS: During the breeding season individual adults (Fig. 183) and young can be identified in the field, within a range of about 100 m, using a spotting telescope. The following details are from Ohanjanian (1986a):

. . . [it is] possible to identify individual adults by the pattern on their cheeks ... Cheeks were not simply white but were patterned in different shades of grey, from near black to white. [In one pair, one adult] . . . had solid grey cheeks . . . its mate had grey cheeks with a distinct "C" of white in the middle; its mate had a prong of red protruding up into solid white cheeks . . . Young could be easily identified by the pattern of stripes on their heads and necks.

The diet of the Red-necked Grebe is poorly known. In some studies, fishes are the most important single items (e.g. Wetmore 1924; Chamberlain 1977). On lakes without fishes, and notably during the breeding period, aquatic insects comprise the chief food (Munro, J.A. 1941b; Riske 1976).

At Creston, in the west Kootenay region of British Columbia, Ohanjanian (1986a) followed the diet of young Red-necked Grebes from hatching until about 49 days old. During the first week of life Odonata (dragonfly) larvae were significant in the diet, after which fishes become increasingly important. Main fish species, in descending order of importance, were yellow perch, pumpkinseed, and largemouth bass.

The Red-necked Grebe occurred on the "Blue List" from 1974 to 1981 (Tate 1981). On the 1976 list, it was thought to be "on a long, slow decline" throughout its range (Arbib 1975), and that view continued through the 1980 list (Arbib 1979). It was delisted in 1982, due to an apparent increase in numbers seen on coastal Christmas Bird Counts (De Smet 1982), but was maintained as a species of "special concern" (Tate and Tate 1982). The general concern includes conversion of wetlands to residental, agricultural, and recreational use.

Other details of the natural history are discussed by Munro, J.A. (1941b) and Ohanjanian (1986a) for British Columbia, Kevan (1970) and Riske (1976) for Alberta, and De Smet (1983) for Manitoba.

Figure 183. *Variation in cheek patterns of adult Red-necked Grebes. Drawn from specimens RBCM 2 (a) and RBCM 2017 (b) by D. Val Blondahl.*

NOTEWORTHY RECORDS

Spring: Coastal - Island View Beach 11 Mar 1983-137; Central Saanich 10 Apr 1983-175; Cowichan Bay 16 Apr 1968-187; Departure Bay 13 Mar 1930-250 (Munro, J.A. 1941b); Tofino 1 May 1974-150; Nanaimo 3 Apr 1962-76; Campbell River 29 Mar 1975-156 at estuary; Menzies Bay 19 Apr 1966-200, 29 Apr 1966-300; Garvey Point 24 Mar 1976-65; Dolomite Narrows 17 Apr 1985-55. **Interior** - Okanagan Landing 21 Apr 1940-150, 24 Apr 1927-100; Swan Lake (Vernon) 15 Apr 1932-300; Green Lake (70 Mile House) 28 Apr 1939-50 (Munro, J.A. 1941b): Williams Lake 27 Apr 1984-20; Tachick Lake 7 May 1945-200; along Peace River 5 May 1975-150, 6 May 1975-156, 10 May 1975-67 (Penner 1976); Charlie Lake 27 Apr 1986-1, 7 May 1983-35, largest spring concentration; Atlin 16 May 1981-12.

Summer: Coastal - Esquimalt Lagoon 29 Jun 1975-13; Victoria 19 Jul 1971-20; Cowichan Head 29 Aug 1984-215; Cleland Island 31 Aug 1969-100;
Rose Spit 20 Aug 1975-105; Burnaby Strait 8 Jul 1977-17. **Interior** - Carp Lake 25 and 26 Aug 1975-260; Stum Lake 13 Aug 1973-30; Stony Lake (Quintette Mountain) 4 Aug 1976-80; Charlie Lake 20 Aug 1975-11, 21 Aug 1975-22; Fern Lake (Kwadacha Wilderness Park) 19 Aug 1983-18 appeared after snowstorm (Cooper, J.M. and Cooper 1983).

Autumn: Interior - Charlie Lake 22 Oct 1986-32; Swan Lake (Tupper) 2 Sep 1981-20; Tyhee Lake 29 Nov 1987-3, lake open; Eaglet Lake 22 Nov 1987-2; Puntchesakut Lake 3 Sep 1944-25 (Munro, J.A. 1947a); Hanceville 20 Sep 1982-25+; Trapp Lake 17 Sep 1978-38; Revelstoke 27 Sep 1977-17; Columbia Lake 13 Sep 1981-12; Swan Lake (Vernon) 10 Nov 1977-20. **Coastal** - Cumshewa Inlet 30 Sep 1971-100+; Cape Lazo 1 Sep 1951-65; Parksville 3 Sep 1974-50; Tofino 5 Sep 1974-160; Blackie Spit 23 Sep 1984-200; Cordova Spit 4 Sep 1974-111; Island View Beach 20 Sep 1982-200, 5 Oct 1980-95.

Winter: Interior - Kathlyn Lake 1 Dec 1987-2, lake open; Okanagan Landing 25 Feb 1908-13; Kelowna 29 Dec 1972-7; Kootenay Lake 22 Feb 1983-6. **Coastal** - Masset 11 Dec 1971-35; Queen Charlotte City 19 Dec 1971-50; Tasu Sound 29 Jan 1973-39; Port Neville 28 Feb 1986-120; Campbell River 19 Feb 1974-106; Comox 12 Dec 1949-50 (Flahaut 1950b); Cates Bay 12 Feb 1972-200+; Tofino 4 Jan 1976-55; Cordova Spit 5 Feb 1977-127.

Christmas Counts: Interior - Recorded from 7 of 19 localities and on 37% of all counts. Maxima: Nakusp 4 Jan 1981-91 [these were likely Horned Grebes]; Vernon 18 Dec 1983-21; Oliver/Osoyoos 28 Dec 1981-12. **Coastal** - Recorded from 25 of 28 localities and on 81% of all counts. Maxima: Victoria 30 Dec 1973-**258**, all-time Canadian high count (Anderson, R.R. 1976); Ladner 14 Dec 1974-227; Sunshine Coast 17 Dec 1983-126.

Eared Grebe

Podiceps nigricollis Brehm

EAGR

RANGE: Breeds in southwestern Canada from southern Yukon (Jones, E.T. 1985) east to Manitoba and south through the western United States to Baja California and Texas. Winters south to Guatemala. Also in the Old World.

STATUS: Locally *common* to *very abundant* migrant and summer visitant in the Kootenays, Okanagan, and Thompson valleys, Chilcotin-Cariboo Basin, and Peace Lowlands. *Rare* in winter in the central-southern interior. *Rare* to *fairly common* migrant and winter resident in coastal waters of the Strait of Georgia and Juan de Fuca Strait. *Rare* in summer there, and *very rare* elsewhere along the coast. Local breeder.

NONBREEDING: The Eared Grebe occurs across southern portions of the province including southeastern Vancouver Island and locally in the Peace Lowlands; scattered elsewhere. Like other grebes, it is a nocturnal migrant and congregates in loose flocks, but has no known major staging areas in the province. It is likely that birds in the southern portions of the province arrive from Washington, Idaho, and Montana while those in the Peace Lowlands enter from northwestern Alberta (see Salt and Salt 1976). In the interior, main habitats include lakes and larger marshes; sheltered marshes, and nearshore marine waters such as bays, estuaries, lagoons, and harbours are preferred along the coast.

Spring migration in the southern interior may begin in some years as early as late March and early April but is mostly evident

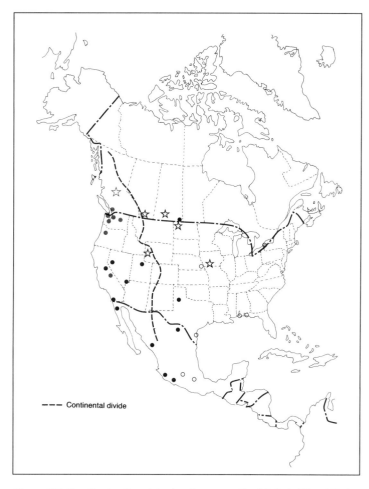

Figure 184. *Banding locations (stars) and recovery sites (circles) of Eared Grebes in North America. Red indicates birds banded in British Columbia. Black indicates birds banded elsewhere: solid circles are recovery sites of birds banded along the Continental Divide; open circles are recovery sites of birds banded in central North America (modified from Jehl and Yochem 1986).*

in late April and early May. In the Peace River area, the movement occurs primarily in the second and third weeks of May. On the coast, the main movement is evident in April with most birds gone by the second week of May.

The summer distribution of nonbreeders in the interior is poorly known although some have been found on lakes separate from breeding birds (A. Breault pers. comm.). Small numbers summer throughout the Strait of Georgia and Juan de Fuca Strait.

Autumn migration in the interior is not well documented because of the difficulty of separating breeding birds from migrants, but probably occurs mostly in September. A. Breault suggests there are probably 3 waves of migrants: nonbreeders, successful breeders, and abandoned young. On the coast, the movement is evident in the latter half of September and carries through October as the wintering population builds. Migrating birds have been recorded from sea level to 1,590 m.

On the coast, the winter population is restricted to the Strait of Georgia and Juan de Fuca Strait, with loose aggregations of seldom more than 20 birds. Flocks of about 100 birds have been reported from the Gulf Islands. In the interior, small numbers winter in open water from Shuswap Lake south through the Okanagan valley. However, the true winter status of the species is obscured because of confusion with the Horned Grebe by many observers (see Christmas Bird Counts in Noteworthy Records and Fig. 184).

BREEDING: The Eared Grebe breeds from the Okanagan valley and east Kootenay, north through the Chilcotin-Cariboo region to Tachick and Nulki lakes, near Vanderhoof. Since the report of Munro, J.A. and Cowan (1947), colonies have become established in the vicinity of Fort St. John and Dawson Creek in the Peace Lowlands. The centre of abundance is the Chilcotin-Cariboo Basin.

The Eared Grebe usually nests colonially, often in tight, compact colonies. Habitat includes shallow, often sheltered, freshwater marshes, lakes (Fig. 185), ponds, and sewage lagoons with moderate to heavy growth of emergent vegetation, usually bulrush. Water bodies are usually larger than 4 ha. Colonies ranged in size from 5 to an estimated 1,000 pairs. For example, a post-nesting census of Cecil Lake on 3 July 1978 revealed 2,826 adults and 2,290 young which suggests a colony of at least 1,000 pairs, considering the normal visibility of the birds in the breeding marshes. The largest colonies (Table 9) were from McMurray, Westwick, and Little White lakes in the Chilcotin-Cariboo, and Cecil, Boudreau, and Boundary (Goodlow) lakes in the Peace Lowlands. Collectively these lakes support about 70% of the provincial population.

Colony size may fluctuate dramatically from year to year which suggests that entire local populations may select different breeding sites due to varying conditions. For example, Westwick Lake supported at least 40 nests in 1940, 469 nests in 1978, and at least 212 active nests in 1986.

Colonies have been located between 420 and 1,220 m elevation.

Nests: Most nests were densely concentrated and located in stands of bulrushes, sedges, cattail, and other emergents growing in shallow water around the perimeter of a marsh. Most were well concealed by emergent growth; some, however, were completely exposed. The latter were usually placed on submerged aquatics including water-milfoils, fennel-leaved pondweed and buttercups.

Small patches of emergents supported very dense colonies. For example, at Rock Lake (1978) 173 nests were found in a dense patch of bulrush that measured 25 x 30 m. At Cecil Lake (1962) 106 nests were concentrated in an area of 30 x 80 m so that some were touching each other. Another colony at 150 Mile House had nests an average of 2 m apart. Most nests were located in water 0.3 to 1.3 m deep and from 3 to 300 m from shore.

Nests were low mounds of rotting aquatic vegetation composed mostly of bulrush, pondweeds, algae, and other plants

Eared Grebe

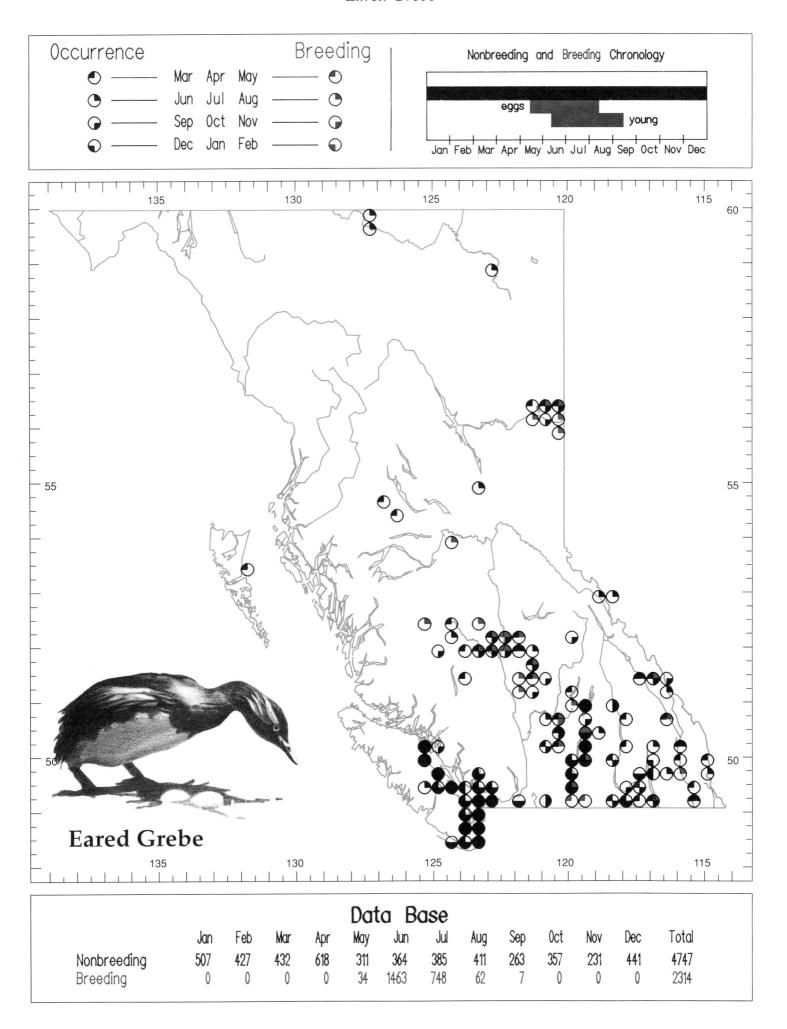

Occurrence   **Breeding**

	Mar Apr May	
	Jun Jul Aug	
	Sep Oct Nov	
	Dec Jan Feb	

Nonbreeding and Breeding Chronology

eggs

young

Jan Feb Mar Apr May Jun Jul Aug Sep Oct Nov Dec

Eared Grebe

Data Base

	Jan	Feb	Mar	Apr	May	Jun	Jul	Aug	Sep	Oct	Nov	Dec	Total
Nonbreeding	507	427	432	618	311	364	385	411	263	357	231	441	4747
Breeding	0	0	0	0	34	1463	748	62	7	0	0	0	2314

Figure 185. *Rock Lake (Riske Creek), August 1975. Eared Grebe breeding colony is located among bulrush patches in the lake (Robert A. Cannings).*

TABLE 9
Eared Grebe: location, history, and size of major colonies in British Columbia.

Location	First Record	Low Survey Results[1]		Year	High Survey Results[1]		Year	Recent Survey Results[1]		Year	Source[2]
Interior - Colonies > 50 nests or pairs
Boudreau Lake	1981				185	P	1985	120	P	1986	2
Boundary Lake (Goodlow)	1978	75	P	1981	500	P	1985	208	P	1986	1,2,3
Cecil Lake	1962	284	A	1978	1000	P	1982	304	Ap	1986	1,2,4
Dawson Creek	1962	12	Ac	1986	84	Ac	1978			1986	1,2
Dry Lake (Hanceville)	1980	30	P	1980	50	N	1983	29	Ap	1985	1,2
Elkhorn Lake	1985	60	Ap	1986	205	Ap	1985			1986	2
Little White Lake	1986				590	P	1986			1986	2
McMurray Lake	1985	343	Ap	1985	440	Np	1986			1986	2
Meadow Lake	1978	37	Ac	1986	79	P	1978			1986	1,2,5
Rock Lake (Riske Creek)	1978	60	P	1980	173	Nc	1978			1980	1
Sorenson Lake	1938	14	Pp	1986	50	P	1949			1986	1,2
Stump Lake (Quilchena)	1986			1986	61	Ac	1986			1986	2
Westwick Lake	1937	23	N	1942	469	Ac	1978	212	Ap	1986	1,2,6
Williams Lake
8432 North	1985	21	Ap	1986	72	Ap	1985			1986	2
Lake 6	1985	37	Ac	1986	81	Ac	1985			1986	2

[1] A - active nests; N - nests; P - pairs. All data are estimates unless noted as follows: c - complete count; p - partial count.

[2] 1 - British Columbia Nest Records Scheme; 2 - Breault et al 1988; 3 - Campbell 1978c; 4 - Campbell 1978d; 5 - Campbell et al. 1979c; 6 - Campbell and Garrioch 1978b.

such as water-milfoils and buttercups (Fig. 186). Most were anchored among stems of emergents or piles of submerged plants. A few were free floating. Measurements for 14 nests follow: outside diameter for portion under water, 55 to 155 cm; outside diameter above water 25 to 41 cm; inside diameter, 13 to 23 cm; height, 8 to 15 cm (Forbes 1985a).

Eggs: Dates for 1,711 clutches ranged from 15 May to 14 August with 56% recorded between 11 and 30 June. The latest date was for 3 adults incubating eggs in a colony near Hanceville that had produced young in July. Clutch size ranged from 1 to 8 eggs (1E-181, 2E-317, 3E-716, 4E-435, 5E-48, 6E-12, 7E-1, 8E-1) with 67% having 3 or 4 eggs. That range includes the mean clutch size of 3.48 reported for 293 clutches by McAllister (1958) in the Cariboo but is higher than the mean of 2.2 eggs for 16 clutches from Creston (Forbes 1985a). The latter figure, however, may be low due to renesting. Incubation period is 20.5 to 21.5 days (McAllister 1958).

Young: Dates for 504 broods ranged from 14 June to 15 September (Munro, J.A. 1941b), with 64% recorded between 30 June and 4 July. Brood sizes ranged from 1 to 8 young (1Y-292, 2Y-149, 3Y-47, 4Y-8, 5Y-3, 6Y-2, 7Y-2, 8Y-1), with 58% having a single young. Number of young in broods is difficult to determine, especially in large colonies where birds disperse and intermingle over large areas. At 14 days old, young feed themselves, and become independent of their parents at 21 days old (Harrison, C. 1978).

REMARKS: Records from 2 coastal areas are undocumented and considered hypothetical: recent spring and autumn occurrences at Tofino, where Hatler et al. (1978) consider this species hypothetical, and at Hansen Lagoon 28 October 1973-4 (Hazelwood 1973).

Known in the Old World as Black-necked Grebe.

Figure 186. *Adult Eared Grebe constructing nest at Williams Lake, 2 July 1977 (Ervio Sian).*

NOTEWORTHY RECORDS

Spring: Coastal - Victoria 26 Mar 1972-10, 18 Apr 1972-27, 9 May 1951-7; Ganges Harbour 8 and 9 Mar 1972-725 at herring spawn; Pitt Marsh 27 Mar 1973-17, 3 Apr 1973-17, 25 Apr 1973-29. **Interior -** Baynes Lake (Skookumchuk) 28 Apr 1948-10 (Johnstone, W.B. 1949); Alki Lake 20 Apr 1934-18; Okanagan Landing 1 May 1942-60; Swan Lake (Vernon) 20 Apr 1980-10; Little White Lake (70 Mile House) 21 May 1982-1,440 adults; 105 Mile Lake 9 May 1970-22, 20 May 1942-80 (Munro, J.A. and Cowan 1947); Rock Lake (Riske Creek) 5 May 1978-77, 14 May 1978-97; Cecil Lake 3 May 1980-300+, 23 May 1976-1,845.

Summer: Coastal - Clover Point 24 Jul 1958-2; Shoal Bay 6 Aug 1949-3; Bazan Bay 13 Aug 1972-2 (Tatum 1973); Comox 25 Aug 1973-6. **Interior -** Island Lake (Fernie) 25 Jun 1976-12; Kamloops 3 Jul 1978-12; Boundary Lake (Goodlow) 4 Jun 1983-331, no nests noted; Fireside 28 June 1985-1.

Autumn: Interior - Fort St. John 13 Oct 1986-1; Cecil Lake 3 Sep 1982-200+; Murtle Lake (Wells Gray Park) 17 Sep 1959-40 (Edwards and Ritcey 1967); Hanceville 20 Sep 1982-10+; Revelstoke 21 Sep 1977-8; Horn Lake (Penticton) 9 Sep 1919-14. **Coastal -** Oyster Bay 1 Oct 1973-10+; Kitsilano 8 Oct 1974-15+; Ganges Harbour 2 to 3 Nov 1971-400, an extraordinary count (Crowell and Nehls 1972a); Cordova Bay 2 Oct 1976-11, 30 Nov 1986-25; Esquimalt Lagoon 4 Sep 1958-3.

Winter: Interior - Shuswap Lake 30 Dec 1973-5; Okanagan Landing 9 Jan 1960-6; Skaha Lake 1 Jan 1968-1; Trail 4 to 6 Feb 1948-1; **Coastal -** Qualicum Beach 13 Jan 1981-12; Chemainus 7 Jan 1975-15; Ganges Harbour 8 Dec 1972-180.

Christmas Counts: Interior - Recorded from 4 of 19 localities and on 15% of all counts. Maxima: Kelowna 20 Dec 1981-14; Vernon 16 Dec 1984-7;

Shuswap Lake 2 Jan 1982-2. **Coastal -** Recorded from 14 of 28 localities and on 48% of all counts. Maxima: Pender Islands 27 Dec 1980-**461**, all-time Canadian high count (Anderson, R.R. 1981); Victoria 2 Jan 1960-123; Vancouver 26 Dec 1966-50. Jehl and Yochem (1986) suggest that very few Eared Grebes winter coastally in the Pacific Northwest. They state that birds in western Canada probably migrate southward east of the Cascade and Sierra Nevada ranges and stage at Mono Lake [California], before continuing to the Salton Sea or Gulf of California (see Fig. 184). Therefore all large winter numbers, including Christmas Bird Counts, should be treated cautiously.

Extralimital Records: Skidegate 15 Apr 1980-1 (sight record with convincing details).

Western Grebe

WEGR

Aechmophorus occidentalis (Lawrence)

RANGE: Breeds in western North America from southern British Columbia and the Canadian prairie provinces south to Mexico. Winters from southern coastal British Columbia south to central Mexico and on some inland waters.

STATUS: *Common* to *very abundant* spring and autumn migrant across the southern portions of the province. Locally *common* to *very common* along the coast in summer; *rare* in the interior away from colonies. *Very abundant* locally on the south coast in winter; *rare* to locally *very common* in the interior. Local breeder.

NONBREEDING: The Western Grebe is the most gregarious of our grebes and is often found, locally, in large flocks that are either compact or strung out in a long line. It ranges along the coast and in the interior from the Peace Lowlands and Babine Uplands, south across the province. In the interior, most birds use larger lakes, larger sloughs, and backwaters of rivers. On the coast, sheltered salt and brackish waters are preferred, including bays, inlets, harbours, channels, lagoons, and estuaries. Small numbers are frequently found on slow-moving coastal rivers, large sloughs, lakes, and the open ocean, usually within 2 to 3 km of shore.

Spring migration occurs mainly from late April to early May across southern portions of the province. It is far more pronounced in the interior. In some years, the movement may still be evident in early June, with flocks of more than 2,000 birds. In early spring, large flocks of up to 6,000 birds have been found in areas of spawning Pacific herring. Most grebes have left the coast by mid-May.

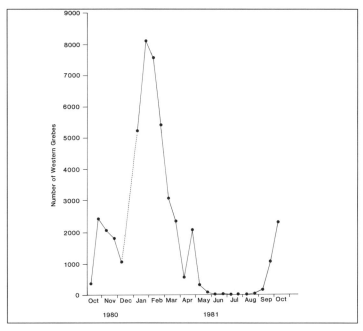

Figure 187. Biweekly counts (averages) of Western Grebes, Comox Harbour to Deep Bay, Vancouver Island, 11 October 1980 to 10 October 1981 (Canadian Wildlife Service unpublished data). The dashed line indicates a period when counts were not made.

Figure 188. A small portion of the largest concentration of Western Grebes ever reported on Christmas Bird Counts in North America: English Bay, 21 December 1969 (R. Wayne Campbell).

Western Grebe

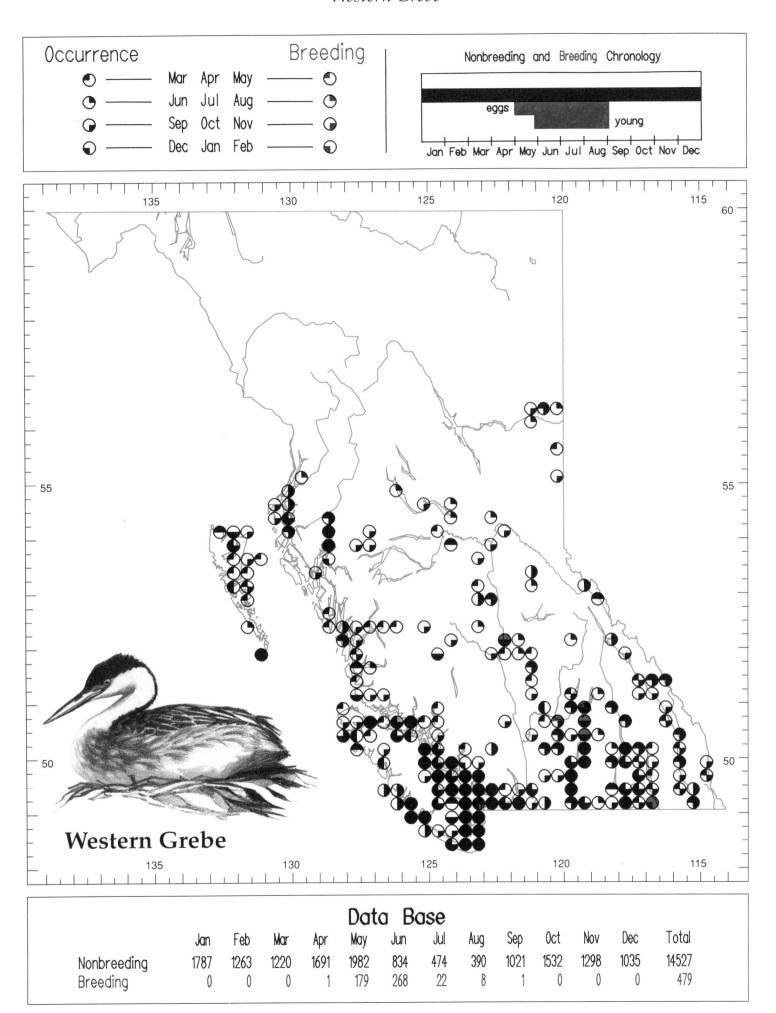

Occurrence

◑	—	Mar	Apr	May	— ◑
◔	—	Jun	Jul	Aug	— ◔
◕	—	Sep	Oct	Nov	— ◕
◑	—	Dec	Jan	Feb	— ◑

Breeding

Nonbreeding and Breeding Chronology

eggs

young

Jan Feb Mar Apr May Jun Jul Aug Sep Oct Nov Dec

Western Grebe

Data Base

	Jan	Feb	Mar	Apr	May	Jun	Jul	Aug	Sep	Oct	Nov	Dec	Total
Nonbreeding	1787	1263	1220	1691	1982	834	474	390	1021	1532	1298	1035	14527
Breeding	0	0	0	1	179	268	22	8	1	0	0	0	479

In summer, flocks, sometimes hundreds of birds, are found along the south coast throughout the Strait of Georgia and Barkley Sound. Smaller numbers occur on larger lakes in the Thompson and Okanagan valleys and the west Kootenay.

The autumn movement may begin as early as late August but is commonly observed from mid-September to mid-October (Fig. 187). At that time, flock sizes may approach 10,000 on the coast and 2,000 in the interior. Numbers build during November and December on the inner south coast where flocks of up to 10,000 birds gather in favourite foraging areas (Fig. 188). In the southern interior, flocks of up to 100 birds may winter on larger, ice-free lakes. The centre of winter abundance is the Strait of Georgia.

Migrants have been recorded from sea level to 1,585 m elevation.

BREEDING: Historically, the Western Grebe has nested at 7 sites in British Columbia (Table 10), of which only 4 remain active: Shuswap Lake, north arm Okanagan Lake, south end Kootenay Lake, and Duck Lake (Creston). The others have disappeared due mainly to industrial development, recreational activities, and unstable water levels. Since habitat still exists but breeding grebes do not, and since the Western Grebe does not appear to move around a lot, it further supports disturbances as the cause of their disappearance from those areas.

The colony at Williams Lake was active for at least 30 years. It was discovered in 1935 (Munro, J.A. 1939b), reached peak numbers in 1941 (Munro, J.A. 1941b) and was last used in 1964 (23 July - 50 adults with 8 young). On 11 August 1971, Riske (1976) censused Williams Lake and found 15 adults but no young or nests. A colony on Kamloops Lake, was used only once in 1973. The colony at Swan Lake (Vernon) was active for at least 45 years. It was discovered in 1933 (Munro, J.A. 1935a), estimated at

40 pairs in the early 1950s, and last suspected of being active in 1978 (Cannings, R.A. et al. 1987). There is one coastal breeding record but the exact nest site is unknown. On 18 September 1986 an adult was observed feeding 2 half-grown young on Westham Island (J. Ireland pers. comm.). There are 4 isolated nesting records without supporting information, here considered hypothetical (see Forbes 1984). The known breeding population today ranges between 182 and 200 pairs (Table 10). Colonies have been located from 300 to 640 m elevation.

The Western Grebe breeds on medium to large lakes, usually with stands of emergent marsh vegetation (e.g. cattail, bulrush, or reed canarygrass - Fig. 189) or flooded shrubs. Other essential requirements for nesting include minimal human disturbance, stable water levels, protection from wind, water deep enough to allow diving, access to open water with substantial fish populations, and a long ice-free period to allow plant growth and breeding (Forbes 1984).

Nests: Nests are usually built in stands of bulrush or cattail but occasionally at the edge of dense patches of willows (Stirling 1964), in open water over stands of water-milfoils (Forbes 1984), or in a grassy marsh. At the Duck Lake colony, mean density of common cattail stems ranged from 1.4 to 16.1 stems/m^2 (Forbes 1984); water depths ranged from 60 to 150 cm.

Nests were large accumulations of vegetation with bases of rotten or decaying vegetation, mostly bulrush, cattail, or reed canarygrass (Fig. 190) and occasionally sticks. The smaller centre platform was often lined with dry stems of emergent vegetation as well as aquatic plants including water-milfoils, buttercups, filamentous algae, and duckweeds. Outside diameters ranged from 38 to 122 cm, with most between 46 and 61 cm. Nest heights ranged from 5 to 15 cm; the depression from 2.5 to 5 cm deep.

Eggs: Human disturbance (e.g. anchored fishermen, power

Figure 189. *Location and habitat of the Western Grebe colony at Shuswap Lake (Salmon Arm), 18 June 1983. The grebes nest amongst the reed canarygrass in the foreground (Ervio Sian).*

Figure 190. *Western Grebe at nest, Shuswap Lake (Salmon Arm), 19 June 1983 (Ervio Sian).*

boating) and changing environmental conditions (e.g. wind, water levels) make it difficult to determine the natural egg-laying period because of forced re-nesting. Clutches have been reported from 29 April (Munro, J.A. 1939b) to 31 August (incubating - Fyfe and Teeple 1968). Egg-laying is synchronous and probably occurs mostly in late May and early June. Sizes for 433 clutches ranged from 1 to 7 eggs (1E-44, 2E-79, 3E-184, 4E-100, 5E-21, 6E-4, 7E-1), with 66% having 3 or 4 eggs. Bent (1919) reports incubation to be "about 23 days" while Lindvall and Low (1982) give a range of 21 to 28 days with an average of 24 days.

Young: Young have been recorded from 5 June (Munro, J.A. 1939b) to 31 August. Calculated dates indicate that young could be found as early as 25 May and as late as September (see Fyfe and Teeple 1968). Under normal conditions, most probably hatch in late June and early July. Sizes for 26 broods ranged from 1 to 4 young (1Y-9, 2Y-13, 3Y-3, 4Y-1) with 13 broods having 2 young. Fledging period is unknown.

REMARKS: The Western Grebe appears on every "Blue List"

from 1973 to 1982 (Tate 1981, Tate and Tate 1982). In the 1980 list, habitat loss was blamed for its current decline, "with more drastic losses predicted in the future" (Arbib 1979). By the 1982 list, the Western Grebe appeared to be "stabilizing at a reduced level" (Tate and Tate 1982). It was delisted to a species of "special concern" in 1986 (Tate 1986).

See Forbes (1985b) for recent studies on feeding ecology.

POSTSCRIPT: On 14 September 1988 a pair of adult Western Grebes, accompanied by 2 less than half-grown, downy young, were seen in a marsh west of the George C. Reifel Bird Sanctuary. On 2 October, presumably the same family group was found in the same area. W.C. Weber (pers. comm.) suggests that occasional pairs probably nest in the brackish marshes off Westham Island.

On 24 March 1989, over 11,000 Western Grebes were counted, in flocks of 4 to 4,000 birds, between Denman Island and French Creek (P.W. Martin pers. comm.). The birds were seaward of huge concentrations of gulls, scoters, and loons where Pacific herring were spawning.

TABLE 10

Western Grebe: location, history, and size of major colonies in British Columbia.

Location	Colony History							
	First Record	Low Survey Results[1]	Year	High Survey Results[1]	Year	Recent Survey Results[1]	Year	Source[2]
Interior - All colonies								
Duck Lake (Creston)	1968	16 N	1968	90 Ac	1982	50 P	1987	1,2
Kamloops Lake	1973			60 P	1973		1973	3,6
Kootenay Lake	1982			4 A	1982		1982	1
Okanagan Lake	1977	18 P	1977	83 Ac	1986		1986	3
Shuswap Lake	1962	26 Nc	1963	65 Nc	1976	C	1987	3
Swan Lake (Vernon)	1933	7 N	1963	40 P	1950	S	1978	3,4,5
Williams Lake	1935	6 N	1949	50 P	1941	E	1965	3

[1] A - active nests; C - nesting confirmed but no count or estimate made; E - colony extinct; N - nests; P - pairs; S - nesting suspected. All data are estimates unless noted as follows: c - complete count.

[2] 1 - Forbes 1984; 2 - Anonymous 1987; 3 - British Columbia Nest Records Scheme; 4 - Cannings, R.A. et al. 1987; 5 - Munro, D.A. 1954; 6 - Forbes 1988.

NOTEWORTHY RECORDS

Spring: Coastal - Saanich 23 Mar 1980-4,000, 22 Apr 1975-2,000; Broken Group 5 Mar 1976-3,000; English Bay 3 Mar 1978-1,000; Belcarra Bay 13 Apr 1974-800; Departure Bay 22 Mar 1938-3,000; Nanoose Harbour 10 Mar 1931-3,500 (Munro, J.A. 1941b); Qualicum Beach 14 Mar 1976-4,800 at Pacific herring spawn (Dawe 1980); Comox 11 Mar 1962-6,000 (Boggs and Boggs 1962c); Sutil Channel 28 Mar 1976-800+, 11 Apr 1976-600; Queen Charlotte City 17 Mar 1976-500; Shingle Bay (Sandspit) 18 Apr 1982 -210; Kitimat 15 Mar 1975-150. **Interior** - Osoyoos Lake 8 Mar 1978-56; Skaha Lake 19 Apr 1978-45, 3 May 1974-400; Balfour 7 May 1950-2,500; Nakusp 5 May 1981-5,000; Lake Windermere 11 May 1981-1,000+; Antlers Beach Park 11 May 1979-300; Kelowna 4 May 1978-1,519; Okanagan Landing 28 Apr 1941-1,500, 9 May 1940-4,500 (Munro, J.A. 1941b); Chapperon Lake 10 May 1981-1,000; Green Lake (70 Mile House) 28 Apr 1939-200 (Munro, J.A. 1941b); Lac la Hache 12 May 1981-200+; Williams Lake 4 May 1970-120; Puntchesakut Lake 24 May 1944-31 (Munro, J.A. 1947a); Swan Lake (Tupper) 7 May 1938-30 (Cowan 1939).

Summer: Coastal - Baeria Rocks 4 Jun 1970-140 (Hatler et al. 1978), 7 Aug 1972-150; Cowichan Bay summer 1970-60 (Tatum 1971); Satellite Channel 9

Jun 1980-95; Iona Island 10 Jun 1976-325; English Bay 1 Jun 1971-800 (Campbell et al. 1972b); Point Grey Beach 3 Aug 1980-100; Oyster Bay 22 Aug 1938-150; Heriot Bay 14 Jun 1924-100 (Pearse 1926). **Interior** - Kootenay River mouth 31 Aug 1968-150; Nicola Lake 2 Jun 1980-65; Shuswap Lake (Salmon Arm) 10 Jun 1977-140, 5 Aug 1951-150, 28 Aug 1970-200+; Cecil Lake 23 Jun 1986-2.

Autumn: Interior - Charlie Lake 7 Oct 1984-14, 27 Oct 1985-1; Eaglet Lake 22 Nov 1987-2; Kinbasket Lake 6 Oct 1951-1,400 (Munro, J.A. 1954); Shuswap Lake 24 Sep 1970-200+; Nicola Lake 12 Oct 1974-2,000; Trout Creek Point 14 Sep 1964-1,000, 22 Sep 1971-200, 2 Nov 1973-75; Golden 4 Oct 1951-300; Argenta 2 Sep 1976-250; Moyie Lake 2 Oct 1951-210; Osprey Lake (Princeton) 4 Oct 1953-300+. **Coastal** - Ocean Falls 29 Sep 1968-80; Campbell River 20 Oct 1975-9,045; Oyster Bay 24 Sep 1976-1,800+, 1 Oct 1976-6,000+, 10 Oct 1976-7,500+, 13 Oct 1976-8,000+; Comox 7 Sep 1949-1,500 an early migration date (Flahaut 1950a); Qualicum Beach 4 Nov 1987-1,674; Hesquiat Harbour 5 Oct 1972-1,705; Nanoose Harbour 24 Oct 1962-5,000; Iona Island 29 Sep 1973-1,500; White Rock 2 Oct 1978-3,000; Vancouver 30 Sep 1972-800, 2 Oct 1972-1,500+, 16 Oct 1968-1,830, 17 Nov 1973-4,000; Satellite

Channel 6 Oct 1974-1,000+, 15 Nov 1973-2,500; Mill Bay (Duncan) 24 Sep 1982-800, 18 Nov 1980-2,500.

Winter: Interior - Williams Lake 7 Dec 1987-1; Kalamalka Lake 29 Dec 1969-30; Okanagan Lake (Penticton) 4 Dec 1973-51, 1 Jan 1980-18; Taghum to Balfour 7 Dec 1980-94; Duck Lake (Creston) 1 Jan 1981-26 (Butler, R.W. et al. 1986). **Coastal** - Queen Charlotte City 24 Feb 1972-150; Kaien Island 25 Feb 1975-46; Quatsino Sound 14 Feb 1973-819; Comox 7 Dec 1924-1,000+; Baynes Sound 17 Dec 1975-2,230, 22 Jan 1976-2,700; Port Alberni 2 Jan 1976-850; English Bay 6 Jan 1979-2,000; Burrard Inlet 10 Jan 1971-2,000; Semiahmoo Bay 22 Feb 1980-1,400; Satellite Channel 23 Dec 1974-1,500, 23 Jan 1974-1,900, 31 Jan 1980-6,000; Crofton 4 Dec 1977-2,000; Ganges Harbour Jan 1972-1,722.

Christmas Counts: Interior - Recorded from 8 of 19 localities and on 41% of all counts. Maxima: Vernon 18 Dec 1983-76; Shuswap Lake 22 Dec 1979-41; Penticton 27 Dec 1982-25. **Coastal** - Recorded from 25 of 28 localities and on 82% of all counts. Maxima: Vancouver 21 Dec 1969-15,450 (see Fig. 188), all-time North American high count (Monroe 1973); Deep Bay 27 Dec 1983-15,174; Duncan 19 Dec 1981-7,215.

Black-footed Albatross

Diomedea nigripes Audubon

BFAL

RANGE: Breeds on western Hawaiian Islands and on Torishima, off Japan. Ranges throughout the north Pacific Ocean.

STATUS: *Fairly common* to *common* visitant from spring to early autumn along the outer coast; *uncommon* the rest of the year.

OCCURRENCE: The Black-footed Albatross is the only albatross seen regularly off the coast. It is widely scattered in offshore waters and is only occasionally seen inshore (e.g. Strait of Georgia, Queen Charlotte Strait). Although it occurs throughout the year, it is most numerous from April through September (Fig. 191), when it is regularly encountered from the 140 m depth contour to the edge of the continental shelf.

Martin and Myres (1969) indicate that the Black-footed Albatross increases in abundance off Vancouver Island as the summer progresses, and also that its behaviour changes with the season. In the spring, they show little or no interest either in trolling boats or in each other. As the summer advances, they are more and more inclined to follow fishing vessels picking up scraps of offal discarded from the dressing tables of long line and trolling vessels. They also tend to congregate in pairs and small parties. This gregarious tendency increases, until by the middle of August, aggregations of up to 20 birds, are commonly seen when the sea is calm.

Wahl (1975) also reports peak numbers and aggregations of the Black-footed Albatross during the autumn, offshore from Washington. Those changes in behaviour and numbers are probably related to birds returning to the breeding grounds, a movement which, according to Palmer, R.S. (1962), takes place in late September and October.

Flocks are rare and generally small, except in the vicinity of commercial fishing vessels and large ships where garbage dumped into the sea may attract aggregations of several hundred albatrosses. Natural concentrations, usually of less than 20 birds, occur in areas of high biotic productivity which are characteristically rich in nutrients and have lower water temperatures (Thompson, D.Q. 1951).

The winter distribution of the birds is poorly known. At Ocean Weather Station PAPA (1958 to 1981) the Black-footed Albatross was no more abundant than the Laysan Albatross from mid-December through mid-March (M.T. Myres pers. comm.). Sanger (1972b) considers the species "common off Vancouver Island" in pelagic waters in December, January, and February, but later indicates that winter distribution in the entire northeastern Pacific still remains poorly known (Sanger 1974a). There are only 3 offshore winter records for the province.

REMARKS: During the nineteenth century the Black-footed Albatross was much more common than at present. Human disturbance at breeding colonies has virtually confined the species to the Leeward chain of the Hawaiian Islands. Rice (1959)

estimates the world population in 1957-58 at 300,000, of which about 160,000 were of breeding age.

The Black-footed Albatross, being essentially a surface feeder, is usually attracted to any floating object. Plastic and aluminum objects discarded at sea are cause for concern as they are picked up by the birds as food. Two birds, washed ashore at Long Beach in autumn, 1971, were grossly underweight and contained 17 man-made objects in their stomachs.

All dead birds should be examined for leg bands. One bird, found off Kyuquot in September 1969, was banded as a nestling near Sand Island, Midway, on 7 March 1967 (Hatler et al. 1978). Young birds leave the breeding grounds in July and wander the oceans for up to 9 years before returning to breed in mid-October (Rice 1959).They may, however, return to the colony as non-breeders when 3 to 4 years old.

Figure 191. *Part of flock of 62 Black-footed Albatrosses 6 km west of Kiokathli Inlet, Queen Charlotte Islands, 11 June 1988 (R. Wayne Campbell).*

NOTEWORTHY RECORDS

Spring: Coastal - Juan de Fuca Strait 20 Mar 1967-1 followed ferry from Victoria to Port Angeles, Washington (Crowell and Nehls 1967b); 21 km w Barkley Sound 23 Apr 1973-4, 20 and 21 May 1973-6; 24 km w Tofino 2 May 1970-5 (Campbell and Shepard 1971); 26 km w Goose Group 18 May 1948-4; 50 km e Kunghit Island 30 May 1982-287 feeding on dumped garbage; 30 km nw Gowgaia Bay 17 May 1986-27 feeding on popcorn (Campbell 1986e); 2 km w Louscoone Inlet 25 May 1986-40 at troller; Reef Island 14 May 1985-1. **Interior** - No records.

Summer: Coastal - Satellite Channel 5 Aug 1957-1; 40 km w Ucluelet 9 Jun 1958-80 feeding on fish offal; Queen Charlotte Sound 16 Jun 1970-100 near a trawler, 26 Jul 1967-15, 11 Aug 1970-20; 51°12'N, 129°36'W 9 Jun 1970-90 feeding on ship garbage; 51°16'N, 129°29'W 10 Jun 1970-140; 51°18'N, 129°22'W 11 Jun 1970-150; 51°19'N, 129°21'W 12 Jun 1970-280 feeding on fish offal; 10 km nw Virgin Rocks 26 Jul 1967-12. **Interior** - No records.

Autumn: Interior - No records. **Coastal** - 24 km w Tofino 13 Sep 1969-125 (Crowell and Nehls 1970a);

La Perouse Bank 2 Sep 1984-15, 1 Oct 1977-17, 14 Oct 1978-4.

Winter: Interior - No records. **Coastal** - 30 km sw Kyuquot Sound 2 Dec 1981-1; 40 km w Estevan Point 22 to 24 Feb 1971-4 (Crowell and Nehls 1971b); 20 km sw Pachena Point 18 Dec 1973-1.

Christmas Counts: Not recorded.

Extralimital Records: e Nanaimo 13 Jun 1900-1 (RBCM 1490) - not 13 June 1904 as listed by Munro, J.A.and Cowan 1947).

Black-footed Albatross

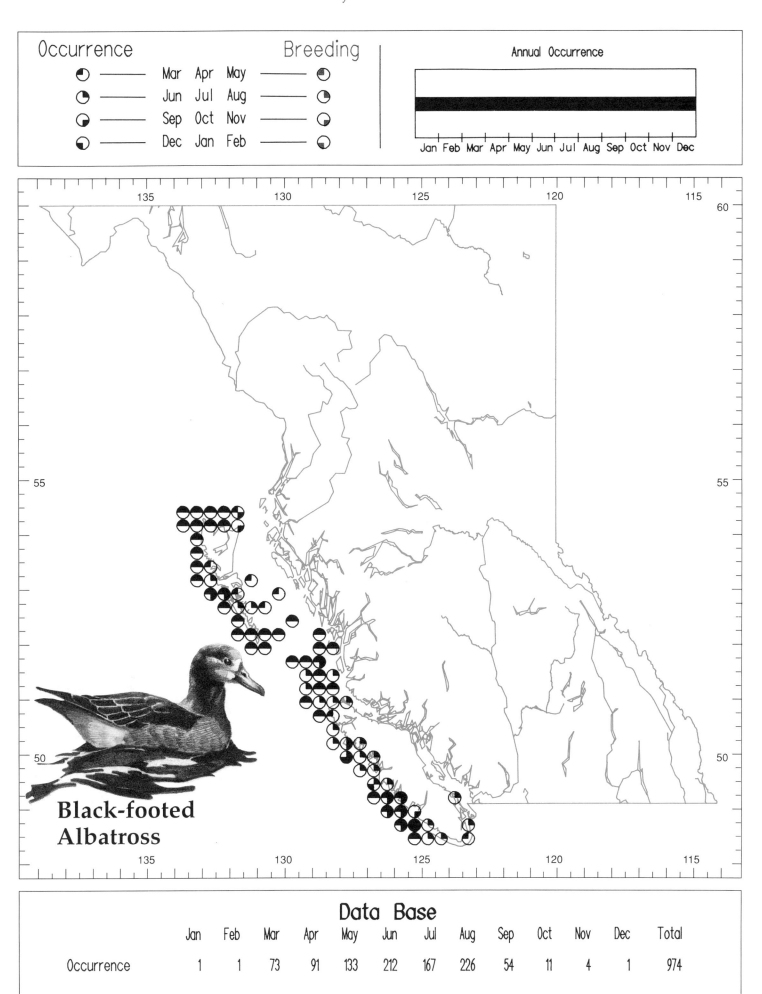

Occurrence

Breeding

	Mar	Apr	May
	Jun	Jul	Aug
	Sep	Oct	Nov
	Dec	Jan	Feb

Annual Occurrence

Jan Feb Mar Apr May Jun Jul Aug Sep Oct Nov Dec

Black-footed Albatross

Data Base

	Jan	Feb	Mar	Apr	May	Jun	Jul	Aug	Sep	Oct	Nov	Dec	Total
Occurrence	1	1	73	91	133	212	167	226	54	11	4	1	974

Laysan Albatross

Diomedea immutabilis Rothschild

LAAL

RANGE: Breeds on the Hawaiian Islands and recently at Bonin Island south of Japan (Hasegawa 1978). Ranges widely throughout the north Pacific Ocean.

STATUS: *Very rare* vagrant along the outer coast.

OCCURRENCE: Although the Laysan Albatross is more numerous than the Black-footed Albatross (Rice and Kenyon 1962), it is less frequently seen at sea throughout the eastern north Pacific Ocean. It is more pelagic (Sanger 1972b) and widely distributed, but follows ships less frequently and is therefore encountered less often. Birds that occur off British Columbia are probably wanderers on the edge of a much larger pelagic movement (Sanger 1974b).

The Laysan Albatross was not observed in Canada until 1968. Since then, it has been recorded in offshore and pelagic waters off British Columbia on 14 occasions, 11 from the west coast of Vancouver Island and 3 from off the Queen Charlotte Islands.

Most records are of single birds seen between February and October. The lack of records in November, December, and January may be partly due to the southward withdrawal to their breeding grounds in mid-October (Rice 1959), and partly to poor observer coverage, as nonbreeders are scattered over the North Pacific throughout the year. Young disperse from breeding colonies in August. Wahl (1975) considers the Laysan Albatross "probably uncommon in winter, uncommon to rare in late summer" off Washington. At Ocean Weather Station PAPA, Laysan Albatrosses have been recorded every month of the year, but with greatest regularity from mid-January to May and mid-September to the end of October (M.T. Myres pers. comm.).

All records, listed in chronological order, are as follows:

(1) La Perouse Bank September 1968-1 (Campbell and Shepard 1973).
(2) 40 km w Ucluelet (48°26'N, 125°40'W) 17 August 1970-1 (Campbell and Shepard 1973).
(3) 40 km w Estevan Point 24 February 1971-1 (RBCM Photo 149; Fig. 192). The photograph was published in *American Birds* (Crowell and Nehls 1971b).

(4) 8 km w northern end Vancouver Island (Cook Bank) 26 October 1971-1 (RBCM Photo 225; Campbell and Shepard 1973).
(5) w Brooks Bay 30 October 1973-1.
(6) 23 km w Tofino 21 May 1981-1.
(7) Long Beach 22 June 1981-1 freshly dead bird washed ashore (RBCM 18273).
(8) w Tasu Sound 25 July 1982-1.
(9) 32 km w Rennell Sound 22 April 1984-1.
(10) 40 km sw Amphitrite Point 11 September 1984-1.
(11) 40 km w Kyuquot Channel 6 March 1986-2. One found caught on a halibut long-line about 16 km west of Hotsprings Cove (RBCM 18957; Campbell 1986a) and preserved.
(12) sw La Perouse Bank 15 March 1986-1 (RBCM Photo 1091; Fig. 193).
(13) 77 km sw Cox Point (Tofino) 11 June 1986-1.
(14) 12 km s Cape St. James 8 September 1987-1 (Campbell 1988a).

REMARKS: There is an additional record of a beached bird from Anthony Island, June 1986. It consisted of skeletal remains, which suggests that it probably washed ashore in late spring.

In the past, large numbers of Laysan Albatrosses were killed for their feathers. Also, between 1955 and 1964, about 54,000 were killed during United States Navy control programs (Fisher, H.I. 1966). As a result, some breeding colonies were extirpated (Rice and Kenyon 1962). During the past 15 years, however, populations have been increasing and some recolonization is occurring both in the Hawaiian Islands (Harrison, C.S. et al 1984) and on the Bonin Islands south of Japan (Hasegawa 1978; Kurata 1978).

The world population in 1957-58 was estimated to be 1,500,000 of which about 800,000 were breeding-age birds (Rice 1959).

POSTSCRIPT:
(15) 1.6 km s Anthony Island 29 May 1988-1 with 3 Black-footed Albatrosses.

Figure 192. Laysan Albatross, the first documented Canadian record, 48°00'N, 127°01'W, 24 February 1971 (RBCM Photo 149; R. Wayne Campbell).

Figure 193. Laysan Albatross, southwest of La Perouse Bank, 15 March 1986 (RBCM Photo 1091; Philip Lambert).

Laysan Albatross

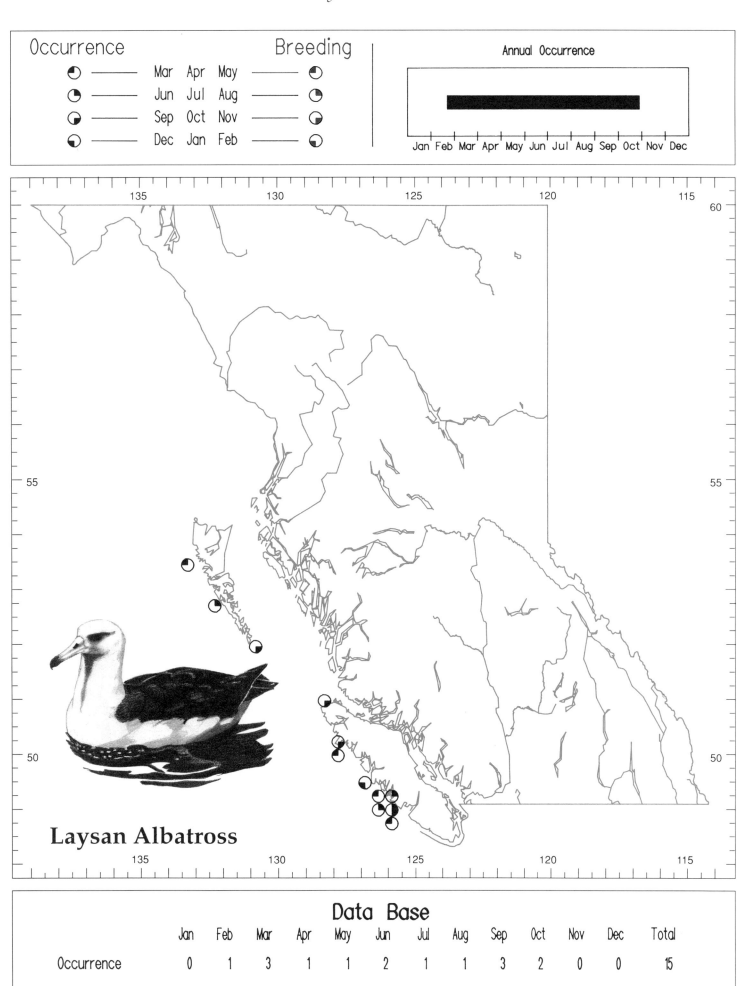

Occurrence

◑ ———	Mar	Apr	May
◔ ———	Jun	Jul	Aug
◕ ———	Sep	Oct	Nov
◕ ———	Dec	Jan	Feb

Breeding

Mar Apr May	———	◑
Jun Jul Aug	———	◔
Sep Oct Nov	———	◕
Dec Jan Feb	———	◕

Annual Occurrence

Jan Feb Mar Apr May Jun Jul Aug Sep Oct Nov Dec

Laysan Albatross

Data Base

	Jan	Feb	Mar	Apr	May	Jun	Jul	Aug	Sep	Oct	Nov	Dec	Total
Occurrence	0	1	3	1	1	2	1	1	3	2	0	0	15

Northern Fulmar

NOFU

Fulmarus glacialis (Linnaeus)

RANGE: Breeds in the north Pacific Ocean from the Alaska peninsula and Aleutian Islands into the Bering Sea. Winters south to California. Another population breeds in the Canadian Arctic, Greenland, Iceland, and northern Eurasia, and winters offshore south to northern France and the central east coast of the United States.

STATUS: Probably *common* visitant offshore in winter and *fairly common* at other times of the year. Locally *abundant*. *Very rare* in inner coastal areas.

OCCURRENCE: The Northern Fulmar occurs regularly throughout the year in offshore waters. It is occasionally seen from shore. It prefers cold waters (3.5 to 7°C - Kuroda 1960); with high salinity (32.14 to 32.73‰- Sanger 1970). Large flocks occur locally in areas of upwelling (e.g. La Perouse Bank), along lines of convergence, and other areas of turbulence (e.g. Rose Spit). Other concentrations are associated with offal discarded from commercial fishing vessels. Fulmars enter Hecate Strait, Queen Charlotte Strait, and Juan de Fuca Strait infrequently; they are casual in the Strait of Georgia.

Although fulmars are present offshore throughout the year, their seasonal status is not well known. Records indicate they are most often seen from June to September, the period when most observers are in the field. An accurate status designation is further complicated by the lack of regular long-term censuses, the solitary behaviour of fulmars except when food is locally plentiful, and their irregular "flight years" (Jehl 1973a; Wahl 1975).

Sanger (1970) reports that numbers and records off Washington and Oregon are at a maximum in winter and a minimum in summer. Wahl (1975) considers the Northern Fulmar as "common in winter well offshore, with numbers decreasing in spring and variable numbers seen at fishing vessels in July and into fall". At Ocean Weather Station PAPA, fulmars are most abundant from December through March but are also found there from May to July. Numbers are low in April and again in August and September. Winter numbers vary greatly from year to year (M.T. Myers pers. comm.). British Columbia information suggests similar seasonal cycles in abundance. There may be, however, a pronounced dispersal to and from northern breeding colonies in the spring and autumn. Martin and Myres (1969) note "an apparent decrease in numbers . . . during the spring and early summer, followed by an increase in late summer" off Vancouver Island and the Goose Group banks.

Exhausted fulmars frequently wash up on beaches after storms. The main storm season occurs from October to February; most birds have been found in November and December.

REMARKS: The Northern Fulmar has 3 disjunct populations. One (*F. g. rodgersii*) occurs in the north Pacific Ocean. In the Atlantic Ocean, birds are separated into 2 distinct populations: *F .g. glacialis* and *F. g. auduboni*.

The Northern Fulmar is polymorphic. The subspecies *F. g. rodgersii*, which breeds from Siberia to Alaska and occurs as a nonbreeding wanderer off British Columbia, exhibits greater extremes of colour variation than the other 2 races (Palmer, R.S. 1962). Four plumage categories have been described by Fisher, J. (1952): double light, light, dark, and double dark. In the Pacific population, white birds (double light and light) breed mainly in northern regions (e.g. St. Matthew Island) and dark birds (dark and double dark) in the southern regions (e.g. Commander Islands; Palmer, R.S. 1962; Shuntov 1974). The distribution at sea of those colour morphs is poorly known; all have been observed off British Columbia in every month of the year. Examination of 229 records (specimens and observations) shows 52% double dark, 26% dark, and 22% light and double light plumage birds. Records are too few to evaluate seasonal variation in plumage for British Columbia birds. Wahl (1975) estimates that off Washington about 10% of the birds are light or double light.

While nonbreeding birds frequently loaf on colonies outside their breeding range, the following observations suggest that the Northern Fulmar may breed on Triangle Island, off the northwestern tip of Vancouver Island. Up to 9 adults, mostly double dark birds, have been seen on cliffs since 1974 when nesting was first suspected (Vermeer et al. 1976b). Birds have been seen there as early as 12 May and as late as 9 September. On 3 June 1976, as many as 6 adults were seen on nests, and on 26 June, 3 adults remained on their nests until disturbed by a helicopter landing. Nest contents could not be determined (K.R. Summers pers. comm.). On 24 June 1977, a pair was watched courting on an old Pelagic Cormorant nest, and 3 possible nest sites were occupied. The nests could not be checked for eggs or young. Breeding remains unconfirmed.

The Northern Fulmar was previously known as Fulmar.

NOTEWORTHY RECORDS

Spring: Coastal - La Perouse Bank 25 Mar 1946-12+ (Martin and Myres 1969); w Tofino 15 May 1970-11 (Campbell and Shepard 1971); s Triangle Island (Scott Islands) 23 May 1978-9; Queen Charlotte Sound 1 Apr 1976-18; 5 km w Flamingo Inlet 17 May 1986-14; s Reef Island 28 May 1986-10 flying south with hundreds of Sooty Shearwaters. **Interior** - No records.

Summer: Coastal - Oak Bay 19 Jul 1962-2 feeding with Bonaparte's Gulls and Heermann's Gulls; w Ucluelet 24 Jul 1984-700; La Perouse Bank 13 to 15 Aug 1946-flocks of up to 15 (Martin and Myres 1969); w Ucluelet 31 Aug 1986-1,000 counted on birding trip (Mattocks and Harrington-Tweit 1987b); w Tofino 31 Jul 1971-35 counted on birding trip (Campbell and Shepard 1972); w of Rugged Point 22 Jun 1975-4; Queen Charlotte

Strait 1 Jul 1969-7; Cox and Lanz Islands 5 Jul 1986-100+, all single dark birds; Queen Charlotte Sound 26 Jul 1967-19 (Crowell and Nehls 1967c), 11 Aug 1970-36 (Crowell and Nehls 1971a); 30 km e Cape St. James 5 Aug 1986-100; 6 km w Louscoone Inlet 15 Jun 1986-9; White Point (Cape Knox) 3 Jun 1975-9; 16 km n Masset Sound 13 Aug 1957-14 (Mills 1960a); n Rose Spit 11 Jul 1975-200. **Interior** - No records.

Autumn: Interior - No records. **Coastal** - n Masset 26 Oct 1953-2 (RBCM 10253, 10254); w Tofino 5 Sep 1982-50+; Long Beach 31 Oct 1981-25 washed ashore (UBC 14241, 14247), 16 Nov 1981-4 washed ashore dead; La Perouse Bank 3 and 4 Sep 1983-800, 5 Sep 1982-50, 26 Sep 1981-50; w Bamfield 1 Oct 1977-8 (Shepard, M.G. 1978), 9 Nov 1969-2; e Chemainus Nov 1895-1 specimen

(Fannin 1898); e Duncan 7 Oct 1981-1 (RBCM 17266); Bamberton 29 Nov 1986-1 found dead. Haro Strait 23 Oct 1983-9, 22 Nov 1981-15 to 20; Victoria 27 Nov 1973-1 struck a downtown building (Crowell and Nehls 1974a); s Clover Point 26 Oct 1963-6.

Winter: Interior - No records. **Coastal** - Hecate Strait 28 Feb 1983-41; 40 km w Estevan Point 22 to 24 Feb 1971-54 (Crowell and Nehls 1971b); 11 km s Carmanah Point 11 Dec 1975-6; La Perouse Bank 13 Feb 1977-23; Bazan Bay 15 Dec 1973-1; Haro Strait 19 Feb 1982-3; s Clover Point 22 Jan 1972-7 (Tatum 1973); s Race Rocks 29 Jan 1982-3.

Christmas Counts: Interior - Not recorded. **Coastal** - Recorded once: Victoria 27 Dec 1964-1.

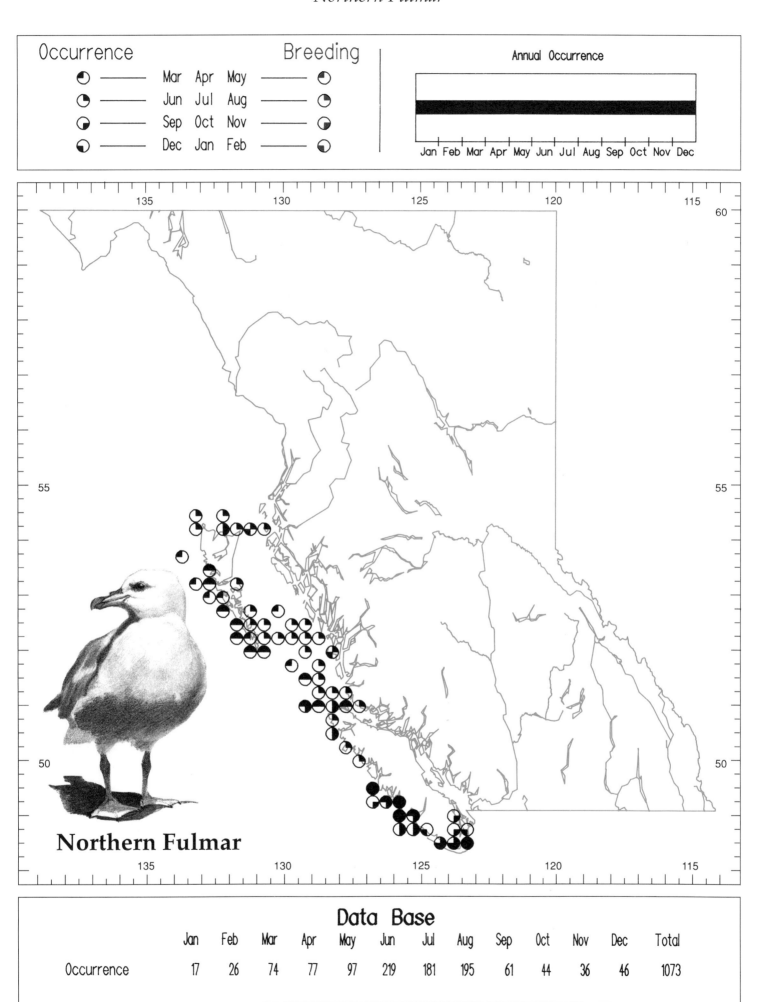

Occurrence

◑	———	Mar	Apr	May	———	◑
◔	———	Jun	Jul	Aug	———	◔
◕	———	Sep	Oct	Nov	———	◕
◕	———	Dec	Jan	Feb	———	◕

Breeding

Annual Occurrence

Jan Feb Mar Apr May Jun Jul Aug Sep Oct Nov Dec

Northern Fulmar

Data Base

	Jan	Feb	Mar	Apr	May	Jun	Jul	Aug	Sep	Oct	Nov	Dec	Total
Occurrence	17	26	74	77	97	219	181	195	61	44	36	46	1073

Pink-footed Shearwater

PFSH

Puffinus creatopus Coues

RANGE: Breeds on islands off Chile, migrating north offshore along the Pacific coast of South and North America.

STATUS: *Rare* in spring, *fairly common* to *common* in summer and autumn along the outer coast. Locally, *very common* at times.

OCCURRENCE: The Pink-footed Shearwater, the province's second most numerous shearwater, tends to stay well offshore and is rarely seen from land. Guzman and Myres (1983), during pelagic surveys off British Columbia, found this large shearwater to be rare inside the 90 m depth contour. Wahl (1975) indicates that, off Washington, Pink-footed Shearwaters are mostly seen beyond the 70 m contour.

The Pink-footed Shearwater can be either solitary or gregarious and often associates with other shearwaters, especially Sooty Shearwaters. It congregates in good feeding areas (e.g. La Perouse Bank) in flocks of up to 300 birds. It has been recorded from 26 April to 14 October, with 85% of all records occuring from July through September, the period when birds gradually return to their southern breeding grounds. Fledging and dispersal from colonies begins in March and April (Harrison, P. 1983); most spring migrants appear in British Columbia waters in May and June.

REMARKS: The Pink-footed Shearwater and the Flesh-footed Shearwater *(P. carneipes)* constitute a superspecies but are sometimes considered to be conspecific (American Ornithologists' Union 1983).

See Schlatter (1984) for details of distribution, abundance, population trends, and threats to world populations of the Pink-footed Shearwater, all of which breed in Chile.

NOTEWORTHY RECORDS

Spring: Coastal - w Pachena Point 22 May 1946-1; 30 to 35 km sw Cape Beale 26 Apr 1974-1; w Cape Beale 31 May 1948-1; w Clayoquot Sound 5 May 1946-1 (all Martin and Myres 1969); w Kyuquot 28 Apr 1940-1 (Martin 1942); Rennell Sound 25 May 1983-2 with 15 Sooty Shearwaters. **Interior** - No records.

Summer: Coastal - 65 km sw Ucluelet 29 Aug 1968-30; La Perouse Bank Aug 1949-flocks of up to 20 (Martin and Myres 1969); Long Beach 27 Jul 1983-6; w Tofino 29 July 1972-12 in flock; w Solander Island 27 Aug 1967-6; nw Vancouver Island 27 Aug 1968-8 (Crowell and Nehls 1968d); 19 km s Goose Group 17 Aug 1948-10 (Guiguet 1953a); 16 km s Gowgaia Bay 8 Aug 1957-1 (Mills 1960a); w Portland Bay 9 Aug 1957-1 (Mills 1960a); 16 km n Masset Sound 13 Aug 1957-1 (Mills 1960a); n Rose Spit 11 July 1975-1. **Interior** - No records.

Autumn: Interior - No records. **Coastal** - 16 km e Reef Island 3 Sep 1946-1 (Munro, J.A. and Cowan 1947); w Tofino 4 Sep 1983-300 (Campbell 1983d), 12 Sep 1970-21, 13 Sep 1969-125 (Campbell and Shepard 1971); Swiftsure Bank 4 Sep 1949-20+ (Martin and Myres 1969); La Perouse Bank 2 Sep 1984-120, 3 Sep 1983-100, 4 Sep 1983-300, 26 Sep 1981-50, 1 Oct 1977-6, 14 Oct 1978-1.

Winter: No records.

Extralimital Records: s Clover Point 22 Sep 1958-1 with 500 Sooty Shearwaters after a storm.

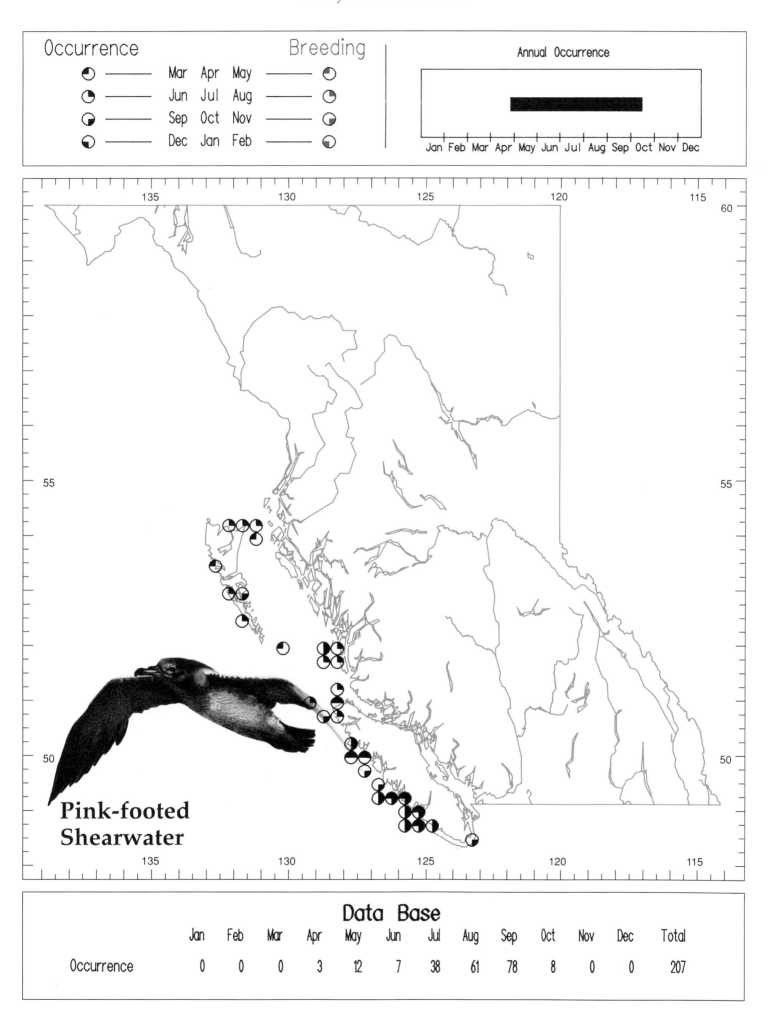

Occurrence

Mar Apr May
Jun Jul Aug
Sep Oct Nov
Dec Jan Feb

Breeding

Annual Occurrence

Jan Feb Mar Apr May Jun Jul Aug Sep Oct Nov Dec

**Pink-footed
Shearwater**

Data Base

	Jan	Feb	Mar	Apr	May	Jun	Jul	Aug	Sep	Oct	Nov	Dec	Total
Occurrence	0	0	0	3	12	7	38	61	78	8	0	0	207

Flesh-footed Shearwater

FFSH

Puffinus carneipes Gould

RANGE: Breeds on islands off Australia and New Zealand; part of population winters in north Pacific Ocean.

STATUS: *Rare* to *uncommon* summer and autumn visitant offshore.

OCCURRENCE: The Flesh-footed Shearwater was first recorded near the British Columbia coast in 1937 (Martin 1942), and has remained an uncommon but regular visitor in offshore waters. Guzman and Myres (1983) indicate that in spring, no birds were seen closer inshore than between the 90 and 180 m depth contours. The paucity of records for the northern half of the coast, including the Queen Charlotte Islands, may simply reflect lack of observer effort since the species ranges into the Bering Sea and Gulf of Alaska (Kessel and Gibson 1978).

The Flesh-footed Shearwater is a transequatorial migrant with populations in 2 main localities. Serventy et al. (1971) recognize 2 subspecies, *P. c. carneipes* of western Australia and *P. c. hullianus* of New Zealand, which migrate to separate regions. The latter race is apparently the one that winters in the north Pacific Ocean. The same authors mention that along the western side of North America the bird prefers to keep to warm waters; some birds, probably immatures, may even winter off California. Adults return to breeding grounds in late September and disperse in late April and early May.

The Flesh-footed Shearwater has been recorded near the British Columbia coast from 2 May to 14 October. Although numbers apparently vary between years (Wahl 1975), the main movement along the British Columbia coast probably occurs in mid-summer. Most observations are of 1 or 2 birds, but flocks of up to 60 have been seen on the Goose Group banks off northern Vancouver Island (Martin and Myres 1969). At sea, they may be more gregarious. Unlike the Sooty Shearwater, the Flesh-footed Shearwater readily follows commercial fishing vessels and may even dive for offal thrown overboard. It is quite capable of "bringing the viscera of a 30 lb. salmon to the surface" (Martin and Myres 1969). Seldom, however, do they come close to the boats.

REMARKS: The Flesh-footed Shearwater, formerly called the Pale-footed Shearwater, is considered by some authors to be conspecific with the Pink-footed Shearwater.

NOTEWORTHY RECORDS

Spring: Coastal - w Tofino 2 May 1970-2+ (Campbell and Shepard 1971), 8 May 1971-2 (Campbell and Shepard 1972). **Interior** - No records.

Summer: Coastal - La Perouse Bank 14 Jul 1946-2 (Martin and Myres 1969), 24 Jul 1984-2; w Tofino 31 Jul 1971-1 (Campbell and Shepard 1972); w Cape Scott 15 Jul 1940-1 (Martin 1942); w Triangle Island (Scott Islands) 28 and 29 Jun 1946-8 (Martin and Myres 1969); Goose Group banks in 1948, 10 Jun-25, 13 Jun-50 to 60, 27 Jul-25, 3 Aug-15, 14 Aug-4, 17 Aug-1, early Jul 1946-flocks of up to 30 seen (Martin and Myres 1969); 24 km n Tow Hill Jul 1957-1 (Mills 1960a). **Interior** - No records.

Autumn: Interior - No records. **Coastal** - 19 km w Tofino 13 Sep 1969-2 (Crowell and Nehls 1970a); 40 km w Bamfield 14 Oct 1978-1; La Perouse Bank 2 Sep 1984-1, 4 Sep 1983-2+.

Winter: No records.

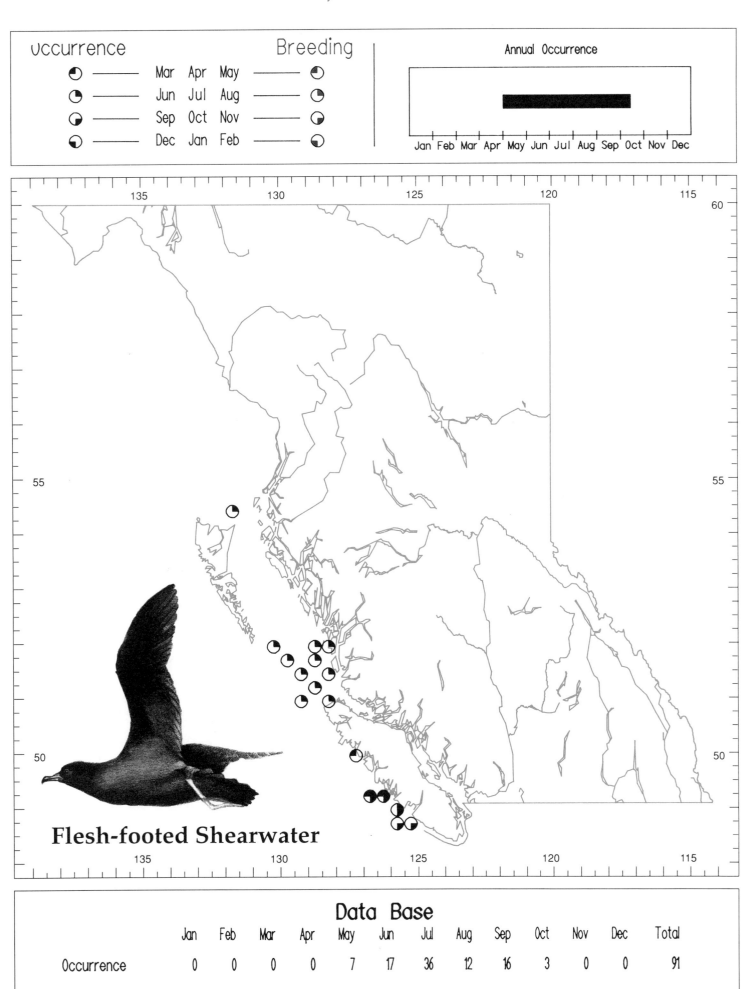

Flesh-footed Shearwater

	Jan	Feb	Mar	Apr	May	Jun	Jul	Aug	Sep	Oct	Nov	Dec	Total
Occurrence	0	0	0	0	7	17	36	12	16	3	0	0	91

Buller's Shearwater

Puffinus bulleri Salvin

RANGE: Breeds in New Zealand area and disperses to north Pacific Ocean during nonbreeding season.

STATUS: *Very rare* visitant in summer, variably *fairly common* to *common* autumn migrant offshore. At times locally *very common*.

CHANGE IN STATUS: The Buller's Shearwater was formerly considered hypothetical in British Columbia (Munro, J.A. and Cowan 1947; Godfrey 1966) on the basis of 2 birds seen in pelagic waters off the northern end of Vancouver Island on 7 August 1926 (Nichols 1927). Presumably due to a massive population expansion in their New Zealand breeding grounds during the past 2 decades (Bartle 1968; Jenkins 1969, 1974), numbers of Buller's Shearwaters have recently appeared in the northwestern and northeastern Pacific Ocean. Birds were first recorded in southeastern Alaska in the autumn of 1974, and they became regular fall visitors off the Washington coast during the 1970s (Mattocks et al. 1976).

This gray and white shearwater was first reported close to the British Columbia coast off Tofino on 13 September 1969. The following year, a specimen was collected on 26 September 40 km west of Tofino (UBC 13571; Campbell 1971a). Since then, Buller's Shearwaters have been seen regularly, mostly in autumn, off the west coast of Vancouver Island.

OCCURRENCE: Buller's Shearwaters leave their breeding colonies in April and return in late August and September (Serventy et al. 1971). Recent surveys by Wahl (1985) indicate that the birds arrive in subarctic waters in June and slowly expand northward and eastward as far as the Gulf of Alaska by August. The mid-ocean distribution after August is poorly known. Many birds, presumably nonbreeders, occur along the west coast of North America, at least from British Columbia to southern California, until late October or early November. They have been reported off the entire outer coast of the province between 1 July and 8 November; nearly 64% of records are from September. The species is apparently more numerous off Washington than off British Columbia (see Wahl 1975). In autumn, there appear to be 2 peak movements off Washington state: 7 to 11 September and 3 to 15 October (Guzman and Myres 1983). These peaks, however, may be artifacts of the peaks of pelagic censuses. No comparable data exist for British Columbia.

Numbers vary from year to year along the west coast of North America, apparently governed by water temperature and salinity (Harrison, P. 1983). During pelagic birding trips off Washington from 1966 to 1975, peak numbers of Buller's Shearwaters were noted in the autumns of 1970 and 1973 (Wahl 1975). The largest number (93) reported off British Columbia was in autumn 1977.

Buller's Shearwaters are usually seen flying individually or in loose groups, often associating with Sooty and Pink-footed Shearwaters. They seldom feed on offal from fishing vessels but are frequently found feeding along convergence lines. There are no areas of upwelling in British Columbia where Buller's Shearwaters are known to concentrate: the closest is off the Olympic Peninsula, Washington (Shepard, M.G. 1976a; Guzman and Myres 1983).

REMARKS: The Buller's Shearwater was previously known as the New Zealand Shearwater. Some authors have recently referred to the species as the Gray Shearwater or the Gray-backed Shearwater (Palmer, R.S. 1962; Blake 1977; Tuck, G. 1978).

NOTEWORTHY RECORDS

Spring: No records.

Summer: Coastal - w Kyuquot and Cape Beale 1 to 10 Jul 1971- seen daily in pelagic waters (Guiguet 1972); 40 km w of Kyuquot Sound 15 Aug 1973- 2; e Sandspit 6 Aug 1985-1; n Masset 25 Aug 1984-1. **Interior** - No records.

Autumn: Interior - No records. **Coastal** - w Dixon Entrance 2 Nov 1971-1 (Crowell and Nehls 1972a); Queen Charlotte Sound 16 to 20 Oct 1978-1 to 3 birds (Guzman 1981); 50 km w of Estevan Point 19 Sep 1973-10; 45 km w of Tofino 12 Sep 1970-10 (Campbell 1971a); 64 km w of Tofino 26 Sep 1970-25 (Campbell 1971a); La Perouse Bank 17 Sep 1977-6, 23 Sep 1978-4, 1 Oct 1977-93 (Shepard, M.G. 1978), 8 Nov 1986-2.

Winter: No records.

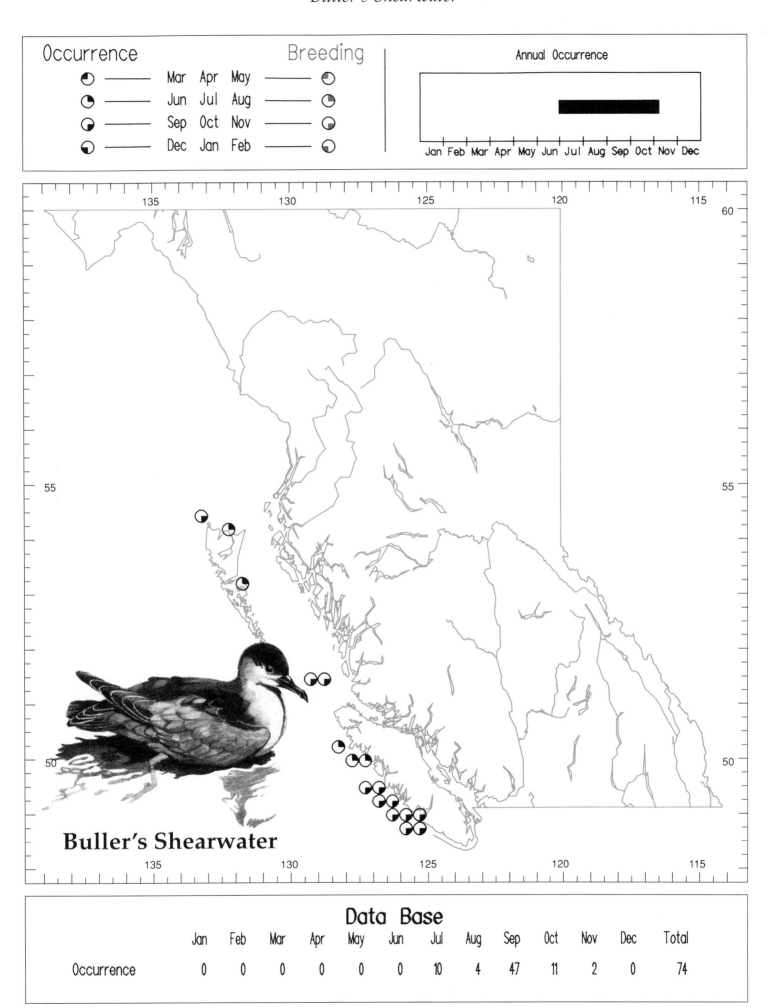

Buller's Shearwater

Occurrence

◑ ————	Mar Apr May	———— ◑
◔ ————	Jun Jul Aug	———— ◔
◵ ————	Sep Oct Nov	———— ◵
◗ ————	Dec Jan Feb	———— ◗

Breeding

Annual Occurrence

Jan Feb Mar Apr May Jun Jul Aug Sep Oct Nov Dec

Data Base

	Jan	Feb	Mar	Apr	May	Jun	Jul	Aug	Sep	Oct	Nov	Dec	Total
Occurrence	0	0	0	0	0	0	10	4	47	11	2	0	74

Sooty Shearwater
Puffinus griseus (Gmelin)

RANGE: Breeds in the southern hemisphere, chiefly on islands off New Zealand, Australia, and southern South America. Spends nonbreeding season in temperate parts of the north Atlantic and north Pacific oceans.

STATUS: *Very common* to *very abundan*t visitant along the outer coast in spring, summer, and autumn; *very rare* in winter. *Very rare* in summer and autumn in inner coastal areas.

OCCURRENCE: The Sooty Shearwater is the most abundant shearwater that can be seen from shore along the coast of British Columbia. In May, it often occurs within the 90 m depth contour, but the largest numbers are found farther offshore between the 90 and 180 m contours. In September, it is found with similar frequency in both zones (Guzman and Myres 1983). Small numbers occur infrequently in summer and autumn in Queen Charlotte Strait and the Strait of Georgia.

The general migratory movements of the Sooty Shearwater, which vary according to where they breed, have been described by Phillips, J.H. (1963) and Shuntov (1974). The Australasian population moves into the north Pacific Ocean after breeding. Birds destined for the southwestern Pacific region move in a broad front and follow a circular route towards the northeastern Pacific Ocean returning in autumn, well offshore of North America. Sooty Shearwaters from South American populations move along the South and North American shores during north and south migrations.

Sooty Shearwaters appear on the west coast of North America in migratory waves arranged by age classes. Subadults arrive off northern California in March and April, followed by breeders in late May and June, and then nonbreeders and fledglings in early July (Guzman 1981; Briggs and Chu 1986). The same pattern occurs in British Columbia. Spring migrants off the central west coast of Vancouver Island have been recorded in 2 distinct waves. In 1977, the waves occurred between 4 and 8 May and 13 and 15 May, and in 1978 between 2 and 5 May and 9 and 16 May (Guzman and Myres 1983). A similar wave was noted off the southwestern coast of Moresby Island between 14 and 16 May 1985. Autumn migration, far less spectacular than spring migration, also occurs in waves and takes place mostly in September.

Most shearwaters migrating to Alaska in spring bypass the coast of British Columbia by taking a transoceanic route across the northeastern Pacific Ocean from northern California and

Oregon (Guzman and Myres 1983). Guzman (1981) suggests the movement of Sooty Shearwaters along the British Columbia coast is of "secondary importance compared to the total size of the population moving offshore to Alaskan waters." During migration watches at sea off the Brooks Peninsula from 14 May to 27 June 1973, the net northward movement of Sooty Shearwaters was 119,000 birds in May and 89,800 in June (Campbell and Summers In press). Numbers off British Columbia in spring are generally much lower than off Oregon and Washington. It is likely, as Guzman and Myres (1983) suggest, that natural sources of shearwater foods such as small fishes and squids are not "generally abundant or reliable enough off Vancouver Island in May to maintain a high early summer population, so the birds are hungry and most of them continue on to Alaskan feeding grounds." Even off California, Sooty Shearwaters are lean when they arrive in May (Chu 1984).

Recent observations by A.J. Gaston (pers. comm.) suggest that substantial numbers of Sooty Shearwaters (500,000 to 1,000,000) regularly spend spring and early summer in Hecate Strait (see Fig. 194), many of them moulting too heavily to be in the process of migration. Birds complete their moult between May and August (Guiguet 1953a). From mid-April to mid-June, the shearwaters appear there in large numbers during periods of strong easterly winds.

Records for British Columbia span the period 23 February to 17 December; over half of them are from the summer months. Shearwaters congregate where food supplies and oceanographic conditions are favourable and constant. Such areas include the Goose Group banks, off Scott Islands, La Perouse Bank, and Swiftsure Bank.

REMARKS: Examination of 107 specimens of Sooty Shearwaters collected off British Columbia from April through October supports the theory of migration waves by age classes. There appears to be no differential seasonal migration by sexes.

See Richdale (1963) for a comprehensive review on the biology of the Sooty Shearwater.

POSTSCRIPT: On 23 May 1989, at least 300,000 Sooty Shearwaters were estimated flying south past Houston Stewart Channel, Queen Charlotte Islands, during a 6-hour period (A.G. Whitney pers. comm.).

NOTEWORTHY RECORDS

Spring: Coastal - w Ucluelet 19 to 29 Mar 1946-a few, 14 to 23 Apr 1946-flocks of several thousand (Martin and Myres 1969); 40 km w Ucluelet 14 May 1977-50,000 (Guzman 1981); 60 km w Ucluelet 14 May 1977-50,000 (Guzman 1981); 29 km w Tofino 8 May 1977-10,100 (Guzman 1981); w Kyuquot 21 Mar 1940-several (Martin 1942); w Triangle Island (Scott Islands) 23 May 1974-1,000+; Milbanke Sound 13 May 1967-650; w Kunghit Island 15 and 16 May 1985-110,000; w Hibben Island 31 Mar 1976-3; w Frederick Island 26 May 1952-2,000+; n Langara Island 20 Apr 1975-6,000 (Guzman 1981); 8 km e Copper Island 15 May 1985-10,000+; e Ramsay Island 22 May 1977-500,000; e Reef Island 21 Apr 1985-some, 14 May 1985-250,000 to 500,000, 24 May 1985-100,000; Prince Rupert to Skidegate 24 Apr 1981-400, 4 May 1986-15,000+. **Interior** - No records.

Summer: Coastal - s Victoria 14 Aug 1939-150 (Munro, J.A. and Cowan 1947); s Sooke 26 Aug 1951-800 in fog; w Ucluelet 24 Jul 1984-5,000; w

Long Beach 28 Jun 1980-3,000, 15 Jul 1967-5,000, 2 Aug 1974-3,000; w Cleland Island 17 Jun 1975-264, 24 Jul 1970-6,000, 24 Jul 1967-4,000 (Campbell and Stirling 1968b); Goose Group 26 Jun 1948-250 on banks; Ikeda Point to Lyman Point 4 Jun 1985-5,000; s Scudder Point 8 Aug 1957-400 (Mills 1960a); e Reef Island 2 Jun 1985-thousands passing northwards and southwards; w Anthony Island 11 Aug 1979-150; between Tasu Sound and Marble Island 9 Aug 1957-300 (Mills 1960a); between Tian Islets and White Point 12 Aug 1957-5,000 (Mills 1960a); n Rose Spit 4 Jul 1957-8,000, 13 Aug 1957-15,000 (Mills 1960a). **Interior** - No records.

Autumn: Interior - No records. **Coastal** - Skidegate Inlet 4 Oct 1971-100; s Cape St. James 15 Oct 1978-200; Pine Island 14 Sep 1983-200; Port Hardy 20 Sep 1938-1,000; w Quatsino Sound 11 Sep 1970-1,700; s Cape Mudge 9 Nov 1983-10; 5 km s Cape Mudge 24 Oct 1983-12; off Oyster River 4 Nov 1925-1,000+; s Hornby Island 5 Sep

1926-400 to 500 feeding; w Tofino 5 Sep 1982-5,000, 25 Sep 1971-1,400 (Campbell and Shepard 1972); w Ucluelet 27 Sep 1986-3,500; Cape Beale to La Perouse Bank 4 Sep 1983-6,000, 23 Sep 1978-7,000, 1 Oct 1977-312, 14 Oct 1978-500; s Clover Point 22 Sep 1958-500, 9 Nov 1983-500; s Sooke 22 Sep 1951-4,500 eating Pacific herring; w Race Rocks 8 Nov 1983-1,000.

Winter: Interior - No records. **Coastal** - between Tofino and Ucluelet 28 Feb 1974-2; w Race Rocks 11 Dec 1983-4; s Victoria Dec 1909-1 (RBCM 1393), 23 Feb 1904-1 (Bent 1922); e Albert Head 17 Dec 1983-1.

Christmas Counts: Interior - Not recorded. **Coastal** - Recorded from 1 of 28 localities and on 1% of all counts. Maxima: Victoria 17 Dec 1977-40 [some of these were likely Short-tailed Shearwaters] and 17 Dec 1983-1.

Sooty Shearwater

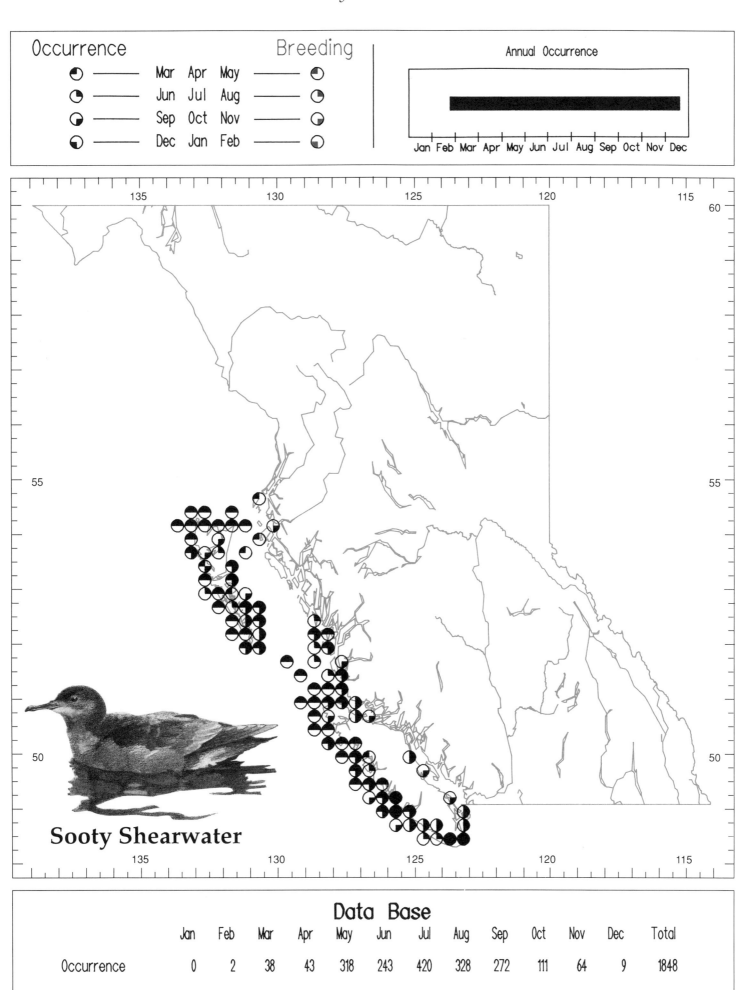

Occurrence

	Mar Apr May	
	Jun Jul Aug	
	Sep Oct Nov	
	Dec Jan Feb	

Breeding

Annual Occurrence

Jan Feb Mar Apr May Jun Jul Aug Sep Oct Nov Dec

Sooty Shearwater

Data Base

	Jan	Feb	Mar	Apr	May	Jun	Jul	Aug	Sep	Oct	Nov	Dec	Total
Occurrence	0	2	38	43	318	243	420	328	272	111	64	9	1848

Short-tailed Shearwater
Puffinus tenuirostris (Temminck)

STSH

RANGE: Breeds off southeast Australia. Migrates to north Pacific Ocean for nonbreeding season.

STATUS: Irregular. *Very rare* visitant to pelagic waters in spring, *fairly common* in late summer and autumn, and *very rare* in winter. *Casual* in the Strait of Georgia. Locally *very abundant* at times, in late spring and late autumn.

OCCURRENCE: The Short-tailed Shearwater is a trans-equatorial migrant. It has been reported to take a figure-eight course around the Pacific Ocean (Nelson, B. 1979), but that is questioned by Shuntov (1964) and others (King, W.B. 1967; T.W. Wahl pers. comm.), and may only involve nonbreeders. M.T. Myres (pers. comm.) suggests that adults go straight across the Pacific Ocean to Alaskan waters. In addition, banding returns show that birds in Japanese waters are mostly first-year birds; insignificant numbers of adults are recovered (Myres, M.T. In prep.). The birds leave their Australian breeding grounds in late April and May, and fly swiftly across the equator to the north Pacific and Arctic oceans (Serventy 1957, 1961, 1967). From May to August, the main wintering (nonbreeding) areas are off southern Kamchatka, and the Aleutian Islands. Some move north into the Bering and Chukchi seas. Adults begin their return trip in late August, and arrive at their breeding areas quite regularly during the last week of September. Nonbreeders travel later, in October and November (Serventy et al. 1971).

Establishing the status of the Short-tailed Shearwater along the west coast of North America has been complicated by the difficulty in separating it from the similar, but slightly larger, Sooty Shearwater (see Harrison, P. 1983). Short-tailed Shearwaters enter the Gulf of Alaska in May (Isleib and Kessel 1973; Guzman 1981) and mostly remain offshore. Generally, they occur in low numbers along the coast to California; under certain wind conditions they may reach coastal areas of British Columbia (Guzman and Myres 1983).

Most of the small number of Short-tailed Shearwater occurrences off the outer coast of British Columbia have been between May and November. All records for the Strait of Georgia are from February and the autumn. There are 14 specimen records for the period of May to October.

Nearly 90% of all records are of individuals or flocks of less than 10 birds, usually associated with Sooty Shearwaters (Fig. 194). Four unusual late-spring and autumn aggregations have been recorded near the British Columbia coast. On 19 May 1972, P.W. Martin (*in* Guzman and Myres 1983) encountered a "tremendous concentration . . . on Swiftsure Bank," which he concluded was at least 24 km across and "contained hundreds of thousands of individuals." A specimen (RBCM 11905) was collected. On 22 May 1977, the same observer noted that Short-tailed Shearwaters "constituted a significant proportion of the large movement of shearwaters moving southeast down the west side of Hecate Strait." R.M. Stewart (*in* Guiguet 1972), reported it in "vast numbers off the mouth of Masset Inlet" in the fall of 1945. Finally, Short-tailed Shearwaters were reported frequently near Green Island, Chatham Sound from 4 October to 3 December 1977, with peak numbers (2,530+) on 11 November (Hart, F.G. 1978).

The Short-tailed Shearwater has been recorded in the province from 27 April to 28 February. Records listed below have been carefully examined and include specimens and observations of Short-tailed Shearwaters seen with Sooty Shearwaters by experienced observers.

REMARKS: There are 2 errors in the literature concerning specimen records. The date of the William Head specimen reported in J.A. Munro and Cowan (1947) (RBCM 1498) should be 23 Feb 1904, not 23 Feb 1901, and the date for the Swiftsure Bank specimen reported in Guzman and Myres 1983 (RBCM 11905) should be 19 May 1972, not 28 May 1972.

The Short-tailed Shearwater was previously known as the Slender-billed Shearwater.

POSTSCRIPT: In late spring and early summer 1988 there was a small influx off the central coast. The largest flocks reported were: Cape St. James 22 May 1988-18 with fewer Sooty Shearwaters; Goose Group 8 June 1988-118.

Figure 194. *Mixed feeding flock of Sooty and Short-tailed shearwaters and gulls, east of Cumshewa Inlet, 5 June 1985 (Alan G. Whitney).*

NOTEWORTHY RECORDS

Spring: Coastal - Cape Beale (Bamfield) 27 Apr 1974-some migrating with Sooty Shearwaters (P.W. Martin *in* Guzman and Myres 1983); Swiftsure Bank 19 May 1972-hundreds of thousands (see text), 26 May 1972-few; 25 km w Tofino 10 May 1970-2; 8 km w Gowgaia Bay 15 May 1985-2; 5 km w Sunday Inlet 17 May 1982-2; 15 km se Langara Island 7 May 1983-1. **Interior** - No records.

Summer: Coastal - w Cree Island 9 Aug 1964-1; Goose Group banks 26 Jun to 27 Jul 1948-single birds on four occasions, one collected 26 Jun (RBCM 9752 - Guiguet 1953a; Martin and Myres 1969); 13 km w Louscoone Inlet 15 Jun 1986-2; w Marble Island 9 Aug 1957-1 (Mills 1960a); 3 km w White Point (Beresford Bay) 12 Aug 1957-1 (Mills 1960a); n Masset 3 Jun 1920-1 (MVZ 81711), 5 Jun 1920-2 (NMC 17486; MVZ 99106), 2 Jul 1940-1

(RBCM 10248); 16 km ne Cape Ball River 13 Aug 1957-1 (Mills 1960a). **Interior** - No records.

Autumn: Interior - No records. **Coastal** - n Masset 20 Sep 1937-1 (RBCM 10249); nw Green Island 4 Oct 1977-21, 9 Oct 1977-350 feeding with Black-legged Kittiwakes, 11 Nov 1977-2,530+, 18 Nov 1977-1,000+ feeding with Black-legged Kittiwakes (Hart, F.G. 1978); w Clayoquot Sound 9 Oct 1907-1 (NMC 3623); La Perouse Bank 26 Sep 1981-1, 1 Oct 1977-2, 8 Nov 1986-15; William Head to Race Rocks 7 Oct 1979-1, 22 Oct 1983-1; e Port Hardy 9 Sep 1937-1 (MVZ 81712), 20 Sep 1938-20, 25 Sep 1937-1 (MVZ 99107); s Cape Mudge 9 Nov 1983-50+ with 10 Sooty Shearwaters; Comox Harbour 4 Oct 1925-a few among Sooty Shearwaters; Tsawwassen 26 Nov 1977-1 w ferry terminal; Active Pass 26 Nov 1977-2; e Albert Head 24 Oct 1891-4 (Fannin 1891); s

Clover Point 2 Nov 1983-22, 5 Nov 1983-10, 25 Nov 1979-1; Haro Strait 23 Oct 1983-4, 15 Nov 1981-7.

Winter: Interior - No records. **Coastal** - nw Green Island 3 Dec 1977-200+ (Hart, F.G. 1978); Hecate Strait 28 Feb 1983-2; n Masset 21 Dec 1986-5; 2 km n Christensen Point 14 Dec 1975-1; 5 km s Sartine Island 14 Dec 1975-3; se William Head 23 Feb 1904-1 (RBCM 1498; Kermode 1904); sw Race Rocks 11 Feb 1978-1; Haro Strait 17 Jan 1979-2; s Clover Point 2 Jan 1959-1 (Boggs and Boggs 1960), 7 Dec 1982-1, 2 Dec 1983-2.

Christmas Counts: Interior - Not recorded. **Coastal** - Recorded once: Victoria 17 Dec 1977-2, all-time Canadian high count (Anderson, R.R. 1978), with 40 Sooty Shearwaters, more of which were likely Short-tailed Shearwaters.

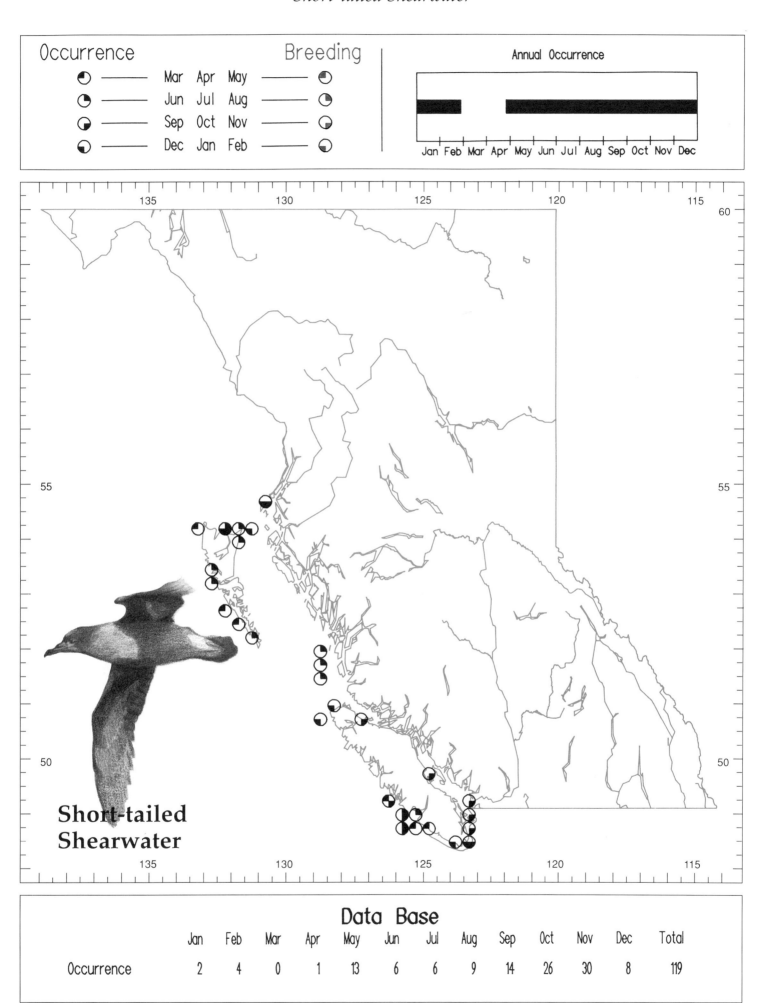

Short-tailed Shearwater

Occurrence

◖ ———	Mar Apr May	——— ◖
◔ ———	Jun Jul Aug	——— ◔
◓ ———	Sep Oct Nov	——— ◓
◑ ———	Dec Jan Feb	——— ◑

Breeding

Annual Occurrence

Jan Feb Mar Apr May Jun Jul Aug Sep Oct Nov Dec

Data Base

	Jan	Feb	Mar	Apr	May	Jun	Jul	Aug	Sep	Oct	Nov	Dec	Total
Occurrence	2	4	0	1	13	6	6	9	14	26	30	8	119

Black-vented Shearwater

BVSH

Puffinus opisthomelas Coues

RANGE: An eastern Pacific Ocean species that breeds on islands off the Pacific coast of Baja California. Disperses north and south after breeding.

STATUS: *Very rare* vagrant to the south coast.

OCCURRENCE: The Black-vented Shearwater breeds in its southern range during our winter. Fledging and dispersal from colonies begins in June and July, and birds may return to breeding colonies as early as November, but the phenology of breeding varies greatly from year to year and from colony to colony (Everett 1988). During the nonbreeding season, timing of dispersal, numbers, and distribution of shearwaters are strongly correlated to maximum water temperatures (Ainley 1976). Post-breeding dispersal is mainly northward following the warm Davidson Current along the California coast to Monterey, during which time the birds probably moult (see Anthony, A.W. 1896; Loomis 1918). In some years, birds arrive at Monterey in August and September, but most records are from mid-October to late November (Stallcup 1976).

In British Columbia, the Black-vented Shearwater has been found mainly near shore, from Queen Charlotte Sound south along the west coast of Vancouver Island to the vicinity of Victoria. It has also been recorded at 52°51'N, 136°01'W, well off the west coast of the Queen Charlotte Islands (17 July 1976; Guzman and Myres 1983). These are the northernmost fully documented records of the species. Summer sightings of small black-and-white shearwaters in the Gulf of Alaska refer to the Manx Shearwater (*Puffinus puffinus*) (Kessel and Gibson 1978).

Records for the province are from the period 3 July to November; there is one February occurrence. All involve 1 or 2 birds; 5 are represented by specimens.

All records, listed in chronological order, are as follows:

(1) e Albert Head 24 October 1891-2 (1 male, 1 female; RBCM 1494, 1495).
(2) e Albert Head November 1891-2 (1 male, 1 unknown; RBCM 89; USNM 153194).
(3) e Albert Head February 1895-1 male (NMC 1982).
(4) w Cape Scott 15 July 1940-1 with Sooty Shearwaters (Martin 1942).
(5) Goose Group 14 August 1948-1 on banks (Martin and Myres 1969).
(6) Juan de Fuca Strait 28 September 1953-1 (Poole 1966).
(7) w Solander Island 3 July 1954-1.
(8) sw Cleland Island 24 July 1967-1 with Sooty Shearwaters (Campbell and Stirling 1968b).
(9) w Amphitrite Point 28 September 1986-1.

REMARKS: The Black-vented Shearwater was formerly considered a subspecies of the Manx Shearwater (*P. puffinus*) of the north Atlantic Ocean.

It is difficult to identify members of the *Puffinus* group in the field, especially *opisthomelas* and *puffinus*, because plumage characteristics overlap due to individual variation, feather wear, and moult. The dark undertail coverts of the Black-vented Shearwater still remains the most reliable field mark (see Hoskins et al. 1979; Jehl 1982).

Everett (1988) summarizes the biology of this little-studied species.

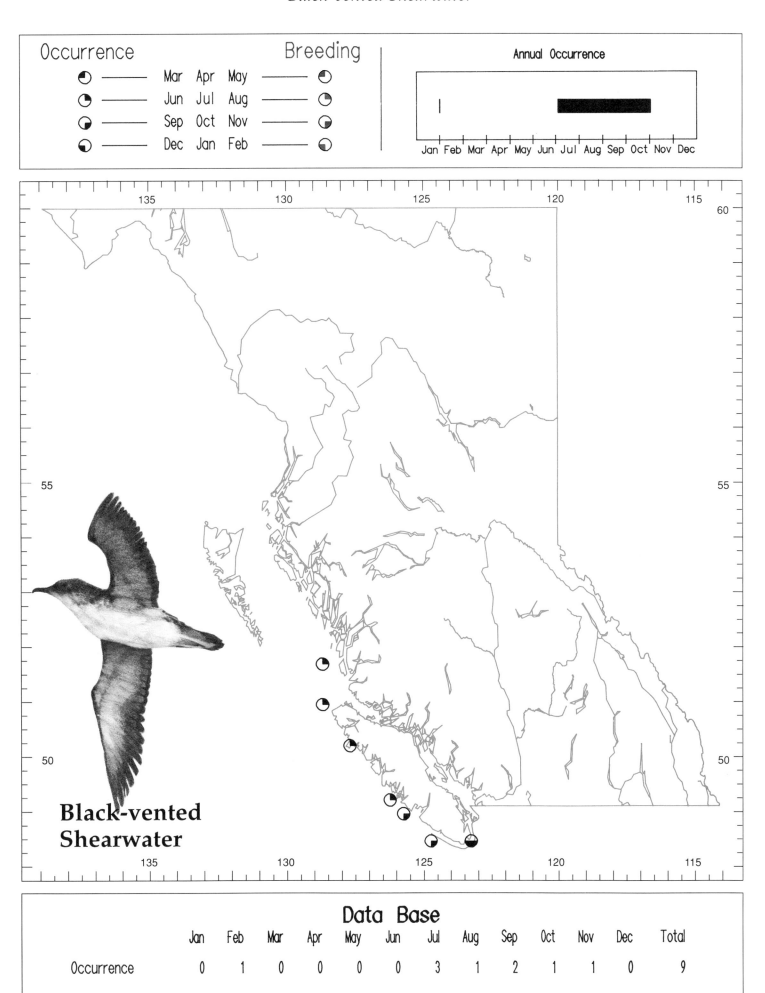

Occurrence

Breeding

		Mar	Apr	May		
		Jun	Jul	Aug		
		Sep	Oct	Nov		
		Dec	Jan	Feb		

Annual Occurrence

Jan Feb Mar Apr May Jun Jul Aug Sep Oct Nov Dec

**Black-vented
Shearwater**

Data Base

	Jan	Feb	Mar	Apr	May	Jun	Jul	Aug	Sep	Oct	Nov	Dec	Total
Occurrence	0	1	0	0	0	0	3	1	2	1	1	0	9

Fork-tailed Storm-Petrel

Oceanodroma furcata (Gmelin)

FTSP

RANGE: Breeds around the north Pacific Ocean from the Kuriles in the west, through the Aleutians, the Gulf of Alaska and southward to northern California. In winter, ranges at sea as far south as Japan, Hawaii, and central California.

STATUS: Variously *very common* to *very abundant* in spring, summer, and autumn and *casual* in winter along the outer coast. *Casual* spring, *very rare* mid-summer, *rare* to *uncommon* late summer and early autumn, and *very rare* winter in the Strait of Georgia and Juan de Fuca Strait. *Casual* in the interior. Widespread colonial breeder along the outer coast.

NONBREEDING: The Fork-tailed Storm-Petrel occurs along the British Columbia coast, but prefers outer coastal areas. Inland occurrences are very unusual (Fig. 195) but are reported throughout the species' range (Geist 1939). It is the most commonly seen storm-petrel in nearshore areas, where it frequents protected waters of inlets, harbours, and bays. Large numbers historically foraged on offal from the coastal fish canneries, but the canneries are now closer to mainland industrial centres and further from the storm-petrel's preferred natural foraging areas.

The Fork-tailed Storm-Petrel is usually seen singly or in loosely scattered flocks of less than 20 birds, but may gather in groups ranging up to 5,000 individuals under certain weather conditions or over concentrations of food. The largest flocks have been reported during foggy conditions. Storm-petrels have a well developed sense of smell (Bang 1966; Grub 1972; Wenzel 1980) and may be seen in strings, following the scent of fish oil on the water.

In spring, birds move from pelagic wintering areas to the breeding colonies from early March through April, but specific details are lacking. Vagrants have occurred in Juan de Fuca Strait and Strait of Georgia from late March to late May.

Autumn migration or post-breeding dispersal, occurs from mid-August through October, with peak numbers recorded between late August and early September. The autumn movement is regularly noticeable at the northern end of the Strait of Georgia (Guiguet 1953a). In early August 1981, southwest of Barkley Sound, Fork-tailed Storm-Petrels occurred at densities of 0.13 to 0.71/km^2 between 48°31'N, 125°30'W and 49°00'N, 128°00'W (T.R. Wahl pers. comm.).

The winter distribution offshore is poorly known. Most inner coastal records are from Juan de Fuca Strait.

BREEDING: The Fork-tailed Storm-Petrel breeds along the coast of western Vancouver Island from Seabird Rocks to Triangle Island (Scott Islands); the entrance to Queen Charlotte Sound; off the central mainland coast; and around the Queen Charlotte Islands, except for the sandy north and east coasts of Graham Island.

All colonies are on islands, usually wooded, but always shrub or grass covered. Most are shared with Leach's Storm-Petrels. Most sites are small islets with relatively open stands of Sitka spruce, usually with dense shrub or luxuriant grass and forb cover and enough soil to permit burrowing (Fig. 196). Open litter under dense forest is also used. Treeless habitats have dense stands of salmonberry, salal, grasses, or forbs. Infrequently, small colonies have been located on vegetated, rocky slopes and among beached logs .

The numbers of Fork-tailed Storm-Petrels at colonies in British Columbia are well known except on the east and west coasts of Moresby Island where the proportions of Fork-tailed and Leach's storm-petrels have not been determined. The total is estimated to be 189,300 pairs that breed at over 40 sites (Rodway In press). Colonies vary in size from a few pairs to 51,000 pairs. British Columbia is towards the southern end of a much larger breeding population centred in the Aleutian Islands and Gulf of Alaska. The total Alaskan population is estimated to be 1,578,000 pairs (United States Department of the Interior 1988). About 2,000 pairs breed in Washington (Speich and Wahl 1989).

Figure 195. Fork-tailed Storm-Petrel, Serpentine River, 16 January 1984 (RBCM Photo 1113; Ervio Sian).

Fork-tailed Storm-Petrels are most concentrated in Queen Charlotte Strait. The largest known colony is on the Storm Islands where about 51,000 pairs bred in 1987. The major breeding colonies in the province are shown in Table 11.

Nests: Most nests were burrows excavated in the soft soil of open or semi-open forests. Often, understory vegetation provides some protection and structural stability, but burrows are typically fragile and easily trampled. In grassy areas, burrows usually begin at the base of grass clumps but always end entirely in the soil. Burrow entrances are frequently located under shrub and tree roots or under dead falls. Some nests are found in spaces beneath drift logs (Fig. 197; Campbell and Stirling 1968b) and occasionally in unused burrows of alcids.

Burrows extend up to 150 cm in length with a diameter near the entrance between 4 and 6 cm. Usually there is a slightly larger nest chamber lined with soft vegetation.

Eggs: Dates for 161 clutches ranged from 29 April to 27 July, with 82% recorded between 10 May and 16 June. Calculated dates suggest eggs could be found from 4 April through July although very late clutches may represent abandoned nests. All clutches consisted of a single egg. The incubation period is between 37 and 67 days, a variance of 31 days (see Boersma et al. 1980, Quinlan 1979, and Simons 1981). This is due to egg neglect, an adaptation in response to storms and un-dependable food resources that delay incubation shifts.

Young: Dates for 122 broods in burrows ranged from 29 May to 18 August, with 63% recorded between 26 June and 20 July. Calculated dates from known-aged chicks indicate unfledged young can be found through September. All broods contained a single young. The mean nestling period ranges from 50 to 68 days within an average time of 61.5 ± 2.7 days (Quinlan 1979; Simons 1981).

REMARKS: The early nestling stage is a period of high mortality for Fork-tailed Storm-Petrel chicks; at that time disturbance should be minimized by visitors to breeding colonies. Simons (1981) mentions:

> . . . the following hatching may be critical to the survival of the chick. The adult assisted the chick in hatching by placing its bill inside the partially opened shell and shaking its head from side to side. This may be a common behaviour, as I have often found that the shell has been partially pecked away on eggs that did

Fork-tailed Storm-Petrel

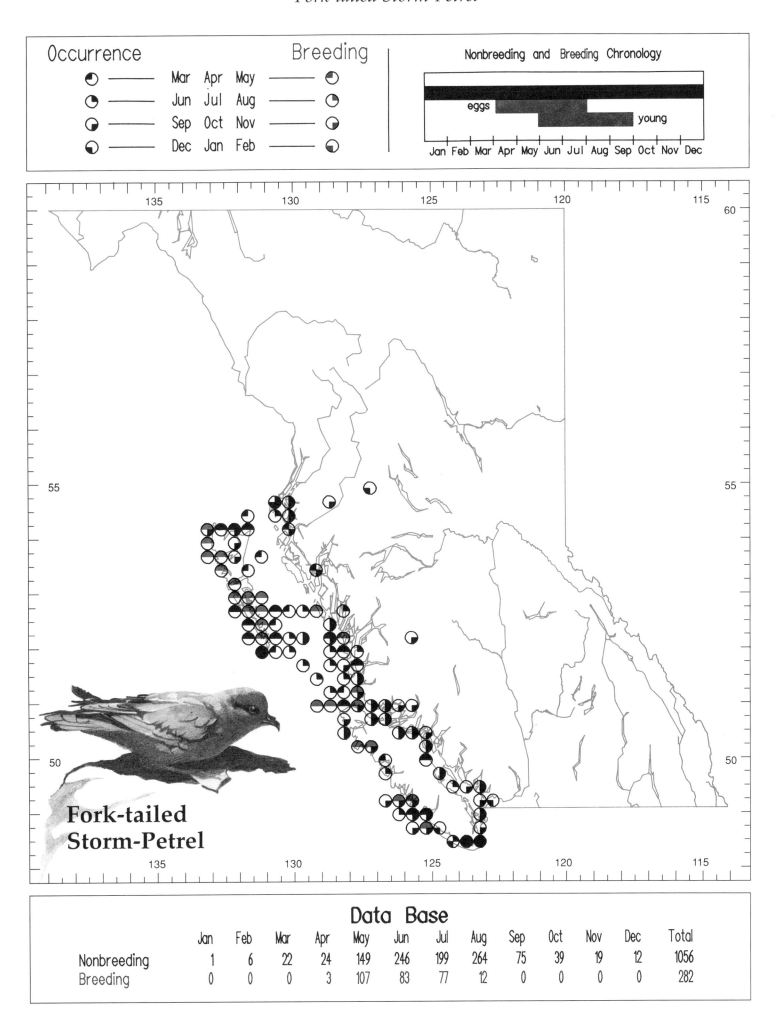

Occurrence / Breeding

Occurrence		Breeding
◑ —	Mar Apr May	— ◑
◔ —	Jun Jul Aug	— ◔
◕ —	Sep Oct Nov	— ◕
◕ —	Dec Jan Feb	— ◕

Nonbreeding and Breeding Chronology

eggs   young

Jan Feb Mar Apr May Jun Jul Aug Sep Oct Nov Dec

**Fork-tailed
Storm-Petrel**

Data Base

	Jan	Feb	Mar	Apr	May	Jun	Jul	Aug	Sep	Oct	Nov	Dec	Total
Nonbreeding	1	6	22	24	149	246	199	264	75	39	19	12	1056
Breeding	0	0	0	3	107	83	77	12	0	0	0	0	282

Figure 196. *Lihou Island, a typical colony where both Fork-tailed and Leach's storm-petrels breed, 8 May 1986 (Michael S. Rodway).*

TABLE 11

Fork-tailed Storm-Petrel: location, history, and size of major colonies in British Columbia.

Location	Colony History									
	First Record	Low Survey Results[1] Year			High Survey Results[1] Year			Recent Survey Results[1] Year		Source[2]
South Coast - Colonies > 2000 nests or pairs										
Beresford Island	1987				2900	At	1987		1987	1
Gillam Island	1975	300	A	1977	42000	At	1988		1988	1,3
Storm Islands	1976	3800	A	1982	50800	At	1987		1987	1,2,3,
Tree Islets	1909	50	A	1976	8300	At	1986		1986	1,4
North Coast - Colonies > 3500 nests or pairs										
Agglomerate Island	1971		S	1977	10000[3]	A	1971	5500[3] At	1985	5,6,8
Bischof Islands	1971	50[3]	N	1985	5000	A	1971		1985	4,6,8
Hippa Island	1977	5000	A	1977	10900	At	1983		1983	1,5
Langtry Island	1977	4000	A	1977	12300[3]	At	1985		1985	5,8
'Lepas' Islet	1927	300	A	1972	3500	A	1977		1977	4,5
Lihou Island	1977		0	1977	13700[3]	At	1986		1986	5,9
Luxmoore Island	1986				5100[3]	At	1986		1986	9
Moore Islands	1970	5700[3]	A	1976	8600	At	1988		1988	1,4
Rankine Island	1960	3500	A	1977	2000	At	1985		1985	4,5,8
Rock Islet	1977	3000	A	1977	4700	At	1986		1986	5,8
Rogers Island	1977	9000	A	1977	28700[3]	At	1986		1986	5,9
Sinnett Islets	1976	450	A	1976	19200	At	1988		1988	1,4

[1] A - active burrows; E - colony extinct; N - nests; S - nesting suspected. All data are estimates unless noted as follows: t - transect estimate.

[2] 1 - Rodway In press; 2 - Young 1930; 3 - Campbell 1976a; 4 - British Columbia Nest Records Scheme; 5 - Campbell and Garrioch 1979; 6 - Summers 1974; 7 - Drent and Guiguet 1961; 8 - Rodway et al. 1988; 9 - Rodway et al. 1989.

[3] Total number of storm-petrel burrows, species ratios not determined.

not hatch. When the chick was free of the shell, the adult brooded it immediately and continued to do so until the chick's down was dry. Chicks were commonly brooded for a total of 1-8 days following hatching . . . they were dependent on the frequent attention of their parents for survival.

Very little is known about where the Fork-tailed Storm-Petrel forages off British Columbia, its feeding habits, or foods. It is well known, however, that food resources are important in influencing reproductive success (see Ashmole 1963, 1971; Lack 1967). In Alaska, Boersma (1986) found that during development, chicks of the Fork-tailed Storm-Petrel are left unattended for several days. If adults do not return regularly with enough food

the chick becomes torpid until feeding resumes. His findings suggest that the metabolism of chicks is adjusted to a gorge-and-fast feeding pattern resulting from the species' exploitation of scarce and unpredictable food resources.

See Harris, S.W. (1974), Quinlan (1979), Simons (1979, 1981) and Boersma et al. (1980) for additional life history information on the Fork-tailed Storm-Petrel.

The species was formerly known as Fork-tailed Petrel.

POSTSCRIPT: On 19 October 1988 a weakened Fork-tailed Storm-Petrel was found at Houston. It died in captivity (RBCM 19964). Houston is over 250 km from the closest marine waters.

Figure 197. Fork-tailed Storm-Petrel with egg, Cleland Island, 18 May 1970 (R. Wayne Campbell).

NOTEWORTHY RECORDS

Spring: Coastal - Victoria 31 Mar 1976-1, 27 Apr 1982-1; Ucluelet Inlet 7 Mar 1985-300+ (Campbell 1985b); Mitlenatch Island 26 May 1974-1; Esperanza Inlet 10 Mar 1976-1; Queen Charlotte Sound 13 May 1967-31; Fitz Hugh Sound 23 Mar 1976-1; Goose Group 18 May 1948-30; Milbanke Sound 13 May 1967-40; Cape St. James 11 Apr 1982-1, 15 May 1982-10+; Huston Inlet 26 Mar 1976-3; Hecate Strait 26 Mar 1976-3, 4 May 1986-40; Masset 20 Apr 1979-1; Rose Spit 12 May 1952-a few; Egeria Bay (Langara Island) 29 Mar 1976-25; Cox Island (Langara Island) 30 Apr 1966-1 (Campbell 1969a). **Interior** - No records.

Summer: Coastal - Constance Bank 26 Aug 1976-600; La Perouse Bank 21 Aug 1949-500+; 32 to 40 km w Tofino 15 Jul 1979-30, 29 Jul 1972-91, 31 Aug 1964-50; Stanley Park (Vancouver) 25 Aug 1966-1; Bowen Island 24 Aug 1983-1; Mitlenatch Island 15 Aug 1979-50+, 31 Aug 1966-9; Discovery Passage 6 Aug 1968-3; Solander Island 27 Aug 1967-9; Kelsey Bay 21 and 22 Aug 1983-45

(Campbell 1983d); Cluxewe River 8 Aug 1981-10 off estuary; Pine Island 1 Jul 1969-13, 25 Jul 1976-5,000 in two feeding groups; Namu 20 Jun and 6 Jul 1976-30 to 100 feeding in harbour under wharf on offal from fish plant from 0030 to 0215; Hunter Island 17 Aug 1948-25 (Guiguet 1953a); Queen Charlotte Sound 20 Jun 1968-148 (Crowell and Nehls 1968d); 30 km e Cape St. James 5 Aug 1986-130; Garcin Rocks to Rankine Island 12 Jun 1987-500; 16 km e Rose Harbour 6 Aug 1977-25. **Interior** - No records.

Autumn: Interior - see Extralimital Records. **Coastal** - Green Island 6 Oct 1976-2, 17 Nov 1977-1; Skeena River (Terrace) 24 Sep 1984-1 (Campbell 1984b); Masset Inlet 27 Oct 1974-1, 4 Nov 1976-1 found dead on beach; Cape St. James 8 Nov 1981-6 at lighthouse; Wentworth Rock 12 Sep 1967-36; Port Neville 5 Sep 1977-22+; Johnstone Strait 24 Sep 1975-7, 4 Nov 1971-2; Discovery Passage 1 Sep 1981-1 (RBCM 18115); Comox 6 Oct 1942-1 male (RBCM 12189);

Vancouver 6 Sep 1934-1 female (RBCM 12190); Bamfield 1 Oct 1977-107; La Perouse Bank 1 Sep 1985-1,418, 3 Sep 1981-120, 25 Sep 1976-62, 26 Sep 1981-100, 1 Oct 1977-107; Clover Point 26 Oct 1963-40 after severe storm, 19 Nov 1983-6.

Winter: Interior - see Extralimital Records. **Coastal** - Green Island 2 Dec 1978-1 caught and released at lighthouse; Cape St. James 10 Dec 1981-1 hit lighthouse; Serpentine River 16 Jan 1984-1 (RBCM Photo 1113, see Fig. 195; Mattocks 1984); Esquimalt 11 Dec 1955-1; Clover Point 4 Feb 1954-1; Victoria Dec 1892-2 (RBCM 1499, 1500), winter 1973-1 female (NMC 59278); Juan de Fuca Strait 22 Feb 1971-1.

Christmas Counts: Not recorded.

Extralimital Records: Interior - Atnarko River 25 Sep 1938-1 found dying (ROM 82054); Smithers 9 Jan 1983-1 found exhausted on snow (Campbell 1983a).

Leach's Storm-Petrel

Oceanodroma leucorhoa (Vieillot)

RANGE: Breeds in the north Pacific Ocean from northen Japan, the Kurile and Aleutian islands, the Gulf of Alaska, and southeast along the Pacific coast of North America to Baja California. Also breeds in the north Atlantic Ocean from southern Labrador, Greenland, Iceland, and the Faroe Islands, south to Massachusetts and the British Isles. Winters in equatorial waters.

STATUS: Locally *very common* to *very abundant* in summer, especially in the vicinity of breeding colonies along the outer coast. *Common* to *very common* at sea in summer, *uncommon* in spring and autumn. *Casual* in winter off extreme northern and southern Vancouver Island. *Very rare* in inshore waters. Breeds along the outer coast; locally off the central mainland coast.

NONBREEDING: The Leach's Storm-Petrel is widely distributed off the British Columbia coast. It is a highly pelagic species that usually forages seaward of warmer coastal waters and is not abundant until sea surface temperatures exceed 14°C (Martin and Myres 1969). It occurs singly, or in small, loose groups. In summer, groups of 50 or more birds may be seen and heard flying around forested islands (e.g. Florencia Islet) where breeding is not known to occur. Otherwise, it rarely occurs near land except when exhausted or dying birds come ashore after storms.

Some Leach's Storm-Petrels winter off the British Columbia coast; there are 5 records from December and February. March records may be early spring arrivals. In early April, 100 nautical miles (185 km) off Washington, T.R. Wahl (pers. comm.) noted a northwest movement of one to a few birds at a time continuously all day. In British Columbia, the storm-petrels return to breeding colonies throughout May. In early August 1981, 100 to 500 km west of Vancouver Island, Leach's Storm-Petrels occurred at densities of 0.42 to 1.72/km^2 (mostly 1.35 to 1.72 birds/km^2) between 48°40'N, 127°00'W and 49°50'N, 136°00'W (T.R.Wahl pers. comm.). Autumn departure begins in mid-September and continues through late October and perhaps early November.

The Leach's Storm-Petrel has been reported in the province between 22 February and 9 March and between 1 May and 14 December.

BREEDING: The Leach's Storm-Petrel breeds along the coast of western Vancouver Island from Seabird Rocks to Triangle Island (Scott Islands), near the entrance to Queen Charlotte Strait, off Aristazabal Island, and around the Queen Charlotte Islands except for the sandy north and east coasts of Graham Island.

Most colonies are on small, wooded islands, often in company with Fork-tailed Storm-Petrels (see Fig. 196). The forested islands have an overstory of Sitka spruce and an understory of grasses, forbs, salal, and salmonberry; non-forested islands often have similar shrub, forb, and grassy vegetation. The storm-petrels also nest on islets where the only ground cover is grass (Fig. 198).

The Leach's Storm-Petrel breeds at more than 41 sites along the coast. Its centre of abundance is in Queen Charlotte Strait where an estimated 276,600 pairs nest. The total population for the province is estimated to be over 550,000 pairs (Rodway In press). In Alaska, the breeding population is estimated to be 1,771,000 pairs (United States Department of the Interior 1988). In Washington there may be 25,000 or more pairs nesting (Speich and Wahl 1989).

Colonies vary in size from a few pairs to 191,000 pairs. There are 26 sites with more than 500 pairs and 21 sites with more than 4,000 pairs (Table 12). The largest known colony is on the Storm Islands where an estimated 191,000 pairs bred in 1987.

Nests: Nests are almost exclusively in burrows excavated by the adults. Burrows are usually started under a root, stump, log, or clump of grass where they angle into the soft earth. Burrows in open areas are fragile and collapse easily. Occasionally, unused burrows of Cassin's Auklets, Rhinoceros Auklets, and Ancient Murrelets are used.

Burrows extended 50 to 115 cm deep, terminating in an incubation chamber (Fig. 199). The largest such chamber measured 20 x 18 x 11 cm. Burrow entrances ranged from 6 to 10 cm in diameter. Where the soil was very shallow (e.g. Gillam Islands), the nest chamber was on bedrock. Nest materials often included a small collection of dry grasses, leaves, and fine twigs.

Eggs: Dates for 573 clutches ranged from 14 May to 20 August with 66% recorded between 20 June and 18 July. The clutch found on 20 August was being incubated and near hatching. Clutch size ranged from 1 to 2 eggs (1E-569, 2E-4), with 99% having 1 egg. Two-egg clutches may be the product of 2 females. The incubation period is 41 to 42 days (Gross 1935).

Young: Dates for 186 broods ranged from 11 July to 26 October with 58% recorded between 26 July and 28 August. Young hatching in late August may not fledge until early November (Gross 1935). All broods contained a single young (Fig. 200). The young, deserted by the adults at about 40 days, live on fat reserves and leave for the sea at 65-76 days (Gross 1935; Harris, M.P. 1969).

REMARKS: Ainley (1980) concludes that body measurements support the merging of *O. l. beali*, which was the subspecies breeding in British Columbia, with *O. l. leucorhoa*.

Leach's Storm-Petrel was formerly known as Leach's Petrel.

Figure 198. *Michael G. Shepard at Leach's Storm-Petrel colony on Cleland Island, 17 June 1975 (R. Wayne Campbell). Very few colonies exist in British Columbia where the only ground cover is tall grasses.*

Leach's Storm-Petrel

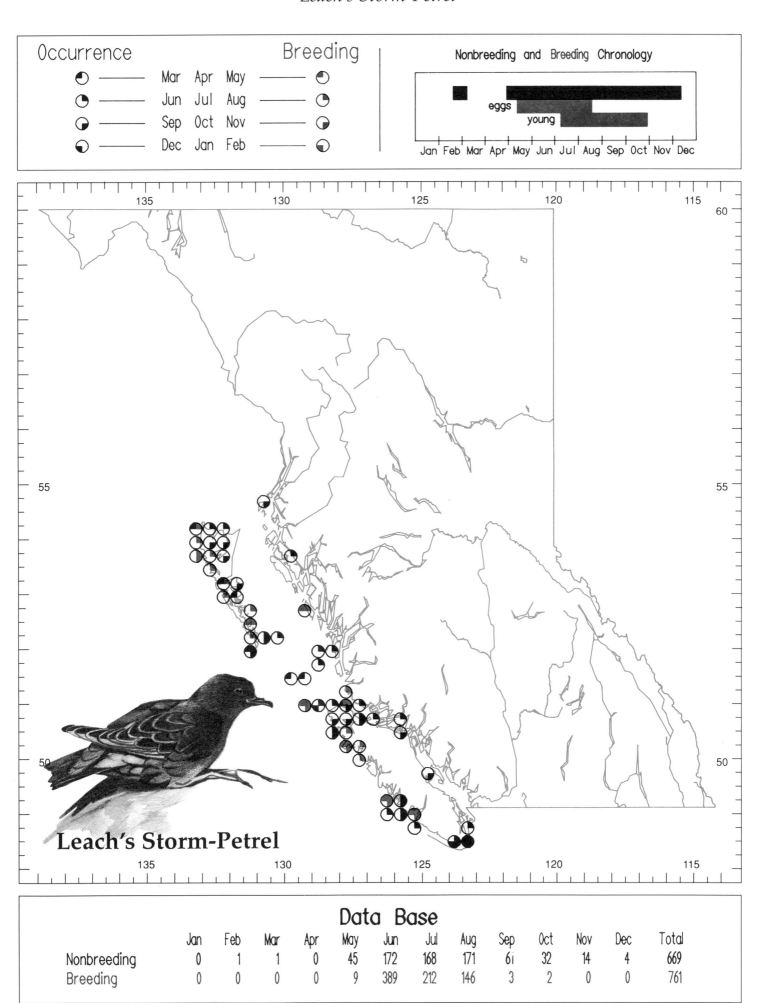

Occurrence

	Mar Apr May	
	Jun Jul Aug	
	Sep Oct Nov	
	Dec Jan Feb	

Breeding

Nonbreeding and Breeding Chronology

eggs

young

Jan Feb Mar Apr May Jun Jul Aug Sep Oct Nov Dec

Leach's Storm-Petrel

Data Base

	Jan	Feb	Mar	Apr	May	Jun	Jul	Aug	Sep	Oct	Nov	Dec	Total
Nonbreeding	0	1	1	0	45	172	168	171	61	32	14	4	669
Breeding	0	0	0	0	9	389	212	146	3	2	0	0	761

Figure 199. *Exposed nest chamber of a Leach's Storm-Petrel, Cleland Island, 10 July 1967 (R. Wayne Campbell).*

TABLE 12.
Leach's Storm-Petrel: location, history, and size of major colonies in British Columbia.

Location	First Record	Low Survey Results[1]		Year	High Survey Results[1]		Year	Recent Survey Results[1]		Year	Source[2]
South Coast - Colonies > 5000 nests or pairs											
Beresford Island	1987				12500	At	1987			1987	1
Buckle Group	1934	1200	A	1976	27000	At	1987			1987	1,4,7
Cleland Island	1925	3000	A	1975	13100	A	1982	5700	A	1988	1,3,7,8
Gillam Islands	1975	3000	A	1975	72000	At	1988			1988	1,3
Reid Islets	1968	100s	A	1968	11500	At	1987			1987	1,4
Solander Island	1975	2000	A	1975	75000	At	1988			1988	1,3
Storm Islands	1929	1250	A	1975	191000	At	1987			1987	1,2,3
Thomas Island	1975	1200	A	1975	11600	At	1982	7300	At	1988	1,3,8
Tree Islets	1909	100s	A	1968	47000	At	1986			1981	4
North Coast - Colonies > 4000 nests or pairs											
Agglomerate Island	1971	1000	A	1977	10000[3]	A	1971	5500[3]	At	1985	5,6,9
Anthony Island	1977	6400	A	1977	8600[3]	At	1985			1985	5,10
Hippa Island	1977	3000	A	1977	12800	At	1983			1983	1,5
Langtry Island	1985				12300[3]	At				1985	9
'Lepas' Islet	1927	500	A	1972	4500	A	1977			1977	4,5
Lihou Island	1977	10000	A	1977	13700[3]	At	1986			1986	5,10
Luxmoore Island	1986				5700[3]	At	1986			1986	10
Moore Islands	1970	100	A	1970	6000	At	1988			1988	1,4
Rankine Islands	1960	6800	A	1977	12300	At	1985			1985	4,5,9
Rock Islet	1977	3000	A	1977	12300	At	1985			1985	5,9
Rogers Island	1977	10000	A	1977	28700[3]	At	1986			1986	5,10
Sinnett Islets	1976	720	A	1976	11200	At	1988			1988	1,4

[1] A - active burrows. All data are estimates unless noted as follows: t - transect estimate.

[2] 1 - Rodway In press; ; 2 - Young 1930; 3 - Campbell 1976a; 4 - British Columbia Nest Records Scheme; 5 - Campbell and Garrioch 1979; 6 - Summers 1974; 7 - Drent and Guiguet 1961; 8 - Rodway et al. In prep; 9 - Rodway et al. 1988; 10 - Rodway et al. 1989.

[3] Total number of storm-petrel burrows, species ratios not determined.

Figure 200. *Leach's Storm-Petrel with chick, Cleland Island, 18 August 1974 (R. Wayne Campbell).*

NOTEWORTHY RECORDS

Spring: Coastal - Cleland Island 1 May 1973-2; Cape St. James 9 Mar 1978-50+ at lighthouse; Skidegate Inlet 24 May 1981-1; Cox Island (Langara Island) 13 May 1947 - birds not yet arrived for breeding. **Interior** - No records.

Summer: Coastal - Discovery Island 5 Jul 1979-1; Florencia Islet 11 Jul 1975-60 over nonbreeding island at night; Long Beach 2 Jun 1968-2; Tofino Inlet 18 Aug 1975-1; Quatsino Sound 6 Jul 1966-11; Port Neville 24 Aug 1976-1 adult 2 km from open marine waters; Pine Island 2 Aug 1987-1;

Virgin Rocks to Cape Scott 25 Jul 1968-59; Garcia Rocks to Rankine Island 12 Jun 1987-100. **Interior** - No records.

Autumn: Interior - No records. **Coastal** - Eden Lake (Naden Harbour) 2 Nov 1975-1 blown 16 km inland by storm; Ship Island 16 Oct 1974-2; Luxana Bay 9 Sep 1981-6; Port Hardy 29 Oct 1935-1 male (MCZ 281257), 5 Nov 1950-1 male (UBC 3266); Winter Harbour Oct 1968-15; Pulteney Point 25 Nov 1975-1 at light station; Comox 20 Oct 1930-1 male (UBC 408); Long

Beach 4 Nov 1982-1 found dead; Cowichan Bay 13 Oct 1986-1 (Mattocks and Harrington-Tweit 1987a); Trial Island 15 Nov 1981-3; Ogden Point 28 Sep 1987-1 (RBCM 19214).

Winter: Interior - No records. **Coastal** - Triangle Island (Scott Islands) 22 Feb 1970-1; 13 km s Scott Islands 14 Dec 1975-1; French Beach 4 Dec 1977-1; Victoria 3 Dec 1961-1 female (RBCM 10751); 4 Dec 1923-1 male (RBCM 4754).

Christmas Counts: Not recorded.

American White Pelican
Pelecanus erythrorhynchos Gmelin

AWPE

RANGE: Breeds locally from south-central British Columbia, the prairie provinces, and extreme western Ontario south to southern California, northern Utah, southern Montana, South Dakota, and locally on the Texas coast. Winters from the southern United States to Guatemala.

STATUS: *Common* to *abundant* migrant and summer visitant locally in the Chilcotin-Cariboo region. *Rare* spring and autumn transient in the west Kootenay, Okanagan, Nicola, and Thompson valleys; *very rare* in summer, *casual* in winter there. *Very rare* in the east Kootenay; *casual* in the far north. *ery rare* on the coast. One known breeding colony in the province.

NONBREEDING: The American White Pelican is locally distributed across southern British Columbia and the central-southern portion of the province; widely scattered elsewhere. It frequents a variety of freshwater and marine habitats from sea level to 1,220 m elevation. In the interior, large and small lakes are used in migration (88%; n=108), where open water, beaches, spits, sandbars, and mouths of rivers are used. Other habitats include rivers and ponds. Single birds have been seen in a garbage dump and in an open grain field, the latter with 1,000 Sandhill Cranes (*Grus canadensis*). On the coast, freshwater habitats are preferred (e.g. lakes, ponds, rivers, and sewage lagoons) but bays, sandy beaches, lagoons, islands, and harbours are visited in marine areas.

The American White Pelican is highly migratory. The continental population is divided by the Rocky Mountains into a western and eastern component. Banding returns indicate these 2 populations do not mix and each occupies separate summer and winter ranges (see Fig. 210).

The western population winters primarily in western Mexico. In March, migrants start moving northward through the western United States, some stopping at colonies en route. Pelicans enter British Columbia via eastern Washington and northern Idaho.

The major migratory route through the province appears to be north through the Okanagan valley, then northwest through the Nicola and Thompson valleys to Stum Lake in the Chilcotin Plateau. Migrants have been reported from early March through May. Most records, some of up to 200 birds, are between the second week of April and the first week of May. Arrival at the breeding colony (Fig. 203) coincides with spring melt. Pelicans arrive in the Chilcotin Plateau in mid-April (mean arrival date, 17 April), about 1 to 2 weeks before ice breakup. In some years, spring migrants appear at Lower Arrow Lake in the west Kootenay. There are only 2 spring records for the coast.

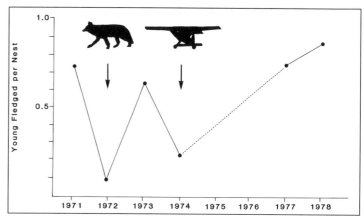

Figure 202. *Effect of coyote predation and human disturbance on the annual productivity of American White Pelicans at Stum Lake, British Columbia, 1971 to 1978 (after Dunbar 1984).*

In summer, pelicans forage primarily in the Chilcotin Plateau area between 3 km (Beaver Lake) and 142 km (Towdystan Lake) from the breeding colony (Fig. 201). They do not forage at the colony itself. According to Dunbar (1984), use of lakes for foraging depends on distance from the colony, abundance and availability of food, and presence of loafing sites. The lake most consistently used for feeding is Chilcotin Lake, 71 km west of the colony. Other important foraging sites are Beaver, Alex Graham, Rosita, Toutri, Alexis, and Palmer lakes.

Summer records more than 145 km from the breeding area probably represent nonbreeding subadults or, in southern areas, dispersal of birds from colonies in the northern United States (such as Idaho—Findholt and Trost 1981; Sloan 1982). For example, Dunbar (1984) reports:

> . . . a non-breeding two-year-old pelican, banded and wing-marked in the Warner Valley, Oregon, was observed at Stum Lake on June 22, 1977. This subadult was approximately 1,000 km from its natal colony.

Autumn migration generally follows the spring route, but is more prolonged. Flock sizes are smaller (usually less than 10 birds) and the birds disperse more widely. The southward movement occurs from early September to late November. Most birds pass through from late September to mid-October.

There are only 3 winter records. Extreme dates (excluding the winter records) for the coast are 23 April to 16 November, and for the interior are 10 March to 29 November.

BREEDING: The only known breeding location for the American White Pelican in British Columbia is at Stum Lake, 70 km northwest of Williams Lake (Figs. 201 and 204). Early reports by B.H. Thompson (1933) of suspected nesting at several other lakes (e.g. Anahim, Puntzi, and Pelican) were likely observations of foraging flocks.

Breeding at Stum Lake was first confirmed in 1939 (Munro, J.A. 1945a). The first census (140 nests) occurred in 1953 (Lies and Behle 1966). During the following 27 years, the colony varied in size from a low of 85 nests in 1968 to a maximum of 152 nests in 1967 (Dunbar 1984). Surveys in 1984 and 1986 showed 120 and 130 nests respectively, slightly above a 15-year average in the 1970s and 1980s of 112 nests (D. Dunbar pers. comm.). Fluctuations in annual reproductive success have been attributed to human disturbance (e.g. collectors, photographers, low-flying aircraft) and predation by coyotes (Fig. 202). Such disturbance results in delay of egg-laying or loss of eggs and young (Bunnell et al. 1981). For example, in 1986, all 130 nests were abandoned in mid-May after probable human disturbance. Some pelicans subsequently re-nested and produced 20 young which were still flightless on 1 October (A. Roberts pers. comm.).

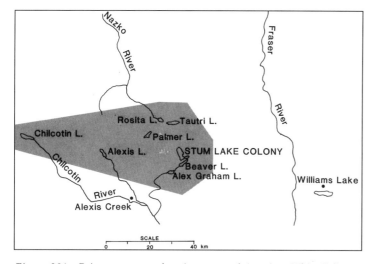

Figure 201. *Primary summer foraging range of American White Pelicans breeding at Stum Lake, British Columbia (after Dunbar 1984).*

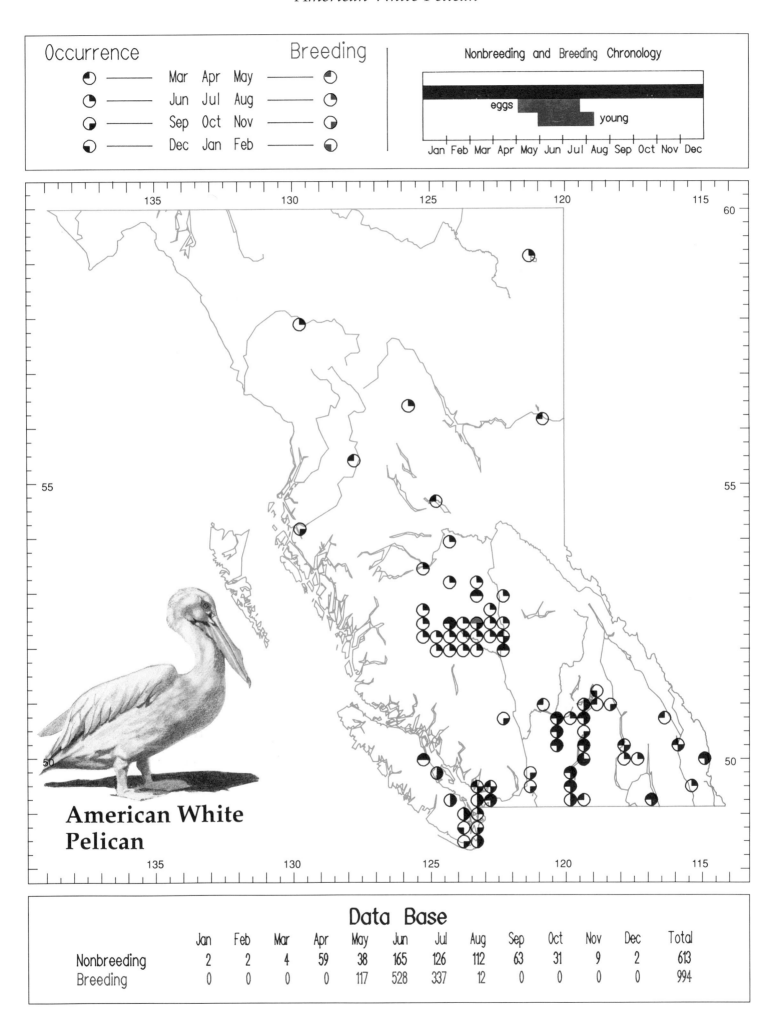

American White Pelican

Occurrence / Breeding

Occurrence			Breeding
◑ ———	Mar	Apr	May ——— ◑
◕ ———	Jun	Jul	Aug ——— ◕
◔ ———	Sep	Oct	Nov ——— ◔
◕ ———	Dec	Jan	Feb ——— ◕

Nonbreeding and Breeding Chronology

eggs   young

Jan Feb Mar Apr May Jun Jul Aug Sep Oct Nov Dec

Data Base

	Jan	Feb	Mar	Apr	May	Jun	Jul	Aug	Sep	Oct	Nov	Dec	Total
Nonbreeding	2	2	4	59	38	165	126	112	63	31	9	2	613
Breeding	0	0	0	0	117	528	337	12	0	0	0	0	994

Stum Lake is situated in the Chilcotin Plateau which is considered part of the Sub-Boreal Spruce Biogeoclimatic Zone of Annas and Coupe (1979). It covers about 900 ha and is protected and managed as a provincial park (White Pelican Park). It has a mean depth of 2.5 m, is slightly alkaline (pH=8.6), and lies at an elevation of 1,220 m. The nesting islands are usually low (to 6.7 m in height), bare, rocky outcroppings (Fig. 204). They are situated 80 to 600 m from shore and cover areas of 90 to 1,000 m^2 (Dunbar 1984). In 1986, the pelicans nested atypically on a forested island between well-spaced white spruce and western birch trees. There was, however, evidence of old nests on the island (A. Roberts pers. comm.).

Nests: Nest-building is initiated within 3 or 4 days after the pelicans arrive during the latter half of April. Nests, frequently closely spaced, were usually situated on the flatter areas of the nesting islands and were built among dead trees, logs, and rocks above a fringe of stinging nettle.

They were either heaped mounds of dirt, sticks, reeds, and assorted debris (88%; n=622) or shallow depressions in sand or gravel (12%), loosely lined with feathers, twigs, fish bones, or small stones.

Eggs: Dates for 345 clutches ranged from 4 May to 23 July. Peak egg-laying occurs during the second and third weeks of May (Dunbar 1984). Sizes for 437 clutches ranged from 1 to 4 eggs (1E-113, 2E-314, 3E-8, 4E-2), with 72% having 2 eggs (Fig. 205). Dunbar (1984) calculated mean clutch size at 1.95 eggs per nest during years without disturbance (1977, 1978) and at 1.69 eggs per nest during years of disturbance (1973, 1974, 1980). Incubation period is unknown. Bendire (1882), however, gives 29 days for eggs hatched under a domestic hen.

Young: Dates for 62 broods (Figs. 206 and 207) ranged from 30 May to 11 August. (The late record of flightless young on 1 October noted above was unusual, so it was not included in the calculations.) Most young, however, hatched during the latter half of June and fledged in late July and early August. The colony fledged from 10 to 89 young per year between 1971 and 1980 (Dunbar 1984). The same author indicated that the colony averaged 0.74 fledged young per nest or 0.44 young per egg laid in years with no disturbance. Fledging period is about 49 to 70 days (Harrison, C. 1978).

REMARKS: In autumn, pelicans from Stum Lake migrate west of the Rocky Mountains (Fig. 210) towards the southwestern United States. Birds have been recovered in Vancouver (Campbell 1970c), Washington, Oregon, Idaho, Utah, California, and Mexico. There is one spring recovery (Munro, J.A. and Cowan 1947): a bird banded at Molly Lake, Yellowstone National Park, Wyoming on 23 July 1933 was recovered 1,500 km away on the Tachi River, British Columbia on 19 May 1936.

In the late 1960s, the North American population of white pelicans was estimated at 30,000 pairs, about 15,000 pairs in Canada and an equal number in the United States (Lies and Behle 1966; Vermeer 1971). The 1979 surveys in the United States only indicated that populations may be declining (Sloan 1982). However, recent information suggests the population has increased on the continent to over 50,000 breeding pairs and its breeding grounds have expanded (Committee on the Status of Endangered Wildlife in Canada news release, 19 June 1987). It appears on the "Blue List" from 1972 to 1981 but was delisted in 1982 to a species of "special concern" due to vulnerability of nesting habitat (Tate and Tate 1982; Tate 1986). Originally on Canada's endangered species list because it was at risk from pesticides and destruction of nesting sites, it was removed from that list in 1987. It is, however, still officially listed as Endangered by the British Columbia Wildlife Act.

The American White Pelican was formerly known as the White Pelican.

POSTSCRIPT: In 1988, 150 nests were counted at the Stum Lake colony and by 16 June most eggs had hatched.

Figure 203. American White Pelicans at Stum Lake, spring 1973 (Ervio Sian).

Figure 204. *American White Pelicans and Herring Gulls at Stum Lake breeding colony, June 1973 (Ervio Sian).*

Figure 205. *American White Pelican eggs at Stum Lake, 12 June 1973 (Ervio Sian).*

Figure 206. *American White Pelican chick in nest scrape at Stum Lake, 16 June 1972 (Ervio Sian).*

Figure 207. American White Pelican feeding young at Stum Lake colony, 20 July 1971 (Ervio Sian).

Figure 208. American White Pelican, Portage Inlet, Victoria, 14 June 1986 (RBCM Photo 1143; Tim Zurowski).

Figure 209. American White Pelican at Eddontenajon Lake, 25 July 1981 (RBCM Photo 891; Richard L. Heathman).

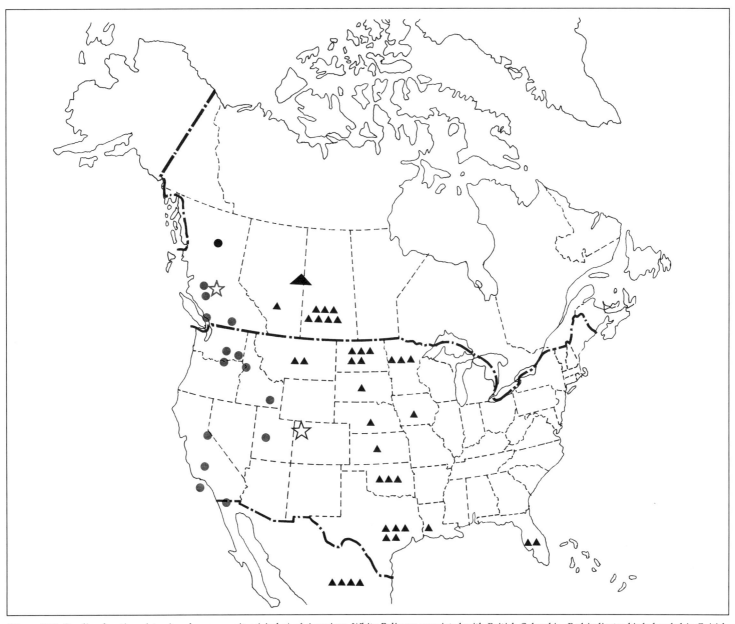

Figure 210. *Banding locations (stars) and recovery sites (circles) of American White Pelicans associated with British Columbia. Red indicates birds banded in British Columbia, black indicates birds banded elsewhere. Included for comparison are the recoveries (small triangles) of pelicans banded at the Primrose Lake, Saskatchewam colony (large triangle). There appears to be little mixing of birds between the 2 colonies (Saskatchewan data from Vermeer 1977).*

NOTEWORTHY RECORDS

Spring: Coastal - Pitt Meadows 23 Apr 1961-5 (Campbell 1970c); Willow Point 27 May 1986-1. **Interior** - Osoyoos Lake 26 May 1929-30 (Laing 1932); Duck Lake (Creston) 30 May 1983-33; Okanagan Lake 14 Mar 1963-8, 24 Apr 1962-32, 17 May 1967-16; Columbia Lake 18 May 1968-3 (Wilson, M.C. et al. 1972); Nicola Lake 14 Apr 1985-51 (Rogers, T.H. 1985c); Stump Lake (Quilchena) 15 Apr 1971-46, 23 Apr 1946-63+; Wilmer 1 May 1985-1; Salmon Arm 10 Mar 1946-5; junction North Thompson and South Thompson rivers 7 May 1926-200 (Racey 1933); Alkali Lake (Cariboo) 14 Apr 1958-55.

Summer: Coastal - Victoria 14 June 1986-1 (RBCM Photo 1143; Fig. 208); Fulford Harbour 1 Jul 1978-1; Roberts Bank 11 Jul 1983-13 (RBCM Photo 860); Deep Bay 17 Jun 1930-5 (Laing 1932); Courtenay 19 Jun 1932-7; Willow Point 18 Aug 1976-3. **Interior** - Duck Lake (Creston) Jun 1974-15 (RBCM Photo 943); Fernie 7 Aug 1953-50;

Skaha Lake 23 Jul 1963-65 (Rogers, T.H. 1963b); Naramata 14 Jun 1982-27; Burton 16 Jun 1983-120 (Rogers, T.H. 1983d); Slocan Lake 16 June 1983-32 (Campbell 1983d), 18 Jun 1983-60; Salmon Arm 12 to 13 Jun 1972-19; Tappen Bay 2 Jun 1987-16 adults (Campbell 1987e); Chilcotin Lake Jun to Jul 1978-60 to 70 foraging all summer (Dunbar 1984); Anahim Lake 17 Aug 1987-45; Kluskoil Lake 8 Jul 1977-13; Pantage Lake 10 Jul 1969-30; Aiken Lake 27 to 29 Aug 1987-1.

Autumn: Interior - Stum Lake 29 Sep 1986-20 young still being fed, left lake 8 Oct; Williams Lake 14 Oct 1986-5 immatures; Revelstoke (garbage dump) 13 to 16 Oct 1977-1 chased by gulls and ravens; Columbia Lake 6 Sep 1941-4 (Johnstone, W.B. 1949); Nakusp 14 Sep 1977-8; Kalamalka Lake 18 to 20 Nov 1968-1; Penticton Nov 1954-12 to 14; Vaseux Lake 14 Nov 1932-15; Creston 1 Oct to 29 Nov 1983-3, 12 Nov 1984-3 (Rogers, T.H. 1984a). **Coastal** - Courtenay 8 Nov

1940-2; Denman Island 12 Sep 1964-5; 32 km n Vancouver 15 Oct 1960-11 flying at 900 m; Jericho Beach 29 Sep to 14 Oct 1985-1 (RBCM Photo 1048); Nicomekl River 15 Oct to 11 Nov 1982-1 (RBCM Photo 1088 on 22 Oct); Saanich Inlet 15 Sep 1964-5; Esquimalt Lagoon 22 Sep 1964-5; Victoria 10 Oct 1958-15.

Winter: Interior - Seymour Arm (Shuswap Lake) all winter 1967/1968-1 photographed (Stevens and Belton 1969); Kelowna late Sep 1980 through May 1981-1 (Cannings, R.A. et al. 1987). **Coastal** - Cherry Point 28 Feb 1947-1 (Anonymous 1947).

Christmas Counts: Not recorded.

Extralimital Records: Coastal - Port Essington Oct 1912-1 (RBCM 200). **Interior** - Kotcho Lake 26 Jun 1982-1; Eddontenajon Lake 25 Jul to 16 Aug 1981-1 (RBCM Photo 891; Fig. 209); junction Peace and Pine rivers 14 May 1980-2.

Brown Pelican

BRPE

Pelecanus occidentalis Linnaeus

RANGE: Breeds locally, on islands on the Pacific coast, from southern California to Chile, including the Galapagos Islands; on the Atlantic Coast from North Carolina south around Florida and west to southern Texas. Also breeds in the West Indies, off the Yucatan Peninsula and Belize, and the coast of Venezuela.

STATUS: *Very rare* transient and winter visitant to coastal waters around southern Vancouver Island. *Casual* elsewhere on the south coast.

OCCURRENCE: The Brown Pelican was first recorded in British Columbia at Burrard Inlet in November 1880 (Fannin 1891). During the following 100 years it was reported on 15 occasions, from July to January, with most of those reports from August and November. This late summer-autumn trend continued into the 1980s when nearly 70 percent of all records were reported. The first spring records also occurred during the 1980s. A major influx came in 1983 (53% of 1980s records) when a change in the El Niño current produced warmer coastal waters. There were no records in 1984.

In 1985, the Brown Pelican was recorded from sometime in January to 15 April, and from 18 July to 20 December. Most records (79%) were in the Juan de Fuca Strait, from Port Renfrew to Victoria, at the extreme south end of Vancouver Island. Most observations were of single birds although a flock of 24 birds was recorded.

The Brown Pelican frequents shallow, coastal marine areas such as bays, offshore islands, spits, breakwaters, and open sandy beaches. Occasionally, it has been seen from commercial fish boats 4 km at sea. The ratio of adults to immatures in late summer and fall was 22:7.

REMARKS: A large-scale population collapse of the Brown Pelican, attributed to pesticide contamination, occurred in much of its northern range during the 1950s and 1960s (Schreiber and DeLong 1969; Schreiber and Risebrough 1972). Since the phase-out of DDT in North America, the recovery of the birds has been spectacular (J. Jehl pers. comm.). That recovery likely accounts for the recent increase in the number of records for British Columbia.

The occurrence of the Brown Pelican in British Columbia coincides with dispersal patterns from colonies in Mexico and California. Anderson, D.W. and Anderson (1976) note a general dispersal in late summer and autumn (late July through early November), the period when most occurrences (77%) have been recorded in British Columbia. The same authors, however, point out that dispersal and numbers fluctuate each year in relation to environmental changes that affect populations of major food fish.

British Columbia specimens are referred to as *P. o. californicus* (American Ornithologists' Union 1957).

Figure 211. Brown Pelican, Sooke Basin, 15 April 1982 (RBCM Photo 1238; Tim Zurowski).

NOTEWORTHY RECORDS

Spring: Coastal - Sooke Basin 15 Apr 1982-1 (RBCM Photo 1238; Fig. 211); Victoria 1 to 7 Mar 1986-1; Discovery Island 22 Mar 1982-1; Mandarte Island Mar 1982-1 found dead (UBC 14386). **Interior** - No records.

Summer: Coastal - Race Rocks 8 Aug 1939-4 (Munro, J.A. and Cowan 1947); Port Renfrew 3 Aug 1985-16 (Campbell 1985d), 23 Aug 1983-24+ (Hunn and Mattocks 1984); Cape Beale 29 Aug 1983-1; Bamfield 29 Aug 1985-6 (Campbell

1986a); Folger Island 6 Aug 1972-1; Long Beach 28 Jul 1979-1 immature; Passage Island 27 Aug 1983-1; Round Island (Alert Bay) 18 Jul 1913-1 (Bicknell 1914). **Interior** - No records.

Autumn: Interior - No records. **Coastal** - Seymour River (Burrard Inlet) Nov 1880-1 (Fannin 1891); Carmanah Point 11 Nov 1983-15; Island View Beach 1 to 7 Nov 1959-2; Victoria 2 to 18 Sep 1985-1; Esquimalt 28 Nov 1904-1 (RBCM 317); Pedder Bay 16 Nov 1983-1 (RBCM Photo

904); Race Rocks 15 Oct 1983-4 adults, 1 immature.

Winter: Interior - No records. **Coastal** - Powell River 3 Dec 1987-2; Trevor Channel 1 to 7 Dec 1981-1 adult; Oak Bay Feb 1983-1; Victoria 19 Dec 1932-1 (Kermode 1933); Albert Head 8 Dec 1983-2; Race Rocks Jan 1898-1 (RBCM 1510).

Christmas Counts: Not recorded.

Brown Pelican

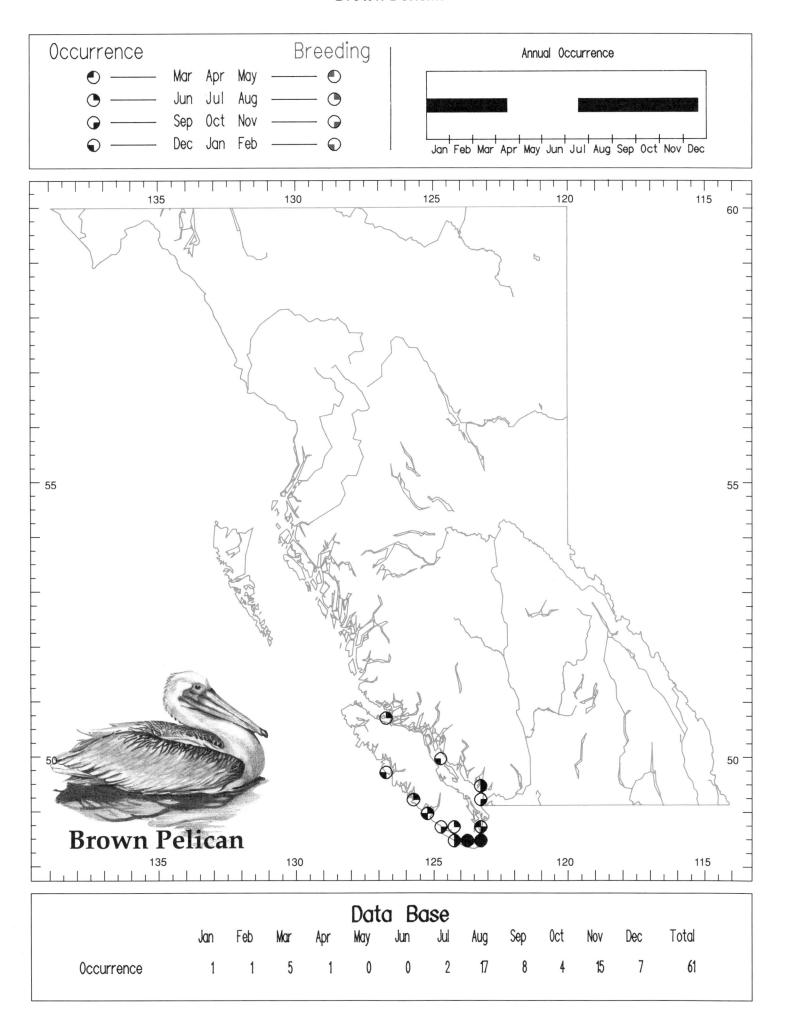

Occurrence

- Mar Apr May
- Jun Jul Aug
- Sep Oct Nov
- Dec Jan Feb

Breeding

Annual Occurrence

Jan Feb Mar Apr May Jun Jul Aug Sep Oct Nov Dec

Brown Pelican

Data Base

	Jan	Feb	Mar	Apr	May	Jun	Jul	Aug	Sep	Oct	Nov	Dec	Total
Occurrence	1	1	5	1	0	0	2	17	8	4	15	7	61

215

Double-crested Cormorant

DCCO

Phalacrocorax auritus (Lesson)

RANGE: Widespread in North America. Breeds from south-western Alaska, central Alberta, James Bay, and Newfoundland south to Mexico and the Bahamas. Winters along the Pacific coast, on the Atlantic coast from New England to Florida, and along the Gulf Coast to Central America.

STATUS: *Common* to *very abundant* resident in the Strait of Georgia and Juan de Fuca Strait. *Uncommon* in winter and *rare* in summer along the outer coast except on the Queen Charlotte Islands where it is an *uncommon* nonbreeding resident. *Very rare* in the interior. Local breeder to the inner south coast.

CHANGE IN STATUS: The Double-crested Cormorant has become established as a breeding species in British Columbia within the last 60 years (Campbell 1976b). It was first reported breeding in the Strait of Georgia in 1927, its occurrence perhaps being the result of dispersal from colonies along the northern Washington coast (Munro, J.A. 1937; Speich and Wahl 1989). By 1946, there were 2 colonies (Munro, J.A. and Cowan 1947) with a total population of about 50 pairs; by 1960, 4 colonies and about 150 pairs (Drent and Guiguet 1961); by 1975, 6 colonies and 671 pairs (Campbell 1976a); and by 1987, 13 colonies and about 2,000 pairs. Some of the smaller colonies are being abandoned due to human disturbance (e.g. Rose Islets) but new sites continue to be established and are growing in size (e.g. Great Chain Island).

Bones of the Double-crested Cormorant are abundant at archaeological sites throughout the Strait of Georgia which indicates occupancy of the area for the past 5,000 years (Hobson, K.A. and Driver 1989). Their recent arrival as a breeding species may have been a re-invasion after a decline for some unspecified reason.

The increase in numbers has also been noticeable in the size of wintering populations. The 1958 Christmas Counts for Vancouver, Ladner, and Victoria totalled 146 Double-crested Cormorants; the 1984 total was 1,123. In addition, the average winter population for these 3 localities has steadily increased, nearly tripling from 1960 through 1984 (Fig. 212).

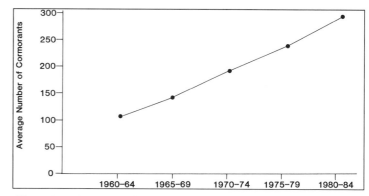

Figure 212. *Average number of Double-crested Cormorants tallied during 5-year periods from 1960 through 1984 for the Vancouver, Ladner, and Victoria Christmas Bird Count areas.*

Figure 213. *Roosting Double-crested Cormorants at Whiffin Spit, 24 September 1983 (Mark Nyhof).*

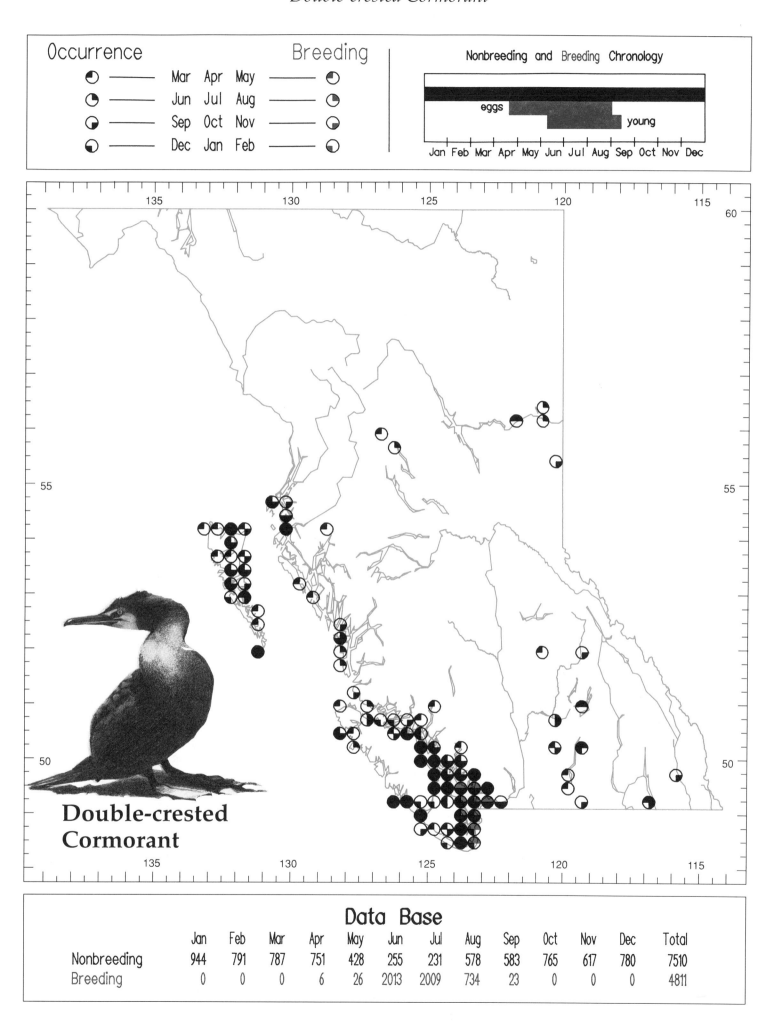

Double-crested Cormorant

Occurrence

◐	——	Mar Apr May	—— ◑
◔	——	Jun Jul Aug	—— ◕
◵	——	Sep Oct Nov	—— ◶
◖	——	Dec Jan Feb	—— ◗

Breeding

Nonbreeding and Breeding Chronology

eggs   young

Jan Feb Mar Apr May Jun Jul Aug Sep Oct Nov Dec

Data Base

	Jan	Feb	Mar	Apr	May	Jun	Jul	Aug	Sep	Oct	Nov	Dec	Total
Nonbreeding	944	791	787	751	428	255	231	578	583	765	617	780	7510
Breeding	0	0	0	6	26	2013	2009	734	23	0	0	0	4811

NONBREEDING: The Double-crested Cormorant is found in all coastal areas, including inlets, but is most abundant in the vicinity of the Strait of Georgia and Juan de Fuca Strait. In the southern interior, it has been recorded from Osoyoos Lake and Duck Lake (Creston) north to Messiter; less frequently in the central and northern interior.

The Double-crested Cormorant prefers marine habitats such as bays, inlets, harbours, lagoons, and estuaries but it regularly visits coastal freshwater lakes on southern Vancouver Island and the Fraser Lowlands. It frequently roosts with Pelagic and Brandt's cormorants on islets, wharves, log booms (Fig. 213), pilings, jetties, and dead trees. In the interior, it frequents lakes and large, slow rivers.

Seasonal movements are most pronounced on the outer coast and probably involve the race *P. a. cincinatus,* which breeds in southeastern Alaska. The spring movement occurs from mid-March to late May but is heaviest during late April and early May. A few nonbreeding birds spend the summer on the outer coast. Autumn migration is evident from late August to early November. In winter, small numbers are widely scattered in protected waters along the outer coast.

Movements on inner coastal waters are more limited and less well known. There appears to be an influx of migrant flocks in early September but the birds are widely distributed in winter. They congregate, again, in February and March when Pacific herring and Pacific sand lance are spawning.

In the interior, extreme dates of occurrence are 11 April and 28 October except for a single winter record.

BREEDING: The Double-crested Cormorant breeds from Chain Islands north to Franklin Island and east to Christie Islet. A single nest was also found on a piling in the Fraser River 30 km inland near the Port Mann bridge (Campbell and Gibbard 1984).

Most colonies are located on bare areas of rocky islands, either on top of low islands or on slopes of higher ones (Fig. 215). The only "mainland" colony, other than the one near the Port Mann Bridge, was situated at the base of a cliff at Bare Point (Chemainus) — an active and noisy industrial area; it was not used by the birds in 1987. Both it and the colony on Ballingal Islets are situated in trees. Many pairs take advantage of pilings near Crofton. The Double-crested Cormorant frequently nests with Pelagic Cormorants in mixed colonies. Colony elevations varied from 4 to 17 m above the high tide line.

Occupancy at smaller colonies, such as Rose Islets, Canoe Islet, or Pam Rock, varies from year to year depending on human disturbance, weather, and predation, but is more stable at larger colonies. The largest colony recorded, approached 1,500 pairs in 1981 (Table 13). The total breeding population in British Columbia in 1987 was 1,982 pairs (Vermeer et al. 1989). The Alaskan population is about 2,750 pairs and the Washington population about 1,650 pairs (United States Department of the Interior 1988; Speich and Wahl 1989).

Nests: Most nests were constructed on bare rock, but trees (Fig. 216), driftlogs, pilings, and man-made structures were also used. Nests ranged from sparse collections of twigs and seaweed (Fig. 217) to elaborate structures of sticks, well-lined with grasses, seaweed, rootlets, feathers, and assorted marine debris including rope, plastic bags, fishing lures, and paper. Most were heavily covered by excrement which became more noticeable as the breeding season progressed. The largest nest was 0.9 m high and 0.7 m across.

Eggs: Dates for 3,628 clutches ranged from 20 April (Drent et al. 1964) to 2 September with 54% recorded between 22 June and 10 July. Late dates reflect attempts at replacing egg losses to gulls and crows. Clutch size ranged from 1 to 11 eggs (1E-638, 2E-763, 3E-1,335, 4E-756, 5E-128, 6E-3, 7E-1, 8E-1, 9E-2, 11E-1) with 79% having 2 to 4 eggs. In 15 of 27 nests monitored by van Tets (1959), the incubation period was 27 or 28 days.

Young: Dates for 1,183 broods ranged from 10 June to 14 September with 68% recorded between 10 July and 15 August. Brood size ranged from 1 to 8 young (1Y-213, 2Y-351, 3Y-396, 4Y-189, 5Y-25, 6Y-4, 7Y-2, 8Y-3) with 63% having 2 or 3 young (Figs.

218 and 219). Fledging period is 35 to 42 days (Lewis, H.F. 1929). It is unlikely that small young found in late August and September would survive to fledge. Drent et al. (1964) suggest that some pairs may attempt to raise 2 broods per season in British Columbia.

REMARKS: See Robertson (1971) for additional information on breeding biology.

The Double-crested Cormorant appears on the "Blue List" from 1972 to 1981 (Tate 1981). It was delisted in 1982 but maintained as a species of "special concern" because of the western Great Lakes population, and the potential effects of acid rain.

The diet of the Double-crested Cormorant has been studied by Robertson (1974a). He has shown that during the summer this species is primarily a bottom feeder and does not prey on commercially valuable species. Most prey species (Fig. 214) included penpoint and crescent gunnels, shiner perch, snake prickleback, and Pacific sand lance. The gunnels and perch contributed 72.2% to total biomass.

POSTSCRIPT: In 1988 the total breeding population had expanded to 2,032 pairs at 15 sites (Rodway In press).

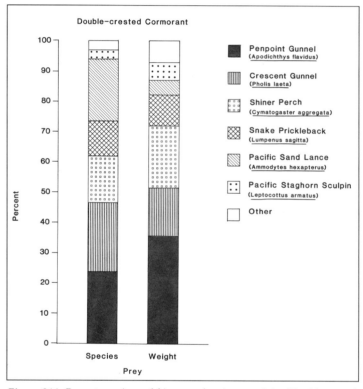

Figure 214. Percent species and biomass of major prey fed to Double-crested Cormorant chicks at Mandarte Island, British Columbia, 1969 to 1971 (adapted from Robertson 1974a).

Figure 215. *Double-crested Cormorant colony, Mandarte Island, 10 July 1981 (R. Wayne Campbell). Note observation hut built by researchers from the University of British Columbia.*

Figure 216. *Double-crested Cormorant colony, Ballingal Islets Park, 27 July 1976 (R. Wayne Campbell).*

Figure 217. *Comparison in structure between nests of the Double-crested Cormorant (left) and Pelagic Cormorant (right), Greater Chain Island, 10 July 1981 (R. Wayne Campbell).*

Figure 218. *Double-crested Cormorant nestlings at Mandarte Island, 10 July 1981 (R. Wayne Campbell). Note the size difference between young, the result of egg predation by Glaucous-winged Gulls and Northwestern Crows.*

Figure 219. *Near fledging Double-crested Cormorants at Christie Islet, 2 August 1973 (R. Wayne Campbell).*

TABLE 13
Double-crested Cormorant: location, history, and size of major colonies in British Columbia.

Location	First Record	Low Survey Results[1]		Year	High Survey Results[1]		Year	Recent Survey Results[1]		Year	Source[2]
South Coast - Colonies > 50 nests or pairs											
Ballingall Islets	1933	14	N	1974	74	N	1957	25	Nc	1987	1,2,3,7
Bare Point[3]	1973	118	N	1981	198	N	1983	0		1987	1,2,6
Chain Islets	1976	2	N	1976	510	Nc	1987			1987	1,2,5
Christie Island[4]	1941	1	N	1963	169	N	1981	119	Nc	1987	1,2,3
Five Finger Island	1959		C	1959	138	Nc	1987			1987	2,3
Franklin Island	1967	11	N	1968	91	N	1978	5	Nc	1987	1,2
Mandarte Island	1927	3	N	1927	1463	N	1981	972	Nc	1987	1,2,8
Rose Islets	1963	2	Nc	1987	182	N	1968			1987	2,4
Sand Heads	1987				86	Nc	1987			1987	2
Shoal Islands	1987				65	Nc	1987			1987	2

[1] C - nesting confirmed but no count or estimate made; N - nests. All data are estimates unless noted as follows: c - complete count.

[2] 1 - British Columbia Nest Records Scheme; 2 - Vermeer et al. 1989; 3 - Drent and Guiguet 1961; 4 - Rodway and Campbell 1977; Campbell 1983f; 6 - Vermeer and Rankin 1984; 7 - Munro, J.A. 1937; 8 - Munro, J.A. 1928.

[3] On 8 July 1988, 25 active nests were counted at Bare Point (A.M. Breault pers. comm.)

[4] Includes Pam Rock.

NOTEWORTHY RECORDS

Spring: Coastal - Clover Point 3 Mar 1976-72, 23 May 1983-54; Portage Inlet 19 Mar 1979-75, 14 Apr 1980-65 adults; Nitinat Lake 24 Apr 1980-12 on small islet; Long Harbour 7 Mar 1976-120; Tofino 2 May 1970-12 (Hatler et al. 1978); Departure Bay 10 Mar 1931-250 (Munro, J.A. and Cowan 1947); Stanley Park (Vancouver) 22 Mar 1974-50; Reifel Island 1 May 1982-500; Thunder Bay 30 Mar 1977-50; Masset Inlet 14 Apr 1935-100 (Munro, J.A. and Cowan 1947); Green Island 17 May 1978-2. **Interior** - Vaseux Lake 17 May 1987-1 immature; Summerland 11 Apr 1970-1; Okanagan Landing 25 May 1926-1 male (MVZ 99165); Salmon Arm 21 May 1987-2; Canim Lake 19 May 1986-1 adult (Campbell 1986c); One Eye Lake 17 May 1960-1 (Paul 1964); Tetana Lake May 1938-1 (Munro, J.A. and Cowan 1947).

Summer: Coastal - Gonzales Point (Victoria) 13 Jun 1983-57, 2 Jul 1982-42; Sidney 21 Aug 1982-152 off spit; Bamfield 29 Jul 1977-5; Tsawwassen 15 Jun 1981-35 roosting on jetty; Mitlenatch Island 5 Jun 1964-32 roosting, 23 Jun 1965-20+ (Campbell and Kennedy 1965); Pulteney Point 21 Aug 1976-92; Brooks Peninsula 9 Aug 1981-6; Masset 1 Jun 1939-1 female (RBCM 11329). **Interior** - Leach Lake 28 Jun 1983-1; South Thompson River (11 km e Kamloops) 7 Jun 1982-1 immature; Tranquille 14 Aug 1982-1 immature; Anglemont 1 Jul 1982-1; Takla Lake 14 Jul 1939-1 (Stanwell-Fletcher and Stanwell-Fletcher 1943); Peace River at Lynx Creek 18 Aug 1986-1 immature (McEwan, C. and Johnston 1987); Fort St. John 13 Jun 1986-1 adult, 1 immature (Campbell 1986c).

Autumn: Interior - Cutbank Lake 15 Sep 1977-1; Messiter 26 Oct 1986-1 (Rogers, T.H. 1987); Kamloops 4 Oct 1982-1 immature; Fort Steele 28 Oct 1912-1 (Brooks and Swarth 1925); Osoyoos Lake 17 Sep to 1 Oct 1928-1; **Coastal** - Prince Rupert 13 Oct 1972-12; Sewall 13 Sep 1975-30; Queen Charlotte City 7 Sep 1981-24 adults; Hornby Island 14 Nov 1978-17; Qualicum Beach 9 Nov 1970-15; Crescent Beach 23 Nov 1976-32; Tsawwassen 25 Oct 1987-110 on jetty breakwater; Active Pass 8 Nov 1974-30; Cowichan Bay 18 Nov 1980-29; Bedwell Bay 26 Nov 1975-65; Sidney Spit 30 Sep 1984-2,000+ flying south in continuous lines; Esquimalt Lagoon 25 Sep 1980-91; Gonzales Point (Victoria) 23 Sep 1985-449, 2 Nov 1985-395; Whiffin Spit 14 Oct 1981-85 mostly immatures.

Winter: Interior - Okanagan Lake Dec 1897-1 (Munro, J.A. and Cowan 1947). **Coastal** - Wainwright Basin 2 Feb 1978-57 (Martin 1978); Tasu Sound 29 to 31 Jan 1973-8; Cape St. James 26 Dec 1981-8; Seymour Narrows 4 Dec 1977-26; Powell River 12 Jan 1982-4; Westham Island 28 Feb 1974-80; Departure Bay 8 Jan 1965-2,500+, 21 Jan 1935-250 (Munro, J.A. and Cowan 1947); Active Pass 3 Feb 1973-400+; Folger Island 11 Feb 1976-38; Portage Inlet 26 Jan 1978-59, 15 Feb 1979-125.

Christmas Counts: Interior - Not recorded. **Coastal** - Recorded from 23 of 28 localities and on 81% of all counts. Maxima: Victoria 15 Dec 1979-**636**, all-time Canadian high count (Anderson, R.R. 1980); Vancouver 18 Dec 1983-379; Ladner 23 Dec 1984-336.

Brandt's Cormorant

BRCO

Phalacrocorax penicillatus (Brandt)

RANGE: Restricted to the Pacific coast of North America. Breeds from south-coastal Alaska south in increasing numbers to central California, then decreasing in numbers to Baja California. Winters mainly from south coastal British Columbia southward.

STATUS: Locally, and seasonally, an *abundant* to *very abundant* resident. *Fairly common* to *common* elsewhere along the coast, chiefly as a migrant. *Very abundant* throughout the year, as a nonbreeding bird, in the southern Gulf Islands. *Common* to *abundant* elsewhere in the Strait of Georgia and Juan de Fuca Strait. Local breeder on the south-central west coast of Vancouver Island and at the entrance to Juan de Fuca Strait.

CHANGE IN STATUS: Although nesting was suspected in British Columbia during the first half of the twentieth century (Brooks and Swarth 1925; Drent and Guiguet 1961; Martin and Myres 1969), breeding was not confirmed until 1965 when a colony of 110 nests was located on Sea Lion Rocks off Long Beach (Stirling and Buffam 1966; Fig. 221). That remained the only known breeding site through 1967 and 1968 (Campbell and Stirling 1968a). Thereafter, the birds spread to other sites off Long Beach and in Barkley Sound where 4 colonies were found. Some were only temporary and occupancy shifted from one year to the next with only 2 sites occupied at one time. Hatler et al. (1978) summarized their numbers and distribution from 1965 to 1975. A peak population of 150 pairs was found in 1970. By 1982, there were less than 50 pairs breeding in the province. There have been no surveys off Long Beach or in Barkley Sound since then. In 1987, 3 nests with young were found at Race Rocks in Juan de Fuca Strait.

They may have bred on Sartine Island off the northwest tip of Vancouver Island. Vermeer et al. (1976a) observed 20 nests with "attending adults" from a boat in 1975. Nest contents were not checked and the birds may have been in a preliminary

Figure 220. Banding locations (stars) and recovery sites (circles) of Brandt's Cormorants associated with British Columbia. Red indicates birds banded in the province, black indicates birds banded elsewhere.

Figure 221. Brandt's Cormorant colony at Sea Lion Rocks, 10 August 1969 (R. Wayne Campbell).

Brandt's Cormorant

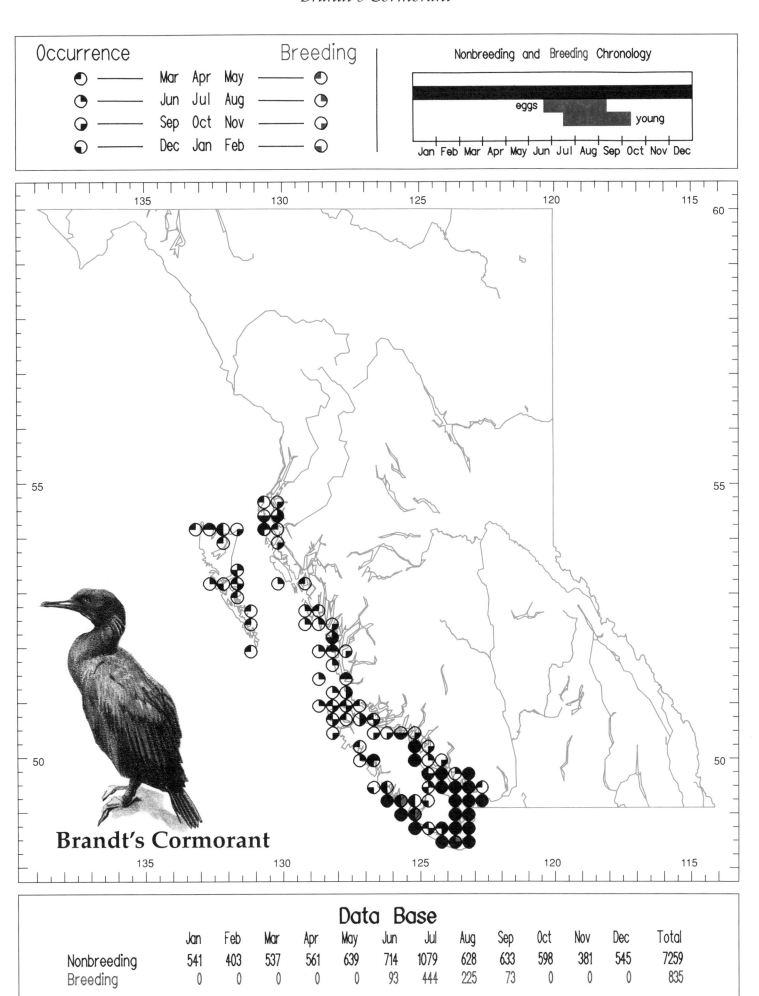

Brandt's Cormorant

Data Base

	Jan	Feb	Mar	Apr	May	Jun	Jul	Aug	Sep	Oct	Nov	Dec	Total
Nonbreeding	541	403	537	561	639	714	1079	628	633	598	381	545	7259
Breeding	0	0	0	0	0	93	444	225	73	0	0	0	835

phase of colonization during which courtship and nest building occur without egg-laying (van Tets 1959). Brandt's Cormorants were not present on Sartine Island or any other Scott Island when landings were made during surveys in 1987 (M. Lemon pers. comm.).

Band returns suggest that California is the origin of birds breeding in British Columbia. The southern population has experienced a great increase in numbers since the turn of the century (Ainley and Lewis 1974), but may be declining again due to the effect of a string of El Niño events. If so, it may be a species that undergoes long term cycles or pulses in its distribution.

NONBREEDING: The Brandt's Cormorant occurs along the British Columbia coast throughout the year. It is not known to frequent mainland inlets. Marine waters are preferred and, unlike the Double-crested Cormorant, the Brandt's Cormorant avoids fresh or brackish waters. It is rarely seen in offshore waters except during migration, and avoids land, even by flying around spits and jetties. It frequents bays, lagoons, harbours, and narrows with strong currents where nearby rocks or islets provide roosting sites. The centre of abundance is the Gulf Islands and Juan de Fuca Strait. Other significant but smaller concentrations occur in Clayoquot Sound and Barkley Sound.

Seasonal movements are not well understood. They are most pronounced on the outer south coast. The spring movement occurs from about mid-March to mid-May. It is not known whether the breeding population originates from the wintering population or from the southern groups, or both. For example, an adult colour-banded on the Farrallon Islands off California in 1971 was seen on Starlight Reef in 1974 (Hatler et al. 1978).

The first post-breeding dispersal of birds from colonies in the western United States occurs in July and August when many are seen flying northward just offshore. Only small numbers go farther than Clayoquot Sound. In September and October, there is a general but gradual movement southward to California (Fig. 220; Hatler et al. 1978) but some birds overwinter. Along the north coast, including the Queen Charlotte Islands, the Brandt's Cormorant is mainly a vagrant.

In the Strait of Georgia and Juan de Fuca Strait, seasonal movements vary greatly between locations. They represent changes in local foraging and roosting areas (Fig. 222). In Active Pass, a favourite foraging area, small numbers appear in late September and build to a peak of many thousands in February and March (Edwards 1965). That peak corresponds with the spawning of Pacific herring, a relationship also evident in neighbouring areas such as Ganges Harbour (Carson and Howsam 1978). On Mandarte Island, small numbers are present in May and June; in July adults begin returning. By the end of August, the population may reach 1,000 birds (Drent et al. 1964). In mid-September, on San Juan Island, Washington, D.A. Manuwal (pers. comm.) has seen 3,000 to 4,000 Brandt's Cormorants. At least 800 birds roost on Mandarte Island and smaller numbers are found on other Gulf Islands in winter.

The total winter population in the inner coastal waters ranges between 10,000 and 15,000 birds.

BREEDING: The Brandt's Cormorant breeds on the west coast of Vancouver Island in Barkley Sound, off Long Beach and at Race Rocks. Known colonies are all on bare rocky islands (Table 14; Fig. 223). During the 22 years Brandt's Cormorants have bred in the province, individual colonies have ranged in size from 3 to 110 breeding pairs. The breeding population has decreased gradually from a peak of 150 pairs in 1970 to about 60 pairs in 1982. Numbers fluctuate greatly from year to year. Colonies are shared with Pelagic Cormorants and Glaucous-winged Gulls.

Figure 222. *Local movements of Brandt's Cormorants in Haro Strait, December 1975 (R. Wayne Campbell).*

Figure 223. Brandt's Cormorant colony, Great Bear Rock, 24 July 1970 (R. Wayne Campbell).

	TABLE 14.				
	Brandt's Cormorant: location, history, and size of major colonies in British Columbia.				

Location	First Record	Low Survey Results[1] Year	High Survey Results[1] Year	Recent Survey Results[1] Year	Source[2]
South Coast - All colonies					
Great Bear Rock	1970	61 N 1970	107 Nc 1971	0 1982	1,4,5
Race Rocks	1987		3 Nc 1987	1987	2
Sea Lion Rocks	1965	5 Nc 1973	110 N 1965	29 Nc 1977	1,2,3,6
Starlight Reef	1972	0 1976	82 Nc 1974	31 Nc 1982	1,2,4
"White" Island	1969		27 Nc 1969	0 1975	1

[1] N - nests. All data are estimates unless noted as follows: c - complete count.

[2] 1 - Hatler et al. 1978; 2 - British Columbia Nest Records Scheme; 3 - Stirling and Buffam 1966; 4 - Rodway et al. In prep.; 5 - Guiguet 1971; 6 - Campbell and Stirling 1968a.

Forty-three pairs breed in Alaska, while the Washington population is estimated at 277 pairs (United States Department of the Interior 1988; Speich and Wahl 1989).

Nests: Nests were built close together on bare rock on the lee side of islands, usually on the shoulder or top of slopes (Fig. 225). Precipitous sites were not used. Nests were compact, circular structures built almost entirely of Torrey's surf-grass (Fig. 224). Seaweeds, marine debris, and bits of driftwood were used infrequently. Nests become covered by guano as the breeding season progresses.

Most nests ranged from 40 to 80 cm in outside diameter and were 15 to 36 cm in height.

Eggs: The Brandt's Cormorant is the latest breeder of the 3 cormorants in the province. Dates for 593 clutches ranged from 20 June to 9 September with 52% recorded between 3 July and 4 August. Clutch size ranged from 1 to 6 eggs (1E-86, 2E-160, 3E-239, 4E-102, 5E-5, 6E-1) with 67% having 2 or 3 eggs (Fig. 225). Incubation period is 28 to 32 days (Speich and Wahl 1989).

Young: Dates for 242 broods ranged from 15 July to 9 September with 52% recorded between 4 and 30 August. Calculated dates indicate unfledged young could be found as late as 10 October. Brood size ranged from 1 to 6 young (1Y-38, 2Y-78, 3Y-81, 4Y-39, 5Y-3, 6Y-3) with 66% having 2 or 3 young (Fig. 226). Nestling/fledging period is 40 to 42 days (Speich and Wahl 1989).

REMARKS: van Tets (1959) presents an overview of the natural history and nonbreeding behaviour of the species in British Columbia.

POSTSCRIPT: Several significant roosting concentrations were noted in 1988 and 1989: Thornton Islands 11 July 1988-200 and 22 January 1989-610 (Rodway et al. In press); Steele Rock 12 June 1988-116 and Mission Islands 22 January 1989-300.

On 29 July 1989 a small colony of 39 pairs of Brandt's Cormorants was found breeding on Sartine Island (Fig. 227) in the Scott Islands off the northwestern tip of Vancouver Island. Twenty-three nests contained young (1Y-10, 2Y-7, 3Y-4, 4Y-1, 5Y-1), 8 nests were empty, and 8 nests had unknown contents (M.S. Rodway pers. comm.).

Figure 224. *Brandt's Cormorant nest and eggs, "White" Island (Portland Point), 4 August 1969 (R. Wayne Campbell).*

Figure 225. *Brandt's Cormorant colony showing location and position of nests on Sea Lion Rocks, 3 July 1967 (R. Wayne Campbell).*

Figure 226. *Brandt's Cormorant nestlings at Starlight Reef, 4 August 1974 (R. Wayne Campbell).*

Figure 227. *Sartine Island, 29 July 1989 (Kenneth R. Summers). A new colony of Brandt's Cormorant was found in the rock crevices near the centre of the figure. This is the most northern colony in the province.*

NOTEWORTHY RECORDS

Spring: Coastal - Victoria 20 Mar 1964-1,500+ migrating during the day, 24 May 1983-64; Active Pass 20 Mar 1964-4,000 (Edwards 1965), 1 Apr 1978-3,847, 2 Apr 1976-3,700; Ganges Harbour 4 Mar 1978-5,905, 11 Mar 1978-7,040 (Carson and Howsam 1978); Mackenzie Bay 16 Mar 1981-1,500; Dodd's Narrows to Yellow Point 31 Mar 1939-350 (Munro, J.A. and Cowan 1947); Mission Point (Gibsons) 15 Mar 1987-5,000+; Mitlenatch Island 17 May 1963-100 (van Tets 1963); Menzies Bay 23 Apr 1966-420; Kyuquot May 1940-50 (Munro, J.A. and Cowan 1947); Masset Inlet 14 Apr 1935-50 (Munro, J.A. and Cowan 1947); Smith Island 20 Mar 1978-30 (Martin 1978). **Interior** - No records.

Summer: Coastal - Clover Point 18 Jun 1982-15; Cattle Point 20 Aug 1976-1,000; Sidney Island 28 Jul 1983-600; Cape Beale 6 Aug 1969-800+ flying northward during a four hour count; Great Bear Rock 24 Jul 1970-155 subadults roosting; Amphitrite Point 15 Jun 1949-250+ (Martin and Myres 1969); Sea Lion Rocks Jul 1965-"1,000+ roosting cormorants flew off ... leaving the breeding birds on their nests" (Stirling 1966a); Calvert Island 19 Jun 1976 - 22; Goose Group 15 Jun 1948-1 female (UBC 3150); McInnes Island 23 Jun 1976-32. **Interior** - No records.

Autumn: Interior - No records. **Coastal** - Hansen's Lagoon 28 Oct 1973-201 (Hazelwood 1973); Tofino Inlet 13 Sep 1969-1,500 (Campbell and Shepard 1971); Great Bear Rock 3 Sep 1983-1,200; Cape Beale 14 Oct 1978-150; Active Pass 28 Oct 1977-1,500, 14 Nov 1970-1,200; Chain Islets 13 Sep 1958-2,000 roosting; Trial Islands 7 Oct 1981-5,000 on the water; Race Rocks 27 Sep 1977-133+, 26 Oct 1986-2,000 on rocks with hauled out sea lions.

Winter: Interior - No records. **Coastal** - Masset 14 Dec 1972-380 (Robertson 1974); Discovery Passage 26 Feb 1971-365 (Crowell and Nehls 1971a); Clayoquot Sound 11 to 13 Dec 1972-380 (Robertson 1974); Lemmen's Inlet 21 Dec 1981-550, 12 Jan 1982-700+; Folger Island 11 Feb 1976-110; Ganges Harbour 26 Feb 1978-7,236 (Carson and Howsam 1978); Active Pass 23 Dec 1974-7,000 (Rodway and Campbell 1977); Esquimalt Lagoon Dec 1959-2,400 (Stirling 1960b); Greater Chain Island 5 Jan 1976-120; between Trial Islands and Race Rocks 18 Feb 1979-1,000.

Christmas Counts: Interior - Not recorded. **Coastal** - Recorded from 22 of 28 localities and on 63% of all counts. Maxima: Pender Island 20 Dec 1983-**3,667**, all-time Canadian high count (Monroe 1984); Nanaimo 26 Dec 1968-2,262; Victoria 15 Dec 1979-1,664.

Pelagic Cormorant

PECO

Phalacrocorax pelagicus Pallas

RANGE: Breeds from northern Alaska south through the Bering Sea to the Aleutian Islands and along the Pacific coast of North America to central Baja California. Also breeds on the northeast coast of Asia.

STATUS: *Common* to *abundant* resident and *fairly common* to *common* migrant along the coast. Widespread coastal breeder.

NONBREEDING: The Pelagic Cormorant is widespread and occurs along the inner and outer coastal areas of the province throughout the year. It rarely occurs very far up inlets, and there are no records from freshwater locations.

The Pelagic Cormorant prefers rocky coasts and forages in bays, harbours, lagoons, surge narrows, and coves. It usually roosts on rocky unvegetated islets, reefs, and cliffs but also uses log booms, spits, promontories, and man-made structures such as bridges, wharves, and light stations. Diurnal roost sites may be selected due to their proximity to foraging areas (Hobson, K.A. and Sealy 1986). Pelagic Cormorants usually occur as scattered individuals and small flocks, but in late winter or early spring, aggregations of hundreds occur to feed at Pacific herring spawning sites. Immature birds frequently roost at breeding colonies.

Spring migration occurs mostly in late March and April while the autumn movement begins in September and continues through October. Migratory movements are most noticeable along the outer coasts.

Population shifts occur among Pelagic Cormorants throughout their range. Most movements are related to seasonal changes in fish availability. Largest numbers occur throughout the year in the Strait of Georgia.

BREEDING: The Pelagic Cormorant breeds throughout inner and outer coastal areas. Colonies are located on cliffs of forested and grassy, rocky islands (Fig. 228), and headlands but the cormorants also use caves, beached driftlogs, and man-made structures such as navigation beacons (Fig. 230), bridge pylons, empty ship hulls, and abandoned towers (Manuwal and Campbell 1979; Carter, H.R. et al. 1984; Hobson, K.A. and Wilson 1985).

There are 145 historical breeding sites in the province (Rodway et al. In prep.). The population is centred on the south coast where 55% occur in the Strait of Georgia and 28% on the west coast of Vancouver Island. Major colonies are listed in Table 15. Not all sites are used every year, but 59% of the sites were used on the most recent surveys. Sites range from a single nest (Lyell Island in 1986) to 550 nests (Mandarte Island in 1983). On the outer coast, Solander Island (see Fig. 97) supports the largest colony: 416 nests in 1976. The largest colony on the Queen Charlotte Islands is on Tian Islets (Fig. 232) where 98 nests were found in 1986. The total breeding population in British Columbia is estimated at 4,196 pairs (Rodway In press). There has been a decline in both the number of breeding sites and breeding pairs in Queen Charlotte Strait, on the northern mainland coast and in the Queen Charlotte Islands between 1977 and 1986, from 661 pairs nesting at 34 sites to 274 pairs nesting at 22 sites (Rodway In press). Populations in Alaska are estimated at 22,000 pairs (United States Department of the Interior 1988) and in Washington at 2,500 pairs (Speich and Wahl 1989).

Nests: Nests are positioned on narrow ledges of cliffs (Fig. 229), within sea caves, or on faces near the top of small rocky islets. In Barkley Sound, 72% of 29 breeding sites were on ledges in caves (Carter, H.R. et al. 1984). On man-made structures, narrow beams, ledges, walkways, and gunnels are used. All large

Figure 228. *Pelagic Cormorant colony on Mitlenatch Island, 26 July 1965 (R. Wayne Campbell).*

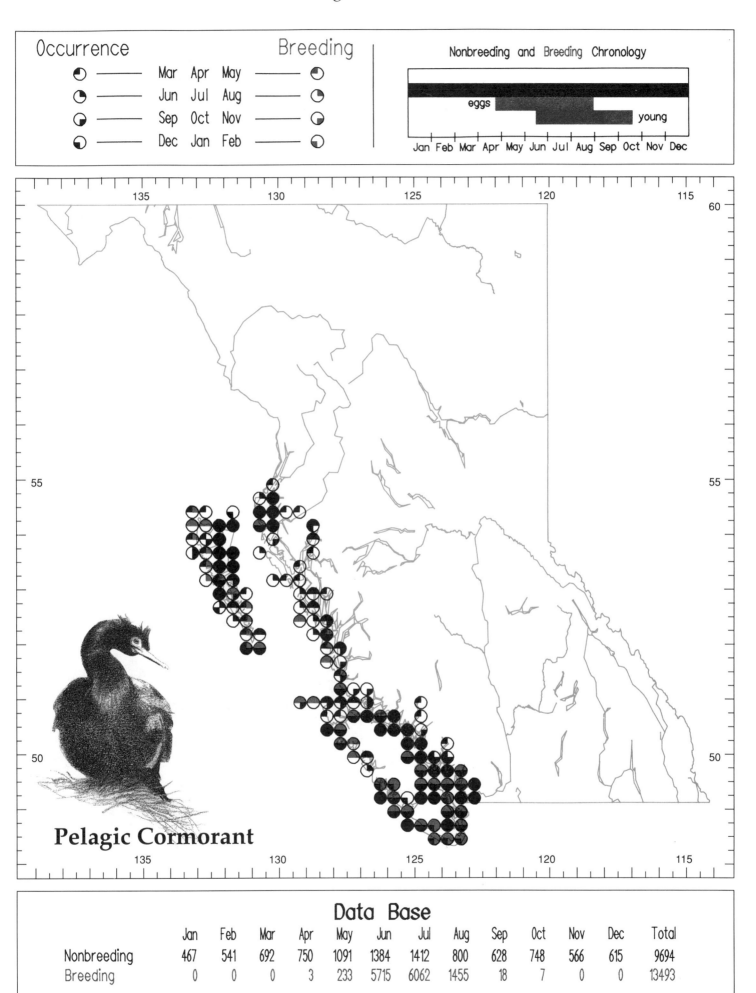

Occurrence

◐ ———	Mar Apr May	——— ◑
◔ ———	Jun Jul Aug	——— ◔
◕ ———	Sep Oct Nov	——— ◕
◑ ———	Dec Jan Feb	——— ◑

Breeding

Nonbreeding and Breeding Chronology

eggs

young

Jan Feb Mar Apr May Jun Jul Aug Sep Oct Nov Dec

Pelagic Cormorant

Data Base

	Jan	Feb	Mar	Apr	May	Jun	Jul	Aug	Sep	Oct	Nov	Dec	Total
Nonbreeding	467	541	692	750	1091	1384	1412	800	628	748	566	615	9694
Breeding	0	0	0	3	233	5715	6062	1455	18	7	0	0	13493

colonies are on cliffs. Elevations of nests ranged between 1.8 and 25 m above the high tide line.

Nests are usually compact structures, but vary in size depending on the substrate. They are composed of seaweeds, grasses, feathers, and general marine debris that can include rope, plastic, and other man-made objects (see Fig. 217). By the end of the breeding season, the nest is caked with excrement. Nests are lined with dry vegetation. Occasionally, eggs are laid on bare rock with only a scattering of materials. Nests may be used for several successive seasons, especially along the inner coast. The largest nest reported was 41 cm high and 48 cm in diameter.

Eggs: Dates for 10,927 clutches ranged from 25 April (Hobson, K.A. and Wilson 1985) to 30 August with 52% recorded between 19 June and 8 July. On Mandarte Island from 1957 to 1959, laying began in mid-May and most first clutches were started before mid-June (Drent et al. 1964). Sizes for 10,913 clutches ranged from 1 to 8 eggs (1E-1,796, 2E-2,048, 3E-3,422, 4E-3,241, 5E-369, 6E-26, 7E-8, 8E-3) with 61% having 3 or 4 eggs. Incubation period averages 31 days (Drent and Guiguet 1961).

Young: Dates for 2,566 broods ranged from 18 June to 20 October with 51% recorded between 15 July and 13 August. Brood size ranged from 1 to 7 young (1Y-468, 2Y-899, 3Y-775, 4Y-365, 5Y-49, 6Y-8, 7Y-2) with 65% having 2 or 3 young (Fig. 233). Nestling/fledging period is unknown.

REMARKS: Two subspecies are known to occur in British Columbia. *P. p. pelagicus* breeds from the Queen Charlotte Islands northward but visits the southern coasts of the province in winter. *P. p. resplendens* breeds from extreme southern British Columbia northward for an undetermined distance. The northern subspecies is slightly larger and has a heavier bill (Palmer, R.S. 1962).

The Pelagic Cormorant is a bottom feeder and selects prey from the littoral-benthic zone (Robertson 1974a). Just over 85% of prey items in the diet of chicks at Mandarte Island (Fig. 231) included crested gunnel, Pacific sand lance, and shrimp species.

Figure 229. *Location of Pelagic Cormorant colony on Mitlenatch Island, August 1965 (R. Wayne Campbell).*

Figure 230. Small colony of Pelagic Cormorants on a navigational beacon in Oak Bay, 12 July 1981 (R. Wayne Campbell).

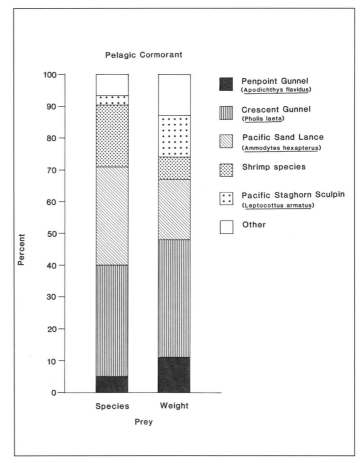

Figure 231. Percent species and biomass of major prey fed to Pelagic Cormorant chicks at Mandarte Island, British Columbia, 1969 to 1971 (adapted from Robertson 1974a).

Figure 232. Location of Pelagic Cormorant colony on Tian Islets, Queen Charlotte Islands, 10 June 1988 (R. Wayne Campbell).

TABLE 15.
Pelagic Cormorant: location, history, and size of major colonies in British Columbia.

Location	First Record	Low Survey Results[1]		Year	High Survey Results[1]		Year	Recent Survey Results[1]		Year	Source[2]
South Coast - Colonies > 50 nests or pairs											
Augustus Point	1972	3	N	1980	81	N	1977	0	c	1981	4,9
Ballenas Islands	1952	0	Nc	1987	55	Nc	1968			1987	3,4,8
Bare Point	1952	50	N	1959	373	N	1983	142	Nc	1987	3,8,10
Beresford Island	1950		C	1950	161	Nc	1987			1987	20,23
Buckle Group	1934	6	Nc	1987	52	N	1975			1987	7,23
Chain Islets	1924	14	N	1943	371	N	1979	248	Nc	1987	3,4,8
Christie Islet	1924	7	N	1955	51	N	1983	44[3]	Nc	1987	3,4,8
Chrome Island	1974	54	N	1974	141	Nc	1987			1987	3,7
Deep Sea Bluff	1792	0	Nc	1982	53	Nc	1962			1982	4,22
East Point	1958	12	Nc	1987	54	N	1974			1987	3,4,7
Five Finger Island	1977	7	N	1977	189	N	1980	17	Nc	1987	3,4
Florencia Island	1968	14	N	1968	86	N	1973	27	N	1982	4,11,12
Franklin Island	1968	14	N	1981	128	N	1970	22[4]	Nc	1987	3,4
Gabriola Island	1960	25	N	1960	390	N	1968	0	c	1987	3,8,9
Galiano Island[5]	1957	2	N	1978	60	N	1981	72[6]	Nc	1987	3,4,9
Galiano Island[7]	1976	44	N	1976	79	N	1978	24	c	1979	4,9
Gordon Head	1951	7	Nc	1958	75	Nc	1955	24	Nc	1987	3,8
Hudson Rocks	1959	30	N	1959	181	N	1981	142	Nc	1987	3,4,8
Mandarte Island	1909	4	N	1923	603	N	1981	536	Nc	1987	3,4,8
Merry Island	1968	2	N	1981	58	N	1976			1987	3,4
Mittlenatch Island	1949	24	N	1949	600	N	1982	315	Nc	1987	1,2,3
Munsie Rocks	1975				91	N	1975	0	c	1988	7,23
Nipple Rocks	1975	28	N	1982	50	N	1975			1982	7,11
O'Leary Islets	1975	41	N	1978	83	N	1975	41	Nc	1988	4,7,23
Passage Island	1968	2	N	1968	180	N	1981	16	Nc	1987	3,4
Prospect Point[8]	1981	1	N	1981	93	Nc	1987			1987	3,4,10
Race Rocks	1924	45	N	1960	437	N	1978	120	Nc	1987	3,4,15
Sartine Island	1950		S	1950	137	Nc	1987			1987	20,23
Second Narrows[9]	1983	10	A	1983	90	Nc	1987			1987	3,21
Sisters Islets	1968	14	N	1968	88	N	1978	0	c	1987	3,4
Snake Island	1958	5	N	1964	174	N	1978	74	Nc	1987	3,4,8
Solander Island	1954	12	N	1976	416	N	1975	464	Nc	1988	4,7,8,23
St. John Point	1955	9	N	1974	127	N	1983	101	Nc	1987	3,5,10
Swiss Boy Island	1969	25	N	1975	50	N	1969	0		1982	13,14
Tent Island	1972	4	N	1972	74	Nc	1987			1987	3,9
Thornton Island	1975	31	N	1982	62	N	1975	125	Nc	1988	7,11,23
Trial Island	1956	50	N	1959	107	N	1960	0		1974	3,4,8
Triangle Island	1949	33	N	1984	1200	P	1949	144	N	1985	20,23
Volcanic Islets	1975	4	Nc	1975	89	Nc	1988			1988	7,23
White Islets	1968	3	N	1969	50	N	1979	13	Nc	1987	3,4
Whyac	1973				50	N	1973			1973	7
North Coast - Colonies > 50 nests or pairs											
Dugout Rocks	1976	148	N	1976	18					1988	4,23
Langara Island	1920	52	Nc	1986	500	N	1927			1986	11,17,18
Murchison Island	1969			1982	100	N	1971	0		1986	4,6,19
Tian Islets	1977	28	N	1977	98	Nc	1986	0		1988	6,11,16

[1] A - active nests; C - nesting confirmed but no count or estimate made; N - nests; P - pairs; S - nesting suspected. All data are estimates unless noted as follows: c - complete count.

[2] 1 - Pearse 1958; 2 - Kennedy, K. and Foottit 1967; 3 - Vermeer et al. 1989; 4 - British Columbia Nest Records Scheme; 5 - Pearse 1956; 6 - Rodway 1988; 7 - Campbell 1976a; 8 - Drent and Guiguet 1961; 9 - Rodway and Campbell 1977; 10 - Vermeer and Rankin 1984; 11 - Rodway et al. In prep.; 12 - Hatler et al. 1978; 13 - Carter, H.R. et al. 1984; 14 - Guiguet 1971; 15 - Munro, J.A. 1925a; 16 - Campbell and Garrioch 1979; 17 - Darcus 1930; 18 - Brooks and Swarth 1925; 19 - Summers 1974; 20 Carl et al. 1950; 21 - Hobson, K.A. and Wilson 1985; 22 - Menzies 1792; 23 - Rodway In press.

[3] Includes Pam Rock.

[4] Includes Merry Island.

[5] Central cliffs.

[6] Exact location not given.

[7] North cliffs.

[8] Includes Siwash Rock.

[9] Second Narrows Bridge

Figure 233. *Adult Pelagic Cormorant with brood on Mitlenatch Island, 25 August 1969 (R. Wayne Campbell).*

NOTEWORTHY RECORDS

Spring: Coastal - Gordon Head 30 Apr 1972-125 (Tatum 1973); Hudson Rocks 25 Mar 1972-300+; Tofino Inlet 31 Mar 1962-5, 1 Apr 1962-200, 1 May 1974-200; Comox 17 Mar 1929-50+ after Pacific herring, mid-Apr 1949-1,000 feeding on Pacific herring (Flahaut 1949); Mitlenatch Island 17 May 1963-350 adults, 50 immatures (van Tets 1963); Menzies Bay 23 Apr 1966-139; Seymour Narrows 13 Apr 1976-200; Quathiaski Cove 2 Mar 1965-65; Johnstone Strait 2 Apr 1939-90 (Munro, J.A. and Cowan 1947); Lama Passage 7 Apr 1976-200; Ivory Island 7 Apr 1977-100; Skedans Islands 26 Apr 1983-30 at fish ball-up, 26 May 1971-200 (Summers 1974); Lawn Point (Tlell) 20 Mar 1981-350 on Pacific herring spawn; Masset Inlet 14 Apr 1935-1,500 (Munro, J.A. and Cowan 1947); Naden Harbour 23 Mar 1976-100; Kitimat 24 Apr 1975-122 on dock; Yakan Point 1 Mar 1979-120. **Interior** - No records.

Summer: Coastal - Race Rocks 6 Jul 1977-406, 12 Aug 1977-754+; Chain Islets 6 Aug 1975-200; East Point 21 Jun 1977-85 adults, 45 immatures; Alley Rock 30 Aug 1977-80; Gabriola Island 5 Aug 1969-1,000; Plover Reefs 18 Jun 1975-40; Cleland Island 4 Aug 1961-55; Keefer Rock 19 Jun 1981-73; Buckle Group 12 Jul 1975-47; Cape St. James 12 Jun 1979-100, 23 Jul 1979-162; Howay Island 6 Jul 1977-45 adults, 70 immatures; Ramsay Island 27 Jun 1971-50 (Summers 1974); w Aristazabal Island 24 Jun 1976-34 immatures. **Interior** - No records.

Autumn: Interior - No records. **Coastal** - Port Neville 30 Nov 1975-50; Point Holmes (Comox) 10 Oct 1953-100; Siwash Rock (Vancouver) 18 Nov 1973-21; Tofino Inlet 13 Sep 1970-200 (Campbell and Shepard 1971); Wya Point 4 Nov 1970-30+; Active Pass 14 Oct 1968-110; Trial Islands 22 Oct 1975-233; Ten Mile Point (Victoria) 12 Sep 1962-2,000 to 3,000.

Winter: Interior - No records. **Coastal** - Masset 14 Dec 1982-62; Puffin Cove 26 Dec 1970-54 (Campbell 1972b); Port Neville 6 Jan 1976-50; Quathiaski Cove 12 Dec 1976-60+; Comox 12 Dec 1949-100 (Flahaut 1950b); Egmont 6 Feb 1976-15; Lighthouse Park (West Vancouver) 28 Jan 1979-30; Tofino 3 Jan 1976-126; Departure Bay 8 Jan 1965-450+; Active Pass 15 Feb 1973-300; Greater Chain Islet 23 Dec 1976-100+.

Christmas Counts: Interior - Not recorded. **Coastal** - Recorded from 22 of 28 localities and on 79% of all counts. Maxima: Victoria 22 Dec 1962-**2,345**, all-time Canadian high count (Anderson, R.R. 1976); Nanaimo 28 Dec 1966-1,047; Deep Bay 30 Dec 1979-391.

American Bittern

AMBI

Botaurus lentiginosus (Rackett)

RANGE: Breeds from southeastern Alaska, central British Columbia, and southern Mackenzie east to central Quebec and Newfoundland and locally south to lower Colorado River and the lower Mississippi Valley and Florida. Winters from southwestern British Columbia and middle and southern United States southward.

STATUS: *Uncommon* summer visitant in the interior north to the Peace and Fort Nelson lowlands. On the coast, *uncommon* resident in the Fraser Lowlands. *Rare* on Vancouver Island; *casual* on the Queen Charlotte Islands. Breeds.

NONBREEDING: The American Bittern is distributed along the coast from southern Vancouver Island north to the Campbell River area and east through the Fraser Lowlands to Hope. It is also widely distributed through the valleys and plateaus of central and southern British Columbia, including the Peace Lowlands. It prefers wet habitats with tall vegetation such as cattail, bulrushes, and willows, and occurs from sea level to 1,450 m elevation. Rarely, it occurs in agricultural fields (e.g. alfalfa). In the interior, marshes are preferred (89% of records). Other habitats include sloughs, lake edges, swamps, river banks, sewage ponds, and fields. Freshwater and estuarine marshes are preferred on the coast. The latter habitat is especially important in winter.

The American Bittern is usually solitary and secretive during migration. In the southern interior, spring migrants arrive mostly in late April and early May. In the Chilcotin-Cariboo, birds arrive during the second and third weeks of May, and in the Peace Lowlands, most arrive in late May. Post breeding dispersal occurs in August in northern areas. Autumn migration occurs mainly in late September and early October in southern areas. Extreme dates for the interior are 4 April (Creston) to 6 November (Okanagan). There are no winter records for the interior.

Seasonal movements are less pronounced on the coast. There appears to be a dispersal of wintering birds (and perhaps migrants) during the first half of April. Autumn arrival occurs mainly during late September and early October. Small numbers winter in marshes in the Fraser Lowlands and on southeastern Vancouver Island.

BREEDING: The American Bittern breeds locally from Osoyoos and Creston northward through the central valleys and plateaus to Bear Lake, 80 km north of Prince George. Small numbers also breed in the Fraser Lowlands. Nests have been found from near sea level to 1,300 m elevation.

It breeds typically in wet areas with dense growths of emergent vegetation or tall grasses. Sites include freshwater sloughs, marshes, swamps, and shallow, protected sections of lakes. Occasionally, dry fields and marshes are used. There is one record from a brackish, tidal, cattail marsh.

Nests: Nests were well concealed and usually built over water up to 36 cm deep. Fourteen of seventeen nests were situated in stands of cattail and bulrushes. The nests were platforms and small mounds of reeds, and other plant material, up to 60 cm in diameter and 15 to 40 cm in height. One nest was a depression on the ground in a dry hay field 45 m from a creek; it was sparsely lined with grasses. Although bitterns are usually solitary nesters, 2 nests were found within 35 m of each other on Dinsmore Island.

Eggs: Dates for 28 clutches ranged from 5 April (Penticton, 1898-2 eggs, RBCM 53) to 10 July, with 17 clutches recorded between 20 May and 10 June. Clutch size ranged from 2 to 6 eggs (2E-2, 3E-1, 4E-6, 5E-16, 6E-3), with 16 clutches having 5 eggs. Incubation period is about 24 days (Mousley 1939).

Young: Dates for 12 broods ranged from 24 May to 19 August, with 7 broods recorded between 9 June and 20 July. Calculated dates indicate that young could be found as early as 1 May. Brood size ranged from 1 to 6 young (1Y-4, 2Y-1, 3Y-4, 4Y-1, 5Y-1, 6Y-1), with 9 broods having 1 to 3 young. Nestling period is about 14 days. The fledging period is unknown.

REMARKS: There have been a number of observations of the American Bittern from Vancouver Island, the east Kootenay, and the Peace Lowlands that suggest the possibility of breeding in those areas. To date, however, nests with eggs or young have not been documented.

The American Bittern appears on the "Blue List" from 1976 to 1986 inclusive (Tate 1981; Tate and Tate 1982; Tate 1986). In 1982, it was "reported severely down in the northern Great Plains, western Great Lake, and Appalachian regions", but stable or slightly increasing farther south and west (Tate and Tate 1982). By 1986, Tate (1986) noted: "we are now in the midst of a continent-wide decline of the American Bittern and most other marsh dependent species."

NOTEWORTHY RECORDS

Spring: Coastal - Buttertubs Marsh Mar 1983-3, Mar 1985-1 (RBCM Photo 1136); Pitt Meadows 16 May 1980-4, 20 May 1976-5. **Interior** - Osoyoos Lake 31 May 1951-5; Creston 18 May 1948-3 (Munro, J.A. 1958a); Vaseux Lake 20 May 1922-4 flying; Wasa 15 May 1938-3 (Johnstone, W.B. 1949); Swan Lake (Vernon) 20 Apr 1980-2; Williams Lake 14 May 1980-3; Driftwood River 7 May 1941-1 (Stanwell-Fletcher and Stanwell-Fletcher 1943); Swan Lake (Tupper) 14 May 1938-1 (Cowan 1939).

Summer: Coastal - Campbell River (Langley) 21 Aug 1982-3; Lulu Island 27 Aug 1927-4; Lakelse Lake 7 Aug 1976-1. **Interior** - Slocan 11 Jun 1981-2; Okanagan Lake 4 Jun 1926-6; Canim Lake 9 Jun 1985-3; Williams Lake 5 Jun 1937-4; Bowron Lake 6 Jun 1975-4; Tupper Creek (Tupper) 28 Jun 1938-1 (RBCM 8246); Fort St. John 6 Jun 1984-2; Boundary Lake (Goodlow) 15 Jul 1981-3; Helmet (Kwokullie Lake) 6 Jun 1982-2.

Autumn: Interior - Buckhorn Lake 13 Sep 1986-1; Chezacut 24 Sep 1933-1 (MCZ 281283); Vernon 26 Sep 1907-2; Kelowna 6 Nov 1957-1 (NMC 47511). **Coastal** - Comox 24 Sep 1924-1 (RBCM 12211); Pitt Meadows 11 Sep 1976-3; Sumas 20 Oct 1894-4; Reifel Island 12 Oct 1975-4, 11 Nov 1971-4, 25 Nov 1974-3; Lulu Island 3 Nov 1895-8; Richmond 23 Nov 1985-5; Saanich 28 Sep 1980-1.

Winter: Interior - No records. **Coastal** - Sea Island 22 Jan 1966-11; Westham Island 23 Dec 1984-8, 17 Jan 1971-5; Buttertubs Marsh 26 Feb 1983-1; Swan Lake (Victoria) 8 Feb 1982-1.

Christmas Counts: Interior - Not recorded. **Coastal** - Recorded from 7 of 28 localities and on 14% of all counts. Maxima: Ladner 23 Dec 1984-9, all-time Canadian high count (Monroe 1985b); Vancouver 27 Dec 1970-3; Pitt Meadows 15 Dec 1974, 4 Jan 1976 and 27 Dec 1977-2; Nanaimo 26 Dec 1982-2 and 1 Jan 1985-2.

Extralimital Records: Coastal - Masset 4 Mar 1942-1 (RBCM 11325), 23 Dec 1939-1 (RBCM 10572).

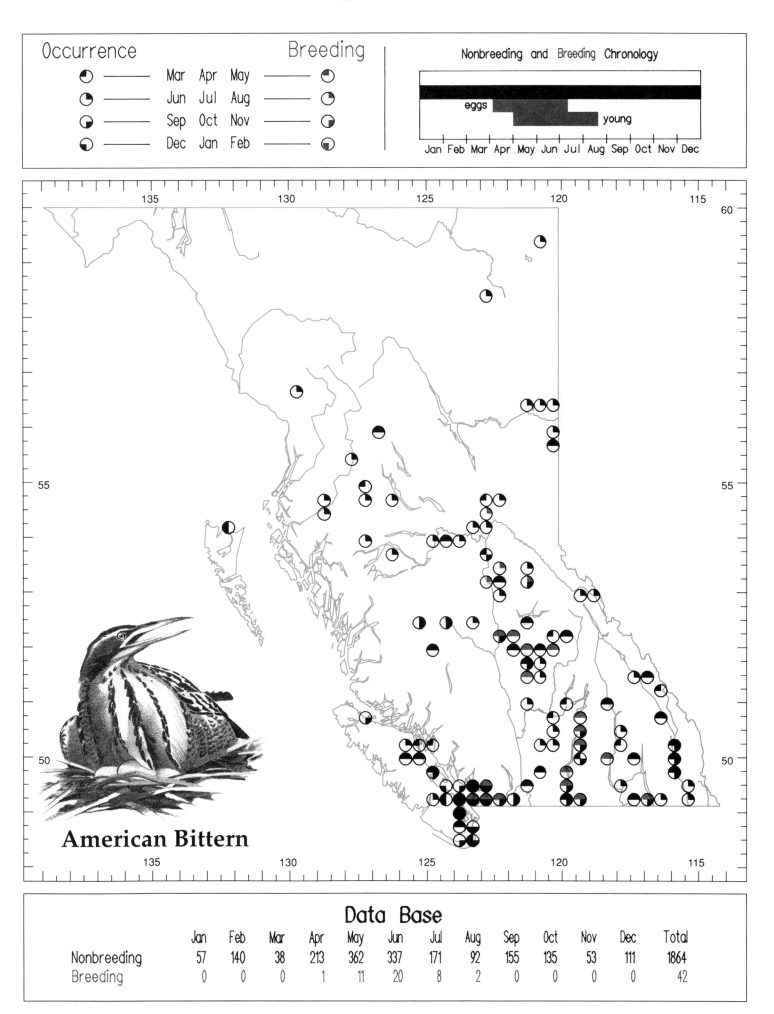

Occurrence

Breeding

	Mar	Apr	May	
	Jun	Jul	Aug	
	Sep	Oct	Nov	
	Dec	Jan	Feb	

Nonbreeding and Breeding Chronology

eggs

young

Jan Feb Mar Apr May Jun Jul Aug Sep Oct Nov Dec

American Bittern

Data Base

	Jan	Feb	Mar	Apr	May	Jun	Jul	Aug	Sep	Oct	Nov	Dec	Total
Nonbreeding	57	140	38	213	362	337	171	92	155	135	53	111	1864
Breeding	0	0	0	1	11	20	8	2	0	0	0	0	42

Great Blue Heron

GBHE

Ardea herodias Linnaeus

RANGE: Breeds from southeastern Alaska and coastal British Columbia east to the Gaspe Peninsula and Nova Scotia south to Mexico, the West Indies and Galapagos Islands. Post-breeding dispersal occurs north into nonbreeding areas. Winters from coastal British Columbia, central United States, and southern New England south to northern South America.

STATUS: Sedentary or migratory. Resident on the coast, where it is *very common* in the south, *common* in the north and *fairly common* on the Queen Charlotte Islands. *Fairly common* resident in the southern interior where waters do not freeze. Widespread breeder in southern British Columbia; local breeder on north coast.

NONBREEDING: The Great Blue Heron is widely distributed throughout the year along the coast, including Vancouver Island and the Queen Charlotte Islands, and throughout the interior south of latitude 52°N. Occurrences elsewhere probably represent nonbreeding wanderers.

The Great Blue Heron is found in a variety of salt, brackish, and freshwater environments. On the coast, it frequents sheltered and shallow bays, lagoons, inlets, coves, tidal mud flats (Fig. 234), sloughs, marshes, rivers, and irrigation ditches. Jetties and log booms are frequently used as communal roosting sites. Solitary birds and small groups often roost in coniferous trees. In the interior, herons may be seen around lakeshores, rivers, sloughs, marshes, and ponds. On the south mainland coast, southeastern Vancouver Island, and occasionally in the interior, wet and dry agricultural fields are used for foraging. Birds have been recorded from sea level to 2,100 m elevation.

There is little information available on seasonal movements or fluctuations in abundance. Data suggest spring migrants arrive at colonies in March and April. Nonbreeding birds probably disperse northward in May and June. In late July and August, there is a further dispersal of herons, probably comprised of young dispersing from breeding colonies in British Columbia and the northern United States. For example, 16 recoveries from young herons banded in Vancouver (University of British Columbia Endowment Lands colony) were remarkably scattered: 9 were found in the Fraser Lowlands, 3 were found in Washington, 3 were found in the interior of British Columbia as far north as Kamloops, and 1 was found at Astoria, Oregon

(Campbell et al. 1972b). Migrants depart southward in September and October. The Fraser River delta is the major wintering area in the province. The largest wintering populations in the interior are found in the Okanagan valley.

Herons are most numerous on the coast during the summer months when foraging aggregations from nearby colonies may approach 300 individuals. In the interior, the largest numbers are found during spring migration, mostly in March.

BREEDING: On the coast, the Great Blue Heron breeds primarily along south-eastern Vancouver Island, the southern Gulf Islands, and the Fraser Lowlands, east to Hope. Isolated pairs breed near Prince Rupert and on the southern Queen Charlotte Islands. There are no other documented breeding records for the northern mainland coast, and none from northern or western Vancouver Island. In the interior, the heron breeds from the Okanagan valley north to Clearwater, in the west Kootenay north to New Denver, and in the east Kootenay north to Golden. The centres of abundance are the Fraser Lowlands, southeast Vancouver Island, and the southern Gulf Islands. Breeding occurs at elevations between sea level and 1,100 m.

Colonies are usually located in mature forests (deciduous, coniferous, or mixed) that are relatively free from disturbance and near suitable foraging areas. Occasionally, colonies can be found in areas of high disturbance (e.g. Stanley Park, Vancouver [Fig. 237]; Sea Island. On the coast, colonies are usually situated on islands (Figs. 235 and 236) or mainland sites near tidal mud flats. Inland colonies are usually situated on the banks of slow-moving rivers, sloughs, or marshy lakes. Colonies can be ephemeral, abandoned one year only to be used the next. A colony at Brisco was abandoned in 1979 when an Osprey used one of the nests, and a new colony was built about 500 m south. In 1980, the herons returned to the old site.

Forbes et al. (1985a) list 110 breeding sites in British Columbia through 1984, of which 76% were still active when last visited. Eighty-four sites were along the coast; the remaining 26 were east of the Cascades. Sizes of 95 colonies ranged from 1 to 169 nests (1 to 10 nests-44, 11 to 20 nests-14, 21 to 30 nests-11, 31 to 50 nests-11, 51 to 100 nests-10, 101 to 169 nests-5). Major coastal and interior colonies are given in Table 16.

Figure 234. Great Blue Herons foraging on tidal flats off Tsawwassen jetty, 2 June 1981 (R. Wayne Campbell).

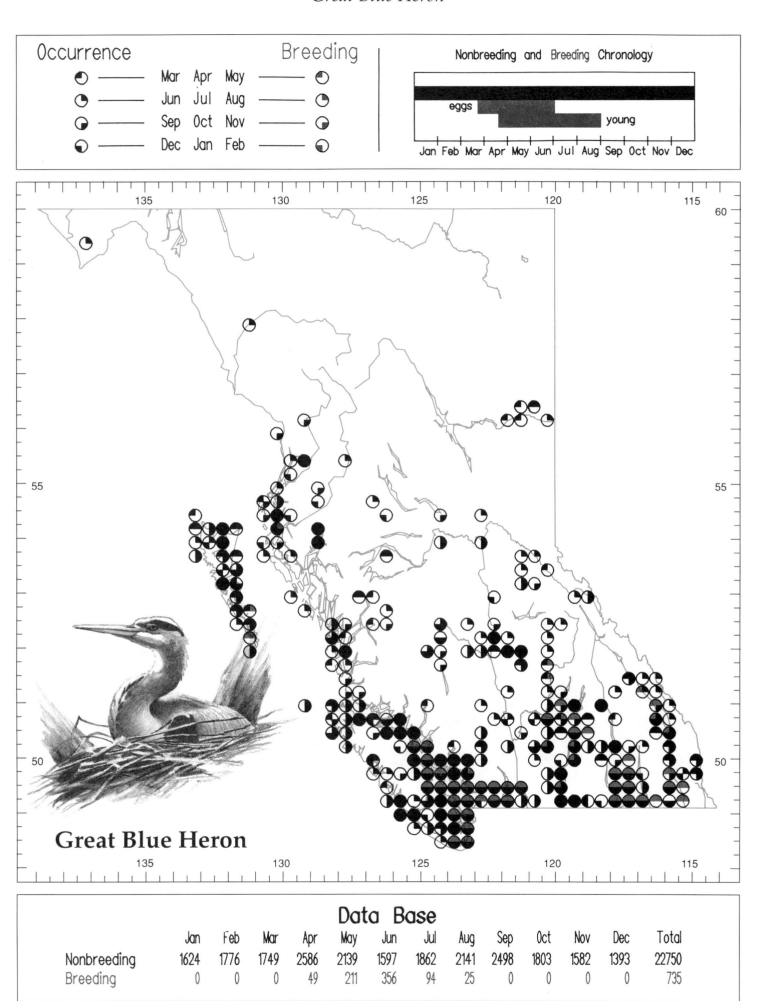

Great Blue Heron

	Jan	Feb	Mar	Apr	May	Jun	Jul	Aug	Sep	Oct	Nov	Dec	Total
Nonbreeding	1624	1776	1749	2586	2139	1597	1862	2141	2498	1803	1582	1393	22750
Breeding	0	0	0	49	211	356	94	25	0	0	0	0	735

Heronries may occupy up to 2 ha of forest (e.g. University of British Columbia Endowment Lands). Up to 39 nests may be situated in a single tree; 1 colony contained nests in 83 individual trees.

Nests: Nest-building begins in March on the coast (27 Mar 1984, Derby Reach) and in April in the interior (21 Apr 1984, Nelson). Nests were large stick platforms (n=93) up to 1 m in diameter and 38 cm in depth (Fig. 236). The nest cup was a shallow depression lined with small twigs, bark strips, fresh evergreen boughs, or rushes. Fifteen species of trees were reported as nest sites. On the coast, red alder (33%) was the most often used nest tree; black cottonwood (70%) was the main species used in the interior (Forbes et al. 1985a). The most frequently used conifer was Douglas-fir. Other tree species used on the coast included bigleaf maple, arbutus, western hemlock, western redcedar and Sitka spruce. In the interior, poplar, western white pine, and ponderosa pine were also used as nest trees. Heights of 926 nests ranged from 7 to 70 m, with 67% recorded between 17 and 30 m.

Eggs: Dates for 137 clutches ranged from 1 April to 2 July, with 66% recorded between 16 April and 10 June. Calculated dates indicate that eggs could be found as early as 23 March. Clutch size ranged from 1 to 8 eggs (1E-12, 2E-26, 3E-24, 4E-39, 5E-28, 6E-6, 7E-1, 8E-1), with 66% having 3 to 5 eggs. Incubation period is 25 to 29 days (Harrison, C. 1978).

Young: Dates for 583 broods ranged from 20 April to 31 August, with 55% recorded between 2 and 20 June. Brood size ranged from 1 to 8 young (1Y-89, 2Y-271, 3Y-137, 4Y-76, 5Y-2, 6Y-5, 7Y-1, 8Y-2), with 70% having 2 to 3 young (Fig. 238). In southwestern British Columbia, 15 colonies fledged 2.5 young per successful nest (1977 to 1981), and in the southeast, 6 colonies fledged 2.7 young per successful nest (1981 to 1983; Forbes et al. 1985b). Fledging period is about 60 days (Harrison, C. 1978).

REMARKS: Prior to 1947, the Great Blue Heron was known to breed in coastal areas of the province, but only at 2 breeding sites in the interior (see Cannings, R.A. et al. 1987). By 1974, 6 interior sites were documented by Mark (1976), and a decade later 26 colony sites were known (Forbes et al. 1985a). Numbers appear to be increasing throughout southern areas of the interior but the magnitude of the increase is not known. Even in the early 1920s, Brooks (Bent 1926:114) reported an increase there. It could be that the recent increases are more apparent than real and are due mainly to better coverage by more observers.

Recently, high levels of organochlorine residues have been found in egg contents from heronries on the south coast and Vancouver Island. Of particular concern were the elevated levels of dioxins. In 1987, biologists found every egg destroyed beneath the nests of a colony adjacent to an industrial area near Crofton, which also held the highest dioxin levels of the 5 heronries sampled. While predation had not been ruled out, the elevated dioxin levels are a matter for concern. Studies are now being planned that will assess the embryotoxic effects of dioxins in heronries in south coastal British Columbia (see Elliott et al. 1988).

The Great Blue Heron appears on the "Blue List" for 1980 and 1981 (Tate 1981). In 1982, the species was delisted, but maintained as a species of "special concern" (Tate and Tate 1982).

Two subspecies are recognized in the province (American Ornithologists' Union 1957). *A. h. fannini* breeds along the coast, while *A. h. herodias* breeds in the interior.

Forbes et al. (1985a) discuss a number of recommendations for management of the Great Blue Heron in British Columbia.

POSTSCRIPT: On 9 May 1989, a colony with 9 active nests was found at Tahsis – the first reported colony on the west coast of Vancouver Island. It was situated in red alder trees within 0.5 km of the Tahsis shopping area (A.M. Breault pers. comm.).

Figure 235. *Location of Great Blue Heron colony on Prevost Island, July 1974 (R. Wayne Campbell).*

Figure 236. *Great Blue Heron nests at colony on Prevost Island, July 1974 (R. Wayne Campbell).*

TABLE 16.
Great Blue Heron: location, history, and size of major colonies in British Columbia.

Location	First Record	Low Survey Results[1]		Year	High Survey Results[1]		Year	Recent Survey Results[1]		Year	Source[2]
South Coast - Colonies > 35 nests or pairs											
Alouette River North	1974	10	N	1974	65	N	1987			1987	1,2
Chilliwack											
Salwein	1976	50	Nc	1976	130	N	1987			1987	1,2
Crescent Beach	1967	37	A	1977	42	A	1979		E	1987	1,2
Crofton	1955	40	N	1970	85	A	1974		E	1979	1
Denman Island	1979	35	Ac	1987	70	N	1981			1987	1,3
Fort Langley											
Edgewater Bar	1974	16	A	1977	59	N	1987			1987	1,2
Fraser Mills	1960				38	Ac	1960			1960	1
Gabriola Island	1979	20		1979	138	A	1983	39	Ac	1987	4,3
Nanaimo-Cedar	1981				91	N	1981		E	1983	4
Pender Harbour	1963	25	N	1981	44	A	1979			1981	1
Port Coquitlam											
Indian Reserve	1973	26	A	1980	169	A	1977	26	A	1981	1,9
Nature Park	1971				68	A	1971		E	1973	1,7
Prevost Island	1974				59	N	1974			1974	1
Sechelt	1978	7	Pc	1987	35	A	1980			1987	1,3
Secretary Island	1932	1	N	1932	44	N	1935			1935	1
Shoal Islands	1982	20	N	1982	60	Ac	1987			1987	1,3
Sidney Island	1974	30	N	1974	87	Ac	1987			1987	1,3
Vancouver											
Stanley Park	1921	19	A	1977	44	A	1978	19	Ac	1987	1,3,10,11
UBC	1970	22	A	1972	183	Ac	1987			1987	1,3,6,8
Victoria											
Beacon Hill Park[3]	1981				3	N	1981	40	Np	1987	4
Interior - Colonies > 20 nests or pairs											
Brisco North	1974	34	N	1981	40	A	1982			1982	1
Duck Lake (Creston)	1947	54	A	1982	122	A	1975	79	A	1987	1,5
Fairmont	1941	2	A	1941	35	A	1982			1982	1
Goat River (Creston)	1967	25	A	1982	33	A	1984			1984	1
Otter Lake (Vernon)	1962	12	N	1962	25	N	1977	23	A	1980	1
Parson	1968	10	A	1980	60	A	1982			1982	1
St. Mary's River	1976	14	A	1980	25	A	1982			1982	1
Shuswap River (Enderby)	1978	7	N	1978	20	N	1980			1980	1
Wilmer	1976	5	A	1980	30	N	1976		E	1981	1

[1] A - active nests; E - colony extinct; N - nests; P - pairs. All data are estimates unless noted as follows: c - complete count; p - partial count.

[2] 1 - Forbes et al. 1985a; 2 - R.W. Butler pers. comm.; 3 - Butler, R.W. In press; 4 - British Columbia Nest Records Scheme; 5 - Anonymous 1987; 6 - Campbell et al. 1972a; 7 - Campbell et al. 1972b; 8 - Campbell et al. 1974; 9 - Jerema 1973; 10 - Mark 1974; 11 - Racey 1921.

[3] In 1988 there were 64 nests (Breault 1988). The same author summarizes the current status and productivity for colonies in the Strait of Georgia.

Figure 237. *Great Blue Heron colony at Stanley Park (Vancouver), June 1924. This colony, the oldest in the province, is still active today despite increased human activities in the park (RBCM Photo 1227; D. W. Gillingham).*

Figure 238. *Great Blue Heron nest, egg, and chicks in Coquitlam colony, 25 May 1971 (R. Wayne Campbell).*

NOTEWORTHY RECORDS

Spring: Coastal - Esquimalt Lagoon 22 Mar 1959-50; Sidney Island lagoon 18 May 1984-120; Somenos Lake 21 Mar 1981-45; Cowichan Bay 15 Mar 1976-77; Nanaimo 1 to 30 Apr 1977-60; Crescent Beach 21 May 1983-106; Tsawwassen jetty 18 May 1984-175; Iona Island 16 Mar 1975-50; Pitt Meadows 7 Mar 1976-81; Chilliwack 9 Mar 1982-60; Hope 18 Mar 1984-43; Queen Charlotte City 20 Mar 1981-7. **Interior** - Vernon 27 Mar 1982-55; Brisco 31 Mar 1978-19; Revelstoke 25 Apr 1978-7; McBride 24 Apr 1977-65; Halfway River (Peace River) 29 Apr 1979-2.

Summer: Coastal - Sooke River estuary 22 Jul 1978-54; Sidney Spit 28 Jul 1983-100, 16 Aug 1986-103; Turtle Island 16 Jun 1970-50; Tofino Inlet 30 Aug 1977-26; Crescent Beach 16 Jul 1983-246, 5 Aug 1974-275, 24 Aug 1983-165; Tsawwassen jetty 15 Jun 1981-232; Roberts Bank 6 Jun 1985-300, one group of 257; Chilliwack 24 Jun 1983-60; Porpoise Bay 20 Jul 1978-23; Nanoose Harbour 14 Jul 1977-33 (Dawe and Lang 1980); Comox Harbour 29 Jun 1969-31; Prince Rupert 12 Aug 1979-9; Masset 5 Jun 1985-6. **Interior** - Creston 21 Jun 1976-25+; Trail 23 Aug 1981-3; Revelstoke 21 Jul 1977-13; Azure Lake 30 Jun 1971-6; Torpy River 20 Jul 1977-3; Fort St. John 17 Aug 1984-1 immature.

Autumn: Interior - Fort St. James 13 Oct 1978-1; Isaac Lake Sep 1973-1; Chilcotin River e Hanceville 14 Nov 1986-1; Revelstoke 15 Sep 1977-17; Adams Lake (Chase) 27 Oct 1980-3; Tranquille 21 Sep 1980-8; Trail 13 Sep 1983-4; Castlegar 27 Nov 1983-5. **Coastal** - Skidegate Inlet 9 Oct 1976-6; Campbell River 15 Sep 1974-7; Comox 7 Sep 1930-50; Crescent Beach 2 Sep 1981-150, 4 Oct 1983-152, 12 Nov 1962-120; Tofino Inlet 12 Sep 1974-40; Saanich 24 Nov 1984-21;

Winter: Interior - Quesnel 2 Jan 1979-1; Williams Lake 26 Dec 1974-1; Chilanko Forks 16 Dec 1987-1; Lac la Hache 8 Jan 1946-5; Castlegar 24 Jan 1977-10, 1 Feb 1981-12; Columbia River (Robson ferry) 4 Dec 1977-1. **Coastal** - Alliford Bay 13 Jan 1942-6; Bella Bella 7 Dec 1976-9; Courtenay 27 Jan 1928-16; Porpoise Bay 24 Feb 1979-30; Harrison Mills 18 Feb 1978-17; Pitt Meadows 17 Feb 1976-45; Crescent Beach 15 Feb 1963-42; Sea Island 9 Dec 1979-53; Cowichan Bay 14 Dec 1974-36; Esquimalt Lagoon 1 Feb 1983-35.

Christmas Counts: Interior - Recorded from 11 of 19 localities and on 54% of all counts. Maxima: Vernon 18 Dec 1983-29; Kelowna 20 Dec 1981-18; Oliver/Osoyoos 28 Dec 1981-18; Vaseux Lake 23 Dec 1981-18. **Coastal** - Recorded from 26 of 28 localities and on 93% of all counts. Maxima: Ladner 27 Dec 1981-**251**, all-time Canadian high count (Anderson, R.R. 1982); Vancouver 18 Dec 1977-248; Victoria 15 Dec 1984-152; Pitt Meadows 27 Dec 1977-152.

Extralimital Records: Interior - Telegraph Creek 5 Jul 1919-1 (Swarth 1922); Kelsall Lake 29 Jul 1965-1.

Great Egret

Casmerodius albus (Linnaeus)

GREG

RANGE: Breeds from central Washington, southern Oregon and California south throughout western Mexico to southern South America, and from southern Saskatchewan, southwestern Manitoba, Minnesota, Illinois, Ohio, southern Ontario, and Maine south through the West Indies and South America. Winters from southern United States southward. Also in Old World.

STATUS: *Very rare* on the south inner coast and in the southern interior; *accidental* on the Queen Charlotte Islands.

CHANGE IN STATUS: The Great Egret was severely persecuted for the millinery trade and was at its lowest numbers during the first 2 decades of the twentieth century (Palmer, R.S. 1962). Under legal protection, a recovery peak was attained in the mid-1930s. The species has an extensive postbreeding dispersal prior to autumn migration (Coffey 1948); during the period 1940 to 1960 it dispersed northward into Washington state (Canaris 1950; Rieck 1962). It was first recorded in British Columbia in September 1970 (Campbell et al. 1972a) and has been reported in 12 of the 17 years to 1987. It is still considered a good find by birders.

OCCURRENCE: The Great Egret has been reported on the coast in the vicinity of Juan de Fuca Strait, the Strait of Georgia, the Fraser Lowlands, and the Queen Charlotte Islands. Interior records are scattered from Osoyoos and Creston north to Wilmer (see Figs. 239 and 240), Tranquille, and Stum Lake. There are 31 spring, 9 summer, 23 autumn, and 14 winter sightings. This pattern is consistent with its occurrence in Washington state (Mattocks et al. 1976). In spring 1987, however, an unprecedented invasion occurred in the province. The Great Egret was reported from 2 coastal and 3 interior locations (Campbell 1987c).

Sixty-eight per cent of our records (n=23) were from aquatic habitats, which included marine (e.g. bays, spits, log booms, and beaches) and fresh water (e.g. ponds, rivers, and sloughs). Terrestrial sites included fields and golf courses.

The Great Egret has been recorded in British Columbia from 23 April to 24 December.

REMARKS: In North America the Great Egret was formerly known as Common or American Egret. In Old World literature it is known as Great White Egret.

POSTSCRIPT: On 9 and 13 January 1988 a Great Egret was observed feeding on small fishes along ditches in Richmond (M. Gebauer pers. comm). These records extend the period the species has been recorded in the province.

Figure 239. Great Egret at Oliver, 18 April 1988 (Stephen R. Cannings).

Figure 240. Great Egret at Wilmer, 8 June 1987 (RBCM Photo 1158; Larry Halverson).

NOTEWORTHY RECORDS

Spring: Coastal - Saanich 16 May 1975-1; Cowichan Bay 29 Apr (Campbell 1987d) to 3 May 1987-1; Reifel Island 26 and 27 Apr 1985-1 (RBCM Photo 1104), 1 May 1987-2 adults; Serpentine Fen 9 and 10 May 1987-2 adults, probably the same birds as those seen on Reifel Island, and likely the 8 additional sightings of a Great Egret from various locations on the Fraser River delta (Crescent Beach, Nicomekl River, Musqueam Indian Reserve) to 28 May 1987 involved one of these birds; Pitt Meadows 23 and 24 April 1985-1 (Campbell 1985c). **Interior** - Osoyoos Lake 29 Apr 1987-4; Creston 30 Apr 1987-2, 14 May 1987-3 (Campbell 1987d; RBCM Photo 1163); Kelowna 14 May 1975-1 (Cannings, R.A. et al. 1987); Tranquille 26 May 1981-1 (RBCM Photo 887); Stum Lake 23 May 1987-1.

Summer: Coastal - Billings Spit 16 Aug 1976-1; Victoria 27 Aug 1977-1 on golf course; Bird's Eye Cove 29 Jul 1977-1; Sea Island 11 June 1980-1 (Harrington-Tweit et al. 1980); Serpentine Fen (Surrey) 13 July 1986-1 (Mattocks 1986b); Coquitlam 7 Jul 1972-1 (Crowell and Nehls 1972c). **Interior** - 3 km s Creston 4 Jul 1987-1 (Campbell 1987d); Tranquille 31 Aug 1978-1; Wilmer 8 Jun 1987-1 (Campbell 1987d; RBCM Photo 1158; Fig. 240).

Autumn: Interior - No records. **Coastal** - Campbell River (Discovery Passage) 16 to 23 Nov 1980-1 (RBCM Photo 655); Alouette River 6 Sep 1976-1; Reifel Island 9 Sep 1970-1 (Campbell et al. 1972a), 11 Sep 1973-1; Serpentine Fen (Surrey) 11 Sep 1970-1 (Campbell et al. 1972a); Mud Bay (Surrey) 2 to 6 Oct 1980-1; Cowichan Bay 23 Sep to 8 Oct 1972-1 (RBCM Photos 243, 328); Sooke 11, 12 and 25 Nov 1975-1.

Winter: Interior - No records. **Coastal** - Duncan 1 Dec 1980-1; Lulu Island 20 and 24 Dec 1978-1 (RBCM Photo 847); Steveston 3 Dec 1987 to 30 March 1988-1.

Christmas Counts: Interior - Not recorded. **Coastal** - Recorded once: Vancouver 17 Dec 1978-1, all-time Canadian high count [tied with Point Pelee] (Anderson, R.R.1979).

Extralimital Record: Masset 24 Sep 1983-1 (Campbell 1983d; RBCM Photo 886).

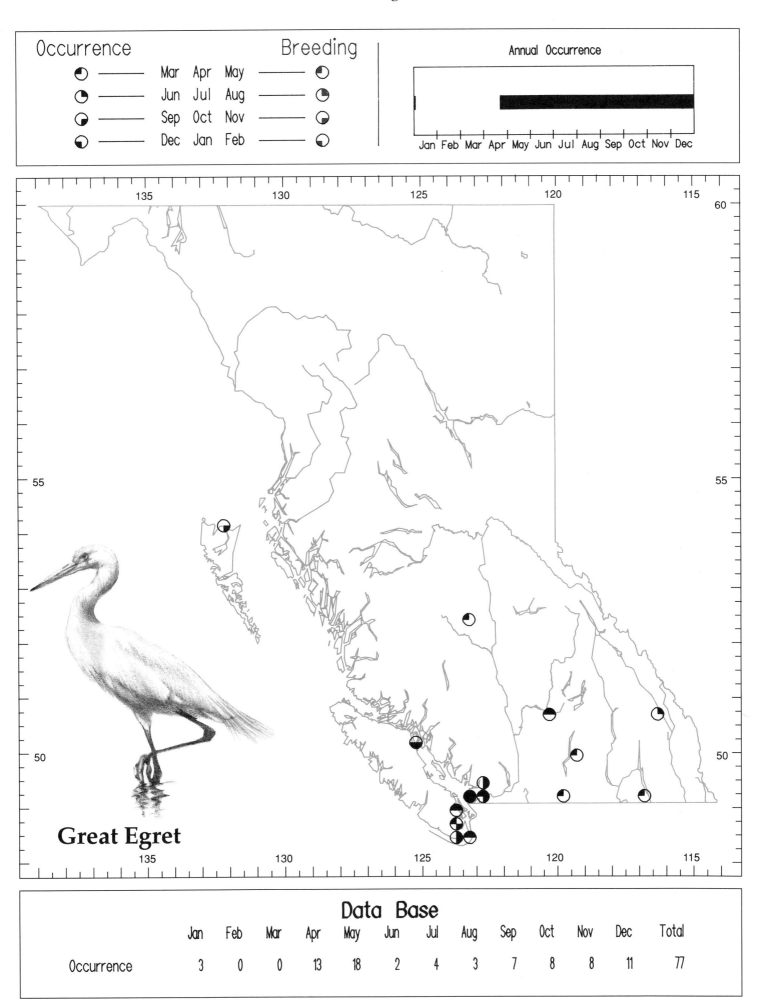

Great Egret

Occurrence

◕	———	Mar	Apr	May
◔	———	Jun	Jul	Aug
◑	———	Sep	Oct	Nov
◕	———	Dec	Jan	Feb

Breeding

———	◕
———	◔
———	◑
———	◑

Annual Occurrence

Jan Feb Mar Apr May Jun Jul Aug Sep Oct Nov Dec

Data Base

	Jan	Feb	Mar	Apr	May	Jun	Jul	Aug	Sep	Oct	Nov	Dec	Total
Occurrence	3	0	0	13	18	2	4	3	7	8	8	11	77

Cattle Egret

CAEG

Bubulcus ibis (Linnaeus)

RANGE: Breeds locally in the Western Hemisphere from Oregon, Idaho, Utah, Colorado, North Dakota, southern Saskatchewan, Minnesota, Wisconsin, southern Ontario, Ohio, and Maine south through Middle America, to the West Indies and South America. Post-breeding dispersal occurs north to southern Canada. Winters in the Americas through much of breeding range. Widespread in the Old World.

STATUS: *Casual* spring and *rare* to *uncommon* late autumn and winter visitant to the south coast. *Casual* on the north coast including the Queen Charlotte Islands. In the southern interior, *casual* in late spring and summer, *rare* from late autumn into winter. *Very rare* in the northern interior.

CHANGE IN STATUS: The Cattle Egret was first reported in British Columbia near Victoria on 26 November 1970, and first documented at Saseenos 3 years later (Campbell and Weber 1977). A bird seen at Salmon Arm on 22 November 1974 was the first interior record. Through the mid-1970s the Cattle Egret was considered *very rare* from late autumn into winter. An influx occurred during the late 1970s and early 1980s (Merilees and McNall 1981; Kragh 1982). The egret's range in the province is still expanding.

OCCURRENCE: The Cattle Egret has been reported along the coast, including the Queen Charlotte Islands, and in the central-southern interior. Wanderers have strayed into the north-central interior. Seventy-three percent of all records are from coastal areas.

The Cattle Egret has been recorded in British Columbia between 6 April and 1 August, and between 1 October and 12 February. On the coast, it has been reported between 6 April and 23 May and between 1 October and 10 February. In the interior, it has been reported between 14 May and 31 July and between 2 October and 11 January.

Ninety-seven per cent of all records are for the period October through February. November (51%) and December (28%) are the peak months. Egrets that arrive on the coast in November, linger into the winter (38% of records) whereas those in the interior disperse elsewhere (4% of records). Their inability to survive below-freezing temperatures may limit their occupation of British Columbia unless they can develop, as they have in Ontario, a migratory habit.

Cattle Egrets frequent a wide variety of open habitats. They prefer agricultural lands (71%; n=237) such as dry and wet fields, pastures, and cultivated fields, where they associate with domestic stock such as cattle, sheep, horses, goats, bison, ducks, and chickens. Other habitats include marshes and sloughs,

beaches and bays, sewage lagoons, jetties, garbage dumps, and lawns of residential areas, parks, airports, cemeteries, golf courses, and lighthouses.

REMARKS: The range of the Cattle Egret is expanding rapidly throughout the world; it is now found on every continent except Antarctica. An Old World species, it first arrived in the Western Hemisphere in northern South America between 1877 and 1882. Its arrival to the new world is generally accepted as an example of a natural extension of range, that is, expansion unaided by man's activities. It spread to Florida in the early 1940s and began breeding there in 1953 (Palmer, R.S. 1962). The population increased rapidly and began to spread throughout North America. It reached the west coast of the United States at California in 1964 (McCaskie 1965), and was breeding near San Diego in 1979 (McCaskie 1979). It was first recorded in Washington state in 1967 (Mattocks et al. 1976) and Alaska in 1981 (Gibson, D.D. and Hogg 1982).

Figure 241. *Cattle Egret, Anglemont, 28 September 1986 (RBCM Photo 1147; Diane Hopp).*

NOTEWORTHY RECORDS

Spring: Coastal - Delta 6 Apr 1980-2; Reifel Island 19 May 1980-1 (RBCM Photo 985); Tofino 9 May 1981-1 adult; Kawkawa Lake 15 May 1981-1; Cape St. James 23 May 1979-1 (Merilees and McNall 1981). **Interior** - Creston 16 May 1980-2 (RBCM Photo 953).

Summer: Coastal - No records. **Interior** - Osoyoos 14 Jun to 14 Jul 1982-1 (Cannings, R.A. et al. 1987), 31 Jul 1982-1; Oliver 3 Jul 1982-1 immature.

Autumn: Interior - Fort Nelson 27 Oct 1980-1 immature; Kispiox River 2 Oct 1981-1 (RBCM Photo 726); Smithers 22 Nov 1981-1; Quesnel 11 Nov 1984-1; Anahim Lake 15 Oct 1982-5; Revelstoke 15 to 24 Nov 1981-2, photographed on 20 Nov (RBCM Photo 730); Anglemont 28 Sep 1986-

1 (RBCM Photo 1147; Fig. 241); Nakusp 9 Nov 1980-4; Genelle 10 Nov 1980-2 immatures; Oliver 1 to 15 Nov 1980-2 (RBCM Photo 740); Grand Forks 13 Nov 1984-9, 24 Nov 1987-1. **Coastal** - Terrace 13 Nov 1980-2+ (RBCM Photo 667); Prince Rupert 6 Nov 1980-2 (RBCM Photo 670) and 25 Nov 1984-1 (RBCM 18419); Tlell 8 Oct 1980-1; Port Neville 1 Oct 1976-1 (RBCM Photo 501); Kains Island 8 Nov 1984-3; Oyster River 26 Oct 1981-3; Squamish 26 Oct 1980-2; Lantzville 25 Oct 1980-9; Tofino 19 Nov 1984-2 (RBCM Photo 1004), 21 to 25 Nov 1987-1 immature (RBCM Photo 1202); Fraser River delta 30 Nov 1980-20, census; Ladysmith Oct 1981-5.

Winter: Interior - Vernon 11 Jan 1981-1 (RBCM Photo 744); Nakusp 11 to 17 Dec 1981-2; Oliver 1

and 2 Dec 1980-2. **Coastal** - Prince Rupert 6 Dec 1984-1; Masset 18 Dec 1982-1; Bella Coola 6 Dec 1979-1; Kains Island 7 Dec 1984-1; Tahsis 8 Dec 1984-8 (Campbell 1985a); Powell River 10 Dec 1979-1 immature; Agassiz 30 Dec 1981-1; Hatzic 10 Feb 1982-1; Port Alberni 5 Jan 1980-1; Tofino 4 Dec 1979-4; Cedar 5 to 12 Dec 1980-3; Ladner 1 Dec 1980-6; Port Renfrew 8 Dec 1984-11.

Christmas Counts: Interior - Not recorded. **Coastal** - Recorded from 9 of 28 localities and on 3% of all counts. Maxima: Ladner 29 Dec 1979-3, all-time Canadian high count (Anderson, R.R. 1980); Victoria 15 Dec 1984-2. Masset, Skidegate Inlet, Sunshine Coast, Pitt Meadows, Vancouver, White Rock, and Duncan, all have recorded single birds.

Cattle Egret

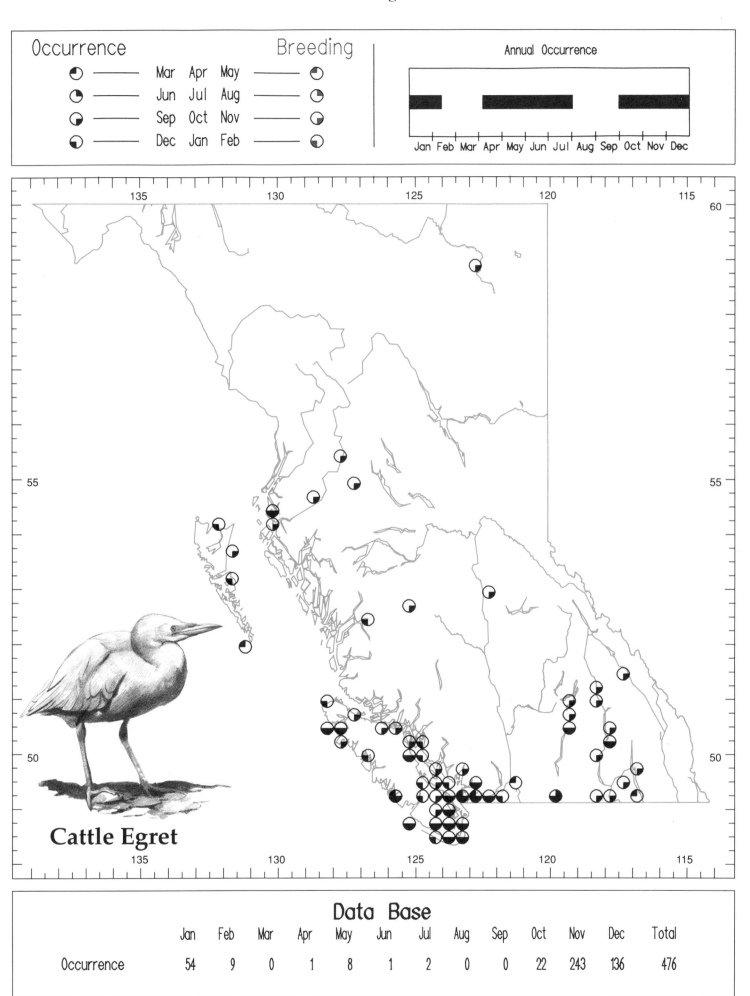

Occurrence

◑ ——	Mar Apr May	—— ◑
◐ ——	Jun Jul Aug	—— ◐
◒ ——	Sep Oct Nov	—— ◒
◓ ——	Dec Jan Feb	—— ◓

Breeding

Annual Occurrence

Jan Feb Mar Apr May Jun Jul Aug Sep Oct Nov Dec

Cattle Egret

Data Base

	Jan	Feb	Mar	Apr	May	Jun	Jul	Aug	Sep	Oct	Nov	Dec	Total
Occurrence	54	9	0	1	8	1	2	0	0	22	243	136	476

Green-backed Heron

Butorides striatus (Linnaeus)

GRHE

RANGE: Breeds from southwestern British Columbia and Washington south to southern California, Arizona, and New Mexico, and from North Dakota, southern Ontario, and New Brunswick south to the Gulf Coast and southern Florida. Winters mainly from southern United States southward. Also occurs in Central and South America and the Old World.

STATUS: Locally *uncommon* summer and *rare* winter visitant to southeastern Vancouver Island and the Fraser Lowlands. *Casual* in the interior. *Casual* on the west coast of Vancouver Island. Local breeder.

CHANGE IN STATUS: The Green-backed Heron was first reported in British Columbia near Chilliwack on 1 October 1953 (Wells 1954). By 1958, it had been seen at Sea Island (Hughes 1961), and was first reported on Vancouver Island in 1963 at Duncan (Stirling 1965a). The establishment and spread of the heron in British Columbia from 1953 through 1970 is documented by Campbell (1972d). Vagrants appeared in the Okanagan valley in 1971, the west Kootenay in 1973, and the east Kootenay in 1984.

It now occurs throughout the year, in small numbers, in extreme southwestern British Columbia.

NONBREEDING: The Green-backed Heron occurs regularly along Vancouver Island from Victoria north to Campbell River and on the southern mainland from the Fraser River delta east to Hope. It is seen very infrequently elsewhere, except in the vicinity of Alta and Green lakes, 90 km north of Vancouver.

The Green-backed Heron is found in a variety of environments but prefers aquatic habitats, either fresh, marine, or brackish, with thickets, shrubs, and small trees nearby. On the coast, it prefers ponds (38%; n=525), rivers (17%), sloughs (14%), and lakes (12%), but also uses marshes, sewage ponds, bays, irrigation ditches, beaches, inlets, city parks, and golf courses. Most records (84%) are from within 10 km of marine shores. Preferred habitats in the interior are lakes and sloughs.

There appear to be 5 general periods in the annual cycle of the Green-backed Heron (adapted from Rydzewski (1956) and Campbell (1972d): return and resettlement (March and April), breeding (May to late July), nomadic (late July to mid-September), migratory (mid-September to early November) and winter (mid-November through February). Most records are for the nomadic period (39%) followed by breeding (27%), migration (16%), return and resettlement (9%) and winter (9%). The increase in records during the nomadic period probably represents post-breeding dispersal of birds (mostly immatures) from southern breeding areas, a common habit of members of the heron family (Palmer, R.S. 1962).

The Green-backed Heron occurs throughout the year in coastal areas. Most occurrences (83%), however, are from the period April through September. In the interior, it has been recorded between 13 May and 3 August.

Most records are of 1 or 2 birds. The largest group reported, 5 individuals, was probably a family.

BREEDING: The Green-backed Heron breeds on southeastern Vancouver Island from Victoria to Courtenay and Port Alberni, on the mainland throughout the Fraser Lowlands east to Chilliwack, and in the vicinity of Alta and Green lakes near Garibaldi Park. It breeds from sea level to 610 m elevation.

The species usually breeds as solitary pairs and prefers fresh water or brackish sloughs, slow-moving rivers, and lakes all with thickets or woodlands of willows and alders along the shore.

Nests: Only 6 nests have been located. Five were built in red alders; willows and hawthorns provided additional support for one nest. Another nest was in a Douglas-fir. All nests were stick and twig platforms placed near the end of branches. Nest heights ranged from 3.8 to 9.1 m above ground.

Eggs: Dates for 4 clutches ranged from 24 May to 5 July. Calculated dates, using details from Palmer, R.S. (1962), suggest the egg date period may extend from 16 May to 31 July. Clutch size ranged from 4 to 6 eggs (4E-2, 5E-1, 6E-1). Incubation period is 19 to 21 days (Palmer, R.S. 1962).

Young: Dates for 22 broods ranged from 9 June to 2 September (recently fledged). Sizes for 27 broods ranged from 1 to 4 young (1Y-7, 2Y-14, 3Y-4, 4Y-2). The nestling period is about 16 to 17 days; age at first flight is 21 to 23 days (Palmer, R.S. 1962).

REMARKS: Formerly known as the Green Heron (*Butorides virescens*), the North American population of which was merged with the Striated Heron and renamed the Green-backed Heron (American Ornithologists' Union 1983).

NOTEWORTHY RECORDS

Spring: Coastal - Swan Lake (Victoria) 12 Apr 1981-2; Reifel Island 21 Mar 1973-1; Langley 6 Mar 1977-1; Strawberry Island (Fraser River) 4 May 1973-3; Page Lake 7 Mar 1982-1; Coquitlam River 21 Mar 1966-1, 31 May 1981-3; Vancouver 26 May 1980-3; Klaskish River mouth 22 May 1978-1 adult. **Interior** - Duck Lake (Creston) 28 May 1973-1 (Butler, R.W. et al. 1986); Skaha Lake 13 May 1971-1 (Cannings, S.R. 1972).

Summer: Coastal - Quick's Bottom 19 Jul 1978-3 adults; Bamfield 11 Jul 1979-1; Blackie Spit 23 Aug 1983-3 (2 adults, 1 immature); Campbell River (Langley) 3 Aug 1981-3; Richmond 27 Aug 1986-6; Vancouver 30 Aug 1979-5; Pitt Lake 18 Aug 1974-4; Agassiz 24 Jun 1980-3; Cranberry Lake (Powell River) 25 Jul 1984-1. **Interior** - Manning Park 14 Jun 1973-1; Wardner 14 Aug 1984-1 (Rogers, T.H. 1985a); Anderson Lake 23 Jun 1968-2; Kamloops 3 Aug 1983-2 immatures.

Autumn: Interior - No records. **Coastal** - Sproat Lake 4 Sep 1984-1 adult; Pitt Meadows 30 Sep 1978-4 (2 adult, 2 immatures); Tofino 18 Sep 1971-1 (Crowell and Nehls 1972a); Chilliwack 17 Oct 1953-1 (Wells 1954); Jericho Beach 15 and 19 Sep 1983-4; Reifel Island 1 Sep 1968-4 (2 adults, 2 immatures); Fort Rodd Hill 24 Nov 1974-1.

Winter: Interior - No records. **Coastal** - Comox 27 Dec 1973-1; Chilliwack 16 Dec 1980-1; Marpole 20 Jan 1971-1 (Campbell et al. 1972b); Salmon River (Langley) 20 Dec 1977-1 adult; Ladner 20 Feb 1975-1; Duncan 3 Dec 1977-1; Victoria 21 Jan 1971-3.

Christmas Counts: Interior - Not recorded. **Coastal** - Recorded from 6 of 28 localities and on 6% of all counts. Maxima: Chilliwack 15 Dec 1979-5, all-time Canadian high count (Anderson, R.R. 1980); Pitt Meadows 15 Dec 1974-2; Duncan 18 Dec 1976, 15 Dec 1979 and 19 Dec 1981-all 2.

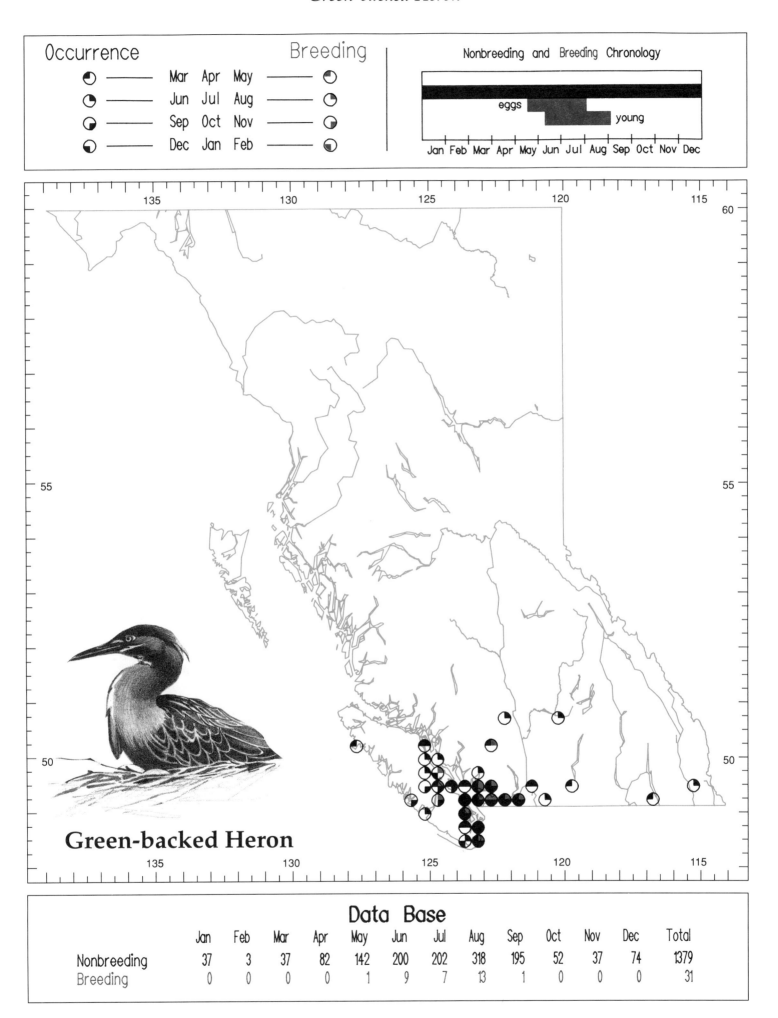

Green-backed Heron

Occurrence

	Mar	Apr	May	
	Jun	Jul	Aug	
	Sep	Oct	Nov	
	Dec	Jan	Feb	

Breeding

Nonbreeding and Breeding Chronology

eggs   young

Jan Feb Mar Apr May Jun Jul Aug Sep Oct Nov Dec

Data Base

	Jan	Feb	Mar	Apr	May	Jun	Jul	Aug	Sep	Oct	Nov	Dec	Total
Nonbreeding	37	3	37	82	142	200	202	318	195	52	37	74	1379
Breeding	0	0	0	0	1	9	7	13	1	0	0	0	31

Black-crowned Night-Heron

BCNH

Nycticorax nycticorax (Linnaeus)

RANGE: Breeds in North America throughout much of United States and central-southern and southeastern Canada. Post-breeding dispersal is widespread. Winters in southwestern and southeastern United States and along Atlantic Coast from southern New England southward. Widely distributed in the Old World.

STATUS: *Rare* summer, recently *rare* local winter visitant on the extreme south mainland coast. *Casual* on Vancouver Island. *Very rare* in the southern interior. Local breeder.

CHANGE IN STATUS: The Black-crowned Night-Heron was included in the "extralimital" list by Munro, J.A. and Cowan (1947) on the basis of a specimen collected at Summerland in 1927. However, Brooks (1909a) reported an earlier occurrence at Okanagan Landing in 1908. During the next 40 years or so it continued to be very rare, but by the mid-1970s it was being reported frequently. So far in the 1980s, the Black-crowned Night-Heron has been seen every month of the year, mostly in the vicinity of Reifel Island (48% of all records are from that area). It has been most frequently reported from March through September, but since 1982, from 3 to 6 birds have wintered each year at Reifel Island.

NONBREEDING: The Black-crowned Night-Heron has been reported from the extreme southern tip of Vancouver Island and the Fraser Lowlands east to Chilliwack, and in the interior, from Osoyoos Lake and Creston north through the central-southern interior to Clearwater Lake (Wells Gray Park). Eighty-five per cent of all records are from the vicinity of Reifel Island and the north end of Osoyoos Lake.

Brackish sloughs surrounded by tall willows and red alder (coast), and freshwater marshes with dense willow and birch growth (interior) are preferred habitats. It has also been seen along river banks, at ponds and ditches, and there is one record of a bird perched in a tree on a golf course.

On the coast, spring migrants arrive in March; autumn departure usually occurs in October. Nearly 54% of the records are from the post-breeding period of July through November. In the interior, extreme dates are 20 April to 12 October.

Most records are of single birds. A flock of 11 birds at Osoyoos Lake in late summer is the largest yet reported in British Columbia. The ratio of adults to immatures for 81 sightings was exactly 1:2. The recent increase in sightings in British Columbia appears to be correlated with a major increase in breeding populations in Washington state (R. Friesz pers. comm.).

BREEDING: There are 2 records. On 24 May 1973, a clutch of 3 eggs was collected from a twig nest in willows bordering a slough on Reifel Island. The eggs were confirmed as Black-

crowned Night-Heron. The other record is of a single fledged young with some natal down present, perched in a red alder on Reifel Island on 19 July 1975.

Breeding chronology was developed using an incubation period of 24 days and a fledging period of 42 days (Gross 1923). Calculated dates suggest eggs are laid between 20 May and 15 June and young are found between 10 June and 19 July.

REMARKS: The Black-crowned Night-Heron appears on the "Blue List" from 1972 through 1981 (Tate 1981). On the 1976 list, it was believed to be declining from Quebec and Ontario, through middle America to the West Coast and south to Texas (Arbib 1975). By 1981 the species seemed to have recovered (Tate 1981). It was delisted on the 1982 list to a species with "special concerns" because it had "not yet begun returning to areas from which it was extirpated in the last 10 years" (Tate and Tate 1982).

The common name was formerly spelled Black-crowned Night Heron.

Figure 242. *Black-crowned Night-Heron, Camp River (Chilliwack), 26 March 1976 (RBCM Photo 479; Dan McPhee).*

NOTEWORTHY RECORDS

Spring: Coastal - Saanich 6 May 1987-2; Somenos Lake 19 May to 31 Jul 1987-1 to 6 birds; Reifel Island 26 May 1976-2 adults (Shepard, M.G. 1976c), 14 Mar 1981-1 immature, 22 Mar 1986-3, 1 May 1987-4 adults; Chilliwack 26 Mar 1976-1 adult (RBCM Photo 479; Fig. 242), May 1979-1 (RBCM 17277). **Interior** - Osoyoos Lake 4 May 1985-1; Swan Lake (Vernon) 20 Apr 1980-2; 10 km s of Revelstoke 3 May 1982-1 adult; Revelstoke 28 Apr 1984-1 adult (Campbell 1984b).

Summer: Coastal - Glen Lake 30 Jul to 9 Aug 1963-1 immature (Stirling 1965; Davidson 1966); Somenos Lake 7 Jun 1987-1; Delta 25 Aug 1973-2; Serpentine Fen (Surrey) 18 Aug 1987-4; Reifel Island 18 Jun 1976-2 adults, 5 Jul 1974-2 adults

(Shepard, M.G. 1975a); Pitt Lake 1 and 4 Jun 1987-4. **Interior** - Osoyoos Lake (north end) 27 Jul through 31 Aug 1981-2 immatures seen almost daily, 7 on 19 Aug; 1 Aug 1974-11 immatures (Cannings, S.G. 1974); Duck Lake (Creston) 27 Jun 1973-1 (Butler, R.W. et al. 1986); Okanagan Landing 3 Aug 1908-1 (Brooks 1909a); Swan Lake (Vernon) Aug 1984-1 (Rogers, T.H. 1985a); Clearwater Lake (Wells Gray Park) 20 Aug 1977-1 (RBCM Photo 472).

Autumn: Interior - Swan Lake (Vernon) 9 to 17 Sep 1979-1 immature; Summerland 18 Sep 1927-1 (Tait 1932; RBCM 6784); Osoyoos Lake (north end) 1 Sep to 12 Oct 1981-2 immatures seen almost daily. **Coastal** - Lulu Island 18 Sep 1955-1

immature (Hughes 1956); Reifel Island 28 Oct 1986-2 immatures, 22 Nov 1986-4, 7 Nov 1987-5 adults, 1 immature; Ladner 4 Oct 1975-2; Oak Bay 28 Sep 1977-1 immature.

Winter: Interior - No records. **Coastal** - Reifel Island 27 Jan 1980-1 immature, 4 Feb 1984-1 immature (RBCM Photo 882), 25 Feb 1985-1 adult, 29 Dec 1985-2 adults, 1 immature, 28 Dec 1986-2 adults, 2 immatures.

Christmas Counts: Interior - Not recorded. **Coastal** - Recorded from 1 of 28 localities and on 2% of all counts. Maxima: Ladner, single birds recorded twice: 27 Dec 1983 and 23 Dec 1984.

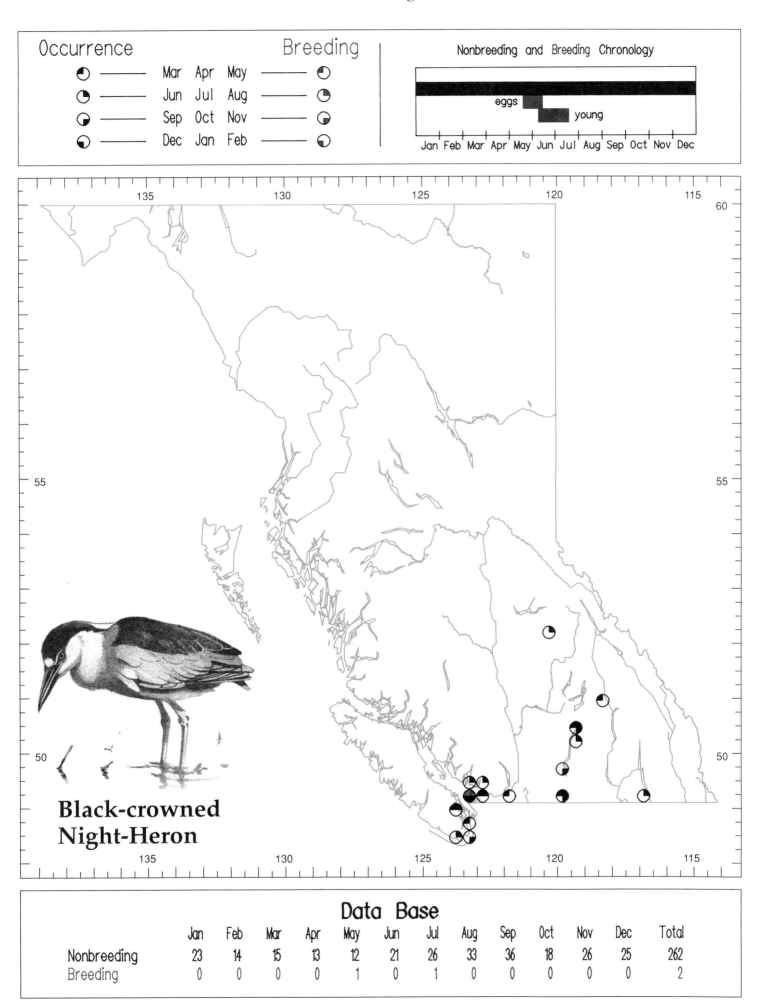

Occurrence   Breeding

	Mar Apr May	
	Jun Jul Aug	
	Sep Oct Nov	
	Dec Jan Feb	

Nonbreeding and Breeding Chronology

eggs   young

Jan Feb Mar Apr May Jun Jul Aug Sep Oct Nov Dec

Black-crowned Night-Heron

Data Base

	Jan	Feb	Mar	Apr	May	Jun	Jul	Aug	Sep	Oct	Nov	Dec	Total
Nonbreeding	23	14	15	13	12	21	26	33	36	18	26	25	262
Breeding	0	0	0	0	1	0	1	0	0	0	0	0	2

Tundra Swan

Cygnus columbianus (Ord)

TUSW

RANGE: In North America, breeds near the Arctic coast between the Bering Sea and Hudson Bay. Winters mainly on the Pacific coast from Washington to California, on the Atlantic coast from Maryland to North Carolina, and from the southern Great Basin south to New Mexico; also in Eurasia.

STATUS: *Fairly common* to *common* migrant on the coast; locally *common* to *abundant* migrant in the interior. Locally *uncommon* to *common* in winter along the coast; *uncommon* to locally *abundant* in winter in the southern interior. *Very rare* in summer.

OCCURRENCE: The Tundra Swan appears to follow at least 3 migration corridors through British Columbia between its wintering grounds in the western United States and the breeding grounds in Alaska (mostly) and the Yukon (Fig. 243). Those corridors are used in both spring and autumn. Spring migrants outnumber autumn migrants. Sladen (1973), from use of neck collars, determined 3 main corridors: coastal, interior, and northeastern. Bellrose (1976) divides the interior route into 2 corridors.

Swans that migrate along the coast of British Columbia breed in western Alaska. The northward movement occurs from late March to late May, and reaches a peak in the second and third weeks of April. Autumn migrants, usually in flocks of less than 50 birds, arrive from mid to late October. Bellrose (1976) estimates that most of the 10,000 to 15,000 swans that breed in south-coastal Alaska migrate south along the coast of Vancouver Island. Most move on by the middle of November to winter in the San Francisco Bay area. Small numbers may winter along the coast of British Columbia, but only the Fraser River delta and Nicomen Slough regularly support populations of up to 100 individuals.

The Tundra Swan is mainly a transient of the interior of the province (Fig. 244); over 70% of our records are from there. Valleys with large lakes, such as the Okanagan valley, and valleys in the west and east Kootenays, are used as migration corridors. Spring migrants probably come from eastern Washington, Idaho, Oregon, and some southwestern states. Spring migration occurs from mid-March through early May in southern interior areas; the peak is during the first half of April. Tundra Swans formerly staged in

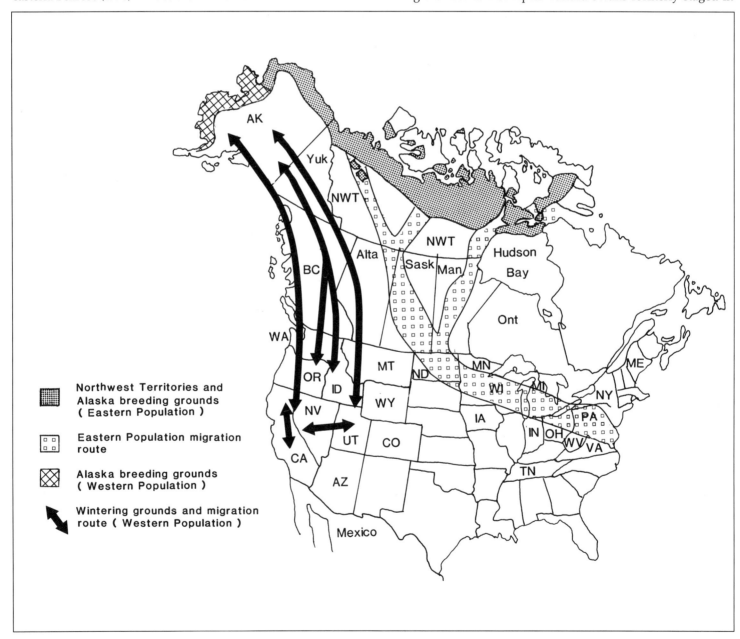

Figure 243. *Major migration corridors of the Tundra Swan in North America (adapted from Sladen 1973 and Bellrose 1976).*

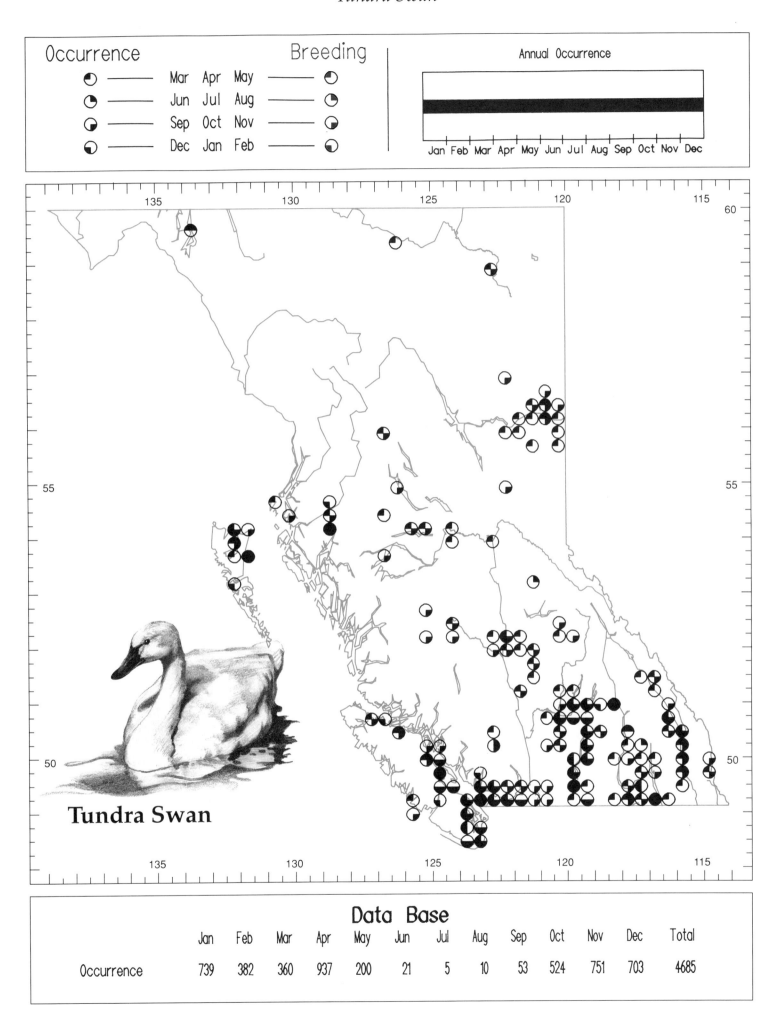

Occurrence

◑ ———	Mar Apr May	——— ◑
◕ ———	Jun Jul Aug	——— ◔
◵ ———	Sep Oct Nov	——— ◔
◖ ———	Dec Jan Feb	——— ◖

Breeding

Annual Occurrence

Jan Feb Mar Apr May Jun Jul Aug Sep Oct Nov Dec

Tundra Swan

Data Base

	Jan	Feb	Mar	Apr	May	Jun	Jul	Aug	Sep	Oct	Nov	Dec	Total
Occurrence	739	382	360	937	200	21	5	10	53	524	751	703	4685

Figure 244. *Tundra Swans in migration, 37 km southwest of Williams Lake near Riske Creek, 27 March 1988 (Brian Nuttall).*

large numbers in the Creston valley, but their numbers have decreased steadily since 1969 (Fig. 245). Records indicate that those southern valleys are still used regularly each spring, but swan numbers and locations vary considerably from year to year. The swans use open water in lakes (Fig. 246) and rivers of the central southern interior north as far as the Chilcotin-Cariboo. Records of flocks farther north are few in number, which seems to indicate that the majority of the birds pass directly through the northern part of the province to staging areas in the Yukon and Alaska. Autumn migration through the interior occurs from late September through mid-November. That passage peaks in late October and early November. There are winter records as far north as Williams Lake, but most of the winter records are from the Thompson and Okanagan valleys (Figs. 247 and 249). The most significant numbers have been counted on the South Thompson River near Kamloops. During mild winters, groups of up to 75 birds may remain on some larger lakes. The largest number censused in the interior was 1,200 birds on 12 December 1951 (Bellrose 1976).

Tundra Swans that use the corridor across northeastern British Columbia in spring migration (Fig. 248) come from Utah and Montana, move through western Alberta, and cross British Columbia towards their breeding grounds in the Yukon and Alaska. The spring movement occurs from mid-April through late May although peak numbers are reported from late March to early May. The Peace River and, to a lesser extent, run-off ponds in the Fort St. John area are used for resting and feeding stopovers. During a May 1975 survey, 7,500+ swans were counted in the area. We do not know if this is an annual occurrence. The return flight in autumn, peaks during the second and third weeks of October. There are no winter reports for the area.

Over 99% of all British Columbia records are from the period September through May. There were, however, summer occurrences scattered throughout the province. Some early June records may have been late migrants. One or 2 healthy birds have been reported to spend the entire summer at some locations, and to depart in autumn.

Tundra Swans frequent fresh or brackish aquatic habitats. They are less frequently found on salt water. On the coast, they are found mostly in flooded fields (22% of records), sloughs (18%), lakes (16%), and bays (16%). Other habitats include estuaries, slow-moving rivers, ponds, inlets, and beaches. In the interior, deep and shallow lakes (51%) and slow-moving rivers (23%) are used most often by the swans. Other habitats include the mouths of creeks, sloughs, flooded fields, ponds, and airports. They have been recorded from sea level to 1,400 m elevation.

In the Pacific population for the period 1961 to 1973, 18.5% were immatures [i.e. brownish-gray plumage] (Lynch and Voelzer 1974). Examination of British Columbia records for the same period, showed 20.2% immatures overall; 26.9% for the coastal flyway and 19.8% for the interior region. More recently, the proportion of immatures in the Tundra Swan population in the southern central interior was much higher and ranged from 23% to 38% for the period 1976 to 1988 (Fig. 250). That is consistently higher than the number of juveniles wintering in the United States continental population, which is estimated to be 15% (Bellrose 1976). The difference between the coastal and interior areas may be due to varying weather conditions at Alaskan breeding areas.

REMARKS: The relationship of *C. columbianus* to *C. bewickii* [Bewick's Swan] is uncertain at the species level. Vaurie (1959) treats them as separate species, while Delacour (1954), Mayr and Short (1970), and R.S. Palmer (1962) consider them conspecific.

The Victoria Christmas Bird Count record of 41 Tundra Swans on 2 January 1966 should be used with caution. At that time the Tundra Swan was assumed to be much more common than the Trumpeter Swan and the identification may have been made solely on that basis (J.E.V. Goodwill pers. comm.). In addition all coastal records of large flocks, old and new, should be carefully scrutinized. For example, reported flocks of 150 birds on 15 April and 3 October 1939 and 500 on 9 November 1937 at Port Hardy and 400 at Lulu Island on 12 November 1924 may have been all Trumpeter Swans or both species together. See also Remarks in Trumpeter Swan.

The North American population of the Tundra Swan was formerly known as the Whistling Swan *(Olor columbianus)*.

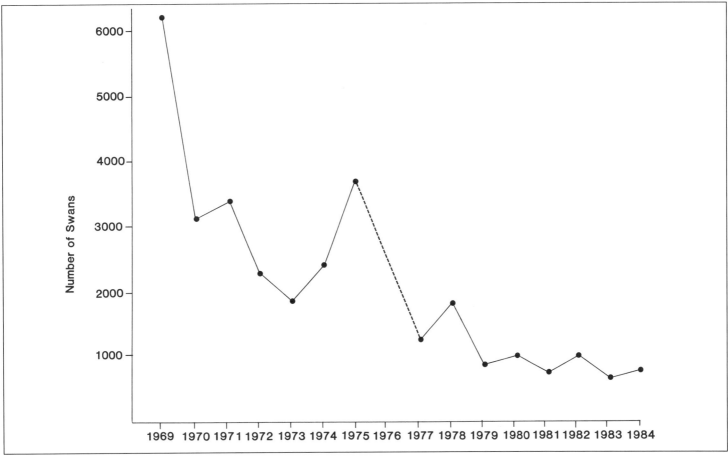

Figure 245. Peak counts of Tundra Swans in the Creston valley, 1969 to 1984 (from Butler, R.W. et al. 1986). The dashed line indicates a period when counts were not made.

Figure 246. Leach Lake in the Creston valley, 18 May 1988 (R. Wayne Campbell). This lake is an important stopover area for migrating Tundra Swans in spring in British Columbia.

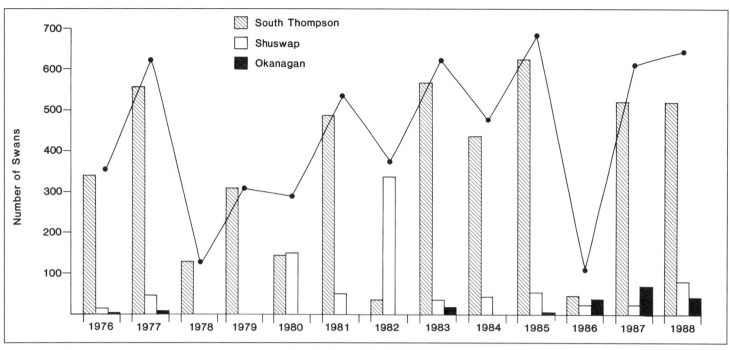

Figure 247. *Mid-winter (January) census of Tundra Swans in 3 areas of the Thompson-Okanagan Plateau, British Columbia from 1976 through 1987. Survey areas include the South Thompson (the valley of the South Thompson River from Kamloops Lake to the outflow of Little Shuswap Lake), Shuswap (all of the Shuswap Lakes and the drainage of the Shuswap River from and including Mabel Lake), and Okanagan (Armstrong south to Kelowna and Peachland south to the international border). Solid line indicates total number of swans reported for each winter (courtesy of Richard R. Howie).*

Figure 248. *Tundra Swans in migration at Fort St. John, 10 May 1973 (R. Wayne Campbell).*

Figure 249. *Syd Roberts (left) and Sandy Rathbone counting swans at Shuswap Lake, 10 January 1988 (Richard R. Howie).*

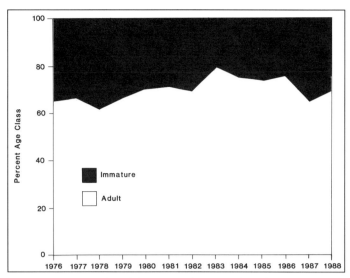

Figure 250. *Proportion of immatures (n = 5,777) in the Tundra Swan population wintering on the South Thompson River, Shuswap Lake, and Okanagan valley areas of British Columbia from winter 1976 to winter 1987 (see Figure 247 for details of census units).*

NOTEWORTHY RECORDS

Spring: Coastal - Cowichan Bay 18 Mar to 18 Apr 1966-35; Tofino 27 Mar 1980-50; Ladner 8 Mar 1978-47; Campbell River 26 May 1924-18 flying north; Masset Inlet 13 Apr 1978-22. **Interior** - Creston valley 6 Mar 1987-14, 28 Mar 1962-4,000 to 5,000, 14 Apr 1956-2,005 (Munro, J.A. 1958a); Tatley Sloughs 13 Mar 1981-104; Columbia Lake 25 Mar 1941-115 (Johnstone, W.B. 1949); South Thompson River (Kamloops) 11 Mar 1979-440, between Kamloops and Chase, 31 Mar 1962-3,000+; 103 Mile Lake 7 Apr 1944-200+ (Munro, J.A. 1945a); near Rock Lake (Riske Creek) 2 Apr 1983-66, 3 Apr 1983-175; Francois Lake 21 Apr 1943-78 (Munro, J.A. and Cowan 1947); Tetana Lake late Apr 1938-293 migrating to northwest (Stanwell-Fletcher and Stanwell-Fletcher 1940); Peace River census in May 1975, 3rd-7,553, 10th-131, 17th-398 (Penner 1976); n Fort St. John 3 Apr 1986-3, 24 Apr 1985-108, 27 Apr 1985-167; Fort Nelson 26 Apr 1983-3, first arrival; Atlin 16 May 1981-3 (Campbell 1981).

Summer: Coastal - Westham Island 14 Jul to 24 Aug 1968-2; Green Lake (Whistler) 1 Jun 1984-1

adult; Port Neville 8 Jun 1975-13 flying north; Tlell 25 Aug 1974-1 adult. **Interior** - Vaseux Lake 24 Jun 1949-3; Lardeau 27 Jun 1976-2; Fort Steele 31 Jul 1985-1 (RBCM Photo 1049); Wasa 14 Jul 1948-1 (Johnstone, W.B. 1949); Revelstoke 3 to 14 Jun 1977-4 and 17 Aug 1978-2 (Bonar 1978a); Kamloops 16 Aug 1979-1 adult; Bowron Lake 15 Jun 1974-4 (Tierney 1974); Fort St. John 6 and 12 Jun 1983-1 adult, 21 Aug 1986-4 adults; Atlin 7 Jun 1981-1 adult.

Autumn: Interior - Cecil Lake 14 Oct 1984-300, 24 Oct 1986-141; Babine Lake 19 Oct 1944-125+ (Munro, J.A. 1947a); Francois Lake 27 Oct 1941-150+ (Munro, J.A. and Cowan 1947); Ootsa Lake 15 Sep 1942-80 (Munro, J.A. and Cowan 1947); Chilcotin Lake 27 Oct 1977-114; Wells Gray Park 21 to 31 Oct 1961-46 (Edwards and Ritcey 1967); South Thompson River (near Kamloops) 21 Oct 1961-165+, 22 Nov 1981-261; Swan Lake (Vernon) 21 Oct 1961-140; Columbia Lake 31 Oct 1978-34; Kelowna 25 Oct 1939-101 (Munro, J.A. 1939c). **Coastal** - Yakoun River 8 Nov 1973-4; Port Neville 17 Sep 1975-31; Alta Lake 7 to 10 Nov 1944-13

birds in 3 flocks (Racey 1948); Kawkawa Lake 2 Nov 1924-12+; Harrison Bay 30 Nov 1974-82; Iona Island 11 Nov 1984-45; Ucluelet 12 Nov 1973-34; Swan Lake (Victoria) 19 Oct 1961-35.

Winter: Interior - Williams Lake 1 Dec 1983-6; Revelstoke 11 Jan 1983-7; Sorrento 25 Dec 1970-73+; South Thompson River 1 Jan 1980-605, 13 Jan 1985-685 (Rogers, T.H. 1985b); Athalmer 20 Feb 1981-11; Okanagan Lake 20 Feb 1970-23. **Coastal** - Cumshewa Inlet 8 and 10 Jan 1979-2; Harrison Bay 2 Dec 1973-31; Nicomen Slough 7 Feb 1977-89; Pitt Meadows 28 Feb 1976-33; Roberts Bank 29 Dec 1979-62.

Christmas Counts: Interior- Recorded from 6 of 19 localities and on 24% of all counts. Maxima: Shuswap Lake 28 Dec 1983-441; Kamloops 15 Dec 1984-81; Vaseux Lake 28 Dec 1974-19. **Coastal** - Recorded from 11 of 28 localities and on 19% of all counts. Maxima: Ladner 23 Dec 1978-88; Chilliwack 29 Dec 1973-65; Victoria 2 Jan 1966-41 (see Remarks).

Trumpeter Swan

Cygnus buccinator Richardson

TRUS

RANGE: Breeds in 3 distinct areas of North America (Fig. 251). The Pacific Coast population breeds in interior and coastal south-central Alaska, and winters along the coast from Alaska south to Oregon. The Rocky Mountain population consists of 2 sub-populations. The Interior Canada subpopulation breeds in Alberta, northeastern British Columbia, southern Yukon, south-western Northwest Territories and southwest Saskatchewan, and winters in the Tri-state area (Wyoming, Idaho, Montana). The Tri-state subpopulation remains throughout the year in the Tri-state area.

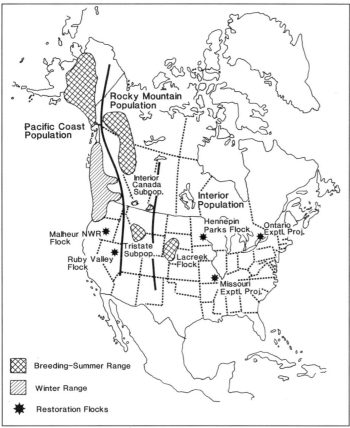

Figure 251. *General breeding-summering and winter ranges of the Trumpeter Swan in North America (from data compiled by Canadian Wildlife Service, Trumpeter Swan Society, and United States Fish and Wildlife Service. See also Anonymous 1986).*

STATUS: On the coast, an *uncommon* migrant and *common* to locally *abundant* winter visitant; *very rare* in summer. *Rare* migrant and *rare* to locally *common* winter visitant in the south and central interior; *very rare* in the Kootenays. In the northern interior locally *uncommon* migrant, summer visitant, and breeder.

NONBREEDING: The Trumpeter Swan is mainly a winter visitant along the coast; 70% of all records are from coastal areas, and of those, 91% are from the period October through March.

Birds wintering on the south coast appear to follow an interior migration route north through the Francois Lake region to Tagish Narrows, Yukon, some 100 km north of Atlin, and on to their Alaskan breeding areas (Mackay 1957; McKelvey and Burton 1983). Swans begin to leave coastal areas in late February and early March, and the main exodus is over by early April. In mid-April, however, some Trumpeter Swans, probably from Oregon and Washington, are often seen with small numbers of migrating Tundra Swans. The autumn movement may occur in mid- to late October, or may be delayed until November

depending on the time of freeze-up in Alaska. In average years, the main influx occurs during the latter half of November. Their numbers increase during December.

Main coastal wintering concentrations occur on Vancouver Island and in the Fraser Lowlands. Wintering birds begin leaving the interior (e.g. Okanagan valley, Lonesome Lake) in late February and early March and are thought to follow the interior route used by coastal birds (R.W. McKelvey pers. comm.). Spring migrants from the Tri-state area reach the Peace Lowlands from mid-to-late April. In autumn, birds return to Lonesome Lake beginning the third week of October and to the southern interior in late October and early November. Main wintering areas, from north to south, are Stuart River, Francois Lake, Crooked River, and Lonesome Lake.

A few nonbreeding birds are usually scattered along the coast in summer. In the interior, small groups of up to 4 birds have been reported, mostly from northern areas.

The Trumpeter Swan frequents sheltered, often shallow, aquatic habitats. On the coast, their habitats include estuaries (51% of records), agricultural fields (19%-Fig. 252), sloughs (5%), bays (5%), and lakes (3%). Other habitats include lagoons, ponds, rivers, tidal mud flats, beaches, and inlets. Interior habitats include unfrozen lakes (71%), marshes (12%), sloughs (8%), ponds (5%), and slow-moving rivers (4%).

The proportion of cygnets in the Trumpeter Swan population wintering on Vancouver Island from 1968-69 to 1970-71 varied from 22 to 26% (Smith, I.D. and Blood 1972). The proportion of cygnets in 463 winter flocks on Vancouver Island from 1980-81 through 1985-86 was 23%. Thus, the proportion of cygnets in wintering populations appears to have remained relatively constant during the past two decades.

BREEDING: Although breeding was suspected (see Munro, J.A. and Cowan 1947), it was not documented in British Columbia until 1976. The Trumpeter Swan is now a local but widespread breeder north of latitude 54°, primarily in the Peace Lowlands and Boreal Forest regions of the province (see McKelvey et al. 1988). Breeding birds in the northeast are likely from the Interior Canada subpopulation, while the birds breeding in the west-central and extreme northwest are probably part of the Pacific Coast population. The population to which the birds breeding in the extreme north-central portion of the province belong is unknown (Anonymous 1984). Recent surveys (McKelvey 1986) revealed a summer population of 27 pairs, which produced 31 cygnets. Sixteen of those pairs were centred in the Peace River area and produced 23 cygnets. That low productivity may be a reflection of the relatively young age of that part of the sub-population (McKelvey 1981a).

Trumpeter Swans breed from 24 to 823 m elevation. Breeding habitat is forested and includes large and small, shallow, fresh water lakes with emergent vegetation (96%; n=20), and occasionally marshes along rivers.

Nests: Only 3 nests with eggs have been reported, although there are a number of observations of pairs beside newly constructed nests (e.g. McKelvey 1981a). All were built on the edge of or among emergent vegetation including bulrushes, sedges, horsetails, and cattail. Water depths at 2 nests were between 1 and 2 m. Nests were piles of marsh vegetation including grasses, sedges, and horsetails.

Eggs: Dates for 3 clutches ranged from 8 June to 21 June. Two nests contained 5 eggs and one contained 4 eggs. Clutches of 6 eggs are probable (see below). Incubation period is 33 to 37 days (Banko 1960; Hansen et al. 1971).

Young: Dates for 17 broods ranged from 23 June to mid-September. Brood size ranged from 1 to 6 young (1Y-7, 2Y-1, 3Y-3, 4Y-5, 6Y-1), with 9 broods having 2 to 4 young. Fledging period is about 91 to 105 days (Hansen et al. 1971).

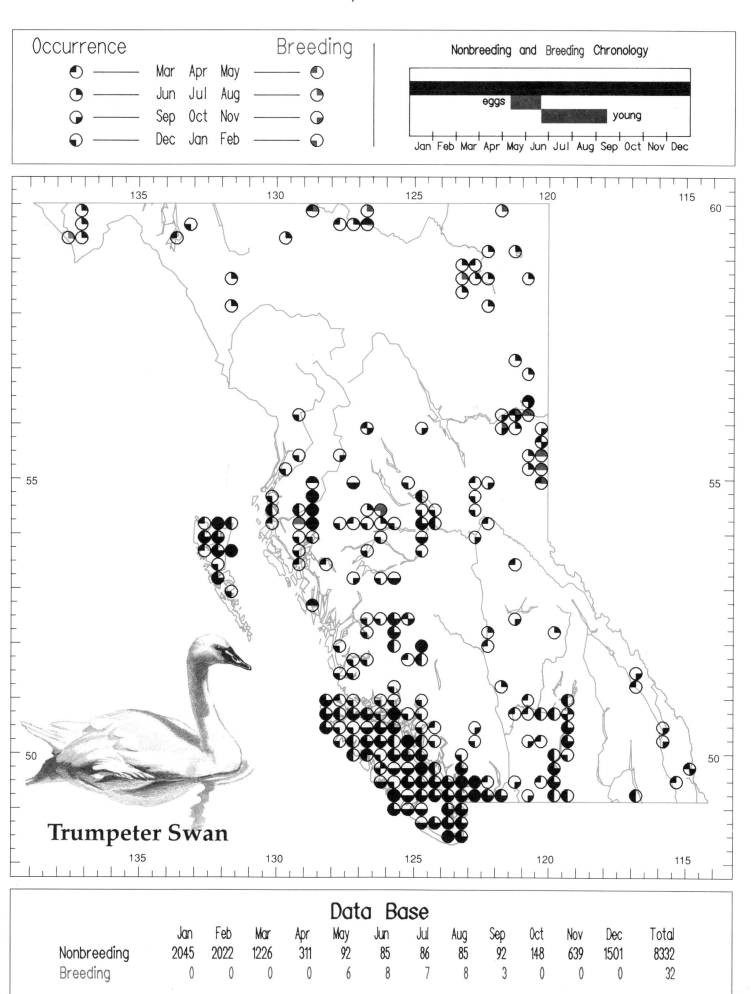

Trumpeter Swan

Occurrence   **Breeding**

	Mar	Apr	May
	Jun	Jul	Aug
	Sep	Oct	Nov
	Dec	Jan	Feb

Nonbreeding and Breeding Chronology

eggs   young

Jan Feb Mar Apr May Jun Jul Aug Sep Oct Nov Dec

Data Base

	Jan	Feb	Mar	Apr	May	Jun	Jul	Aug	Sep	Oct	Nov	Dec	Total
Nonbreeding	2045	2022	1226	311	92	85	86	85	92	148	639	1501	8332
Breeding	0	0	0	0	6	8	7	8	3	0	0	0	32

Figure 252. *Wintering Trumpeter Swans at Anderton Road, Comox, December 1980 (Richard W. McKelvey).*

REMARKS: In the 19th century, the Trumpeter Swan was apparently widely distributed from southeastern Alaska, across Canada, and throughout much of North America (Banko 1960; Lumsden 1984). Due to overharvest, habitat alteration, and a commercial market for swan skins in the late 1800s and early 1900s, the population declined drastically, and by the 1930s reached an all-time low. Trumpeter Swans were then considered by many to be a vanishing species.

Concern for the species resulted in substantial management efforts that protected the swans and their habitat. Although the wild, interior population of North American birds is still largely confined to the fringes of its former range, the Trumpeter Swan is no longer considered in danger of extinction (Anonymous 1984). Today, the population of non-captive birds is estimated at 11,000, most of which breed in Alaska (Anonymous 1986) and winter in British Columbia (Anonymous 1984).

There is little evidence to suggest that Pacific populations were ever as low as generally reported in the 1930s and 1940s (Banko 1960). In fact, numbers may have been increasing slowly. For example, at Lonesome Lake in British Columbia, the wintering population increased naturally from 14 birds in 1912-13 to 30 birds in 1931-32 (Gould, E. 1981). A similar increase occurred on the Campbell Lake system on Vancouver Island. There, the wintering population increased from 20 to 30 birds in the early 1920s, 40 to 50 birds in the 1950s, and 80 to 90 birds in the 1970s (R.G. Davies pers. comm.).

During the past 40 years, the known Pacific population has increased substantially. Late summer surveys in Alaska yielded 2,847 swans in 1968, 4,170 in 1975, 7,696 in 1980 (King, J.G. and Conant 1981), and 9,459 in 1985 (Anonymous 1986). Smith, I.D. and Blood (1972) indicate that the Vancouver Island winter population could have increased by 129% over the period 1969 to 1971, to a minimum of 1,076 birds. Davies (1978, 1981a, 1981c), in his inventory of wintering Trumpeter Swans on Vancouver Island,

indicates a maximum increase of 90% for the period 1973 to 1981 (Fig. 253). Christmas Bird Counts from Comox probably best illustrate the trend. There, numbers increased steadily from 4 birds in 1963 to 712 in 1984.

There are 2 breeding records for the southwest mainland coast: introduced birds (i.e. feather clipped and later free-flying) nested successfully at Burnaby Lake in 1965 and 1966 and at Stanley Park (Vancouver) in 1967 and 1968. They have since been extirpated.

A detailed account of the winter feeding ecology and management of the Trumpeter Swan on southeastern Vancouver Island is provided by McKelvey (1981b) and McKelvey and Verbeek (1988).

The Trumpeter Swan and Whooper Swan (*Cygnus cygnus*) have been considered conspecific by some authors. Other authors have even considered them as 2 species, and the Tundra Swan (*C. columbianus*) to be a single species (American Ornithologists' Union 1983).

The Trumpeter Swan appears on the "Blue Lists" of 1980 and 1981 (Tate 1981). It was delisted in 1982, but was retained as a species of "special concern" primarily because of the low capacity of existing wintering habitat for the interior birds. Since "nearly all of the [interior] Canadian birds winter in the tri-state area ... a single disease outbreak [could] obliterate the Canadian population" (Tate and Tate 1982).

The Trumpeter Swan was formerly placed in the genus *Olor.*

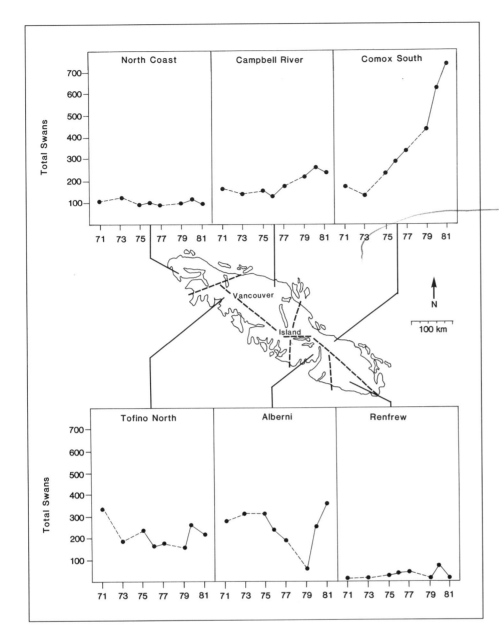

Figure 253. Total number of Trumpeter Swans counted within 6 regions of Vancouver Island during mid-winter surveys between 1971 and 1981. Census units are North Coast (Brooks Peninsula to Hope Island), Campbell River (Tsitika River to Oyster River), Comox South (Oyster River to Sooke), Renfrew (Sooke to Nitinat River), Alberni (Nitinat River to Ucluelet), and Tofino (Ucluelet to Brooks Peninsula) [adapted from Davies 1978, 1981a, and 1981c].

NOTEWORTHY RECORDS

Spring: Coastal - Prospect Lake (Victoria) 27 Mar 1953-22; Saanich 7 Mar 1987-66; Courtenay/Comox, aerial surveys 1 Mar 1985-392, 9 Mar 1985-306; Exstew River 24 Mar 1985-8; Big Bay (Chatham Sound) 17 Apr 1975-41 (Martin 1978); Kumdis Bay 14 Apr 1962-80+ flying northwest. **Interior** - Creston 6 to 7 May 1948-15; Vaseux Lake 2 Mar 1980-12; Lambly Lake 26 Apr 1977-7; Princeton 11 Mar 1979-6; Klinaklini River 1 Mar 1967-37; Fraser Lake (Fraser Lake) 24 Mar 1977-24; Crooked River (100 km n Prince George) 9 Apr 1985-6; Driftwood valley 10 Apr 1938-190 flying northward (Stanwell-Fletcher and Stanwell-Fletcher 1943); Fort St. John 15 Apr 1983-2; Parker Lake (Fort Nelson) 17 May 1986-1 immature; Palmer Lake (Atlin) 18 May 1981-12.

Summer: Coastal - Sooke River mouth 22 Jul 1978-1; Sheringham Point 25 Aug 1969-2; Tofino 2 Jul 1987-1 immature; Port Moody 8 and 9 Jun 1987-1 adult; Comox 9 Aug 1953-1; Perry Lake (Tahsis Inlet) 10 Jun 1973-2; lower Campbell Lake 1 Jul 1922-2; Lakelse Lake 6 Jun 1976-2. **Interior** - Clinton 19 Aug 1948-2; Clearwater Lake (Kleena Kleene) 31 Jul 1956-1 (Paul 1959); Williams Lake Jul and Aug 1971-3; Stillwater River (Wells Gray Park) 21 Jun to 10 Jul 1956-1 (Ritcey 1956); Swan

Lake (Tupper) 3 Jun 1976-4; Kotcho Lake 20 Jun 1982-2; Cassiar 13 Jul 1962-1; O'Connor and Tatshenshini rivers 11 Jun 1983-2; Goat Creek (Kelsall Lake) 16 Jun 1980-3.

Autumn: Interior - Cecil Lake 3 Sep 1982-3; Moberly Lake 21 Oct 1981-47; Keynton Lake 11 Oct 1981-13; Kathlyn Lake 21 Nov 1981-17 arrived; Fraser Lake (Fraser Lake) 20 Oct 1981-62; Nithi River 30 Oct 1980-1,766; Anahim Lake 7 Nov 1978-49; Nicholson 24 Oct 1976-15; Vernon 26 Oct 1969-18 (Rogers, T.H. 1970a); Columbia Lake 1 Oct 1948-2 (Johnstone, W.B. 1949), 31 Oct 1978-11; Nicola Lake 20 Oct 1976-14; Vaseux Lake 15 Oct 1972-6, first of season. **Coastal** - Lakelse Lake 9 Nov 1974-47; Masset 7 Nov 1950-47; Kelsey Bay 18 Nov 1973-93; Cranberry Lake (Powell River) 18 Nov 1978-38; Comox Harbour 16 Nov 1983-142; Tofino Inlet 23 Sep 1980-1; Sandhill Creek (Long Beach) 17 Nov 1978-29; Somass River estuary 8 Nov 1973-109; Nanaimo 16 Nov 1984-89; Quesnel Lake 25 Nov 1983-128; Reifel Island 29 Nov 19o86-100; Brunswick Point marsh (Delta) 30 Nov 1978-83.

Winter: Interior - Surprise Lake (Atlin) 3 Jan 1984-1 (RBCM Photo 905); Meziadin Lake 5 Jan 1977-16 in open water at outlet of lake; Crooked

River 19 Jan 1983-71; Stuart River 31 Dec 1967-105; Francois Lake 7 Dec 1976-47; Tahtsa Reach 24 Dec 1949-56 (Mackay 1950); Lonesome Lake 9 Feb 1970-531 (Turner, I.G. 1970); Vaseux Lake 11 Jan 1969-14; Creston winter 1947/48-60 (Munro, J.A. 1958a). **Coastal** - Yakoun River winter 1948/49-100+; South Bentinck Arm 11 Feb 1981-38; Bute Inlet (Homathko River) 11 Feb 1981-136; Cranberry Lake (Powell River) 8 Jan 1981-45; Comox valley 8 Jan 1985-881 (census); Pitt Lake 17 Feb 1980-97; Somass River estuary 16 Dec 1972-182; Nicomen Slough 11 Jan 1982-84; Westham Island foreshore 2 Feb 1985-149; Nanaimo River estuary 11 Jan 1985-234; Grice Bay 25 Jan 1979-27; Cowichan River estuary 14 Jan 1986-173; Cheewhat River 24 Jan 1976-50; Central Saanich 8 Jan 1984-24.

Christmas Counts: Interior - Recorded from 2 of 19 localities and on 4% of all counts. Maxima: Shuswap Lake 28 Dec 1983-13; Oliver/Osoyoos 26 Dec 1984-10. **Coastal** - Recorded from 19 of 28 localities and on 46% of all counts. Maxima: Comox 16 Dec 1984-**712**, all-time North American high count (Monroe 1985a); Nanaimo 26 Dec 1982-243; Deep Bay 27 Dec 1984-221.

Mute Swan

Cygnus olor (Gmelin)

MUSW

RANGE: Native to mid-latitude Eurasia; introduced in North America. Breeds locally from southern British Columbia and Saskatchewan, northern Wisconsin, central Michigan, southern Ontario, southern New York and Connecticut south to central Missouri, Illinois and Indiana. Populations probably include both feral and captive birds. Most populations are sedentary.

STATUS: Introduced. Locally *fairly common* to *very common* resident on southeastern Vancouver Island. *Uncommon* resident in the Gulf Islands and Fraser Lowlands. *Rare* resident in the Okanagan valley. *Casual* elsewhere. Breeds.

CHANGE IN STATUS: The Mute Swan was not listed by J.A. Munro and Cowan (1947), probably because of the difficulty in separating feral and domesticated birds. Mute Swans were apparently first introduced about 1889 in Victoria (Warren, W.H. 1970). The few pairs remained confined to city parks until the 1930s when 20 more swans were imported from Great Britain. Most were released on Elk Lake after a period of acclimatization in Beacon Hill Park. Overwintering mortality of juveniles was initially high and local farmers reportedly shot or poisoned swans that ventured onto their crop lands. Davies (1981b) mentions that it was not until the 1940s and early 1950s, when regular winter feeding and pinioning of young birds was instituted, that the Mute Swan population established itself.

Some dispersal of swans occurred from 1969 to 1972 when free-flying birds were reported west of Sooke, on the Gulf Islands, near Qualicum, and at Cowichan Bay. Small populations soon became established near Sooke and in the Cowichan area. The Cowichan wintering population increased from 7 birds in 1970 to 123 birds in 1982 and during the same period the population around Victoria declined somewhat (from Audubon Christmas Bird Counts). Davies (1981b) suggests that the total population for southeastern Vancouver Island increased from 36 swans in 1969 to 140 swans in 1981, about 12% per year. He also suggests that both winter feeding and mild winter weather conditions may be necessary for the survival of Mute Swans on Vancouver Island.

Feral populations in other areas of the province are unstable, fluctuate greatly, and depend on continued introductions and feeding programs. There is some concern that increasing Mute Swan populations may pose a threat to wintering Trumpeter Swans on Vancouver Island.

NONBREEDING: The Mute Swan is resident in coastal areas of southeastern and southern Vancouver Island and the Gulf Islands in the Strait of Georgia. Mute Swan records from the south mainland coast consist entirely of escapees (or possibly stragglers from Vancouver Island); the species has not become established there. The largest population of captive swans is located at Stanley Park in Vancouver (18 Nov 1974-80). Records from the interior (3%; n=2,503), mainly the Okanagan valley, are probably also of birds that have escaped from captivity (Cannings, R.A. et al. 1987).

Mute Swans are essentially sedentary in British Columbia, although some dispersal and winter wandering does occur, mostly evident on southern Vancouver Island. There they frequent lagoons (42%; n=1,221), lakes (24%) and estuaries (12%). Other habitats include inlets, bays, ponds, rivers, sloughs, harbours, and flooded fields. In the interior, lakes are used.

The proportion of cygnets in the winter Mute Swan population on Vancouver Island from 1980 to 1985 was 46% (n=96 flocks).

BREEDING: Feral breeding populations are established only on southern Vancouver Island from Duncan to Sooke. Captive birds have bred at Stanley Park (Vancouver), Burnaby Lake, Harrison, and Skookumchuck.

Mute Swans are solitary nesters although several pairs may nest together on larger lakes, usually well separated from each other. They prefer to nest on lakes (65%; n=46), but brackish lagoons (26%) and ponds are also used. Sufficient aquatic vegetation and enough escape distance to enable them to take flight by pattering over the water surface seem to be pre-requisites.

Nests: Nests were situated on shore, in shallow water at the edge of emergent growth (e.g. cattails, red alder, willows), on islands, or built on artificial floating platforms. In 3 instances swans used the previous year's nest after repairing it. Nests were large mounds of vegetation, piled to 0.5 m in height, and composed of grasses (29%), reeds (18%) as well as cattails, waterlilies, sticks, and some down. Nest diameters were about 2 m.

Eggs: Dates for 29 clutches ranged from 1 April to 11 July, with 16 clutches recorded between 15 May and 7 June. Clutch size ranged from 1 to 8 eggs (1E-1, 2E-1, 3E-2, 4E-8, 5E-4, 6E-7, 7E-5, 8E-1), with 19 clutches having 4 to 6 eggs. Incubation period for 3 clutches in British Columbia was 35 to 37 days.

Young: Dates for 69 broods ranged from 19 May to 8 September, with 57% recorded between 10 June and 20 July. Brood size ranged from 1 to 7 young (1Y-6, 2Y-10, 3Y-8, 4Y-19, 5Y-5, 6Y-14, 7Y-7), with 54% having 2 to 4 young. Fledging period is about 112 to 154 days (Bellrose 1976).

REMARKS: For information on ecology, productivity and management implications of other feral Mute Swan populations in North America, consult Willey (1968) and Reese (1975). The Mute Swan has also been well studied in Europe, with information summarized by Birkhead and Perrens (1986).

NOTEWORTHY RECORDS

Spring: Coastal - Esquimalt Lagoon 6 Mar 1983-19, 24 May 1983-14; Goldstream River estuary 9 Mar 1983-14; Elk Lake (Saanich) 21 May 1973-20; Cowichan Bay 10 May 1983-44; Somenos Lake 23 Mar 1980-45 adults, 31 May 1987-48; Ganges Harbour 25 Mar 1977-1 adult; Nanoose Creek estuary 4 May 1978-1 (Dawe and Lang 1980); Harrison Lake 10 May 1978-1; Cranberry Lake (Powell River) 1 Mar 1975-2 adults. **Interior** - Vaseux Lake 6 May 1976-2; Okanagan Lake 1 Mar 1976-4, 3 Apr 1977-2 adults.

Summer: Coastal - Esquimalt Lagoon 12 Jul 1982-19 adults, 6 cygnets some moulting birds; Elk and Beaver lakes (Saanich) 4 Aug 1970-25; Cowichan Bay 15 Jun 1985-75 adults moulting, 19 Jul 1987-83, 21 Jul 1983-84; Quamichan Lake 10 Aug 1978-35 adults, 13 immatures; Ganges Harbour 24 Jul 1981-1 adult; Ruby Lake (Sechelt) 13 Jul 1981-2

adults. **Interior** - Swan Lake (Vernon) 7 Jun 1986-1, 9 Jun 1980-4, 23 Jul 1981-2.

Autumn: Interior - Vernon 30 Nov 1980-1; Osoyoos Lake 17 Nov 1979-5. **Coastal** - Cranberry Lake 2 Sep 1974-9; Harrison Lake 20 Nov 1977-1 adult; Nicomen Slough 26 Nov 1980-5; Cowichan Bay 2 Sep 1984-99, 20 Nov 1983-100+; Elk and Beaver lakes 8 Oct 1972-51, largest population this year (Tatum 1973); Esquimalt Lagoon 18 Sep 1982-15, 19 Nov 1982-18.

Winter: Interior - Vernon 9 Feb 1979-1; Okanagan Lake (Summerland) 4 Feb 1987-1. **Coastal** - Nicomen Slough 21 Feb 1982-2 adults; Beach Grove 18 Dec 1980-2; Cowichan River estuary 21 Jan 1983-104; Goldstream River estuary 8 Feb 1983-26; Portage Inlet 24 Jan 1973-20; Elk Lake 17 Jan 1973-14; Esquimalt Lagoon 27 Dec 1982-20.

Christmas Counts: Interior - Recorded from 5 of 19 localities and on 12% of all counts. Maxima: Oliver/Osoyoos 28 Dec 1979-4; Penticton 27 Dec 1980-3; Kelowna 20 Dec 1981-2; Vaseux Lake 28 Dec 1978-2. **Coastal** - Recorded from 7 of 28 localities and on 15% of all counts. Maxima: Duncan 18 Dec 1982-123, all-time Canadian high count (Anderson, R.R. 1983); Victoria 1 Jan 1972-77; Sooke 16 Dec 1984-4.

Extralimital Records: Interior - Alkali Lake (Cariboo) 17 Apr 1972-2 adults began nesting, female killed, male adopted American White Pelican (Anderson, E.A. 1972), 3 Jun 1973-1 adult male again selected pelican as a mate for one week (A. Roberts pers. comm.).

Mute Swan

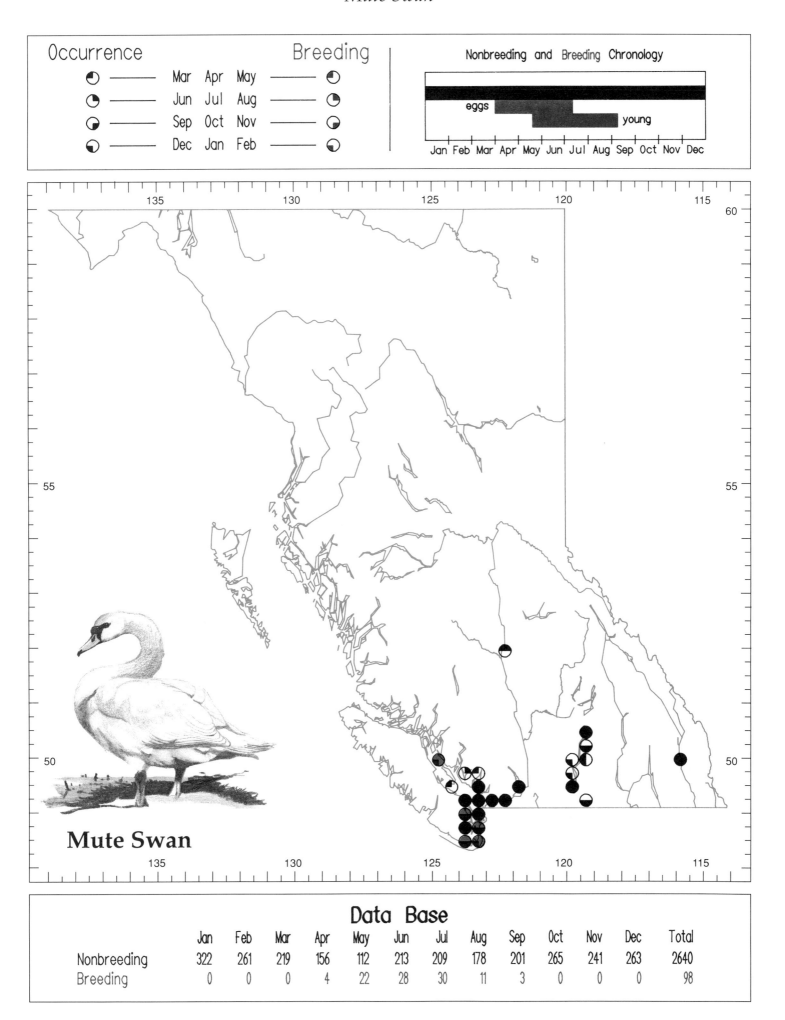

Occurrence

					Breeding
◐	———	Mar	Apr	May	——— ◑
◔	———	Jun	Jul	Aug	——— ◕
◵	———	Sep	Oct	Nov	——— ◵
◶	———	Dec	Jan	Feb	——— ◶

Nonbreeding and Breeding Chronology

eggs

young

Jan Feb Mar Apr May Jun Jul Aug Sep Oct Nov Dec

Mute Swan

Data Base

	Jan	Feb	Mar	Apr	May	Jun	Jul	Aug	Sep	Oct	Nov	Dec	Total
Nonbreeding	322	261	219	156	112	213	209	178	201	265	241	263	2640
Breeding	0	0	0	4	22	28	30	11	3	0	0	0	98

Greater White-fronted Goose

GWFG

Anser albifrons (Scopoli)

RANGE: In North America, breeds in Alaska and western arctic Canada; winters mainly from southwestern British Columbia south through California, in coastal Texas and Louisiana, and in Mexico. Widespread in Eurasia.

STATUS: *Very abundant* offshore transient in spring and autumn. On the coast, usually *fairly common* to *very common* spring and autumn transient; *rare* in summer, *uncommon* in winter. In the interior, an *uncommon* spring and autumn transient; *very rare* in winter in the Okanagan valley.

OCCURRENCE: The Greater White-fronted Goose population in North America is divided into 2 distinct components. The Pacific Flyway component is the largest with an average autumn population (1979 to 1983) of 98,000 birds (C. Dau pers. comm.). These birds breed in the Yukon River delta and each autumn depart on a 3,220 km flight across the Gulf of Alaska to the mouth of the Columbia River. The principal wintering area lies in the Central Valley of California (Dzubin et al. 1964). Both coastal and inland routes are thought to be used during spring migration (C. Dau pers. comm.). The mid-continent (Central Flyway) population is composed of birds from breeding areas in Alaska (other than the Yukon River delta) as well as western Arctic Canada. Most of those birds stage in autumn in southeastern Alberta and southwestern Saskatchewan, and then continue on to wintering grounds on the Gulf Coast of Louisiana, Texas, and Mexico (Miller et al. 1968; Lensink, C.J. 1969). A summary of North American breeding and wintering areas and migration corridors is presented by Bellrose (1976).

The Pacific Flyway Greater White-fronted Goose population has apparently declined by over 50% since the early 1950s, probably because of excessive hunting (Timm and Dau 1979).

For the most part, the Greater White-fronted Goose bypasses British Columbia during its annual migration to and from the Alaskan and western Canadian arctic breeding grounds. The number of geese found regularly along the British Columbia coast each year is small compared to the total population. Infrequently, and probably due to inclement weather conditions, flocks of thousands may be seen. White-fronts occur much less commonly in the interior; only 8% of our records are from there, and most of those are from the central southern portion of the province.

Except during main migration periods, white-fronts are frequently found associating with Canada Geese, Snow Geese, or domestic geese. They frequent a variety of habitats, such as shallow waters of sloughs, marshes, ponds, and lagoons, as well as flooded and dry fields, lakes, mud flats, and golf courses.

Spring migration occurs throughout the province from late March through late May and seems to be gradual. Peak numbers probably occur from mid-April through early May on the coast, in March and April in the southern interior, and in late April and early May in the far north. A few birds may be scattered along the coast in summer. Autumn migration may start as early as late August and carry through into November. The main movement in average years probably occurs from mid-September to mid-October. Small numbers winter along the coast.

REMARKS: Prior to 1947, *A. a. frontalis* was the only subspecies known from British Columbia (Munro, J.A. and Cowan 1947). However, Bauer (1979) suggests the larger and darker subspecies *A. a. elgasi*, (Tule White-fronted Goose) also migrates along the coast of the province. Timm et al. (1982) have since documented the presence of the "tule" goose in British Columbia, but they do not think that a third subspecies (*elgasi*) has been substantiated. They refer all large, dark-coloured birds to the subspecies *A. a. gambelli*.

The Greater White-fronted Goose was formerly known as the White-fronted Goose.

Figure 254. Greater White-fronted Goose, Nakusp, 6 May 1979 (RBCM Photo 688; Gary S. Davidson).

NOTEWORTHY RECORDS

Spring: Coastal - Saanich 3 May 1977-9; Pachena Bay 2 May 1979-300+ flying northwest; Ucluelet 19 Apr 1974-250+ flying north; Long Beach 29 Mar 1978-12 migrating; Crescent Beach 27 Apr 1940-300; Nanaimo 30 April 1968-109; Comox 21 Apr 1969-100; Port Hardy 28 Apr 1951-600, 21 May 1968-600; Goose Group 30 May 1948-70; Tlell 28 Apr 1954-500; Masset 6 May 1947-500; Langara Island 29 April 1966-600 (Campbell 1969a). **Interior** - Creston 2 Apr 1983-200; Osoyoos Lake 15 Mar 1978-6; Nakusp 6 May 1979-1 (RBCM Photo 688; Fig. 254); Kamloops 6 Mar 1982-1 adult; Alkali Lake (Riske Creek) 19 May 1946-7; Alexis Creek 13 May 1960-100 (Erskine and Stein 1964); Smithers 29 May 1944-7; Cecil Lake 13 Apr 1984-16; Fort Nelson 28 Apr 1986-3; Atlin 29 Apr 1931-1 (Munro, J.A. and Cowan 1947).

Summer: Coastal - Swan Lake (Victoria) 24 Jul 1981-1; Long Beach 23 Aug 1970-150 flying south; Tofino 29 Aug 1983-129 migrating in 3 groups;

Ladner 29 Aug 1970-275; Iona Island 4 Jun 1968-13 (Sirk 1968); Courtenay 30 Aug 1923-80; Port Hardy 26 Aug 1937-3,000, 26 Aug 1939-500, 30 Aug 1938-1,000; Sandspit 28 Aug 1978-215 flying; Masset 29 Jul 1947-1 female (UBC 1415). **Interior** - Okanagan Landing 29 Aug 1945-flock; Fort St. John 24 Aug 1986-5; Fern Lake (Kwadacha Wilderness Park) 17 Aug 1983-80 (Cooper, J.M. and Cooper 1983).

Autumn: Interior - Atlin 12 Sep 1935-1 female (RBCM 5984); Fort Nelson 2 Sep 1987-3; Charlie Lake 7 Oct 1984-1; Fort St. John 7 Sep 1985-81; Hazelton 19 Sep 1921-7 (Swarth 1924); Vaseux Lake 10 Sep 1975-1 immature; Creston 16 Sep 1982-75 to 100, 16 Oct 1983-200. **Coastal** - Masset 20 Sep 1981-75; Drizzle Lake 28 Sep 1977-250; Kitimat 3 Oct 1974-46 on golf course; Port Hardy 9 Sep 1934-2,000, 30 Sep 1938-10,000 and more birds passing over all night, 3 Oct 1936-1,000s; Comox 14 Sep 1948-200+; Little Qualicum River

10 Oct 1984-72 on estuary; Stanley Park (Vancouver) 8 Oct 1973-100; Reifel Island 13 Oct 1975-75; Bamfield 2 Sep 1974-140; Saanich 11 Sep 1971-39 (Tatum 1972); Victoria 7 Oct 1975-85.

Winter: Interior - Lonesome Lake 16 and 17 Jan 1970-1 with Trumpeter Swans (Turner, I.G. 1970); Nakusp 11 Dec 1983-1; Taghum 20 Jan 1977-1 with 29 Canada Geese; Penticton 24 Dec 1972-1. **Coastal** - Tlell 1 Dec to 23 Feb 1983-1; Portage Inlet 29 Dec 1970-10; Metchosin 1 Feb 1983-6 on golf course.

Christmas Counts: **Interior** - Recorded once: Vernon 26 Dec 1978-1. **Coastal** - Recorded from 12 of 28 localities and on 20% of all counts. Maxima: Chilliwack 15 Dec 1979-**338**, all-time Canadian high count (Anderson, R.R. 1980); Victoria 17 Dec 1983-15; Ladner 19 Dec 1976-12.

Greater White-fronted Goose

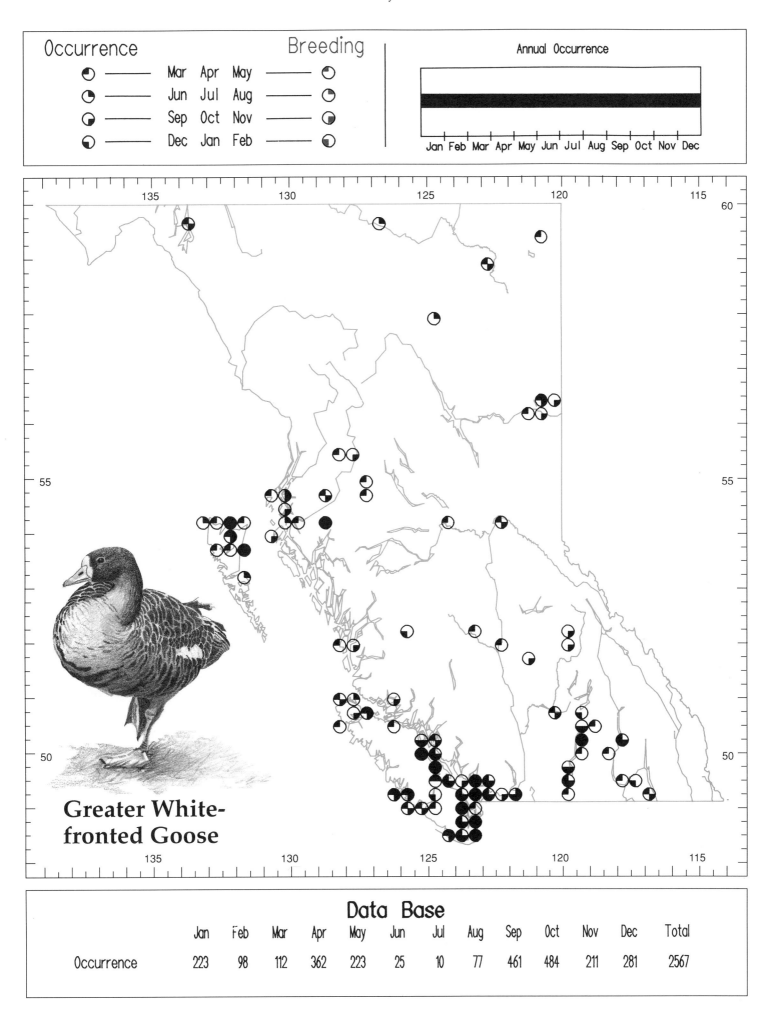

Occurrence

| ◐ ——— Mar Apr May ——— ◐ |
| ◔ ——— Jun Jul Aug ——— ◔ |
| ◕ ——— Sep Oct Nov ——— ◕ |
| ◑ ——— Dec Jan Feb ——— ◑ |

Breeding

Annual Occurrence

Jan Feb Mar Apr May Jun Jul Aug Sep Oct Nov Dec

Greater White-fronted Goose

Data Base

	Jan	Feb	Mar	Apr	May	Jun	Jul	Aug	Sep	Oct	Nov	Dec	Total
Occurrence	223	98	112	362	223	25	10	77	461	484	211	281	2567

Snow Goose
Chen caerulescens (Linnaeus)

RANGE: Breeds in northeastern Siberia (Wrangel Island), northern Alaska, Arctic Canada, and northwestern Greenland. Winters mainly from British Columbia south to California, New Mexico, and Mexico in the west; in the midwest, from coastal Texas and Louisiana, rarely as far north as Nebraska, Iowa, and Louisiana; and on the Atlantic coast from New Jersey to South Carolina.

STATUS: *Very common* spring and *abundant* to *very abundant* autumn migrant on the coast. *Very abundant* winter visitant; irregularly *rare* in summer. *Fairly common*, at times *very common*, spring and *uncommon* autumn migrant in the interior. *Rare* in summer, *very rare* in winter in the southern interior.

OCCURRENCE: The Snow Goose is distributed during migration along coastal British Columbia primarily from Juan de Fuca Strait, north along the inner coast to northern Vancouver Island and the north coastal region. It is widespread but scattered throughout the central and southern interior. The Snow Goose is primarily a winter visitant to the inner coastal area of southeastern Strait of Georgia and Puget Sound where a population, averaging over 24,000 birds, frequents marshes off the Fraser River delta in British Columbia and the Skagit-Stillaguamish river delta in Washington (Jeffrey and Kaiser 1979).

Snow Geese can begin arriving on the marshes of the Fraser and Skagit-Stillaguamish river deltas in mid-September and early October. The birds originate in a discrete area on Wrangel Island in Siberia (see Kozlik et al. 1959; Sladen and Kistchinski 1977). Numbers on the Fraser River delta increase through October, peak in November, and generally decline through January and early February. They peak again in March with the addition of northward migrants (Campbell et al. 1974). In January, over 75% of the total Puget Sound population is on the Skagit-Stillaguamish river deltas (Jeffrey and Kaiser 1979), but by March many of the geese have moved back to the Fraser River delta (W.S. Boyd pers. comm.).

Spring departure begins in late March, but occurs mostly during April. Occasionally, some movement is evident in early May.

Infrequently, 1 or 2 birds have been found scattered along the coast in summer, usually in association with Canada Geese. They are likely unfit birds or escapees from avicultural collections.

In winter, Snow Geese prefer estuarine marshes (Fig. 255) where bulrush rhizomes provide the staple food in their diet (Burton, B.A. 1977). Sedge rhizomes and shoots also seem to be an important food. In the late 1960s and early 1970s Snow Geese wintering on the Fraser River delta left the foreshore only occasionally to feed in adjacent agricultural fields. J.P. Hatfield (pers. comm.) has recently summarized the trend. In March of 1977, he first recorded 2,000+ Snow Geese on the fields of the Alaksen National Wildlife Area. But it was not until the autumn of 1980 that the geese began to field-feed on a regular basis, and field-feeding has occurred every autumn, winter, and spring since then. The number of birds using the fields has risen from around 2,000 in the early 1980s to over 15,000 in 1987.

Snow Geese pass irregularly, in small numbers, through the interior of British Columbia on migration between breeding and wintering grounds; only 9% of our records for the province are from interior locations. Snow Geese have been recorded in the interior from 29 September to 21 June. Spring migration is most pronounced; in southern areas it starts in early April, peaks in early May and lasts through mid-May; and in northern areas it starts sometimes in late March, but usually in mid-April and lasts

Figure 255. *Snow Geese wintering on the Fraser River delta off Reifel Island, 24 November 1974 (Neil K. Dawe).*

Snow Goose

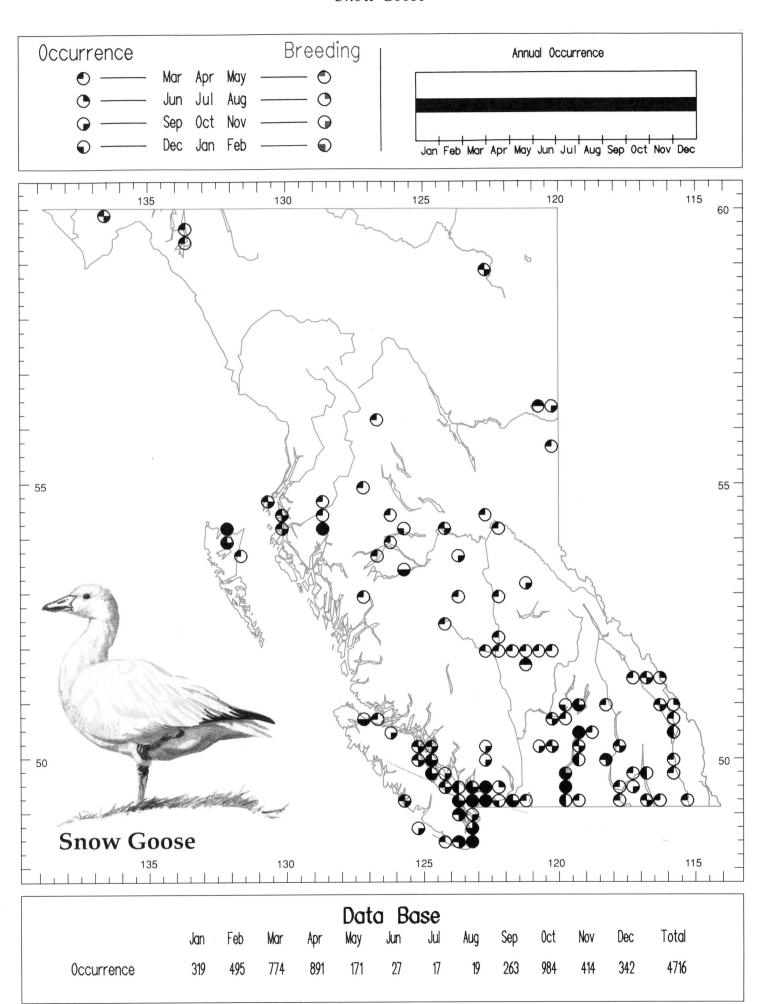

Snow Goose

Occurrence

	Mar	Apr	May	
	Jun	Jul	Aug	
	Sep	Oct	Nov	
	Dec	Jan	Feb	

Breeding

Annual Occurrence

Jan Feb Mar Apr May Jun Jul Aug Sep Oct Nov Dec

Data Base

	Jan	Feb	Mar	Apr	May	Jun	Jul	Aug	Sep	Oct	Nov	Dec	Total
Occurrence	319	495	774	891	171	27	17	19	263	984	414	342	4716

through late May.. There are no records for July or August. The autumn movement, in flocks of usually less than 10 individuals, occurs from late September to late November. Winter records are from the Okanagan valley, the Kootenays, the Shuswap area, and the central interior.

The Puget Sound population fluctuates depending on breeding success on Wrangel Island. The Wrangel Island population was about 100,000 birds in the spring of 1987, higher than the Wrangel Island spring flight average of 80,710 over the period 1970 to 1979 (Wrangel Island Snow Goose - Pacific Flyway Management Plan). Also in 1987, about 140,000 birds left Wrangel Island for the wintering grounds. The population that winters on the Fraser and Skagit-Stillaguamish river deltas (Table 17) has ranged from a high of 51,131 birds in January 1988 to a low of 12,346 birds in January 1975, with a mean for the period 1948 to 1988 of 24,117 birds (Jeffrey and Kaiser 1979; W.S. Boyd pers. comm.).

REMARKS: The white and blue phases of the Snow Goose were formerly referred to as *Chen hyperborea* and *C. caerulescens* respectively (American Ornithologists' Union 1957). The white colour phase predominates in the northeastern race, the Greater Snow Goose (*C. caerulescens atlantica*), while the more southern race, the Lesser Snow Goose (*C. c. caerulescens*), has both white and blue colour phases.

The proportion of blue-phase to white-phase Snow Geese is shifting, so that in mid-continental areas there is a trend towards a more uniform distribution of colour phases (Bellrose 1976). That trend is continuing in western North America where the blue-phase is the least abundant of the two (Dzubin 1979). There are 3 records of blue-phase geese in British Columbia: Sea Island 3 Nov 1969-2; Steveston 21 Mar 1970-50 (Campbell et al. 1972a); Vanderhoof 17 Apr 1970-4 (Noble 1972).

Snow Geese from Wrangel Island separate into 2 distinct wintering subpopulations: the Fraser-Skagit segment and the Oregon-California segment that merges with a contingent from the western Canadian Arctic.

The separation of the Wrangel Island flock probably occurs on the Chukotka coast. According to Syroechkovskiy and Litvin (1986), the migration routes (Fig. 256) correspond to the different wintering groups, as follows:

Fraser-Skagit population - leave Wrangel Island and reach Chukotka, fly through the central parts of the Chukotsk peninsula to Alaska to the deltas of the Yukon-Kuskokwim rivers and beyond that along the Pacific coast of North America to the wintering areas (Pacific Flyway).

Oregon-California population - reach Chukotka, fly along its north coast, then along the northern coast of Alaska to the mouth of the Mackenzie River, upriver by the valley and beyond that through the provinces of Alberta or Saskatchewan and through the states of Montana and Idaho to the wintering area (Central Flyway).

Of the total Wrangel Island population, about 36% winter in the Fraser-Skagit river deltas and 64% in the California-Oregon region. These areas are discrete as well, for:

The same birds from year to year overwinter in one and the same region. Changes by the Snow Geese of wintering regions are rare ...

The Snow Goose does not breed naturally in British Columbia. However, an introduced population was established for a short period at the George C. Reifel Bird Sanctuary in the Fraser River delta. In 1974, the population was 19 pairs. Egg dates ranged from 4 April to 4 June. Clutch size ranged from 1 to 7 eggs (1E-2, 2E-5, 3E-3, 4E-4, 5E-2, 6E-2, 7E-1). Hatching success was 47%. Dates for young (n=11) ranged from 21 May to 16 July. Brood size ranged from 1 to 5 young (1Y-2, 2Y-3, 3Y-3, 4Y-1, 5Y-2).

The Snow Goose is sometimes placed in the genus *Anser* (Johnsgard 1965; Bellrose 1976; Godfrey 1986).

TABLE 17.

Numbers of **Snow Geese** on the Fraser River delta (British Columbia) and Skagit River delta (Washington) at midwinter (2 to 13 January) 1948 to 1988 (Data from Jeffrey and Kaiser 1979 and Canadian Wildlife Service, Delta, British Columbia).

	Number of Snow Geese		
Year	Fraser River	Skagit River	Total
1948	12,500	13,500	26,000
1949	6,000	23,400*	29,400
1950	2,060	16,100	18,160
1951	75	16,000	16,075
1952	4,000	21,700*	25,700
1953	2,200	15,030	17,230
1954	818*	21,740*	22,558
1955	1,500	17,591*	19,091
1956	100	15,000	15,100
1957	3,250	17,123*	20,373
1958	0	26,986*	26,986
1959	130	14,116*	14,246
1960	dna	24,425*	24,425
1961	0	22,180	22,180
1962	dna	27,641	27,641
1963	0	23,600	23,600
1964	dna	21,800	21,800
1965	800	25,300	26,100
1966	dna	15,800	15,800
1967	500	20,350	20,850
1968	dna	22,600	22,600
1969	dna	15,400	15,400
1970	7,000	24,676*	31,676
1971	9,000	26,968*	35,968
1972	dna	23,800	23,800
1973	7,100	11,880	18,980
1974	2,000	10,450	12,450
1975	1,500	10,846*	12,346
1976	0	16,017	16,017
1977	2,140	22,764	24,904
1978	500	15,575*	16,075
1979	dna	dna	dna
1980	dna	28,800*	28,800
1981	dna	dna	40,500*
1982	17,680*	25,410*	43,090*
1983	7,379*	29,831*	37,210*
1984	6,900*	24,700*	31,600*
1985	26,700*	13,500*	40,200*
1986	16,302*	24,212*	40,514*
1987	6,390*	33,664*	40,054*
1988	9,590*	41,541*	51,131*

* - Photographic count   dna - Data not available

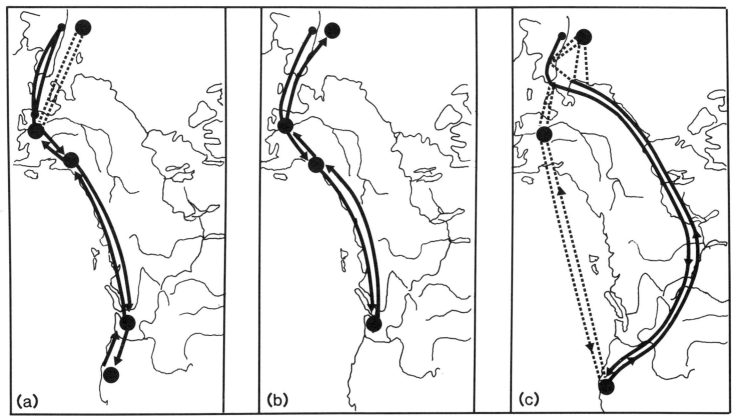

Figure 256. *Major migration corridors of Snow Geese breeding on Wrangel Island, U.S.S.R. and wintering in British Columbia and western U.S.A. (a - migration routes as proposed prior to 1978. b - migration routes of Snow Geese that winter on the Fraser and Skagit-Stillaguamish deltas based on data from individual marking. c - migration routes of Snow Geese that winter in California, U.S.A. based on data from individual marking. The hatched line indicates the previously supposed route). From Syroechkovskiy and Litvin (1986).*

NOTEWORTHY RECORDS

Spring: Coastal - Victoria 28 Apr 1939-19 (Munro, J.A. and Cowan 1947); Saanich 25 Mar 1984-24; Sea Island 2 Apr 1967-10,000 to 12,000, 19 Apr 1967-nearly all gone; Westham Island 26 Apr 1981-3,000; Blackie Spit 15 May 1983-40; Gibsons 3 May 1959-14; Sechelt 9 Apr 1983-60; Cranberry Lake (Powell River) 14 Apr 1980-150, 30 Apr 1981-300+; Tlell 3 May 1935-5; Nadu River 18 Apr 1974-15; Big Bay (Prince Rupert) 17 Apr 1975-150 (Martin 1978); Prince Rupert 23 Apr 1979-175; Green Island 11 May 1978-62. **Interior** - Tugulnuit Lake 30 Apr 1967-8; Okanagan Lake 10 Mar 1971-75, 3 May 1967-40; Okanagan Landing 26 Apr 1925-12 (Munro, J.A. and Cowan 1947); Kamloops to Chase (South Thompson River count) 31 Mar 1962-150; Brisco 25 Apr 1984-4; Brisco to Spillimacheen survey Apr 1967-21 (Demarchi, R.A. and Smith 1967); Sorrento 6 May 1971-32; 122 Mile House 26 to 28 Apr 1946-100 (Munro, J.A. 1955c); Lac la Hache 21 Apr 1944-30 (Munro, J.A. and Cowan 1947); Vanderhoof 18 Apr 1946-16 (Munro, J.A. and Cowan 1947); Aleza Lake 1 to 20 May 1944-117 (Munro, J.A. 1947a); Tupper Creek (Tupper) 7 May 1938-25 (Cowan 1939); n Fort St. John 16 Apr 1986-1; Fort Nelson 6 May 1986-7; Palmer Lake (Atlin) 31 May 1975-20; Atlin 7 May 1933-1 male (RBCM 5982); Chilkat Pass 3 May 1957-6 (Weeden 1960).

Summer: Coastal - Saxe Point 15 Jul to 8 Oct 1971-1 (Tatum 1972); Iona Island 11 Jul 1964-1; Port Mann 3 Jun 1982-1. **Interior** - Okanagan Lake 21 Jun 1978-1; Buffalo Lake 13 Jun 1964-1; Fort St. John 24 to 26 Jun 1984-1.

Autumn: Interior - Fort Nelson 4 Oct 1987-42; Moonlight Lake 21 Oct 1981-1; Kootenay National Park 29 Sep 1981-7; Vernon 24 Nov 1969-7 (Rogers, T.H. 1970a); Vaseux Lake 29 Sep 1951-3. **Coastal** - Green Island 3 Nov 1978-173; Drizzle Lake 15 Oct 1978-130; Port Hardy 21 Oct 1940-2,000; Port Neville 27 Oct 1975-821 in 9 flocks; Alta Lake 7 Nov 1944-75 (Racey 1948); Cortes Island 3 Nov 1977-350; Comox 22 Oct 1946-1,000; Point Grey Beach 30 Sep 1973-500; Reifel Island 11 Nov 1979-30,000; Westham Island 13 Nov 1974-8,000; Gabriola Island 28 Nov 1977-200; Long Beach 6 Oct 1982-220; Pachena Point 11 Oct 1974-150; Martindale (Saanich) 1 Sep 1969-340 (Tatum 1970); Gonzales Bay 9 Oct 1969-120 (Tatum 1970).

Winter: Interior - Francois Lake 7 Dec 1976-2; Adams River mouth 2 Dec 1972-1 (Sirk et al. 1973); Penticton 28 Jan 1973-1. **Coastal** - Port Hardy 2 Dec 1972-1 (Cuthbert 1972); Gibsons 19 Dec 1981-1; Chilliwack 10 Jan 1981-4; Reifel Island 15 Dec 1968-10,000, 10 Jan 1971-20,000; Victoria 8 Dec 1976-3.

Christmas Counts: Interior - Recorded from 3 of 19 localities and on 3% of all counts. Maxima: Oliver/Osoyoos 28 Dec 1982-5; Kelowna 20 Dec 1981-2; Vernon 27 Dec 1981-2. **Coastal** - Recorded from 9 of 28 localities and on 21% of all counts. Maxima: Ladner 23 Dec 1978-**15,101**, all-time Canadian high count (Anderson, R.R. 1979); Vancouver 18 Dec 1983-1,000; White Rock 30 Dec 1984-259.

Ross' Goose
Chen rossii (Cassin)

ROGO

RANGE: Breeds locally in the Canadian low arctic, mostly adjacent to Queen Maud Gulf in the Northwest Territories. Winters in the Central Valley of California (e.g. Sacramento and San Joaquin valleys); rarely elsewhere in the southern United States (e.g. New Mexico and Texas coast).

STATUS: *Very rare* vagrant on the south coast and throughout the central interior of the province.

OCCURRENCE: British Columbia is outside the normal range of the Ross' Goose. Migration corridors lie to the east and south of the province. Birds from breeding grounds near Queen Maud Gulf in the Northwest Territories move south through eastern Alberta and western Saskatchewan to the vicinity of Great Falls - Freezeout Lake, Montana. From there they change their flight to a westerly course towards the Central Valley of California, where most of the continental population winters (Dzubin 1965). Spring migration is a reverse of the autumn route.

The Ross' Goose was first recorded in British Columbia in 1889 and during the next 98 years, through 1987, has been reported in 18 different years. Most records (77%) are from the period 1958 to 1985, which corresponds with increasing continental populations (McLandress 1979). It has been reported 126 times during 23 actual occurrences in the province from the third week of August to 15 May. Records are evenly distributed in spring, autumn, and winter.

All records but 4 are of single birds; the largest reported flock had 7 individuals. Most of the birds have been seen among flocks of Snow Geese, Canada Geese, and mixed flocks of Canada Geese and Greater White-fronted Geese. There is one record of a Ross' Goose among a flock of American Coots.

REMARKS: Hybridization between Ross' and Snow geese occurs infrequently (Trauger et al. 1971).

The Ross' Goose is sometimes placed in the genus *Anser* (Johnsgard 1965; Bellrose 1976; Godfrey 1986).

Figure 257. *Ross' Goose with Canada Geese at Trout Creek Point (Summerland), 8 February 1982 (RBCM Photo 789; Stephen R. Cannings).*

NOTEWORTHY RECORDS

Spring: Coastal - Kuper Island Apr 1895-1 (Kermode 1904); Iona Island 4 May 1974-4 (Shepard, M.G. 1975a); Reifel Island 18 Apr 1985-1 (Mattocks 1985b); Burnaby Lake 2 to 6 May 1984-1 adult (Fix 1984; RBCM Photo 1050). **Interior** - Rawlings Lake spring 1921-1 (Brooks and Swarth 1925); Swan Lake (Vernon) 27 Apr to 1 May 1985-1 (Cannings, R.A. et al. 1987); 149 Mile Lake (150 Mile House) 15 May 1942-1 adult (Munro, J.A. 1945a); Dragon Lake (Quesnel) 2 May 1982-1 adult.

Summer: Coastal - No records. **Interior** - Corn Creek third week Aug 1982-1.

Autumn: Interior - Leo Lake 8 Nov 1962-1 (RBCM 10801); Stuart Lake (Fort St. James) Oct 1889-1 (USNM 117074); Castor Creek 23 Sep 1958-2 (RBCM 16506 and 16507); Salmon Arm 23 Sep to 13 Nov 1970-1 (Schnider et al. 1971); Duck Lake (Creston) Sep 1967-1 (Butler, R.W. et al. 1986). **Coastal** - Cranberry Lake (Powell River) 11 Oct 1981-7; Iona Island 11 Oct 1984-4 (Hunn and Mattocks 1985); Reifel Island 19 and 29 Oct 1984-1 (probably from flock seen at Iona Island).

Winter: Interior - Sicamous 22 and 23 Jan 1982-1 (Campbell 1982a); Duck Lake (Kelowna) 31 Dec

1980-1 adult; Kelowna 28 Dec 1980 to May 1981-1 (RBCM Photo 788); Trout Creek point (Summerland) 8 Feb 1982-1 (RBCM Photo 789; Fig. 257); **Coastal** - Comox Dec 1892-1 (Munro, J.A. and Cowan 1947), Jan 1894-1 (Kermode 1904); Sea Island 30 Jan and 1 Feb 1979-1 adult; Fraser River delta 16 Jan 1897-1 adult male (FMNH 128979).

Christmas Counts: Not recorded.

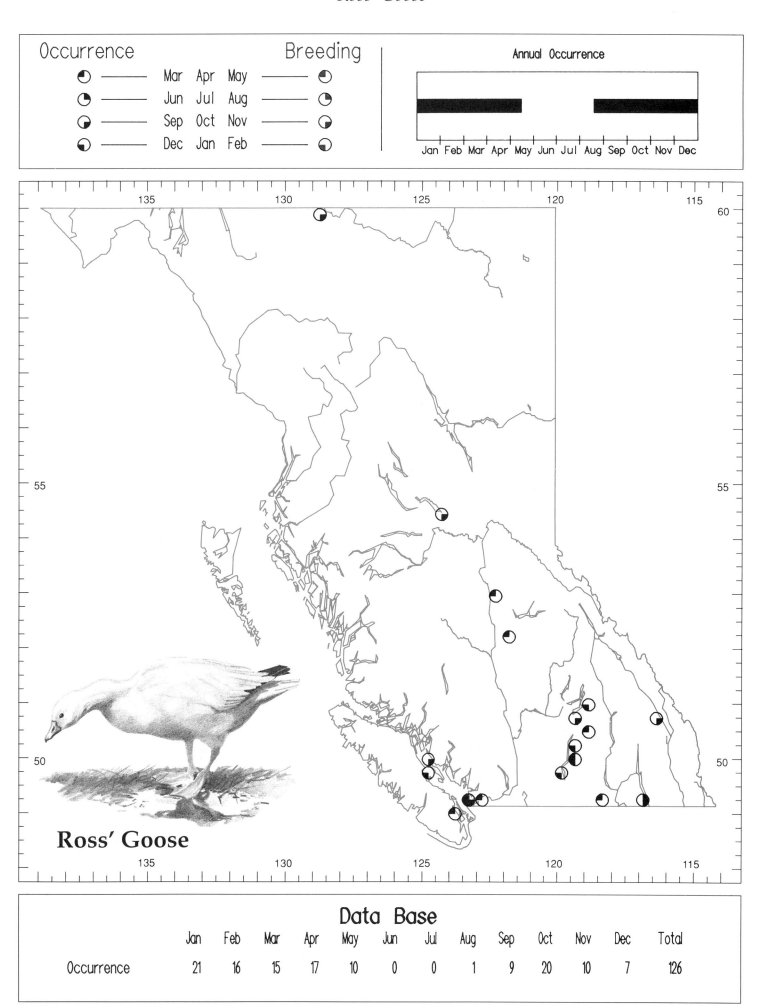

Occurrence

◐	———	Mar Apr May	——— ◐
◔	———	Jun Jul Aug	——— ◔
◔	———	Sep Oct Nov	——— ◔
◑	———	Dec Jan Feb	——— ◔

Breeding

Annual Occurrence

Jan Feb Mar Apr May Jun Jul Aug Sep Oct Nov Dec

Ross' Goose

Data Base

	Jan	Feb	Mar	Apr	May	Jun	Jul	Aug	Sep	Oct	Nov	Dec	Total
Occurrence	21	16	15	17	10	0	0	1	9	20	10	7	126

Emperor Goose

EMGO

Chen canagica (Sevastianov)

RANGE: Breeds along the coast of western Alaska and in northeastern Siberia. Winters throughout the Aleutian Islands, along the Alaska Peninsula, and rarely and irregularly south along the Pacific coast to California. Also in Kamchatka and the Commander Islands.

STATUS: *Very rare* migrant and winter visitant along the coast.

OCCURRENCE: Most of the North American population of Emperor Geese winter in the vicinity of the Aleutian Islands (Headley 1967). However, small numbers are reported most winters along the west coast of the continent south of Alaska (see Munro, J.A. and Cowan 1947; Wilbur and Yocom 1972).

The Emperor Goose was first recorded in British Columbia in 1894 and in 21 of the following years through 1984. It is probably a consistent winter visitor along the coast, but in 1943, 1968, and 1978 it was especially noticeable in the province. It has been reported on 249 occasions from 22 localities between 14 November and 26 May. Winter (57%) and spring (39%) accounted for most of the records, a pattern consistent with that reported by Roberson (1980) for the Pacific coast south of Alaska.

The Emperor Goose frequents rocky shores, breakwaters, jetties, and spits. There are 2 records of birds in cultivated fields. They are often found among flocks of Brant, Snow Geese, Canada Geese, and Glaucous-winged Gulls. Most records (71%) are of individual birds; the largest flock was 6 birds. Most records are of single-day occurrences; the longest was 143 days (19 November 1977 to 10 April 1978) at Reifel Island (Fig. 258).

REMARKS: There are 3 records for the Okanagan valley that R.A. Cannings et al. (1987) consider hypothetical on the basis of a hybrid bird (RBCM Photo 768), a possible escapee, and a sighting that lacked supporting details. Another record exists of an unaged and unsexed bird, collected (MVZ 99250) at the mouth of the Fraser River in 1927 (no other details). We have excluded those records from the account.

The species is frequently placed in the monotypic genus *Philacte* (American Ornithologists' Union 1957), as well as the genus *Anser* (Johnsgard 1965; Bellrose 1976; Godfrey 1986).

Figure 258. *Emperor Goose at Reifel Island, 29 November 1977 (RBCM Photo 546; Ervio Sian). This bird was present for 143 days from 19 November 1977 through 10 April 1978.*

NOTEWORTHY RECORDS

Spring: Coastal - Race Rocks 19 Apr 1984-1 (Fix 1984); Discovery Island 26 Mar 1943-1 female (RBCM 8993); Clover Point 3 Mar 1965-2 (Stirling 1965b); Victoria early March 1968-2 (Crowell and Nehls 1968c); Crescent Beach 24 Mar to 6 Apr 1968-1; s Vancouver 18 Mar 1924-2 (Cumming 1926); Cleland Island 8 to 26 May 1982-3 birds on 8th, 1 thereafter; Campbell River (Discovery Passage) Mar 1968-2 (Stirling 1972b); Sandspit 2 Mar 1984-1 (Campbell 1984a); Masset 28 Apr 1940-1 female (RBCM 11340), 29 Apr 1943-1. **Interior** - No records.

Summer: No records.

Autumn: Interior - No records. **Coastal** - Masset 20 Nov 1936-1 (RBCM 10237); Port Hardy 14 Nov 1956-1 male (PMNH 71547); Fraser River mouth Nov 1922-1 (Munro, J.A. and Cowan 1947); Reifel Island 19 Nov 1977 to 10 Apr 1978-1 (RBCM Photo 546; Fig. 258); White Rock (Surrey) 25 Nov 1971-2.

Winter: Interior - No records. **Coastal** - Masset 3 Jan 1942-1 male (UBC 3345), 3 Jan 1943-1 (Munro, J.A. and Cowan 1947); Cape Scott Dec 1912-1 (UBC 3344); Port Hardy 7 Dec 1932-1; Estevan Point 1 Dec 1930-6 (RBCM 4966); Westham Island 28 Jan 1978-1 adult; White Rock (Surrey) 4 Jan to 6 Apr 1968-1 (Campbell 1968f; RBCM Photo 22), 12 Jan to 16 Mar 1969-1 (Crowell and Nehls 1969a), 1 Feb to 12 Apr 1970-1 (RBCM Photo 133), 26 Dec 1970-1 (Crowell and Nehls 1971a), 1 Jan to 5 Feb 1971-1 (Campbell et al. 1972b; RBCM Photo 146); Chemainus Dec 1894-1 male (Fannin 1895; RBCM 1584); Chain Islets 11 Feb 1978-1 (RBCM Photo 522), 24 Feb 1968-1; Esquimalt Lagoon 13 Dec 1987-1 (RBCM Photo 1197).

Christmas Counts: Interior - Not recorded. **Coastal** - Recorded once: Ladner 26 Dec 1977-1.

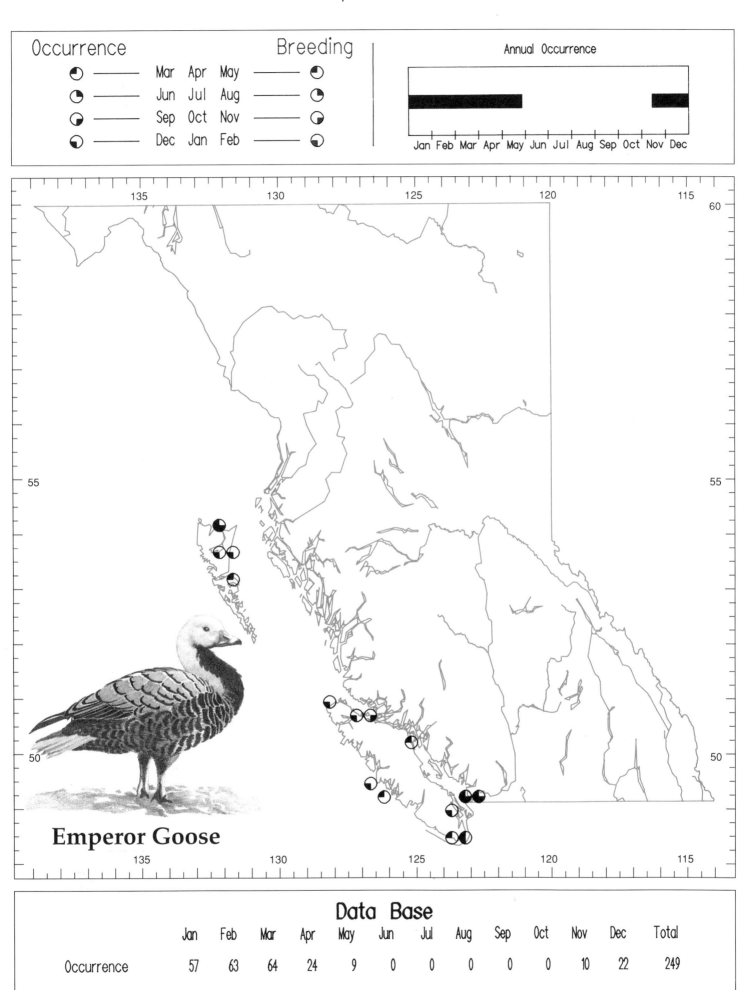

Emperor Goose

Occurrence

◐ ———	Mar Apr May	——— ◐
◔ ———	Jun Jul Aug	——— ◔
◕ ———	Sep Oct Nov	——— ◕
◑ ———	Dec Jan Feb	——— ◑

Breeding

Annual Occurrence

Jan Feb Mar Apr May Jun Jul Aug Sep Oct Nov Dec

Data Base

	Jan	Feb	Mar	Apr	May	Jun	Jul	Aug	Sep	Oct	Nov	Dec	Total
Occurrence	57	63	64	24	9	0	0	0	0	0	10	22	249

Brant

Branta bernicla (Linnaeus)

BRAN

RANGE: Circumpolar. Breeds in arctic North America and Eurasia. In North America, winters along the Pacific coast from southern Alaska and the Queen Charlotte Islands to Baja California and along the Atlantic coast from Massachusetts to North Carolina.

STATUS: *Abundant* to *very abundant* spring migrant, *rare* summer visitant, *rare* autumn migrant and *common* to *abundant* local winter visitant along the coast. Formerly *very abundant* in winter. *Very rare* in the interior.

CHANGE IN STATUS: During the past 100 years, the Brant has declined drastically as a wintering species in British Columbia. In the late 1800s, Fannin (1891) considered Brant an "abundant winter resident." Recollections of a former market hunter, summarized by Leach (1982), best illustrate the populations that were present before the twentieth century.

When Henry Weaver, a market hunter, began fowling in 1895 at the age of 14:

> the shores of Mud Bay and Boundary Bay were at times solid with flocks of [Black] Brant. They came in so continuously to decoys that on one occasion he and eight other hunters took turns shooting from a single blind and picked up 128 birds in the course of a few hours.

Leach also mentions:

> Market hunters on Vancouver Island and the Lower Mainland [Fraser River delta] were especially busy in December shooting large numbers of Brant for sale at Christmas, when they fetched 50 cents a brace. A market hunter named Franklin shipped two sacks of Brant on a

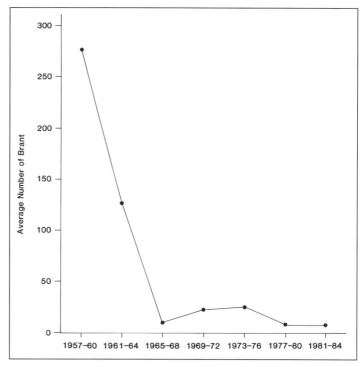

Figure 259. *Average number of Brant tallied during Christmas Bird Counts at Ladner, British Columbia from 1957 through 1984.*

Figure 260. *Part of a flock of 1,665 Brant counted off Little Qualicum River estuary, 21 April 1980 (Neil K. Dawe).*

Brant

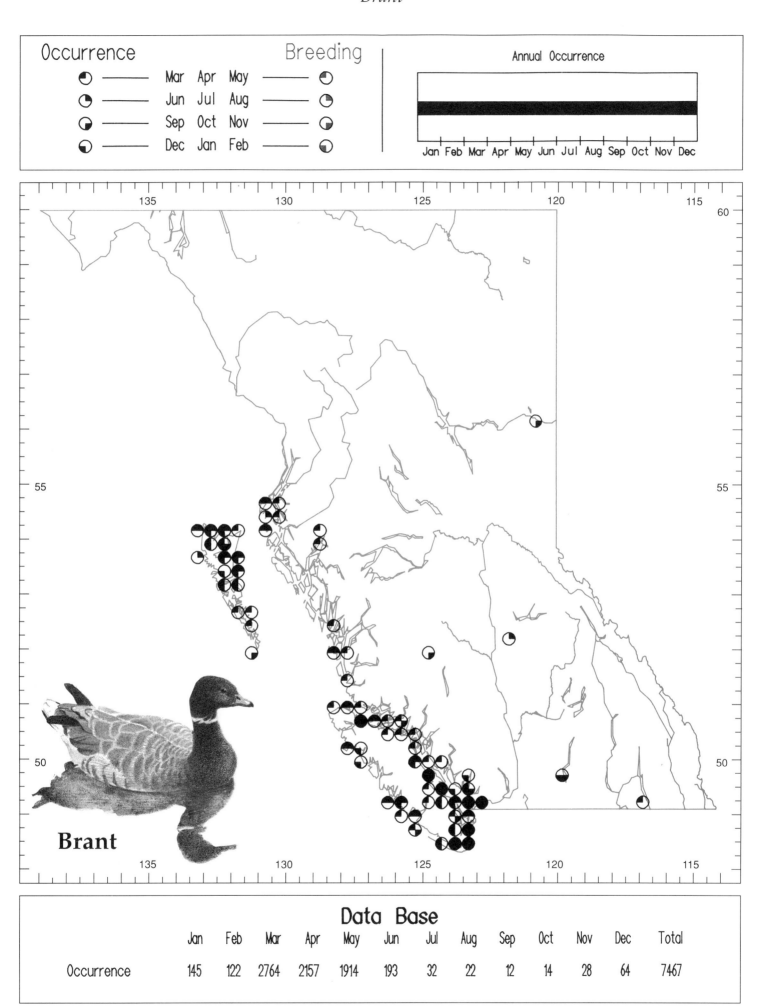

Occurrence | Breeding

	Mar Apr May	
�---	Jun Jul Aug	---
	Sep Oct Nov	
	Dec Jan Feb	

Annual Occurrence

Jan Feb Mar Apr May Jun Jul Aug Sep Oct Nov Dec

Brant

Data Base

	Jan	Feb	Mar	Apr	May	Jun	Jul	Aug	Sep	Oct	Nov	Dec	Total
Occurrence	145	122	2764	2157	1914	193	32	22	12	14	28	64	7467

twice-weekly boat to Victoria and others to Vancouver. In one good year, he and a companion sold 2,500 Brant to Pat Burns and Company before New Year's Day.

By the 1920s, Brooks and Swarth (1925) describe the Brant as a "common winter visitant to the coast . . . in former years more generally distributed than at present." By the mid-1940s, the Brant was still considered a winter visitant, but much more abundant as a spring transient (Munro, J.A. and Cowan 1947).

The decline of wintering Brant continued during the next 30 years; this is well documented by annual surveys and censuses, mostly from the Queen Charlotte Islands and Boundary Bay. The population of Brant at Masset in January 1952 was estimated at 1,000 birds (Leopold and Smith 1953). Today (1986), flocks of up to 6 birds are reported there infrequently. However, annual Christmas Bird Counts at Skidegate Inlet (90 km to the south) have shown an increase from 129 birds in 1982 to 283 in 1984, and some birds are frequently seen on the Yakoun River estuary and at Sandspit.

The decline is also documented in the vicinity of Boundary Bay. In December 1944 and 1946, at least 500 Brant were counted off Crescent Beach (Holdom 1945, 1947). Numbers peaked there at 1,000+ birds on 14 January 1947, but by 1951 they had decreased to about 200 birds (Munro, D.A. 1952). Christmas Bird Counts at Ladner from 1957 to 1984 also show a decline in the average wintering population (Fig. 259). Numbers dropped from 600 to 83 birds between 1960 and 1962. The decline continued to 4 birds in 1983; none were found in 1984. Between 1975 and 1984, the winter population, based on Christmas Bird Counts at Skidegate Inlet, Ladner, and White Rock (Surrey), averaged only 28 birds per count (n=23).

During the past 30 years, the proportion of Brant that winter along the Pacific coast north of Baja California declined from 50% to 65% of the population to less than 10% (Kramer et al. 1979). That decline coincided with increasing numbers of Brant wintering in Baja California and along the west coast of Mexico (see Smith, R.H. and Jensen 1970). The population shift was attributed to harassment and disturbance of birds by people (Denson 1964). Winter surveys, however, from 1951 to 1974, indicate the population along the Pacific coast has remained relatively stable at 140,000 birds (Smith, R.H. and Jensen 1970; Bellrose 1976). In 1987 the population was reported to be 146,992 birds (Conant 1988). Of those, 116,696 were counted in Mexico, 8,385 in Alaska, and 21,911 at other locations.

OCCURRENCE: The Brant is widely distributed along coastal British Columbia, particularly the inner coast; it is rarely found in the interior. It occurs principally on estuaries, beaches (Fig. 260), bays, lagoons, and mud flats. It is extremely rare any distance from the ocean. In British Columbia, it occurs chiefly as a spring migrant, during which time thousands are widespread along the coast littoral. Some of that northward movement, however, occurs well offshore (see Martin and Myers 1969; Hatler et al. 1978).

Spring populations build in California bays in early January and peak in mid-March (Moffit 1939). Spring migration occurs from late February through mid-May and peaks in late March and early April in extreme southern British Columbia. Aerial counts at Boundary Bay during the spring of 1958 (Taylor, E.W. 1959) show a rapid build-up to a peak in late March followed by a gradual decline throughout April and May. Similar trends have been noted at the Little Qualicum River estuary (Dawe 1980), following a Pacific herring spawn there, while near Campbell River the peak movement occurs slightly later (Fig. 261). Most of the spring movement is visible passing northward up the Strait of Georgia. Areas of concentration are Boundary Bay and the east coast of Vancouver Island from Victoria to Campbell River. Daily fluctuations of numbers there probably indicate a continual turnover of migrants. E.W. Taylor (1959) notes that spring migration in the Boundary Bay area appears to be more gradual than in other areas of concentration in the Pacific Northwest.

Small numbers, usually individuals but occasionally flocks of up to 200, may occur in summer on estuaries and bays, along the coast. Flocks reported in June are probably non-breeding wanderers. First-year birds are common in north-bound flocks into late June (T. Tolish pers. comm.).

Fall migrants are rare along the British Columbia coast. Most of the population stages at Izembek Lagoon, Alaska and then departs en masse offshore, in a rapid, direct flight to wintering grounds in Mexico (Hansen and Nelson 1957; Jones, R.D. 1973). Small numbers of Brant occur along the British Columbia coast from late August through October. Those birds are likely non-breeding adults or immatures. Occasionally, the direct autumn flight from Alaska is witnessed at sea off Vancouver Island. R.D.

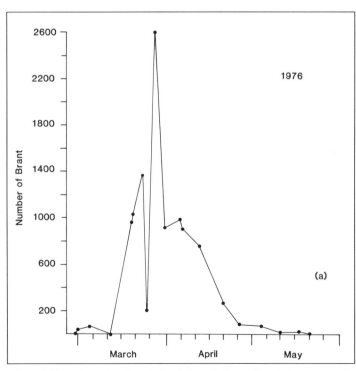

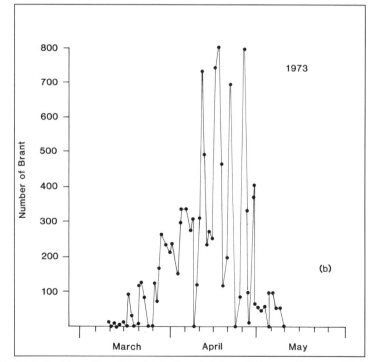

Figure 261. *Spring migrations of Brant through the northern Strait of Georgia: (a) - Little Qualicum River (1976); (b) - Campbell River (Discovery Passage, 1973), British Columbia. Campbell River data courtesy of the Mitlenatch Field Naturalists, Campbell River.*

Jones (pers. comm.) suggests that migration routes illustrated by Einarsen (1965) and Bellrose (1976) should be modified. He contends that wind conditions prevailing at the time the southward migration occurs are such that great turbulence would be encountered if the birds swung as far east as those routes show. Moreover, Einarsen and Bellrose indicate coastal travel over at least a part of the trip, which is contrary to what Moffit (1939) observed. Jones contends that since westerly winds blow around the north side of the Pacific High, the majority of birds fly a strictly seaward route south on the back quadrant of a low centre to pick up the westerlies and fly favourable winds to Baja.

Only small numbers of Brant now winter in British Columbia; Masset and Skidegate inlets alone support sizeable winter populations.

Flocks of Brant that appear in British Columbia in February and March are composed almost entirely of mated pairs. W.T. Munro (1979b) shows that 90% of the Brant harvested in the province are adults. The late winter/early spring hunting seasons in British Columbia, when in effect, concentrate the kill on birds that would soon be nesting.

The distribution of Brant in the province is closely related to the distribution of eel-grass (*Zostera marina*) which is the Brant's most important food (Cottam et al. 1944). Examination of gut contents from 50 Brant shot by hunters in Boundary Bay in early March 1988 showed that 94% of the diet (by volume) was *Z. marina*, the remaining plant food being *Z. japonicus*, a smaller, non-indigenous eelgrass; trace amounts of Pacific herring eggs were found in some birds (A. Reed pers. comm.). Observations in the Qualicum Beach and other areas indicate that the algae, sea lettuce (*Ulva lactuca*), is taken in large quantities later on during spring migration.

REMARKS: Two well-marked forms occur in British Columbia. *B. b. nigricans* (Black Brant), the common subspecies, breeds in northeastern Siberia, Alaska, and western subarctic Canada. Band recoveries and visual observations indicate that virtually all of the birds overwintering in British Columbia are of that subspecies (A. Reed pers. comm.). A light-bellied form intermediate between *B. b. nigricans* and *B. b. hrota* (Atlantic Brant), which breeds in the islands of the Canadian western high arctic (Boyd and Maltby 1979), also migrates past coastal British Columbia en route to its main wintering haunt in Padilla Bay, Washington; it occasionally occurs in small numbers during spring migration in Boundary Bay and along the eastern coast of Vancouver Island (A. Reed pers. comm.).

A bibliography on Brant, with emphasis on *B. b. nigricans*, is presented by Hout (1967).

Known in Old World literature as Brent Goose.

POSTSCRIPT: Recent observations during spring migration on the east coast of Vancouver Island have been reported by Dawe and Nygren (1989). In the Parksville-Qualicum Beach area, Brant spent time preening and apparently feeding well out in the Strait of Georgia during high tide. As the tide began to drop, small flocks would arrive on the newly exposed bars and sandflats where they routinely began maintenance activities followed by feeding activity as the tide receded. The highest numbers were usually counted about 2 hours after high tide.

Although there was an obvious movement of Brant, 30 individually marked birds were observed in the area for at least 2 weeks; 4 birds stayed between 30 and 45 days.

Brant from at least 2 separate breeding populations were noted in the area: some from the Yukon-Kuskokwim River deltas and some from the Teshekpuk Lake area of northern Alaska.

NOTEWORTHY RECORDS

Spring: Coastal - Whiffin Spit 20 Apr 1972-1,434; Chatham Islands 27 Apr 1959-2,000 to 3,000; Oak Bay 2 May 1977-600; James Island 26 Mar 1963-1,545, 6 Apr 1964-850; Pachena Point 29 Mar 1975-125 (largest flock, 19 Mar to 29 Apr); Tofino Inlet 30 Mar 1978-300, 15 Apr 1927-1,000+, 2 May 1974-4,000 (Crowell and Nehls 1974c); Boundary Bay, 15 Mar 1958-25, 26 Mar 1958-3,157, 31 Mar 1958-4,383, 7 Apr 1958-3,750, 16 Apr 1958-1,365, 23 Apr 1958-960, 30 Apr 1958-376 and 7 May 1958-291 aerial counts (Taylor, E.W. 1959); Canoe Pass (Delta) to Point Roberts (Washington) 22 Mar 1950-7,500 (Munro, D.A. 1952); Nanoose Harbour 24 Mar 1961-3,473; Gibsons 11 Apr 1981-321; Qualicum Beach 24 Apr 1946-8,050; Little Qualicum River estuary 4 Mar 1976-1,030, 23 Mar 1976-1,359, 27 Mar 1976-2,600, 5 Apr 1976-991, 12 Apr 1976-750, 20 Apr 1976-264, 26 Apr 1976-88, 3 May 1976-74, 10 May 1976-6, 17 May 1976-6 (Dawe 1980); Big Qualicum River 9 Apr 1966-4,300; Little River (Comox) 7 Apr 1954-5,000 (Einarsen 1965); Oyster River 21 Apr 1958-1,690; Harwood Island 21 Apr 1958-950; Clerke Point 11 to 31 May 1973-4,039 counted during migration watches (Campbell and Summers In press); Pulteney Point 5 May 1977-7,000 (largest numbers from 15 Apr to 22 May); Skidegate Inlet 18 Apr 1982-1,190, 1 to 7 May 1985-1,000 to 1,500; Yakoun River 10 Mar 1957-375, 15 Apr 1950-2,000, 11 May 1983-177; Rose Spit 23 Apr 1979-309, 24 Apr 1979-621, 25 Apr 1979-1,188, 26 Apr 1979-2,332, 28 Apr 1979-1,226,

29 Apr 1979-1,298, 30 Apr 1979-2,059, 2 May 1979-31, 3 May 1979-1,555, 4 May 1979-5,197. **Interior** - see Extralimital Records.

Summer: Coastal - Royal Roads 3 Jun 1984-19; Oak Bay 9 Jul 1966-7; Sandhill Creek (Long Beach) 14 Jul 1983-13; Cleland Island 24 Jul 1967-2, 14 Aug 1967-7, 28 Aug 1967-6 (Campbell and Stirling 1968b); Crescent Beach 7 Jun 1964-11; Boundary Bay 28 Jul 1970-3 (Barnard 1973); Roberts Bank 7 Aug 1982-8; Englishman River 27 Jun 1984-14; Qualicum Beach 7 Jul 1975-30; Comox 5 Jul 1953-20 (Flahaut 1953a), 22 Jul 1922-1 male (NMC 18074); Mitlenatch Island 1 Jul 1965-1 (Campbell and Kennedy 1965), 25 Aug 1968-10 (Foottit 1968); Clerke Point 1 to 27 Jun 1973-103 counted during migration watches (Campbell and Summers In press); Goose Group 24 Jul 1948-7; Hippa Island 28 Aug 1983-57; Yakoun River 9 Jun 1982-200+; Masset Sound, 1 June 1987-200, 9 Jun 1982-162. **Interior** - see Extralimital Records.

Autumn: Interior - see Extralimital Records. **Coastal** - Cape St. James 6 Oct 1981-46, 15 Oct 1978-120; Parksville 30 Nov 1979-10; Lantzville 20 Oct 1985-50+; Roberts Bank 22 Sep 1984-3, 19 Oct 1982-6; Boundary Bay 29 Sep 1960-25, 2 Oct 1965-20; Vesuvius Bay 22 Nov 1977-60; Clover Point 5 Nov 1983-14; Trial Islands 7 Oct 1976-8.

Winter: Interior - see Extralimital Records.

Coastal - Port Clements 8 Jan 1955-150; Yakoun River 22 Jan 1983-62; Sandspit 23 Dec 1982-129 (Campbell 1983b); Fort Rupert 15 Dec 1936-100; Fair Harbour 12 to 23 Dec 1983-20; Mitlenatch Island 21 Dec 1965-3 (Campbell 1965); Mission Point (Sechelt) 24 Jan 1987-30; Little Qualicum River estuary 29 Feb 1976-3 (Dawe 1980); Lantzville 18 Feb 1985-80 flying north; Boundary Bay 27 Jan 1981-176, 5 Feb 1964-1,000+ feeding on euphausids, 19 Feb 1979-230, 15 Dec 1984-50; Stubbs Island (Tofino) 18 Dec 1983-4; Gonzales Bay 10 Dec 1950-26.

Christmas Counts: Interior - Not recorded. **Coastal** - Recorded from 8 of 28 localities and on 16% of all counts. Maxima: Ladner 30 Dec 1961-600, all-time Canadian high count (Anderson, R.R. 1976); Skidegate Inlet 15 Dec 1984-283; White Rock (Surrey) 2 Jan 1972-33.

Extralimital Records: Interior - Creston 22 Mar 1978-1 (Butler, R.W. et al. 1986); Okanagan Lake at Penticton 5 to 12 Dec 1970-2 (Cannings, S.R. 1972; RBCM Photo 217); Aikin's Point (Naramata) and Trout Creek point (Summerland) 13 to 28 Nov 1977-1 with Canada Geese; Trout Creek point (Summerland) 2 Dec 1970-12, Mar 1981-1 (Cannings, R.A. et al. 1987); Kleena Kleene 18 Nov 1964-4; Jones Lake (150 Mile House) 19 Aug 1970-17 stopped for a couple of hours (Roberts, A. 1973); Fort St. John 16 to 22 Sep 1986-1 (Campbell 1986d; RBCM Photo 1124).

Canada Goose

CAGO

Branta canadensis (Linnaeus)

RANGE: Breeds from the Arctic coast of Alaska and northern Canada east to Labrador and Newfoundland and south to central California, northern Utah, southern Kansas, northern Arkansas, western Tennessee, western Kentucky, central Ohio, and rarely to Maine. Winters locally from southern Canada to northern Mexico and the Gulf Coast of the United States. Introduced in the British Isles, Iceland, and New Zealand.

STATUS: *Very abundant* spring and autumn migrant throughout the province; locally *very common* to *very abundant* in winter along the coast and in the southern interior. Resident populations established locally and increasing. Widespread breeder.

CHANGE IN STATUS: During the 1940s, the Canada Goose was mainly a migrant and summer visitant in British Columbia, and the occurrence and distribution of the various subspecies were fairly well understood (Munro, J.A. and Cowan 1947). In the 1960s and 1970s, resident populations became well established and began to increase, partly due to the natural adaptability of the species (e.g. *B. c. moffitti* in the Okanagan valley) but primarily because of transplants of flightless young and breeding stock from a wide variety of races (Fig. 263). Those changes have been documented by R.W. Butler. et al. (1986) for the Creston area, R.A. Cannings. et al. (1987) for the Okanagan valley, Dawe and Davies (1975), Leach (1982) and Christmas Bird Counts (Fig. 262) for the Fraser Lowlands, and I.D. Smith (1972, 1973) for the Nimpkish valley on Vancouver Island. By the late 1970s, the provincial breeding population had increased to an estimated 25,000 birds (Munro, W.T. 1979a).

NONBREEDING: Canada Geese are widely distributed throughout the province and can be found almost anywhere permanent

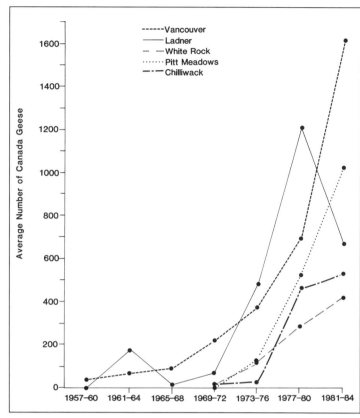

Figure 262. Average numbers of Canada Geese tallied at 5 Christmas Bird Count areas in the Fraser Lowlands, British Columbia, 1957 through 1984.

Figure 263. Canada Geese from the Lower Mainland being released at Mountain Slough, Chilliwack, July 1980. The cages were re-used from some of the earlier introductions of the mid-1970s (Douglas J. Wilson).

Canada Goose

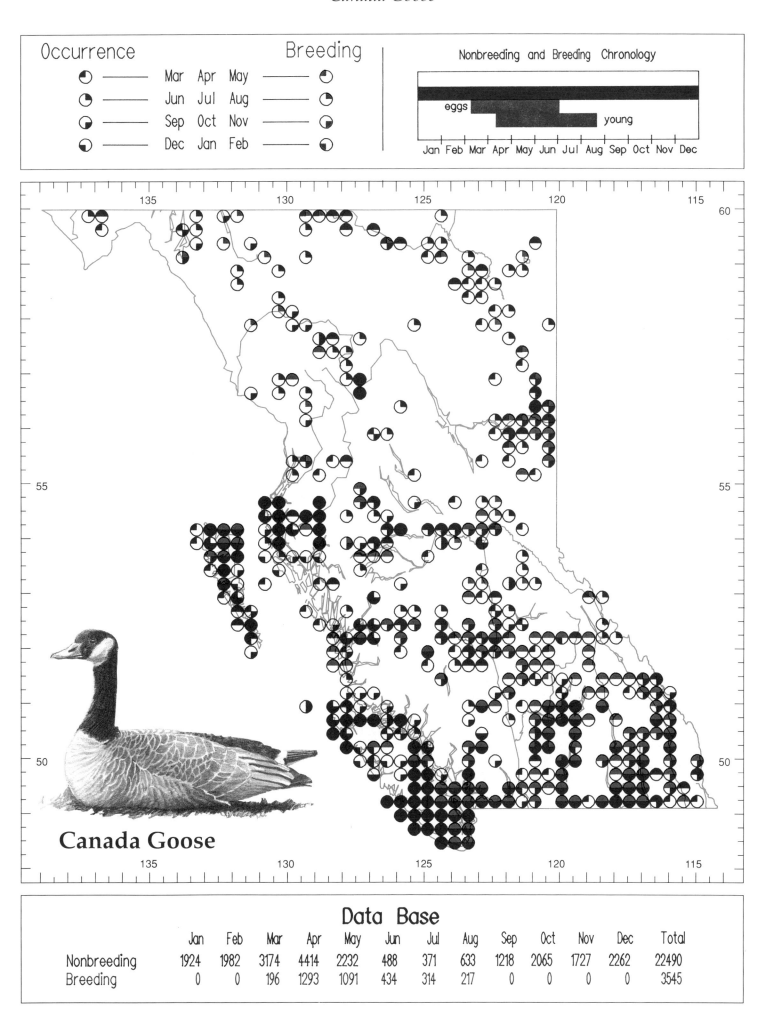

Occurrence

◑ ——	Mar Apr May	—— ◑
◔ ——	Jun Jul Aug	—— ◔
◓ ——	Sep Oct Nov	—— ◓
◕ ——	Dec Jan Feb	—— ◕

Breeding

Nonbreeding and Breeding Chronology

eggs

young

Jan Feb Mar Apr May Jun Jul Aug Sep Oct Nov Dec

Canada Goose

Data Base

	Jan	Feb	Mar	Apr	May	Jun	Jul	Aug	Sep	Oct	Nov	Dec	Total
Nonbreeding	1924	1982	3174	4414	2232	488	371	633	1218	2065	1727	2262	22490
Breeding	0	0	196	1293	1091	434	314	217	0	0	0	0	3545

water and grazing areas are available. They are one of the most adaptable of waterfowl, responding readily to propagation and feeding programs and adjusting to many man-altered environments.

There appear to be 3 routes that migrant Canada Geese use in British Columbia: offshore, coastal, and interior. The offshore movement is the least known. Each autumn, from late August through October, commercial fishermen report southward migrating "geese" up to 48 km offshore. These migrants may be pure flocks of Greater White-fronted Geese (Dzubin et al. 1964), or mixed with *B. c. minima* (Nelson, U.C. and Hansen 1959) and *B. c. occidentalis*. Essentially the same routes are used by spring migrants. The northward movement begins in late March, peaks during the latter half of April, and carries through until at least mid-May.

In autumn, the coastal movement is most noticeable in the vicinity of Tofino on the central west coast of Vancouver Island. Numbers begin building during the first 3 weeks of October, reach a peak during the first week of November, and clearly dwindle by the end of the month (Blood and Smith 1967; Hatler 1973). Spring migration occurs mostly during the latter half of April.

The autumn movement in the interior is protracted, extending from late August through November, and peaking from mid-September through early November. The first spring migrants arrive in southern areas in late February and early March, and in northern areas in late March. That movement peaks in the Chilcotin-Cariboo about mid-April and in the Nechako Lowlands a week later. There may be another large spring movement through the interior that goes almost unnoticed because it occurs at altitudes of up to 4,570 m. Myres and Cannings (1971), during radar studies of migrating geese in the springs of 1965, 1968, and 1969, conclude that between 50,000 and 75,000 geese migrate through the Okanagan valley each year between mid- and late April. The peak passage recorded was on 18 April 1968, when 4,250 geese passed over Penticton in a one hour period. Those migrants may be *B. c. parvipes*, although Grieb (1970) shows that that race usually migrates through eastern Alberta and western Saskatchewan.

Moult migrations, which occur annually in late spring to early autumn, are not well understood in British Columbia. The movements may involve large numbers of birds flying long distances to and from favourite moulting areas (Krohn and Bizeau 1979).

Wintering populations are increasing throughout southern areas of the province. Most are associated with cities where airports, golf courses, and farmlands provide rich grazing opportunities and safety from hunters. Along the coast, major wintering areas include the Fraser Lowlands and southeastern Vancouver Island. In the interior, the Okanagan and Thompson basins and the Revelstoke area support significant populations.

BREEDING: The Canada Goose breeds throughout the province from sea level to 1,250 m elevation. During the past 2 decades, introduced populations have become established and are increasing throughout southern British Columbia. However, natural populations still exist, mostly north of latitude 52°N.

The Canada Goose breeds in a variety of habitats, including inland and coastal marshes, islands in lakes, ponds, sloughs, rivers, tundra, muskeg, and man-made environments such as agricultural fields, reservoirs, sanctuaries, ditches and dykes, and sewage lagoons. All nesting habitats have a source of permanent water nearby. The Canada Goose usually breeds singly, but in refuges, sanctuaries, or on islands it will occasionally nest in loose colonies. For example, in 1979, 223 Canada Goose nests were found on Hatfield's Island, a 1.5 ha island in Vaseux Lake Migratory Bird Sanctuary. Nest density was 149 nests/ha.

Nests: Most nests were associated with lakes, marshes, and slow-moving rivers. The remainder were located in farmlands with irrigation ditches, on sloughs, ponds and bogs, in open mixed woodlands, and in urban areas. Sixty-two percent of 1,244 nests were on islands and 27% were located near the edge of water bodies. Almost all nests were located within 60 m of water, but one nest was found 1.6 km from any water.

Nests (n=632) were positioned on the ground (64%), in Osprey and Bald Eagle nests (13%), on muskrat or beaver lodges (11%), on artificial nest tubs and platforms (9%), and on other man-made structures such as pilings, bridges, and buildings (3% - Fig. 264). Maximum height for a tree nest was 31 m.

Nests were usually mounds of grasses, reeds, cattail, sticks, leaves, twigs, mosses, and sedges; most were lined with down and fine grasses.

Eggs: Dates for 1,405 clutches ranged from 13 March to 6 July, with 52% recorded between 18 April and 2 May. Sizes for 1,374 clutches ranged from 1 to 14 eggs (1E-31, 2E-52, 3E-111, 4E-218, 5E-241, 6E-514, 7E-161, 8E-33, 9E-4, 10E-2, 11E-5, 12E-1, 14E-1), with 55% having 5 or 6 eggs. That is within the latitudinal range in variation in clutch size for Canada Geese in North America reported by E.H. Dunn and MacInnes (1987). Nests containing more than 8 eggs probably represent dump laying by intruding females (Bellrose 1976). Incubation period averages about 28 days (Dow, J.S. 1943; Hanson and Browning 1959).

Young: Dates for 2,076 broods ranged from 15 April to 24 August, with 52% recorded between 14 May and 15 June. Sizes for 2,033 broods ranged from 1 to 27 young (1Y-82, 2Y-178, 3Y-274, 4Y-361, 5Y-388, 6Y-397, 7Y-171, 8Y-85, 9Y-47, 10Y-28, 11Y-9, 12Y-5, 13Y-1, 14Y-4, 15Y-1, 17Y-1, 27Y-1) with 56% having 4 to 6 young. Broods of more than 10 young are likely the result of brood mixing (Fig. 265). Fledging period for British Columbia is 63 days (Bellrose 1976).

Figure 264. *Urban nesting Canada Goose at False Creek, Vancouver, May 1982 (Douglas J. Wilson).*

Figure 265. *Adult Canada Geese with large brood at Westham Island, 26 June 1973 (Ervio Sian).*

NOTEWORTHY RECORDS – CANADA GOOSE

Spring: Coastal - Victoria 30 Apr 1962-5,000 in 3 large flocks; Pachena Point 18 Apr 2,242 in 12 flocks, largest movement in month; Ucluelet Inlet 19 Apr 1974-2,700; Tofino 16 Apr 1982-2,932 in 22 flocks; Crescent Beach 12 Mar 1952-500+; Cultus Lake 4 Mar 1965-375+; Shelter Point 2 May 1976-1,000+ in 7 flocks; Mahatta River 9 May 1978-1,965 in 9 flocks; Masset 22 Mar 1972-1,000, 20 Apr 1979-676, 15 May 1972-466; Naden Harbour 16 Apr 1975-1,000; Green Island 27 Mar 1966-3,000; Kitsault/Alice Arm 10 to 11 Mar 1980-360. **Interior** - Creston 6 Mar 1986-4,845, 12 Mar 1986-6,310, 14 Mar 1986-4,170, 15 Apr 1986-195, aerial censuses; White Lake (Okanagan Falls) 19 Apr 1978-2,420+; Summerland 21 Apr 1970-4,200 in 22 flocks; Brisco 28 Mar 1977-481, aerial survey (Kaiser et al. 1978); Kamloops 13 Mar 1982-2,200; Revelstoke airport 21 Apr 1978-236 (Bonar 1978b); Williams Lake 22 Apr 1970-2,000; Vanderhoof 17 Apr 1970-500 (Noble 1972); Halfway River 18 Mar 1986-8 near mouth; Fort St. John 27 Mar 1983-120+, 15 Apr 1983-400.

Summer: Coastal - Victoria 30 Aug 1969-100+ flying south (Tatum 1970); Beaver Lake (Saanich) 14 Jun 1979-135; Quamichan Lake 11 Jul 1967-80+; Narvaez Bay 12 Jun 1981-150+; Goose Group 15 Aug 1948-150+ migrants; Masset 2 Aug 1982-345 migrants; Kitsault 17 to 19 Jun 1980-155+. **Interior** - Creston 29 Jul 1985-1,125, 18 Aug 1947-400, mixed races (Munro, J.A. 1947b); Ellison Lake 29 Aug 1962-800; Otter Lake (Vernon) 19 Aug 1977-550; Spillimacheen to Golden 17 Aug 1977-722 on aerial survey (Kaiser et al. 1978); Chukachida River 15 Jul 1975-24 adults; Spatsizi River 20 Jul 1977-60; Kotcho Lake 20 Jul 1977-30; junction Dease and French Rivers 25 Aug 1977-200+; Swift River 20 Jul 1986-1 adult female, 99 moulting juveniles.

Autumn: Interior - Atlin 1 Sep 1981-23, 9 Oct 1980-53; Meziadin Lake 29 Sep 1980-55; Cecil Lake 21 Oct 1981-350, 11 Nov 1980-150; Nechako River (Vanderhoof) 20 Sep 1944-1,000+; Barkerville 16 Sep 1962-150; Chilcotin Lake 2 Nov 1977-890; Revelstoke 14 Nov 1983-4,771 (Campbell 1984a); Kamloops 28 Sep 1981-2,500, 22 Nov 1981-1,500; Douglas Lake (Quilchena) 22 Oct 1982-1,200; Otter Lake (Vernon) 20 Sep 1970-2,000; Creston 26 Sep 1985-309, 15 Oct 1985-2,485, 8 Nov 1985-630, aerial censuses. **Coastal** - Masset 10 Oct 1951-1,000, 27 Nov 1982-853; Naden Harbour 26 Sep 1975-500, 10 Oct 1975-1,000; Drizzle Lake 15 Oct 1978-3,000 in 15 flocks; Kumdis Creek 4 Sep 1979-150; Hansen Lagoon 7 Nov 1963-4,000, 17 Nov 1965-600; Port Hardy 2 Oct 1938-5,000, 18 Nov 1936-2,000; Port Neville 10 Oct 1975-5,916 birds in 34 flocks; Cortes Island 17 Oct 1977-2,500; Campbell River (Discovery Passage) 30 Sep 1973-thousands migrating; Oyster Bay 10 Oct 1975-2,500+; Blackie Spit 14 Oct 1984-4,500+; Tofino 9 Nov 1960-6,000+, 15 Nov 1960-10,000 to 12,000; Florence Lake 20 Oct 1979-1,000.

Winter: Interior - Carpenter Lake (Bridge River) Dec 1977-275 (Antifeau 1977); South Thompson River 9 Jan 1983-500; Kamloops Lake 30 Dec 1952-840 (Munro, D.A. 1953); Athalmer 10 Dec 1981-75+; Kelowna 1 Jan 1981-650; Kootenay Lake 6 Dec 1983-79; Penticton 10 Jan 1979-450 on golf course; Creston 12 Dec 1985-300, 28 Jan 1986-325, 5 Feb 1986-240 aerial census. **Coastal** - Big Bay and Pearl Harbour (Chatham Sound) 19 Jan 1978-750 (Martin 1978); Masset 11 Dec 1972-1,000; Taleomey River estuary 10 Jan 1977-295; Hansen Lagoon 14 Feb 1975-150; Widgeon Slough 17 Feb 1972-450; Reifel Island 27 Dec 1979-5,000; Somenos Lake 23 Dec 1978-205; Todd Creek 18 Jan 1982-146.

Christmas Counts: Interior - Recorded from 12 of 19 localities and on 71% of all counts. Maxima: Vernon 27 Dec 1981-1,690; Revelstoke 21 Dec 1983-1,097; Kelowna 20 Dec 1981-963. **Coastal** - Recorded from 23 of 28 localities and on 67% of all counts. Maxima: Ladner 28 Dec 1980-1,731; Vancouver 20 Dec 1981-1,721; White Rock 2 Jan 1983-1,454.

Figure 266. "Cackling" Canada Geese at Cowichan Lake, 19 November 1938 (Ian McTaggart-Cowan).

REMARKS: In many areas throughout North America and Europe, the establishment of local resident flocks of Canada Geese has caused nuisance problems ranging from the high density of goose feces on public parks, beaches, and golf courses, to direct damage of agricultural crops (Hawkins 1970; Conover and Chasko 1985; Parkin and McMeeking 1985). Similar problems now occur in British Columbia (Fig. 267) and appear to be increasing (G. Grigg pers. comm.). Another result of the spread of feral geese is that the indigenous breeders are threatened by interbreeding, as well as by neglect (H. Boyd pers. comm.). In addition, the present taxonomy of Canada Geese in southern areas of the province has been confused by the introduction of mixed subspecies and is likely to remain unclear for a long time. Despite the knowledge of these problems, transplants are still taking place in British Columbia.

See Craven (1981) for an annotated bibliography of the Canada Goose.

Following is a summary of Canada Goose sub-species known or suspected to occur in British Columbia. Migration corridors and chronology for the different subspecies occurring in British Columbia are generally not well documented. Details for the autumn period are perhaps best known because of the number of band recoveries obtained during the hunting season.

Branta canadensis fulva [Vancouver Canada Goose] - Breeds along the coast, from southeastern Alaska south through northern British Columbia. Relatively sedentary; only about 2% of the population actually migrates (Ratti and Timm 1979). Small numbers (50+) of *B. c. fulva* have been found wintering near Tofino (Hatler et al. 1978).

B. c. leucopareia [Aleutian Canada Goose] - Formerly bred in the thousands on the outer Aleutian Islands, but introduced Arctic foxes (*Alopex lagopus*) greatly reduced its numbers. The endangered goose (see Springer et al. 1978) has 3 surviving ancestral populations, which breed only on Buldir Island, Chagulak Island, and the Semidi Islands, Alaska (R.D. Jones pers. comm.). In addition, as a result of restocking efforts that included destruction of the Arctic foxes, they now nest on Agattu Island and have been re-introduced to Amchitka Island (R.D. Jones pers. comm.). In October, the Aleutian Canada Goose makes a transoceanic flight to its wintering grounds in the Central Valley of California (Woolington et al. 1979). J.A.Munro and Cowan (1947) list it as a regular migrant in British Columbia, but it was last recorded in the province in 1945.

B. c. minima [Cackling Canada Goose - Fig. 266] - Breeds mainly on the Yukon-Kuskokwim delta in Alaska and winters in the Central Valley of California (Nelson, U.C. and Hansen 1959). *B. c. minima* is the smallest subspecies of Canada Goose, and is also the easiest subspecies to identify in the field (Johnson, D.H. et al. 1979); because of this we have considerably more information on file for *B. c. minima* than for any other subspecies.

Cackling Canada Geese occur regularly as spring and autumn migrants in the province, but usually in small numbers and often associated with other Canada Geese, Brant, or Greater White-fronted Geese. Infrequently, large, pure flocks are reported from both coastal and interior locations. One such occurrence, from the field notes of K. Racey at Port Hardy on 24 October 1950, deserves mention:

> During the past fortnight we estimate that 10 or 12,000 geese, mainly *minima*, have gone through and of these approximately 2,000 are White-fronted Geese. A strong ESE gale is blowing today.

Most records and largest numbers are from the spring migration period. The Cackling Canada Geese leave their California wintering grounds over an extended period from

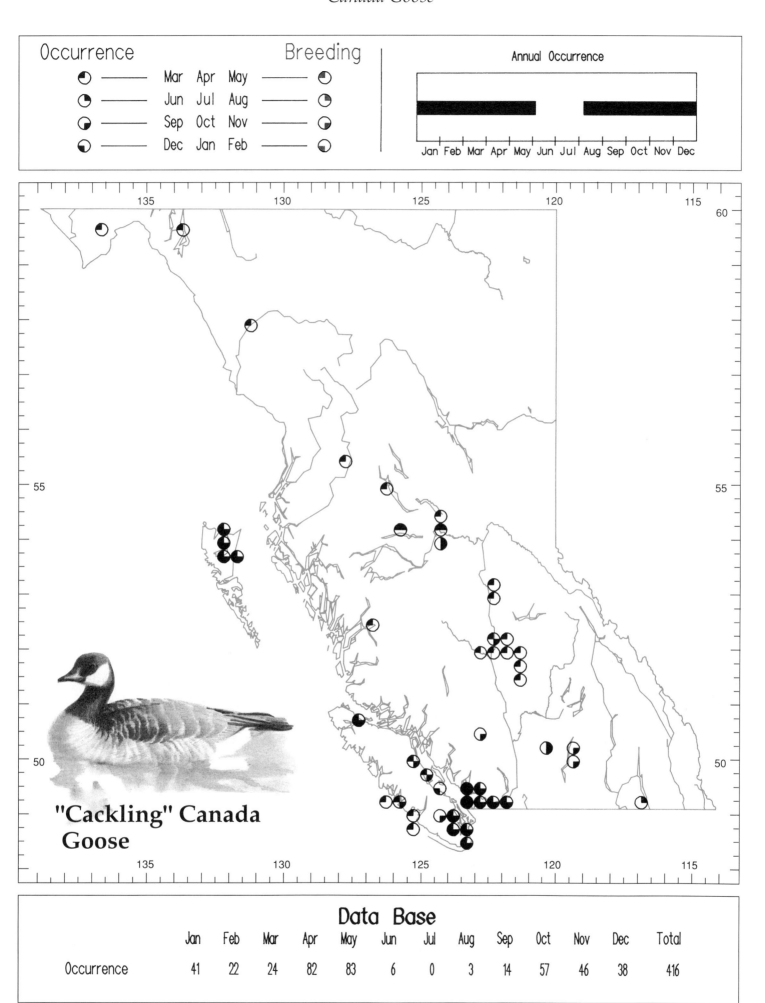

Canada Goose

Occurrence

Mar Apr May
Jun Jul Aug
Sep Oct Nov
Dec Jan Feb

Breeding

Annual Occurrence

Jan Feb Mar Apr May Jun Jul Aug Sep Oct Nov Dec

"Cackling" Canada Goose

Data Base

	Jan	Feb	Mar	Apr	May	Jun	Jul	Aug	Sep	Oct	Nov	Dec	Total
Occurrence	41	22	24	82	83	6	0	3	14	57	46	38	416

February to early April, following 2 corridors through British Columbia. Early migrants may appear along the coast in March, but most pass through between mid-April and mid-May. They are but a tiny fraction of the estimated 150,000 geese that regularly migrate across the northeastern Pacific Ocean from central California to western Alaska (Bellrose 1976). The interior corridor generally follows the Intermontane System (Farley 1979, p. 31) from the Okanagan valley north through regions of the Chilcotin-Cariboo and Fraser basins, and then in a northwesterly direction to western Alaska. Spring migrants have been recorded in the interior between 2 April and 5 June. The peak movement occurs from late April to early May.

Records for the summer period are probably late spring stragglers and early autumn arrivals. Autumn movements are generally a reversal of the spring routes. In September, they stage on Bristol Bay at the base of the Alaska Peninsula (Nelson, U.C. and Hansen 1959), and leave in early October. The majority apparently fly direct to Klamath Basin, California, bypassing the British Columbia coast, although a few are found along the coast each year. Some linger through November and frequently through the winter. There are a few records of autumn migrants in the interior, between 8 August and 12 November.

The size of Cackling Canada Goose flocks range up to 600 individuals on the coast and up to 300+ individuals in the interior, but most groups are of less than 10 birds. Most records are from coastal areas. The Cackling Canada Goose has been recorded in the province between 8 August and 5 June.

B. c. moffitti [Western Canada Goose] - Breeds on both sides of the Rocky Mountains from the Peace River regions of British Columbia and Alberta south to California and Colorado. Birds that breed in interior British Columbia winter mostly in south-central Washington (Hansen and Nelson 1964), but bands placed

on sub-adults in British Columbia have also been recovered from the Northwest Territories, Alberta, Saskatchewan, Michigan, California, and Texas. *B. c. moffitti* probably comprises most of the interior British Columbia population. Prior to introductions, it was also the common nesting race there.

B. c. occidentalis [Dusky Canada Goose] - Breeds largely on the Copper River delta, Alaska and winters primarily in the Willamette valley, Oregon. Part of the *occidentalis* race migrates offshore from mid-September through October, although substantial numbers stop on the Queen Charlotte Islands and Vancouver Island en route to their wintering grounds (Hansen 1962; Chapman, J.A. et al. 1969). The coastal route in British Columbia is probably used mostly by *B. c. occidentalis*. J.A. Chapman et al. (1969) indicate that up to and including the 1965-66 hunting season, band recoveries for that race reported by hunters from British Columbia were second only to those reported from Oregon. Of the British Columbia recoveries, 82% were from Vancouver Island, with the remainder mostly from the Queen Charlotte Islands. There was only one recovery from the mainland. See also J.A. Munro and Cowan (1947).

B. c. parvipes [Lesser Canada Goose] - Breeds in interior Yukon, mainland Northwest Territories, and at Tuya Lake in northern British Columbia (Godfrey 1986). Migrates through central British Columbia to winter in Oregon's Willamette valley (Johnson, D.H. et al. 1979) and California (American Ornithologists' Union 1957).

B. c. taverneri [Taverner's Canada Goose] - Breeds in western and northern Alaska and eastward into Canada along the Arctic coast. Winters in central California and recently in the Willamette valley in Oregon (Johnson, D.H. et al. 1979). Most migrate non-stop through British Columbia. W.T. Munro (1979a) lists Tranquille as an autumn staging area and Vanderhoof as a spring staging area.

Figure 267. *Canada Geese grazing in Terry Hughes Memorial Park, New Westminster, 20 December 1988 (R. Wayne Campbell).*

Figure 268. *"Cackling" Canada Geese with Snow Geese at Mosquito Flats (Chilkat Pass), 16 May 1977 (Ervio Sian).*

NOTEWORTHY RECORDS - "CACKLING" CANADA GOOSE

Spring: Coastal - Tofino 23 Apr 1981-250; Oak Bay 16 Mar to 24 Apr 1944-3; Vancouver 10 Mar 1924-1 (Cumming 1926); Serpentine River 7 May 1984-40; Courtenay 27 Apr 1939-5 with Greater White-fronted Geese, 13 May 1943-14 with other Canada Geese; Miracle Beach Park 12 May 1962-40; Port Hardy 21 Apr 1933-500, 25 Apr 1941-10; Bella Coola River 15 May 1935-2 (Munro, J.A. 1936b). **Interior** - 70 Mile House 23 Apr 1940-300 to 400 (Munro, J.A. 1945a); Lac la Hache 20 Apr 1940-100, 20 Apr 1941-70, 30 Apr 1943-70 (Munro, J.A. 1945a); Williams Lake 2 Apr 1974-a few with 30 other Canada Geese, 3 Apr 1977-3; Puntchesakut Lake 4 May 1944-20 (Munro, J.A. 1947a); Vanderhoof 19 to 20 Apr 1970-few with 1000+ mixed Canada Geese (Ebel 1973b), 2 May 1945-150, 4 May 1945-200 (Munro, J.A. and Cowan 1947); Francois Lake spring 1943-flock

remained until 5 June (Munro, J.A. 1947a); Mosquito Flats (Chilkat Pass) 14 to 20 May 1977-11 to 21 birds daily (see Fig. 268).

Summer: Coastal - Westham Island 5 Jun 1971-2 (Campbell et al. 1972b). **Interior** - s Kootenay Lake 8 Aug 1947-16 on beach, 13 Aug 1948-7; Leach Lake 18 Aug to 3 Sept 1947-100 (Munro, J.A. 1950); Quilchena 2 Jun 1973-1; Vanderhoof 29 Aug 1945-50 with other Canada Geese on gravel bars of Nechako River; Francois Lake 5 Jun 1943-100 (Munro, J.A. and Cowan 1947).

Autumn: Interior - Vanderhoof 1 Sep 1945-50; Williams Lake 29 Sep 1969-15, 12 Nov 1984-4; Quilchena 11 Oct 1970-100 with Canada Geese; Pemberton Valley autumn 1944-1 (Racey 1948); Leach Lake 3 Sep 1947-flocks of 45 and 14 birds.

Coastal - Masset 19 Sep 1983-2, 2 Nov 1949-125, 4 Nov 1971-8; Port Hardy 22 Oct 1940-150, 23 Oct 1940-600; Comox 26 Sep 1922-100, 28 Nov 1926-25 to 30; Quamichan Lake 20 Oct 1972-3 (Tatum 1973); Pitt Meadows 20 Oct 1975-104; Stanley Park (Vancouver) 1 Nov 1974-10; Huntingdon 1 Nov 1942-27; Arakun Islands 3 Oct 1972-5 (Hatler 1973); Saanich 20 Sep 1952-2 with 105 other Canada Geese; Oak Bay 29 Oct 1963-4 feeding with 6 Snow Geese, 24 Nov 1943-27.

Winter: Coastal - Masset Inlet 10 Dec 1980-1; Kumdis Slough 8 Jan 1954-17; Tlell River mouth 24 to 26 Jan 1955-10; Port Hardy 3 Dec 1953-2 (PMNH 71554, 71555); Reifel Island 16 Feb 1973-8 with 300 other Canada Geese; Saanich 19 Jan 1981-2; Elk Lake (Saanich) 5 Feb 1954-7 with 21 other Canada Geese.

Wood Duck
Aix sponsa (Linnaeus)

WODU

RANGE: Breeds from southern British Columbia and Montana south to central California and from central Saskatchewan east to Nova Scotia and south to the Gulf Coast. Winters south to central Mexico; western populations winter mainly in California but some northern coastal populations are resident.

STATUS: Locally *common* to *very common* resident in the Fraser Lowlands and on southern Vancouver Island. Elsewhere, a *rare* to *uncommon* summer visitant across southern British Columbia; locally *common* spring and autumn migrant. *Fairly common* to *common* in winter on the south coast; *rare* in the southern interior. *Casual* on the Queen Charlotte Islands; *accidental* in the Peace Lowlands. Local breeder.

NONBREEDING: The Wood Duck is distributed locally across southern British Columbia north to Quesnel and Mount Robson Park from sea level to 1,280 m elevation. Populations in the Fraser Lowlands and on southern Vancouver Island are resident. Migrants arrive in small numbers on the south coast in mid-March and in the southern interior in April.

The Wood Duck frequents waterways such as sloughs, oxbows, lowland ponds, swamps, flooded fields, sewage lagoons, and sluggish rivers that are usually associated with dense stands of mature forest, emergent vegetation, and overhanging brush such as red alder or willows. Frequently, the Wood Duck is seen in small groups foraging along the edge of sheltered backwaters, in vegetation bordering shallow shorelines, in emergents such as cattail, and among waterlilies, It is rarely seen on marine waters.

Males group together after incubation begins, and post-breeding flocking also occurs before the southward migration. In the east Kootenay, the autumn movement is more noticeable than the spring movement and occurs between late August and early October, peaking in mid-September (Howie 1975). Overwintering populations of Wood Ducks are increasing on the south coast as they take advantage of artificial feeding stations in parks and wildlife reserves. A few winter in the Okanagan Basin.

BREEDING: The Wood Duck breeds on southern Vancouver Island north on the west coast to Tofino and on the east coast to Cortes Island, throughout the Fraser Lowlands and throughout the southern interior north to Williams Lake and Anahim Lake. It has been reported from sea level to 1,200 m elevation.

The Wood Duck breeds in mature deciduous woodlands adjacent to lowland ponds, sloughs, slow-moving rivers, and quiet backwaters in both fresh and brackish water environments. The centre of abundance is the Fraser Lowlands where populations can reach a density of 1 pair/ha in Maple Ridge, Pitt Meadows, White Rock, Burnaby Lake, and Westham Island.

In the interior, the centre of abundance is the Creston area. Bellrose (1976) estimates a breeding population of 3,000 birds for British Columbia.

Breeding populations increased dramatically in the Fraser Lowlands during the 1970s coinciding with a conservation program to provide additional nest sites. Several thousand nest boxes were erected during the decade (Campbell et al. 1972b, 1974; Leach 1972; Van Drimmelen 1973; Trethewey and Cooper 1975). On the South Alouette River, the Wood Duck population increased from one pair in 1968 to 50+ pairs in 1979. Inadequate maintenance of nest boxes has resulted in local declines of breeding numbers in the 1980s. Nest box programs have also increased populations locally in the Creston and Enderby areas.

Nests: Nests were usually situated near water: 52% of 141 nests were near sloughs, 40% were on river banks, and 8% were along lake shores; but 96% of 276 nests were in nest boxes. Only 9 natural nests were found. They were in cavities in mature deciduous trees, either in holes excavated by other animals (e.g. Pileated Woodpecker; *Dryocopus pileatus*) or in rotted-out knot holes and stub ends. Nest trees included black cottonwood, trembling aspen, red alder, and bigleaf maple. One nest was found in a crow's old nest. Natural nest cavities ranged from 5 to 25 m above ground.

Eggs: Dates for 292 clutches ranged from 7 April to 13 July with 51% recorded between 7 May and 1 June. Downy young found between 5 and 11 May indicate clutch initiation can occur on 28 March. Sizes for 298 clutches ranged from 1 to 29 eggs (1E-1, 2E-3, 3E-4, 4E-6, 5E-6, 6E-12, 7E-16, 8E-22, 9E-33, 10E-29, 11E-32, 12E-31, 13E-18, 14E-14, 15E-14, 16E-21, 17E-9, 18E-8, 19E-4, 20E-4, 21E-3, 22E-1, 23E-2, 24E-2, 27E-2, 29E-1) with 55% having 8 to 13 eggs. At least 12% of all clutches greater than 16 eggs were the product of more than one female. Incubation period averages 30 days, but ranges from 25 to 37 days (Bellrose 1955; Breckenridge 1956).

Young: Dates for 216 broods ranged from 5 May to 9 September with 50% recorded between 5 June and 5 July. Sizes for 213 broods ranged from 1 to 19 young (1Y-4, 2Y-12, 3Y-26, 4Y-22, 5Y-28, 6Y-26, 7Y-22, 8Y-21, 9Y-20, 10Y-18, 11Y-3, 12Y-6, 13Y-1, 14Y-1, 16Y-1, 17Y-1, 19Y-1) with 58% having 3 to 7 young. Fledging period is about 56 to 70 days (Bellrose 1976).

REMARKS: There is no conclusive evidence that Wood Ducks breed on the Queen Charlotte Islands, as suggested by Munro, J.A. and Cowan (1947) and Godfrey (1986), or on all of Vancouver Island as noted in Godfrey (1986).

During the late 1970s, 25 to 50 fledgling Wood Ducks were introduced to Smithers and Prince George. Apparently those introductions were unsuccessful.

NOTEWORTHY RECORDS

Spring: Coastal - Blenkinsop Lake 31 May 1980-5 males; Duncan 21 Mar 1981-20, 1 Apr 1987-40 males, 2 females; Burnaby Lake 1 May 1977-40 (20 pairs); Pitt Meadows 3 Apr 1966-36; Cortes Island 13 Mar 1985-2, first arrivals; Kimsquit River 17 Apr 1985-pair on beaver pond 3 km from mouth. **Interior** - Duck Lake (Creston) 20 Apr 1983-11, 31 May 1980-53, (52 males); Wasa 7 Apr 1982-1; Nakusp 5 Apr 1982-2; Spillimacheen to Golden 13 Apr 1977-25 (Kaiser et al. 1978); Kersley 29 May 1966-4; Williams Lake 12 Mar 1983-2.

Summer: Coastal - Pitt Meadows 4 Aug 1972-52; Cranberry Lake (Powell River) 30 Aug 1981-9; Black Creek (Courtenay) 29 Jun 1971-25. **Interior** - Osoyoos Lake 2 Jun 1977-pair, 25 Jul 1974-11; Creston 25 Jul 1985-29; Okanagan Lake 10 Aug

1978-15 on north arm; Fort St. John 14 to 25 Jun 1984-1 male (Rogers, T.H. 1984d).

Autumn: Interior - Moberly Marsh 5 Oct 1977-19 (Kaiser et al. 1978); Brisco 14 Sep 1977-20 (Kaiser et al. 1978); Monte Creek 8 Nov 1942-1 (MVZ 99417); Vernon 3 Oct 1939-200 in 7 flocks (Cannings, R.A. et al. 1987); Creston 9 Sep 1984-20, 18 Oct 1982-10. **Coastal** - Masset 2 Nov 1946-2 (RBCM 10233, 10234); Lost Lagoon 29 Sep 1973-40, 7 Nov 1979-55; Duncan 15 Sep 1984-90+, 21 Oct 1984-84; Thetis Lake 26 Oct 1980-21.

Winter: Interior - Kamloops 20 Dec 1987-1; Mara Lake 26 Jan 1977-1; Vernon 5 to 20 Jan 1979-1; Vaseux Lake 8 Dec 1963-4. **Coastal** -Masset 9 Jan 1941-1 (RBCM 11354); Campbell River (Discovery Passage) 27 Dec 1977-3; Mud Lake (Langley) 30

Jan 1980-50; Stanley Park (Vancouver) 13 Jan 1979-82; Burnaby Lake 3 Jan 1974-21; Serpentine Fen (Surrey) 5 Dec 1978-108; Duncan 19 Jan 1974-14, 15 Feb 1977-14; Swan Lake (Saanich) 23 Dec 1979-10, 26 Feb 1979-6.

Christmas Counts: Interior - Recorded from 2 of 19 localities and on 6% of all counts. Maxima: Vaseux Lake 28 Dec 1978-3; Vernon 26 Dec 1976-3. **Coastal** - Recorded from 10 of 28 localities and on 36% of all counts. Maxima: Pitt Meadows 30 Dec 1979-122; Vancouver 18 Dec 1983-101; White Rock 30 Dec 1978-80.

Extralimital Records: Fort St. John 14 and 25 Jun 1984-1.

Wood Duck

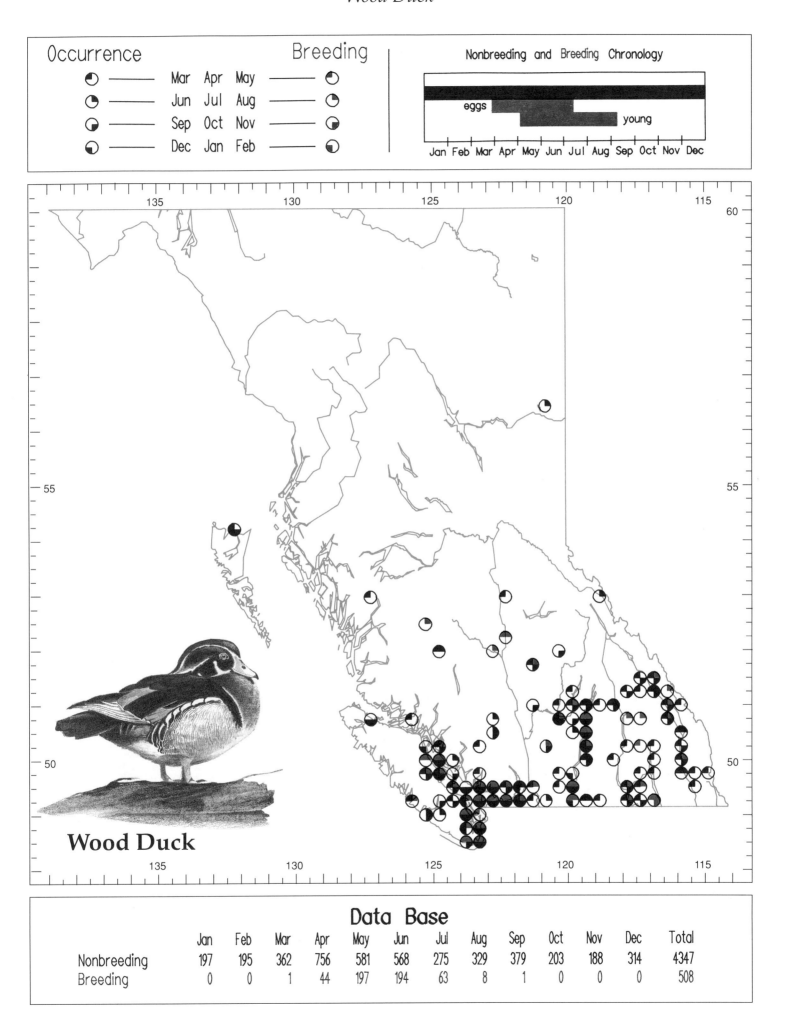

Occurrence

| | | Mar | Apr | May | | |

Breeding

Nonbreeding and Breeding Chronology

eggs

young

Jan Feb Mar Apr May Jun Jul Aug Sep Oct Nov Dec

Occurrence

Mar Apr May
Jun Jul Aug
Sep Oct Nov
Dec Jan Feb

Data Base

	Jan	Feb	Mar	Apr	May	Jun	Jul	Aug	Sep	Oct	Nov	Dec	Total
Nonbreeding	197	195	362	756	581	568	275	329	379	203	188	314	4347
Breeding	0	0	1	44	197	194	63	8	1	0	0	0	508

Wood Duck

Green-winged Teal

Anas crecca Linnaeus

GWTE

RANGE: In North America, breeds from central Alaska and the Yukon delta east to Newfoundland except the Arctic archipelago, south to California and Arizona in the west and Pennsylvania in the east. Winters mainly from the northern United States to Central America; on the Pacific coast north to the Aleutian Islands. Also occurs in the Old World.

STATUS: *Common* to *very abundant* migrant along the coast, *fairly common* to *abundant* in the interior. *Common* to *very abundant* winter visitant on the southwest coast, *common* to *abundant* on the north coast, and *fairly common* in early winter in the southern interior. Widespread breeder.

NONBREEDING: The Green-winged Teal occurs throughout the province. On the coast, it prefers tidal mudflats, which are used more by this species than by any other duck. It is very rarely seen on pelagic waters, but may rest during migration in marine lagoons, or just offshore in rafts of several hundred birds. In the interior, shallow marshes and flooded, weedy fields are most often used. Other habitats used on the coast and in the interior include sloughs, estuaries, ponds, creek mouths, slow-moving rivers, and sewage lagoons. It rarely uses dry grain fields.

The Green-winged Teal forages in emergent vegetation, along shorelines and in wet, shallow, muddy areas. It loafs on exposed shorelines, mudflats, shallow marshes, and lakes.

Spring migration may begin in late February in the south, but the main movement begins in late March and peaks in mid-to-late April. In the north, migrants arrive in early April with the peak movement occurring later in the month and continuing through May. Small numbers of nonbreeders are widely scattered in early summer. Post breeding males, followed by females and young, gather on marshes in June and July.

The autumn movement begins in mid-August in the interior and in mid-September on the coast. The movement is protracted and continues through December, peaking in late October to early November on the coast and late September to mid-October in the interior. J.A. Munro (1949) suggests the coastal movement is 4 times larger than the interior movement.

Thousands winter in tidal marshes and flooded fields associated with agricultural lands along the southern coast, most noticeably on the Fraser and Chemainus river estuaries. Our highest wintering estimates indicate that at least 6% of the total Pacific Flyway population of 280,000 birds is found in south coastal British Columbia. Smaller numbers winter on north coast estuaries. A few winter in the Okanagan valley and west Kootenay as long as open water is available, but most leave by early January.

BREEDING: The Green-winged Teal breeds throughout the interior of the province. On the coast, it breeds on southern Vancouver Island, the Fraser Lowlands and on the northern Queen Charlotte Lowlands. It breeds from sea level to 1,525 m.

In the interior, preferred habitats are grassy, brushy, or lightly wooded upland areas near fresh water marshes. On the coast, habitats include sloughs and ponds, usually associated with estuaries.

The centre of abundance is in the Chilcotin-Cariboo and Peace River areas. Bellrose (1976) estimates the breeding population at 12,000 birds. That figure, however, may be low as the Green-winged Teal is now known to be more widely distributed in northern areas of the province.

Nests: Very few nests have been discovered in the province, since the Green-winged Teal prefers nest sites with dense cover. Described habitats for 18 of 25 nests included marshes (8), woodlands (7), and rangeland (3). Other general habitats included alpine tundra and boreal forest adjacent to seismic lines. Specific sites for 24 nests included clumps of small bushes (12), grasses (7), rushes (2), and bases of trees (3). Distance from water for 7 nests ranged from 3 to 100 m with 6 being less than 30 m from water. J.A. Munro (1949) indicates nests have been found up to 230 m from water.

Nests were shallow hollows in the ground: 21 of 24 nests were lined with down; 14 contained grasses as well. Other materials included mosses, leaves, and twigs.

Eggs: Dates for 39 clutches ranged from 29 April to 12 July with 54% recorded between 20 May and 27 June. Sizes for 38 clutches ranged from 1 to 11 eggs (1E-1, 2E-1, 5E-1, 6E-5, 7E-7, 8E-8, 9E-12, 10E-1, 11E-2) with 53% having 8 or 9 eggs. Clutch size probably ranges to at least 13 eggs, as indicated by broods. Incubation period is 21 to 23 days (Bent 1923).

Young: Dates for 293 broods ranged from 24 May to 22 August with 50% recorded between 3 July and 22 July. Sizes for 270 broods ranged from 1 to 19 young (1Y-4, 2Y-13, 3Y-12, 4Y-27, 5Y-35, 6Y-43, 7Y-47, 8Y-31, 9Y-25, 10Y-17, 11Y-11, 12Y-2, 13Y-1, 16Y-1, 19Y-1) with 58% having 5 to 8 young. Broods of 16 and 19 young are likely the product of more than one female. Fledging period is about 35 days (Hooper, D.C. 1951).

REMARKS: The Old World race, known as the Common Teal or Teal (*Anas crecca crecca*) was previously considered a separate species. It occurs as a regular winter visitant to the south coast (Campbell 1967).

See Moisan et al. (1967) for a discussion of the distribution, migration, and population dynamics of the Green-winged Teal.

NOTEWORTHY RECORDS

Spring: Coastal - Tsehum Harbour 12 Mar 1977-218; Long Beach 30 Apr 1981-500+ in raft offshore; Fraser River delta 28 Mar 1967-5,244, 20 Apr 1967-7,955, 4 May 1967-9,280 (Burgess 1970); Comox 7 May 1943-300; Masset 1 May 1979-72; Rose Spit 28 Apr 1979-300, 4 May 1979-616 day count. **Interior** - Creston 6 Mar 1986-40, 1 Apr 1985-375, 18 Apr 1985-426; White Lake (Oliver) 14 Apr 1968-50; Wasa 21 Apr 1979-53; Columbia Lake 29 Mar 1978-37; Kelowna 16 Mar 1977-24; Revelstoke 18 Apr 1977-200 (Bonar 1978b); Sloane Slough 14 May 1981-44; Cecil Lake 24 Apr 1983-250; Atlin 20 Apr 1934-earliest (Munro, J.A. 1949).

Summer: Coastal - Whiffin Spit 16 Aug 1980-12; Sea Island 25 Jun 1971-18 males (Campbell et al. 1972b); Iona Island 24 Jun 1973-70; Kitimat 23 Aug 1975-40. **Interior** - Creston 4 Jul 1984-51; Vaseux Lake 25 Jun 1976-12; Swan Lake (Vernon) 10 Aug 1977-135; Revelstoke 26 Aug 1977-254 (Bonar 1978b); Rock Lake (Riske Creek) 25 Jul 1978-18;

Wilde Lake 24 Jul 1980-20; Hudson Hope 17 Aug 1975-56; Kotcho Lake 26 Jun 1982-21 (Campbell and McNall 1982); Atlin 12 Jun 1975-1 pair.

Autumn: Interior - Charlie Lake 26 Sep 1982-81; Fort St. John 11 Sep 1986-130, 31 Oct 1982-4, latest record; Chilcotin Lake 2 Nov 1977-19; Revelstoke 21 Sep 1977-207 (Bonar 1978b); Swan Lake (Vernon) 1 Oct 1937-800+ (Munro, J.A. and Cowan 1947); Nakusp 4 Nov 1975-26; Sirdar 10 Sep 1947-800 (Munro, J.A. 1949); Creston 28 Sep 1984-300, 15 Oct 1985-600, 8 Nov 1983-201. **Coastal** - Port Simpson 2 Sep 1969-200; Masset 9 Oct 1971-200; Kumdis Slough 5 Sep 1979-1,500; Port Hardy 29 Oct 1936-2,000; Kelsey Bay 17 Oct 1983-350; Laddie Island 2 Sep 1982-150; Iona Island 25 Sep 1973-10,000; Reifel Island 12 Nov 1974-3,000; Fraser River delta 13 Oct 1966-16,890 (Burgess 1970); Crescent Beach 21 Nov 1976-450; Tsehum Harbour 3 Nov 1978-233.

Winter: Interior - Coldstream 27 Feb 1951-14 (Cannings, R.A. et al. 1987); Nakusp 1 Jan 1977-6; Vaseux Lake 21 Dec 1974-25; Creston 5 Feb 1986-10. **Coastal** - Masset 15 Feb 1983-278; Kumdis Slough 19 Dec 1953-350; Pallant Creek 20 Jan 1979-15; Iona Island 25 Feb 1973-3,000; Reifel Island 14 Dec 1974-4,840; Fraser River delta 22 Dec 1966-10,000; Chemainus River estuary 1 Jan 1975-1,000 (Blood 1976); Cowichan River estuary 22 Jan 1982-440; Todd Creek flats (Saanich) 29 Jan 1982-440; Hastings flats (Saanich) 15 Dec 1981-400.

Christmas Counts: Interior - Recorded from 8 of 19 localities and on 31% of all counts. Maxima: Vaseux Lake 23 Dec 1981-45; Vernon 23 Dec 1979-33; Kelowna 20 Dec 1981-18. **Coastal** - Recorded from 27 of 28 localities and on 81% of all counts. Maxima: White Rock 3 Jan 1982-**8,842**, all-time Canadian high count (Anderson, R.R. 1982); Ladner 27 Dec 1982-5,082; Vancouver 26 Dec 1973-3,513.

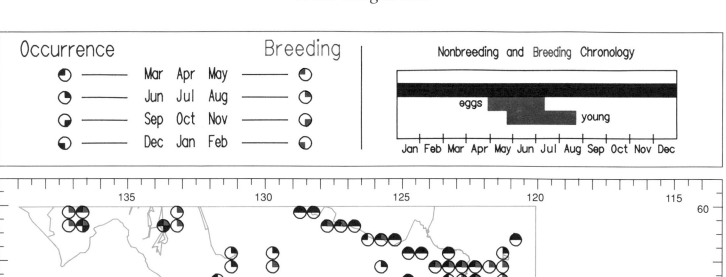

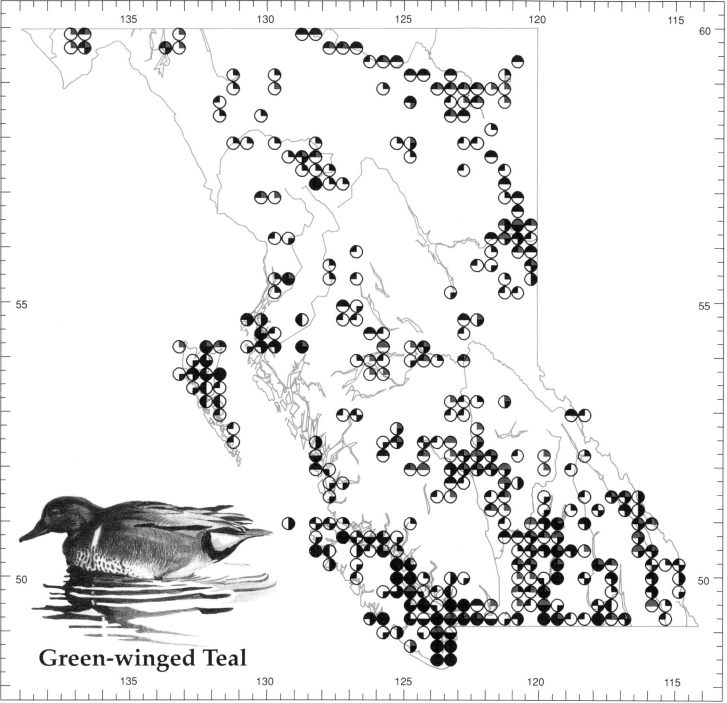

Green-winged Teal

Data Base

	Jan	Feb	Mar	Apr	May	Jun	Jul	Aug	Sep	Oct	Nov	Dec	Total
Nonbreeding	697	714	869	2243	1198	731	368	1289	2191	1753	1180	895	14128
Breeding	0	0	0	1	18	82	197	41	0	0	0	0	339

American Black Duck

Anas rubripes Brewster

RANGE: Breeds very locally in Alberta and Saskatchewan and generally from northwestern Manitoba east to Labrador and Newfoundland and south to western Minnesota, Wisconsin, Ohio, Pennsylvania, Maryland, and eastern Virginia. Winters from southeastern Canada to Texas, the Gulf States and Florida. Introduced locally in western North America.

STATUS: Introduced. On the coast, an *uncommon* local resident near Victoria, Yellow Point, Stanley Park (Vancouver), and on the Fraser River delta; *rare* elsewhere. *Casual* in the interior. Local breeder.

CHANGE IN STATUS: The American Black Duck was first brought into British Columbia in the late 1960s as captive display stock for the George C. Reifel Waterfowl Refuge in Delta. Apparently all birds were killed by predators. In 1970, another small flock of pinioned birds was established at the refuge and the following year at least 4 ducks escaped and were free-flying. One was seen there with a female Mallard on 22 March 1971 and 4 were reported flying together on 9 August 1971 (Campbell et al. 1972b).

During the 1970s small numbers of black ducks were also brought into various locations in the Fraser Lowlands by aviculturists. Some of those birds also escaped and reports of free-flying birds came from as far east as Chilliwack.

The only known introduction on Vancouver Island occurred during the late 1970s when 10 to 20 birds were released at Michael Lake near Yellow Point. Stock was apparently from the Fraser Lowlands.

The total feral population on the southwest coast is unknown but is probably less than 100 birds.

NONBREEDING: The American Black Duck occurs as a local resident, in small numbers, on the south coast in the vicinity of Vancouver, Reifel Island, Michael Lake, and Victoria. It has been recorded from Victoria to Courtenay on Vancouver Island, near Powell River, and from Vancouver and the Fraser River delta east to Chilliwack. In the interior, it has been recorded only on Cecil Lake in the Peace Lowlands.

The American Black Duck frequents brackish and freshwater marshes and sloughs, lagoons, farmlands, ponds (Fig. 269), parks, shallow lakes with emergent growth, and marine foreshores where it associates with Mallards.

There is no information on seasonal movements although there appears to be a small autumn and winter dispersal from local resident populations. Mattocks and Hunn (1980) suggest that black ducks seen in Victoria and Saanich may have originated from populations in Everett, Washington.

The origin of birds recorded in the interior is not known.

BREEDING: The American Black Duck breeds locally in the vicinity of Reifel Island, Ladner, and Pitt Meadows. There are only 3 records, all of broods, as follows: Pitt Meadows 23 May 1974-female with 10 young (Class I) from a pair known to have escaped from a flock in 1973; Reifel Island 5 June 1980-female with 5 young (Class I); Ladner 17 June 1982-female with 6 young (Class II) on sewage lagoon.

REMARKS: The American Black Duck was formerly known as Black Duck. *A. rubripes* frequently hybridizes with *A. platyrhynchos*. American Ornithologists' Union (1983) notes, however, that these 2 forms, "differ somewhat behaviourally and they tend to segregate as species."

Figure 269. *American Black Duck with female Mallard at Yacht Pond (Victoria), February 1983 (Mark Nyhof).*

NOTEWORTHY RECORDS

Spring: Coastal - Victoria 2 Mar 1984-7; Michael Lake 7 Apr 1985-5; Reifel Island 6 May 1981-4; Silver Creek (Mission) 17 May 1975-1; Courtenay 4 May 1987-1 pair at sewage lagoon. **Interior** - See Extralimital Records.

Summer: Coastal - Victoria 7 Jun 1984-1, 15 Jun 1985-1; Reifel Island 26 Aug 1978-3; Maplewood Flats (North Vancouver) 3 Aug 1980-1; Mission 5 Aug 1982-1; Stanley Park (Vancouver) 31 Aug 1975-1; Cranberry Lake (Powell River) 27 Jul 1977-1. **Interior** - No records.

Autumn: Interior - No records. **Coastal** - Cranberry Lake (Powell River) 27 Sep to 6 Oct 1980-1; Michael Lake 3 Nov 1981-7; West Vancouver 18 Oct 1979-2; Stanley Park (Vancouver) 17 Sep 1979-2; Reifel Island 21 Oct 1976-5; Blackie Spit 3 Nov 1984-1; Discovery Island autumn 1976-1 (RBCM 16168).

Winter: Interior - No records (See Christmas Counts). **Coastal** - Courtenay 13 to 16 Dec 1986-1; Stanley Park (Vancouver) 12 Dec 1980-1; Westham Island 2 Feb 1978-4; Reifel Island 16 Feb 1973-15; Boundary Bay 16 Feb 1984-2; Holland

Point (Victoria) 21 Dec 1983-3; Goodacre Lake 2 Dec 1985-2 adults.

Christmas Counts: Interior - Recorded once: Vaseux Lake 23 Dec 1980-1 [considered hypothetical by Cannings, R.A. et al. (1987)]. **Coastal** - Recorded from 5 of 28 localities and on 4% of all counts. Maxima: Ladner 27 Dec 1981-10; Chilliwack 15 Dec 1984-4; Vancouver 16 Dec 1984-3.

Extralimital Records: Cecil lake 4 May 1982-2, 4 May 1986-1 (McEwan, C. and Johnston 1986).

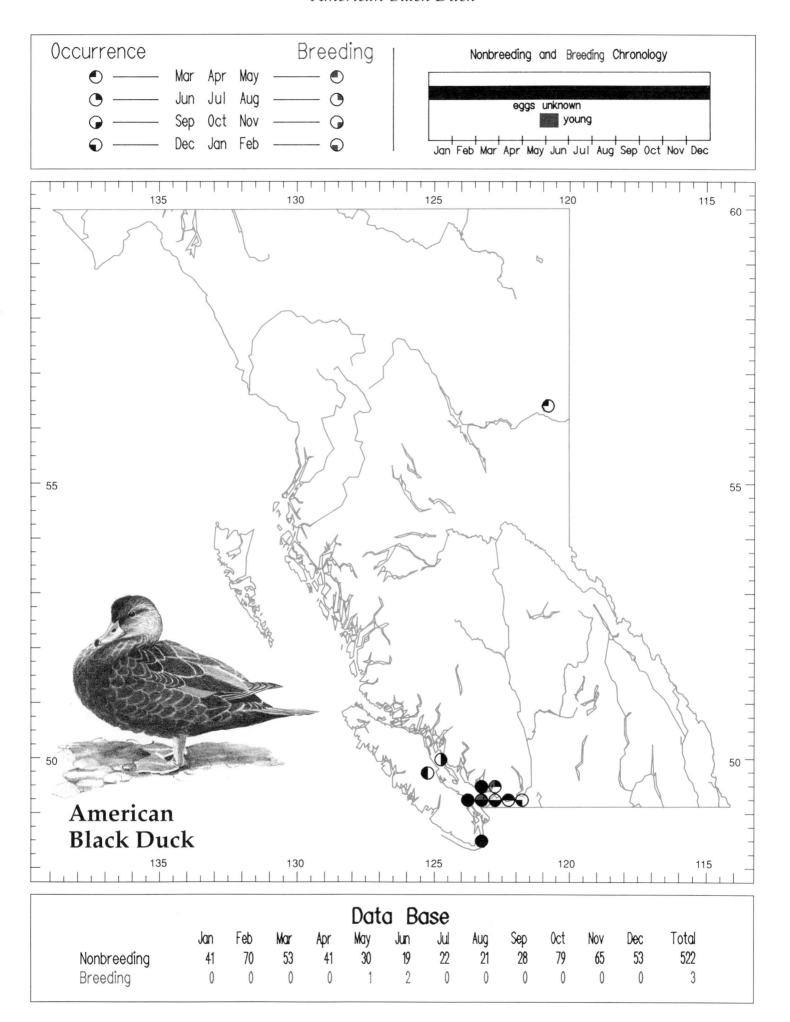

American Black Duck

Occurrence

◑	———	Mar Apr May
◔	———	Jun Jul Aug
◐	———	Sep Oct Nov
◕	———	Dec Jan Feb

Breeding

Mar Apr May	——— ◑
Jun Jul Aug	——— ◔
Sep Oct Nov	——— ◐
Dec Jan Feb	——— ◕

Nonbreeding and Breeding Chronology

eggs unknown
■ young

Jan Feb Mar Apr May Jun Jul Aug Sep Oct Nov Dec

Data Base

	Jan	Feb	Mar	Apr	May	Jun	Jul	Aug	Sep	Oct	Nov	Dec	Total
Nonbreeding	41	70	53	41	30	19	22	21	28	79	65	53	522
Breeding	0	0	0	0	1	2	0	0	0	0	0	0	3

Mallard
Anas platyrhynchos Linnaeus

MALL

RANGE: In North America breeds from north-central and southwestern United States north to northern Alaska and the Northwest Territories excluding the Maritimes and eastern Arctic. Winters mainly from southern Canada south to central Mexico; also on the Pacific coast north to the Aleutian Islands. Also resident in Eurasia.

STATUS: *Common* to *very abundant* migrant. In winter, *common* to *very abundant* on the coast; locally *common* to *abundant* in the southern interior; locally *rare* to *uncommon* in the northern interior. Widespread breeder.

NONBREEDING: The Mallard is the most abundant and widely distributed duck in British Columbia and has been recorded from sea level to 3,000 m elevation. It occurs virtually everywhere open water is present. Shallow marshes are preferred, but Mallards also frequent lakes, rivers, sloughs, estuaries, ponds, ditches, wet fields, and coastal marine waters. In urban environments, ponds, puddles, and other damp areas attract Mallards, especially in parks. On the south coast, the Mallard loafs on estuaries and offshore in bays and inlets. It forages on nearby farmlands, preferring flooded fields to dry fields (Hirst and Easthope 1981), as well as in tidal marshes and estuaries (Eamer 1985). Salmon spawning rivers are used in all coastal areas in autumn and winter. In the interior, preferred habitats include marshes, wet and dry fields, and lakeshores.

The Mallard is an extremely early spring migrant; in the interior, it is frequently seen on the first open waters of lakes and rivers. The movement begins in the south in mid-February and continues in the north through early May. Spring flocks are small—10 to 200 birds. Post-breeding males begin to flock together for the summer moult by mid-May in the south and late June in the north. In autumn, migration begins in late August and continues through December, and is the most protracted movement of all the dabbling ducks. Flocks of up to several thousand birds occur. Mallards will remain as far north as conditions permit. The major influx of migrants into southern British Columbia in some years may not occur until November.

In winter, tens of thousands occur along the coast; the major concentration is on the Fraser River delta (Fig. 270; Butler, R.W. and Campbell 1987). At least 39,000 birds have wintered in the southern coastal area (Appendix 2) which is about 2% of the Pacific Flyway population of 1,970,000 as indicated by Bellrose (1976) and at least twice the wintering numbers reported by the same author. In the interior, much smaller numbers winter as far north as the Peace River; in recent years, however, several thousand have wintered near Vernon. Wintering populations increased dramatically in the interior after grain farming was initiated in the early 1930s (Munro, J.A. 1943). Near urban centres, supplemental feeding of Mallards by the general public has greatly influenced the winter distribution of the species in the province.

Eamer (1985) found that dabbling ducks, primarily Mallard and American Wigeon, moved between coastal sites and flooded fields depending on the degree of flooding in the fields and the presence or absence of freezing temperatures. She believes that single sites should not be considered in isolation, but rather as part of a wetlands complex.

BREEDING: The Mallard breeds in wetlands throughout the province from sea level to 1,300 m elevation. Habitats include

Figure 270. *Mallards at Reifel Island, 19 December 1981 (Ervio Sian). On the Ladner count that year, the Mallard reached all-time high numbers for Christmas Bird Counts in Canada.*

Mallard

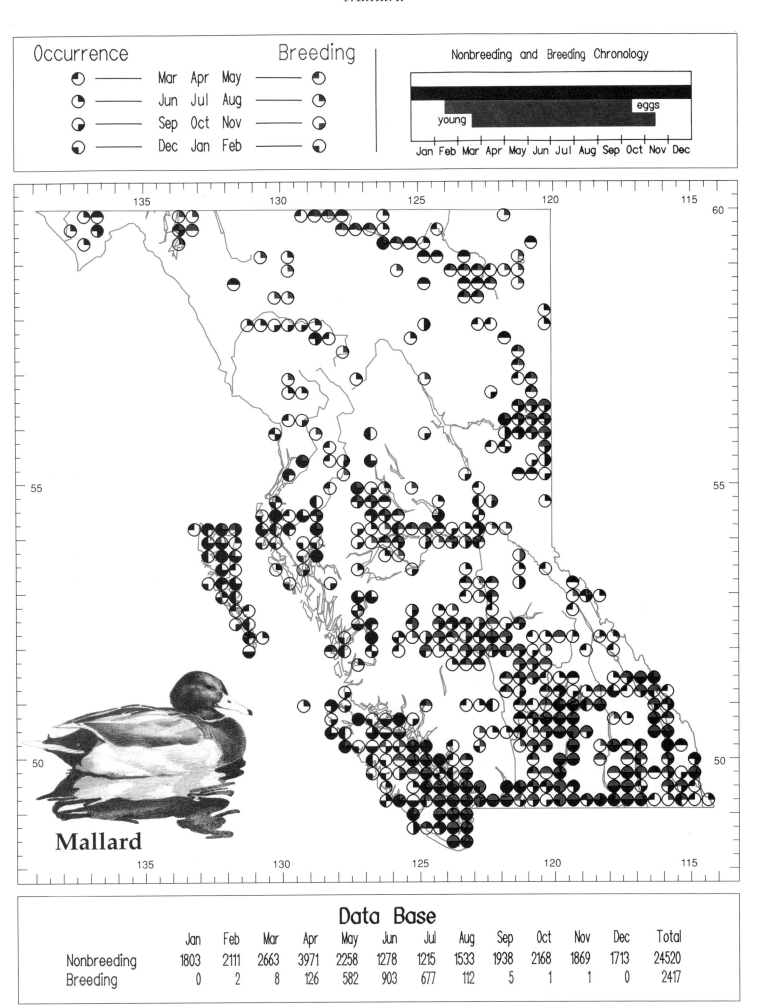

Occurrence

		Breeding
◔ —	Mar Apr May	— ◑
◔ —	Jun Jul Aug	— ◔
◕ —	Sep Oct Nov	— ◔
◕ —	Dec Jan Feb	— ◑

Nonbreeding and Breeding Chronology

young | eggs

Jan Feb Mar Apr May Jun Jul Aug Sep Oct Nov Dec

Data Base

	Jan	Feb	Mar	Apr	May	Jun	Jul	Aug	Sep	Oct	Nov	Dec	Total
Nonbreeding	1803	2111	2663	3971	2258	1278	1215	1533	1938	2168	1869	1713	24520
Breeding	0	2	8	126	582	903	677	112	5	1	1	0	2417

sloughs, marshes, lakes, swamps, islands, and riparian woodlands. In urban and rural environments, parks, golf courses, ditches, agricultural fields, vacant lots, and private yards are used wherever fresh water is near (Fig. 273).

The Mallard is a solitary breeder but loose aggregations of up to 14 nests have been found on small islands near Creston. The centre of abundance is in the Chilcotin-Cariboo. The breeding season is unusually long and may extend from February to November on the south coast.

Nests: Nests were usually situated on dry land near water (Fig. 271). Major habitats for 235 nest sites included marshes (37%), woodlands (15%), lake edges (14%), islands (12%), pastures (8%), and riverbanks (4%). Of 22 nests, 17 were within 40 m of water; 5 others were from 200 m to 1.6 km from water.

Most nests (88%; n=224) were shallow depressions in the ground filled with various quantities of down and loose accumulations of leaves, grasses, needles, sedges, or mosses. In other situations, nests were constructed differently. For example, nests on logs, among flooded willow clumps, in tree crotches, and on artificial platforms (7%; n=224) were heaps of aquatic plants and other vegetation. Nests in cattail beds were down-filled platforms of interwoven cattail stems.

Most nests (76%; n=224) were well concealed by vegetation, including grasses (22%), brushy thickets (16%), saplings (9%), cattail and rushes (8%), roots and logs (6%), and single shrubs (5%). Twenty-one per cent of the nests were situated at the bases of trees in relatively exposed situations. Six nests were found in trees: 3 in willow crotches, 2 in large natural cavities 2 to 3 m above ground, and 1 in an American Crow nest 4 m above ground.

One nest site, situated in a woodland at Cluculz Lake, was occupied for 6 consecutive years. A nest at Milch Lakes was rebuilt on top of a recently flooded nest, while a nest in Howe Sound was within a Glaucous-winged Gull colony. Two nests on Reifel Island contained Ring-necked Pheasant eggs.

Eggs: Dates for 242 clutches ranged from 28 February to 10 July with 50% recorded between 29 April and 27 May. Records of downy young on 20 March and 15 November indicate egg laying could occur as early as 15 February and as late as 15 October.

Sizes for 355 clutches (Fig. 272) ranged from 1 to 24 eggs (1E-3, 2E-5, 3E-4, 4E-9, 5E-14, 6E-23, 7E-37, 8E-62, 9E-69, 10E-54, 11E-43, 12E-19, 13E-5, 14E-5, 19E-1, 21E-1, 24E-1) with 52% having 8 to 10 eggs. Clutches of 19, 21, and 24 eggs are likely the product of at least 2 females. Incubation period is 26 to 30 days, with a 28 day average (Girard 1941).

Young: Dates for 1,111 broods ranged from 20 March to 15 November with 53% recorded between 22 May and 28 June. Downy young (Class I) on 15 November (lower Fraser River valley) would not fledge until early January; it is not known if they survived. Sizes for 1,987 broods ranged from 1 to 22 young (1Y-42, 2Y-97, 3Y-157, 4Y-193, 5Y-261, 6Y-310, 7Y-266, 8Y-235, 9Y-149, 10Y-128, 11Y-60, 12Y-51, 13Y-11, 14Y-9, 15Y-4, 16Y-5, 17Y-2, 18Y-4, 19Y-1, 21Y-1, 22Y-1) with 54% having 5 to 8 young. Fledging period ranges from 42 to 60 days depending on the latitude of breeding (Hochbaum 1944; Lensink, C.J. 1954).

REMARKS: Eamer (1985) discusses winter habitat and foods of the Mallard on southeastern Vancouver Island. She found that the Mallard selects a wide variety of food types from the estuarine marshes and marine deltas including algae (*Ulva* sp., *Enteromorpha* sp.), marine snails, insect larvae, Pacific silverweed roots and stems, sedge achenes, and other assorted seeds. Seeds, however, did not dominate the diet to the extent reported in Burgess (1970) for Mallards on the Fraser delta.

The Mallard is the single most important game duck in British Columbia, and hunting seasons are planned around its migration and seasonal distribution. About 100,000 (55% of the duck harvest) are taken in the province each year.

See Anderson, D.R. and Henny (1972), Anderson, D.R. et al. (1974) and Pospahala et al. (1974) for summary information on population ecology of the Mallard in North America.

Figure 271. *Female Mallard on nest at Reifel Island, 28 April 1974 (Neil K. Dawe).*

Figure 272. *Exposed clutch of Mallard eggs at Burnaby Lake, 24 June 1965 (R. Wayne Campbell).*

Mallard

Figure 273. *Urban Mallard with brood at Victoria, June 1973 (R. Wayne Campbell). Of all the ducks, Mallards are the most adaptable to man-made changes in the environment.*

NOTEWORTHY RECORDS

Spring: Coastal - Fraser River delta 9 Mar 1967-5,499, 18 May 1967-151 (Burgess 1970); Asseek River 8 Apr 1979-700; Kitimat 9 Apr 1975-576; Sialun Bay 24 Mar 1980-300 on small lake. **Interior** - Creston 6 Mar 1986-1,035, 24 Mar 1983-2,574, 6 Apr 1984-3,825; Wasa Lake and sloughs 28 Mar 1977-463 (Kaiser et al. 1978); Sorrento 30 Mar 1972-1,000; Chilanko Forks 19 Apr 1968-3,000; 93 km n Williams Lake 31 Mar 1977-584; Halfway River 21 Mar 1984-30 first arrival; Fort St. John 12 Apr 1985-50, 19 Apr 1985-350, 24 Apr 1985-400, 25 Apr 1985-100, 4 May 1981-2,000 (Siddle 1981); Atlin 20 Apr 1981-12, first arrival.

Summer: Coastal - Reifel Island 28 Aug 1974-12,000; Addington Point 17 Jul 1972-130; Minette Bay 19 Jun 1975-42 (Hay 1976); Masset 18 Jul 1982-8. **Interior** - Duck Lake and Leach Lake 25 Aug 1948-4,500 (Munro, J.A. 1958a); Creston 29 Jul 1985-1,775; Rock Lake (Riske Creek) 4 Aug 1978-210; Cecil Lake 24 Aug 1984-400+; Pine Tree Lake 1 Jun 1978-9 males.

Autumn: Interior - Moonlight Lake 21 Oct 1981-900; Peace River (Farrell Creek to Lynn Creek) 23 Nov 1986-76 in three flocks; Vanderhoof 20 Sep 1944-2,000; Chilcotin Lake 22 Sep 1977-841, 1 Nov 1977-1,987; Horsefly Bay (Quesnel Lake) 8 Oct 1979-700; Duck Lake (Creston) 15 Sep 1967-13,300, 9 Oct 1984-5,355, 25 Oct 1986-1,706, 8 Nov 1985-1,500. **Coastal** - Port Clements 1 Nov 1954-1,600; Hansen Lagoon 7 Nov 1963-1,800; Reifel Island 14 Sep 1973-6,000; Fraser River delta 24 Nov 1966-14,134 (Burgess 1970); Martindale Flats (Saanich) 11 Nov 1983-2,500.

Winter: Interior - Lynx Creek and Peace River junction 24 Dec 1985-75; Prince George 2 Feb 1969-3 (Rogers, T.H. 1969); Sorrento 13 Dec 1970-900; South Thompson River between Chase and Pritchard 18 Jan 1949-3,700; Okanagan Lake 11 Jan 1977-880 on north arm; Mud Lake (Fairmont) 30 Jan 1982-400; Creston 17 Jan 1986-90, 26 Feb 1985-340. **Coastal** - Yakoun River 4 Dec 1956-1,150 at estuary; Taleomey River 10 Jan 1977-400 at estuary; Clayoquot Sound 11 to 13 Dec 1972-1,448 on survey (Robertson 1974); Fraser River delta 22 Dec 1966-13,273 (Burgess 1970); Chemainus River 1 Jan 1975-1,000 at estuary (Blood 1976); Martindale Flats (Saanich) 2 Jan 1976-2,500.

Christmas Counts: Interior - Recorded from 15 of 19 localities and on 81% of all counts. Maxima: Vernon 18 Dec 1983-5,200; Oliver/Osoyoos 28 Dec 1980-1,832; Revelstoke 21 Dec 1983-761. **Coastal** - Recorded from 26 of 28 localities and on 92% of all counts. Maxima: Ladner 27 Dec 1981-**18,012** (see Fig. 270), all-time Canadian high count (Anderson, R.R. 1982); Victoria 20 Dec 1980-5,906; Vancouver 21 Dec 1980-4,640.

Northern Pintail

Anas acuta Linnaeus

NOPI

RANGE: In North America breeds from northern Alaska across northern Canada to Labrador, south to California and across the central United States to Maine. Winters from southeast Alaska to northern South America on the Pacific coast, across the southern United States and on the Atlantic coast from Long Island to Georgia. Also occurs in Eurasia.

STATUS: *Common* to *very abundant* migrant. In winter, *common* to *abundant* on the coast, *rare* to locally *common* in the interior. Widespread breeder.

NONBREEDING: The Northern Pintail is widely distributed throughout the province. It occurs from sea level to 2,500 m elevation. On the coast, preferred habitats include tidal marshes, shallow foreshore waters, estuaries, exposed eelgrass beds, mudflats, agricultural fields (Fig. 274), and lagoons. During migration it also occurs in pelagic waters. The Northern Pintail often associates with other species such as Mallard, American Wigeon, and Brant. Inland coastal and interior habitats include river banks, flooded fields, ponds, marshes, sloughs, and lakes.

The Northern Pintail is a very early spring and autumn migrant. In the interior, it appears in spring as soon as open water forms along the edges of frozen lakes and sloughs. The spring movement occurs from late February through April in the south and in April and early May in the north. On the south coast, that movement begins in late February, peaks in March, and carries on into April. On the north coast, spring migrants arrive during the latter half of March, with the peak movement in April. By May, only small flocks of unmated males and late pairs remain. In June, post-breeding males gather into flocks to moult.

The autumn migration begins in early August on the coast

and late August in the interior. Band recoveries indicate that the early arrivals are from Alaska. Migration continues through early December on the coast but the peak movement occurs from September to October. In the interior, the autumn movement peaks in September and is usually over by late October. In 1987, there was a very small migration on the Fraser River delta in August because of a breeding failure in Alaska.

In winter, small numbers, usually less than 100, occur on open waters of the southern interior. Bellrose (1976) notes that the first sizeable numbers of wintering pintail in the Pacific Flyway occur in the Puget Sound region, Washington; however, during mild winters, thousands are present on the south coast of British Columbia and hundreds are present on the north coast. For example, the average number of Northern Pintail observed in Christmas Bird Counts from 4 count areas on the east coast of Vancouver Island (Victoria, Duncan, Nanaimo, and Comox) from 1973 to 1987 is over 1,400 birds. For the same period in the Lower Mainland wintering numbers have averaged nearly 21,000 birds (Fig. 275) and, on occasion, have exceeded 50,000 birds, which is about 3% of the Pacific Flyway winter population.

The major migration corridor is along the coast where up to one million Northern Pintail pass through annually to and from breeding grounds in Alaska (Bellrose 1976). A secondary corridor through the interior leads birds to breeding grounds in the Yukon, while a third corridor over the open Pacific Ocean between Alaska and California is indicated by sightings of migrants on Swiftsure Bank and 160 km off Tofino in August (Martin and Myres 1969).

The Northern Pintail usually migrates in groups of 10 to 200 birds, but flocks of up to 1,500 birds have been seen. Major staging areas on the coast are Clayoquot Sound and the Fraser River delta.

Figure 274. *Northern Pintails and Mallards in barley stubble field on Westham Island, early morning, 23 August 1973 (Neil K. Dawe).*

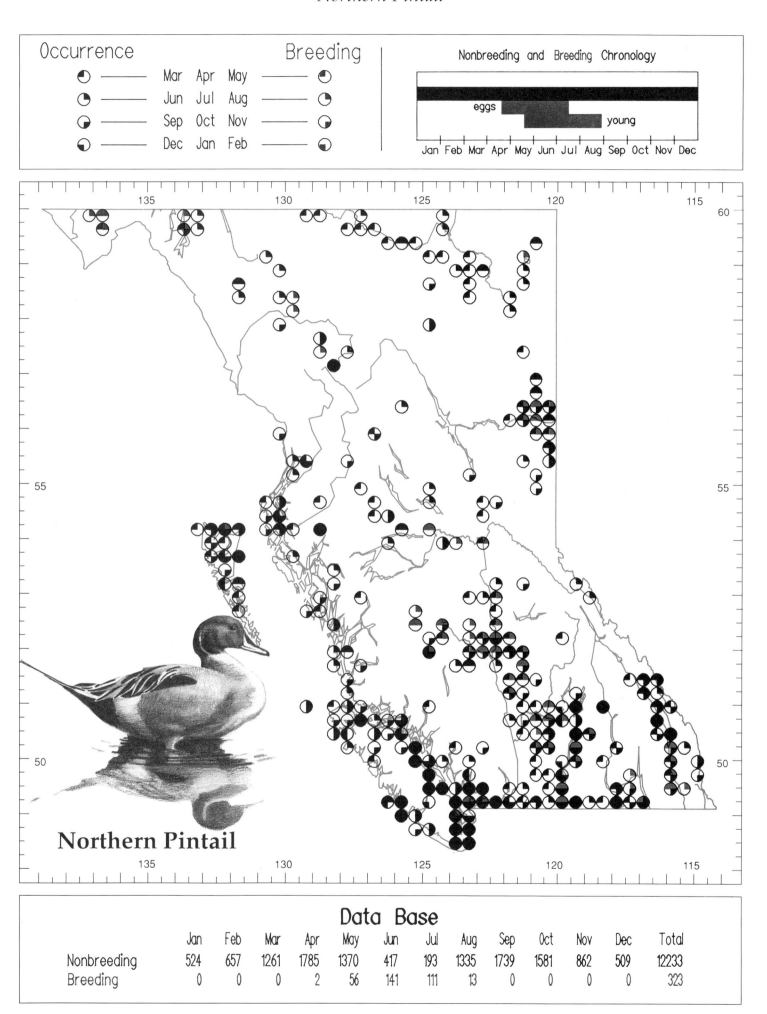

Northern Pintail

Occurrence

◐ ———	Mar Apr May	——— ◐
◓ ———	Jun Jul Aug	——— ◓
◑ ———	Sep Oct Nov	——— ◑
◒ ———	Dec Jan Feb	——— ◒

Breeding

Nonbreeding and Breeding Chronology

eggs

young

Jan Feb Mar Apr May Jun Jul Aug Sep Oct Nov Dec

Data Base

	Jan	Feb	Mar	Apr	May	Jun	Jul	Aug	Sep	Oct	Nov	Dec	Total
Nonbreeding	524	657	1261	1785	1370	417	193	1335	1739	1581	862	509	12233
Breeding	0	0	0	2	56	141	111	13	0	0	0	0	323

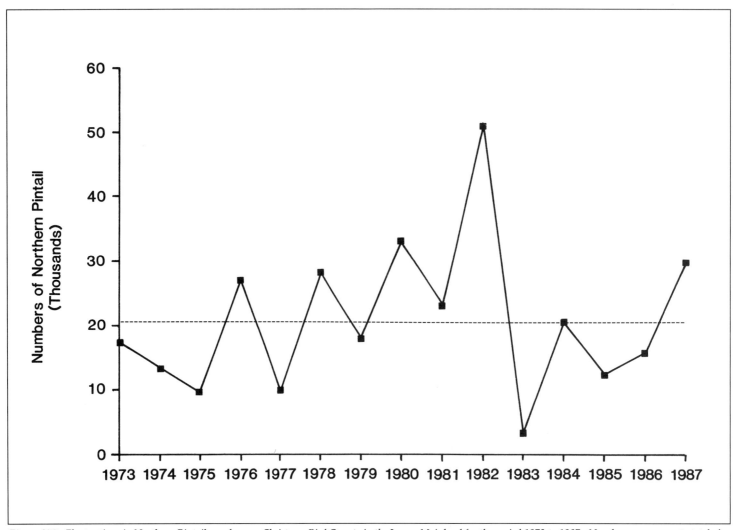

Figure 275. *Fluctuations in Northern Pintail numbers on Christmas Bird Counts in the Lower Mainland for the period 1973 to 1987. Numbers are aggregate totals for the Ladner, Pitt Meadows, Vancouver, and White Rock count areas. The horizontal dashed line indicates the average number observed on those counts over the 15-year period.*

BREEDING: The Northern Pintail breeds throughout the interior of the province, east of the Coast Ranges and locally on the coast on southern Vancouver Island, the Fraser Lowlands and Queen Charlotte Lowlands. It breeds from near sea level to 1,070 m elevation.

The centres of abundance are in the central-south interior, the Peace Lowlands, and the east Kootenay. Bellrose (1976) estimates that up to 42,000 birds breed in British Columbia.

A wide variety of general habitats are used, but those with sparse or low vegetation, not necessarily near water, are preferred. Specific habitats include drier margins of lakes, sloughs, ponds, lagoons (Fig. 276), dry grasslands, shrubby fields, edges of mixed forests, damp meadows, and subalpine bogs.

Nests: Nests (n=57) were shallow depressions in the ground located in grasses, sedges, or grass clumps (37%), at the base of sapling clumps (21%), under a bush (16%), on small islands (12%), in dry reed beds (7%), or between boulders (7%). Nests situated in grasses, under shrubs, or on dry slough margins were usually well camouflaged, but nests situated under a dense forest canopy, against boulders or logs, or on overgrazed rangeland were frequently completely exposed (Fig. 277). Distances from water for 27 nests ranged from 1 to 400 m, but 63% were found over 30 m from water. Almost half of the nests (47%; n=70) were constructed of down only, 31% contained down and grasses, 16% contained down and other materials, and 6% contained only leaves, twigs, or grasses. One nest measured 20 cm in diameter.

Eggs: Dates for 85 clutches ranged from 23 April to 16 July with 53% recorded between 19 May and 9 June. Calculated dates indicate that eggs could be found as early as 20 April. Sizes for 86 clutches ranged from 2 to 10 eggs (2E-1, 3E-3, 4E-5, 5E-7, 6E-16, 7E-15, 8E-24, 9E-10, 10E-5) with 64% having 6 to 8 eggs. Broods of 11, 12, and 13 young indicate clutch size could include up to 13 eggs. Incubation period ranges from 22 to 25 days and averages 23 days (Hochbaum 1944; Fuller 1953).

Young: Dates for 227 broods ranged from 19 May to 28 August with 53% recorded between 16 June and 15 July. Sizes for 212 broods ranged from 1 to 13 young (1Y-7, 2Y-8, 3Y-12, 4Y-23, 5Y-26, 6Y-50, 7Y-28, 8Y-24, 9Y-11, 10Y-13, 11Y-6, 12Y-2, 13Y-2) with 60% having 5 to 8 young. Fledging period ranges between 36 and 57 days (Gollop and Marshall 1954; Lensink, C.J. 1964).

REMARKS: The Northern Pintail was formerly known as the Pintail.

Figure 276. *Fort St. John sewage lagoon, May 1988 (R. Wayne Campbell). Agricuiltural fields associated with sewage lagoons are becoming important nesting locations for many puddle ducks including the Northern Pintail.*

Figure 277. *Northern Pintail nest site at Chilco Ranch, Hanceville, 4 June 1980 (John M. Cooper). This exposed nest is unusual in that most nests are well concealed by vegetation.*

NOTEWORTHY RECORDS

Spring: Coastal - Fraser River delta 9 Mar 1967-9,389, 11 Apr 1967-5,276, 4 May 1967-430 (Burgess 1970); Cleland Island 21 May 1982-2 pairs; Queen Charlotte City 20 Mar 1981-200; Kitimat 23 May 1975-16 (Hay 1976). **Interior** - Creston 5 Mar 1984-480, 6 Apr 1984-1,200, 22 Apr 1985-1,792; Nicola Lake 4 Mar 1984-100; Sorrento 30 Mar 1972-2,000; Chezacut Lake 25 Mar 1940-1,500 (Munro, J.A. and Cowan 1947); Watlas Lake 30 May 1976-32; Fort St. John 9 Apr 1985-100, mostly drakes, 14 Apr 1985-400, 26 Apr 1985-1,000, 27 Apr 1985-500; Cecil Lake 4 May 1981-2,000 (Siddle 1982); Chilkat Pass 21 May 1977-8 pairs.

Summer: Coastal - James Island 24 Aug 1963-2 flocks of 1,500 each; Barkley Sound 19 Aug 1968-1,500 in 1 flock; Westham Island 6 Aug 1973-10, 17 Aug 1973-1,000; Iona Island 18 Aug 1973-1,025; Qualicum Beach 22 Jul 1976-50; Kitimat 29 Aug 1975-85 (Hay 1976). **Interior** - Creston 4 Jul 1984-20; Kilpoola Lake 22 Jun 1978-18; Salmon Arm 26 Aug 1973-850 (Cannings, R.J. 1973); Revelstoke 29 Aug 1977-661 (Bonar 1978b); Abuntlet Lake 13 Jun 1948-260 males; Nulki Lake 28 Aug 1945-1,100 (Munro, J.A. and Cowan 1947); Scott Lake (Dawson Creek) 2 Jun 1980-9; Fort St. John 8 Jun 1986-34.

Autumn: Interior - Fort St. John 8 Oct 1986-250, 31 Oct 1982-2; Swan Lake (Tupper) 2 Sep 1981-500; Chezacut Lake 8 Oct 1940-2,000 (Munro, J.A. and Cowan 1947); Revelstoke 21 Sep 1977-716 (Bonar 1978b); Brisco 14 Sep 1977-328; Windermere Lake 27 Nov 1983-4; Kamloops 9 Nov 1980-50; Creston 9 Oct 1984-1,100, 25 Oct 1986-140, 28 Nov 1982-75. **Coastal** - Kumdis Slough 5 Sep 1979-1,500; Port Hardy 28 Sep 1934-10,000; Reifel Island 7 Oct 1966-3,564 (Burgess 1970); Westham Island 7 Sep 1973-17,000, 14 Sep 1973-4,000, 28 Oct 1973-500; Crescent Beach 25 Nov 1976-8,000; Mud Bay (Surrey) 6 Sep 1971-5,000 (Campbell et al. 1972b); Grice Bay 24 Nov 1965-3,000 (Baldridge and Crowell 1966).

Winter: Interior - Chase 18 Jan 1949-48; Okanagan Lake 13 Dec 1965-30 on north arm; Okanagan Landing 26 Feb 1967-hundreds; Creston 2 Dec 1982-75, 15 Feb 1983-25; Osoyoos Lake 22 Feb 1977-50. **Coastal** - Masset 18 Dec 1982-228; Yakoun River 4 Dec 1956-950 at estuary; Matsqui 27 Feb 1972-1,490; Brunswick Point 2 Feb 1983-4,000; Fraser River foreshore 22 Dec 1966-17,791, 9 Feb 1967-6,315 (Burgess 1970); Fry's Corner (Surrey) 2 Feb 1970-1,500; Ladner 22 Dec 1962-5,000.

Christmas Counts: Interior - Recorded from 7 of 19 localities and on 23% of all counts. Maxima: Vernon 26 Dec 1976-40; Vaseux Lake 31 Dec 1976-18; Shuswap Lake 28 Dec 1983-2. **Coastal** - Recorded from 24 of 28 localities and on 75% of all counts. Maxima: Ladner 27 Dec 1982-**48,981**, all-time Canadian high count (Anderson, R.R. 1983); White Rock 30 Dec 1984-13,011; Vancouver 27 Dec 1970-3,652.

Blue-winged Teal
Anas discors Linnaeus

BWTE

RANGE: Breeds from east-central Alaska, southern Yukon and southern Mackenzie south through western Canada and east to Newfoundland; south to southern California, New Mexico, middle Texas, Louisiana and North Carolina. Winters from southern United States south to Ecuador, Brazil, Argentina, and the West Indies.

STATUS: *Fairly common* to *very common* migrant and summer visitant throughout the southern interior and Peace Lowlands; *abundant* locally prior to autumn migration. *Fairly common* migrant and summer visitant on the inner coast north to Campbell River; *rare* elsewhere including the Queen Charlotte Islands. In winter, *very rare* in the southernmost interior and locally in the inner south coast. Widespread breeder.

NONBREEDING: The Blue-winged Teal occurs throughout the province and may be found almost anywhere near water from sea level to 2,200 m elevation. It frequents shallow water at the edge of emergent cover or along shorelines of marshes, ponds, flooded fields, ditches, lagoons, backwaters of large rivers, and estuaries. On the coast, sheltered bays, inlets and coves, and offshore islands are used.

Migration occurs mainly through the interior. Spring migrants may arrive on the south coast in February or March, but generally the main spring movement throughout southern British Columbia begins in late April and early May, peaks in mid-May and is over by late May. In the north, the main spring movement begins in late April, peaks from mid-to-late May and is usually over by early June. Flocks of males arrive first, followed by paired birds or flocks of mixed sexes with males predominating. Numbers in British Columbia fluctuate from year to year often depending on water conditions in other parts of their range. For example, influxes were noted in the Columbia River valley (Kaiser et al. 1978) and at Revelstoke (Bonar 1978b) in the spring of 1977, and in the Chilcotin-Cariboo in the spring of 1980 and 1981 (Ducks Unlimited Canada 1983).

In June and July, small flocks of males and apparently nonbreeding pairs are reported throughout their range. The summer moult occurs from mid-July to mid-August, when birds may accumulate in flocks of up to 600 individuals on larger marshes.

The autumn migration begins throughout the province in early August, peaks in late August and early September, and declines steadily to the end of the month; by mid-October most birds are gone.

Records from November through January are unusual anywhere in the province, but in mild winters a few sometimes remain on the inner south coast and in the Okanagan valley and the Kootenays.

BREEDING: The Blue-winged Teal breeds on southeastern Vancouver Island, and in the Fraser Lowlands east through the southern and central interior, and in the northern interior from the Peace River west through the Boreal Forest to Atlin. There is one record for the Queen Charlotte Islands: 8 downy young at Delkatla Wildlife Sanctuary on 24 June 1983. Breeding has been reported from sea level to 1,200 m elevation. The Blue-winged Teal breeds in a wide variety of forested and open habitats near small bodies of water, including grassy meadows, swamps, freshwater and brackish marshes, bogs, beaver ponds, edges of ditches, sloughs, small shallow lakes, agricultural fields, and hedgerows.

The centre of abundance is in the Chilcotin-Cariboo; substantial numbers also breed in the Okanagan valley, Nechako Lowlands, and Peace River areas. Bellrose (1976) estimates that 120,000 birds breed in the province.

Nests: Nests were situated on the ground, usually near water, and were well concealed by vegetation. Wooded areas were avoided. Of 67 nests, 24% were found at the edge of marshes, 24% in fields, 13% in meadows, and 12% at the edge of lakes. Specifically, 45% of 67 nests were situated among clumps of grasses, 15% in sedges, 13% at the base of small trees, and 9% in vegetation over water. In overgrazed rangelands, nests can be completely exposed.

Nests were usually small cups of tightly woven grasses, sedges, cattail, or bulrushes formed into a slight hollow and filled with moderate amounts of down. Nests have been found as far as 50 m from water but most (15 of 17) were found within 23 m of water. One nest measured 13 cm in diameter.

Eggs: Dates for 91 clutches ranged from 2 May to 15 July with 51% recorded between 2 and 20 June. Calculated dates indicate that eggs could be found on the coast as early as 6 April. Clutch size ranged from 1 to 12 eggs (1E-3, 2E-3, 3E-3, 4E-2, 5E-1, 6E-5, 7E-8, 8E-15, 9E-19, 10E-19, 11E-10, 12E-3) with 58% having 8 to 10 eggs. Incubation period is normally 23 to 24 days (Dane 1966).

Young: Dates for 315 broods ranged from 8 May to 13 September with 50% recorded between 5 and 28 July. Sizes for 331 broods ranged from 1 to 12 young (1Y-11, 2Y-12, 3Y-19, 4Y-30, 5Y-42, 6Y-49, 7Y-54, 8Y-50, 9Y-29, 10Y-17, 11Y-15, 12Y-3) with 59% having 5 to 8 young. Fledging period is 35 to 44 days (Gollop and Marshall 1954).

REMARKS: Plumages of female, young, and eclipse male Blue-winged and Cinnamon teal are very difficult to distinguish in the field; see Palmer, R.S. (1976a).

NOTEWORTHY RECORDS

Spring: Coastal - Witty's Lagoon 13 Mar 1979-8, 23 May 1980-23; Saanich 27 Apr 1974-22 males; Serpentine Fen (Surrey) 17 May 1981-30; Westham Island 24 Mar 1935-14 (Munro, J.A. and Cowan 1947); Iona Island 28 May 1981-48; Cranberry Lake (Powell River) 11 May 1977-22; Masset 1 May 1983-2 males, 15 May 1972-18. **Interior** - Creston 27 Apr 1984-16; Merritt 15 Apr 1968-20; Okanagan Landing 26 Mar 1946-early arrival (Cannings, R.A. et al. 1987), 22 May 1933-8 pairs; Vernon 26 Mar 1946-2; Wilmer 12 May 1978-2 pairs, 18 males; Revelstoke 4 May 1977-62, 31 May 1977-69 (Bonar 1978b); Tetana Lake 10 Apr 1941-1 pair (Stanwell-Fletcher and Stanwell-Fletcher 1943); Sloane Slough 14 May 1981-19 pairs, 56 males, 8 females; Fort St. John 26 Apr 1980-2 males; Cecil Lake 12 May 1980-100+, 29 May 1980-45 males, 2 females.

Summer: Coastal - Swan Lake (Victoria) 1 Jun

1981-31, 6 Jul 1981-12 males; Duncan 24 Aug 1974-48; Tsawwassen 14 Aug 1962-150; Iona Island 4 Jun 1977-79 males, 3 females, 6 Jun 1985-250 (Harrington-Tweit and Mattocks 1984); Black Creek (Courtenay) 29 Jun 1971-12 males, 13 females; Courtenay 26 Jun 1977-26. **Interior** - Creston 18 Jun 1984-19, 29 Jul 1985-35; Yellow Lake (Richter Pass) 18 Jun 1977-5 pairs; Swan Lake (Vernon) 24 Aug 1943-600; Revelstoke 3 Jun 1977-66, 26 Aug 1977-111 (Bonar 1978b); 103 Mile Lake 8 Aug 1935-230 (Munro, J.A. and Cowan 1947); Fort St. John 21 Jun 1984-60 males.

Autumn: Interior - Fort St. John 20 Oct 1986-1; Kelly Lake (Tupper) 15 Sep 1977-50; 10 km s Fort Fraser 13 Sep 1980-500; Revelstoke 21 Sep 1977-165 (Bonar 1978b); Swan Lake (Vernon) 18 Sep 1943-300, 1 Nov 1933-2 (Munro, J.A. 1939d); Knutsford 2 Sep 1977-75; Wasa 1 Sep 1977-30. **Coastal** - Mace Creek 15 Sep 1983-30; Hansen

Lagoon 28 Oct 1973-30 (Hazelwood 1973); Reifel Island 17 Sep 1965-350+; Crescent Beach 12 Nov 1965-15; Duncan 12 Oct 1975-40.

Winter: Interior - Vernon 26 Dec 1973-14; Kelowna 30 Dec 1934-1 (UBC 3441). **Coastal** - Campbell River 10 Jan 1973-1; Iron River 17 Jan 1976-1; Cranberry Lake (Powell River) 11 Dec 1981-1; Westham Island 8 Jan 1969-1 (RBCM 15,200), 20 Feb 1972-1 male.

Christmas Counts: Interior - Recorded from 3 of 19 localities and on 4% of all counts. Maxima: Kelowna 20 Dec 1981-4; Lake Windermere 26 Dec 1982-4; Nakusp 2 Jan 1983-3. **Coastal** - Recorded from 7 of 28 localities and on 4% of all counts. Maxima: Ladner 26 Dec 1970-7; Vancouver 18 Dec 1977-3. The all-time Canadian high count (Anderson, R.R. 1976) of 30 birds at Nanaimo on 26 Dec 1967 lacks supporting documentation.

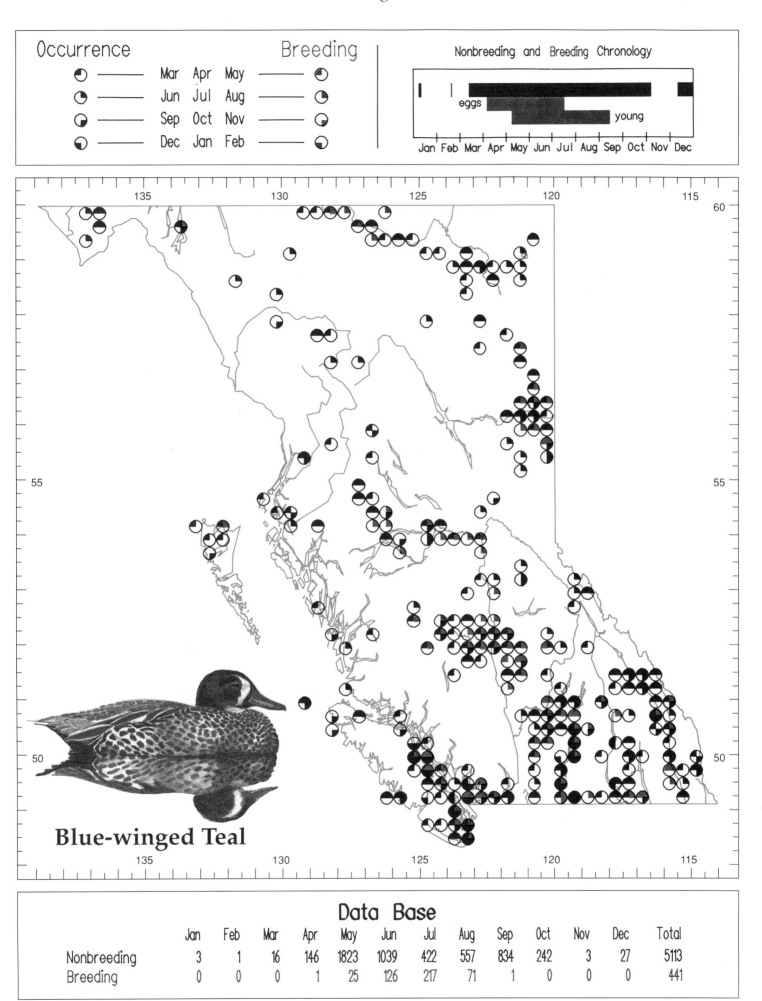

Blue-winged Teal

Data Base

	Jan	Feb	Mar	Apr	May	Jun	Jul	Aug	Sep	Oct	Nov	Dec	Total
Nonbreeding	3	1	16	146	1823	1039	422	557	834	242	3	27	5113
Breeding	0	0	0	1	25	126	217	71	1	0	0	0	441

Cinnamon Teal
Anas cyanoptera Vieillot

CITE

RANGE: Breeds from southern British Columbia and southern Alberta south throughout the western United States to central Mexico. Winters from southern California south through Central America to Colombia, primarily in western and central Mexico. Resident in much of South America.

STATUS: *Uncommon* to *fairly common* migrant and summer visitant throughout British Columbia south from the Chilcotin-Cariboo; locally *very common*. *Rare* summer visitant to the Peace Lowlands; *very rare* elsewhere. In winter, *very rare* on the inner coast; *accidental* in the Okanagan. Breeds.

NONBREEDING: The Cinnamon Teal, one of the least abundant dabbling ducks, occurs mainly throughout the interior south of Quesnel and on the south coast. Small numbers occur regularly in the Peace Lowlands. Scattered individuals have been recorded from Prince George and the northern Queen Charlotte Islands north to Chilkat Pass. It has been found from sea level to 1,100 m elevation.

The Cinnamon Teal frequents sloughs, marshes, and ponds with emergent vegetation. On larger marshes, it is usually found in shallow bays and inlets, not too far from cover. Other habitats include flooded fields, ditches, sewage ponds, willow swamps, and even the tiniest puddles on farms and open rangelands. On marine waters it is found in lagoons, estuaries, and bays with eel-grass.

Spring migration records suggest that it rarely occurs in flocks of more than 2 or 3 pairs. The spring movement begins on the south coast in mid-March, and in the southern interior in mid-April. Numbers increase into May, and may peak from late April to mid-May. In the north, migrants arrive in late April on the coast and early May in the Peace Lowlands. Small groups of males, mixed flocks, and lone pairs occur throughout June and into early July in the southern interior.

Autumn departure dates are not well known. The Cinnamon Teal is certainly present throughout the summer, but after the mid-July moult, identification in the field is virtually impossible. In the Okanagan, it apparently departs in September (Cannings, R.A. et al. 1987); on the south coast some linger through November. Winter records are unusual on the south coast; there is only one interior record.

BREEDING: The Cinnamon Teal reaches the northern limit of its breeding range in southern British Columbia. On the coast, it breeds from Victoria north to Powell River and throughout the

Fraser Lowlands. In the interior, it breeds throughout the east Kootenay, southern west Kootenay, and from the southern Okanagan valley north to Nimpo Lake in the Chilcotin-Cariboo. Breeding has been recorded from sea level to 1,220 m.

The Cinnamon Teal breeds near water by sloughs, marshes, ponds, wet meadows, ditches, sewage lagoons, and slow-moving streams.

The centre of abundance is the Chilcotin-Cariboo. Bellrose (1976) estimates the population at 6,000 to 10,000 breeding birds. E. Hennan (pers. comm.) suggests that breeding numbers have recently increased and the Cinnamon Teal now probably breeds in the Nechako Lowland region. That may be due to influxes resulting from substantial habitat deterioration in the main breeding grounds in Utah.

Nests: Most nests (85%; n=29) were situated close to water near marshes. Others were on small islands or at the edge of streams and ditches. Three nests were 0.6 m, 4.5 m, and 15 m from water. Of 22 nests, 14 were found in tall, dense grasses, others were in bulrushes, horsetails, sedges, willows, and vetches, and 2 were at the bases of fenceposts. Nests were grass and down-lined hollows in the ground. Grasses were reported more frequently as a nest material than was down. Several nests with incubated eggs contained no down at all.

Eggs: Dates for 38 clutches ranged from 19 April to 28 June with 53% recorded between 15 May and 10 June. Calculated dates indicate that eggs could be found as early as 12 April. Sizes for 40 clutches ranged from 1 to 12 eggs (1E-1, 4E-1, 5E-2, 7E-4, 8E-5, 9E-10, 10E-11, 11E-4, 12E-1, 14E-1) with 54% having 9 or 10 eggs. A brood of 14 young suggests clutch size may reach 14 eggs. One clutch contained 2 Ring-necked Pheasant eggs. Incubation period is 21 to 25 days (Spencer 1953).

Young: Dates for 44 broods ranged from 16 May to 24 August with 51% recorded between 13 June and 16 July. Brood size ranged from 2 to 14 young (2Y-1, 3Y-4, 4Y-6, 5Y-3, 6Y-5, 7Y-5, 8Y-4, 9Y-7, 10Y-4, 11Y-2, 12Y-2, 14Y-1) with 58% having 6 to 10 young. Fledging period is about 49 days (Spencer 1953).

REMARKS: All northern records include males in breeding plumage. See Palmer, R.S. (1976a) for information on distinguishing females, young, and eclipse-plumaged males.

All recoveries of birds banded in British Columbia are from the Pacific coast states.

For further information on aspects of the life-history of the Cinnamon Teal, see Spencer (1953).

NOTEWORTHY RECORDS

Spring: Coastal - Quick's Bottom 17 Mar 1979-1, 30 Apr 1982-5 pairs; Martindale Flats (Saanich) 14 Mar 1981-1; Serpentine Fen (Surrey) 17 May 1981-21; Burnaby Lake 1 May 1977-15 pairs; Knight Inlet mid-May 1984-1 (RBCM Photo 1168); Sewall 1 May 1983-1; Masset 25 Apr 1983-1; New Aiyansh 30 Apr 1987-2. **Interior:** Osoyoos 17 Mar 1985-1; Duck Lake (Creston) 8 Apr 1985-6, 22 Apr 1985-42, 21 May 1979-26 including 10 pairs, 31 May 1984-23; Tamarack Lake 25 May 1977-7; Swan Lake (Vernon) 20 Apr 1980-25; Revelstoke 4 May 1977-48, 26 May 1977-40 (Bonar 1978b); 108 Mile Lake 11 May 1977-13; Williams Lake 10 Apr 1964-4; Telkwa 3 May 1976-2; Fort St. John 3 May 1985-1 male; Liard River 14 May 1981-20 on aerial survey; Haines Road (Chilkat Pass) 14 May 1977-1.

Summer: Coastal - Quick's Bottom 5 Jun 1981-5 males, 13 Jun 1979-2 pairs; Beach Grove 29 Aug 1973-10; Reifel Island 9 Jun 1973-20; Matsqui 4 Jul 1982-1 pair; Comox 8 Jun 1971-7. **Interior** - Osoyoos Lake 1 Aug 1976-6; Creston 30 Jul 1985-22; Richter Lake (Richter Pass) 18 June 1976-4 pairs; Richter Pass 20 Jun 1976-10 males; Wasa 30 Aug 1977-20; Alleyne Lake 24 Jun 1974-2 pairs; Lac du Bois 24 Jul 1949-3 males; Revelstoke 8 Jul 1977-28, 17 Aug 1978-2 (Bonar 1978b); Cecil Lake 2 Jul 1978-3 males, 1 female; Boundary Lake (Goodlow) 16 Jun 1985-4.

Autumn: Interior - Knutsford 2 Sep 1977-16; Swan Lake (Vernon) 30 Sep 1939-1 (ROM 83577); Okanagan Landing 7 Sep 1944-1; Wasa 1 Sep 1977-4. **Coastal** - Comox 11 Sep 1979-2 males;

Burnaby Lake 21 Oct 1981-1; Iona Island 14 Sep 1974-30; Reifel Island 4 Nov 1975-1 male; Blackie Spit 30 Oct 1978-1; Duncan 2 Sep 1986-15 on sewage ponds (Hunn and Mattocks 1986).

Winter: Interior - Summerland 28 Dec to 1 Jan 1967-1. **Coastal** - Burnaby Lake 18 Dec 1983-1 (RBCM Photo 969); Reifel Island 21 Dec 1975-2 males, 2 Feb 1970-4; Glen Valley 21 Feb 1976-2 pairs; Esquimalt Lagoon 2 Jan 1983-1 male.

Christmas Counts: Interior - Not recorded. **Coastal** - Recorded from 3 of 28 localities and on 2% of all counts. Maxima: Ladner 27 Dec 1982-8, 27 Dec 1983-8, both all-time Canadian high counts (Monroe 1984); Vancouver 18 Dec 1983-3; Deep Bay 29 Dec 1982-1.

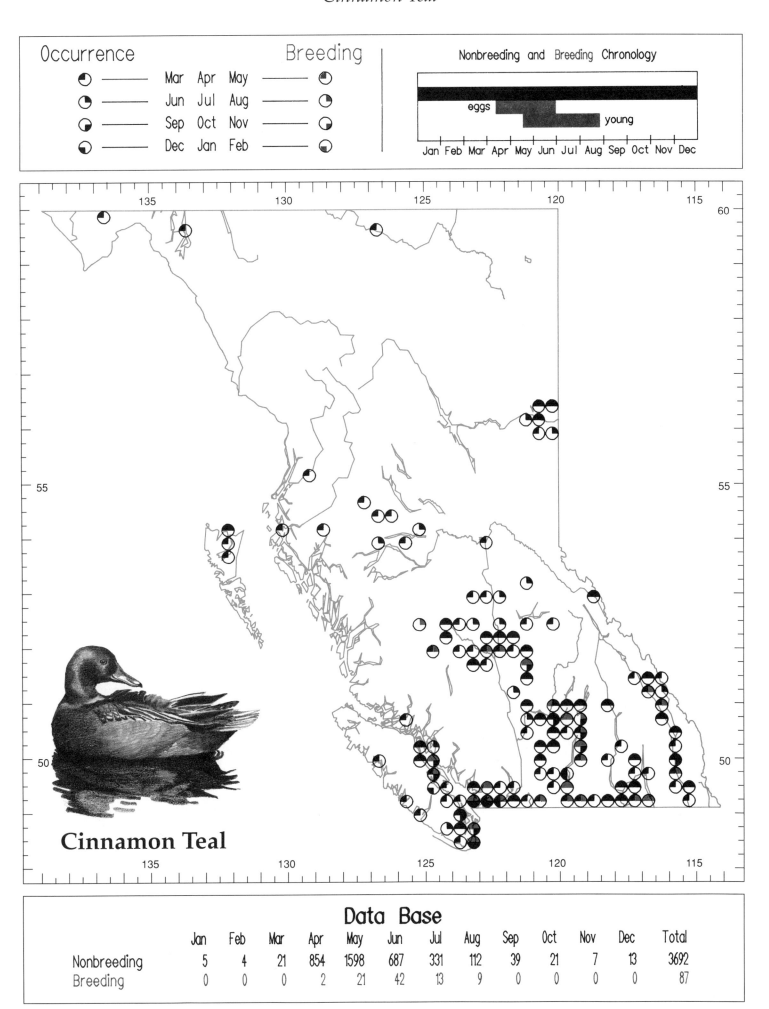

Cinnamon Teal

Occurrence

		Mar Apr May	
		Jun Jul Aug	
		Sep Oct Nov	
		Dec Jan Feb	

Breeding

Nonbreeding and Breeding Chronology

eggs

young

Jan Feb Mar Apr May Jun Jul Aug Sep Oct Nov Dec

Data Base

	Jan	Feb	Mar	Apr	May	Jun	Jul	Aug	Sep	Oct	Nov	Dec	Total
Nonbreeding	5	4	21	854	1598	687	331	112	39	21	7	13	3692
Breeding	0	0	0	2	21	42	13	9	0	0	0	0	87

Northern Shoveler

Anas clypeata Linnaeus

RANGE: Breeds from Alaska and Yukon south and east to Saskatchewan and Manitoba, south to northern California, Colorado, Nebraska, and Wisconsin, and locally in eastern Canada east to the Maritimes. Winters from coastal British Columbia south to California and Texas, Louisiana, and Mexico. Also occurs in the Old World.

STATUS: *Common* to locally *abundant* migrant throughout the province; *fairly common* to *common* summer visitant. In winter, *fairly common* on the coast, although *abundant* on the Fraser River delta and on southeastern Vancouver Island; locally *fairly common* to *very common* in the central south interior. Breeds.

NONBREEDING: The Northern Shoveler occurs throughout the province from sea level to 1,600 m elevation. It frequents sheltered bays, estuaries, shallow lakes, marshes, and flooded agricultural fields. Largest concentrations have been recorded on sewage ponds and outfalls. It occurs infrequently on exposed marine coasts.

Across southern British Columbia spring migration may begin in March, but it usually begins in early to mid-April. The movement peaks in late April and early May. Most have passed through by late May. In the north, migrants begin to arrive from mid to late April; the movement peaks in May and may continue through into early June. Nonbreeding birds, mostly males, are widely but sparsely distributed throughout the province in June and July. Autumn migrants begin to arrive in northern areas in early August and in southern areas from mid to late August. The movement peaks in September and early October and is generally over by late October. On the south coast, numbers build throughout November.

Hundreds winter on the coast, mainly in the vicinity of the Fraser River delta and southeastern Vancouver Island. At least 1,930 birds have wintered in the southern coastal area (Appendix 2) which is considerably more than the estimate of a few hundred mentioned by Bellrose (1976). In mild winters, a few remain scattered throughout the Okanagan valley.

BREEDING: The Northern Shoveler breeds in small numbers on the inner south coast and from Creston and the southern Okanagan valley north to Atlin and the Peace River area. It breeds from sea level to 1,100 m elevation, in open and semi-open habitats, in the vicinity of marshes, sloughs, ponds, bogs, lakes, ditches, and slow-moving streams.

Centres of breeding abundance in the province are the Chilcotin-Cariboo and Peace Lowlands; shovelers are sparsely distributed elsewhere. Bellrose (1976) estimates 6,000 birds breed in the province.

Nests: Of 21 nests, 16 were situated on dry, grassy sites, 4 to 800 m from water; they were found near marshes (9), gas well berms (4), lake edges (3), and in fields (3) and rangeland (2). Four nests were found in dry, dead "reeds", 3 in grass clumps, 3 in tall grasses, 1 in "reeds" over water, and 1 under brush. Nests are usually shallow depressions in the ground. Most were lined with down and grasses; 1 nest was lined with "reeds" and another with bracken fern.

Eggs: Dates for 26 clutches ranged from 11 April to 22 June with 54% recorded between 9 and 14 June. A brood recorded on 4 May on the coast indicates eggs could be found about 1 April. Clutch size ranged from 4 to 19 eggs (4E-2, 5E-2, 6E-1, 7E-5, 8E-3, 9E-7, 10E-3, 11E-1, 12E-1, 19E-1) with 58% having 7 to 9 eggs. The largest clutch may have been the product of more than one female. Incubation period is 23 to 28 days (Girard 1939; Delacour 1956).

Young: Dates for 114 broods ranged from 4 May to 30 September with 60% recorded between 1 and 24 July. Brood size ranged from 1 to 12 young (1Y-3, 2Y-6, 3Y-8, 4Y-6, 5Y-18, 6Y-18, 7Y-14, 8Y-11, 9Y-16, 10Y-9, 11Y-3, 12Y-2) with 54% having 5 to 8 young. Fledging period ranges between 36 and 39 days in Alaska (Hooper 1951; Lensink, C.J. 1954) and 52 and 66 days in Manitoba (Hochbaum 1944).

REMARKS: See Girard (1939) and Poston (1974) for additional information on the natural history of the Northern Shoveler.

The Northern Shoveler was formerly known as the Shoveller.

NOTEWORTHY RECORDS

Spring: Coastal - Victoria 1 May 1966-100 (Crowell and Nehls 1966b); Ladner 3 Mar 1976-156; Nanaimo 16 Mar 1977-6 pairs; Iona Island 3 May 1985-235; Comox 28 May 1977-10; Rose Spit 29 Apr 1979-36, 4 May 1979-117, 5 May 1979-145 (day counts). **Interior** - Duck Lake (Creston) 1 Apr 1985-12, 20 Apr 1986-200, 22 Apr 1985-394; Columbia Lake 1 Apr 1976-1, 12 Apr 1970-42 (Wilson, M.C. et al. 1972); Nakusp 16 Apr 1986-150; Kamloops 16 Mar 1986-5; Sorrento 3 Mar 1972-1; Revelstoke 4 May 1977-53 (Bonar 1978b); Chezacut 19 Apr 1940-25 (Munro, J.A. and Cowan 1947); Vanderhoof 4 May 1945-250 (Munro, J.A. and Cowan 1947); 3 km w Cache Creek 19 Apr 1980-2; Charlie Lake 7 May 1983-300+; Kledo Creek 13 May 1981-102; Atlin 16 May 1981-14 (Campbell 1981).

Summer: Coastal - Ladner 26 Aug 1973-42 at sewage lagoon; Sea Island 4 June 1977-95; Cleland Island 16 Jun 1982-2; Walken Islands 6 Aug 1968-18; Port Simpson 19 Aug 1969-10; Masset 6 Jun 1982-12. **Interior** - Creston 18 Jun 1984-21; Leach Lake 29 Aug 1947-100 (Munro, J.A. 1958a); Stump Lake (Quilchena) 14 Jun 1937-11 pairs (Munro, J.A. and Cowan 1947); Fort St. John 26 Aug 1982-75; Boundary Lake (Goodlow) 16 Jun 1985-25 males; Haworth Lake 3 Aug 1976-15; Kotcho Lake 26 Jun 1982-12 males, 2 females (Campbell and McNall 1982).

Autumn: Interior - Fort St. John 7 Sep 1985-100, 20 Sep 1986-400, 1 Oct 1983-16, 31 Oct 1982-1; Mitchell Lake (Kamloops) 9 Nov 1980-125; Swan Lake (Vernon) 4 Nov 1933-75 (Munro, J.A. 1939d); Stump Lake (Quilchena) 28 Nov 1981-15; Lightning Lake 17 Sep 1978-32; Creston 27 Sep 1982-50, 25 Oct 1986-20, 8 Nov 1983-10. **Coastal** - Masset 25 Sep 1981-24; Tlell 2 Nov 1942-2 (ROM 68385); Port Hardy 30 Sep 1938-50, 2 Oct 1938-100; Cranberry Lake (Powell River) 5 Sep 1981-27; Iona Island 3 Sep 1971-200 (Crowell and Nehls 1972a), 30 Oct 1975-460, 5 Nov 1975-470, 26 Nov 1975-280; Ladner 1 Nov 1972-760 at sewage lagoon; Duncan 30 Oct 1978-130, 16 Nov 1977-187.

Winter: Interior - Sorrento 23 Jan 1973-2; Swan Lake (Vernon) 21 Dec 1944-100 (Munro, J.A. 1945b). **Coastal** - Masset 11 Feb 1973-12; Yakoun River 4 Jan 1954-12 on estuary; Burnaby Lake 28 Feb 1966-115+; Iona Island 3 Dec 1975-190; Ladner 4 Dec 1974-425, 20 Jan 1973-196; Cowichan Bay 22 Jan 1974-209; Victoria 4 Jan 1947-150+, 6 Feb 1950-200+; Oak Bay 8 Dec 1945-300+.

Christmas Counts: Interior - Recorded from 3 of 19 localities and on 4% of all counts. Maxima: Kelowna 20 Dec 1981-34; Vernon 26 Dec 1976-19; Vaseux Lake 28 Dec 1974-1. **Coastal** - Recorded from 17 of 28 localities and on 20% of all counts. Maxima: Duncan 17 Dec 1977-**988**, all-time Canadian high count (Anderson, R.R. 1978); Vancouver 17 Dec 1978-657; Victoria 2 Jan 1960-476.

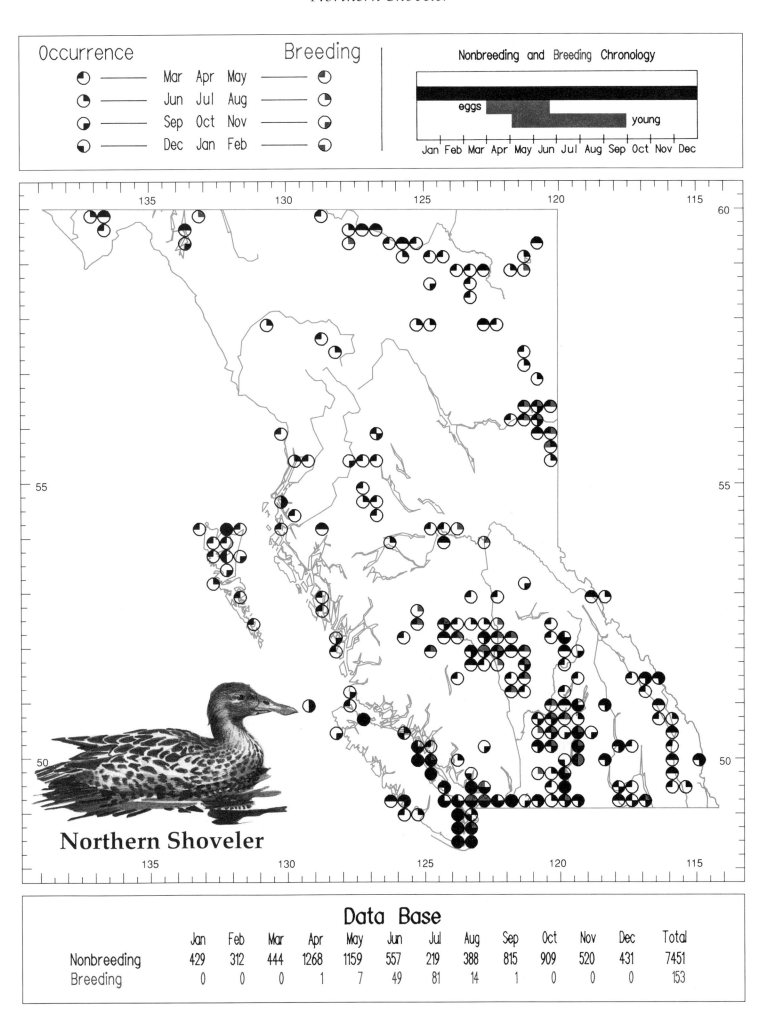

Northern Shoveler

	Jan	Feb	Mar	Apr	May	Jun	Jul	Aug	Sep	Oct	Nov	Dec	Total
Nonbreeding	429	312	444	1268	1159	557	219	388	815	909	520	431	7451
Breeding	0	0	0	1	7	49	81	14	1	0	0	0	153

Gadwall

GADW

Anas strepera Linnaeus

RANGE: Breeds in North America from central Alaska, southern Yukon, southwestern Mackenzie, east across the Canadian prairies, southern Ontario and Quebec, locally in the Maritimes, south to southern California in the west and North Carolina in the east. Winters from southern Alaska, coastal and southern British Columbia, the American midwest, and Chesapeake Bay south to Mexico and the Caribbean. Also winters in the Old World.

STATUS: Locally *common* to *abundant* migrant on the southwest coast and central-southern interior. *Uncommon* to *fairly common* migrant in the east Kootenay and the Peace Lowlands; *rare* on the northern coast and in the northern interior. In winter, locally *fairly common* to *abundant* on southern Vancouver Island, the Fraser Lowlands and the Okanagan Basin; *fairly common* some years on the Queen Charlotte Islands; *casual* elsewhere. Local breeder.

CHANGE IN STATUS: Recently the Gadwall has increased its range substantially in central and eastern North America (Henny and Holgersen 1974). That trend has also occurred in the Pacific Northwest. The Gadwall was not known to breed west of the Pacific and Cascade Range in British Columbia, Washington, and Oregon prior to the mid-1960s (Munro, J.A. and Cowan 1947; Jewett, S.G. et al. 1953; Gabrielson and Jewett 1970). Small numbers began breeding in 1966 and 1967 in the Fraser River delta in British Columbia and in northwestern Washington. Over the next 2 decades, populations became well established (Canning and Herman 1983). The small natural population was enhanced by the Pitt Waterfowl Society and Ducks Unlimited Canada through the importation of about 1,500 eggs from Alberta. Those that hatched were reared in captivity and released near Maple Ridge between 1975 and 1984. Today the breeding population in the Fraser Lowlands is estimated at 100 pairs (Butler, R.W. and Campbell 1987).

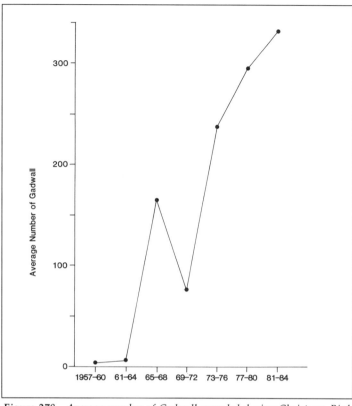

Figure 278. *Average number of Gadwall recorded during Christmas Bird Counts at Vancouver, Ladner, and Victoria, British Columbia, 1957 through 1984.*

Figure 279. *Male Gadwall in eclipse plumage at Creston, 24 July 1983 (David F. Fraser).*

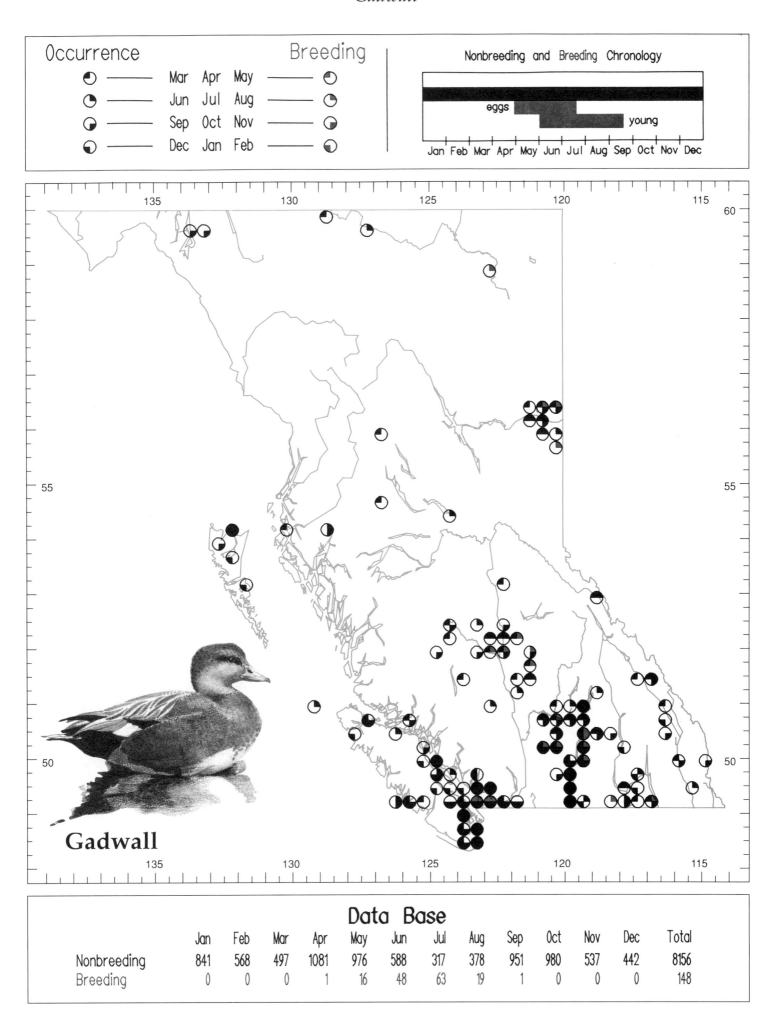

Occurrence   Breeding

◑ ——	Mar	Apr	May	—— ◔
◔ ——	Jun	Jul	Aug	—— ◔
◑ ——	Sep	Oct	Nov	—— ◑
◕ ——	Dec	Jan	Feb	—— ◑

Nonbreeding and Breeding Chronology

eggs   young

Jan Feb Mar Apr May Jun Jul Aug Sep Oct Nov Dec

Gadwall

Data Base

	Jan	Feb	Mar	Apr	May	Jun	Jul	Aug	Sep	Oct	Nov	Dec	Total
Nonbreeding	841	568	497	1081	976	588	317	378	951	980	537	442	8156
Breeding	0	0	0	1	16	48	63	19	1	0	0	0	148

In the interior, the Gadwall expanded its breeding range into the Chilcotin-Cariboo in the early 1950s (Erskine and Stein 1964), the west Kootenay in 1975 (Butler, R.W. et al. 1986), and the Peace Lowlands in the late 1970s.

J.A. Munro and Cowan (1947) report that the Gadwall wintered regularly, but not abundantly, on the coast from Victoria to Masset, and occasionally in the interior. Annual Christmas Bird Counts have shown that winter populations have continually increased on the south coast since the late 1960s (Fig. 278) and in the southern interior since the mid-1970s.

NONBREEDING: The Gadwall is widely distributed throughout southern British Columbia and the Peace Lowlands; it is scattered elsewhere. It occurs from sea level to 1,300 m elevation.

On the coast, it frequents estuaries, brackish and fresh water marshes, mudflats, flooded fields, and sewage lagoons. In the interior, lakes, marshes, wet grassy areas, large slow-moving rivers, sewage lagoons, and ponds (Fig. 279) are preferred habitats. The Gadwall uses deeper, more open waters than other dabbling ducks and often forages with American Coots.

On the south coast, spring migration begins in late March and early April and peaks later in April. However, local dispersal may occur. For example, wintering populations on the Saanich Peninsula generally decline from March to May, the same period when numbers increase on the Fraser River delta. In the southern interior, the spring movement occurs throughout April but peaks in late April and early May. In the Peace Lowlands, it begins in late April and peaks in late May.

A large nonbreeding population, numbering in the hundreds, summers on the Fraser River delta in June and early July. This unusual aggregation of nonbreeders may indicate that these birds cannot find suitable habitat in the few remaining wetlands of this urbanized area. The presence of the flock may argue against further enhancement of the local population. Significant post-breeding aggregations have been reported in August, only at Swan Lake (Vernon) and locally on the Fraser River delta.

Autumn migration occurs from late August through October; it generally peaks in September. The only large numbers are found on the south coast and the central-southern interior.

In winter, most birds are found on southeastern Vancouver Island, the Fraser Lowlands, and in the Okanagan Basin. Small numbers winter along the coast north to the Queen Charlotte Islands. At least 971 birds have wintered in the southern coastal area (Appendix 2), which accounts for nearly 3% of the Pacific Flyway population as reported in Bellrose (1976).

BREEDING: The Gadwall breeds in small numbers in central-southern British Columbia from Creston and Grand Forks north through the Thompson-Okanagan Plateau to Williams Lake in the Chilcotin-Cariboo Basin. Local populations also exist in the Fraser Lowlands and in the Peace Lowlands. The Gadwall breeds from sea level to 1,100 m elevation.

In the interior, breeding sites are associated with marshes, potholes, lakes, or sewage lagoons in grasslands or open areas within forests. Coastal breeding habitats include brackish marshes, farmlands, sewage lagoons, and lakes.

Nests: Most nests (23 of 27) were found near marshes; 18 nests were situated in tall grass, 5 were under clumps of blackberries, nettles, or brush, 3 were among sedges, and 1 nest was found on a rock jetty. Nests were usually situated in drier areas near water: 12 nests ranged between 1.5 and 180 m from water, 8 of those within 9 m of water.

Of 24 nests, 18 were shallow hollows in the ground; the remainder were shallow saucers of dry reeds. All nests contained various quantities of down (Fig. 280); 8 were also lined with grasses.

Eggs: Dates for 46 clutches ranged from 16 May to 19 July with 57% recorded between 28 May and 15 June. Calculated dates indicate that eggs could be found as early as 29 April. Sizes for 48 clutches ranged from 1 to 13 eggs (1E-1, 3E-2, 4E-1, 5E-1, 6E-2, 7E-3, 8E-8, 9E-13, 10E-7, 11E-8, 12E-1, 13E-1), with 58% having 8 to 10 eggs. Incubation period is 24 to 27 days (Oring 1966).

Young: Dates for 98 broods ranged from 2 June to 19 September with 51% recorded between 1 and 24 July. Sizes for 83 broods ranged from 1 to 21 young (1Y-1, 2Y-2, 3Y-3, 4Y-9, 6Y-12, 7Y-7, 8Y-15, 9Y-11, 10Y-10, 11Y-6, 12Y-3, 13Y-2, 19Y-1, 21Y-1) with 52% having 7 to 10 young (Fig. 281). Small, late broods are common in August in the Fraser River estuary and may indicate a high proportion of replacement nests, perhaps because of high densities of predators such as domestic cats, raccoons, and opossums. Groups of 19 and 21 young are likely the result of brood mixing. Fledging period is about 49 to 56 days (Oring 1968).

REMARKS: See Oring (1966, 1968) for information on the breeding biology and plumages of the Gadwall.

***Figure 280.** Gadwall nest and eggs at Boundary Lake, 24 June 1984 (Chris Siddle).*

Figure 281. *Female Gadwall with brood at Vernon, 3 August 1984 (Chris Siddle).*

NOTEWORTHY RECORDS

Spring: Coastal - Quicks Bottom 2 Mar 1983-76, 5 Apr 1982-28; Iona Island 4 May 1980-400, 24 May 1981-500; Port Neville 13 May 1974-8; Ridley Island 25 Mar 1979-2. **Interior** - Creston 7 Mar 1985-40, 16 Mar 1972-10, 24 Mar 1983-274, 22 Apr 1985-253; Wasa 19 Apr 1979-3; Salmon Arm 24 Apr 1946-40; Glenmore 23 Apr 1938-60+; Campbell Range (Kamloops) 15 May 1966-6; 103 Mile Lake 12 Apr 1978-4; Fort St. John 21 Apr 1983-2, 14 May 1986-14, 27 May 1984-100; Leo Lake 14 May 1981-4.

Summer: Coastal - Iona Island 2 Jun 1981-500, 25 June 1985-2,000, 29 Jun 1975-650, 4 Jul 1971-150, 29 Aug 1973-50; Cranberry Lake (Powell River) 30 Aug 1981-19; Johnstone Strait 24 Aug 1987-20; Triangle Island (Scott Islands) 27 Aug 1978-2; Masset 5 Jun 1984-3. **Interior** - Creston 17 Jun 1983-115, 20 Jul 1982-160; Leach Lake 27 Jun 1956-2; Richter Lake (Richter Pass) 25 Jun 1967-2; Swan Lake (Vernon) 10 Aug 1977-150; Shuswap Lake 25 Jun 1963-4; Fort St. John 29 Aug 1984-13.

Autumn: Interior - Atlin 14 Sep 1972-6; Fort St. John 24 Sep 1983-12, 23 Oct 1983-3; Kleena Kleene 20 Nov 1965-20; Emerald Lake (Yoho National Park) 24 Oct 1976-15 (Wade 1977); Invermere 5 Sep 1977-5; Swan Lake (Vernon) 30 Sep 1939-250; Douglas Plateau 13 Sep 1981-75; Nelson 23 Nov 1985-15; Vaseux Lake 10 Sep 1975-70+; Creston 26 Sep 1985-488, 27 Sep 1982-550, 9 Oct 1984-425, 19 Nov 1982-250. **Coastal** - Masset 28 Nov 1971-10; Kitimat 27 Nov 1979-2; Port Hardy 3 Sep 1936-20; Iona Island 4 Sep 1974-55, 27 Sep 1977-80+, 3 Oct 1973-200, 5 Nov 1973-20.

Winter: Interior - Okanagan Lake 27 Jan 1977-23 at north end; Nicola Lake 29 Dec 1986-3; Kelowna 1 Jan 1981-80; Vaseux Lake 3 Jan 1970-30; Creston 2 Dec 1982-90. **Coastal** - Masset 15 Feb 1983-35; Yakoun River 4 Jan 1954-15; Quatsino 14 Feb 1973-20; Sechelt 22 Feb 1987-2; Sea and Iona islands 6 Dec 1972-200, 26 Jan 1974-200; Quicks Bottom 18 Feb 1983-58.

Christmas Counts: Interior - Recorded from 8 of 19 localities and on 42% of all counts. Maxima: Vaseux Lake 23 Dec 1981-169; Vernon 18 Dec 1983-99; Penticton 27 Dec 1983-86. **Coastal** - Recorded from 16 of 28 localities and on 34% of all counts. Maxima: Duncan 27 Dec 1970-921; Victoria 30 Dec 1967-589; Vancouver 20 Dec 1981-382.

Eurasian Wigeon
Anas penelope Linnaeus

EUWI

RANGE: Breeds in Iceland and across northern Eurasia. Winters in the Old World south to northern Africa, Turkey, Indochina, and Japan. In North America, it occurs regularly during autumn and winter along the Pacific and Atlantic coasts, and in spring mainly in southeastern Alaska. Irregular in the interior of the continent.

STATUS: *Uncommon* to *fairly common*, but regular migrant and winter visitant on the south coast; *casual* in summer. *Very rare* on the Queen Charlotte Islands. In the interior, a *rare* spring migrant, *casual* in summer and autumn.

OCCURRENCE: The Eurasian Wigeon occurs regularly on the inner south coast, mainly along southeastern Vancouver Island and in the Fraser Lowlands. It has also been recorded infrequently along the west coast of Vancouver Island and the Queen Charlotte Islands, but not as yet along the northern mainland coast. It is widely distributed in the interior from Quesnel and Anahim Lake south. There are 3 records for the Peace Lowlands. It has been found from sea level to 2,050 m elevation.

The Eurasian Wigeon is most often found within larger flocks of American Wigeon and therefore frequents similar habitats. On the coast, those habitats include uplands with short grass such as flooded fields, fallow fields, parks, golf courses, and airports. Marine habitats include estuaries and protected coves with eelgrass. In the interior, lakeshores, river deltas, creek mouths, ponds, marshes, and slow-moving rivers are preferred.

The apparent trend in North America is for spring migrants to disperse mainly through the interior of the continent, whereas autumn migrants tend to be more coastal (Hasbrouck 1944; Palmer, R.S. 1976a). That trend is evident in British Columbia, where most interior records (82%; n=44) are for the spring period. Spring migrants move north beginning in March, probably with flocks of American Wigeon. The peak movement is evident in mid-April and is over by early May.

In summer, the Eurasian Wigeon has only been recorded on Vancouver Island. Autumn migrants begin to appear in mid-September but most arrive in October. Numbers increase and reach their maxima during the winter months.

Most large coastal winter flocks of American Wigeon contain at least one Eurasian Wigeon. Single males are most frequently reported, probably because of the difficulty in identifying females. The single largest group was 22 males counted in a flock of 2,000 American Wigeon. The Eurasian Wigeon also associates with Mallard, Northern Pintail, and, in marine waters, Barrow's Goldeneye.

REMARKS: Edgell (1984) analysed records of the Eurasian Wigeon in North America from 1947 to 1981. He documents a dramatic increase in numbers since 1965, especially on the Pacific coast, a trend also noted in British Columbia (Fig. 282). From 1965 to 1981 total winter records increased nearly twenty-fold. He indicates that this represents a real increase in numbers, which parallels increased sightings of several other Palearctic species of Anatidae occuring in North America. The North American winter population is estimated at 1,000 birds.

The Eurasian Wigeon was formerly known as the European Widgeon (*Mareca penelope*).

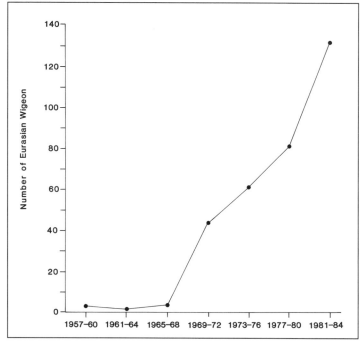

Figure 282. *Aggregate totals for Eurasian Wigeon on the south coast recorded during annual Christmas Bird Counts at Vancouver, Ladner, and Victoria, British Columbia, 1957 through 1984.*

NOTEWORTHY RECORDS

Spring: Coastal - Victoria 5 May 1984-1 male; Beach Grove 20 Mar 1982-3 males; Woodhus Creek 30 Mar 1987-3; Menzies Bay 29 Apr 1966-12; Klaskish River 14 May 1978-1 male on estuary; Kimsquit River 18 Apr 1985-1 male on estuary; Sewall 10 Apr 1982-4 pairs, 28 Apr 1983-1 male. **Interior** - Duck Lake (Creston) 19 Mar 1976-1 male, 15 Apr 1980-1 male (Butler, R.W. et al. 1986), 22 Apr 1985-8; Castlegar 9 Mar 1981-1 male; Wasa 7 Apr 1982-2, 21 Apr 1987-1 male; Kelowna 12 May 1978-1 pair; Beresford 2 May 1987-1 male; Tranquille 30 Mar 1980-3; Burges and James Gadsen Park 9 and 17 Apr 1987-4 males; 150 Mile House 19 Mar 1983-1; Fort St. John 3 Apr 1986-1 (McEwan, C. and Johnston 1986); Charlie Lake 21 to 22 May 1983-1 (Siddle 1982); Cecil Lake 17 May 1986-1 male.

Summer: Coastal - Comox 15 Jul 1953-1 male. **Interior** - No records.

Autumn: Interior - Lake O'Hara 10 Sep 1987-4; Kamloops 4 Nov 1980-1; Kelowna 30 Oct 1978-1; Nelson 26 Oct 1971-1; Duck Lake (Creston) 23 Oct 1981-1 (Butler, R.W. et al. 1986). **Coastal** - Naden Harbour 7 Nov 1974-1 male; Port Hardy 15 Nov 1986-3 males; Jericho Park (Vancouver) 12 Nov 1982-12; Boundary Bay 17 Sep 1982-1 male; Bings Creek 18 Nov 1980-5; Esquimalt Lagoon 28 Sep 1978-1.

Winter: Interior - Kamloops Jan 1967-1 (Jacobson 1974); Kelowna 22 Dec 1973-3 (Cannings, R.A. et al. 1987); Kootenay Lake Dec 1971-1; Okanagan Falls 6 Feb 1971-1 (BCPM Photo 844). **Coastal** -

Masset 21 Dec 1978-1 male; Queen Charlotte City 4 Jan 1987-2; Tofino 1 Jan 1986-1 male; Jericho Park (Vancouver) 12 Nov 1982-12; Sea Island 6 Feb 1967-12; Reifel Island 10 Dec 1980-22 males with 2,000 American Wigeon, 22 Jan 1984-9; Somenos Flats (Duncan) 28 Jan 1984-8; Saanich Peninsula 28 Feb 1982-27 on survey; Swan Lake (Victoria) 25 Jan 1977-8.

Christmas Counts: Interior - Not recorded. **Coastal** - Recorded from 17 of 28 localities and on 35% of all counts. Maxima: Victoria 15 Dec 1984-21, all-time North American high count (Monroe 1985a); Ladner 27 Dec 1983-20 and 23 Dec 1984-20; Vancouver 17 Dec 1978-13.

Eurasian Wigeon

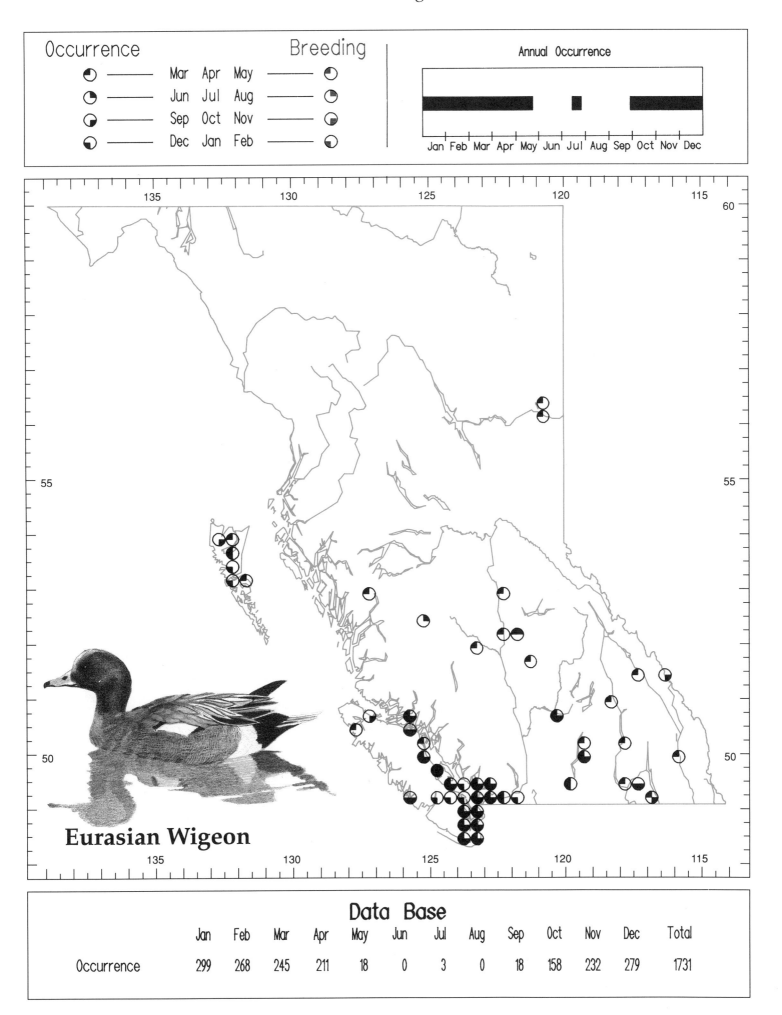

Occurrence · Breeding

Mar Apr May
Jun Jul Aug
Sep Oct Nov
Dec Jan Feb

Annual Occurrence

Jan Feb Mar Apr May Jun Jul Aug Sep Oct Nov Dec

Data Base

	Jan	Feb	Mar	Apr	May	Jun	Jul	Aug	Sep	Oct	Nov	Dec	Total
Occurrence	299	268	245	211	18	0	3	0	18	158	232	279	1731

American Wigeon
Anas americana Gmelin

AMWI

RANGE: Breeds from northern Alaska and northern Yukon across most of sub-arctic western Canada to James Bay, south to Oregon, Utah, Wyoming, and the Dakotas; locally east to the Maritimes. Winters from southern Alaska, coastal and south-central British Columbia, to New England and south through California, Texas, Louisiana, and Florida to Central America and the West Indies.

STATUS: *Abundant* to *very abundant* migrant and winter visitant on the south coast; locally *abundant* on the north coast. *Abundant* to *very abundant* migrant in the southern interior; *common* to *abundant* migrant in the northern interior. Locally, *common* to *abundant* winter visitant on open waters of the central south interior. Widespread breeder in the interior; local on the south coast.

NONBREEDING: The American Wigeon occurs throughout the province from sea level to 1,300 m elevation.

On the coast, the American Wigeon mostly occurs in sheltered waters; it is seldom found along the exposed outer coast. Preferred habitats include estuaries, mudflats, lagoons, and shallow bays with seaweeds and eel-grass. Inland, agricultural fields, sloughs, marshes, lakes, golf courses, and airports are used. In the interior, marshes, sloughs, large and small lakes, slow-moving rivers, fields, and golf courses are frequented.

The American Wigeon is an early spring migrant. On the coast, the wintering population is swelled by migrants in March and early April, but most of the birds depart by late April. In the southern interior, the northward movement begins in March and usually peaks during the first half of April. In the northern interior, the movement starts from early to mid-April and peaks from late April to early May.

A few birds occur along the coast throughout the summer. About mid-June, post-breeding males gather on lakes and marshes in the southern interior to moult.

Autumn migration generally begins from mid to late August. In the interior, it peaks in mid-October, declines rapidly thereafter in the north and gradually through November in the south. On the coast, migrants arrive steadily throughout September, October, and November.

In winter, the American Wigeon is the most numerous dabbling duck along the coast, where it concentrates mainly on estuaries and nearby agricultural areas (Eamer 1985). The largest population, estimated at 62,000 birds, is found on the Fraser River delta (Butler, R.W. and Campbell 1987); that population is over twice that reported by Bellrose (1976) and about 7% of the Pacific Flyway winter population. Populations of 1,000 to 2,000

birds winter in estuaries such as those of the Cowichan, Nanaimo, Englishman, and Yacoun rivers, and in Clayoquot Sound (Hatler 1973). In the southern interior, hundreds winter on open lakes and rivers such as Kootenay Lake, Okanagan Lake, Shuswap Lake, and the South Thompson River.

BREEDING: The American Wigeon breeds throughout most of British Columbia east of the Coast Ranges and locally on the south coast from Duncan and the Fraser Lowlands north to Powell River. It breeds from sea level to 1,200 m elevation; 75% of all records were between 660 and 1,090 m elevation. The American Wigeon breeds in the vicinity of freshwater sloughs, ponds, lakes, marshes, and rivers.

Its centre of breeding abundance is the Chilcotin-Cariboo and Peace River parklands, where it is one of the most numerous dabbling ducks. It breeds regularly, but in smaller numbers, in the central-southern interior, the Kootenay, Nechako Lowlands, and Peace River boreal regions. Bellrose (1976) estimates the breeding population in British Columbia at 60,000 to 80,000 birds.

Nests: Few nests have been discovered in British Columbia because the American Wigeon tends to nest in brushy, upland habitats, sometimes far from water. Nests (n=22) were shallow hollows in the ground mostly lined with various quantities of down (13) and other materials such as leaves (5) grasses (3), and twigs, mud, and reeds (1 each). Nests were usually very well concealed; 13 nests were under overhanging shrubs, 5 were under trees, and 3 were in grass clumps. Seven nests were found between 1 and 240 m from water.

Eggs: Dates for 43 clutches ranged from 7 May to 4 August with 53% recorded between 9 and 25 June. Calculated dates indicate that eggs could be found on 30 April. Sizes for 32 clutches ranged from 3 to 11 eggs (3E-1, 4E-1, 5E-2, 6E-1, 7E-2, 8E-11, 9E-5, 10E-6, 11E-3) with 69% having 8 to 10 eggs. Broods of 12 and 13 young indicate a clutch size of up to 13 eggs. Incubation period is 23 to 25 days (Delacour 1956; Hochbaum 1944).

Young: Dates for 589 broods ranged between 28 May to 1 September with 55% recorded between 2 and 22 July. Sizes for 534 broods ranged from 1 to 19 young (1Y-6, 2Y-14, 3Y-31, 4Y-36, 5Y-72, 6Y-88, 7Y-72, 8Y-75, 9Y-60, 10Y-40, 11Y-16, 12Y-9, 13Y-4, 15Y-5, 16Y-1, 17Y-1, 18Y-3, 19Y-1) with 57% having 5 to 8 young. Groups of 15 to 19 young are likely the result of brood mixing. Fledging period is 37 to 44 days in Alaska (Hooper, D.C. 1951; Lensink, C.J. 1954) and 45 to 48 days in Manitoba (Hochbaum 1944).

REMARKS: Formerly known as American Widgeon (*Mareca americana*).

NOTEWORTHY RECORDS

Spring: Coastal - Victoria 22 Mar 1980-750; Fraser River delta 9 Mar 1967-12,296, 20 Apr 1967-11,597, 18 May 1967-130 (Burgess 1970); Fry's Corner (Surrey) 4 Apr 1977-3,500; Kimsquit River 1 May 1985-100+; Yakoun River 28 Apr 1984-350+ on estuary, 5 May 1977-2; Rose Spit 23 Apr 1979-395 on day count, 5 May 1979-31. **Interior** - Creston 24 Mar 1983-10,465, 18 Apr 1985-2,511, 5 May 1984-530; Wasa 28 Mar 1977-106; Sorrento 4 Apr 1971-1,000+; Fort St. John 4 Apr 1984-1; Cecil Lake 22 Apr 1984-600; Atlin 16 May 1981-22 (Campbell 1981).

Summer: Coastal - Swan Lake (Victoria) 26 Jun 1979-5; Crescent Beach 19 Aug 1949-19; Masset 6 Jun 1985-9. **Interior** - Duck Lake (Creston) 3 Jul 1982-2,125, 18 Aug 1966-2,500 (Greyell 1966); Chilcotin Lake 23 Jun 1977-100 mostly males; Abuntlet Lake 13 June 1948-70 males; Nulki Lake 24 Jul 1945-276 (Munro, J.A. 1947a); Fort St. John

6 Jun 1983-21 pairs; Cecil Lake 3 Jul 1978-134; Boundary Lake (Goodlow) 21 Aug 1983-300; Fern Lake (Kwadacha Wilderness Park) 21 Aug 1983-11 (Cooper, J.M. and Cooper 1983).

Autumn: Interior - Boundary Lake 5 Oct 1986-800; Cecil Lake 21 Oct 1981-250, 24 Oct 1986-300; Fort St. John 31 Oct 1982-3; Fraser Lake 20 Oct 1981-1,000; Revelstoke 15 Sep 1977-502, 21 Sep 1977-745, 1 Nov 1977-255 (Bonar 1978b); Brisco 11 Oct 1976-3,000; Vaseux Lake 14 Oct 1973-1,390; Creston 14 Sep 1982-8,205, 26 Sep 1983-6,497, 18 Oct 1982-15,255, 27 Oct 1983-5,520, 25 Nov 1986-590. **Coastal** - Port Clements 24 Nov 1955-850; Tofino Inlet 13 Nov 1972-1,200 (Hatler et al. 1978); Iona and Sea islands 5 Sep 1979-500; Fraser River delta 29 Sep 1966-13,200, 27 Oct 1966-11,623, 24 Nov 1966-10,331, all aerial surveys (Burgess 1970); Cherry Point 13 Nov 1976-4,000; Central Saanich 18 Nov 1973-2,500.

Winter: Interior - Sorrento 19 Dec 1970-150+; Chase 18 Jan 1949-36; Kootenay Lake (Nelson) 2 Dec 1978-725, mid-Feb 1980-300; Creston 27 Jan 1983-300; Oliver 31 Dec 1976-95. **Coastal** - Yakoun River 12 Dec 1982-1,000+, 12 Jan 1983-748 on estuary; Taleomey River 10 Jan 1977-350; Fraser River delta 9 Dec 1965-16,500, 9 Feb 1967-7,635, aerial surveys; Westham Island 23 Dec 1972-6,950, 18 Jan 1973-10,000; Central Saanich 4 Jan 1979-4,000.

Christmas Counts: Interior - Recorded from 8 of 19 localities and on 49% of all counts. Maxima: Vernon 26 Dec 1976-355; Vaseux Lake 23 Dec 1981-242; Oliver/Osoyoos 28 Dec 1981-108. **Coastal** - Recorded from 24 of 28 localities and on 83% of all counts. Maxima: Ladner 27 Dec 1981-**42,726**, all-time Canadian high count (Anderson, R.R. 1982); Victoria 17 Dec 1977-14,889; Vancouver 18 Dec 1977-9,437.

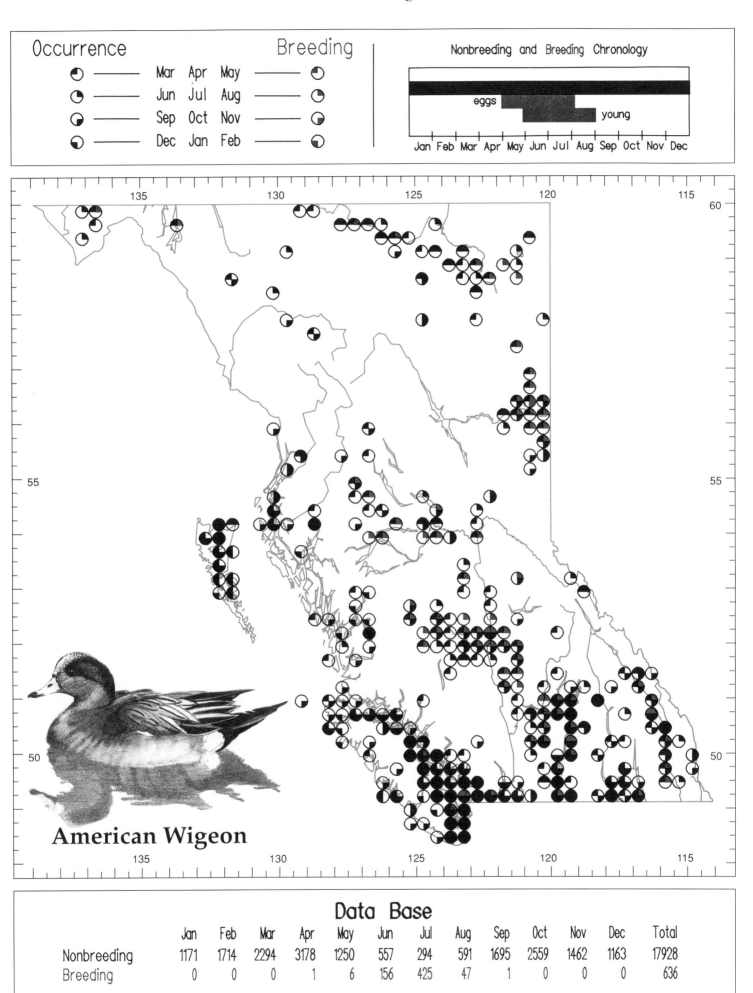

American Wigeon

Data Base

	Jan	Feb	Mar	Apr	May	Jun	Jul	Aug	Sep	Oct	Nov	Dec	Total
Nonbreeding	1171	1714	2294	3178	1250	557	294	591	1695	2559	1462	1163	17928
Breeding	0	0	0	1	6	156	425	47	1	0	0	0	636

Canvasback
Aythya valisineria (Wilson)

CANV

RANGE: Breeds from central Alaska, northern Yukon, west and southern Mackenzie to southern Manitoba, south locally to northern California, east across the central and northern states to Iowa. Winters mainly from southern British Columbia on the Pacific coast and from Massachusetts on the Atlantic coast south to the Gulf coast and Mexico.

STATUS: *Fairly common* to *very common* migrant through most of southern British Columbia and the Peace Lowlands; *very rare* elsewhere. *Uncommon* to *common* summer visitant to the central southern interior; *fairly common* in the Peace Lowlands. *Uncommon* on the coast in summer. In winter *fairly common* to *very common* in the southern interior; *rare* in the west Kootenay; *rare* on the outer and north coast including the Queen Charlotte Islands. Breeds.

NONBREEDING: The Canvasback occurs throughout southern British Columbia from Vancouver Island east to the Kootenays and north to the Chilcotin-Cariboo region. Farther north its distribution becomes sparse. It occurs from sea level to at least 1,500 m elevation.

The Canvasback frequents a variety of coastal marine and freshwater habitats including estuaries (47%; n=473), saltwater lagoons (31%), rivers, lakes, inlets, sewage lagoons (Fig. 283), bays, ponds, and occasionally flooded fields. Interior birds are most often found on lakes (79%; n=353), followed by ponds, rivers, sloughs, and sewage ponds.

Spring migration begins in February and continues into May. On the coast, numbers increase by late February and remain relatively high through March and the first 2 weeks of April after which most have departed. In the interior, numbers increase from March to mid-April, when the main movement occurs. Migration may continue well into May. In the Peace River area, spring migration does not start until the latter part of April. Small numbers of nonbreeders remain on the coast through the summer.

Autumn migration, less noticeable and more protracted than the spring movement, begins in late August and continues through November. Most birds have usually left the interior breeding grounds by October. Birds arrive at the coast by early September and numbers continue to build, peaking in November. Banding recoveries indicate that in autumn most Canvasbacks reared in British Columbia travel due south towards wintering grounds in California (Fig. 284)

The winter distribution of the Canvasback includes Vancouver Island and the Fraser Lowlands on the south coast, and the extreme southern interior north through the Okanagan valley to Vernon, and occasionally west to Douglas Lake and the Kamloops area. The Canvasback occasionally winters on the Queen Charlotte Islands, the north coast, the west Kootenay and the Creston valley. The Fraser River delta is the centre of winter abundance along the coast; in the interior, the greatest concentration occurs in the south Okanagan from Vaseux Lake to Summerland (Fig. 285). Bellrose (1976) estimates the winter population at 170 birds, which is too

Figure 283. *Canvasbacks and scaup at Iona Island sewage lagoon, 12 May 1970 (R. Wayne Campbell). The Fraser River delta is the most important wintering area for Canvasbacks in British Columbia.*

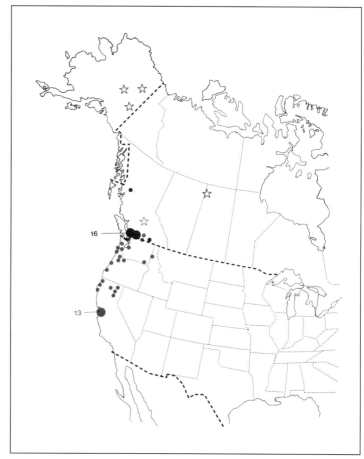

Figure 284. *Banding locations (stars) and recovery sites (circles) of Canvasbacks associated with British Columbia. Red indicates birds banded in British Columbia, black indicates birds banded elsewhere.*

Canvasback

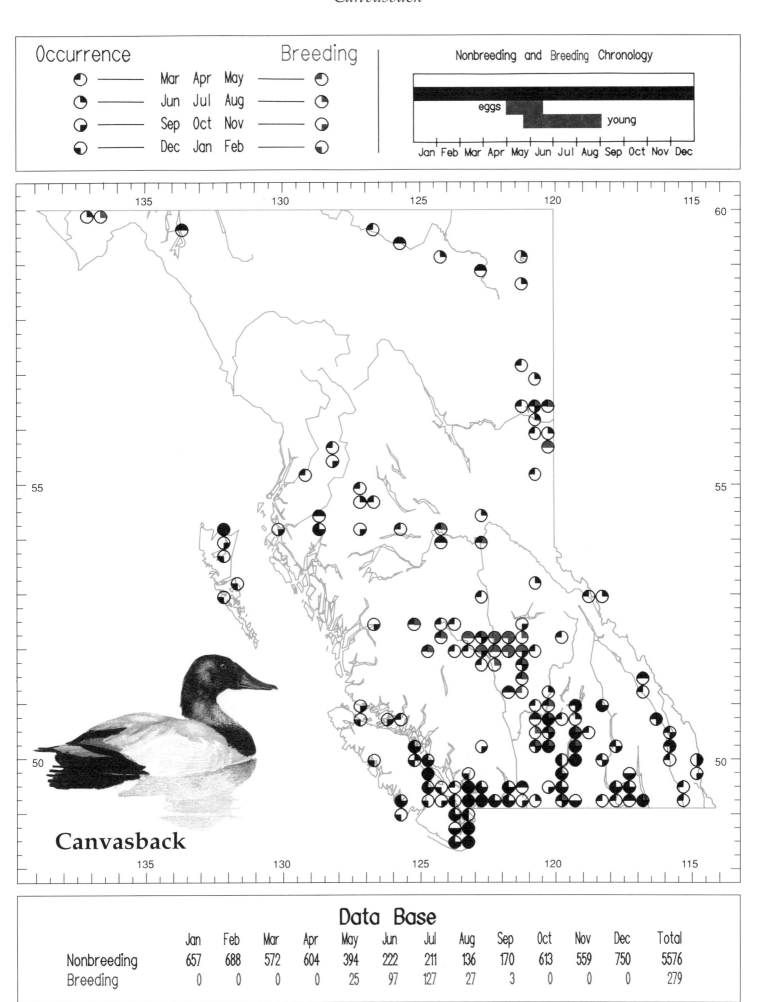

Canvasback

Data Base

	Jan	Feb	Mar	Apr	May	Jun	Jul	Aug	Sep	Oct	Nov	Dec	Total
Nonbreeding	657	688	572	604	394	222	211	136	170	613	559	750	5576
Breeding	0	0	0	0	25	97	127	27	3	0	0	0	279

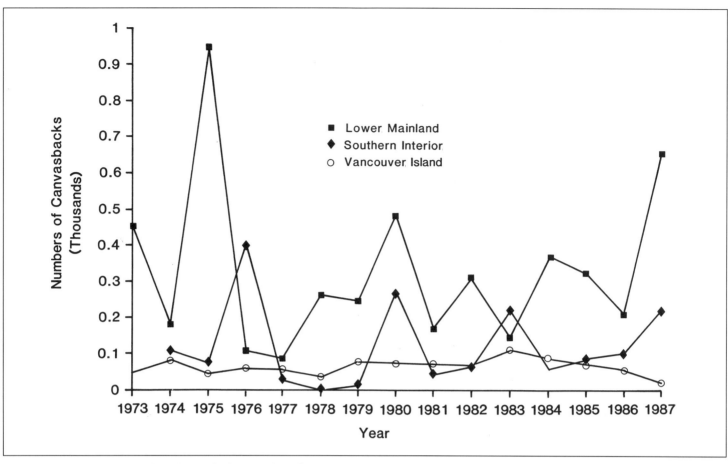

Figure 285. *Fluctuations in numbers of Canvasbacks reported on Christmas Bird Counts from the Lower Mainland (Ladner, Pitt Meadows, Vancouver, White Rock), Okanagan (Penticton, Vaseux Lake, Vernon), and Vancouver Island (Comox, Duncan, Nanaimo, Victoria) count areas. Numbers are aggregate totals for the count areas within the regions.*

low. In some winters over 1,000 Canvasbacks can be found in the province, which is about 3% of the Pacific Flyway winter population. (See also Christmas Counts below and Appendix 2.)

BREEDING: The Canvasback breeds in the central and southern interior from Creston and Richter Pass north through the Thompson-Okanagan Plateau and Chilcotin-Cariboo to Prince George, Vanderhoof and Atlin and throughout the Peace Lowlands. The centre of abundance is the Chilcotin-Cariboo region from about 100 Mile House north to Williams Lake and west to Riske Creek. Bellrose (1976) estimates that 3,000 birds breed in British Columbia. The Canvasback breeds from 550 to 1,200 m elevation.

Breeding habitat includes fresh water and alkali lakes, marshes, ponds, and sloughs. Lakes are used most often (72%; n=339) and include both large, deep, and small, shallow bodies of water. Most have extensive marshes or shorelines bordered by dense emergent vegetation (Fig. 286). Bulrush marshes or stands are favoured, although cattail marshes are sometimes used. J.A. Munro (1958b) considers cattail marshes marginal Canvasback habitat. Alkali lakes are used primarily as brood ponds.

Nests: Most nests (87%; n=47) were situated in dense stands of emergent vegetation including bulrush (68%), reeds, rushes, cattail, and grasses. Four nests were over open water. All but one of the nests were located on water, the depth of which ranged from 0.3 to 0.6 m (n=12). Nine nests were located from 3 to 11 m from shore. Nests consisted of a depression in a large, often bulky, mound of dry, emergent vegetation (bulrush, cattail, or occasionally, rushes and grass), often down-lined, ranging from a few cm to over 40 cm in height. One nest had a basal diameter of over 1 m tapering to a top diameter of 35 cm.

Eggs: Dates for 47 clutches ranged from 12 May to 17 June with 54% recorded between 27 May and 4 June. Calculated dates indicate that eggs could be found as early as 30 April. Clutch size

ranged from 3 to 14 eggs (3E-1, 5E-5, 6E-2, 7E-6, 8E-8, 9E-9, 10E-8, 11E-4, 12E-3, 14E-1) with 53% having 8 to 10 eggs. Five nests were parasitized by Redheads. Incubation period is 24 to 29 days with an average of 25 days (Erikson 1948).

Young: Dates for 318 broods ranged from 22 May to 2 September with 52% recorded between 28 June and 20 July. Brood size ranged from 1 to 14 young (1Y-4, 2Y-17, 3Y-27, 4Y-41, 5Y-62, 6Y-42, 7Y-45, 8Y-30, 9Y-27, 10Y-13, 11Y-3, 12Y-3, 13Y-2, 14Y-2) with 60% having 4 to 7 young. Young are often moved from natal ponds to adjacent ponds that may have less cover but are richer foraging sites (J.-P. Savard pers. comm.). Fledging period is reached in 56 to 68 days (Dzubin 1959).

REMARKS: The migrant and wintering populations of the Canvasback have been in a 30-year decline (see Bellrose 1976; Tate and Tate 1982). The species appears on the "Blue List" for the period 1975 to 1981 and as a species of "Special Concern" in 1982 and 1986 (Tate 1986), because of that decline. As Tate (1986) notes, we must reverse the loss of quantity and quality of wetlands for the sake of the Canvasback and, indeed, all wetland species.

See Erickson (1948) for information on the life history and ecology of the Canvasback.

Figure 286. *Typical nesting habitat for Canvasbacks near Fort St. John, May 1988 (R. Wayne Campbell).*

NOTEWORTHY RECORDS

Spring: Coastal - Esquimalt Lagoon 14 May 1977-1; Iona Island 2 Mar 1979-211, 31 Mar 1982-300, 12 Apr 1974-400, 24 May 1973-30; Delkatla Inlet 29 Mar 1979-5; Kitimat 23 May 1975-1. **Interior** - Creston 7 Mar 1985-330, 24 Apr 1985-320; Sirdar 7 May 1956-200, 8 May 1956-100, 9 May 1956-50 (Munro, J.A. 1958a); Windermere Lake 31 Mar 1978-48; Nicola Lake 14 Mar 1982-275; Kamloops 29 Mar 1985-44, 5 Apr 1985-138, 13 Apr 1985-32 (Butler, R.W. and Savard 1985); Riske Creek 10 Apr 1985-152, 11 Apr 1985-201, 13 Apr 1985-107, 17 Apr 1985-20 (Butler, R.W. and Savard 1985); Lac la Hache to Williams Lake 12 Apr 1962-100, 16 Apr 1962-257, 24 Apr 1962-74 (Erskine 1964); Williams Lake 13 Mar 1979-1, 17 Mar 1983-11; Prince George 19 Apr 1983-1; Fort St. John 23 Apr 1983-2; Charlie Lake 7 May 1983-880; Parker Lake (Fort Nelson) 11 May 1979-6, 14 May 1978-52.

Summer: Coastal - Crescent Beach 10 Aug 1957-10; Iona Island 12 Jul 1975-8; Masset 1 Aug 1940-1 (RBCM 11335). **Interior** - Minnie Lake 10 Aug 1939-200; Radium Hot Springs 6 Jul 1969-2 (Christman 1969); Edgewater 9 Jun 1973-8 (Hennan 1975); Bald Mountain (Riske Creek) 10 Jul 1978-8 males in eclipse plumage; Kotcho Lake 20 Jul 1977-95; Como Lake 3 Jul 1980-2.

Autumn: Interior - Charlie Lake 24 Oct 1982-1; Kitwancool Lake 25 Oct 1980-1; McBride Lake 29 Sep 1974-46; Williams Lake 4 Nov 1983-4; Scotch Creek 5 Nov 1962-4; Separation Lake 4 Sep 1950-5; Wilmer Lake 16 Oct 1977-16; Nicola Lake 23 Oct 1979-45; Vaseux Lake 8 Oct 1975-30, 22 Oct 1975-33, 29 Oct 1975-66; Creston 28 Sep 1986-265, 25 Oct 1986-350, 8 Nov 1985-2,325. **Coastal** - Delkatla Inlet 14 Nov 1981-5; Kitimat 28 Oct 1978-7; Granite Bay 16 Nov 1973-50; Tofino Inlet 22 Nov 1981-101; Westham Island 25 Sep 1971-8, 27 Oct 1971-50 (Campbell et al. 1972b); Roberts Bank 16 Nov 1981-200, 26 Nov 1982-400+; Esquimalt Lagoon 9 Oct 1976-6, 11 Nov 1970-95.

Winter: Interior - Kamloops 26 Dec 1981-1, 28 Feb 1982-60; Nicola Lake 19 Feb 1983-1; Okanagan Landing 27 Feb 1968-500; Penticton 27 Jan 1980-100; Vaseux Lake 22 Feb 1974-48; Creston 19 Dec 1984-40, 17 Jan 1983-250, 15 Feb 1983-200. **Coastal** - Kitimat 19 Dec 1981-1; Tasu Sound 29 to 31 Jan 1973-5; Browning Passage 7 Dec 1969-400 (Hatler et al. 1978); Harrison Bay 4 Dec 1976-96, 19 Jan 1977-68; Widgeon Slough 17 Feb 1972-46; Iona Island 29 Jan 1966 -500 (Crowell and Nehls 1967a); Sea Island 27 Dec 1970-112, 9 Feb 1974-200; Esquimalt Lagoon 1 Dec 1972-90, 6 Dec 1975-68, 29 Jan 1980-50.

Christmas Counts: Interior - Recorded from 7 of 19 localities and on 31% of all counts. Maxima: Penticton 27 Dec 1976-357; Vaseux Lake 31 Dec 1976-36; Vernon 18 Dec 1983-21. **Coastal** - Recorded from 22 of 28 localities and on 78% of all counts. Maxima: Ladner 21 Dec 1975-753; Vancouver 26 Dec 1973-383; Victoria 21 Dec 1963-232.

Redhead

REDH

Aythya americana (Eyton)

RANGE: Breeds locally but sparingly, in Alaska and from British Columbia and southwestern Mackenzie to central Minnesota, northern Iowa, south to northern Texas and southern California; sporadically in eastern North America. Winters from British Columbia and the northern and middle United States south to Guatemala, Cuba, Jamaica, and the Bahamas.

STATUS: *Abundant* migrant through the Okanagan and Creston valleys, becoming *fairly common* to *uncommon* north to the Chilcotin-Cariboo; *uncommon* to *fairly common* migrant in the Columbia valley; *rare* elsewhere. *Fairly common* summer visitant in the southern interior and Chilcotin-Cariboo areas; *uncommon* in the Creston valley and Peace Lowlands; *very rare* summer visitant elsewhere in the province. *Abundant* winter visitant to the south Okanagan valley; *very common* to *abundant* some years in the west Kootenay and Creston valleys; *rare* winter visitant to the south coast; *very rare* on the Queen Charlotte Islands. Breeds.

NONBREEDING: The Redhead is distributed locally throughout most of southern British Columbia. On the coast, it occurs on southern Vancouver Island and the Fraser Lowlands, rarely farther north to northern Vancouver Island and the Queen Charlotte Islands. In the interior, it occurs locally from the extreme southern portions of the province north through the major valleys (Okanagan, Creston, Columbia, Thompson) to the Chilcotin-Cariboo region. Farther north it is sparsely distributed through the Nechako Lowlands, Peace Lowlands, Boreal Forest, and the Northern Mountain and Plateau regions to the Yukon border.

The Redhead frequents freshwater and, occasionally, marine habitats throughout its nonbreeding range in British Columbia.

Interior birds favour large, deep lakes in winter (75%; n=366). Other habitats include ponds, sloughs, rivers, flooded fields, and freshwater and sewage lagoons. On the coast, Redheads prefer lakes (55%, n=123) followed by saltwater inlets (12%), saltwater lagoons (11%), flooded fields, sewage lagoons, reservoirs, ponds, and saltwater bays.

In the south, spring migration gets underway by mid-February and continues until mid-May. Farther north, birds arrive in April and May with the melting of spring ice. In the Okanagan and Creston valleys, numbers usually peak in late March.

Small numbers of Redheads summer on the coast. In the interior, flocks of moulting males can be found on select lakes by the end of June and small groups of nonbreeding yearling males have also been noted. Autumn migration often begins in early September, peaks in the second half of October, and continues into November in the southern valleys. The main southward movement occurs through the Okanagan and Creston valleys, but large numbers of Redheads occasionally move south through the Columbia valley. Banding recoveries indicate that most Redheads reared in British Columbia travel in autumn due south towards wintering grounds in southern California and western Mexico. A few have been recovered east of the Rocky Mountains (Fig. 288).

The Redhead is the only duck that winters in larger numbers in the interior than on the coast. Coastal winter distribution includes the Fraser Lowlands and southern Vancouver Island on the south coast; rarely on the Queen Charlotte Islands. In the interior, the Redhead winters from the Okanagan valley, north to Shuswap Lake, and east to the West Arm of Kootenay Lake and the Creston valley. The centre of winter abundance is Okanagan Lake, from Summerland south (Fig. 287). Bellrose (1976) notes that a "few" Redhead winter in southern British Columbia, but

Figure 287. Redheads with scaup and other diving ducks at Naramata, 22 December 1986 (Stephen R. Cannings).

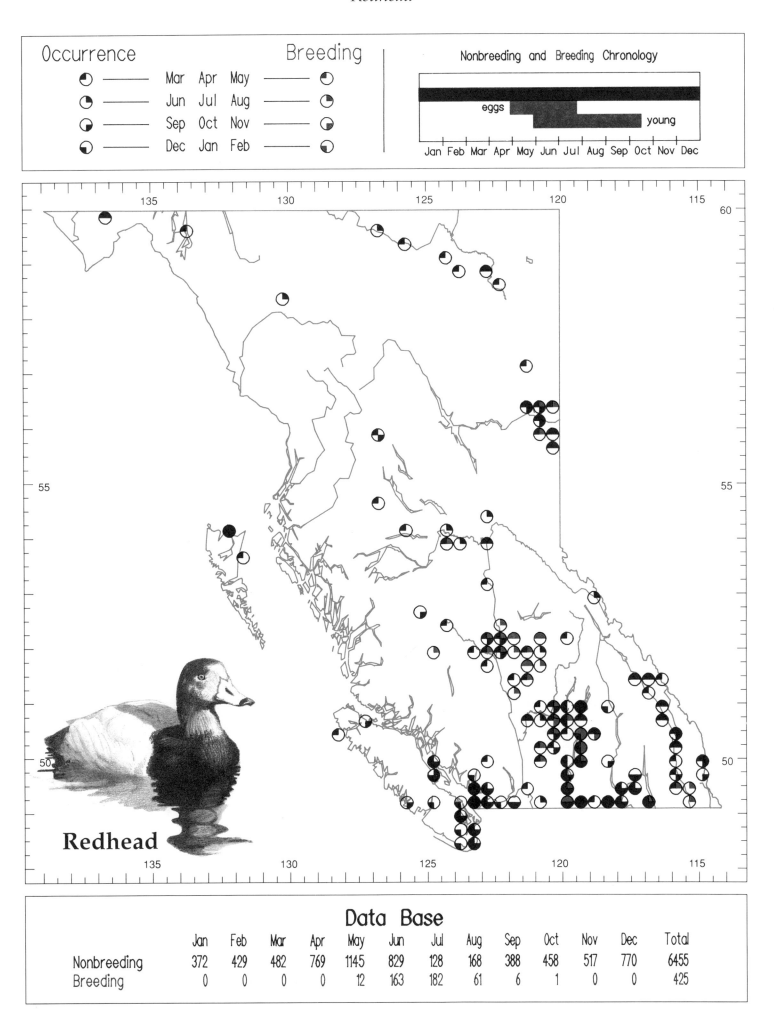

Occurrence

	Mar	Apr	May	
	Jun	Jul	Aug	
	Sep	Oct	Nov	
	Dec	Jan	Feb	

Breeding

Nonbreeding and Breeding Chronology

eggs

young

Jan Feb Mar Apr May Jun Jul Aug Sep Oct Nov Dec

Redhead

Data Base

	Jan	Feb	Mar	Apr	May	Jun	Jul	Aug	Sep	Oct	Nov	Dec	Total
Nonbreeding	372	429	482	769	1145	829	128	168	388	458	517	770	6455
Breeding	0	0	0	0	12	163	182	61	6	1	0	0	425

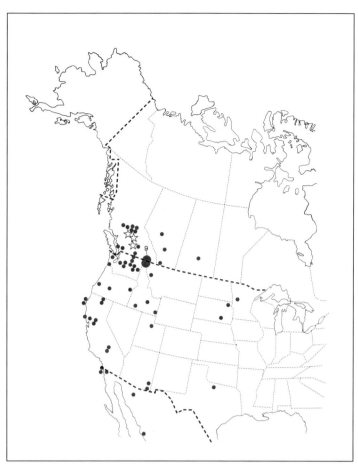

Figure 288. *Banding locations (stars) and recovery sites (circles) of Redheads associated with British Columbia (updated from Weller 1964). Red indicates birds banded in British Columbia.*

our records indicate that in some years over 2,500 birds can winter (see Christmas Counts below and Appendix 2).

BREEDING: The Redhead breeds in 2 distinct regions of the province. One population breeds from the southern east Kootenay, the Creston valley and in the central southern interior from the Okanagan valley north through the Merritt and Kamloops areas and widely throughout the Cariboo and eastern Chilcotin regions north to Soda Creek, but rarely in the Bulkley Basin. A second population nests in the Peace Lowlands from Scott Lake north to Boundary Lake. Bellrose (1976) suggests an estimated breeding population in the province of 7,000 birds.

The Redhead breeds on shallow freshwater lakes, marshes, sloughs and ponds from 330 to 1,000 m elevation. Most were observed on lakes (73%; n=242) with emergent vegetation on the shoreline or a larger expanse of emergent marsh.

Nests: Most nests (93%; n=30) were situated in dense stands of emergent vegetation. Twenty-seven nests were located over water ranging in depth from a few centimetres to over one metre One nest was on mud and one was on a rock ledge by water. An American Coot nest and a muskrat lodge were used as the substrates on two other occasions. Most nests were large structures of dead vegetation 30 to 45 cm above the water with a central depression lined with dry vegetation and down. Nest materials included reeds, rushes, cattail, and grasses. Extensive dry-land nesting by Redheads in Utah is documented by McKnight (1974). He concludes that the "aberrant" nesting behaviour was precipitated by large quantities of proteinaceous food available to Redheads seeking territories.

Eggs: Dates for 52 clutches ranged from 23 May to 9 July with 53% recorded between 3 June and 22 June. Calculated dates indicate that eggs could be found as early as 28 April and as late as 24 July. Clutch size ranged from 2 to 16 eggs (2E-3, 3E-1, 4E-6,

5E-4, 6E-6, 7E-3, 8E-8, 9E-7, 10E-6, 11E-1, 13E-2, 14E-3, 16E-2) with 58% having 6 to 10 eggs. It is difficult to determine normal clutch sizes in Redheads because of their semi-parasitic habit of laying eggs in the nests of other waterbirds, including other Redheads. We have observations of 4 species being parasitized by the Redhead: Pied-billed Grebe, Canvasback, Lesser Scaup, and American Coot. Incubation period is about 24 days (Low 1945).

Young: Dates for 287 broods ranged from 28 May to 16 October (flightless young) with 55% occurring between 20 June and 19 July. Brood size ranged from 1 to 18 young (1Y-9, 2Y-4, 3Y-13, 4Y-26, 5Y-37, 6Y-45, 7Y-49, 8Y-34, 9Y-27, 10Y-10, 11Y-14, 12Y-7, 13Y-3, 14Y-2, 15Y-3, 17Y-3, 18Y-1) with 57% having 5 to 8 young. Broods having more than 15 young may be the products of more than 1 female. Fledging period ranges from 56 to 73 days (Weller 1957).

REMARKS: The pattern of distribution and abundance for the Redhead has changed considerably during this century. J.A. Munro and Cowan (1947) state that the Redhead was scarce or absent in winter in the Okanagan valley, where it was once formerly abundant. Since then, the trend has reversed and the Redhead is now as abundant there in winter (Fig. 289) as it probably was in the early 1900s. However, declines have been noted for breeding Redheads in the Okanagan valley (Cannings, R.A. et al. 1987).

In the east Kootenay, W.B. Johnstone (1949) mentions the Redhead only as a rare spring migrant. Spring numbers are still modest, but autumn migrations over the past decade have produced concentrations of up to 1,700 birds on Windermere Lake.

J.A. Munro (1950) thought the bird was "probably a regular spring transient" to the Creston area. He mentions only 2 summer records, the latter of which is likely an early autumn movement (11 August 1948-90). During spring and autumn migration, the Creston valley now supports the largest known Redhead migration in the province. Recent spring numbers of Redheads at Creston have exceeded 8,500 birds; it is now a common breeding bird in the valley, and autumn numbers can exceed 7,500 birds. In addition, large numbers of Redheads now often winter in the west Kootenay and Creston valley. On the other hand, analysis of waterfowl harvest records at Creston suggest lower autumn numbers in the 1980s than in the previous decade (Butler, R.W. et al. 1986).

Observations of Redheads in extreme northeastern British Columbia may be of birds moving to their Alaska breeding grounds, or they may be part of a northward shift in the species' breeding range, of birds apparently displaced through a reduction in wetlands (Palmer, R.S. 1976b). The Redhead, like several other species nesting on the prairies or in the Great Basin, tends to move into peripheral habitats when conditions are not optimal in its primary range.

See Weller (1957) for a discussion of growth, weights, and plumages of the Redhead.

The Redhead appears on the 1982 "Blue List" as a species of "special concern" due to apparent declines in parts of the eastern United States (Tate and Tate 1982).

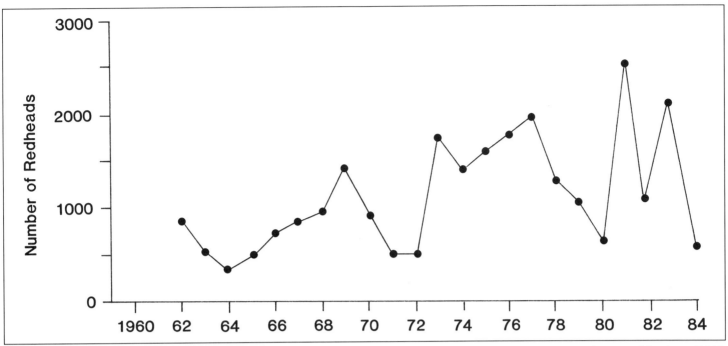

Figure 289. *Aggregate totals for Redheads in the Okanagan valley recorded during annual Christmas Bird Counts at Vernon, Kelowna, and Penticton, British Columbia, 1962 to 1984 (modified from Cannings, R.A. et al. 1987).*

NOTEWORTHY RECORDS

Spring: Coastal - Victoria 3 Mar 1956-31; Duncan 18 Mar 1974-6; Siwash Island 8 Mar 1972-38; Grant Bay 1st week May 1969-8; Tlell 15 and 27 May 1987-1; Delkatla Inlet 30 Apr 1979-2. **Interior** - Creston, all aerial censuses 5 Mar 1984-8,900, 15 Mar 1985-3,250, 17 Mar 1982-3,750, 6 Apr 1984-3,050, 24 Apr 1985-3,850; Vaseux Lake 15 Mar 1978-182; Penticton 6 Mar 1980-300; Cranbrook 10 Mar 1982-1; Okanagan Landing 10 Mar 1973-1,200 stayed only one day; Nicola Lake 6 Mar 1982-35; Canal Flats 21 Apr 1981-14; Windermere Lake 31 Mar 1978-45; Separation Lake 15 Mar 1981-60; North Kamloops 29 Mar 1985-8, 21 Apr 1985-21, 12 May 1985-25, on 2 Jun 1985 all birds had gone (Butler, R.W. and Savard 1985); Alkali Lake (Riske Creek) 2 Apr 1977-48 on small ice-free sections at each end of lake; Lac la Hache 21 Mar 1977-2; Charlie Lake 22 Apr 1985-1 pair; Boundary Lake (Goodlow) 7 May 1983-10; Clanga Lake (Fort Nelson) 5 May 1980-2; Como Lake 17 May 1977-4.

Summer: Coastal - Westham Island 17 Jul 1974-3; Delkatla Inlet 5 Jun 1984-1. **Interior** - Creston 20 Jul 1982-3,050, aerial census; Island Lake (Canal Flats) 25 Jun 1976-1; Swan Lake (Vernon) 15 Jul 1977-42, 25 Aug 1978-100; Brisco 21 Jun 1981-9; Riske Creek 26 Jun 1978-12 males, mostly in eclipse plumage; Tachick Lake 4 and 12 Jul 1945-40, chiefly nonbreeding yearling males; Summit Lake (Prince George) 1 Aug 1975-2; Dease Lake 7 Jun 1962-3; Coal River 24 Jun 1981-10; Haines Road, Mile 84.5 (Chilkat Pass) 23 Jun 1980-1.

Autumn: Interior - Charlie Lake 12 Sep 1982-2, 30 Oct 1986-5; Anahim Lake 26 Oct 1979-15 (Hennan 1979); Riske Creek 15 Oct 1978-5; Sorrento 23 Oct 1970-100; Swan Lake (Vernon) 6 Oct 1977-124, 3 Nov 1977-71; Douglas Lake (Quilchena) 3 Sep 1979-25; Windermere Lake 18 Oct 1977-1,040 at south end (Kaiser et al. 1978), 25 Oct 1979-1,700, 10 Nov 1978-250; Elkview 16 Oct 1984-62; West Arm (Kootenay Lake) 29 Sep 1983-3; Penticton 30 Oct 1973-200, 9 Nov 1980-600, first flock of fall, 11 Nov 1973-600; Vaseux Lake 15 Sep 1973-200+, 6 Oct 1973-375, 14 Oct 1974-452, 27 Oct 1973-395, 12 Nov 1972-500; Creston, aerial censuses, 28 Sep 1986-4,745, 9 Oct 1984-4,600, 25 Oct 1986-7,850, 8 Nov 1985-2,800, 14 Nov 1984-5,100. **Coastal** - Delkatla Inlet 4 Oct 1981-2; Cranberry Lake (Powell River) 2 Nov 1979-8; Vancouver 7 Nov 1962-10 (Boggs and Boggs 1963a); Grice Bay 22 Nov 1981-3; Duncan 31 Oct 1977-6.

Winter: Interior - Sorrento 19 Dec 1970-100+; Vernon 31 Dec 1950-400 (Grant, J. 1951); Penticton 29 Jan 1978-1,200+, 29 Feb 1980-2,000 (Cannings et al. 1987), 4 Dec 1973-1,845, 15 Dec 1980-2,500+, 28 Dec 1977-1,400; Nelson 18 Dec 1982-10; West Arm (Kootenay Lake) 1 Dec 1983-101, 2 Dec 1978-600, 2 Dec 1980-600, 8 Dec 1979-251; Creston, aerial censuses, 19 Dec 1984-175, 1 Jan 1981-206, 4 Feb 1982-150, 16 Feb 1984-600, 27 Feb 1984-805. **Coastal** - Masset 18 Dec 1983-1 male (Campbell 1983b), 11 Jan 1983-1; Pitt Lake 29 Jan 1972-61; Beaver Lake (Saanich) 28 Jan 1984-9.

Christmas Counts: Interior - Recorded from 7 of 19 localities and on 36% of all counts. Maxima: Penticton 27 Dec 1981-2,533; Vernon 26 Dec 1975 and 1976-350; Nakusp 3 Jan 1982-41. **Coastal** - Recorded from 12 of 28 localities and on 16% of all counts. Maxima: Pitt Meadows 27 Dec 1983-17; Ladner 23 Dec 1978-16; Comox 18 Dec 1983-12.

Ring-necked Duck

Aythya collaris (Donovan)

RANGE: Breeds from Alaska, southern Yukon, and most of southern Canada south to northeastern California and east across the north-central United States to Massachusetts; also north-central Florida. Winters mainly from the southern United States (north on the Pacific coast to Alaska, on the Atlantic coast to New England) south to Middle America and the West Indies.

STATUS: *Fairly common* to *common* migrant locally and *uncommon* to *fairly common* summer visitant through most of the province east of the Coast Ranges with the exception of the Northern Mountains and Plateaus and the Northern and Central Rocky Mountains region where the species is *very rare*. *Rare* summer visitant to the south coast. *Uncommon* to *common* winter visitant to the south coast and southern interior regions; *very rare* on the Queen Charlotte Islands; *casual* elsewhere in the province. Breeds.

NONBREEDING: The Ring-necked Duck is widely distributed throughout most of the province including Vancouver Island and the Queen Charlotte Islands. It is absent or very scarce along the mainland coast from Powell River north to the Kitimat area and in the Northern Mountain region. It occurs from sea level to 1,750 m elevation.

The Ring-necked Duck frequents a variety of freshwater habitats. Wintering birds can occasionally be found on marine waters, particularly during periods of severe weather when freshwater areas are frozen. Near the coast, birds are found primarily on lakes, ponds, and flooded fields; other coastal habitats include saltwater lagoons, sewage ponds, bogs, swamps, freshwater and saltwater sloughs, saltwater inlets, reservoirs, rivers, creeks, and estuaries. Interior habitat includes lakes, ponds, sewage lagoons, rivers, sloughs, and marshes.

Spring migration starts in February as birds begin leaving the coast. The main coastal movement occurs through the first 2 weeks in March with numbers decreasing through April; most birds have departed by early May. In the interior, birds begin moving by mid-March, but in the central and northern regions the main movement does not occur until after the middle of April or early May. Small numbers of nonbreeders remain at the coast during the summer. In the interior, flocks of moulting males can be found on certain lakes from mid-June to the end of July, sometimes later. The autumn migration can begin in late August but the main movement in the interior does not occur until the end of September or early October; on the coast, the main movement occurs from October through mid-November.

Major wintering areas on the coast include eastern Vancouver Island, principally from Duncan south to Victoria, and the Port Alberni area. Small numbers (mainly males) winter in the Okanagan and Nicola valleys, if lakes remain unfrozen.

BREEDING: The Ring-necked Duck is a widespread but uncommon breeder throughout the interior of the province from the Okanagan valley and the Kootenays north through the Chilcotin-Cariboo and Fraser Basin; also the Peace Lowlands and the northern Boreal Forest region of northeastern British Columbia. Except for the east coast of Vancouver Island and the Fraser Lowlands, where the bird is a local breeder, there are no breeding records for the coast or the Northern Mountains and Plateaus and Northern and Central Rocky Mountains regions of the province.

It breeds on freshwater lakes (69%; n=149), marshes, ponds, and sloughs, often in wooded situations, mainly from 300 m to 1,200 m elevation. J.A. Munro (1958b) notes that nesting birds in the Cariboo parklands seem restricted to slightly acid lakes where yellow waterlily covers much of the water surface.

Nests: Most nests (72%; n=14) were situated in stands of emergent vegetation or grass clumps in varying degrees of concealment; two nests were completely exposed. Six nests were located on the ground; six were over water. Three nests ranged from 0.3 m to 3 m from water; one nest on the water was 1 m from shore. Nests on the ground were usually in a small hollow lined with vegetation and down; nests on the water were cupped clumps (or rafts) of vegetation and down. Materials included grasses, bulrush, sedges, and cattail.

Eggs: Dates for 14 clutches ranged from 21 May to 18 July. Clutch size ranged from 5 to 12 eggs (5E-1, 6E-2, 7E-1, 8E-2, 9E-3, 10E-4, 12E-1), with 50% having 9 or 10 eggs. Incubation period is about 25 to 29 days with an average of 26 days (Mendall 1958).

Young: Dates for 164 broods ranged from 15 June to 31 August with 54% recorded between 9 July and 7 August. Brood size ranged from 1 to 11 young (1Y-5, 2Y-10, 3Y-10, 4Y-22, 5Y-27, 6Y-25, 7Y-30, 8Y-21, 9Y-9, 10Y-3, 11Y-2) with 63% having 5 to 8 young. Fledging period is about 49 to 56 days (Mendall 1958).

REMARKS: Prior to 1947, the Ring-necked Duck was known to occur north only to the Bulkley valley, but it is now known to occur with some regularity north to the Yukon border in northeastern British Columbia. Bellrose (1976) estimates a breeding population in British Columbia of almost 28,000 birds.

NOTEWORTHY RECORDS

Spring: Coastal - Beaver Lake (Saanich) 5 Mar 1977-107, 12 Mar 1977-38; Somenos Lake 6 Mar 1974-30, 15 Mar 1974-16; Hubard Marsh (Comox) 11 Apr 1971-22; Cape Scott Park 4 to 9 May 1975-6; Delkatla Inlet 18 May 1987-1 male. **Interior** - Osoyoos Lake 15 Mar 1965-46; Wilmer 31 Mar 1981-9, 3 Apr 1985-7, 15 Apr 1985-49, 22 Apr 1985-66, 30 Apr 1985-32, 13 May 1985-6 (Butler, R.W. and Savard 1985); Separation Lake 16 Mar 1981-11; Revelstoke 18 Apr 1977-12; Alkali Lake (Riske Creek) 2 Apr 1977-63 on small ice-free section; Riske Creek 10 Apr 1985-20, 15 Apr 1985-61, 20 Apr 1985-51, 25 Apr 1985-51, 2 May 1985-8 (Butler, R.W. and Savard 1985); Williams Lake 14 Mar 1978-1, 15 Apr 1962-16; Prince George 14 Apr 1985-2, 5 May 1985-54, 26 May 1985-5 (Butler, R.W. and Savard 1985); Quick 24 Apr 1983-1; 20 km sw Ft. St. John 23 Apr 1983-1; Kledo Creek 13 May 1981-24; Atlin 16 May 1981-3 (Campbell 1981).

Summer: Coastal - Swan Lake (Saanich) 6 Jun 1981-3; Iona Island 27 Jun 1974-2 (Crowell and Nehls 1974d); Agassiz 3 Jul 1985-1 pair. **Interior** - Vaseux Lake 27 Jul 1974-3; Swan Lake (Vernon) 22 Jul 1977-20 males, 19 Aug 1977-68; Rose Hill 15 to 25 Jun 1966-38 males, 16 to 20 Jun 1969-10 males; Fireside 16 Jul 1981-20 moulting birds.

Autumn: Interior - Chilkat Pass 22 Sep 1972-6; Spatsizi River 6 Sep 1976-2; Charlie Lake 6 Oct 1986-25; Boudreau Lake 9 Sep 1981-50; Dawson Creek 3 Oct 1982-1; Kathlyn Lake 30 Nov 1987-2 males; Chilcotin Lake 22 Sep 1977-26; Puntzi Creek 19 Oct 1980-27; Williams Lake 10 Sep 1979-11, 20 Sep 1979-127, 2 Oct 1979-65, 25 Oct 1979-2, 4 Nov 1983-1; Napier Lake 22 Sep 1982-21; Richie Lake 11 Oct 1981-80; Nicola Lake 3 Nov 1984-35; Windermere Lake 18 Oct 1977-145 at south end (Kaiser et al. 1978); Sirdar 8 Sep 1947-4 (Munro, J.A. 1950); Vaseux Lake 3 Sep 1975-5, 24 Sep 1975-28, 10 Oct 1975-60, 29 Oct 1975-58, 13 Nov 1975-51. **Coastal** - Masset 18 Nov 1983-25; Cranberry Lake (Powell River) 28 Sep 1981-95, 1 Oct 1981-133, 3 Nov 1980-150, 26 Nov 1980-10; Westham Island 13 Oct 1974-14; Somenos Lake 10 Nov 1982-147; Swan Lake (Saanich) 22 Sep 1977-3, 1 Oct 1977-25, 22 Nov 1980-50.

Winter: Interior - Kathlyn Lake 1 Dec 1987-2 males; Williams Lake 26 Dec 1969-1; South Thompson River (Chase to Pritchard) 18 Jan 1949-14; Taghum 24 Jan 1977-3; 1 km e Brilliant 10 Dec 1984-80 on Kootenay River; Vaseux Lake 2 Dec 1973-45, 10 Jan 1970-31; Christina Lake 20 Jan 1977-5. **Coastal** - Masset 15 Feb 1983-7; Kitimat 18 Dec 1978-2; Cranberry Lake (Powell River) 9 Dec 1979-30; Somass River 16 Jan 1981-78 on estuary; Nicomen Slough 29 Dec 1977-114, 30 Jan 1977-48; Somenos Lake 13 Dec 1973-84, 23 Dec 1973-250, 23 Jan 1974-86, 20 Feb 1974-23; Beaver Lake and Elk Lake (Saanich) 12 Dec 1959-400 (Poynter 1960).

Christmas Counts: Interior - Recorded from 7 of 19 localities and on 32% of all counts. Maxima: Vaseux Lake 23 Dec 1982-78; Kelowna 20 Dec 1981-19; Shuswap Lake 28 Dec 1983-14. **Coastal** - Recorded from 20 of 28 localities and on 55% of all counts. Maxima: Victoria 15 Dec 1984-**408**, all-time Canadian high count (Monroe 1985b); Duncan 16 Dec 1973-394; Port Alberni 4 Jan 1976-81.

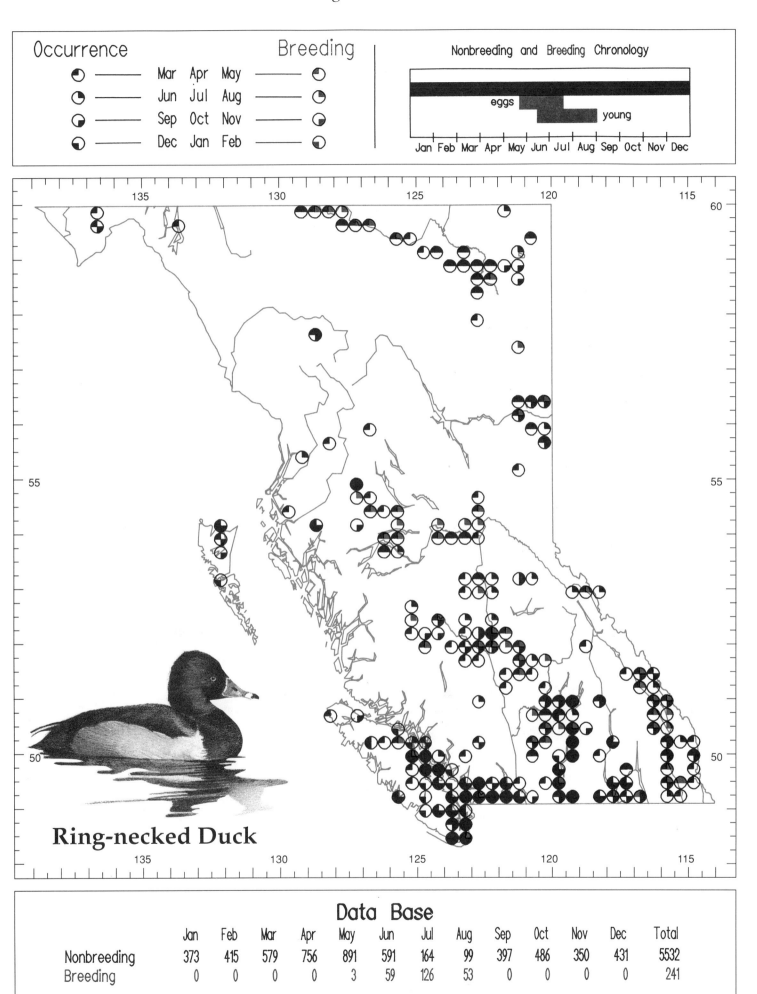

Occurrence
Breeding

	Mar Apr May	
Jun Jul Aug	
Sep Oct Nov	
Dec Jan Feb	

Nonbreeding and Breeding Chronology

eggs   young

Jan Feb Mar Apr May Jun Jul Aug Sep Oct Nov Dec

Ring-necked Duck

Data Base

	Jan	Feb	Mar	Apr	May	Jun	Jul	Aug	Sep	Oct	Nov	Dec	Total
Nonbreeding	373	415	579	756	891	591	164	99	397	486	350	431	5532
Breeding	0	0	0	0	3	59	126	53	0	0	0	0	241

Tufted Duck

Aythya fuligula (Linnaeus)

TUDU

RANGE: Breeds throughout northern Eurasia. Winters in southern Eurasia, northern Africa, Philippines, and Japan. In North America nonbreeders occur regularly, in small numbers, in migration to the western and central Aleutian Islands. A few birds winter along the Pacific coast to southern California. Casual on the Atlantic coast.

STATUS: *Rare* winter visitant to the south inner coast; *casual* in summer. *Casual* in spring and *accidental* in autumn in the interior.

CHANGE IN STATUS: The Tufted Duck was first recorded on the Pacific coast of North America south of Alaska, in California, during the winter of 1948-49 (Cogswell 1977). It was first reported in British Columbia in 1961 (Hughes 1963). From 1961 to 1975 the Tufted Duck appeared in 10 of the 16 years on at least 30 occasions on the south coast (Campbell and Weber 1976). From 1976 to 1987 it was reported in 9 different years, and in every year since 1980. The Tufted Duck is now expected to be found annually, especially on the south mainland coast.

OCCURRENCE: The Tufted Duck has been found in the Greater Victoria area on southern Vancouver Island, in the southern Gulf Islands and on the mainland from the Fraser River delta to Harrison Lake. There are 3 vagrant interior occurrences: 2 from Williams Lake and 1 from Okanagan Lake.

The Tufted Duck frequents marine, brackish, and fresh water habitats. Marine waters of bays, inlets, and harbours were most often used (35%; n=49), followed closely by brackish lagoons (31%). Other habitats included sewage ponds, lakes, reservoirs, and sloughs.

Ninety-five percent of all records were of single birds. The largest group was 3 adult males. Eighty-eight percent of records were males (45% adults, 16% immatures, 27% undetermined age); 12% were females.

The Tufted Duck has been recorded in British Columbia between 27 September and 12 July. Most birds arrive in October and November. There appears to be an increase of records in spring, suggesting that some of the birds may be migrants. The average length of stay, excluding the 3 longest periods, is about 2 weeks. The longest continuous stay was 104 days, from 16 February to 30 May.

The geographic origin of Tufted Ducks occurring in British Columbia is probably Alaska (or perhaps Siberia) where they accompany migrating flocks of Greater Scaup. While in the province, the Tufted Duck also associates with Surf Scoters, White-winged Scoters, Lesser Scaups, and Ring-necked Ducks.

Figure 290. *Female Tufted Duck at Lost Lagoon (Vancouver), 25 January 1986 (RBCM Photo 1077; Tim Zurowski).*

NOTEWORTHY RECORDS

Spring: Coastal - Clover Point 25 Mar to 6 Apr 1970-1 male, first record for Vancouver Island (Tatum 1971; RBCM Photo 233 on 25 Mar), 5 Apr 1973-1 pair (Crowell and Nehls 1973c); Ganges 9 Mar 1972-1 (RBCM Photo 392); Duncan 28 Mar 1987-1 male; Ladner 16 Feb to 30 May 1974-1 male (RBCM Photo 341 on 13 Mar); Stanley Park (Vancouver) 7 Apr 1986-1 (RBCM Photo 1116); McKay Creek (North Vancouver) 16 Mar 1975-1 male (Campbell and Weber 1976); Harrison Lake 21 Mar 1971-1 male (Campbell and Weber 1976). **Interior** - See Extralimital Records.

Summer: Coastal - Iona Island 7 and 8 Jun 1986-1, 7, and 15 Jun 1975-2 males, 12 Jul 1975-1 male moulting into eclipse plumage; Stanley Park (Vancouver) 6 Jun 1968-1 adult male. **Interior** - No records.

Autumn: Interior - See Extralimital Records. **Coastal** - Stanley Park (Vancouver) 27 Sep 1971-1 male (Crowell and Nehls 1974a), 10 to 17 Oct 1967-1 male (RBCM Photo 92), 3 to 25 Nov 1987-1 female, 4 to 11 Nov 1961-1 male (Hughes 1963); Reifel Island 11 to 17 Nov 1968-3 adult males; White Rock 26 Nov 1980-1 adult male; Central Saanich 17 Nov to 2 Dec 1984-1.

Winter: Interior - No records. **Coastal** - Stanley Park (Vancouver) 4 Jan to 28 Feb 1986-1 to 2 females (RBCM Photo 1077; Fig. 290); Iona Island 26 to 28 Jan 1984-1, 8 Feb 1971-1 male (Campbell et al. 1972b); Ganges Harbour 9 Feb 1972-1 male (Crowell and Nehls 1972b); Long Harbour 13 Feb 1972-1 adult male; Victoria 8 Feb to 6 May 1971-1 adult male (Tatum 1972).

Christmas Counts: Interior - Not recorded. **Coastal** - Recorded from 2 of 28 localities and on 1% of all counts. Maxima: Victoria 21 Dec 1974-1; Vancouver 26 Dec 1975-1, 18 Dec 1983-1 [records are all-time Canadian high counts (Anderson, R.R. 1976)].

Extralimital Records: Interior - Williams Lake 2 May 1982-1 male (Campbell 1982c; RBCM Photo 802), 15 Mar 1984-1 adult male with flock of Ring-necked Ducks on open creek; Okanagan Landing 13 to 15 October 1987-1 immature male with Greater Scaup, Redheads, and Ring-necked Ducks (Campbell 1988a).

Tufted Duck

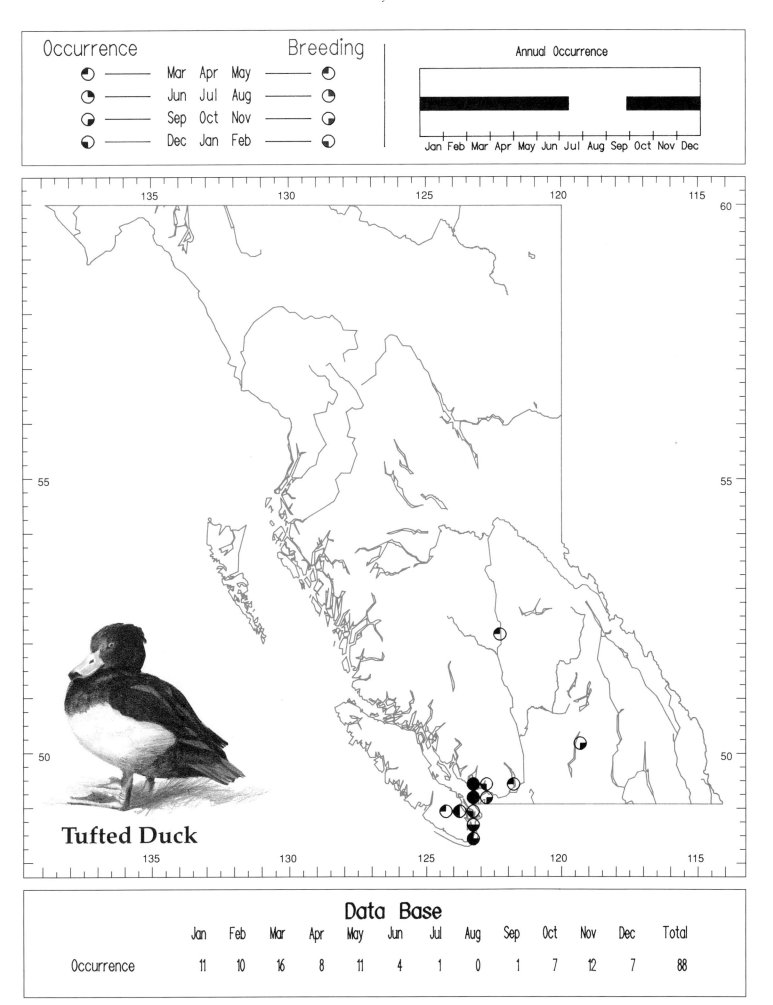

Occurrence　　　　　**Breeding**

Occurrence	Mar Apr May	Breeding
◐ ———	Mar Apr May	——— ◐
◔ ———	Jun Jul Aug	——— ◔
◕ ———	Sep Oct Nov	——— ◕
● ———	Dec Jan Feb	——— ●

Annual Occurrence

Jan Feb Mar Apr May Jun Jul Aug Sep Oct Nov Dec

Tufted Duck

Data Base

	Jan	Feb	Mar	Apr	May	Jun	Jul	Aug	Sep	Oct	Nov	Dec	Total
Occurrence	11	10	16	8	11	4	1	0	1	7	12	7	88

Greater Scaup

GRSC

Aythya marila (Linnaeus)

RANGE: Holarctic. Breeds in North America from Alaska and Yukon east across northwestern and southern Mackenzie to extreme northern Manitoba and Ontario. Also breeds in Eurasia from Iceland and Scandinavia east to northern Russia and Siberia. In North America winters along the Pacific coast from Alaska to Baja California; on the Atlantic coast from Newfoundland south to Florida and on the eastern Great Lakes.

STATUS: *Common* to *abundant* migrant and *uncommon* to *common* summer visitant along coastal British Columbia. *Common* migrant and *rare* to *fairly common* summer visitant to the interior. *Common* to *abundant* winter visitant to the coast and the southern interior.

OCCURRENCE: The Greater Scaup is distributed all along the British Columbia coast; in the interior, it occurs in smaller numbers from the Okanagan valley and the west Kootenay (rarely the east Kootenay), north through the Chilcotin-Cariboo region. Farther north its distribution becomes sporadic in the Fraser Basin and Northern Mountains and Plateaus region; it is rarely reported from the Peace Lowlands and Boreal Forest regions. It has been reported from sea level to 1,750 m elevation.

The Greater Scaup frequents a variety of marine and freshwater habitats throughout its range in British Columbia. On the coast those include estuaries, bays (see Fig. 291) and harbours, lakes, saltwater lagoons, inlets, sounds, and occasionally, flooded fields and ponds. Interior birds frequent lakes, rivers, ponds, and sewage lagoons; occasionally they occur on flooded fields. Spring migration begins on the coast in March when larger concentrations build where Pacific herring are spawning. Small groups reach the interior lakes as soon as there is open water. For example, the main movement usually begins in early April at Kamloops, but sometimes occurs throughout March. The migration continues into June. The coastal movement is far greater than the interior movement and records suggest that

a large part of the migratory population overflies the province.

Small numbers of Greater Scaup summer along the coast and occasionally in the interior, particularly north of 56°N latitude. One large concentration of birds at Butte Lake may have been a moulting flock. Some birds may begin the autumn migration in September, but the main movement does not occur until mid-October. It continues through November, when most birds arrive on the wintering grounds. Birds winter all along the coast. In the interior, wintering Greater Scaup can be found from the Okanagan valley, occasionally east to the west Kootenay, north to the Thompson Basin, and rarely to Williams Lake. Greatest concentrations occur around the Strait of Georgia, particularly southern Vancouver Island and the Fraser River delta. Bellrose (1976) notes that about 5,700 Greater Scaup winter on the coast of British Columbia, but recent data indicate that at least 3 times that number have wintered there (Appendix 2).

REMARKS: The Greater Scaup is reported to breed in the St. Elias Mountains, Haines Triangle (Munro, J.A. and Cowan 1947; Weeden 1960; Godfrey 1986); however, the downy young collected there have since been confirmed as those of Lesser Scaup (R.D. James and W.E. Godfrey pers. comm.). The confusion between the two species on both the breeding and wintering areas has been noted by a number of authors including R.S. Palmer (1976b) and R.A. Cannings et al. (1987).

Known in Old World literature as the Scaup.

NOTEWORTHY RECORDS

Spring: Coastal - Clover Point 26 Mar 1972-900, 17 Apr 1973-400, 5 May 1973-250; Ganges Harbour 11 Mar 1978-700, 21 Mar 1978-2,800 at herring spawn area (Carson and Howsam 1978); Tofino 1 May 1974-200; between Flewett Pt. and Dodd Narrows 25 Mar 1977-5,600; Gabriola Island 26 Mar 1978-4,500; Mud Bay (Boundary Bay) 5 Mar 1976-564, 6 May 1976-130; Roberts Bank 17 Apr 1981-3,000, 12 May 1976-1,293 in 3 flocks; Sea and Iona islands 17 Mar 1974-800, 30 Mar 1974-1,000, 27 Apr 1974-1,000, 10 May 1974-600; Iona Island 11 Mar 1979-1,600; Sea Island 8 Apr 1979-2,000; Vancouver Harbour 24 Feb 1952-1,625 near sewer outfalls; Nanoose Harbour 22 March 1978 - 4, 250 following Pacific herring spawn (Dawe and Lang 1980); 28 Mar 1975-5,000, 29 Mar 1976-11,300; Little Qualicum River 26 Mar 1982-2,025, 12 Apr 1976-1,840 (Dawe 1980), 18 May 1974, departure; Baynes Sound 14 Mar 1979-1,000+; Powell River 29 Mar 1981-400; Campbell River 22 May 1975-4; Pulteney Point 5 May 1976-20, first noticeable northward movement, 8 May 1976-320 last spring sighting; Delkatla Inlet 29 Mar 1979-5, 21 Apr 1972-155; Rose Spit 25 Apr 1979-199, 29 Apr 1979-149, 4 May 1979-36, 5 May 1979-99, all flying north in flocks of 2 to 35 birds; Prince Rupert 29 Mar 1976-500, 29 Apr 1975-50. **Interior** - Duck Lake (Creston) 13 Mar 1949-90; Penticton 13 Mar 1980-50; Sparwood 23 May 1984-38; Sorrento 1 Mar 1971-150, 3 Apr 1971-250+, 6 May 1971-2, latest date; Nicola Lake 14 Mar 1982-8; Kamloops 7 Mar 1982-4, 8 Mar 1982-150; Riske Creek 14 May 1978-2, most gone by this date; 105 Mile House 6 May 1977-200; Williams Lake 26 Mar 1978-20, 14 Apr 1980-70;

Westwick Lake 5 May 1977-50; Nulki Lake 2 May 1945-300+ (Munro, J.A. and Cowan 1947); Prince George 4 Apr 1986-10; Francois Lake 7 Apr 1978-12; Nilkitkwa Lake 22 May 1978-4; Fort St. John 27 Apr 1986-1; Charlie Lake 20 May 1979-9; Gnat Lake 29 May 1979-2.

Summer: Coastal - Oak Bay 9 Jul 1977-2; Browning Passage 3 Jun 1982-150; Sea and Iona islands 22 Jun 1974-270 summering (Shepard, M.G. 1975c); Howe Sound 31 Jul 1971-15 (Campbell et al. 1972b); Miracle Beach 13 Jul 1959-2 (Stirling 1961); Kitimat 26 Jul 1975-27; Masset 18 Jul 1982-65. **Interior** - Okanagan River 31 Aug 1977-1; Manning Park 23 to 24 Jul 1973-3 (Crowell and Nehls 1973d); Williams Lake 1 Jun 1963-25; Stalk Lakes 10 Jul 1976-14; Summit Pass 23 Jun 1972-1; Cold Fish Lake 9 Jul 1976-3 pair (Osmond-Jones et al. 1977); Butte Lake 2 Jul 1977-150, mostly males; Kelsall Lake 24 Jun 1980-5.

Autumn: Interior - McBride-Stikine rivers 9 Sep 1977-1 at junction; Fort St. John 16 Sep 1986-1; Manson Lakes 22 Oct 1972-6; Riske Creek 14 Oct 1978-30; Kamloops 21 Nov 1982-85; Nicola Lake 28 Nov 1981-3; Sorrento 25 Oct 1970-30+; Elkview 13 Oct 1984-6; Kootenay Lake 18 Nov 1979-40; Vaseux Lake 9 Oct 1978-10. **Coastal** - Pearl Harbour 5 Nov 1977-287 (Martin 1978); Delkatla Inlet 11 Nov 1982-84; Discovery Passage 30 Sep 1967-175; Saranac Island 9 Nov 1981-2,500+; Grice Bay 22 Nov 1981-400; Frank Island 24 Sep 1982-300 flying southeast in 5 separate flocks; Tsawwassen 3 Oct 1979-1,500; Ocean Park 28 Nov 1978-3,000; Sidney 21 Nov 1975-3,000 (Rodway

and Campbell 1977); Brentwood Bay to Cordova Bay 20 Oct 1952-1,500 to 2,000 (Flahaut 1953a); Oak Bay 28 Sep 1969-10.

Winter: Interior - Kleena Kleene 26 Jan 1952-2 (Paul 1959); Kamloops 17 Dec 1978-3, 3 Jan 1983-85 on South Thompson River; Adams River 13 Dec 1970-300+ at mouth (Schnider et al. 1971); South Thompson River (Chase to Pritchard) 18 Jan 1949-725; Kamloops 18 Jan 1985-105; Revelstoke 21 Dec 1983-1; Swan Lake (Vernon) 8 Dec 1944-200 (Munro, J.A. 1945b); Okanagan Lake Jan 1919-2,000 (Munro, J.A. and Cowan 1947); Penticton 1 Jan 1980-100; Thrums 22 Jan 1977-33. **Coastal** - Pearl Harbour 19 Jan 1978-202 (Martin 1978); Masset 14 Dec 1971-100; Minette Bay 15 Feb 1975-15 (Hay 1976); Port Clements 19 Feb 1955-325; Port Neville 12 Jan 1978-24; Mud Bay (Baynes Sound) 18 Feb 1976-575; Somass River 24 Jan 1976-200+ on estuary; Tofino 4 Jan 1976-390; Pitt Lake 19 Jan 1974-200; Iona Island 27 Feb 1972-1,689; Beach Grove 9 Feb 1986-4,000; Departure Bay 8 Jan 1965-500+; Clover Point 19 Dec 1969-1,500, 24 Jan 1971-1,100+.

Christmas Counts: Interior - Recorded from 7 of 19 localities and on 47% of all counts. Maxima: Penticton 22 Dec 1984-345; Shuswap Lake 28 Dec 1975-182; Vaseux Lake 31 Dec 1976-79. **Coastal** - Recorded from 23 of 28 localities and on 86% of all counts. Maxima: White Rock 4 Jan 1981-7,017; Vancouver 27 Dec 1959-4,706; Victoria 21 Dec 1963-3,139.

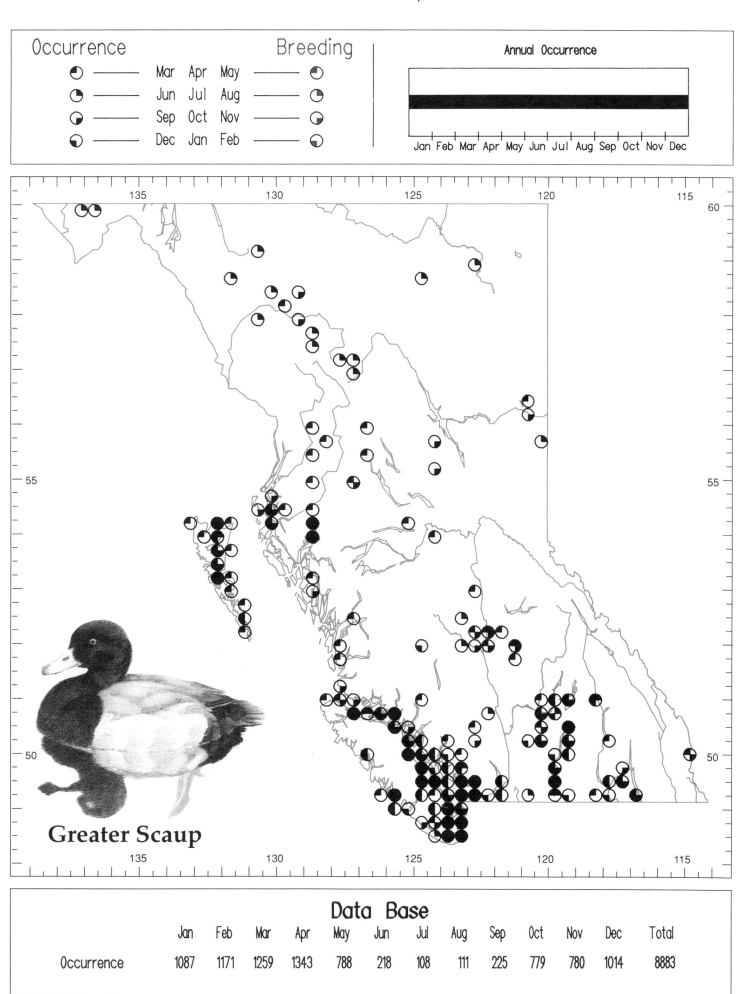

Greater Scaup

Occurrence

◑ ———	Mar Apr May	——— ◑
◔ ———	Jun Jul Aug	——— ◔
◕ ———	Sep Oct Nov	——— ◕
◕ ———	Dec Jan Feb	——— ◕

Breeding

Annual Occurrence

Jan Feb Mar Apr May Jun Jul Aug Sep Oct Nov Dec

Data Base

	Jan	Feb	Mar	Apr	May	Jun	Jul	Aug	Sep	Oct	Nov	Dec	Total
Occurrence	1087	1171	1259	1343	788	218	108	111	225	779	780	1014	8883

Lesser Scaup

LESC

Aythya affinis (Eyton)

RANGE: Breeds from Alaska, Yukon, and across northern Canada from the tree limit east to central Quebec, south to southern interior British Columbia, northern Idaho and across the northern states to northwestern Minnesota. Winters mainly from southern British Columbia and southern Utah east to Maryland and south through the United States, Middle America, to northern South America and the West Indies.

STATUS: *Fairly common* to *very common* migrant and summer visitant throughout the province with the exception of the coast where it is *uncommon* in summer. *Uncommon* to *very common* winter visitant to coastal British Columbia and the extreme central-southern portion of the province. Widespread breeder throughout the interior of the province.

NONBREEDING: The Lesser Scaup is widely distributed throughout British Columbia. On the coast, it occurs primarily on southeastern Vancouver Island and the Fraser Lowlands. Records are scarce from northern Vancouver Island and north along the mainland coast from Prince Rupert to the Terrace area. On the Queen Charlotte Islands, its distribution includes only northeastern Graham Island. It has been found from sea level to 1,980 m elevation.

The Lesser Scaup frequents a variety of marine and freshwater habitats throughout the province. On the coast, birds are most often found on open waters of straits adjacent to points, rocky islets or beaches, on bays (Fig. 291) and harbours, estuaries, lakes, ponds, and saltwater lagoons. Other habitats near the coast include reservoirs, sewage ponds, inlets, sloughs, and flooded fields. Birds in the interior frequent lakes, ponds, rivers, sewage lagoons and occasionally sloughs, creeks, flooded fields, and

marshes. Mulholland (1985), in the southern United States, considers 4 variables sufficient to evaluate wintering habitat on coastal areas: percentage of area supporting pelecypods, percentage of area supporting emergent vegetation (more vegetation = less suitable habitat), water depth (1 to 3 m is optimal), and minimal human disturbance to feeding areas.

Spring migration begins in March on the coast and continues into early May. In the interior, early migrants sometimes arrive in late February and early March but most birds do not appear until early to mid-April, after the ice recedes; numbers peak in late April and early May. In the northern part of the province, the main movement occurs about mid-May. A few summer along the south coast. In the interior, large numbers of nonbreeding birds begin congregating on select lakes by early July to moult. They are soon followed by post-breeding males, whose moult can continue into late August. Autumn migration likely begins in late August in the northern areas, although differentiating rafts of moulting males from early migrants is difficult on the basis of available information. Males complete the wing moult ahead of the females, so migrating flocks are often composed entirely of males, or females and young. In the Chilcotin-Cariboo, there is a reduction in numbers by late August. The main autumn movement occurs from mid-September through October in the north interior, and may carry on until the end of November in the south interior, and late November on the coast. Some birds remain in the interior until freeze-up forces them south. Bellrose (1976) states that most birds west of the Great Plains follow a coastal corridor from Alaska to Guatemala. However, Munro, J.A. (1941a) notes the lack of information on Lesser Scaup migration along the coast north of the Fraser River, and our data show little in the way of a coastal movement as well. It seems likely that

Figure 291. Greater and Lesser scaup wintering off Stanley Park (Vancouver), 31 December 1984 (Chris Siddle).

Lesser Scaup

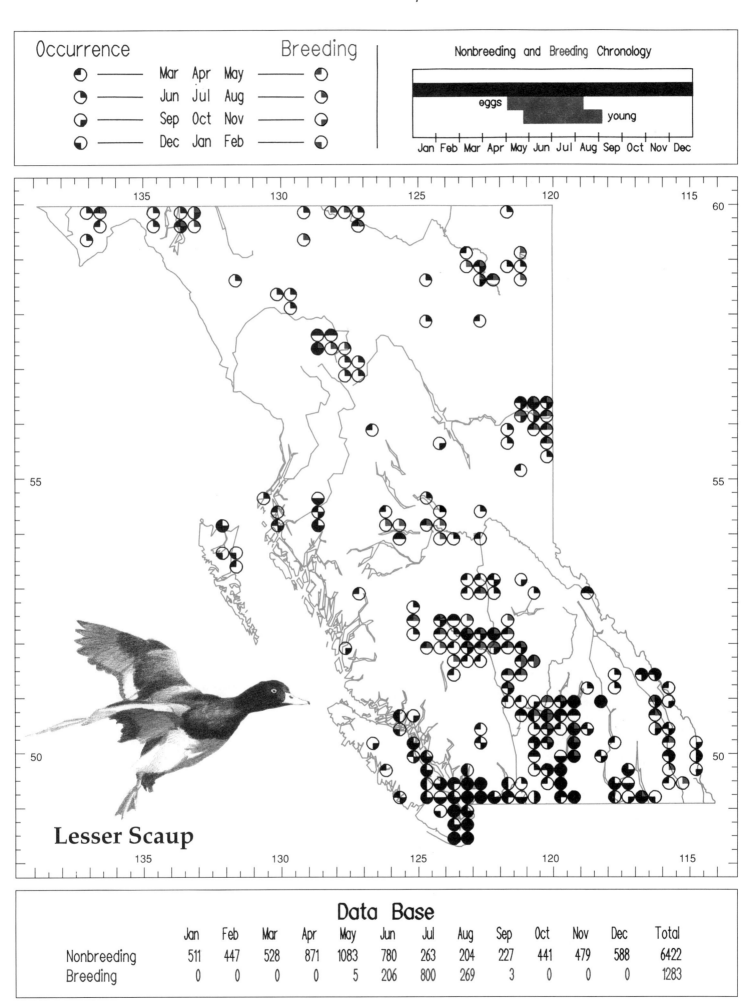

Occurrence

◕ ———	Mar	Apr	May
◔ ———	Jun	Jul	Aug
◔ ———	Sep	Oct	Nov
◑ ———	Dec	Jan	Feb

Breeding

——— ◕
——— ◔
——— ◔
——— ◑

Nonbreeding and Breeding Chronology

eggs — young

Jan Feb Mar Apr May Jun Jul Aug Sep Oct Nov Dec

Lesser Scaup

Data Base

	Jan	Feb	Mar	Apr	May	Jun	Jul	Aug	Sep	Oct	Nov	Dec	Total
Nonbreeding	511	447	528	871	1083	780	263	204	227	441	479	588	6422
Breeding	0	0	0	0	5	206	800	269	3	0	0	0	1283

birds wintering along the coast migrate directly from the interior of the province.

The major wintering areas include southern Vancouver Island from Victoria north to Duncan, and the extreme western Fraser Lowlands, particularly the Fraser River delta. In the interior, major areas include the southern Okanagan valley and the west arm of Kootenay Lake.

BREEDING: The Lesser Scaup breeds throughout the interior of the province. It is a rare breeder in the north Okanagan, Creston, and Columbia valleys, but numbers of breeding birds increase northward through the Rocky Mountain Trench and the Thompson-Okanagan Plateau to the Cariboo-Chilcotin and the Peace River areas. Small numbers breed in the Bulkley Basin, Boreal Forest, and the Northern Mountains and Plateau regions. The Chilcotin-Cariboo Basin, from 100 Mile House north to Stum Lake and west to Kleena Kleene and Chilcotin Lake, is the centre of breeding abundance. J.A. Munro (1958b) states that the Lesser Scaup is probably the most abundant breeding duck in the Cariboo parklands, although he notes that perhaps only half the population is sexually mature. Bellrose (1976) reports a breeding population of 50,000 birds for British Columbia. The Lesser Scaup breeds near freshwater and alkaline lakes (70%; n=867) marshes, sloughs, and ponds from 300 to 1,400 m elevation.

Nests: Most nests (42%; n=81) were on islands (Fig. 292), followed by farmland (28%, including hay and alfalfa meadows, rangeland, and cereal grain fields), and the main shores of water bodies (23%). Nests in agricultural areas were occasionally lost to mowing. Other locations included wet sedge meadows, peninsulas, and wooded groves. Most nests were concealed in dense clumps of grass (43%; n=95), including agricultural crops, or thick growths of emergent vegetation (33%). Other sites included a nettle patch, shrubs (Labrador tea [Fig. 293], birches, willows), and under a pile of boughs. Two nests were located in coot's nests and one nest was found on a muskrat lodge. Two nests were completely exposed. Forty nests were categorized as being either on the shoreline (43%), up to 60 m from shore (34%), or over water (23%). Nests varied from a simple scrape with no material to a heap of reeds and grasses lined with down. Nests with no material contained less than 3 eggs, suggesting nest material is added as the clutch is laid. Most nests (75%; n=81) were constructed of grass and down and ranged from only a grass cup, to mostly down. Other materials included sedges, bulrush, cattail, and rushes. We have 3 records of 2 active nests within 3 m of each other; Lesser Scaup are known to nest semi-colonially (Palmer, R.S. 1976b).

Eggs: Dates for 197 clutches ranged from 28 May to 10 August with 58% recorded between 21 June and 12 July. Calculated dates indicate that eggs could be found as early as 2 May. Clutch size ranged from 1 to 22 eggs (1E-1, 2E-6, 4E-1, 5E-5, 6E-14, 7E-31, 8E-38, 9E-44, 10E-36, 11E-10, 12E-6, 13E-1, 15E-1, 18E-2, 22E-1) with 60% having 8 to 10 eggs. The larger clutches were likely the results of more than one female. Incubation is 21 to 27 days with an average of about 25 days (Vermeer 1968).

Young: Dates for 674 broods ranged from 23 May to 4 September with 56% recorded between 18 July and 4 August. Brood size ranged from 1 to 29 young (1Y-8, 2Y-15, 3Y-18, 4Y-41, 5Y-53, 6Y-97, 7Y-84, 8Y-104, 9Y-76, 10Y-59, 11Y-33, 12Y-27, 13Y-14, 14Y-12, 15Y-14, 16Y-7, 18Y-4, 19Y-4, 20Y-1, 22Y-1, 26Y-1, 29Y-1) with 54% having from 6 to 9 young. Aggressive interactions between female parents and adoptions of deserted young may result in amalgamation of broods into large groups (Bellrose 1976; Palmer, R.S. 1976b). One brood, containing 26 young, was composed of 4 age-classes of young. Two broods were accompanied by Redhead young, suggesting nest parasitism had taken place. Fledging period ranges from 45 to 50 days (Rogers, J.P. 1962; Lensink, C.J. 1964).

REMARKS: See Gehrman (1951) for a discussion on the ecology of the Lesser Scaup in Washington. Austin and Frederickson (1986) discuss the moult of the female Lesser Scaup following breeding.

Figure 292. *This island in Kotcho Lake supports significant numbers of breeding Lesser Scaup and Bonaparte's, Mew, and Herring gulls; 26 June 1982 (R. Wayne Campbell).*

Figure 293. Lesser Scaup nesting habitat on island in Kotcho Lake, 26 June 1982. A loosely arranged scaup colony nested amongst the blooming Labrador tea (R. Wayne Campbell).

NOTEWORTHY RECORDS

Spring: Coastal - Victoria 2 Mar 1976-100, 26 Mar 1972-200, 24 Apr 1976-100, 3 May 1976-50; Duncan 9 Mar 1983-120, 25 Mar 1978-200, 7 Apr 1980-250; Iona Island 2 Mar 1979-1944, 19 Apr 1979-124; Port Alberni 3 Apr 1983-41; Lulu Island 27 Mar 1979-1 early; Stanley Park (Vancouver) 2 Mar 1974-220, 23 Apr 1973-50, 18 May 1970-4; Pitt River 27 Mar 1973-112 (Jerema 1973); Harrison Lake (Agassiz) 10 May 1978-202; Cranberry Lake (Powell River) 23 May 1981-4; Dead Tree Point 7 Apr 1956-200 first sighting; Kitimat 9 Apr 1975-2, 29 May 1975-1; Delkatla Inlet 30 Apr 1980-50; Prince Rupert 29 Mar 1979-17, 29 Apr 1975-5. **Interior** - Princeton 16 May 1964-4; Vaseux Lake 23 Mar 1978-60, 24 Apr 1971-30; Sirdar 9 May 1956-495, 18 May 1956-246, 21 May 1956-7 migrating (Munro, J.A. 1958a); Cranbrook 6 May 1981-2; West Arm (Kootenay Lake) 22 Mar 1979-10; Wasa 9 Apr 1982-2; Windermere Lake 21 Mar 1978-20; Swan Lake (Vernon) 27 Apr 1968-60, 4 May 1966-53; Wilmer Lake 23 Apr 1982-45; Robbins Range 15 to 22 May 1966-40; Sorrento 24 Apr 1971-50+; Revelstoke 18 Apr 1977-26 (Bonar 1978a); Sink Lake 19 May 1975-2 (Wade 1977); Rush Lake 9 May 1978-255; Merritt 15 Apr 1968-30; Richie Lake 15 Mar 1981-160; Stump Lake (Quilchena) 9 May 1975-150+; Separation Lake 21 Apr 1950-350; Crown Lake 13 Apr 1968-50 on available open water; 5 km n 70 Mile House 6 Apr 1978-1 early migrant; Williams Lake 13 Mar 1979-1, 23 Mar 1978-19, 12 Apr 1979-48, 17 Apr 1980-80; Chilcotin Lake 4 May 1977-54; 24 km s Prince George 26 Apr 1979-2; Murray River 24 May 1977-2; Sloan Slough 14 May 1981-85; Fort St. John 7 Apr 1984-1 first spring arrival; Charlie Lake 1 May 1983-100, 14 May 1983-500, 21 May 1983-100; Prophet River 26 May 1981-2; Black Fox Lake 28 May 1976-2; Parker Lake (Fort Nelson) 5 May 1980-79, 14 May 1978-200; Atlin 3 May 1933-

earliest arrival, 16 May 1981-67; 1 km s Blanchard River on Haines Road (1.5 km s Yukon border) 14 May 1977-2.

Summer: Coastal - Swan Lake (Saanich) 18 Jul 1982-1; Sidney 2 Jul 1976-2; Quamichan Lake 13 Jul 1974-1; Lost Lagoon 5 Jun 1971-8 (Campbell et al. 1972b); Green Island 9 to 16 Jun 1978-1. **Interior** - Wapta Lake 8 Aug 1967-1 (Wade 1977); Minnie Lake 2 Aug 1951-1,000 post breeding males and nonbreeding yearlings; Stump Lake (Quilchena) 8 Aug 1949-700 mostly males; Rose Hill Jul 1966-134 mostly males; Moose Lake (Mount Robson) 18 Jun 1973-1 (Cannings,S.G. 1973); Stum Lake 20 Jul 1973-400 (Ryder 1973); Nulki Lake 24 Jul 1945-738 including yearling males and females and post breeding males, 5 Aug 1945-300 presumably had finished the moult; Cecil Lake 19 Aug 1984-207 raft of 200 males; Charlie Lake 28 Aug 1982-99 eclipse plumage birds; Parker Lake (Fort Nelson) 19 Jul 1985-50 males – 25 starting to moult; Kotcho Lake 26 Jun 1982-109 (Campbell and McNall 1982); Dease Lake 17 Jun 1962-5.

Autumn: Interior - Atlin 17 Oct 1931-last seen (Munro, J.A. and Cowan 1947); near Gladys Lake (Atlin) 11 Oct 1980-44; Parker Lake 25 Oct 1987-51; Boundary Lake (Goodlow) 5 Oct 1986-350; Charlie Lake 7 Sep 1985-1,000, 1 Oct 1983-250, 23 Oct 1982-160 mostly females and young, 2 Nov 1986-700, 5 Nov 1983-70; Cecil Lake 21 Oct 1981-1,400; Chilcotin Lake 22 Sep 1977-40; Williams Lake 19 Nov 1978-1 diving off edge of ice; Hanceville 20 Sep 1982-500+; Nicola Lake 18 Oct 1976-65; Campbell Lake (Quilchena) 5 Sep 1950-200; Stump Lake (Quilchena) 28 Nov 1981-300; Golden 11 Nov 1976-175; Wapta Lake 20 Oct 1975-2+ in snow (Wade 1977); Windermere Lake

18 Oct 1977-190; Sparwood 19 Nov 1983-22 (Fraser 1984); Thrums 5 Nov 1979-230; Vaseux Lake 6 Oct 1983-12, 13 Nov 1975-29; Sirdar 10 Sep 1947-40 (Munro, J.A. 1950). **Coastal** - Prince Rupert 28 Nov 1974-75; Delkatla Inlet 25 Sep 1981-12, 28 Oct 1981-46, 5 Nov 1981-67, 14 Nov 1981-47; Minette Bay 22 Sep 1974-9; Cranberry Lake (Powell River) 23 Sep 1981-36 all males; Stanley Park (Vancouver) 30 Sep 1973-11, 31 Oct 1971-80; Blackie Spit 4 Sep 1979-1; Fulford Harbour 29 Nov 1980-110; Somenos Lake 23 Nov 1981-50 to 100; Esquimalt Lagoon 25 Oct 1980-30, 5 Nov 1975-71, 19 Nov 1975-210, 26 Nov 1975-410.

Winter: Interior - Williams Lake 22 Dec 1974-5; Kamloops 8 Dec 1985-2; Coldstream 28 Jan 1954-5; Penticton 4 Dec 1973-647, 5 Jan 1974-70; west arm Kootenay Lake 2 Dec 1978-300, 15 Feb 1981-500; Creston Jan -300 (Butler, R.W. et al. 1986); Osoyoos Lake 28 Dec 1973-2. **Coastal** - Port Clements 29 Jan 1955-210, 22 Feb 1955-250; Tlell River mouth 12 Jan 1955-225; Cranberry Lake (Powell River) 8 Feb 1980-60; Stanley Park (Vancouver) 27 Jan 1973-150; Matsqui 27 Feb 1972-121; Burnaby Lake 27 Jan 1973-110; Iona Island 4 Feb 1976-400 to 500; Somenos Lake 26 Jan 1981-110 in flooded fields; Clover Point 26 Dec 1976-420.

Christmas Counts: Interior - Recorded from 7 of 19 localities and on 36% of all counts. Maxima: Penticton 22 Dec 1984-270; Vernon 16 Dec 1984-139; Shuswap Lake 22 Dec 1979-40. **Coastal** - Recorded from 22 of 28 localities and on 67% of all counts. Maxima: White Rock 30 Dec 1978-**2,795**; Vancouver 16 Dec 1984-2,561; recorded as the all-time Canadian high count (Monroe 1985b) but in 1978 White Rock had a total of **2,795** birds (Schouten 1979); Duncan 17 Dec 1977-1,080.

King Eider
Somateria spectabilis (Linnaeus)

KIEI

RANGE: Breeds in northern Alaska and arctic Canada south along Hudson and James bays. In western North America, winters on Bering Sea and Aleutian Islands and on the Atlantic coast from Labrador to Long Island. Also found in Eurasia.

STATUS: *Very rare* vagrant along the coast.

OCCURRENCE: The King Eider has been found in 6 areas along the coast: Chatham Sound, Masset, Skidegate Inlet, Port Hardy, Sooke, and on the extreme south mainland coast. All records are from protected waters including bays, inlets, and harbours.

The King Eider was first recorded in British Columbia in 1938, and during the next 48 years was found in 13 different years, 11 of which were during the 1970s and 1980s. Fourteen individual birds are represented in the 32 monthly records; of those, 9 were females (2 adults, 7 undetermined age), and 5 were males (1 adult, 2 immature, 2 undetermined). The longest continuous period of occurrence was 185 days. King Eiders have been recorded in the province between 7 August and 20 May, with most records (42%) from the winter months.

All records, listed in chronological order, are as follows:

(1) Hardy Bay 18 October 1938-1 male (MVZ 99553; Brooks 1942).

(2) Sooke 11 January 1942-1 female (RBCM 8966; Carl 1942).

(3) Masset 4 December 1945-1 female (RBCM 10226).

(4) Queen Charlotte City 15 December 1971 to 16 January 1972-1 female (Crowell and Nehls 1972b). Photographed on 19 December 1971 (RBCM Photo 838).

(5) Vancouver (including Stanley Park and Point Grey) 17 November 1973 to 20 May 1974-1 immature male, presumably the same individual frequenting both areas. Photographed on 18 November and 7 February (RBCM Photo 326; Fig. 294).

(6) Port Edward (Chatham Sound) 22 February 1975-1 adult female with 160 Surf Scoters and 60 Oldsquaws.

(7) Sandspit 14 May 1977-1 female.

(8) Iona Island 7 August to 9 October 1982-1 immature male (Campbell 1982a). Photographed (RBCM Photo 988) on 9 October.

(9) Vancouver (including Stanley Park and Ambleside Park) 17 November 1983 to 19 February 1984-1 adult female. Photographed (RBCM Photo 1111) on 5 January 1984 off Ambleside Park. Also see Mattocks (1984).

(10) Vancouver (including Stanley Park, Deep Cove, Burrard Inlet and shore of North and West Vancouver) 4 November 1984 (not 5 November as reported by Hunn and Mattocks 1985) to 6 April 1985-1 nearly full adult plumaged male. It was photographed on 4 December 1984 (RBCM Photo 1196) and 20 February 1985 (RBCM Photo 1089). The latter was published in *American Birds* (Mattocks 1984a).

(11) Stanley Park (Vancouver) 1 March to 9 April 1986-1 female.

(12) Stanley Park (Vancouver) 6 April to 23 May 1986-1 male.

REMARKS: In addition, there is a published record we consider hypothetical because it lacks convincing documentation: 2 females seen from a ferry in Fulford Harbour on 6 February 1984 (Mattocks 1984).

Although Barry (1968) calculates that there are at least 1,000,000 King Eiders in North America, very few winter south of the Bering Sea and Aleutian Islands. Isleib and Kessel (1973) estimate several hundred King Eiders winter in the Gulf of Alaska. Birds appearing along the British Columbia coast, then, are individuals that infrequently wander south, mostly in winter (Burr 1967).

Figure 294. Immature male King Eider at Stanley Park (Vancouver), 7 February 1974 (RBCM Photo 326; Ervio Sian).

NOTEWORTHY RECORDS

Christmas Counts: Interior - Not recorded. **Coastal** - Recorded from 1 of 28 localities and on 1% of all counts. Maxima: Vancouver, single birds recorded on 26 Dec 1973, 18 Dec 1983, and 16 Dec 1984.

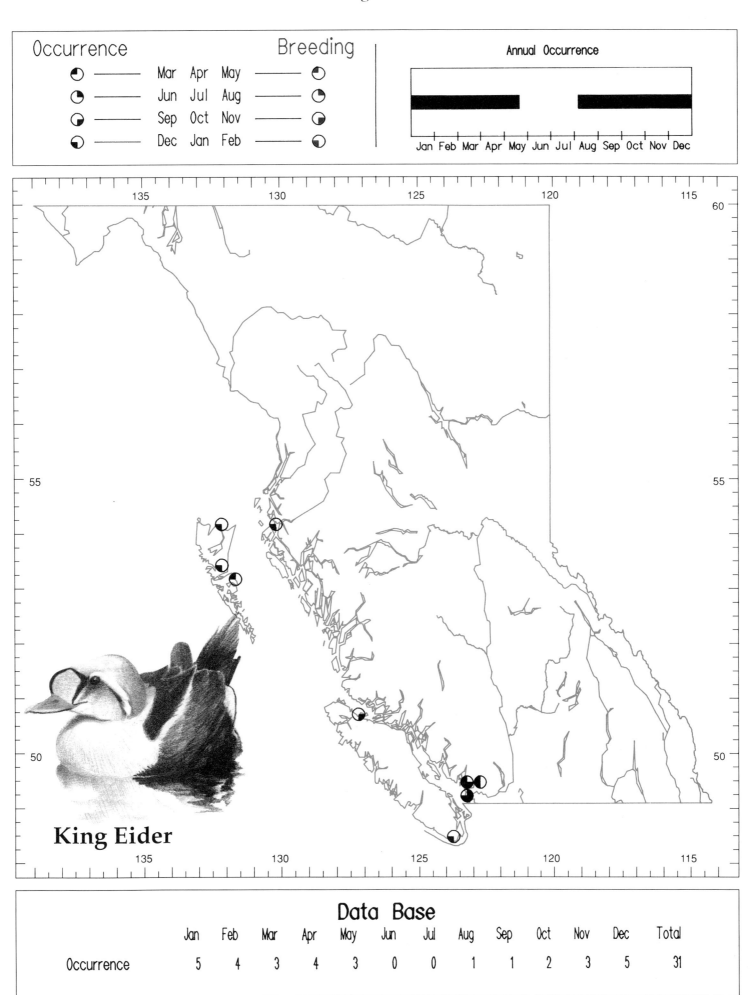

King Eider

Data Base

	Jan	Feb	Mar	Apr	May	Jun	Jul	Aug	Sep	Oct	Nov	Dec	Total
Occurrence	5	4	3	4	3	0	0	1	1	2	3	5	31

Harlequin Duck

HADU

Histrionicus histrionicus (Linnaeus)

RANGE: Breeds in North America from western Alaska and northern Yukon south to California and Wyoming and from southern Baffin Island south at least to central Quebec and eastern Labrador. Also breeds in Greenland, Iceland, and eastern Asia. Winters in North America on the Pacific coast from Alaska to central California; on the Atlantic coast from southern Labrador to New York; rarely on the Great Lakes. Also winters in eastern Eurasia.

STATUS: *Fairly common* to locally *very common* migrant and summer visitant to coastal British Columbia; widespread but *uncommon* migrant and summer visitant to the interior excluding the Boreal Forest and Peace Lowlands. *Fairly common* to locally *common* in winter along the coast; *rare* winter visitant to the west Kootenay, *very rare* elsewhere in the interior. Widespread breeder.

NONBREEDING: The Harlequin Duck is distributed primarily along coastal British Columbia from southern Vancouver Island and the southwest mainland coast north to the Queen Charlotte Islands and Portland Inlet on the north mainland coast. It is widely but sparsely distributed, throughout the interior except in the Liard Basin, the Cassiar and Muskwa ranges, and the Fort Nelson Lowlands where it is a very rare visitor.

The Harlequin Duck frequents both marine and freshwater habitats throughout the province. On the coast, birds usually frequent the often turbulent waters adjacent to rocky islets and rocky shores and bays, feeding amongst kelp beds and moving to the islets and exposed rocks or reefs to loaf and preen. Coastal habitats infrequently used include saltwater lagoons, inlets, and harbours. In the interior, birds are most often found

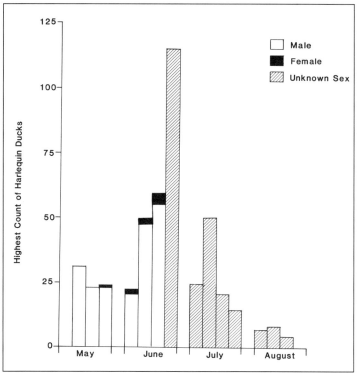

Figure 295. *Maximum counts, by week, of moulting Harlequin Ducks on Cleland Island, British Columbia, 11 May to 20 August 1970.*

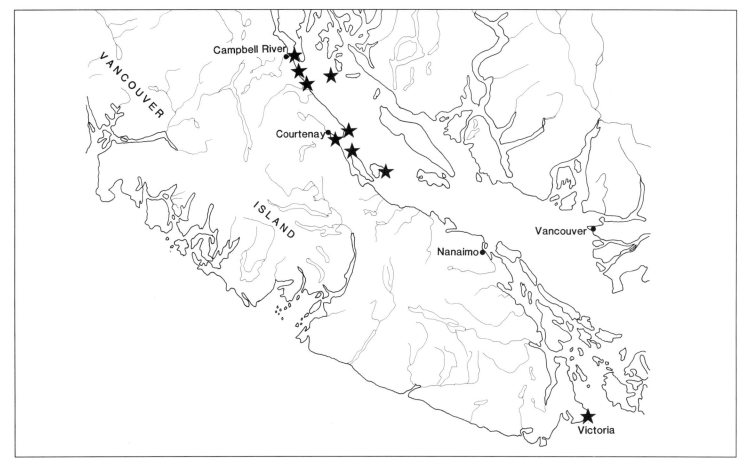

Figure 296. *Major moulting sites (stars), containing over 100 birds, for the Harlequin Duck in British Columbia. From south to north, they include the Chain Islets, Helliwell Park, Seal Islet, Comox Bay, Cape Lazo, Oyster Bay, Mitlenatch Island, Shelter Point, and the Campbell River area. Two sites from the north coast are not shown: Chatham Sound and west McIntyre Bay (modified from Savard 1988).*

332

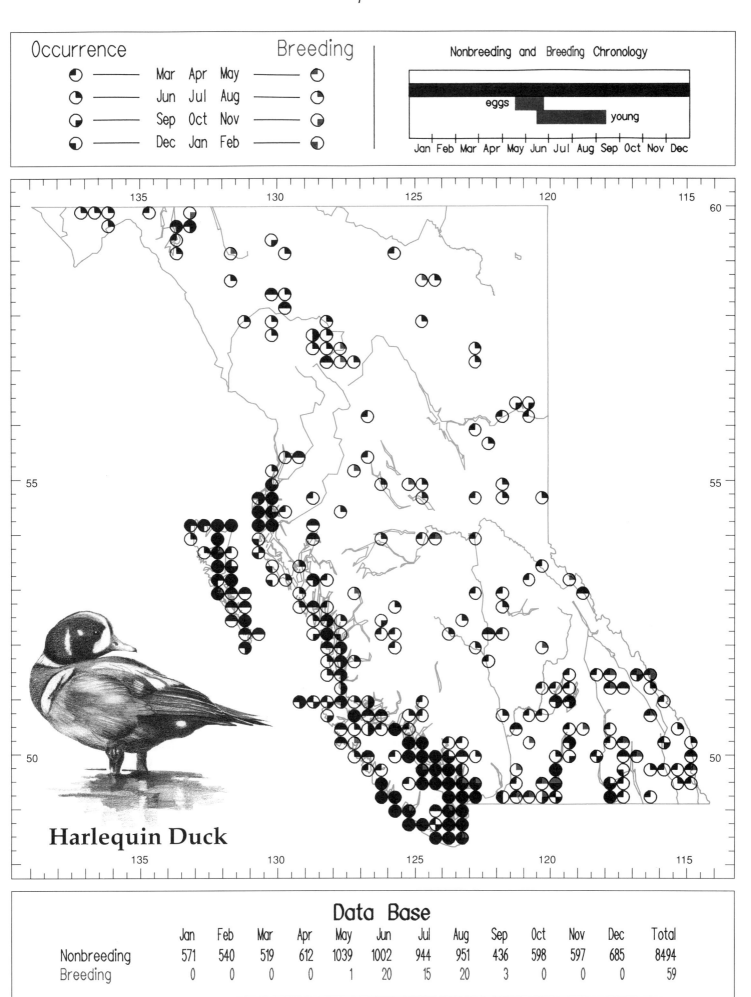

Harlequin Duck

Occurrence — **Breeding**

Mar	Apr	May
Jun	Jul	Aug
Sep	Oct	Nov
Dec	Jan	Feb

Nonbreeding and Breeding Chronology

eggs   young

Jan Feb Mar Apr May Jun Jul Aug Sep Oct Nov Dec

Data Base

	Jan	Feb	Mar	Apr	May	Jun	Jul	Aug	Sep	Oct	Nov	Dec	Total
Nonbreeding	571	540	519	612	1039	1002	944	951	436	598	597	685	8494
Breeding	0	0	0	0	1	20	15	20	3	0	0	0	59

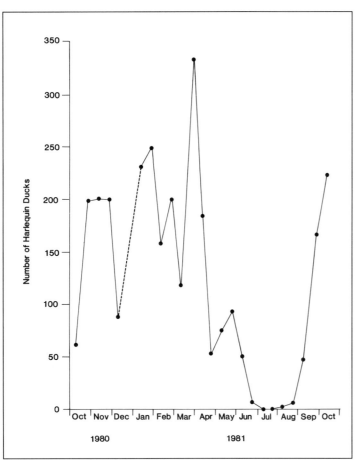

Figure 297. Biweekly counts (averages) of Harlequin Ducks, Comox Harbour to Deep Bay, Vancouver Island, 11 October 1980 to 10 October 1981 (Canadian Wildlife Service unpublished data). The dashed line indicates a period when counts were not made.

winter regularly in the west Kootenay (Ellison, M. and Merilees 1980) and the southern Okanagan valley (Cannings, R.A. et al. 1987); very rarely elsewhere. Major known wintering areas include the Victoria area, eastern Vancouver Island mainly from Qualicum Beach north to Campbell River, and the northern Queen Charlotte Islands.

Nonbreeding populations are unknown, but it is estimated that in British Columbia numbers may range into the high 10,000s which are the highest in Canada. For example, results of a survey of a 50 km stretch of coastline on eastern Vancouver Island (Fig. 297) showed the following seasonal results (birds per km): spring 7.7, summer 1.5, autumn 5.8, and winter 5.7.

BREEDING: On the coast, the known breeding distribution of the Harlequin Duck includes only Vancouver Island, the Fraser Lowlands, the Sumallo River, and the Queen Charlotte Islands. It is a scattered breeder throughout the interior, excluding the Peace Lowlands. We have no breeding records from the mainland coast north of the Coquitlam River and, with the exception of 3 brood records from Mount Robson Park, there are only 2 breeding records from the central interior of the province. An estimated 7,000 to 8,000 Harlequin Ducks breed in the province (Bellrose 1976).

Breeding areas include both marine and freshwater habitats from near sea level to 2,100 m elevation. Sites include coastal and interior rivers, creeks (Fig. 298), and glacial streams (often turbulent), where most broods were noted, coastal and interior lakes and ponds, and coastal islands and rocky shores. Of 17 breeding records, 12 were from elevations in excess of 1,000 m.

Nests: Only 4 nests have been found in British Columbia. Because of their rarity, full details are provided for each record.

(1) Shatford (Sheep) Creek 24 May 1936-7 eggs. Nest was on the ground under a clump of bushes at the foot of a small Douglas-fir tree, less than 1 m from the creek bank (Parham 1937; Tait 1949; Cannings, R.A. et al. 1987, p. 108; RBCM Photo 991).

(2) Shingle Creek 1 Jun 1947-6 eggs, incubation advanced (RBCM Photo 288). Nest was on the ground under a root overhang, in a depression in a newly cut creek bank. The female had completely covered the eggs with down (Tait 1949).

(3) Moricetown 16 June 1985-6 eggs, one of which was damaged and about 1 m from nest. Nest was on a cliff ledge directly over the Bulkley River (RBCM Photo 1201). It was composed of mosses, leaves, feathers, and lined with down. The female was incubating.

(4) Masset Inlet 24 Jun 1986-4 eggs, 2 young, 1 egg pipping. Nest was on a small, 2-m-high rock off the west side of Kwaikans Island (RBCM Photo 1123). The nest was composed of grass and was surrounded by dune wildrye. Three pairs of Harlequin Ducks were flushed from the island before the nest was found.

Eggs: Dates for 4 clutches ranged from 24 May to 24 June. Calculated dates indicate that eggs could be found as early as 17 May. Clutch size ranged from 6 to 7 eggs (6E-2, 7E-2). Incubation period is 28 or 29 days (Bengtson 1966).

Young: Dates for 41 broods ranged from 16 June to 13 September with 53% recorded between 10 July and 12 August. Brood size ranged from 1 to 10 young with 61% having 4 or 5 young (1Y-3, 2Y-3, 3Y-5, 4Y-11, 5Y-14, 6Y-2, 7Y-1, 8Y-1, 10Y-1). The brood with 10 young was apparently the product of 1 female. Fledging period is estimated at 35 to 42 days (Palmer, R.S. 1976b).

REMARKS: Known in the Old World as the Harlequin.

on rivers, lakes, and creeks, the rivers and creeks often with fast, turbulent waters.

In early spring, the Harlequin Duck can be locally abundant in areas where Pacific herring spawn. The onset of spring migration is difficult to determine from coastal data due to the large numbers of nonbreeders that summer there; it is perhaps best noted by the birds' arrival on fresh water, which can be as early as the first week of April. As in autumn, it is primarily a lateral movement. Most pairs have arrived on the interior nesting areas by mid-May.

On the coast, males begin to outnumber the females by mid-May; that bias towards males is most evident from early June to early July, and may be earlier on the outer coast (Fig. 295), as breeding males leave incubating females and move to marine waters to moult. The moult begins in late May, continuing through August and occasionally into late September as post-breeding females complete their moult. Moulting harlequins are found wherever rocky islets and shores occur along the British Columbia coast. Major concentrations of moulting birds occur at the northern end of the Strait of Georgia (e.g. Mitlenatch Island, Shelter Point - Fig. 296). Autumn migration is difficult to identify because of the early post-breeding return of males to the sea and the straggling departure of females and young from the nesting grounds. Most birds have left the breeding areas by August.

Male:apparent-female ratios sampled from coastal flocks were 1.5:1 (n=55; 544 birds) in winter and 1.4:1 (n=30; 297 birds) in March and April. Sex ratios became more biased towards the males in May 4.3:1 (n=20; 495 birds), and summer ratios through to the end of July heavily favoured males by 18.2:1 (n=27; 1,633 birds).

Harlequin Ducks winter on the sea along the coast of British Columbia including Vancouver Island and the Queen Charlotte Islands. In the interior, small numbers have recently begun to

Figure 298. *Two pairs of Harlequin Ducks on Shingle Creek (Penticton), 9 May 1981 (Richard J. Cannings).*

NOTEWORTHY RECORDS

Spring: Coastal - Chatham Islands 25 Mar 1983-45; Finlayson Point 24 Apr 1977-28 in compact migrant flock; Cleland Island 24 May 1982-24 males; Taylor River 26 Mar 1984-1; Qualicum Beach 31 Mar 1978-130; Bowser 26 Mar 1975-778 following Pacific herring spawn (Dawe 1976); Denman Island 15 Mar 1981-200; Yale 8 Mar 1964-1 pair; Cheakamus River 23 Apr 1966-2; Tahsis River 17 Apr 1979-2; Mitlenatch Island 22 May 1963-11, 24 May 1963-187, 96% drakes (van Tets 1963); Namu 6 Apr 1981-80 at Pacific herring spawn, first large congregation; Alder Island (Burnaby Island) 21 Apr 1985-255; Lyell Island 8 May 1982-2 pairs; Bischof Islands 30 May 1982-13, 3 beginning to moult; Kunga Island 15 May 1983-25 all males; Sandspit 6 May 1979-287, sexes equal; Lawn Point (Tlell) 20 Mar 1981-247 on Pacific herring spawn. **Interior** - Ashnola River 5 Apr 1958-1; Trout Creek (Summerland) 8 May 1966-1 pair; Kaslo 6 May 1973-2 pairs, spring arrival; Kootenay River 3 May 1983-2; New Denver 2 May 1976-6; Okanagan Landing 18 Apr 1975-1; Sorrento to Chase 12 Apr 1971-1 pair; Kamloops 2 May 1984-6; Mount Revelstoke National Park 20 May 1977-1; n Knot Lakes 20 May 1975-1 pair; Williams Lake 6 May 1983-4, 14 May 1985-6 on creek; Isaac River 27 May 1974-several pairs around log jam; Nechako River 5 May 1983-1 pair; Kerry Lake 8 May 1968-1 pair; Carbon Creek 14 May 1977-10 males, 9 females; Bear Lake 24 May 1939-6 pairs (Stanwell-Fletcher and Stanwell-Fletcher 1943); Peace River near Moberly River 20 May 1985-1 pair; Pine Creek (24 km e Atlin) 18 May 1981-1 first seen.

Summer: Coastal - Chain Islets 19 Jun 1982-60, mainly faded adult-plumage males, 22 Jun 1973-100, mainly males, 19 Jul 1976-110; Strongtide Islet 9 Jul 1953-125, mostly moulting males; Mandarte Island mid-Jun 1977-150, 5% females; Ballingall

Islets 4 Aug 1979-71, flightless; Folger Island 26 Jul 1970-26 males in complete moult; Crescent Beach 21 Jul 1986-30 in eclipse plumage; White Rock 2 Jul 1980-100 moulting males (Savard 1981); Cleland Island 12 Jun 1975-55; LaCroix Group 19 Jun 1975-116, 94% males; Qualicum Beach 6 Jun 1977-62, mostly males (Dawe 1980), 23 Jun 1974-110; Norris Rocks 4 Jun 1978-150; Hornby Island 1 Jul 1977-120 in moult; Cape Lazo 24 Aug 1963-150; Mitlenatch Island 5 Jun 1963-366 males, 18 females, 5 Jul 1963-400 males, 4 females (van Tets 1963); Shelter Point 21 Jul 1975-220, 26 Aug 1973-200+ males moulting from eclipse to breeding plumage; Bunsby Islands 26 Jun 1975-85; Storm Islands 13 Jun 1976-116, mostly males; Holmes Point 29 Aug 1955-300; Triangle Island (Scott Islands) 7 Jul 1978-17, flightless; Currie Islet 20 Jun 1976-52, mostly males; McKenney Islands 25 Jun 1976-62, mostly males; Skincuttle Island 6 July 1977-84; Hallet Island 17 Jul 1977-63; Lawyer Islands 16 Jun 1979-155, mostly males; McIntyre Bay 30 Jul 1977-156; Green Island 4 Jul 1978-50+ moulting males. **Interior** - Spanish Lake 2 Jun 1966-2 pairs; Williams Lake 24 Aug 1985-2 on creek; Smith Island (Stuart Lake) 7 Jun 1977-1; Kitchener Lake 22 Jun 1976-1; Nuttlude Lake 16 Jul 1963-3; Buckinghorse Creek 16 Jul 1976-4 females (Osmond-Jones et al. 1977); Muskwa River 22 Aug 1983-3 (Cooper, J.M. and Cooper 1983); Lower Gnat Lake 12 Jun 1978-2 pairs; Kakuchuya Creek 3 Jun 1979-1; Cottonwood River (Cassiar) 2 Jun 1978-2 pairs; Pine Creek (25 km w Atlin) 17 Jun 1975-6; Kelsall River 25 Jun 1958-2 (Weeden 1960).

Autumn: Interior - Kahan Lake (Cassiar) 20 Sep 1976-2; Cold Fish Lake 26 Sep 1976-3; Cecil Lake 21 Sep 1985-2 males; Charlie Lake 7 Nov 1986-1 female (Campbell 1987a); Adams River 25 Oct 1982-2; Okanagan Falls 15 Nov 1987-1 female, 21

Nov 1974-1; Trail 23 Oct 1980-3 pairs; Similkameen River (Keremeos) 5 Sep 1960-1. **Coastal** - Green Island 8 Sep 1977-62, 4 Nov 1977-44; Skidegate 15 Sep 1979-7; Swan Islands 25 Sep 1977-3, 27 Oct 1977-12; Elizabeth Rocks 14 Sep 1967-12; Hansen Lagoon 28 Oct 1973-4 (Hazelwood 1973); Campbell River 1 Oct 1962-100; Shelter Point 20 Sep 1976-175+, mainly eclipse plumage birds; Oyster Bay 9 Sep 1977-200+; Hornby Island 20 Sep 1978-6 males, 5 females in full nuptial plumage, 28 Oct 1978-20 pairs; Oak Bay 28 Oct 1977-108, Discovery Island 26 Sep 1959-300 (Poynter 1960).

Winter: Interior - Mission Creek (Kelowna) 16 and 17 Dec 1984-1 female (Campbell 1985a); Penticton 27 Dec 1977-1; Castlegar 26 Feb 1981-pair; Brilliant 16 Jan 1977-1; Trail 14 Dec 1978-4, 19 Jan 1984-3. **Coastal** - Dixon Entrance 13 Feb 1978-114 (Savard 1978); Deepwater Point 17 Feb 1974-30+ on herring spawn; Pearl Harbour 19 Jan 1978-103 (Martin 1978); Skidegate Inlet 15 Feb 1978-51 (Savard 1978); Swan Islands 22 Feb 1978-12; Idol Point 30 Jan 1975-12; Evans Inlet 12 Jan 1977-6; Mitlenatch Island 19 to 22 Dec 1965-30 to 50 (Campbell 1965); Little Qualicum River 19 Dec 1973-50+ on estuary; Chilliwack 19 Dec 1983-1; Chain Islets 6 Jan 1974-49; Chatham Islands and Discovery Island 27 Dec 1964-258 (Davidson 1965); Race Rocks 17 Jan 1977-76, 23 Feb 1977-40.

Christmas Counts: Interior - Recorded from 2 of 19 localities and on 5% of all counts. Maxima: Vaseux Lake 23 Dec 1983-2; Penticton 26 Dec 1978-1. **Coastal** - Recorded from 19 of 28 localities and on 62% of all counts. Maxima: Deep Bay 29 Dec 1982-**886**, all-time Canadian high count (Anderson, R.R. 1983); Victoria 27 Dec 1964-417; Comox 20 Dec 1981-385.

Oldsquaw
Clangula hyemalis (Linnaeus)

OLDS

RANGE: Circumpolar. Breeds in North America from Alaska east across most of northern Canada. Also breeds in Greenland, Iceland, Scandinavia, and east across arctic Russia. Winters along the Pacific coast of North America from the Bering Sea south rarely to California; from Greenland, eastern North America, and Labrador south, including the Great Lakes, to South Carolina. In Europe, winters from Iceland, Scandinavia and western Russia south to central Europe and in Asia from Caucasia to Iran, Korea, eastern China and Japan.

STATUS: *Uncommon* to locally *very common* winter visitant and migrant along coastal British Columbia; *very rare* winter visitant and *rare* migrant in the interior. In summer, *very rare* to *uncommon* along the coast; *very rare* in the interior. Breeds (one old record).

NONBREEDING: The Oldsquaw is distributed primarily along coastal British Columbia; it is a sporadic wanderer to the interior of the province.

The Oldsquaw frequents a variety of coastal waters. Most birds were observed in the deeper waters of straits, bays, harbours, channels, and fiords, although usually they were adjacent to points, spits, peninsulas, rocky islets, or reefs. Other habitats include estuaries, offshore waters, mudflats, and rarely, larger lakes and rivers. R.S. Palmer (1976) describes the Oldsquaw as almost pelagic, but few records in British Columbia are from beyond sight of land. In the interior, birds are found on lakes (to 1,500 m elevation), ponds, sloughs, rivers, and sewage lagoons. Spring migration may begin by late February, although it is difficult to detect as local movements to Pacific herring spawning sites tend to mask the northward movement. Most observations record flocks numbering less than 50 birds; however, during the Pacific herring spawn, Oldsquaw concentrations in the thousands are not uncommon, particularly in the Ganges, Powell River, and Qualicum Beach areas. The inshore and northward coastal movement continues through

May on the south coast and early June in the north, although few individuals remain along the south coast after mid-April. In summer, individuals, possibly moulting birds, early migrants, or unfit birds, remain scattered along the coast; a few remain on northern lakes. Boundary Bay supports the largest known summer population on the coast (Vermeer and Levings 1977; Savard 1981). Oldsquaws are late migrants from their northern breeding areas; the autumn movement in British Columbia is concentrated in October and November with numbers increasing along the south coast into December. In the interior, most Oldsquaw reports from the Okanagan valley and west Kootenay involve autumn migrants; spring migrants make up the bulk of the observations from the Chilcotin-Cariboo and Peace Lowlands. Major wintering areas along the coast include the Strait of Georgia from Comox south to Victoria and the northern Queen Charlotte Islands.

BREEDING: There is one breeding record for the province: a flightless young was taken at Log Cabin, north of White Pass, on 1 September 1927, with primaries still in sheaths (Brooks 1927). Several flying broods were also observed. That record is some distance from the known regular breeding range (Palmer, R.S. 1976b; Bellrose 1976). Since 1927, there have been no nests, eggs, or young found for Oldsquaw, nor any evidence that the birds still breed in the province.

REMARKS: Known in the Old World as Long-tailed Duck.

POSTSCRIPT: Between 17 and 19 July 1989, a brood of 4 downy young and another of 8 were identified on Blackfly Lake (59 15'N, 130 51'W) in northwestern British Columbia (W. Nixon pers. comm.)

NOTEWORTHY RECORDS

Spring: Coastal - Baynes Channel 2 Mar 1975-300 feeding on euphausiids; Ross Bay 15 May 1983-11; Sidney Spit 12 May 1974-17; Ganges 11 Mar 1978-1,150 feeding on herring spawn (Carson and Howsam 1978), 25 Mar 1977-920; Centennial Park (Tsawwassen) 26 Apr 1982-200; Tsawwassen 15 May 1971-1 off jetty, latest departure (Campbell et al. 1972b); Tofino Inlet 2 May 1976-60; Nanoose Harbour 14 Mar 1974-1,600, 12 Apr 1973-2,000+; Little Qualicum River 15 Mar 1979-2,800, 20 Mar 1978-1,290, 22 Mar 1979-3,230, 26 Mar 1982-3,254 all records from areas of Pacific herring spawn, 29 Mar 1977-3 (Dawe 1980); Campbell River (Discovery Passage) 12 May 1975-120+; Atrevida Reef 30 Mar 1977-1,600; Powell River 21 Mar 1982-8,500; Pulteney Point 26 Mar 1976-500+ daily at sunset, from about 19 March hundreds flying northwest, to the end of March when a much smaller local movement occurred all day, 10 Apr 1976-365 flying west over 10 minute period, last major spring sighting; Huston Inlet 27 Mar 1976-80; Skidegate Inlet 4 May 1986-400+; Lawn Point (Tlell) 20 Mar 1981-300; Browning Entrance 2 May 1975-2,500 to 3,000 (Martin 1978); Drizzle Lake 14 May 1978-1; between Yakan Point and Tow Hill 2 May 1979-1,250. **Interior** - Creston 5 Apr 1980-1; west arm Kootenay Lake 26 Mar 1971-1; Vernon 24 Mar 1984-1 (Rogers, T.H. 1984c); Savona 28 Apr 1985-1 (Rogers 1985c); Kloh Lake 22 May 1980-2 (Ducks Unlimited Canada 1983); Dutch Lake 9 May 1984-150; Riske Creek 16 May 1978-1, 25 May 1986-2 (Rogers 1986c); Williams Lake 29 Apr 1985-22, 10 May

1968-16; Moose Lake (Mount Robson) 25 May 1972-1; Tabor Lake 12 May 1981-30; Wilde Lake 14 May 1981-4; Charlie Lake 24 Apr 1986-1 first arrival, 12 May 1984-74, 30 May 1984-14; Parker Lake (Fort Nelson) 21 May 1979-29; Como Lake 20 May 1977-2.

Summer: Coastal - Victoria 17 Jun to 3 Jul 1971-5; Boundary Bay 11 Jul 1953-1, Jul 1974-397 (Vermeer and Levings 1977); Tsawwassen 2 Jul 1977-3 off jetty; Nanoose Harbour 17 Aug 1976-2; Mitlenatch Island 19 Jun 1966-3; Pulteney Point 29 Aug 1976-1, first autumn sighting; Rose Spit 21 Jul 1974-1. **Interior** - Slocan River 11 Jun 1981-8; Williams Lake 23 Jun 1973-1; Bowron Lake 3 Jul 1971-4 (Runyan 1971); Ootsa Lake 4 Jun 1977-1; Boundary Lake (Goodlow) 15 Jul 1981-20; Stalk Lakes 12 Jul 1976-2 in eclipse plumage; Nogah Creek 19 Jul 1977-6; Hatin Lake 1 Jun 1979-35+; Atlin Lake 24 Jul 1980-1; Kelsall Lake 25 June 1958-1 (Weeden 1960).

Autumn: Interior - Cecil Lake 8 Oct 1979-50; Charlie Lake 27 Oct 1985-5, 2 Nov 1986-1 female, last fall record; Round Lake 29 Nov 1987-4, lake all open—unusually mild; Puntzi Lake 16 Oct 1976-1; Kleena Kleene 25 Oct 1963-1; Alkali Lake (Riske Creek) 14 Oct 1968-1; Williams Lake 3 Nov 1985-1; Adams River 13 Oct 1965-6 at mouth; Revelstoke 23 to 25 Nov 1983-1; Nelson 23 Nov 1982-48; Elkview 17 Oct 1984-1 (Fraser 1984). **Coastal** - Masset 22 Oct 1971 and 7 Nov 1971-100's; Onion Lake (Kitimat) 5 Nov 1983-10; Campbell River (Discovery Passage) 20 Nov 1975-50+; Hornby

Island 8 Oct 1977-1 first seen this autumn; Qualicum Beach 9 Oct 1982-1; Meares Island 9 Nov 1981-155; Sea Island 24 Oct 1973-45; Saanich Peninsula 30 Oct 1962-135 (Hancock 1963); Clover Point 29 Sep 1974-6, 9 Oct 1959-5 first autumn record, 24 Nov 1979-64.

Winter: Interior - Williams Lake 26 Dec 1974-1; Vernon 30 Dec 1951-7; Okanagan Landing 26 Dec 1972-12 (Rogers, T.H. 1973b); Robson 19 Dec 1983-1. **Coastal** - Prince Rupert 27 Jan 1979-150; Rose Spit 17 Dec 1987-20,380 counted flying eastward from 0945 to 1100 hrs; Masset 17 Dec 1982-195, 19 Feb 1983-32; Oval Bay 15 Feb 1978-200; Kumdis Slough 29 Jan 1975-288; Tlell River 4 Dec 1975-6; Robbers Nob 29 Dec 1977-64; Port Neville 28 Feb 1986-71; Cortes Island 15 Dec 1975-65; Mitlenatch Island 19 to 22 Dec 1965-250+ migrating through Discovery Passage (Campbell 1965); Stanley Park (Vancouver) 30 Jan 1965-35; Iona Island 9 Feb 1979-27; Ganges 26 Feb 1978-2,120 (Carson and Howsam 1978); Baynes Channel 7 Feb 1979-650; Cordova Bay 27 Feb 1978-500; Oak Bay 5 Feb 1977-200+; Chatham Islands 3 Dec 1983-100; Clover Point 27 Dec 1978-57, 28 Jan 1980-250.

Christmas Counts: Interior - Recorded from 1 of 19 localities and on 1% of all counts. Maxima: Vaseux Lake 31 Dec 1975-1. **Coastal** - Recorded from 21 of 28 localities and on 72% of all counts. Maxima: Victoria 20 Dec 1980-783; Ladner 28 Dec 1980-498; Hecate Strait 30 Dec 1980-303.

Oldsquaw

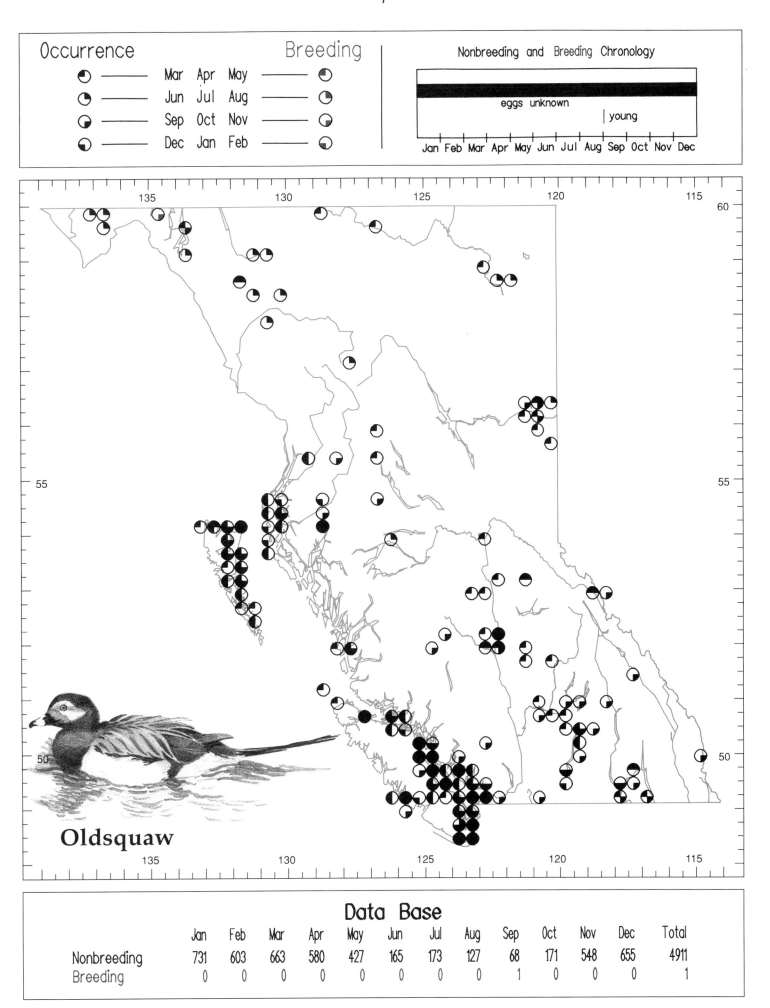

Occurrence

	Mar Apr May	
	Jun Jul Aug	
	Sep Oct Nov	
	Dec Jan Feb	

Breeding

Nonbreeding and Breeding Chronology

eggs unknown

young

Jan Feb Mar Apr May Jun Jul Aug Sep Oct Nov Dec

Data Base

	Jan	Feb	Mar	Apr	May	Jun	Jul	Aug	Sep	Oct	Nov	Dec	Total
Nonbreeding	731	603	663	580	427	165	173	127	68	171	548	655	4911
Breeding	0	0	0	0	0	0	0	0	1	0	0	0	1

Black Scoter

BLSC

Melanitta nigra (Linnaeus)

RANGE: Circumpolar. Breeds in Alaska, and central and eastern Canada; also in Eurasia. Summers widely. Winters in North America on the Pacific coast from the Aleutian Islands south to southern California, uncommonly on the Great Lakes, and from Newfoundland to South Carolina; also in Eurasia.

STATUS: *Uncommon* to locally *very common* winter visitant and migrant along the coast. *Very rare* in summer along the coast. *Very rare* migrant in the interior.

OCCURRENCE: The Black Scoter is distributed along the coast from southern Vancouver Island and the southwest mainland coast, north to the Queen Charlotte Islands, Prince Rupert, and the Chatham Sound region. Records are few for the mainland coast between the north end of Vancouver Island and Kitimat, probably because of poor observer coverage. The Black Scoter very rarely wanders to the interior.

The Black Scoter frequents a variety of coastal waters throughout its provincial range including estuaries, bays and harbours, inlets, sounds, and lagoons usually where water depths are less than 11 m and where mussel beds occur. In the interior, birds are found on lakes, rivers, and sewage ponds. Spring migration begins in March, and numbers decline through mid-May, by which time most birds have gone. Small numbers, likely nonbreeding yearlings, summer along the coast.

The autumn migration begins in early September and continues through November, with the peak movement occurring in late October. Major wintering areas include the Qualicum Beach, Baynes Sound (Fig. 299), and Campbell River areas on the east coast of Vancouver Island, and the Crescent Beach to Roberts Bank area on the south mainland coast.

REMARKS: In order to recognize 2 taxonomic groups that may be species, the American Ornithologists' Union (1987) divides the Black Scoter into 2 groups: an *americana* group that occurs principally in North America and eastern Siberia, and a *nigra* group confined to Eurasia. The 2 groups are sometimes considered separate species: *M. americana* (American Scoter) and *M. nigra* (Black Scoter).

The Black Scoter was previously known as Common Scoter. Unlike Surf and White-winged scoters, male Black Scoters vocalize on their wintering areas.

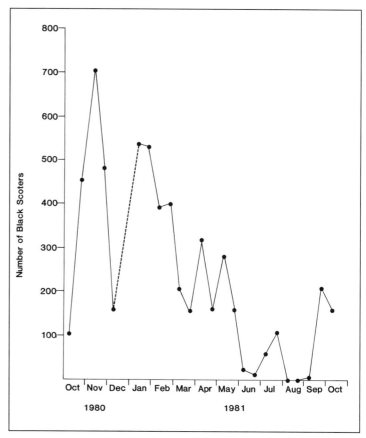

Figure 299. Biweekly counts (averages) of Black Scoters, Comox Harbour to Deep Bay, Vancouver Island, 11 October 1980 to 10 October 1981 (Canadian Wildlife Service unpublished data). The dashed line indicates a period when counts were not made.

NOTEWORTHY RECORDS

Spring: Coastal - Whiffin Spit 8 May 1971-19; Sidney to Mandarte Island 19 Mar 1983-28; Ocean Park 22 Mar 1979-180; Nanoose Harbour 12 Apr 1973-100+; Little Qualicum River 26 Mar 1975-109, 12 Apr 1976-346, 22 Apr 1977-201, 15 May 1975-103, 27 May 1975-32 (Dawe 1976, 1980); Spanish Banks 30 Mar 1974-164, 16 Apr 1974-66; Comox 7 Mar 1974-120; Stories Beach 22 Apr 1974-200, 13 May 1974-100+; Campbell River 29 Mar 1975-150 near estuary; Robbers Nob 23 May 1977-100; west of Sandspit 10 and 28 Apr 1979-200, 6 May 1978-100; Tlell 8 May 1979-687 (Savard and Kaiser 1982); Entry Point to Wiah Point 8 May 1977-106; Rose Spit 28 Apr 1979-70; Green Island 29 May 1978-6 last sighting. **Interior** - 108 Mile House 10 May 1891 - small flock (Kermode 1904); Anahim Lake 22 May 1948-2.

Summer: Coastal - Clover Point 30 Jun 1975-1; Duncan 26 Jul 1970-5; Long Beach 28 Aug 1962-15; Florencia Bay 15 Jul 1974-5; Qualicum Beach 13 Jul 1977-15, 19 Aug 1977-32; Willow Point 28

Jul 1977-1; Port Neville 30 Jun 1976-13; Darby Channel 8 Aug 1977-41; Masset 18 Jul 1982-4. **Interior** - Kamloops 8 Jun 1935-1, 31 Aug 1978-1; Moose Lake (Mount Robson) 3 Aug 1972-1; Spatsizi River (Hyland Post) 21 Jul 1977-6; Fern Lake (Kwadacha Wilderness Park) 14 to 16 Aug 1979-1 (Cooper, J.M. and Adams 1979).

Autumn: Interior - Beatton Park 18 Oct 1987-1 adult female; Trail 31 Oct to 5 Nov 1975-1. **Coastal** - Masset 25 Oct 1971-15; Masset Sound 19 Nov 1983-416 (boat count); Green Island 22 Sep 1978-3, first autumn sighting, 20 Oct 1978-19, largest autumn concentration, 8 Nov 1977-25 in 2 flocks; Port Neville 8 Sep 1975-40; Campbell River to Oyster Bay 20 Oct 1975-3,044 (20 km ground survey); Oyster Bay 14 Sep 1976-8, 5 Nov 1975-150; Courtenay 1 Sep 1962-30; Point Grey Beach 13 Oct 1980-200; Little Qualicum River 8 Oct 1974-14, 8 Oct 1975-11, 31 Oct 1977-217, 24 Nov 1975-172 (Dawe 1976, 1980); Iona Island 27 Oct 1979-150, 7 Nov 1973-61; Ocean Park 30 Sep 1979-42; Saltspring Island 30 Sep 1961-35 (Boggs and

Boggs 1962a); Discovery Island 15 Sep 1962-10.

Winter: Interior - No records. **Coastal** - Naden Harbour 19 Feb 1974-500 over Pacific herring; Masset Sound 3 Feb 1983-75, 17 Dec 1982-264; Green Island 23 Dec 1978-8, typical winter sighting; Copper Creek (Sandspit) 26 Feb 1979-10; Grant Bay 4th week Jan 1969-1; Hornby Island 8 Jan 1983-200; Little Qualicum River 1 Jan 1974-307, 15 Feb 1974-170, 14 Dec 1973-500 to 1,000; Point Grey Beach 24 Feb 1974-178 (Shepard, M.G. 1974), 1 Dec 1973-150; Iona Island 27 Jan 1973-80 (Crowell and Nehls 1973b); Ocean Park 14 Jan 1979-225; Chatham Islands 20 Jan 1955-55.

Christmas Counts: Interior - Not recorded. **Coastal** - Recorded from 22 of 28 localities and on 65% of all counts. Maxima: Deep Bay 19 Dec 1976-**1,095**, all-time Canadian high count (Anderson, R.R. 1977); White Rock 22 Dec 1974-899; Campbell River 18 Dec 1977-774.

Black Scoter

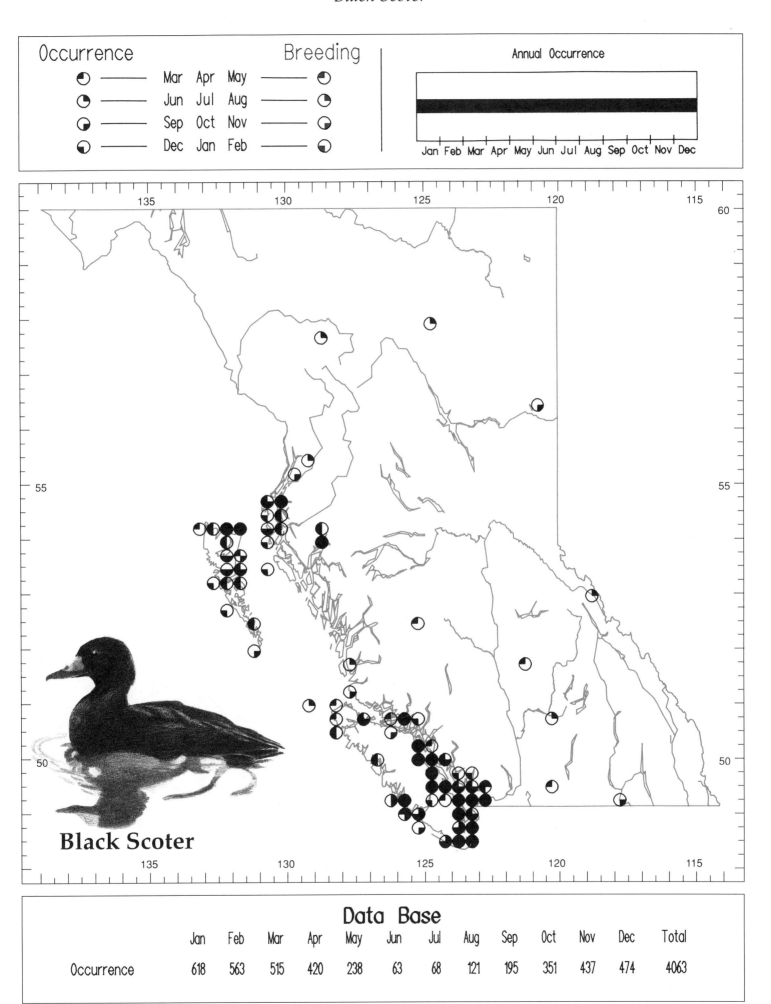

Surf Scoter

SUSC

Melanitta perspicillata (Linnaeus)

RANGE: Breeds from the Mackenzie delta east to northern Ontario and eastern Quebec and Labrador, south to western and central Alaska, northern British Columbia, central Alberta, and northern Saskatchewan. Winters primarily along the Pacific coast from Alaska south to California, on the Great Lakes, and on the Atlantic coast from New Brunswick to Florida; rarely the Gulf coast.

STATUS: *Common* to *very abundant* migrant and *common* to *abundant* summer visitant to coastal British Columbia; *uncommon* to locally *common* migrant and summer visitant to the interior. *Abundant* to *very abundant* winter visitant on the coast; *accidental* in winter in the interior. Breeds in the northeastern portion of the province.

NONBREEDING: The Surf Scoter is generally distributed in large numbers along coastal British Columbia including the coasts of Vancouver Island and the Queen Charlotte Islands (Fig. 300). It is widely distributed in small numbers throughout the interior. It has been found from sea level to 1,200 m elevation.

It frequents a variety of freshwater and marine habitats. On the coast, birds are most often reported from the relatively open but shallower (<6 m) waters of straits usually adjacent to beaches, spits, and points, as well as the more protected waters of bays, harbours, and lagoons. The Surf Scoter is one of the few waterbirds to make use of the deep fiords. From late autumn through early spring, flocks, mixed with Barrow's Goldeneye, cluster along the inlets' walls at waterfalls and creek mouths. They are less often seen on the estuaries at the heads of inlets except during migration. Habitat used infrequently includes creeks, rivers, and lakes. In the interior, lakes are most often used,

but occasionally birds are reported from sloughs, sewage lagoons, ponds, and rivers.

In late winter and spring, spectacular numbers of Surf Scoters are often seen where Pacific herring are spawning. An unusually large concentration was noted by Martin (1978) who reports a flock of 300,000 scoters, almost exclusively Surf Scoters, from Big Bay, suggesting that the birds move considerable distances to those sites. It is also likely that the time of that Pacific herring spawn coincided with the northward movement of the scoters. Bellrose (1976) reports an estimated breeding population in North America of 257,000 to 765,000 Surf Scoters which, together with Martin's (1978) records, suggests that a sizable proportion of the North American population depends on British Columbia's coastal habitats for their survival.

Spring migration can begin in late March with the arrival from the south of many females (see sex ratios in Remarks; also Palmer, R.S. 1976b), but the main coastal movement occurs from mid-April to mid-May. There is also a less conspicuous lateral movement suggesting that most migrants overfly the province when travelling to and from their subarctic nesting grounds. However, based on the large numbers of flocks reported on interior lakes during spring, there appears to be at least one major lateral migration corridor. Records suggest that birds along the south coast follow a band centred on the Chilcotin-Cariboo region, bounded by Kamloops on the south and Quesnel on the north, running from the south coast east through the Mount Robson area, perhaps to breeding grounds in northern Alberta. Birds can arrive on interior lakes by late March, but most records are from late April and May, after most ice recedes. Many birds, likely pre-breeders, remain along the coast in summer. They are later joined by males that have left the breeding grounds to moult

Figure 300. Spring aggregation of Surf Scoters at Skidegate Inlet, 29 May 1984 (John M. Cooper).

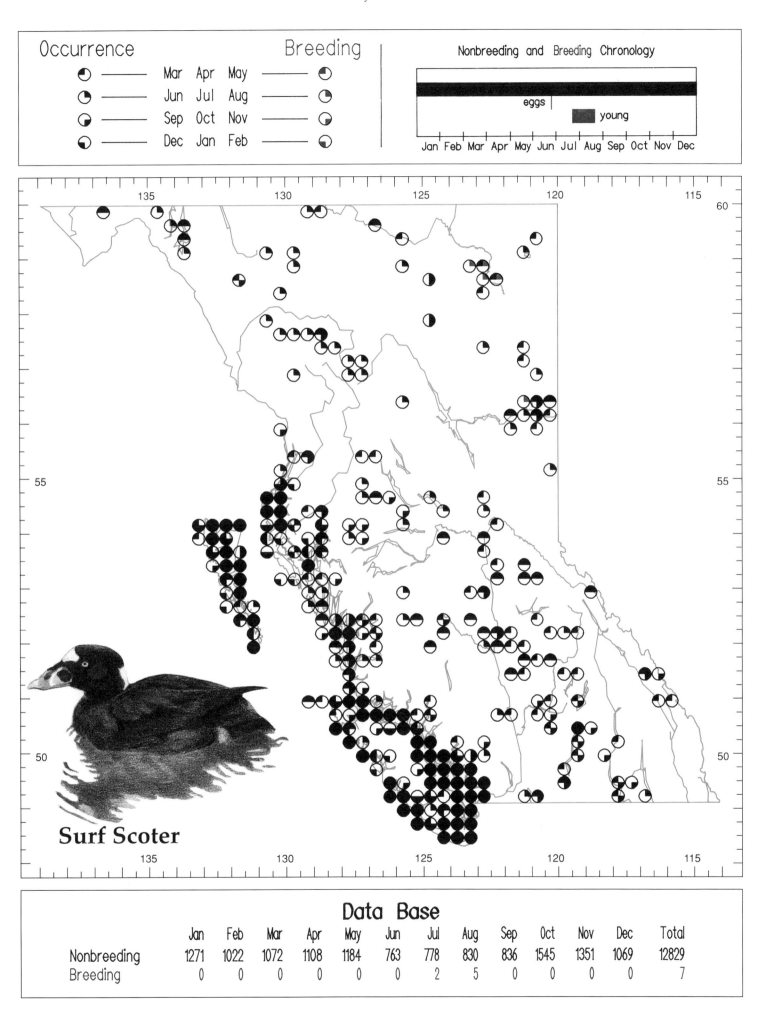

Surf Scoter

Occurrence

◐	———	Mar Apr May	———	◐
◔	———	Jun Jul Aug	———	◔
◖	———	Sep Oct Nov	———	◗
◕	———	Dec Jan Feb	———	◕

Breeding

Nonbreeding and Breeding Chronology

eggs young

Jan Feb Mar Apr May Jun Jul Aug Sep Oct Nov Dec

Data Base

	Jan	Feb	Mar	Apr	May	Jun	Jul	Aug	Sep	Oct	Nov	Dec	Total
Nonbreeding	1271	1022	1072	1108	1184	763	778	830	836	1545	1351	1069	12829
Breeding	0	0	0	0	0	0	2	5	0	0	0	0	7

at sea. Small numbers of both sexes remain on interior lakes to complete their moult. Autumn migration begins slowly in the northern interior by late August and is less noticeable than the spring movement.

Large numbers begin reaching the coastal wintering grounds by late September and build through October and November. Surf Scoters winter along the length of the British Columbia coast, including the waters adjacent to Vancouver Island and the Queen Charlotte Islands. We have but one winter record for the interior. Major wintering areas include the south mainland coast from White Rock, north to the Sunshine Coast, and the Baynes Sound area of Vancouver Island (Fig. 301). Winter bird counts from 23 coastal areas in 1983 totalled over 13,000 Surf Scoters (Appendix 2), which is 10% of the Surf Scoter population that winters south of the Aleutian Islands (Bellrose 1976).

A seasonal sample from Surf Scoter flocks along the coast revealed the following male:apparent-female ratios: in winter, males were favoured 3.2:1 (n=56; 2,601 birds); this dropped to 2.5:1 (n=41; 1,348 birds) for the period March-April and 1.7:1 (n=54, 653 birds) in May as birds left for the breeding grounds. The return of post-breeding males to the coast was noted as the summer ratios increased to 3.5:1 (n=76; 822 birds). Our early spring ratios are similar to those reported by Bellrose (1976), calculated from hunters' bags.

BREEDING: The Surf Scoter breeds occasionally in the Peace and Fort Nelson lowlands of northeastern British Columbia. Habitats include freshwater lakes surrounded by spruce and muskeg or mature coniferous/deciduous stands from 300 to 360 m elevation. The known breeding range in the province is much reduced from that reported by R.S. Palmer (1976b), Bellrose (1976), and Godfrey (1986).

Nests: There are no documented nests from the province.

Eggs: Calculated dates, using an estimated age of broods and assuming an incubation period similar to the other scoters (Bellrose 1976), indicate that eggs could be found as early as 25 June. Clutch size reported by Bent (1925) ranged from 5 to 7 eggs.

Young: Dates for 6 broods ranged from 22 July to 20 August. Brood size ranged from 4 to 14 young (4Y-2, 5Y-1, 7Y-1, 13Y-1, 14Y-1).

REMARKS: Most of the available information on nesting for the Surf Scoter dates back to the 19th century and is only fragmentary (Bellrose 1976). Our data shed little further light on the breeding biology of the species. However, with careful work and perseverence, dedicated observers in northeastern British Columbia have the opportunity to fill that gap in our understanding of the species.

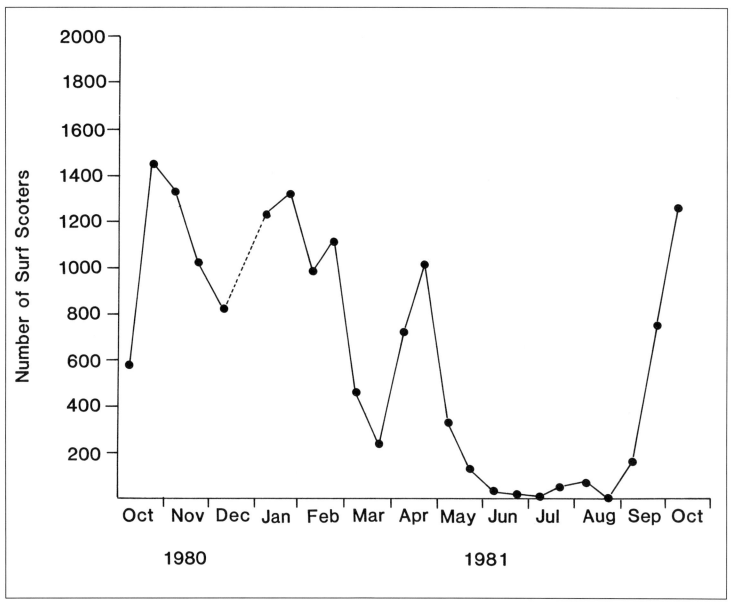

Figure 301. *Biweekly counts (averages) of Surf Scoters, Comox Harbour to Deep Bay, Vancouver Island, 11 October 1980 to 10 October 1981 (Canadian Wildlife Service unpublished data). The dashed line indicates a period when counts were not made.*

NOTEWORTHY RECORDS

Spring: Coastal - Gonzales Point (Victoria) 18 Apr 1983-1,802 flying NE in flocks of 15 to 150; Clover Point 21 Apr 1977-773 flying E in flocks of 35 to 120 in 1.5 hours, 16 May 1982-60; Ganges Harbour 11 Mar 1978-5,200 on herring spawn (Carson and Howsam 1978) 25 Mar 1977-3,537; Hesquiat Harbour 7 Mar 1976-10,000; Clayoquot spit 25 Mar 1971-4,000 on herring spawn (Hatler et al. 1978); Long Beach 21 May 1981-1,000+; Iona Island 4 May 1980-1,500+; Gabriola Island 25 Mar 1977-3,800; Thetis Island 14 Apr 1979-3,000; Nanoose Harbour 12 Apr 1973-4,600+; Little Qualicum River 5 Apr 1977-1,000, 15 Apr 1975-1,147, both on estuary (Dawe 1976), 20 Apr 1976-977 (Dawe 1980); between Lasqueti and Texada Islands 5 May 1977-3,000 to 5,000; Powell River 21 Mar 1982-8,500; Atrevida Reef 30 Mar 1977-1,200; Ickna Creek 8 Apr 1979-600; Lama Passage 7 Apr 1976-500; Indian Rock (Queen Charlotte Sound) 29 Mar 1972-525; Section Cove 24 Apr 1985-1,500; Gillatt Island 18 Apr 1982-1,300, 12 May 1977-2,200+; Kitkatla Inlet 11 to 12 May 1977-100,000 scoters, almost exclusively Surf, on boat survey, (Martin 1978); Billy Bay 8 May 1979-30,000 on aerial survey (Savard and Kaiser 1982); Lawn Point (Tlell) 20 Mar 1981-2,050 on herring spawn; Rose Spit 4 May 1979-1,231 flying N in 52 flocks of 2 to 170; Big Bay (Tsimpsean Peninsula) 16 to 17 Apr 1975-300,000 scoters, almost exclusively Surf, on boat survey, (Martin 1978); Finlayson Island 24 Mar 1981-6,500 on aerial survey; Port Simpson 24 Mar 1981-2,000 on aerial survey. **Interior** - Salmon Lake (Westwold) 9 May 1982-12; Tunkwa Lake 12 May 1968-75; Dutch Lake 9 May 1984-75 to 100; 100 Mile House 4 May 1986-50, first spring record; Lac la Hache 9 Apr 1978-1, 12 May 1981-200+; Williams Lake 24 Mar 1964-3, 21 Apr 1979-15, day after ice left, 9 May 1982-75, 10 May 1968-53; Puntzi Lake 26 Apr 1977-75+; Moose Lake (Mount Robson) 25 May 1972-120; Ten Mile Lake (Cinema) 10 May 1968-112; Nilkitkwa Lake 23 May 1978-200+; Charlie Lake 1 May 1983-7, 17 May 1986-200; Parker Lake (Fort Nelson) 13 May 1979-29; Cold Fish Lake 27 May 1976-4, lake mostly frozen; Atlin 8 May 1931-352, 16 May 1981-5; Leo Lake 14 May 1981-24, lake mostly frozen.

Summer: Coastal - Esquimalt Lagoon 1 Jun 1977-95 yearlings; Victoria 5 Jul 1980-80; Satellite Channel 10 Aug 1972-150 (Tatum 1973); Sidney Island 1 Jul 1953-55 males; Florencia Bay 2 Aug 1974-425; Pachena Bay 2 to 20 Jul 1979-206, 25 Aug 1977-500; Stubbs Island (Tofino) 16 Jul 1960-25+; Tsawwassen 29 Jul 1973-600 off jetty; Boundary Bay 7 Aug 1980-2,000 to 4,000 (Savard 1981); Miami Islet 20 Jun 1978-78, many moulting males, 17 Jul 1968-500; White Islets (Roberts Creek) 9 Jun 1981-640 feeding on blue mussels; Franklin Island 8 Aug 1979-300, most flightless; Pam Rock 8 Jun 1981-75, mostly nonbreeding males, feeding on mussels, 8 Aug 1979-500; Christie Islet 10 Jun 1978-66, mostly moulting males, 11 Aug 1977-800, moulting subadults; Hornby Island 1 Jun 1981-225; Hernando Island 11 Aug 1969-1,000, 80% unable to fly (Foottit 1969); Brooks Peninsula 4 to 15 Aug 1981-30, maximum numbers - moulting birds; Darby Channel 8 Aug 1977-157; Hunt Island 17 Jun 1948-900; Skidegate Inlet 19 Jul 1977-100; Coste Rocks 2 and 4 Jul 1975-800, mostly males; Rose Spit 15 Jul 1977-1,000 offshore; off Ranger Islet 19 Jul 1967-200, mostly males; Portland Inlet 21 Jul 1966-200+; Kwinamass Bay 12 Jul 1967-100 males; Hastings Arm 8 Aug 1986-5,000, 14 Aug 1976-3,000 (J.-P. Savard pers. comm.). **Interior** - Kleena Kleene 27 Jun 1951-12 nonbreeders (Paul 1959); Williams Lake 21 Jul 1979-9; Lake Kathlyn 1 Jul 1974-13 males; Peace River (Hudson's Hope) 26 Jul 1985-28; Fort St. John 21 to 23 Jul 1983-1 male; Tatlatui Lake 1 Jul 1976-10; Kitchener Lake 23 Jun 1976-15; Fern Lake (Kwadacha Wilderness Park) 12 Aug 1983-65 (Cooper, J.M. and Cooper 1983); Parker Lake (Fort Nelson) 29 Jul 1979-24; Summit Pass 23 Jun 1972-18; Kotcho Lake 20 Jun 1982-7; Kinaskan Lake 8 Jul 1979-45 to 50; Tuaton Lake 24 Jul 1976-25+ (Osmond-Jones et al. 1977); Cold Fish Lake 8 Jul 1959-30 males, 10 Jul 1976-68 males (Osmond-Jones et al. 1977); Tagish Lake 15 Jul 1980-7 males; Atlin Lake 4 Jul 1980-8 males.

Autumn: Interior - Cold Fish Lake 19 Sep 1976-15, young and adults; Charlie Lake 29 Sep 1985-120, 2 Oct 1983-127, 20 Oct 1986-2, last record; 6 Oct 1986-143, all in female-like plumage; Morice Lake 30 Sep 1974-5 (LGL Limited 1974); McBride Lake 30 Sep 1974-4 (LGL Limited 1974); Williams Lake 14 Oct 1986-17; Kamloops Lake (Savona) 1 Nov 1980-1; Trapp Lake 4 Sep 1978-20. **Coastal** - Venn Passage 23 Sep 1977-468; Cumshewa Inlet 30 Sep 1971-thousands; Fisher Channel 27 Sep 1968-540, mostly males; Johnstone Strait (Tsitika River) 7 Oct 1979-568 flying SE in 14 flocks of 15 to 75 birds; Campbell River (Discovery Passage) 20 Oct 1975-2,309; Campbell River to Oyster River 11 Oct 1977-3,000; Oyster Bay 30 Sep 1972-100+; Jervis Inlet 28 Nov 1976-1,500 in middle of inlet; Hornby Island 20 Sep 1978-165, mostly males; Ocean Park 26 Oct 1980-1,200; Stanley Park (Vancouver) 27 Sep 1959-800, 6 Oct 1973-2,000, 18 Oct 1981-2,000, 25 Oct 1977-3,000; Ambleside 27 Nov 1983-3,000; Bedwell Bay area 31 Oct 1978-1,200; Tofino Inlet 18 Nov 1982-400; Saanichton Bay 26 Sep 1980-400; McMicking Point 25 Sep 1977-400+.

Winter: Interior - See Christmas Counts. **Coastal** - Chismore Passage 26 Feb 1978-324 (Martin 1978); Kitimat 19 Dec 1981-400; Verney Passage 30 Jan 1975-265; Porcher Inlet 16 Feb 1978-559 on aerial survey (Savard 1978); Skidegate Inlet 15 Feb 1978-401 on aerial survey (Savard 1978); Skedans Bay 30 Jan 1975-900; Port Neville 29 Dec 1977-60; Campbell River (Discovery Passage) 29 Jan 1962-2,500+; Campbell River to Oyster River 14 Feb 1975-1,622; Little Qualicum River 1 Jan 1974-385 on estuary; West Vancouver 16 Dec 1979-3,482; Stanley Park (Vancouver) 4 Dec 1982-4,000; Alberni Inlet 5 Feb 1976-3,685; Captain's Passage 26 Feb 1978-5,018 (Carson and Howsam 1978); off Billings Spit 14 Jan 1978-500, 4 Feb 1978-1,000.

Christmas Counts: Interior - Recorded once: Vernon 26 Dec 1976-1. **Coastal** - Recorded from 23 of 28 localities and on 80% of all counts. Maxima: Vancouver 17 Dec 1978-**5,562**, all-time Canadian high count (Anderson, R.R. 1979); White Rock 28 Dec 1976-4,280; Sunshine Coast 17 Dec 1983-2,474.

White-winged Scoter

WWSC

Melanitta fusca (Linnaeus)

RANGE: Breeds from Alaska to northern Ontario, south to north-central Washington and northern North Dakota. Winters on both the Pacific and Atlantic coasts from the Aleutian Islands as far south as Baja California in the west, and from Newfoundland to Georgia in the east. Also found in Eurasia.

STATUS: *Abundant* to *very abundant* spring and *very common* to *abundant* autumn migrant on the coast; *abundant* to *very abundant* in winter and locally *very common* to *abundant* summer visitant. In the interior, *common* spring and *fairly common* autumn migrant; *very rare* in winter. Breeds in the interior.

NONBREEDING: The White-winged Scoter is widely distributed in coastal waters throughout the year; it occurs throughout the interior from spring through autumn. In the interior, small numbers winter irregularly only in the Thompson-Okanagan Plateau region of the province. It has been found from sea level to 2,000 m elevation (Christman 1969).

The White-winged Scoter frequents marine and brackish waters along the coast including bays, inlets, channels, estuaries, and occasionally large, slow-moving rivers. It appears to prefer more open, deeper waters than the Surf Scoter, especially where sandy or gravelly bottoms support shellfish beds. Such areas include the north and east coasts of the Queen Charlotte Islands, Big Bay near Prince Rupert, much of the Strait of Georgia and the coastal areas of extreme southern Vancouver Island. During migration the White-winged Scoter is regularly encountered in open, coastal waters, mostly within 5 km of the shore.

In the interior, the deeper areas of large lakes and occasionally slow-moving rivers are preferred habitat.

The presence of large numbers of birds on the coast in all seasons makes the timing of migration to and from the coast difficult to ascertain, especially since there is a strong tendency for age and sex classes to be segregated. Spring migration generally occurs in April and May, and autumn migration runs from late September through early November (Fig. 302). Spring migration in the interior is best marked by the arrival of paired birds on interior lakes in the second week of May; it may begin in southern areas in late April. Many nonbreeding subadult birds migrate but most of the first-year birds remain on salt water. Nonbreeders soon return to the coast and are joined by adult males who leave the females early in incubation. Many adult females migrate to salt water in early autumn and may head farther south than the other groups. The young of the year follow before freeze-up in the first weeks of November.

The moulting period is variable and extended, beginning slightly earlier in subadults and adult males. They begin their moult in July or August while the females wait until the young are independent in late August or September. Patch (1922) reports the north beaches of Graham Island to be "littered with feathers" in late August, but flightless birds can be encountered in early winter. Boundary Bay is one of the more important moulting areas.

Courtship occurs throughout the winter, and from mid-winter on, paired birds are not as tightly associated with large flocks as the subadults and unpaired birds.

Flocks of 100 to 500 birds are scattered throughout the Strait of Georgia and around the southern tip of Vancouver Island in all seasons. There are 2 centres of winter distribution: Hecate Strait between Skidegate Inlet and Bonilla Island, and the southern Strait of Georgia. Winter bird counts from 23 coastal areas in 1977

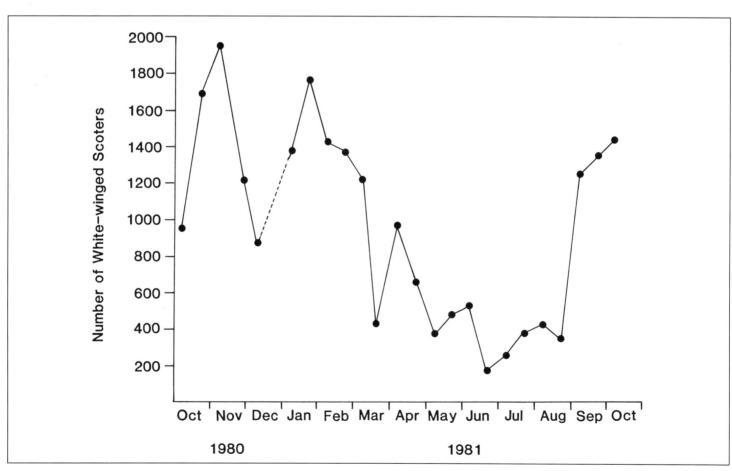

Figure 302. *Biweekly counts (averages) of White-winged Scoters, Comox Harbour to Deep Bay, Vancouver Island, 11 October 1980 to 10 October 1981 (Canadian Wildlife Service unpublished data). The dashed line indicates a period when counts were not made.*

White-winged Scoter

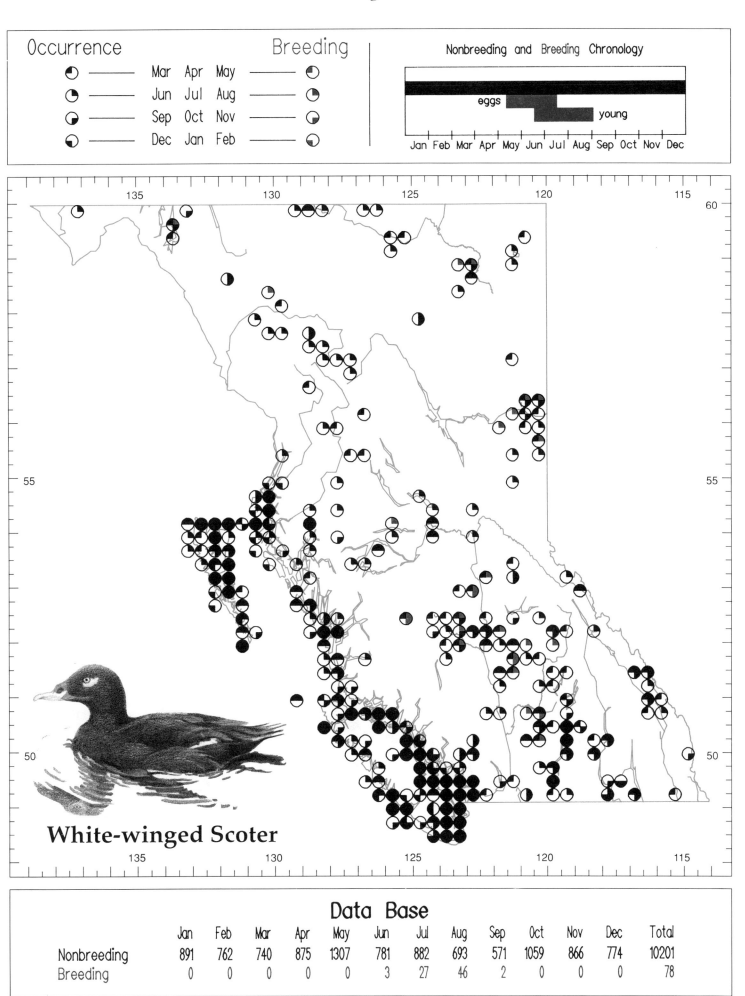

Occurrence

◐ ———	Mar Apr May
◔ ———	Jun Jul Aug
◑ ———	Sep Oct Nov
◕ ———	Dec Jan Feb

Breeding

——— ◑	
——— ◔	
——— ○	
——— ◑	

Nonbreeding and Breeding Chronology

eggs young

Jan Feb Mar Apr May Jun Jul Aug Sep Oct Nov Dec

White-winged Scoter

Data Base

	Jan	Feb	Mar	Apr	May	Jun	Jul	Aug	Sep	Oct	Nov	Dec	Total
Nonbreeding	891	762	740	875	1307	781	882	693	571	1059	866	774	10201
Breeding	0	0	0	0	0	3	27	46	2	0	0	0	78

totalled over 5,000 birds (Appendix 2), which is over 3% of the 142,000 White-winged Scoters reported to winter on the Pacific coast (Bellrose 1976).

BREEDING: The White-winged Scoter breeds in the Thompson-Okanagan Plateau from Douglas Lake north through the Fraser Plateau to Nimpo Lake and Burns Lake, throughout the Peace Lowlands (Fig. 303) and across the Boreal Forest in northern British Columbia west to Atlin. It breeds from 700 to 1,530 m elevation. R.W. McKelvey (pers. comm.) estimates a breeding population of 17,000 birds in the province.

All reports of nests and broods in British Columbia have been from freshwater lakes and ponds, from relatively open country in the central plateau region to forested habitat in northern areas. Freshwater systems include shallow alkaline ponds in the Chilcotin-Cariboo region, acidic bog lakes in the Peace Lowlands, occasionally bulrush sloughs and very large waterbodies such as Atlin Lake. Some lakes seem to be more important than others: Fletcher and Stum lakes in the Chilcotin Plateau, 103 Mile and 105 Mile lakes in the Chilcotin-Cariboo Basin, Cecil and Boundary (Fig. 304) lakes in the Peace Lowlands, and Como Lake near Atlin.

Nests and Eggs: Only 2 nests have been found in British Columbia: 15 June 1980 (9 eggs), built of grass and lined with down, on edge of an exploration road only 8 m from an active oil pump, in thin grasses on the muskeg beside German Lake, east of Fort St. John, and 10 July 1980 (8 eggs), built with some grass but mostly down, on the edge of a small grass island in Como Lake. J.A. Munro and Cowan (1947) mention that a completely formed egg was found in the oviduct of a female shot on 9 June 1938 at Tupper Creek (Tupper).

Calculated dates indicate clutches could be found as early as 12 May (see Young below) and as late as 17 July. Incubation period is 25 to 28 days (Bellrose 1976).

Young: Dates for 88 broods ranged from 19 June to 3 September, with 59% recorded between 23 July and 13 August. Brood size ranged from 1 to 46 young (1Y-3, 2Y-1, 3Y-3, 4Y-6, 5Y-3, 6Y-6, 7Y-12, 8Y-9, 9Y-7, 10Y-8, 11Y-5, 12Y-6, 13Y-2, 14Y-3, 16Y-2, 17Y-1, 18Y-1, 19Y-3, 20Y-1, 23Y-2, 25Y-1, 33Y-1, 38Y-1, 46Y-1), with 53% having 7 to 12 young. Fledging period is 63 to 77 days (Hochbaum 1944).

Broods larger than 16 young (see Bellrose 1976) were reported 12 times and probably result from amalgamation of several separate broods. Most of those "gang" broods occurred after 8 August, and involved young that were 2 to 3 weeks old, but a report on 22 July noted that the young were only 2 to 3 days old. There was one report of a "gang" brood with 2 females. P.W. Brown (1977) mentions, however, that young become independent of the females at about one week of age after which many of the females leave to moult on salt water in mid-August.

REMARKS: The White-winged Scoter is divided into 2 groups: a *deglandi* group that occurs primarily in North America and eastern Asia, and a *fusca* group that is only found in Eurasia (American Ornithologists' Union 1983). They are considered by some authors to be separate species: *M. fusca* (Velvet Scoter) and *M. deglandi* (White-winged Scoter).

Not all White-winged Scoters that winter on the British Columbia coast breed nearby. Two birds banded in central Saskatchewan were recovered on the south coast of British Columbia (Houston and Brown 1983).

See Rawls (1949) and P.W. Brown (1977) for additional information on the life history of this large sea duck.

POSTSCRIPT: In summer 1988, the following noteworthy records were received: Rose Spit 4 June 1988-3,000 along east side; Stum Lake 16 June 1988-265, which included a raft of 238 adult males.

Figure 303. *Typical open country in the Peace Lowlands, May 1978 (R. Wayne Campbell). Numerous ponds and lakes with emergent vegetation in the water and as bands along the shore provide excellent cover for nesting White-winged Scoters.*

Figure 304. *Boundary Lake (Goodlow), July 1978 (R. Wayne Campbell). Islands of emergent vegetation in the lake and bands along the shores provide escape cover for broods of White-winged Scoters.*

NOTEWORTHY RECORDS

Spring: Coastal - Oak Bay 28 Mar 1947-200+ at sewage outlet; Ganges Harbour 11 Mar 1978-2,100 (Carson and Howsan 1978), 23 Mar 1980-3,000; Crescent Beach (White Rock) 5 May 1949-1,000+; Nanoose Harbour 12 Apr 1973-700+; Little Qualicum River 23 Mar 1974-6,000+; Qualicum River 15 Mar 1939-1,000 on herring spawn (Munro, J.A. 1939g); Tofino 1 Apr 1962-300+; Hesquiat Harbour 7 Mar 1976-800; Baynes Sound 21 May 1987-20 adults, 430 immatures; Powell River 9 May 1923-320; Alert Bay 23 May 1968-300; Cumshewa Head 16 Mar 1976-5,000+; Bonilla Island to Banks Island 28 Mar 1978-3,500 (Savard and Kaiser 1982); Skidegate Inlet 9 May 1987-2,800 (Campbell 1987b); central Hecate Strait 21 Apr 1987-814; Rose Spit 25 Apr 1979-146. **Interior** - Trout Creek (Summerland) 13 May 1969-10; Whatshan Lake 16 May 1981-30; Nakusp 11 May 1976-6; Chapperon Lake 9 May 1982-65; Tunkwa Lake 12 May 1968-32; Enid Lake 29 May 1977-2; Adams Lake 17 May 1970-12 at north end; Lac la Hache 12 May 1981-50; Stum Lake 24 May 1987-60; Haines Lake 20 May 1975-19; Isaac Lake 17 May 1979-78; n Fort St. John 27 Apr 1985-1 adult male; Charlie Lake 3 May 1986-1 adult male, 17 May 1986-100 adults, 24 May 1986-300 adults; Bear Lake (e Motase Peak) 24 May 1939-1,240+ (Stanwell-Fletcher and Stanwell-Fletcher 1943); Atlin 21 May 1981-42 (Campbell 1981).

Summer: Coastal - Oak Bay 5 Jul 1978-93, all males; Satellite Channel 19 Aug 1982-150; Boatswain Bank 22 Jul 1983-180; Barkley Sound 3 Aug 1968-2,000; Crescent Beach 5 Jun 1951-50, all males; Nanoose Harbour 10 Jul 1950-165; Denman Island 30 Jun 1929-500 off spit; Comox 1 to 22 Jun 1969-500, late Aug 1954-2,000 (Flahaut and Schultz 1955); Royston 20 Aug 1927-1,000;

Port Neville 13 Jun 1976-100; Hunter Island 17 Jun 1948-300; Kagan Bay 5 Aug 1979-300; Cape Ball River 2 Aug 1974-240, mostly males; Bonilla Island 29 Jul 1980-1,538; McIntyre Bay 14 Jul 1977-1,000+, 14 Aug 1986-1,000+; Big Bay (Prince Rupert) 30 Jul 1980-258. **Interior** - Summerland 8 Jul 1979-70; Trail 9 Jun 1971-1 male; Minnie Lake 20 Jun 1950-50; Kamloops 28 Jun 1940-100, mostly males (Goldman 1940); Fletcher Lake 25 Aug 1983-20; Williams Lake 25 Jun 1971-40 males; Green Lake (70 Mile House) 27 Jul 1936-350 (Munro, J.A. and Cowan 1947); Stum Lake 6 Jun 1973-100+, 20 Jul 1973-250+, 15 Aug 1973-200+ (Ryder 1973); Bowron Lake 18 Jul 1961-11 (Ritcey and Verbeek 1961); Charlie Lake 12 Jun 1982-208, 90% males; Kitchener Lake 24 Jun 1976-70; Parker Lake (Fort Nelson) 20 Aug 1978-18; Kotcho Lake 20 Jun 1982-650 to 700 (Campbell and McNall 1982); Como Lake 6 Jun 1978-34.

Autumn: Interior - Gladys Lake (ne Atlin) 11 Oct 1980-32; Parker Lake (Fort Nelson) 7 Sep 1985-5 immatures; Cold Fish Lake 24 Sep 1976-25; Charlie Lake 26 Sep 1982-50, 2 Oct 1983-43; Puntzi Lake 23 Oct 1976-35+; Quesnel Lake 8 Oct 1979-15; Williams Lake 20 Sep 1984-36; Emerald Lake (Yoho National Park) 29 Oct 1976-9 (Wade 1977); Sorrento 7 Oct 1970-28, 8 Oct 1970-50+ (Schnider et al. 1971); Nelson 20 Sep 1969-5; Trail 14 Nov 1979-1 immature; Vaseux Lake 22 Oct 1975-5; Lightning Lake 13 Oct 1984-1. **Coastal** - Rose Spit 23 Sep 1977-1,926, 17 Oct 1977-387, 14 Nov 1977-673 (Savard 1978); Skedans 18 Oct 1977-590, 15 Nov 1977-1,202 (Savard 1978); Cumshewa Head 30 Sep 1971-tens of thousands; Cape Scott Park 12 Sep to 1 Oct 1953-500; Campbell River (Discovery Passage) 20 Oct 1975-1,259; Elma Bay 20 Nov 1936-1,140; Comox 7 to 9

Oct 1969-500; Little Qualicum River 17 Nov 1975-182; Capilano River 24 Oct 1971-200 off mouth (Campbell et al. 1972b); Crescent Beach 6 Sep 1974-500, 16 Oct 1966-200; Cherry Point 11 Oct 1975-520; Sooke Harbour 14 Nov 1938-3,000.

Winter: Interior - 3 km e Nelson 17 Jan 1971-1; Okanagan Landing 21 to 26 Dec 1944-1, 25 Dec 1913-1, 26 Dec 1972-1, 8 Jan 1914-1; Swan Lake (Vernon) 21 Dec 1944-1 (Munro, J.A. 1945b); Trail 5 Dec 1979-1. **Coastal** - Venn Passage 5 Jan 1978-162, 28 Feb 1978-353 (Martin 1978); Rose Spit 9 Jan 1978-1,132, 16 Feb 1978-121 (Savard 1978); Skedans 11 Jan 1978-4,516, 15 Feb 1978-1,753 (Savard 1978); Bonilla Island 11 Jan 1978-5,250, 15 Feb 1978-3,000 off north end (Savard 1978); Cape St. James 1 Dec 1978-230; Pulteney Point 18 Jan 1977-190, 9 Feb 1977-190, 26 Feb 1976-525, 24 Dec 1975-200; Comox 27 Feb 1974-222; Departure Bay 8 Jan 1965-650; Clayoquot Sound 11 to 13 Dec 1972-293 (Robertson 1974); Little Qualicum River 1 Jan 1974-180 off estuary; Nanoose Harbour 24 Jan 1974-495, 28 Feb 1974-645; Fulford Harbour 9 Dec 1978-486; Bowen Island 6 Feb 1921-800 (Munro, J.A. 1921); Stanley Park (Vancouver) 13 Feb 1966-150; Crescent Beach 14 Jan 1979-275, 25 Jan 1968-450, 22 Feb 1978-1,200, 30 Dec 1942-200+ (Holdom 1943); Chatham Islands 17 Feb 1952-130+ courting; Sooke 5 Feb 1952-80 to 100.

Christmas Counts: Interior - Not recorded. **Coastal** - Recorded from 23 of 28 localities and on 77% of all counts. Maxima: Deep Bay 29 Dec 1982-**2,029**, all-time Canadian high count (Anderson, R.R. 1983); Comox 27 Dec 1976-1,697; Duncan 17 Dec 1977-1,569.

Common Goldeneye

Bucephala clangula (Linnaeus)

COGO

RANGE: Breeds in North America from near tree limit in Alaska east to Newfoundland and south through most of Canada to the northern United States. Winters in North America on the Pacific coast from Alaska south to southern California, southern Ontario, southern Quebec, in the Mississippi and Ohio valleys to the Gulf coast and on the Atlantic coast from Newfoundland south to Virginia and casually to Florida. Also occurs in Eurasia.

STATUS: *Fairly common* to locally *abundant* migrant and winter visitant to the coast; *rare* in summer. *Uncommon* to locally *very common* migrant and summer visitant to the interior. *Uncommon* to *fairly common* winter visitant to the major interior valleys in the southern portion of the province; *very rare* in winter elsewhere in the interior. Breeds throughout the interior; occasionally breeds on the coast.

NONBREEDING: The Common Goldeneye is distributed along coastal British Columbia from the Juan de Fuca Strait north to Alice Arm, although we have few records for the mainland coast between the north end of Vancouver Island and Kitimat. It is widely distributed throughout the southern third of the province, becoming more sporadic through the Sub-Boreal and Boreal Forest regions.

The Common Goldeneye frequents a variety of marine and freshwater habitats. On the coast, favoured habitats include estuaries, bays and harbours, lakes, lagoons (Fig. 305), the shallower waters of straits adjacent to beaches and spits, and occasionally ponds, rivers, and creeks. Interior birds frequent lakes and rivers and, to a lesser extent, ponds, sloughs, creeks, beaches, and marshes.

Large numbers of Common Goldeneyes can be found on the coast in late winter and early spring concentrated at areas where Pacific herring are spawning. Spring migration probably begins by late February on the coast as birds begin arriving on interior lakes by early March. The main movement occurs from late March through mid-April in the south and late April to early May in the north. Unpaired adult males seem to arrive at interior lakes first, followed by mated pairs and yearlings (see also Munro, J.A. 1939a). A few unfit or subadult birds summer along the coast. In the interior, males leave the incubating females for unknown moulting areas.

Autumn migration is late, as many birds remain on interior lakes until freeze-up (early December in some years). Birds can begin arriving in the southern portions of the province by early October; however, the main movement does not begin until late October to late November and early December on the coast.

The Common Goldeneye winters along the coast, principally around Vancouver Island and the adjacent mainland coast, the northern Queen Charlotte Islands and the north mainland coast. In the interior, it winters regularly in the south Okanagan, South Thompson River and Creston valleys, the west Kootenay and locally in the Columbia valley north to Golden; rarely it winters farther north locally to Williams Lake, Prince George, and the Peace Lowlands. The winter centre of abundance is the Vancouver area and the east coast of Vancouver Island from Qualicum Beach north to Comox.

Bellrose (1976) reports only 2,400 goldeneye wintering in British Columbia of which 1,248 are Common Goldeneye; that is considerably lower than the over 5,000 Common Goldeneye reported from Christmas Bird Counts in some years (Appendix 2).

Figure 305. *Courting pair of Common Goldeneye at Esquimalt Lagoon, 25 January 1986 (Tim Zurowski). For many waterbirds, wintering grounds are important for courtship and pair bond formation.*

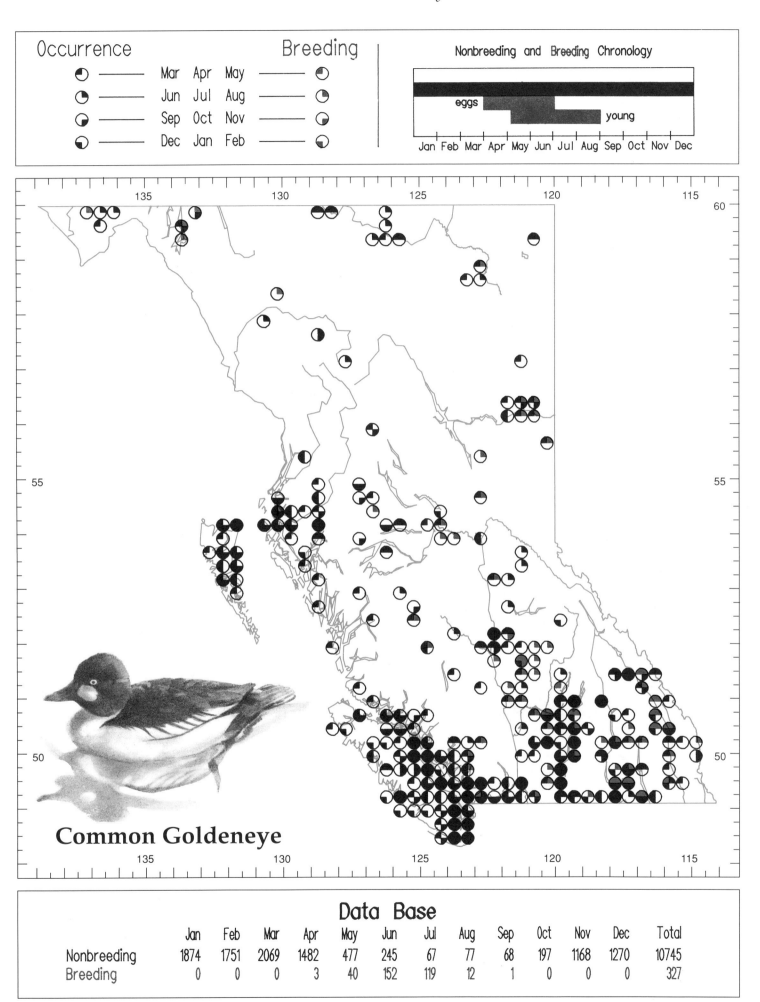

Common Goldeneye

Occurrence

| | Mar Apr May |
| Jun Jul Aug |
| Sep Oct Nov |
| Dec Jan Feb |

Breeding

Nonbreeding and Breeding Chronology

eggs

young

Jan Feb Mar Apr May Jun Jul Aug Sep Oct Nov Dec

Data Base

	Jan	Feb	Mar	Apr	May	Jun	Jul	Aug	Sep	Oct	Nov	Dec	Total
Nonbreeding	1874	1751	2069	1482	477	245	67	77	68	197	1168	1270	10745
Breeding	0	0	0	3	40	152	119	12	1	0	0	0	327

Those wintering numbers are over 4% of the Pacific coast winter population (Bellrose 1976).

BREEDING: The Common Goldeneye is a widespread though uncommon breeder throughout the southern third of the province east of the Coast Ranges becoming more sparsely distributed north through the Fraser Plateau and Fraser Basin regions, Peace and Fort Nelson lowlands, and the far northwestern Boreal Forest regions. It is a very rare breeder west of the Coast Ranges, including the Fraser Lowlands. Breeding on Vancouver Island remains to be confirmed.

The Common Goldeneye frequents lakes (often oligotrophic), rivers and associated flood plains, sloughs, ponds, and creeks, usually with wooded margins, from 180 to 1,550 m elevation (Fig. 306).

Bellrose (1976) reports that from 20,000 to 30,000 Common Goldeneye breed in British Columbia, largely in the Chilcotin-Cariboo region. Based on our data those estimates appear very high.

Nests: Thirteen of 17 nests were situated in nest boxes. Natural sites included cavities in trees (black cottonwood, Douglas-fir), a piling, and in a clump of witches' broom on a dead spruce. All nests were within 90 m of the edge of a lake, slough, or river. Fourteen nests ranged in height from 3.5 to 15 m, with most nests between 3.5 and 5.5 m. Nest material consisted primarily of down with various admixtures of shavings, wood chips, and feathers.

Eggs: Dates for 17 clutches ranged from 11 April (RBCM 586) to 2 July. Calculated dates indicate that eggs could be found as early as 1 April. Clutch size ranged from 2 to 9 eggs (2E-1, 5E-1 6E-4, 7E-3, 8E-5, 9E-3) with 70% having 6 to 8 eggs. Incubation period is 28 to 32 days and averages 30 days (Moyle et al. 1964).

Young: Dates for 214 broods ranged from 6 May to 1 September with 54% between 12 June and 13 July. Brood size ranged from 1 to 22 young (1Y-7, 2Y-18, 3Y-24, 4Y-34, 5Y-28, 6Y-37, 7Y-17, 8Y-15, 9Y-13, 10Y-6, 11Y-5, 12Y-4, 13Y-2, 15Y-1, 17Y-1, 19Y-1, 22Y-1) with 57% having 3 to 6 young. Broods with more than 12 young were likely the result of aggressive encounters between females or the amalgamation of deserted young with other broods. Fledging period is about 56 to 60 days (Carter, B.C. 1958; Moyle et al. 1964).

REMARKS: J.A. Munro (1939a) considers the Common Goldeneye a common migrant, noting only 4 breeding records for the species, 2 of which were based merely on the presence of mated pairs. Later, J.A. Munro and Cowan (1947) report only 3 nesting records for the Common Goldeneye from widely separate localities: Vernon, Vanderhoof, and Tupper. Other researchers up to the early 1960s report similar results: the Barrow's Goldeneye is the common breeding bird of the interior while the Common Goldeneye is only a migrant or does not occur at all (e.g. Stanwell-Fletcher and Stanwell-Fletcher 1943: Munro, J.A. 1947a, 1950, 1958a; Johnstone, W.B. 1949; Carl et al. 1952; Weeden 1960). Only in the Tupper Creek area of the Peace Lowlands is the Common Goldeneye found to be the more abundant summer resident of the two goldeneyes (Cowan 1939). Thus, there appears to have been an expansion of the breeding range of the Common Goldeneye in British Columbia. For example, according to R.W. Butler et al. (1986) the Common Goldeneye is now the more abundant of the two in the Creston valley. Only Common Goldeneye broods have been reported since 1966, and the species now forms 32% of the diving duck species composition, tied with Redhead as the most abundant breeding diving duck in the valley. R.W. Butler et al. (1986) note, however, that identification of broods was uncertain and was based on the most commonly seen pairs. This is a significant change from the 1956 breeding season in the Creston valley when J.A. Munro (1958a) observed only 1 Common Goldeneye, but 12 mated pairs and 34 broods of Barrow's Goldeneye.

The Common Goldeneye now also breeds in the Columbia valley and in the Chilcotin-Cariboo region. Savard (1984, 1986) studied both goldeneyes nesting in the Columbia valley. He found that the Common:Barrow's ratio there ranged between 1:2 and 1:3. In the Columbia valley, the Common Goldeneye uses both ponds and lagoons within the floodplain of the river and lakes and sloughs on the adjacent benchland in about equal proportions, whereas the Barrow's Goldeneye occurs primarily on the benchlands (Savard 1984; Table 18). Savard's other study area at Riske Creek held only Barrow's Goldeneye, but in J. Eadie's (pers. comm.) study area between 100 Mile House and 148 Mile House, some 60 km east of Savard's site, nesting Common and Barrow's goldeneyes occurred in a ratio of about 1:3. Common Goldeneyes appear to have invaded the Chilcotin-Cariboo region since 1982.

While we have many other sight records of female Common Goldeneye with broods from throughout the interior of the province, few of those are supported by specimens, photographs, or adequate field notes. In view of the difficulty of field identification of female goldeneyes, an element of doubt remains as to the precise breeding distribution of the species. On the distribution map we have only included breeding records from experienced observers. We encourage others to fully document all goldeneye nest records in future.

POSTSCRIPT: On 15 July 1989 a female Common Goldeneye with a brood of 10 downy young was observed feeding on Nisnak Lake in Schoen Lake Park (B.J. Brooks pers. comm.). This is the first documented breeding for Vancouver Island.

TABLE 18.
Distribution of Common and Barrow's goldeneyes in 2 main habitat types in the Columbia valley.
Figures represent numbers seen in each habitat (modified from Savard 1984).

	1982		1983	
	Floodplain (9 ponds)	Benchlands (14 ponds)	Floodplain (31 ponds)	Benchlands (24 ponds)
Common Goldeneye	52	83	134	89
Barrow's Goldeneye	0	46	5	106
Total	52	129	139	195

Figure 306. *Typical breeding habitat for the 3* Bucephala *species near Riske Creek, 5 June 1978 (Robert A. Cannings).*

NOTEWORTHY RECORDS

Spring: Coastal - Esquimalt Lagoon 1 Apr 1982-76; Roberts Bay 17 May 1978-1; Cowichan Bay 16 Mar 1974-151; Ganges Harbour 4 Mar 1978-220 on herring spawn (Carson and Howsam 1978); Ladner 11 Mar 1975-60; Gabriola Island 26 Mar 1978-2,000; Vancouver 2 Mar 1974-80, 18 Apr 1971-150, last spring concentration (Campbell et al. 1972b); Somass River 9 Mar 1977-89 on estuary; Nanoose Harbour 22 Mar 1979-720; Little Qualicum River 15 Mar 1979-1,611, 20 Mar 1978-502, 12 Apr 1976-470, 15 May 1975-5, latest departure (Dawe 1976, 1980); Squamish River 25 Mar 1980-30 on estuary; Okeover and Theodosia Inlets 6 Mar 1982-157; Klemtu 5 Apr 1976-2; Copper Bay 21 Mar 1981-88; Sandspit 6 May 1979-210; Lawn Point (Tlell) 20 Mar 1981-355 on Pacific herring spawn. **Interior** - Creston 5 Mar 1984-380, 6 Apr 1984-140; Vaseux Lake 19 Mar 1975-120; Nelson 15 Mar 1969-59; Balfour narrows 11 Mar 1979-50; Elizabeth Lake (Cranbrook) 6 May 1981-10; Wilmer 24 Mar 1985-3, 26 Mar 1985-182, 28 Mar 1985-298, 3 Apr 1985-183, 8 Apr 1985-99, 22 Apr 1985-35, 30 Apr 1985-9, 20 May 1985-3 (Butler, R.W. and Savard 1985); Sorrento 30 Mar 1972-100; Revelstoke 5 Apr 1977-27; Merritt 22 Mar 1979-26, 20 males, most ponds frozen; Lillooet 13 Apr 1968-25, some open water but most still frozen; Riske Creek 3 Mar 1981-12; Alkali Lake 2 Apr 1977-24 in small ice-free sections, 18 Apr 1971-55; Williams Lake 2 Mar 1971-2 males, first arrivals on open creek, 23 Mar 1971-11 males, 5 Apr 1971-11, first female seen; Fraser Lake 24 Mar 1977-3 in small meltwater area; Peace River (Clayhurst) 10 May 1975-119; Peace River 27 Mar 1983-6 first arrival; Fort St. John 6 Apr 1986 1 male, first arrival; Charlie Lake 16 Apr 1983-41, 11 May 1983-120; Fort Nelson 24 Apr 1986-1, first arrival; Parker Lake (Fort Nelson) 13 May 1975-6; Helmet (Kwokullie Lake) 14 to 31 May 1982-1 to 3 pairs almost daily.

Summer: Coastal - Clover Point 15 Aug 1958-1; Cowichan Bay 20 Jul 1974-2 (2 to 3 birds regular here each summer); Ambleside 30 Jul 1975-2; Kwai Lake 12 Jul 1981-1; Alta Lake 27 Aug 1968-2; Comox 14 Jun 1978-2; Granite Bay 2 Jul 1977-1; Kitimat 25 Jul 1975-2. **Interior** - Duck Lake (Creston) 20 Jul 1982-40, 22 Jul 1981-20+; Trout Creek (Summerland) 8 Jun 1966-1; Sorrento 18 Jun 1970-2; Bald Mountain (Riske Creek) 15 Jun 1978-28; Squiness Lake 18 Jul 1975-2, eclipse plumage; Charlie Lake 15 Jun 1982-300, 2 flocks; Fishing Lake 13 Jul 1978-4; Deer River 15 Aug 1978-1 at hotspring; s Fort Nelson 30 Aug 1985-4.

Autumn: Interior - Charlie Lake 3 Oct 1982-1 male, 27 Oct 1984-200, mostly males, 7 Nov 1982-90 almost only duck species left, lake froze 4 days later, 18 Nov 1979-1; Kathlyn Lake 17 to 23 Nov 1981-8; Anahim Lake 27 Oct 1977-31 (Hennan 1979); Williams Lake 17 Oct 1979-6, early; Knutsford 2 Sep 1977-24; Revelstoke 8 Nov 1977-10 (Bonar 1978b); Sorrento 30 Oct 1970-2, early; Windermere 9 Nov 1978-49; Elk River (Sparwood) 19 Sep 1982-5; Sparwood 14 Nov 1983-43; Peckham Lake 24 Nov 1984-6; Okanagan Lake (Kelowna) 4 Nov 1975-1, first of season; Summerland 12 Oct 1969-1, 17 Nov 1968-70; Vaseux Lake 19 Oct 1962-1, early, 10 Nov 1973-44; Creston 28 Sep 1986-65, 25 Oct 1986-135, 8 Nov 1985-75. **Coastal** - Kumdis Slough 14 Nov 1956-25; Tlell 4 Nov 1974-21; near Lawn Hill (Tlell) 19 Oct 1971-1; Port Neville 20 Sep 1975-4, 24 Oct 1977-20; Salmon River (Sayward) 9 Oct 1977-6; Little Qualicum River 31 Oct 1977-1, early arrival, 17 Nov 1975-135, 21 Nov 1977-124, large influx, 23 Nov 1978-103; 29 Nov 1976-129 (Dawe 1976, 1980); Meares Island 22 Nov 1981-28; Stanley Park (Vancouver) 6 Nov 1977-250; Iona Island 13 Nov 1971-51 (Campbell et al. 1972b); St. Mary Lake (Saltspring Island) 22 Nov 1977-50; Tsehum Harbour 30 Nov 1978-93; Esquimalt Lagoon 24 Nov 1975-50.

Winter: Interior - Peace River, e Lynx Creek 19 Feb 1984-2; Kathlyn Lake 1 Dec 1987-12, lake open, unusually mild; Francois Lake 27 Dec 1987-5; Fraser River (Prince George) winter 1968/69-10 (Rogers, T.H. 1969); Williams Lake 6 Dec 1971-125 in small patch of open water as lake froze, 2 Jan 1977-3; Kleena Kleene 29 Jan 1954-3, 17 Feb 1951-4 (Paul 1959); Sorrento 21 Dec 1970-50+; South Thompson River (Chase) 5 Feb 1977-30; Okanagan Lake 11 Jan 1977-18; Columbia River, Athalmer to Radium 4 Jan 1981-87; west arm, (Kootenay Lake) 7 Dec 1980-188, 8 Feb 1981-100; Columbia River near Kootenay River 6 Feb 1977-32; Okanagan Lake (Penticton) 26 Dec 1974-25; Creston 17 Jan 1983-95, 27 Jan 1983-35, 1 Feb 1983-175, 9 Feb 1983-190, 15 Feb 1983-265. **Coastal** - Kumdis Slough 6 Jan 1954-100; Tlell River 3 Dec 1956-12 at mouth; South Bay 12 Jan 1954-300; Quatsino Sound 14 to 16 Feb 1973-142; Port Neville 14 Jan 1976-50; Kelsey Bay 16 Feb 1975-7; Oyster Bay 18 Feb 1975-35; Little Qualicum River 18 Dec 1973-600+, 1 Jan 1974-294, 21 Jan 1974-250; Somass River 16 Feb 1977-58; Squamish River 27 Dec 1977-32; Stanley Park (Vancouver) 17 Dec 1977-250, 1 Jan 1971-220, 5 Feb 1984-210, 28 Feb 1974-300; Ganges Harbour 26 Feb 1978-383 (Carson and Howsam 1978); Cowichan Bay 15 Jan 1974-417; Esquimalt Lagoon 24 Jan 1971-100 (Tatum 1972); Sooke Harbour 21 Jan 1953-2,000+, 5 Feb 1952-1,000+.

Christmas Counts: Interior - Recorded from 12 of 19 localities and on 71% of all counts. Maxima: Shuswap Lake 21 Dec 1982-283; Vaseux Lake 31 Dec 1976-156; Vernon 18 Dec 1983-134. **Coastal** - Recorded from 27 of 28 localities and on 94% of all counts. Maxima: Vancouver 18 Dec 1977-1,729; Comox 27 Dec 1976-789; Deep Bay 27 Dec 1977-694.

Barrow's Goldeneye

Bucephala islandica (Gmelin)

BAGO

RANGE: Breeds in North America from Alaska, southern Yukon, and western Mackenzie south through British Columbia and southwestern Alberta to northern Washington and western Montana; locally at higher elevations farther south. Also breeds in Greenland and Iceland. Winters primarily along the Pacific coast from Alaska south to California and locally in the interior from southern British Columbia south to California and Arizona; on the Atlantic coast from the Gulf of St. Lawrence south to New York, rarely to South Carolina.

STATUS: *Fairly common* to locally *abundant* migrant and winter visitant to the coast; *rare* in summer. In the interior, *uncommon* to locally *very common* migrant and summer visitant to the southern portion of the province, becoming *rare* to locally *fairly common* north of the Chilcotin-Cariboo region. *Uncommon* winter visitant to the South Thompson River, Okanagan valley, and west Kootenay region; *very rare* in winter elsewhere in the interior. A widespread breeder throughout the interior; occasional breeder on the coast.

NONBREEDING: The Barrow's Goldeneye is distributed all along coastal British Columbia, including Vancouver Island and the Queen Charlotte Islands. It is widely distributed throughout the interior, although concentrated in the south-central portion of the province. It occurs from sea level to 2,400 m elevation.

The Barrow's Goldeneye frequents a variety of marine and freshwater habitats. Along the coast, birds are most often reported from bays, harbours, and inlets or fiords with rocky shores and extensive mussel beds. They often congregate near sources of fresh water such as creeks, waterfalls, and even storm drains, frequently forming mixed flocks with Surf Scoters and other waterbirds. Other habitats reported less frequently included lagoons, lakes, rivers, and sloughs. In the interior, birds are found most often on lakes, ponds, and rivers, followed by sloughs, creeks, marshes, and sewage lagoons.

During late winter and early spring, birds concentrate locally in areas where Pacific herring have spawned. About the same time, spring migration begins and small numbers of birds leave for their breeding grounds. The spring movement continues and numbers dwindle through April and into May. This dwindling of numbers along the coast suggests that the birds leave for the breeding grounds in relatively small groups rather than large flocks. This is supported by Savard's (1985a) observation: a marked pair was sighted on its winter territory near Vancouver on 12 April 1984 at 0715 and was subsequently found on its breeding territory, 320 km distant, on 13 April 1984 at 1120. The pair was not seen in any groups prior to its departure. By mid-May most birds have left the coast.

Birds, apparently unpaired adult males, arrive in the interior in early March, with numbers of both sexes and all ages concentrating on the larger ice-free lakes as early as the end of March in the Columbia valley, and mid-April in the Chilcotin-Cariboo. These concentrations can remain on the larger lakes until May in some years depending on the ice conditions at the breeding lakes. Adult and yearling males leave for moulting areas once the females are well into incubation; yearling females remain on the breeding grounds. We have some evidence to suggest that the males move north to moult (see Summer: Interior - Charlie Lake, Boundary Lake, below; and Swarth 1926). To date, however, moulting areas for males in British Columbia are unknown. In the summer, only a few likely unfit birds can be found along the coast, suggesting that the moulting areas are inland.

The summer population in the interior consists of adult and yearling females and young of the year. J.A. Munro (1958b) believes that adult and yearling females leave the Chilcotin-Cariboo region before their summer moult, possibly spending their flightless period on some of the larger lakes in the Nicola

region. Stum Lake may also be an important moulting site for Barrow's Goldeneyes. J.A. Munro (1939a, 1958b) presents data to support the exodus of females to autumn staging areas and then to coastal wintering grounds in this order: yearling females, adult females, and finally the young. Birds concentrate on the larger interior lakes from late August and September, and occasionally into November in some years.

Barrow's Goldeneyes begin arriving on the coast in October, but the main influx occurs from late October through November as birds are forced off the interior lakes during freeze-up. Males are the first to return. Subsequently, pairs which have been separated since early summer reunite on winter territories with most territories occupied by late December (Savard 1985a).

Barrow's Goldeneyes winter along the coast including Vancouver Island and the Queen Charlotte Islands. Some birds move farther south (Fig. 307). Small numbers winter in the interior in the Okanagan, the west Kootenay, and the South Thompson River valleys, rarely elsewhere in the interior. Major wintering areas include the south mainland coast (Indian Arm to Burrard Inlet, Sunshine Coast) and the north mainland coast (Kitimat Inlet, Douglas Channel, Prince Rupert). Bellrose (1976) notes that about 1,200 Barrow's Goldeneye winter in British Columbia. In some years, wintering birds can number about 5,000 (Appendix 2) which would be conservative as the Christmas Bird Count surveys do not cover the many coastal fiords that the species frequents. Prebreeding population estimates of the Barrow's Goldeneye in the province range from 70,000 to 126,000 birds (Bellrose 1976; Munro, W.T. and Goodchild 1981).

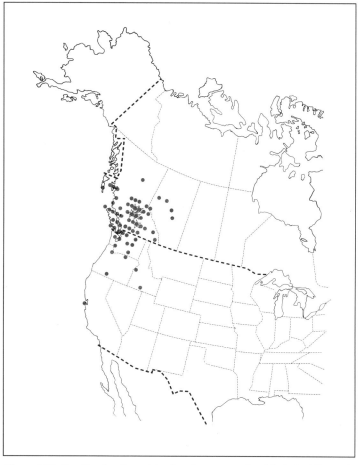

Figure 307. *Banding locations (stars) and recovery sites (circles) of Barrow's Goldeneyes banded in British Columbia. Since adult males leave the breeding areas to moult, most of the mortality on the breeding grounds would involve adult female and immature birds.*

Barrow's Goldeneye

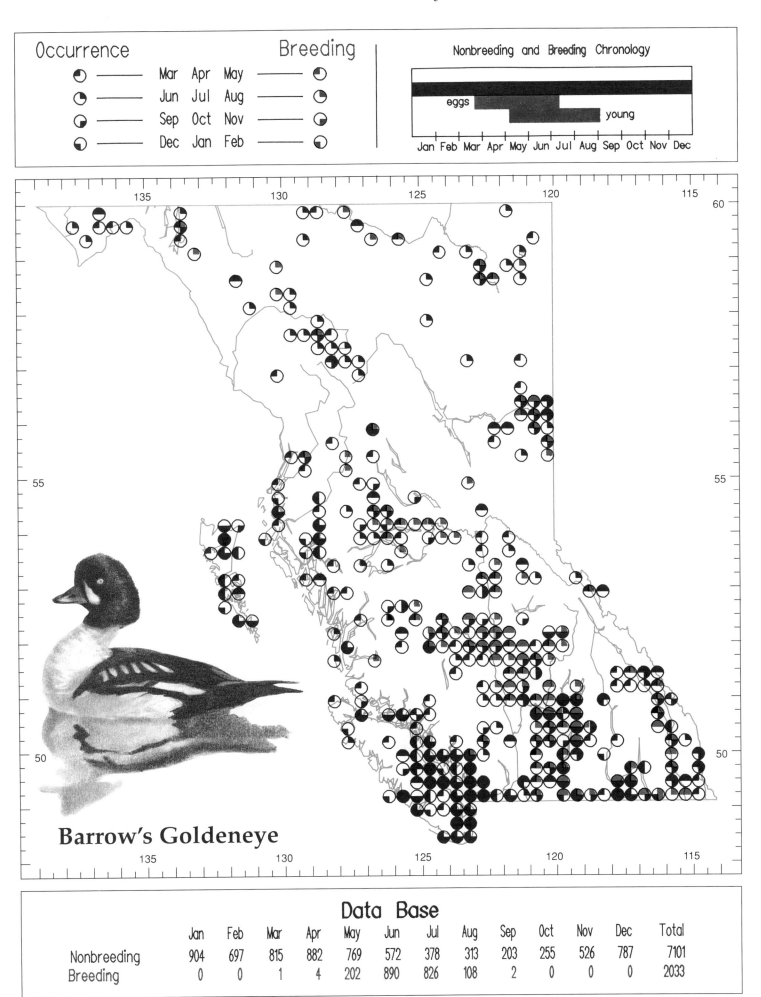

Occurrence / Breeding

Mar	Apr	May
Jun	Jul	Aug
Sep	Oct	Nov
Dec	Jan	Feb

Nonbreeding and Breeding Chronology

eggs

young

Jan Feb Mar Apr May Jun Jul Aug Sep Oct Nov Dec

Data Base

	Jan	Feb	Mar	Apr	May	Jun	Jul	Aug	Sep	Oct	Nov	Dec	Total
Nonbreeding	904	697	815	882	769	572	378	313	203	255	526	787	7101
Breeding	0	0	1	4	202	890	826	108	2	0	0	0	2033

BREEDING: The Barrow's Goldeneye is a widespread breeder throughout most of the interior of the province south of 53°N latitude, where over 95% of our records have been gathered. Farther north the species is an uncommon breeder. It is a very rare breeder west of the Coast Ranges: Brackendale, near Garibaldi, Green Lake (Garibaldi), Alta Lake, Owikeno Lake, and Kitsault Lake are known breeding sites. Its breeding centre of abundance is the Chilcotin-Cariboo region.

Breeding habitat includes lakes associated with aspen parkland (see Fig. 306), open ponderosa pine forests, farmland, rangeland and alpine meadows, as well as the wetter, closed coniferous forests including those of the sub-alpine regions from 300 to 1,830 m elevation. Alkaline lakes are preferred; occasionally the Barrow's Goldeneye breeds near ponds, rivers, and creeks.

Nests: Most nests (67%; n=134) were situated in man-made sites including nest boxes (66%); one nest was in the hay loft of a barn. Natural sites (Fig. 308) included cavities in deciduous trees (14%; trembling aspen-11% and black cottonwood - 3%) and coniferous trees (10%; Douglas-fir-6%, and ponderosa pine, spruces and lodgepole pine - 4%). Only cavities excavated by the Pileated Woodpecker are large enough for Barrow's Goldeneye; other woodpecker-created cavities are suitable only after they have been enlarged by decay, but by that time they are fragile and subject to blowdown. Other natural sites included crow nests (Edwards 1953; Sugden 1963), one nest in a yellow-bellied marmot burrow (Munro, J.A. 1935f), one nest in a hole in a cliff, and one nest on a clump of mistletoe in a spruce tree (Fig. 309; Campbell 1981). Most sites were on the edge or in the water near the edge of a wetland, although 10 nests ranged from 3 to 440 m away from water. On one occasion, downy young were observed following a female along a dirt road 4.8 km from the nearest lake; a similar observation is reported by Bellrose (1976). On another occasion, a brood was observed on a small pond surrounded by rangeland, with the nearest trees 1.6 km away. Nests (n=87) ranged in height from ground level to 18 m with 51% between 2

Figure 308. *Female Barrow's Goldeneye leaving nest site at Becher's Prairie (Riske Creek), 10 June 1978 (Richard J. Cannings).*

Figure 309. *Barrow's Goldeneye nest site on plant growth near top of spruce tree (arrow) at Davie Hall Lake near Atlin, 29 July 1980 (R. Wayne Campbell).*

and 3 m, the bulk of which were in nest boxes. The majority of natural nests (91%) were from 0 to 6 m above the ground. Seven nests had cavity depths ranging from 8 cm to 1.3 m. Four nests had cavity diameters ranging from 18 to 38 cm with 3 between 18 and 22 cm. Nest material consisted primarily of down with various mixtures of shavings, wood chips, or sawdust and occasionally grasses and lichen. Savard (1986) shows that a shortage of nest sites was limiting breeding pair densities in some areas of central British Columbia, but he points out that provision of nest boxes could increase this density. See Savard (1985b) for a discussion of the factors influencing the use of nest boxes by Barrow's Goldeneyes.

Eggs: Dates for 152 clutches ranged from 23 April to 11 July with 55% recorded between 20 May and 10 June. Calculated dates indicate that eggs could be found as early as 22 March (Munro, J.A. 1950). Clutch size ranged from 1 to 20 eggs (1E-9, 2E-5, 3E-3, 4E-6, 5E-14, 6E-16, 7E-19, 8E-20, 9E-7, 10E-19, 11E-11, 12E-4, 13E-5, 14E-6, 15E-2, 16E-1, 17E-4, 20E-1) with 53% having 6 to 10 eggs. Savard (1986) reports an average clutch size for nests in the Cariboo parklands of 9.8 (n=115) for 1983 and 9.7 (n=131) for 1984. The larger clutches reported here are likely the products of 2 or more females. Savard (1986) reports a conservative estimate of the frequency of parasitic laying ranging between 7% and 20%. J. Eadie (pers. comm.) found that 35% of Barrow's Goldeneye nests were parasitized in a study area near 100 Mile House. The incubation period for 8 nests in British Columbia ranged between 29 and 34 days with 5 of the nests between 31 and 32 days.

Occasionally mixed clutches, usually with Bufflehead, occur (Erskine 1959; Palmer, R.S. 1976b).

Young: Dates for 1,384 broods ranged from 7 May to 3 September with 52% recorded between 21 June and 16 July. Brood size ranged from 1 to 31 young (1Y-39, 2Y-58, 3Y-114, 4Y-131, 5Y-160, 6Y-165, 7Y-199, 8Y-152, 9Y-82, 10Y-81, 11Y-45, 12Y-38, 13Y-20, 14Y-27, 15Y-8, 16Y-16, 17Y-7, 18Y-9, 19Y-7, 20Y-4, 21Y-3, 22Y-4, 23Y-1, 24Y-1, 27Y-2, 31Y-1) with 58% having 4 to 8 young. The larger broods are likely the results of aggressive encounters between two females or the amalgamation of deserted young with other broods (Savard 1987a). Fledging period from British Columbia is 56 days (Bellrose 1976).

REMARKS: Based on available but poor population estimates, Savard (1987a) notes that British Columbia supports over 60% of the world population of Barrow's Goldeneye, possibly up to 90%. Given those proportions, it is apparent that wildlife management activities in British Columbia could affect the future of the species.

For a discussion of the research needs for Barrow's Goldeneye, see Savard (1987a). See also Common Goldeneye: Remarks.

POSTSCRIPT: A census of Stum Lake on 16 June 1988 revealed a large early summer concentration of Barrow's Goldeneye. A total of 575 birds were counted of which 497 were males. Stum Lake may be an important staging area for the drakes prior to their departure to more northern moulting areas.

NOTEWORTHY RECORDS

Spring: Coastal - Ganges Harbour 4 Mar 1978-723, 11 Mar 1978-369 on Pacific herring spawn; Nanoose Harbour on 25 Mar 1977-275, 3 Apr 1977-252; Keats Island 3 Apr 1977-275; Sea and Iona islands 27 Apr 1974 450; Vancouver 3 Mar 1978: English Bay-211, Inner Harbour-648, east Burrard Inlet-437, census (McKelvey et al. 1978); Stanley Park (Vancouver) 11 Mar 1973-300, 8 Apr 1973-200, 10 May 1974-30; n Bedwell Bay 13 May 1979-30, mostly females; St. Vincent Bay 31 Mar 1977-208; Hotham Sound 31 Mar 1977-320; head of Jervis Inlet to Patrick Point 2 Apr 1977-447; Deserted Bay 1 Apr 1977-236 probably feeding on Pacific herring spawn; De Cosmos Lagoon 19 Mar 1983-200; Juskatla Inlet 6 May 1977-144; Minette Bay 6 Mar 1975-94, 21 Mar 1975-177, 28 Mar 1975-83, 10 Apr 1975-76, 17 May 1975-16; Prince Rupert 2 Mar 1978-429 (Martin 1978); Kitsault 10 to 11 Mar 1980-496, 13 to 17 May 1980-150+. **Interior** - Richter Pass 15 Apr 1976-16; Trail 7 Mar 1982-40; Sirdar 6 May 1956-12 mated pairs (Munro, J.A. 1958a); Wasa Lake 2 Apr 1976-14+; n end Windermere Lake 31 Mar 1978-68; Invermere 13 Mar 1979-4; Vernon 30 Apr 1975-5 pairs; Salmon Lake (Westwold) 5 May 1984-500; Nicola Lake 15 Apr 1968-20; Shumway Lake 9 May 1975 125; Kamloops 4 Apr 1985-2, 11 Apr 1985-117, 18 Apr 1985-94, 29 Apr 1985-85, 9 May 1985-44 (Butler and Savard 1985); n Savona 14 Apr 1968-15; Crown Lake 13 Apr 1968-50, most of lake frozen; Riske Creek 10 Mar 1981-14, 10 Apr 1985-79, 15 Apr 1985-150, 20 Apr 1985-89, 25 Apr 1985-43 (Butler and Savard 1985); Bridge Creek (100 Mile House) 20 Mar 1983-5 males; 100 Mile House 11 May 1977-96, including yearlings; Westwick Lake 5 May 1977-30; Williams Lake 9 Mar 1979-1 male; 24 km s Prince George 4 Apr 1978-2; Francois Lake 7 Apr 1978-8; Charlie Lake 16 Apr 1983-1 male, first arrival, 5 May 1983-12; Parker Lake (Fort Nelson) 5 May 1980-2; Leo Lake 14 May 1981-4 lake mostly frozen; Chilkat Pass 15 May 1977-3 pairs.

Summer: Coastal - Cordova Channel 26 Jul 1975-1; Pitt Meadows 12 Jun 1971-1 (Campbell et al. 1972b); English Bay 21 to 22 Jun 1975-1; Ambleside 2 Jun 1974-3; Masset Inlet 19 Jun 1980-6. **Interior** - Kilpoola Lake 18 Jun 1977-25; Disdero Lake 4 Aug 1960-110+; Minnie Lake 10 Aug 1939-400 (Munro, J.A. and Cowan 1947); Leighton/Tunkwa Lakes 1 Aug 1950-250, mostly adults, 1 Aug 1951-176, mostly adults; Big Lake (Nemaiah Valley) 18 Aug 1978-250, some flightless; Green Lake (70 Mile House) 27 Jul 1937-150, probably all yearling females; Stum Lake 20 Jul 1973-230 (Ryder 1973); Nulki Lake 24 Jul 1945-279, including 200 yearlings; Charlie Lake 20 Jun 1984-61, including 56 adult males, 20 to 21 Aug 1975-130; Boundary Lake (Goodlow) 10 Jun 1984-18 yearling males.

Autumn: Interior - Atlin 16 Sep 1972-1; Parker Lake (Fort Nelson) 7 Sep 1985-20 immatures; s Fort Nelson 10 Oct 1985-2; Cold Fish Lake 19 Sep 1976-1; Charlie Lake 8 Sep 1985-44, 25 Sep 1983-80 adults, including 70 females, 3 Oct 1982-75 adults, including 73 males, unusual influx, 9 Oct 1986-150, 30 Oct 1983-6; Leg Lake 13 Sep 1980-700; Kamloops 1 Sep 1986-125; Stum Lake 9 Nov 1980-484; Hanceville 20 Sep 1982-200+; Nicola Lake 18 Oct 1976-6; Invermere 3 Sep 1977-9; Castlegar 15 Nov 1980-100; Okanagan Falls 26 Nov 1975-71. **Coastal** - Kitsault 23 to 29 Nov 1979-470; Prince Rupert 8 Nov 1977-316 (Martin 1978); Sewall 13 Oct 1980-2; Okeover and Theodosia Inlets 12 Nov 1981-132; Port Neville 21 Oct 1975-13; Jervis Inlet 28 Nov 1976-250; Indian Arm (n Bedwell Bay) 29 Oct 1978-2,800, 31 Oct 1978-1,520, 14 Nov 1978-500, 29 Nov 1978-400; Stanley Park (Vancouver) 30 Sep 1972 and 1973-2, 28 Oct 1972-500 (Crowell and Nehls 1973a), 11 Nov 1962-200, 24 Nov 1968-220; Halfmoon Bay 11 Nov 1981-117 adults; Boundary Bay 12 Nov 1962-200; Nanaimo River estuary 15 Nov 1978-150, salmon run; Cowichan Bay 21 Nov 1981-100;

Roche Cove 2 Nov 1980-80.

Winter: Interior - Tetana Lake early winter 1937-3 occupied stretch of spring-fed open water, 1 Jan 1939-2 (Stanwell-Fletcher and Stanwell-Fletcher 1940); Francois Lake 27 Dec 1987-2 males; Kleena Kleene 29 Dec 1948-1 (Paul 1959); Wells Gray Park 8 Feb 1953-5, small number spent winter in park (Ritcey 1953); Sorrento 31 Dec 1970-111, 8 Jan 1972-50+; Revelstoke 21 Dec 1982-5; Kamloops 18 Jan 1985-125; Fairmont Hot Springs 26 Feb 1983-12; Balfour 8 Feb 1981-200; Castlegar 22 Jan 1977-76; Okanagan Falls 29 Dec 1977-64. **Coastal** - Kitsault 10 to 12 Dec 1980-900; Prince Rupert 6 Jan 1978-377; n Douglas Channel 9 Feb 1982-1,175 aerial survey; Sue and Devastation channels 9 Feb 1982-749 aerial survey; Masset Inlet 8 Jan 1982-60+; near Namu 22 Feb 1981-24; Port Neville 14 Jan 1976-16; Indian Arm (n Bedwell Bay) 5 Jan 1979-100; Ambleside 8 Jan 1984-500; Stanley Park (Vancouver) 25 Dec 1984-590, 6 Jan 1973-200, 16 Feb 1973-700; Nanoose Harbour 28 Feb 1974-91; Departure Bay 8 Jan 1965-200; Alberni Inlet 5 Feb 1976-168; Clayoquot Sound 11 to 13 Dec 1972-894 (Robertson 1974); lower Sarita River 6 Dec 1978-85; Ganges Harbour 26 Feb 1978-295 (Carson and Howsam 1978); Cowichan River estuary 12 Feb 1974-69; Goldstream River estuary 16 Dec 1982-55.

Christmas Counts: Interior - Recorded from 12 of 19 localities and on 58% of all counts. Maxima: Vaseux Lake 23 Dec 1979-175; Shuswap Lake 19 Dec 1978-138; Vernon 18 Dec 1983-40. **Coastal** - Recorded from 24 of 28 localities and on 82% of all counts. Maxima: Vancouver 27 Dec 1970-3,388, all-time North American high count (Monroe 1973); Nanaimo 27 Dec 1976-2,016; Sunshine Coast 15 Dec 1984-814.

Bufflehead
Bucephala albeola (Linnaeus)

RANGE: Breeds from Alaska east across southern Yukon and southwestern Mackenzie to northern Ontario south to northern Washington and central Ontario; locally in Oregon and California. Winters from Alaska, the Great Lakes, and the Maritimes south in coastal regions to the southern United States and Mexico.

STATUS: *Fairly common* to locally *abundant* migrant and winter visitant along the coast; *rare* in summer. *Fairly common* to locally *very common* migrant and summer visitant in the interior with the exception of portions of the Northern Mountains and Plateaus region where the species is *rare* to *uncommon*. *Rare* to locally *very common* winter visitant south of 52°N latitude. A widespread breeder throughout the interior; occasional breeder on the coast.

NONBREEDING: The Bufflehead is distributed along the coast of British Columbia, including Vancouver Island and the Queen Charlotte Islands. It is widely distributed throughout the interior although it is not as common in the Northern Mountains and Plateaus region and the Northern and Central Rocky Mountains region as in the rest of the province. It occurs from sea level to at least 1,900 m elevation.

Along the coast, birds occur in a wide variety of marine and freshwater habitats although most reports come from marine environments. Small flocks of less than 10 birds are most often reported, although protected waters, such as bays, harbours, lagoons, and estuaries, often hold significant concentrations. Other habitats include lakes, ponds, rivers, inlets (Fig. 311), coves, sewage lagoons, reservoirs, and, occasionally, rocky shores and flooded fields. In the interior, birds are most often reported from both freshwater and alkali lakes; habitats reported less frequently include rivers, ponds, creeks, and sewage lagoons.

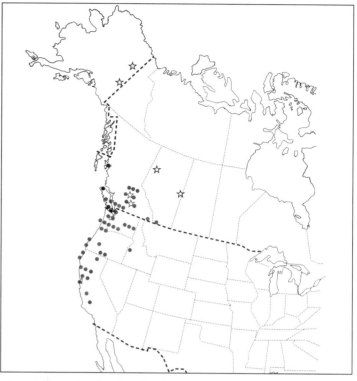

Figure 310. *Banding locations (stars) and recovery sites (circles) of Buffleheads associated with British Columbia. Red indicates birds banded in the province, black indicates birds banded elsewhere.*

Figure 311. *Mike Inlet, Queen Charlotte Islands, 20 May 1988 (R. Wayne Campbell). Protected coastal waters are important habitats for migrating and wintering Buffleheads in British Columbia.*

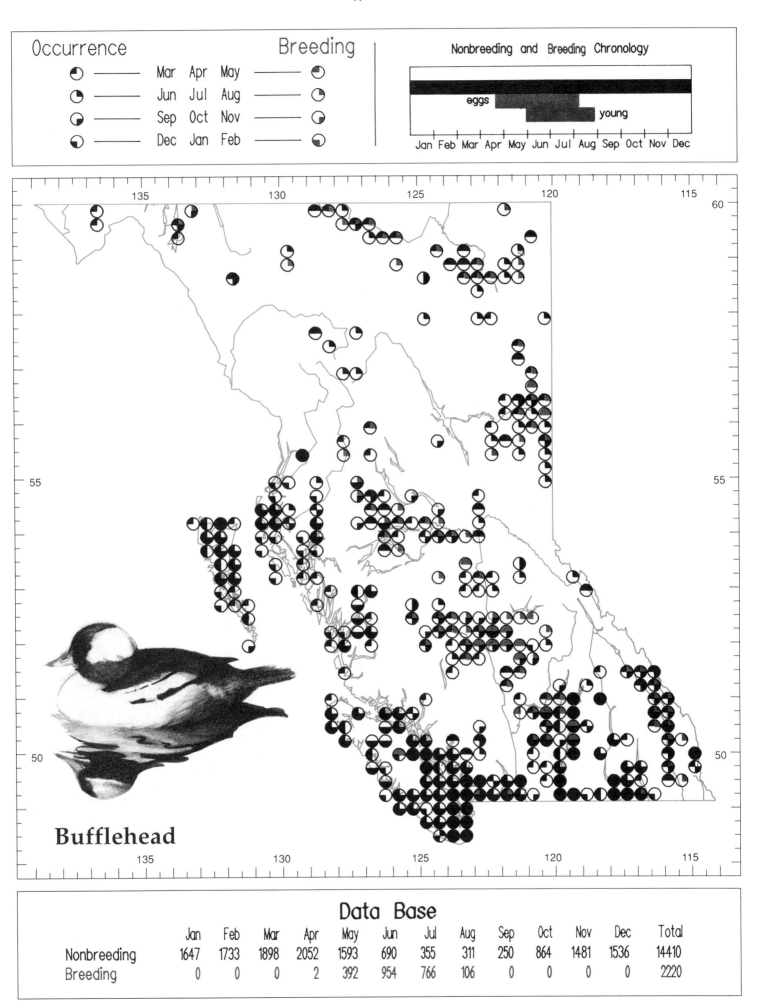

Occurrence

	Mar	Apr	May		
	Jun	Jul	Aug		
	Sep	Oct	Nov		
	Dec	Jan	Feb		

Breeding

Nonbreeding and Breeding Chronology

eggs

young

Jan Feb Mar Apr May Jun Jul Aug Sep Oct Nov Dec

Bufflehead

Data Base

	Jan	Feb	Mar	Apr	May	Jun	Jul	Aug	Sep	Oct	Nov	Dec	Total
Nonbreeding	1647	1733	1898	2052	1593	690	355	311	250	864	1481	1536	14410
Breeding	0	0	0	2	392	954	766	106	0	0	0	0	2220

In a number of areas around southern Vancouver Island, large concentrations of Buffleheads occur around shoals of spawning Pacific herring in late winter and early spring. Numbers decline through late April and May on the coast as birds move to their interior breeding grounds. Arrival in the interior can be as early as mid-March; however, the peak movement occurs through April as birds concentrate on the larger ice-free lakes. By May, the numbers are reduced when birds disperse to their breeding lakes. Unpaired adult males are the first to arrive followed by breeding pairs (see also Munro, J.A. 1942a; Erskine 1972). Yearlings arrive on the summering areas several weeks later than the adults (Erskine 1972). Most birds have left the coast by early May although small numbers, possibly unfit birds, remain through the summer.

Adult males leave their breeding territories once incubation has begun and flocks consisting entirely of males can be found from the end of May to mid-June. Males do not always stay in the same area to moult and although their moulting areas are unknown it is fairly certain they do not go to the coast. Possibly, they moult in the Yukon or Alaska, as large concentrations of males have been sighted there in the autumn. Through July and August, large numbers of yearlings and moulting adult female Buffleheads concentrate on select lakes. Erskine (1972) notes that probably many Buffleheads remain in the same general area from the completion of moult until migration begins. Buffleheads remain on the interior breeding areas until freeze-up forces them to move elsewhere. The main autumn movement to the coast occurs from late October through November.

Buffleheads winter mainly along the coast including the coastal areas of Vancouver Island and the Queen Charlotte Islands. In the interior, they winter from the Okanagan valley east to the west Kootenay, rarely the east Kootenay, and north to the South Thompson River, rarely farther north. The winter centre of abundance is southern Vancouver Island and adjacent islands.

A portion of the birds that winter in British Columbia originates in Alaska and Alberta. Many of the birds reared in the province winter along the Pacific coast south to California (Fig. 310).

BREEDING: The Bufflehead breeds throughout most of the interior of the province including the Peace Lowlands and northern areas of the Boreal Forest; rarely in the Okanagan and Creston valleys and the Northern Mountains and Plateaus region. It seldom breeds on the coast: Sumas Lake (Brooks 1917), near Middle Quinsam Lake (Hancock 1964), and the Pitt Meadows area (Stockman 1972) are the only records. Apparently, most breed south of 53°N latitude, where over 85% of our records were gathered. Estimated numbers of Bufflehead breeding in the province range from 70,000 to 100,000 birds (Bellrose 1976).

The Bufflehead breeds primarily on lakes and occasionally on rivers, sloughs, and ponds in aspen parklands (see Fig. 306), interior Douglas-fir forests, open ponderosa pine forests, farmland, and rangeland from 300 to 1,430 m elevation. Bufflehead nesting in the Columbia valley used both the floodplain and the lakes and ponds of the adjacent benchlands, slightly favouring (56%) the floodplain.

Nests: Of 228 nests, 11 were situated in nest boxes; all the rest were in cavities in living and dead trees (mostly those created by the Northern Flicker [*Colaptes auratus*]; Fig. 312). The most commonly reported natural site was trembling aspen (58%), followed by Douglas-fir (25%), lodgepole pine, ponderosa pine, black cottonwood, spruces, and poplars. Most sites were near the edge of a wetland, although one site was 200 m from the water's edge. Nests (n=218) ranged from 60 cm to 14 m above the ground, with 61% between 60 cm and 3 m. Eight nests had cavity depths ranging from 25 to 46 cm with a mean depth of 37 cm. Four nests had cavity diameters ranging from 9 to 18 cm with a mean diameter of 12 cm. Nest material consisted primarily of down with mixtures of sawdust, straw, duff, and twigs. See Erskine (1978) and Peterson, B. and Gauthier (1985) for additional information on nest sites.

Eggs: Dates for 235 clutches ranged from 29 April to 7 August (incubating hen) with 54% recorded between 29 May and 10 June. Eggs can be present in nests as early as the third week of April (Erskine 1972). Clutch size ranged from 1 to 20 eggs (1E-16, 2E-6, 3E-2, 4E-8, 5E-13, 6E-14, 7E-33, 8E-47, 9E-41, 10E-20, 11E-12, 12E-7, 13E-6, 14E-3, 15E-2, 16E-3, 17E-1, 20E-1) with 51% having 7 to 9 eggs. The large clutches reported here are likely the products of 2 or more females. Erskine (1972) reports an average clutch size of 8.8 eggs for British Columbia. Incubation periods from British Columbia ranged from 28 to 33 days with most clutches hatching 29 to 31 days after the last egg was laid (Erskine 1972).

Young: Dates for 573 broods ranged from 29 May to 27 August with 51% recorded between 24 June and 18 July. Brood size ranged from 1 to 23 young (1Y-16, 2Y-35, 3Y-50, 4Y-63, 5Y-61, 6Y-90, 7Y-80, 8Y-65, 9Y-41, 10Y-27, 11Y-18, 12Y-7, 13Y-3, 14Y-5, 15Y-3, 16Y-1, 17Y-2, 18Y-2, 19Y-2, 23Y-2) with 52% having 5 to 8 young. Broods larger than 12 young are likely the results of brood amalgamation. This occurs when one female excludes another from a pond or when young mix accidentally. Fledging period is about 49 to 56 days (Erskine 1972).

REMARKS: In areas where Bufflehead nest in sympatry with goldeneye, the goldeneye usually dominate Bufflehead in aggressive encounters. Such factors should be considered whenever nest box programs are initiated because an increase in the density of one species may result in a decline in the density of the other (Savard 1987a). However, on a study site in the Chilcotin-Cariboo Basin over the period 1980 to 1984, nest box installation resulted in an increase in the Barrow's Goldeneye population with no apparent change in the Bufflehead population (Fig. 313).

Erskine's (1972) discussion of the future of the Bufflehead in British Columbia is still, for the most part, applicable today.

Figure 312. Bufflehead nest site in mature aspen, Becher's Prairie (Riske Creek), June 1973 (Neil K. Dawe).

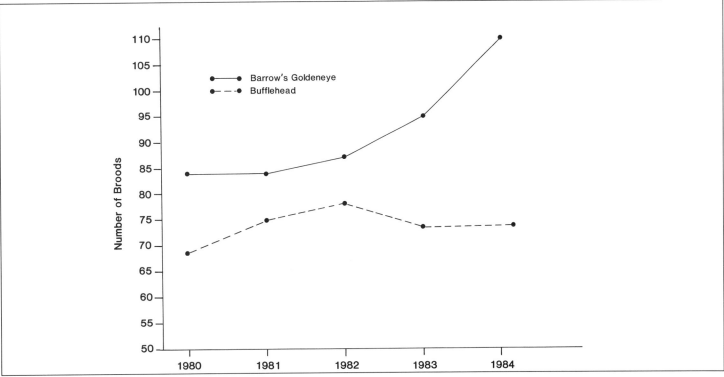

Figure 313. Numbers of Barrow's Goldeneye and Bufflehead broods on a study area in the Chilcotin-Cariboo Basin, British Columbia, 1980 to 1984, following nest box installation (after Savard 1986).

NOTEWORTHY RECORDS

Spring: Coastal - Esquimalt Lagoon 7 Mar 1981-339, 29 Mar 1962-538, 1 Apr 1982-350, 16 Apr 1982-550, 2 May 1974-43, 17 May 1974-2; Ganges Harbour 21 Mar 1978-700, on Pacific herring spawn (Carson and Howsam 1978); Stubbs Island (Tofino) 25 Mar 1984-1,300, on Pacific herring spawn; Gabriola Island 26 Mar 1978-200+; Stanley Park (Vancouver) 11 Mar 1973-150, 18 Apr 1971-50 numbers declining (Campbell et al. 1972b), 10 May 1974-10; Chilliwack 5 May 1982-29; Powell River 29 Mar 1981-500; Okeover and Theodosia Inlets 16 Mar 1982-164; Cortes Island 29 Mar 1977-200; Campbell River (Discovery Passage) estuary 29 Mar 1975-117, 25 May 1975-2; Blenkinsop Bay 13 Apr 1976-425; Port Neville 10 Mar 1975-48, 1 May 1976-4; Section Cove 17 Apr 1985-105; Kumdis Island 5 May 1977-155; Porpoise Harbour 17 Apr 1979-130; Delkatla Inlet 5 May 1979-15. **Interior** - Creston 17 Mar 1982-1,580 aerial survey, 24 Apr 1985-150 aerial survey; Green Lake (Okanagan Falls) 8 Apr 1977-60; Windermere Lake 21 Mar 1978-1; Wilmer 28 Mar 1985-2, 25 Apr 1985-40, 20 May 1985-5 (Butler, R.W. and Savard 1985); Swan Lake (Vernon) 20 Apr 1980-85; Little Shuswap Lake 31 Mar 1962-3; Revelstoke 31 Mar 1978-8, 5 May 1978-45 (Bonar 1978a); near Merritt 22 Mar 1979-16 males only on one of few shallow ponds open; Kamloops 4 Apr 1985-18, 9 Apr 1985-125, 24 Apr 1985-89, 13 May 1985-8 (Butler, R.W. and Savard 1985); Kamloops to Chase 31 Mar 1962-135; Minton Creek (Hanceville) 4 Apr 1980-1 male; Alkali Lake 2 Apr 1977-81 on small ice-free sections at each end of lake; Riske Creek 10 Apr 1985-79, 14 Apr 1985-95, 25 Apr 1985-34, 6 May 1985-15 (Butler, R.W. and Savard 1985); Williams Lake 14 Mar 1979-3 males, 31 Mar 1978-20 males, 2 females, 29 Apr 1984-40; 24 km south of Prince George 13 Apr 1980-1 male; Prince George 14 Apr 1985-1, 21 Apr 1985-49, 28 Apr 1985-22, 12 May 1985-7 (Butler, R.W. and Savard 1985); Vander-hoof 11 Apr to 29 Apr 1985 - very small movement (Butler, R.W. and Savard 1985); Stellako River 24 Mar 1977-3 apparent females; Charlie Lake 10 Apr 1986-1 male; Parker Lake

(Fort Nelson) 7 May 1978-5.
Summer: Coastal - Esquimalt Lagoon 10 Jul 1971-1 (Tatum 1972); Stanley Park (Vancouver) 5 Jun 1971-5 summering birds (Campbell et al. 1972b); Little River 15 Jun 1975-1; near Khyex River 13 Jul 1981-2; Upland Lakes (Kitsault) 23 to 25 Jul 1980-1. **Interior** - Minnie Lake 10 Aug 1935-300 (Munro, J.A. 1942a); Westwick Lake 3 Jun 1937-50 males, 26 Jul 1937-101, only 1 male; near Riske Creek 6 Jun 1978-8 males, 15 Aug 1978-31 apparent females, 25 Aug 1978-66; 103 Mile Lake 4 Aug 1937-500 mostly yearling females (Munro, J.A. 1942a); Swan Lake (Tupper) 27 Aug 1980-106; Charlie Lake 3 Jun 1983-100 virtually all males; 22 Jul 1983-5 apparent females, 26 Aug 1984-65; Boundary Lake (Goodlow) 22 Aug 1984-30 apparent females.

Autumn: Interior - Como Lake 13 Oct 1980-36; Charlie Lake 10 Sep 1983-61, 23 Sep 1984-90 males, some coming into breeding plumage, 13 Oct 1984-400, 30 Oct 1983-160, 5 Nov 1983-50; McKelvey Lake 14 Oct 1978-10; Tyhee Lake 29 Nov 1987-5, lake still open; Anahim Lake 27 Oct 1978-307 (Hennan 1979); Williams Lake 5 Nov 1970-35; Revelstoke 8 Nov 1983-1,523, all-time high count; Tranquille 4 Nov 1987-1,200; Nicola Lake 28 Nov 1981-60; Stum Lake 9 Nov 1980-65; Swan Lake (Vernon) 27 Oct 1977-55, 10 Nov 1977-80; Kootenay Pond 5 Nov 1965-4 (Seel 1965); Wilmer Lake 18 Oct 1977-27; Windermere Lake 8 Nov 1977-39; Elkview 13 Oct 1984-7, 16 Oct 1984-530+, 18 Oct 1984-15; Okanagan Falls 12 Nov 1972-52; Creston 28 Sep 1986-255, 15 Oct 1985-160, 19 Nov 1984-405. **Coastal** - Alice Arm 26 Oct 1956-300; Venn Passage 2 Nov 1977-140 (Martin 1978); Big Bay and Pearl Harbour 5 Nov 1977-291; Masset 4 Nov 1971-120; Minette Bay 22 Oct 1974-4, 28 Oct 1974-40; Kumdis Slough 3 Nov 1956-85; Adam River 17 Nov 1974-100 feeding on dead salmon; Port Neville 2 Oct 1975-26 males; Okeover and Theodosia Inlet 19 Sep 1981-3, 12 Nov 1981-107; Stanley Park (Vancouver) 11 Oct 1971-4, 28 Oct 1972-200, 24 Nov 1968-165; Grice

Bay 22 Nov 1981-800; Fulford Harbour 24 Nov 1977-200; Sidney Island 30 Oct 1962-150, 14 Nov 1962-1,225, 28 Nov 1962-1,910 (Hancock 1963); Esquimalt Lagoon 19 Oct 1976-44, 29 Oct 1975-230, 12 Nov 1962-604, 26 Nov 1975-460.

Winter: Interior - Kathlyn Lake 1 Dec 1987-1, lake still open; Francois Lake 27 Dec 1987-1 male; Canim Lake winter 1983/84-pair stayed all winter in small patch of open water; Williams Lake 22 Jan 1987-1 male; Sorrento 23 Jan 1973-1; South Thompson River between Chase and Pritchard 18 Jan 1949-3; Falkland 1 Feb 1977-3; Athalmer 27 Jan 1982-1; Grave Lake 2 Dec 1982-1; west arm (Kootenay Lake) 7 Dec 1980-160, 8 Feb 1981-150; Okanagan Falls 5 Jan 1974-17, 21 Feb 1974-76; Vaseux Lake 23 Dec 1977-219; Creston 2 Dec 1982-125, 11 Jan 1983-195, 9 Feb 1983-125, 15 Feb 1983-110, all aerial censuses; Kettle River 7 Feb 1980-5. **Coastal** - Big Bay and Pearl Harbour 19 Jan 1978-203 (Martin 1978); Masset 26 Dec 1972-225; Douglas Channel 9 Feb 1982-264 aerial survey; Browning Entrance 15 Feb 1978-148 (Savard 1978); Kumdis Slough 6 Jan 1954-200; Port Neville Inlet 15 Dec 1976-180, 1 Jan 1977-100, 28 Feb 1986-446; Little Qualicum River estuary 18 Dec 1973-300+ (Dawe 1976); Stanley Park (Vancouver) 6 Jan 1973-100; Boundary Bay 16 Feb 1974-150; Clayoquot Sound 11 to 13 Dec 1972-2,483 boat survey (Robertson 1974); Ganges Harbour 19 Feb 1978-229 (Carson and Howsam 1978); Chemainus River estuary 30 Dec 1974-1,150 (Blood 1976); Sidney Island 14 Dec 1962-1,290, 22 Jan 1963-615, 12 Feb 1963-795 (Hancock 1963); Esquimalt Lagoon 21 Jan 1976-278, 20 Feb 1976-380.

Christmas Counts: Interior - Recorded from 11 of 19 localities and on 58% of all counts. Maxima: Vaseux Lake 23 Dec 1979-219; Vernon 18 Dec 1983-120; Penticton 27 Dec 1983-90. **Coastal** - Recorded from 27 of 28 localities and on 94% of all counts. Maxima: Victoria 27 Dec 1975-**1,944**, all-time Canadian high count (Anderson, R.R. 1976); Ladner 28 Dec 1980-1,147; Duncan 17 Dec 1977-1,107.

Hooded Merganser
Lophodytes cucullatus (Linnaeus)

RANGE: Breeds from southern Alaska, central British Columbia and southwestern Alberta to Oregon and Idaho; and from central Saskatchewan across southern Canada to Nova Scotia south to southeastern United States. Winters from southern British Columbia and New England south to California, the Gulf coast and Mexico.

STATUS: *Common* spring and locally *very common* autumn migrant, *rare* to *uncommon* summer visitant and *fairly common* to locally *very common* winter visitant on the south coast; *rare* to locally *uncommon* visitant, on the northern mainland coast and the Queen Charlotte Islands. In the southern interior, *uncommon* to *fairly common* spring and *fairly common* to *common* autumn migrant, *uncommon* summer visitant and locally *fairly common* to *very common* in winter. *Very rare* north of the Fraser Basin and Peace Lowlands. Breeds throughout the southern half of the province.

NONBREEDING: The Hooded Merganser is widely distributed along the coast and throughout the southern two-thirds of the interior; it is widely scattered in northern areas. It occurs from sea level to 1,480 m elevation.

On the coast, the Hooded Merganser is most often seen in estuarine situations and in protected bays and inlets. It also frequents coastal lakes, marshes, sloughs, and in autumn, salmon-spawning streams. In the interior, it occurs on small and large lakes, rivers, beaver ponds, sewage lagoons, and, infrequently, marshes.

Spring migration is not clearly defined. On the south coast, wintering birds have usually left by the end of April, although in some years there appears to be a passage of migrants about mid-April. In the southern interior, most wintering birds have departed by mid-to-late May. In some years, there is an influx of birds into that region about mid-May. For example, more than 100 birds, in pairs and small groups, arrived in the Columbia valley on 11 May 1978; they moved on 2 weeks later.

In summer, males leave the females when incubation begins, and disperse to unknown moulting areas. They move to the coast in autumn where they are eventually joined by the females.

Autumn migration is a gradual dispersal from the interior and only small waves have been observed. In the Peace Lowlands and the Columbia River valley, that movement is evident in early October and may carry through into early November some years. In the Nicola and Okanagan valleys, the main movement usually occurs from about the third week of October through the second week of November. On the south coast, autumn migration is evident in late October and may carry into early December.

The centre of winter distribution on the coast appears to be the Strait of Georgia; in the interior, it is the south Okanagan valley. At least 1,000 birds winter there, slightly more than that reported by Bellrose (1976). See also Appendix 2.

BREEDING: The Hooded Merganser breeds from northern Queen Charlotte Islands, Kitsault, Fort St. James and Prince George generally south through the rest of the province. At present, breeding has not been confirmed for most of the Queen Charlotte Islands, the central mainland coast and northern Vancouver Island. It breeds from near sea level to 1,180 m elevation.

Breeding habitat includes mostly fresh, but occasionally brackish water sites, usually with wooded shorelines. Specific habitats include rivers, lakes, marshes, streams, beaver ponds, and sloughs. Three broods were found in irrigation ditches and two on sewage lagoons.

The centre of the breeding population is probably the southwestern portion of the province. Bellrose (1976) estimates that 2,000 to 4,000 birds breed in British Columbia.

Nests: Most nests (82%; n=38) were in nest boxes, the remainder were in natural sites in either living (4) or dead (3) black cottonwood, western redcedars, or Douglas-firs. Tree diameters ranged from 20 to 90 cm. Heights of 7 nests in natural sites ranged from 4 to 15 m, with 4 between 6 and 9 m. Nest cavities contained leaves, wood chips, or dry moss, and all contained various amounts of down and feathers.

Eggs: Dates for 38 clutches ranged from 27 March to 15 June with 54% recorded between 4 and 25 May. Clutch size ranged from 3 to 15 eggs (3E-1, 6E-4, 7E-3, 8E-9, 9E-12, 10E-3, 11E-4, 13-1, 15E-1), with 55% having 8 or 9 eggs. Incubation period ranges from 29 to 37 days and averages about 33 days (Morse, T.E. et al. 1969).

Young: Dates for 143 broods ranged from 5 May to 5 October with 54% recorded between 7 June and 6 July. Brood size ranged from 1 to 13 young (1Y-6, 2Y-9, 3Y-10, 4Y-23, 5Y-21, 6Y-27, 7Y-14, 8Y-12, 9Y-9, 10Y-6, 11Y-4, 12Y-1, 13Y-1) with 50% having 4 to 6 young. Fledged young have been recorded as early as 9 July. Fledging period is about 71 days (McGilvrey 1966).

REMARKS: See T.E. Morse et al. (1969) and Kitchen and Hunt (1969) for other aspects of the breeding biology of the Hooded Merganser.

NOTEWORTHY RECORDS

Spring: Coastal - Metchosin 24 May 1986-6; Thetis Lake 24 May 1977-25; Beaver Lake (Saanich) 5 Mar 1977-153; Stanley Park (Vancouver) 9 Mar 1963-10; North Alouette River 25 Apr 1970-100; Graham Lake (Denman Island) 18 Mar 1979-5 pairs; Canoe Lake 23 May 1978-8; Lang Island 26 May 1968-1 adult female; Masset 19 Apr 1979-1; Kitimat 29 May 1975-10; Exstew River 24 Mar 1985-4 males, 2 females; Aiyansh 24 Apr 1981-1 adult male. **Interior** - Nakusp 11 Apr 1979-1; Kamloops 29 Mar 1980-4, 20 May 1986-20; Spillimacheen 11 May 1978-12; near Golden 28 Mar 1977-1; Alakali Lake (Riske Creek) 18 Apr 1971-12; Williams Lake 31 Mar 1978-10; 24 km s Prince George 5 May 1983-1 male, 2 females; Nilkitkwa Lake 23 May 1978-1 pair; 33 km w Fort St. John 17 Apr 1986-1 adult male; Fort St. John 2 May 1986-1 adult male, 30 May 1986-1 subadult male; near Clarke Lake 28 May 1978-1 pair (RBCM Photo 605).

Summer: Coastal - Tsehum Harbour 24 Aug 1978-36; Sandhill Creek (Long Beach) 14 Jul 1976-3; Iona Island 27 July 1980-3; Williams Beach (Merville) 16 Jun 1971-25; Drizzle Lake 29 Aug 1981-5; w Greenville 16 Jun 1981-1 female. **Interior** - Glade 21 Jun 1977-6 males; Williams Lake 10 Jun 1978-1 male; Parker Lake (Fort Nelson) 5 Jul 1978-1 female; Tanzilla River 14 Jun 1980-1 pair; Basement Creek 9 Jun 1983-1 female (Campbell et al. 1983).

Autumn: Interior - Charlie Lake 22 Oct 1986-18 males, 1 female, 4 Nov 1986-1 adult female; 24 km s Prince George 25 Oct 1976-1 male; Williams Lake 26 Oct 1970-5 males, 1 female; Sparwood 17 Nov 1983-2 males, 2 females; Vaseux Lake 26 Nov 1975-50. **Coastal** - Masset 28 Oct 1981-39; Queen Charlotte City 26 Oct 1971-9; Cape Scott Park 29 Sep 1935-14; Comox 27 Oct 1949-50 (Flahaut 1950b); Maltby Slough (Tofino Inlet) 11 Nov 1972-18 (Hatler 1973); Ganges 29 Nov 1980-66; Albert Head Lagoon 17 Oct 1980-70; Beacon Park 28 Oct 1974-56.

Winter: Interior - Williams Lake 26 Dec 1974-1 female; Fauquier 3 Dec 1978-3; Skaha Lake 12 Feb 1962-26; Elk River (Fernie) 9 and 12 Dec 1983-1 female; Vaseux Lake 28 Dec 1973-66. **Coastal** - Kitsault 10 to 12 Dec 1980-9; Masset 11 Jan 1983-31; Namu 22 Feb 1981-2 males; Port McNeil 26 Feb 1983-7; Comox 30 Jan 1974-3; Clayoquot Sound 11 to 13 Dec 1972-38 (Robertson 1974); Ganges 9 Dec 1978-27; Albert Head Lagoon 13 Dec 1980-50+; Elk Lake (Saanich) Dec 1970-300 to 400; Beaver Lake (Saanich) 15 Feb 1980-60.

Christmas Counts: Interior - Recorded from 7 of 19 localities and on 43% of all counts. Maxima: Vaseux Lake 28 Dec 1974-109; Penticton 27 Dec 1983-48; Oliver/Osoyoos 28 Dec 1980-42. **Coastal** - Recorded from 25 of 28 localities and on 76% of all counts. Maxima: Victoria 27 Dec 1970-472, all-time Canadian high count (Anderson, R.R. 1976); Pender Islands 27 Dec 1980-112; Vancouver 26 Dec 1965-93.

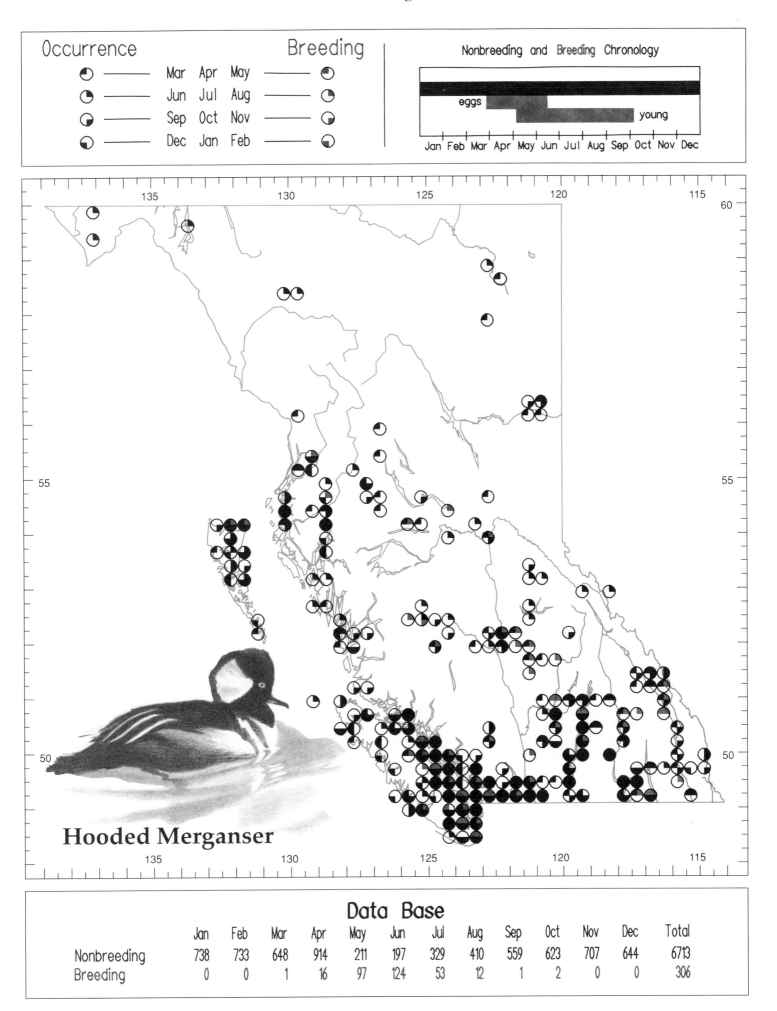

Hooded Merganser

Data Base

	Jan	Feb	Mar	Apr	May	Jun	Jul	Aug	Sep	Oct	Nov	Dec	Total
Nonbreeding	738	733	648	914	211	197	329	410	559	623	707	644	6713
Breeding	0	0	1	16	97	124	53	12	1	2	0	0	306

Common Merganser

Mergus merganser Linnaeus

COME

RANGE: Breeds from southern Alaska, across southern Canada to Newfoundland, south to California, Arizona, and New Mexico, to Michigan and Connecticut. Winters from Alaska to southern California on the Pacific coast, and from Newfoundland to Florida on the Atlantic coast as well as the Gulf coast and northern Mexico. Also occurs in Europe and Asia.

STATUS: Resident on the coast; locally *abundant* spring and autumn migrant, *common* to *very common* in summer, *very common* to locally *very abundant* in winter. In the interior, a *very common* to *abundant* spring and autumn migrant, *fairly common* to *common* summer visitant and locally *common* to *very common* in winter in southern areas, *rare* to *uncommon* in the northern interior. Widespread breeder.

NONBREEDING: The Common Merganser is one of the most widely distributed birds in British Columbia. It occurs regularly throughout the province except in the extremely mountainous area of the Coast Ranges and the Northern and Central Rocky Mountains, and in the muskeg country of the Peace River area. It has been found from sea level to 1,070 m elevation.

On the coast, the Common Merganser is a near-shore species most often seen in fresh and brackish waters, especially in estuaries, protected bays, and inlets. It is also found on lower regions of wide, clear rivers and large sloughs. Usually these habitats have roosting sites that include shoals, beach boulders, gravel/sand bars, logs, or dry spits. It avoids muddy waters and areas where aquatic vegetation persists. In spring, Pacific herring spawning sites and, in autumn, salmon spawning rivers and streams are frequented. In the interior, it prefers open clear waters of medium-sized lakes, rivers, and streams.

Spring migration is gradual and birds depart in pairs and small flocks. On the coast, it occurs from mid-March to early May, but subadults and some resident breeders remain behind in flocks through the spring. In the interior, spring migrants follow the break-up of ice on lakes and rivers. In southern areas, early migrants may appear in late February and early March but the main movement occurs in April and early May. In northern areas, first migrants may arrive in early March. Most breeding adults migrate as mated pairs after courtship in the wintering areas.

Males do not stay on the breeding grounds very long, generally leaving for moulting areas before the eggs have hatched (Fig. 314). Moulting areas are poorly known. The only record of a large group on moult migration is from Eddontenajon Lake, although there are several records of flightless birds and small flocks of males on southern lakes. The moult migrants become flightless in July or early August. Nesting females moult and regain flight with their young.

Autumn migrants, in large flocks of hundreds, occur along the coast mainly from late October to early December, with the main movement in November. In the interior, many mergansers do not attempt autumn migration until it is forced on them by the freezing of lakes and rivers. This may occur anywhere from early October in northern areas to early December in southern areas, although the main influx occurs in southern areas in November.

In winter, males and females reunite for courtship. Small flocks to flocks numbering several hundreds are distributed along the coast in protected marine and brackish waters and freshwater lakes. In the northern interior, a few individuals, particularly males, winter at the edge of the ice on rivers and the outlets of lakes. Flocks approaching 200 individuals may be found locally in southern interior areas. In some years over 4,000

Figure 314. Common Mergansers preening at Grice Bay near Tofino, 26 June 1986 (R. Wayne Campbell).

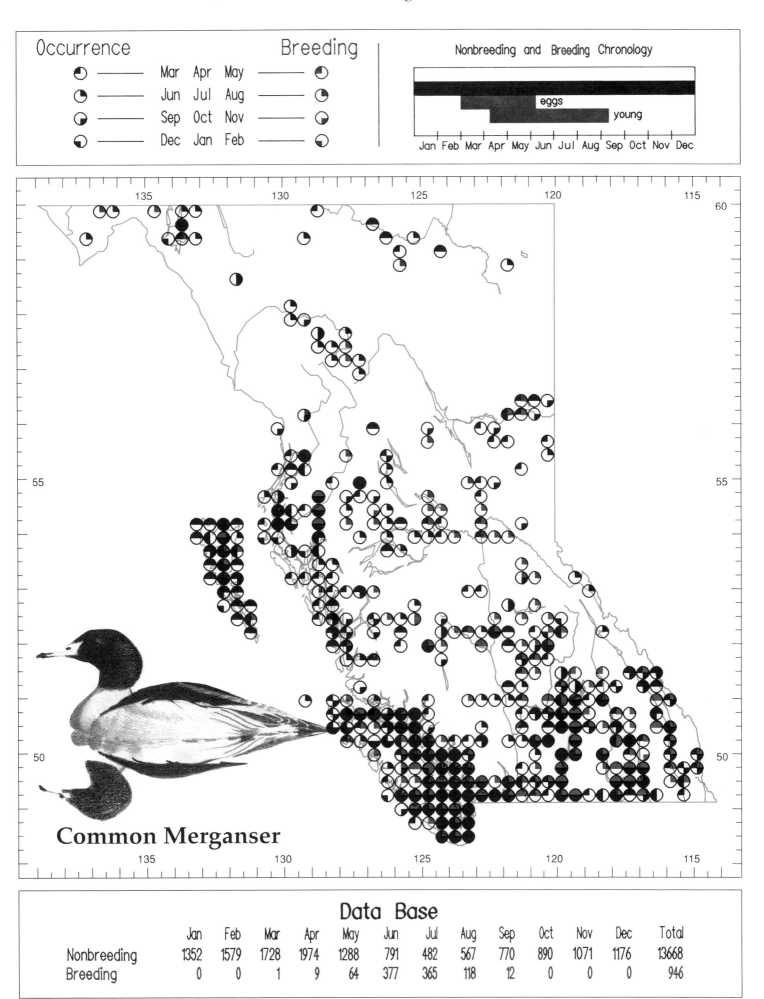

Common Merganser

Occurrence

Mar	Apr	May
Jun	Jul	Aug
Sep	Oct	Nov
Dec	Jan	Feb

Breeding

Nonbreeding and Breeding Chronology

eggs
young

Jan Feb Mar Apr May Jun Jul Aug Sep Oct Nov Dec

Data Base

	Jan	Feb	Mar	Apr	May	Jun	Jul	Aug	Sep	Oct	Nov	Dec	Total
Nonbreeding	1352	1579	1728	1974	1288	791	482	567	770	890	1071	1176	13668
Breeding	0	0	1	9	64	377	365	118	12	0	0	0	946

Common Mergansers have been reported to winter in the province (Appendix 2), which is over 15% of the wintering population of 24,000 in the Pacific Flyway (Bellrose 1976).

BREEDING: The Common Merganser breeds throughout the province except in extremely mountainous areas, from sea level to about 1,000 m elevation. It is more widely scattered and less numerous in northern areas. Bellrose (1976) notes that most of the 8,000 to 12,000 mergansers that breed in the province, are Common Mergansers.

It breeds near fresh water along the forested shores of lakes, streams, rivers (Fig. 315), inlets, and beaver ponds, usually with clear waters, but it avoids isolated mountain lakes. It also breeds on marine shores.

Nests: Most nests (82%; n=53) were found along the shores of freshwater lakes and the banks of large rivers. Others were found along marine shores (15%); the remainder were on islands in lakes. Thirty-one nests were situated in tree cavities, seventeen on the ground, three in nest boxes, and single nests were found in an old chimney and in an abandoned trapper's cabin. Tree nests were in both living and dead coniferous and deciduous trees. Ground nests were in small caves or crevices, or under dense shrubbery. Most of them were built with aquatic vegetation, grasses, bits of wood, leaves, weeds, bark, twigs, and dried mosses and lined with down and feathers. Tree nests were lined only with down and a few feathers. Heights of 31 tree nests ranged from 1.5 to 24 m, with 55% between 5 and 12 m.

Eggs: Dates for 15 clutches ranged from 10 April to 7 June with 57% recorded between 20 April and 10 May. Calculated dates indicate that eggs could be found as early as 1 March (Cannings et al. 1987). Clutch size ranged from 5 to 15 eggs (5E-1, 7E-2, 8E-4, 9E-3, 10E-3, 15E-2) with 73% having 8 to 10 eggs. Incubation period ranges from 28 to 35 days (Bent 1923; Witherby et al. 1943).

Young: Dates for 618 broods ranged from 9 April to 10 September with 52% recorded between 15 June and 20 July.

Brood size ranged from 1 to 50 young (1Y-26, 2Y-24, 3Y-37, 4Y-48, 5Y-70, 6Y-73, 7Y-64, 8Y-57, 9Y-49, 10Y-52, 11Y-28, 12Y-27, 13Y-12, 14Y-18, 15Y-4, 16Y-3, 17Y-2, 18Y-4, 19Y-2, 20Y-5, 21Y-2, 22Y-3, 23Y-1, 24Y-1, 26Y-2, 27Y-1, 29Y-1, 33Y-1, 50Y-1), with 51% having 5 to 9 young (Fig. 316). C.C. Wood (1986) reports a brood range of 6.1 to 11.4 young, along the central east coast of Vancouver Island, and farther north, at Owikeno Lake, Stutz (1965) reports 16 broods with a mean size of 11.4 young. Fledging period is about 65 to 70 days (Erskine 1971).

Broods of up to 27 young have contained the same size and age class but frequently the large broods have a mixture of classes. Spectacularly large broods are more likely to be noticed and reported than smaller ones but there is a clear drop in frequency after 14 young. Very large broods represent the efforts of several females.

REMARKS: The pattern of separate migration for males and females with their young gives rise to an apparent imbalance to the sex ratios that is greater than the actual case. The male:female ratio in the spring for the southern interior is 1:1 but on the south coast it is near 1:3. Early summer ratios are roughly 1:1 throughout the province. Autumn ratios can be 1:3 or more but observations are skewed by the flocking of full grown young with similarly plumaged females. Males tend to migrate a little later. The situation is reversed in winter. In the southern interior twice as many males are seen as females and on the southern coast the huge flocks of males that gather on the lakes near Victoria artificially increase the male to female ratio to 2.5:1. Flocks that contain mostly females and young are smaller and are widely dispersed throughout coastal habitats.

See J.A. Munro and Clemens (1937) and C.C. Wood (1984, 1986) for additional life history information and the relationship between the Common Merganser and fish populations in the province.

The Common Merganser is known as Goosander in Old World literature.

Figure 315. *The forested shores of Hiellen River, is typical breeding habitat for the Common Merganser on the Queen Charlotte Islands (R. Wayne Campbell).*

Figure 316. *Female Common Merganser with brood at Ross Lake (north of Riske Creek), 16 July 1977 (Ervio Sian).*

NOTEWORTHY RECORDS

Spring: Coastal - Sooke River 28 Apr 1979-33; Portage Inlet 31 Mar 1978-28; Beaver Lake (Saanich) 1 Mar 1979-290; Cowichan Bay 16 Mar 1974-180; Tofino Inlet 1 May 1974-100; Tilbury Island 26 Apr 1981-500 feeding on eulachons; Pitt Marsh 3 Mar 1977-134; Hope 19 Mar 1961-92; Quathiaski Cove 2 Mar 1975-94; Port Neville 13 Mar 1977-50; Sea Otter Cover 23 May 1974-15; Hansen Lagoon 17 May 1974-23; Kildidt Lagoon 20 Mar 1983-80; Kumdis Island 5 May 1977-23; Tlell 2 May 1935-47 (Munro, J.A. and Cowan 1947); Minette Bay 29 May 1975-71; Antigonish Creek at Skeena River 24 Mar 1981-133; Prince Rupert 29 Apr 1975-100. **Interior** - Osoyoos Lake 8 Mar 1978-12; Vaseux Lake 15 Apr 1937-137 (Munro, J.A. and Cowan 1947); Duck Lake (Creston) 21 May 1978-80; Wasa Lake 30 Apr 1975-27; Columbia Lake 28 Mar 1977-34 (Kaiser et al. 1978); Windermere Lake 28 Mar 1977-52 (Kaiser et al. 1978); Ellison Lake 10 Apr 1976-62; Kamloops 18 Mar 1978-100; Revelstoke 5 Apr 1977-86; Williams Lake 13 Apr 1976-21; Nilkitkwa Lake 22 May 1978-5; Farrell Creek (Peace River) 27 Mar 1983-2 pairs; Atlin Lake 19 May 1977-2 pairs.

Summer: Coastal - Whiffin Spit 16 Aug 1944-50+; Clover Point 24 Aug 1973-60; Cowichan Bay 3 Jul 1972-44 (Crowell and Nehls 1972c); Sarita River 4 Aug 1976-68 on estuary; Pitt Meadows 2 Jun 1971-106 (Campbell et al. 1972b); Comox Harbour 20 Aug 1927-200; Sewall 12 Jul 1983-20; Kitimat 2 Jul 1975-20; **Interior** - Leach Lake 21 Jul 1966-65, of which 23 were flightless (Greyell 1966); Mount Robson Park 10 Jun 1983-8; Eddontenajon Lake 10 Jun 1976-150, all males; Koshin River (Hatin Lake) 10 Jun 1979-50+; July Creek (Atlin) 30 Aug 1980-5.

Autumn: Interior - Fort St. John 2 Nov 1985-2; Pass Lake (Longworth) 19 Oct 1983-20; Williams Lake 25 Nov 1969-10; One Eye Lake 16 Nov 1949-80 males, 3 females; Revelstoke 16 Oct 1978-49 (Bonar 1978b); Cheem Lake (e Chase) 26 Sep 1977-74; Vernon 15 Nov 1936-350; Napier Lake 21 Oct 1984-45; Goose Lake (Vernon) 7 Nov 1977-125; Okanagan Landing 22 Nov 1969-300; Columbia Lake 16 Oct 1977-65; Vaseux Lake 26 Nov 1974-100, 26 Nov 1975-90; Wardner 9 Nov 1977-236 (Kaiser et al. 1978); Tugulnuit Lake 12 Nov 1977-57. **Coastal** - Drizzle Lake 21 Sep 1981-76; Kumdis Bay 19 Sep 1979-26; Bella Coola 7 Nov 1979-50 on estuary; Taleomey River 6 Nov 1979-32; Port Neville 24 Sep 1978-118; Florencia Bay 18 Oct 1972-119; Theodosia Inlet 19 Sep 1981-70; Little Qualicum River 4 Sep 1976-136 (Dawe 1980); Burnaby Lake 14 Nov 1946-930 (Munro, D.A. 1947); Deer Lake (Burnaby) 26 Nov 1971-182 (Campbell et al. 1972b); Quamichan Lake 23 Nov 1976-150; Elk Lake (Saanich) 22 Nov 1977-250; Esquimalt Lagoon 11 Oct 1979-200; Metchosin 25 Nov 1975-100.

Winter: Interior - Atlin 16 Dec 1980-2; Peace River (ne Hudson Hope 11 Jan 1987-2 males, 1 female, 23 Feb 1986-4 males; Smithers 28 Dec 1982-2; Kamloops 9 Dec 1984-45, 17 Dec 1983-73; Whiskey Island (Okanagan Lake) 11 Jan 1977-26; Kootenay Lake (Boswell) 4 Feb 1987-4; Vaseux Lake 7 Dec 1979-211; Osoyoos Lake 28 Dec 1973-23. **Coastal** - Prince Rupert 25 Jan 1979-49; Galloway Rapids 20 Feb 1981-74; Queen Charlotte City 16 Feb 1972-25; Quatsino Sound 14 Feb 1973-52 (Robertson 1974); Port Neville 31 Jan 1977-46; Kelsey Bay 4 Dec 1977-67; Qualicum River 3 Jan 1977-107; Little Qualicum River 13 Dec 1978-267 (Dawe 1980); Ladysmith 26 Feb 1974-346; Quamichan Lake 23 Dec 1973-500; Iona Island 3 Dec 1972-420; Burnaby Lake 11 Dec 1946-400 (Munro, D.A. 1947); Vedder Canal 27 Jan 1983-100; Cowichan Bay 19 Jan 1974-548; Somenos Lake 15 Jan 1977-117; Beaver Lake (Saanich) 12 Dec 1982-250, 9 Jan 1983-250; Elk Lake (Saanich) 26 Dec 1982-2,000; Goldstream River 1 Jan 1983-102 at mouth.

Christmas Counts: Interior - Recorded from 14 of 19 localities and on 71% of all counts. Maxima: Vernon 18 Dec 1983-530; Vaseux Lake 23 Dec 1981-147; Oliver/Osoyoos 28 Dec 1981-139. **Coastal** - Recorded from 26 of 28 Localities and on 91% of all counts. Maxima: Victoria 27 Dec 1964-1,602; Duncan 18 Dec 1976-1,536; Campbell River 2 Jan 1984-1,219.

Red-breasted Merganser

RBME

Mergus serrator Linnaeus

RANGE: Breeds from Alaska across northern Canada to New-foundland south to northwestern British Columbia, southern Manitoba, central Michigan, and eastern Maine. Winters on the Pacific coast from the Aleutian Islands to northern Mexico, and on the Atlantic coast from Newfoundland to southern United States. Also occurs in Europe and Asia.

STATUS: *Very common* to *abundant* spring and autumn migrant on the coast; *uncommon* in summer, *common* to locally *abundant* in winter. In the interior, a *rare* to locally *uncommon* spring and autumn migrant, *rare* summer visitant in the south and northeast, *uncommon* in the northwest; *rare* winter visitant in the central southern interior. Local breeder.

NONBREEDING: The Red-breasted Merganser is widely distributed along inner and outer coastal areas. In the interior, it occurs throughout southern valleys and is widely scattered throughout the northern two-thirds of the province. It has been found from sea level to 950 m elevation.

The Red-breasted Merganser is more marine in its habits than the Common Merganser, and generally frequents more open and deeper waters. Largest numbers occur in bays, estuaries, and inlets; coastal lakes, rivers, and large sloughs are visited infrequently. In the interior, lakes and large rivers are preferred.

Spring migration on the coast is not well pronounced; it occurs from mid-March to early May, with the main movement in April. Migrants are seen as pairs and small flocks, but occasionally large numbers are found in staging areas, perhaps taking advantage of migrating or spawning fish. In the interior, spring migration may begin in early March in southern areas, and carry through to early June, with a small peak in the first half of May. Routes in southern areas are through the major valleys.

Summer records are numerous only on the coast. They include occasional non-migrants, perhaps males and nonbreeding subadults moving from breeding areas to moulting areas, as well as post-breeding birds. Summer records are rare in the interior.

Autumn migration is prolonged, occurring from late August to early December, but mostly from mid-September to early November. In the interior, this movement is almost unnoticeable. Large numbers usually appear on the south coast as freeze-up begins in the interior.

In winter, the centre of abundance appears to be the Strait of Georgia on the coast and the southern Okanagan valley in the interior. In some years, over 1,700 Red-breasted Mergansers have been reported to winter in the province (Appendix 2), which is about 28% of the 6,000 reported to winter in the Pacific Flyway (Bellrose 1976).

BREEDING: The Red-breasted Merganser breeds only on the Teslin Plateau in extreme northwestern British Columbia near Atlin Lake (Swarth 1936) and on islands in Masset Inlet (RBCM Photo 1133). It breeds from sea level to 770 m elevation.

On the coast, the Red-breasted Merganser breeds on small and large marine islands; in the interior, it breeds on the shores of lakes and rivers. All sites are heavily vegetated with shrubs and trees.

In 1986 M.S. Rodway (pers. comm.) found 7 nests, and estimated at least 20 breeding pairs, in Masset Inlet, which suggests the species in British Columbia may be semi-colonial as it is elsewhere (A.J. Erskine pers. comm.), or at least may nest in definable neighbourhoods.

Nests: All nests (n=8) were on the ground, on small heavily vegetated islets (7), or on forested lakeshores. Nests were from 0.5 to 14 m from the shore and, on the coast, were situated among dune wildrye, Nootka rose, coastal strawberry, Nootka lupine, or salal. Nests were formed of grasses, salal leaves, twigs, or plant stalks, and lined with thick down and some feathers.

Eggs: Dates for 8 clutches ranged from 25 June to 16 July. Calculated dates indicate that eggs could be found at least as early as 12 May. Clutch size ranged from 1 to 10 eggs (6E-1, 8E-1, 9E-5, 10E-1). Incubation period is about 30 days (Johnstone, S.T. 1970).

Young: There are only 2 records of broods, both from the extreme northwest. A brood, unable to fly, was reported from Surprise Lake (Atlin) on 15 September 1934 (Swarth 1936) and on 20 July 1980 an adult female with a brood of 8, about 1 week old, was seen on Atlin Lake. Calculated dates indicate that young could be found as early as 13 July, although 1 of the eggs found in Masset Inlet on 25 June 1986, was pipping.

REMARKS: There are at least 14 other reports of broods from the central and southern interior and southern coastal areas of the province. None, however, included detailed description of the female which greatly resembles the female Common Merganser (Bellrose 1976).

NOTEWORTHY RECORDS

Spring: Coastal - Portage Inlet 27 Apr 1974-137 (Crowell and Nehls 1974c); Patricia Bay 18 Mar 1974-75; Chemainus 1 to 7 Mar 1975-121 (Blood 1976); Roberts Bank 8 May 1982-150; Westham Island 30 Apr 1973-300; Departure Bay 6 Mar 1930-300 to 400 (Munro, J.A. and Cowan 1947); Tofino 1 May 1974-20; Stanley Park (Vancouver) 4 May 1962-125 (Boggs and Boggs 1962c); Qualicum Beach 6 Apr 1976-100; Comox 7 Mar 1974-100; Okeover and Theodosia Inlets 16 Mar 1982-47; Port Neville 6 May 1976-42; Namu 11 Apr 1981-20; Bella Coola 8 Apr 1979-35; Lawn Point (Tlell) 20 Mar 1981-52+ feeding on spawning sandlance; Masset Inlet 14 Apr 1935-100 (Munro, J.A. and Cowan 1947); Kitimat 24 Apr 1975-35; Skeena River at Khyex River 24 Mar 1981-570. **Interior** - Penticton 1 May 1948-5; Okanagan Landing 13 May 1921-9; Columbia Lake 28 Mar 1977-27 (Kaiser et al. 1978); Nakusp 16 Apr 1978-1; 108 Mile Lake 4 May 1986-3 males, 2 females; Williams Lake 13 May 1975-4, 2 pair courting; Charlie Lake 6 May 1986-1 male, 24 May 1986-4; Atlin 19 May 1981-12 (Campbell 1981).

Summer: Coastal - Witty's Lagoon 15 Jul 1975-9, 23 Aug 1975-11; Clover Point 2 Jun 1976-2;

Cowichan Bay 8 Jul 1982-20; Long Beach 2 Jun 1968-2; Crescent Beach 12 Jun 1940-6; Qualicum Beach 6 Jun 1977-4, 2 Aug 1975-7; Port Neville 11 Jul 1976-2; Meyer's Narrows 18 Jul 1969-1 male; Masset 14 Jun 1983-2. **Interior** - Duck Lake (Creston) 16 Jul 1956-3 females (Munro, J.A. 1958a); Glade 21 Jun 1977-1 male; Osoyoos Lake 24 Jun 1986-1 eclipse male (RBCM Photo 1220); Kootenay Lake 15 Jun 1985-2 adult females; Revelstoke 3 Jun 1977-4, 17 Aug 1978-6; Cold Fish Lake 12 Jul 1975-a few; Kotcho Lake 20 Jun 1982-3 adult males, 2 Jul 1982-4 adult males (Campbell and McNall 1982).

Autumn: Interior - Surprise Lake (Atlin) 15 Sep 1924-1 female (MVZ 44632); Warm Bay 16 Sep 1972-6; Charlie Lake 27 Oct 1985-10; Murtle Lake 7 Nov 1956-1 (Edwards and Ritcey 1967); Adams Lake 21 Sep 1980-18; Sorrento 25 Sep 1970-16; Windermere Lake 18 Oct 1977-25; Columbia Lake 9 Nov 1977-75; Kamloops 2 Nov 1980-1; South Thompson River at Monte Creek 11 Oct 1951-12 (Munro, D.A. 1952); Trout Creek Point (Summerland) 17 Sep 1973-1 adult female. **Coastal** - Porcher Island 5 Nov 1975-40 (Martin 1978); Port Neville 20 Nov 1975-300; Comox 29 Oct 1932-100, no adult males; Qualicum Beach 17 Sep 1974-64;

Disappointment Inlet 11 Nov 1962-150; Ganges Harbour 29 Nov 1980-60; Esquimalt Lagoon 27 Sep 1974-175.

Winter: Interior - Sorrento 24 Dec 1970-2 adult males; Kamloops 29 Dec 1985-1; Vernon 21 Feb 1970-9; Okanagan Lake 24 Feb 1970-5; Waneta 26 Dec 1974-13; Castlegar 1 Feb 1981-1; Trail 15 Feb 1968-5. **Coastal** - Masset 19 Feb 1983-33; Port Neville 6 Dec 1975-68; Okeover and Theodosia Inlets 13 Jan 1982-52; Bowen and Gambier Islands 6 Feb 1921-400 (Munro, J.A. 1921); Stanley Park (Vancouver) 3 Feb 1963-117; Westham Island 23 Dec 1972-96; Ladysmith 15 Jan 1974-118; Nanoose Harbour 28 Feb 1974-80; Chemainus 19 Jan 1977-125, 21 to 31 Dec 1974-109, 1 to 6 Jan 1975-86, 22 to 28 Feb 1974-170 (Blood 1976); Clayoquot Sound 11 to 13 Dec 1972-99 (Robertson 1974).

Christmas Counts: Interior - Recorded from 7 of 19 localities and on 23% of all counts. Maxima: Oliver/Osoyoos 28 Dec 1982-10; Vernon 26 Dec 1977-7; Penticton 27 Dec 1983-7. **Coastal** - Recorded from 25 of 28 localities and on 81% of all counts. Maxima: Vancouver 27 Dec 1970-518; Pender Island 27 Dec 1980-403; Victoria 2 Jan 1966-338.

Red-breasted Merganser

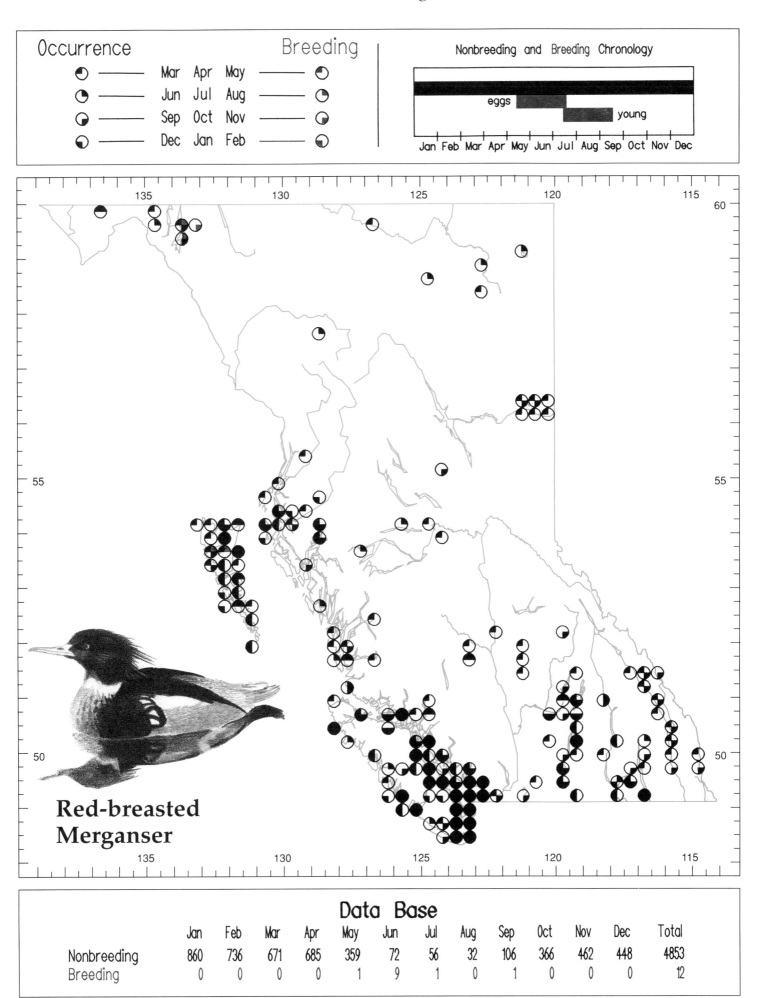

Occurrence

	Mar Apr May	
	Jun Jul Aug	
	Sep Oct Nov	
	Dec Jan Feb	

Breeding

Nonbreeding and Breeding Chronology

eggs

young

Jan Feb Mar Apr May Jun Jul Aug Sep Oct Nov Dec

Data Base

	Jan	Feb	Mar	Apr	May	Jun	Jul	Aug	Sep	Oct	Nov	Dec	Total
Nonbreeding	860	736	671	685	359	72	56	32	106	366	462	448	4853
Breeding	0	0	0	0	1	9	1	0	1	0	0	0	12

Ruddy Duck
Oxyura jamaicensis (Gmelin)

RANGE: Breeds in North America from northeastern British Columbia and southern Northwest Territories east to Manitoba and western Ontario, south to northern Mexico; locally in the east-central portion of the continent. Winters mainly from southern British Columbia and central United States southward. Also resident in West Indies and South America.

STATUS: *Fairly common* to *very common* migrant and winter visitant to the lowlands of southeastern Vancouver Island, locally *rare* summer visitant. *Common* to *abundant* migrant and winter visitant to the Fraser Lowlands, locally *uncommon* summer visitant. *Very rare* elsewhere on the coast. In the interior, a *fairly common* to *very common* migrant and *fairly common* summer visitant in the Peace Lowlands and generally across southern portions of the province. Locally *uncommon* in winter in the Nicola and Okanagan valleys. *Very rare* elsewhere in the interior. Breeds.

NONBREEDING: The Ruddy Duck is widely distributed from southeastern Vancouver Island across the southern third of the province and throughout the Fort Nelson and Peace lowlands. It is extremely unusual to see this little duck anywhere along the coast north of Campbell River. It occurs from sea level to at least 1,400 m elevation.

The Ruddy Duck visits almost any body of fresh or salt water deep enough for diving. During migration periods and in winter, protected bays and lakes are preferred. In marine habitats, favourite sites have soft mud bottoms from which the Ruddy Duck can extract small invertebrates on which it feeds. Boundary Bay, Esquimalt Lagoon, and large sewage lagoons are some areas that support sizable congregations. In fresh water, preferred sites tend to be at least 2 m deep and are often surrounded by an abundant growth of cattail. The Ruddy Duck is rarely seen on rivers or in very deep water.

Spring migration can begin in late February on the southwest coast and early March in the southern interior, but it occurs mainly from late April through the third week of May. First spring migrants in the Peace River region are found in late April. Males begin their moult migrations in July and occasionally large flocks are reported in late summer. Autumn migration can occur from late August through mid-November, but the main movement is from late September through October.

The centre of winter distribution is the southwestern corner of the province, particularly Mud Bay (Boundary Bay). Bellrose (1976) notes that a few hundred Ruddy Ducks winter in coastal British Columbia near Vancouver. Numbers vary annually but the total wintering population in extreme south coastal areas is much higher and in some years may climb to over 11,000 birds (see Appendix 2). During Christmas Bird Counts for 5 major wintering areas from 1970 to 1984, the total number of Ruddy Ducks ranged between 462 and 11,688 birds (Fig. 317) with an average of 2,711 per year.

BREEDING: The Ruddy Duck breeds in the interior from the Nicola and Okanagan valleys to the east Kootenay, north through the Chilcotin-Cariboo to the Nechako Lowland region, and in the Peace River area. It is absent from the west Kootenay north of Creston. On the coast, it breeds locally on Quamichan Lake, Vancouver Island (Munro, J.A. and Cowan 1947) and in the Fraser Lowlands (Campbell 1968c). It breeds from near sea level to 1,200 m elevation.

The Ruddy Duck prefers freshwater lakes, ponds, sloughs, and marshes, usually deeper than 2 m, with emergent vegetation such as bulrushes and cattail for nesting cover (Fig. 318). It seems to prefer areas with slightly shorter and sparser dead vegetation rather than taller and denser green vegetation. The smallest nest site pond was 0.3 ha in size.

Bellrose (1976) estimates a breeding population in the Chilcotin-Cariboo to be 15,000 birds.

Nests: Most nests (91%; n=126) were over water that was 25 to 40 cm deep. They were situated in cattail, bulrushes, and sedge borders, 2 to 33 m from open water. Low (1941) suggests that a desirable water depth is more important in the selection of a nest site than the quality of the cover vegetation. Six nests were among emergent vegetation in the centre of water bodies, four were on grass islands and two were found on dry land (see McKnight 1974).

Nests were meagre to elaborate platforms of short pieces of living (53%; n=54) or dead (47%) cattails, bulrushes (Fig. 319), sedges, pondweeds, leaves, and bits of other nearby water vegetation. Nine nests were lined with substantial amounts of down. Most nests were attached to emergent vegetation and many were concealed by vegetation pulled over the nest, giving it a basket-shaped appearance. Three nests were free-floating.

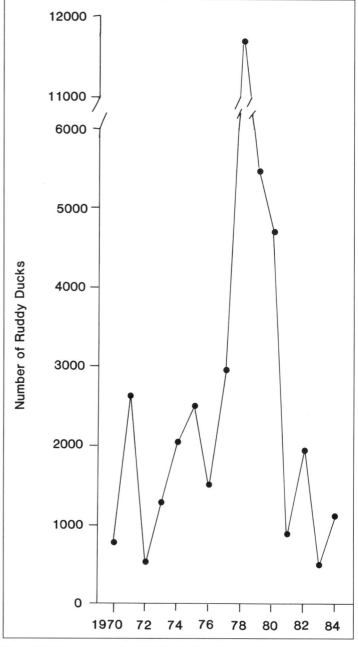

Figure 317. *Aggregate totals of Ruddy Ducks tallied on Christmas Bird Counts at Victoria, White Rock, Ladner, and Vancouver, British Columbia, 1970 to 1984. The all-time high numbers for Canada were reported from White Rock in 1978.*

Ruddy Duck

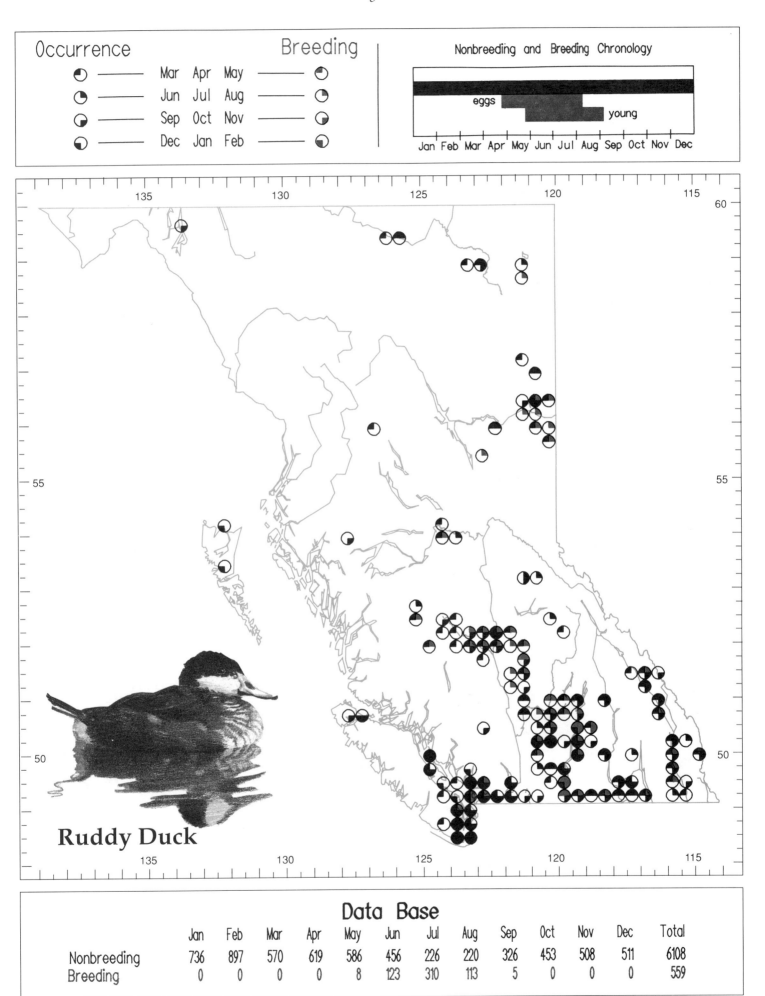

Occurrence

◐	—	Mar	Apr	May
◔	—	Jun	Jul	Aug
◕	—	Sep	Oct	Nov
◕	—	Dec	Jan	Feb

Breeding

Mar Apr May	—	◐
Jun Jul Aug	—	◔
Sep Oct Nov	—	◔
Dec Jan Feb	—	◕

Nonbreeding and Breeding Chronology

eggs young

Jan Feb Mar Apr May Jun Jul Aug Sep Oct Nov Dec

Ruddy Duck

Data Base

	Jan	Feb	Mar	Apr	May	Jun	Jul	Aug	Sep	Oct	Nov	Dec	Total
Nonbreeding	736	897	570	619	586	456	226	220	326	453	508	511	6108
Breeding	0	0	0	0	8	123	310	113	5	0	0	0	559

Figure 320. Ruddy Duck nest with 2 Northern Pintail eggs, 24 km south of Merritt, 20 June 1984 (Mark Nyhof).

Figure 318. Ruddy Duck breeding habitat at un-named lake, 23 km east of Fort Nelson, 1 July 1982 (R. Wayne Campbell).

Figure 319. Ruddy Duck nest and eggs, 24 km south of Merritt, 20 June 1984 (Mark Nyhof).

Nests (n=14) were 13 to 22 cm above water. Outside and inside diameter ranged from 23 to 27 cm and 14 to 16 cm, respectively. Inside depth ranged from 5 to 9 cm.

Eggs: Dates for 132 clutches ranged from 22 May to 7 August with 56% recorded between 16 June and 7 July. This corresponds closely to clutch initiation reported by Somerville (1985) near Riske Creek in the Chilcotin-Cariboo Basin in 1983 and 1984 (Fig. 321). Calculated dates indicate that eggs could be found on 24 April. Somerville (1985) indicates that, in the Chilcotin-Cariboo region, the latest clutch initiation was 14 July, and the peak seemed to coincide with the growth of green emergent vegetation to 70 or 80 cm. Clutch size ranged from 1 to 16 eggs (1E-4, 2E-5, 3E-2, 4E-9, 5E-13, 6E-17, 7E-15, 8E-17, 9E-13, 10E-10, 11E-5, 12E-9, 13E-8, 14E-3, 15E-1, 16E-1), with 57% having 5 to 9 eggs. Incubation period is about 23 days from the last egg laid (Bellrose 1976).

Eggs of Ruddy Ducks have been found with clutches of American Bittern, Northern Pintail (Fig. 320), Canvasback, Redhead, Lesser Scaup, and American Coot.

Young: Dates for 328 broods ranged from 24 May to 4 September with 52% recorded between 12 July and 3 August. Brood size ranged from 1 to 18 young (1Y-13, 2Y-20, 3Y-36, 4Y-48, 5Y-44, 6Y-72, 7Y-45, 8Y-20, 9Y-9, 10Y-12, 11Y-1, 12Y-3, 13Y-1, 14Y-3, 18Y-1), with 64% having 4 to 7 young. Fledging period is 42 to 49 days (Bellrose 1976).

REMARKS: Unlike other species of waterbirds in British Columbia, the Ruddy Duck undergoes 2 complete moults per year and is flightless for 2 three-week periods. One moult takes place in early August during the fledging period of the young; the second takes place in late winter or early spring and the primaries may not be fully grown until after migration is completed (Palmer, R.S. 1976b).

See Somerville (1985) for additional information on details of Ruddy Duck breeding biology in the Cariboo.

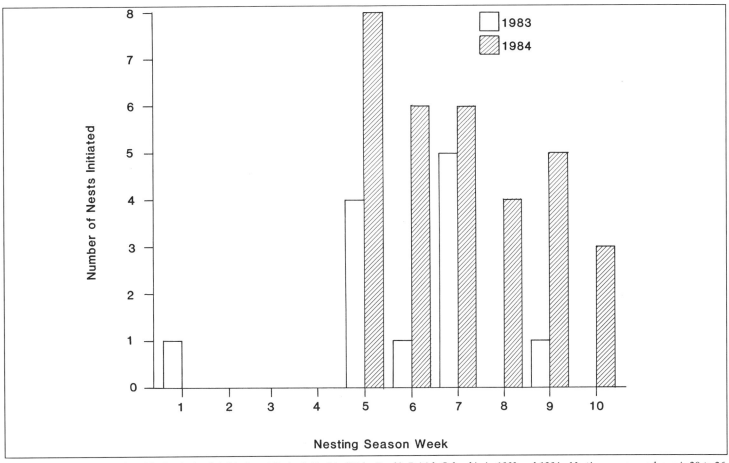

Figure 321. *Comparison of Ruddy Duck clutch initiation at Becher's Prairie (Riske Creek), British Columbia in 1983 and 1984. Nesting season week one is 20 to 26 May, week 10 is 22 to 28 July (after Somerville 1985).*

NOTEWORTHY RECORDS

Spring: Coastal - Esquimalt Lagoon 20 Mar 1971-32; Swan Lake (Saanich) 6 Mar 1976-58; Elk Lake (Saanich) 5 Mar 1977-26; St. Mary Lake (Saltspring Island) 4 Mar 1978-114, 25 Mar 1962-240+; Somenos Lake 25 Mar 1972-40; Quamichan Lake 18 Apr 1950-125+; Ganges Harbour 2 Apr 1949-100+; Iona Island 21 Mar 1971-500 (Campbell et al. 1972b); Burnaby Lake 3 Mar 1966-65, 10 Apr 1971-134; Stanley Park (Vancouver) 11 Mar 1973-80. **Interior** - Creston 11 Mar 1983-5; Richter Lake 24 Apr 1971-16; Vaseux Lake 3 May 1960-30; Okanagan Landing 22 Mar 1943-4, first arrival; Swan Lake (Vernon) 27 Apr 1978-139, 2 May 1936-104 (Munro, J.A. 1939c), 11 May 1933-67 (Munro, J.A. 1939c); Otter Lake 3 Apr 1977-82; Baynes Lake 9 May 1946-262, 11 May 1943-900 to 1,000 (all Johnstone, W.B. 1949) 28 May 1948-80; Island Lake (Canal Flats) 10 May 1972-22, Napier Lake 19 Apr 1933-150, 22 Apr 1940-248, 24 Apr 1941-215; Kamloops 15 Mar 1981-40; Stump Lake 25 May 1987-300; Westwick Lake 29 May 1941-70; Williams Lake 21 Apr 1980-32; Rorison Lake 31 May 1978-19; Tetana Lake 30 May 1938-6 (Stanwell-Fletcher and Stanwell-Fletcher 1943); Rock Lake (Hudson Hope) 24 Apr 1979-40; Boundary Lake (Goodlow) 13 May 1984-173; Fort St. John 15 Apr 1984-1 adult male, first arrival; Beaver Lake (w Fort Nelson) 11 May 1980-6; Liard Hotsprings 15 May 1981-2; Aline Lake 14 May 1981-10.

Summer: Coastal - Portage Inlet 9 Jun 1959-2; Cowichan Bay 24 Aug 1974-1; Iona Island 19 Jun 1981-20; Cranberry Lake (Powell River) 7 Jun 1963-7. **Interior** - Duck Lake (Creston) 17 Jun 1983-40, 25 Jul 1966-12; Meyer's Lake (Bridesville) 8 Jun 1974-13; Kilpoola Lake 5 Jun 1977-15; Swan Lake (Vernon) 31 Jul 1940-100, 24 Aug 1943-700, mostly flightless males; McLeary Lake 1 Aug 1975-12.

Autumn: Interior - Atlin 16 Sep 1972-2; Fort St. John 16 Sep 1982-6, 30 Oct 1986-18, 4 Nov 1986-2; Bowron Lake Park 17 Sep 1975-1; Siwash Lake (Alexis Creek) 8 Nov 1980-1; Williams Lake 20 Sep 1984-26; Fletcher Lake (Hanceville) 20 Sep 1982-50; 103 Mile Lake 2 Oct 1940-80; Sorrento 2 Oct 1970-31; Minnie Lake 29 Oct 1962-105; Separation Lake 15 Sep 1986-150; Swan Lake (Vernon) 12 Sep 1936-161 (Munro, J.A. 1939e), 15 Sep 1932-500 (Munro, J.A. 1939e), 18 Sep 1943-400, more than half males, 30 Sep 1939-300 (Munro, J.A. 1939f); Brisco 5 Oct 1977-15 (Kaiser et al. 1978); Vaseux Lake 4 Oct 1977-11; Osoyoos Lake 13 Sep 1960-8; Duck Lake (Creston) 18 Oct 1982-10. **Coastal** - Coal Harbour 5 Nov 1935-1 female (MVZ 99601); Comox 13 Oct 1952-1; Hardy Bay 5 Nov 1935-1; Stanley Park (Vancouver) 17 Oct 1970-75; White Rock 26 Nov 1980-1,069; Esquimalt Lagoon 26 Nov 1975-20; Victoria 9 Nov 1974-25.

Winter: Interior - Williams Lake 22 Feb 1978-1; Nicola Lake 4 Jan 1987-1; Nelson 8 and 18 Dec 1968-3; Okanagan Lake (Penticton) 22 Dec 1973-22, 28 Dec 1977-23, 1 Jan 1980-20, 29 Jan 1978-20, 3 Feb 1974-20. **Coastal** - Masset 21 Dec 1986-2; Skidegate Inlet 24 Jan 1984-2; Hardy Bay 8 Feb 1938-1; Cranberry Lake (Powell River) 1 Dec 1980-14; Harrison Lake 6 Feb 1971-100; Iona Island 12 Dec 1980-946, 9 Feb 1979-425; Ladner 14 Jan 1981-500 on sewage lagoon; White Rock 5 Feb 1981-907; Somenos Lake 4 Jan 1981-84 in flooded fields; Quamichan Lake 2 Feb 1974-116, 22 Feb 1970-1,000 (Tatum 1971); St. Mary Lake (Saltspring Island) 7 Feb 1960-225; Ganges Harbour Jan 1972-735 (Rodway and Campbell 1977); Bazan Bay 10 Jan 1974-150; Sidney Island 26 Dec 1962-145 (Hancock 1963); Elk Lake (Saanich) 1 Jan 1978-110; Esquimalt Lagoon 28 Jan 1959-145.

Christmas Counts: Interior - Recorded from 3 of 19 localities and on 16% of all counts. Maxima: Vernon 23 Dec 1979-42; Penticton 27 Dec 1976-19; Vaseux Lake 23 Dec 1980-1. **Coastal** - Recorded from 13 of 28 localities and on 10% of all counts. Maxima: White Rock 30 Dec 1978-**11,280**, all-time Canadian high count (Anderson, R.R. 1979); Ladner 2 Jan 1966-3,838; Duncan 18 Dec 1971-587.

Casual, Accidental, Extirpated,
and
Extinct Species

Clark's Grebe
Aechmophorus clarkii (Lawrence)

CLGR

RANGE: Poorly known. Sympatric with Western Grebe but less abundant. Breeds in very small numbers from Washington and southern Canadian prairie provinces south to Mexico. Winters from southern British Columbia (casually) south to central Mexico.

STATUS: *Casual* in the central southern interior, and on the extreme south coast.

OCCURRENCE: At least 6 records are on file. The Clark's Grebe was first recorded in the province on Shuswap Lake, near Salmon Arm, in 1981. The record was overlooked until 1987 when a clearly identifiable photograph (Fig. 322) was published as a Western Grebe in the local newspaper (Munro, D. and Munro 1987). The photograph (RBCM Photo 1162) was taken in late May or early June. Since then the species has been observed on several occasions in the summers of 1982 and 1983 among a nesting colony of Western Grebes at Duck Lake, Creston. On 26 July 1983, L.S. Forbes (pers. comm.) observed a female Clark's Grebe paired with a male Western Grebe. The pair had a single chick which was fed by both adults. The most recent record at Duck Lake is of a single bird seen on 8 July 1987. Breeding colonies should be carefully examined to determine the breeding status of the Clark's Grebe in the province.

There are 2 acceptable coastal records, both of which have been confirmed by J.T. Ratti (pers. comm.). A single bird was present off Ogden Point, Victoria from 13 to 26 October 1986 (Campbell 1986d). It was photographed (RBCM Photo 1142) on 18 October (Fig. 323). Detailed field notes were received for another bird sighted in Boundary Bay on 7 and 8 December 1986.

REMARKS: In 1858, the 2 colour morphs were considered as separate species (Baird 1858). The dark phase was called the Western Grebe (*Podiceps occidentalis*) and the light phase the Clark's Grebe (*P. clarkii*). In 1881, Henshaw suggested that these forms were simply colour phases of the same species. For nearly 100 years afterwards, ornithologists considered the Western Grebe (*Aechmophorus occidentalis*) as a single species. In the late 1970s, Ratti (1979) concluded that the 2 forms "biologically functioned as separate species." That led to the resurrection of *A. clarkii* as a separate species from *A. occidentalis* (American Ornithologists' Union 1985).

See Ratti (1981) and Storer and Nuechterlein (1985) for details on the identification and distribution of the Clark's Grebe. De Smet (1987) summarizes the grebe's status in Canada through 1986.

POSTSCRIPT: On 8 April 1988 a single bird was photographed (RBCM Photo 1229) near Alberni on southern Vancouver Island.

Figure 322. *Adult Clark's Grebe at Salmon Arm, early June 1981. This was the first documented record of the species for the province (RBCM Photo 1162; Deane Munro).*

Figure 323. *Clark's Grebe at Ogden Point, Victoria, 18 October 1986 (RBCM Photo 1142; Tim Zurowski).*

Short-tailed Albatross

STAL

Diomedea albatrus Pallas

RANGE: Breeds on Torishima Island off Japan and ranges at sea through the north Pacific Ocean to the Hawaiian Islands.

STATUS: Formerly of regular occurrence off the British Columbia coast; presently considered *accidental*.

OCCURRENCE: In prehistoric times, the Short-tailed Albatross was the dominant near-shore albatross. McAllister (1980), in his archaeological analysis of the Yuquot midden at Nootka Sound on Vancouver Island, excavated 2,000 Short-tailed Albatross bones. He determined, by carbon dating, that 40% of the bones were from the period A.D. 800 to 1789 and 27% were after 1789. At least 19 individual bird skeletons were from the latter period.

In the late 19th century, the Short-tailed Albatross was reported by Kermode (1904) as "tolerably common on both coasts of Vancouver Island, but more abundant on the west coast." In April 1894, he found it quite common near Cape Beale. In 1889 (exact date unknown), 2 specimens were obtained in Juan de Fuca Strait off Victoria and prepared as display mounts by the British Columbia Provincial Museum. One bird was a male (RBCM 1491) and the other a juvenile female (RBCM 1492; Fig. 324). The final record, in the 19th century, was a bird found dead on a beach at Esquimalt on 4 June 1893 (Macoun and Macoun 1909).

The bird's present status in British Columbia remains uncertain. The only recent record is of an immature photographed on 11 June 1960 (RBCM Photo 296) associating with Black-footed Albatrosses, 64 km west of Vancouver Island (Lane 1962). This record is consistent with records of Short-tailed Albatrosses observed recently at Ocean Weather Station Papa (50°N, 145°W; M.T. Myres pers. comm.). From 1958 to 1981 single birds, often immatures, were reported on at least 10 occasions, as follows: May (1963), June (1964, 1971 - Gruchy et al. 1972), August (1972, 1976), September (1958, 1974), and October (1969). Recent records from Oregon (Wyatt 1963), Alaska (Sanger 1964, 1972a; Yesner 1976; Boggs and Boggs 1964), and other areas of the northern Pacific Ocean (Hasegawa and DeGange 1982) also suggest that the Short-tailed Albatross may once again become part of the avifauna of the northeastern Pacific Ocean. A recent record from Washington (Wahl 1970) is now suspected to have been a very old or aberrant Black-footed Albatross (T. Wahl pers. comm.).

REMARKS: By the 1930s, Short-tailed Albatross populations were reduced almost to extinction due to the activities of feather hunters and possibly by volcanic erruptions on its breeding grounds (Harrison, C. 1979). It was designated an endangered species by the International Council for Bird Preservation (King, W.B. 1981) and given protection; the population has increased slowly and numbered at least 250 individuals in 1981 (Hasegawa 1982).

Figure 324. *Juvenile female Short-tailed Albatross collected in Juan de Fuca Strait off Victoria in 1889 (RBCM 1492; Andrew Niemann).*

Mottled Petrel

MOPE

Pterodroma inexpectata (Forster)

RANGE: Breeds on islands south of the South Island of New Zealand from late October through early June. Ranges into the North Pacific Ocean as far as the southern Bering Sea and the Gulf of Alaska during the nonbreeding season from early May to late October.

STATUS: *Casual* off the west coast of Vancouver Island.

OCCURRENCE: Two records. On 24 February 1971, a Mottled Petrel was found on board the ship, CNAV *Endeavour*, at 49°14'N, 127°01'W, about 24 km west of Flores Island, central Vancouver Island (Campbell and Shepard 1973). It was photographed (RBCM Photo 150; Fig. 325) and released. The other record was a single bird seen on the water on 16 June 1986 at 49°00'N, 126°26'W, about 19 km southwest of Flores Island.

There are 4 significant records from well off the British Columbia coast: 48°00'N, 127°22'W, 23 February 1971 - 1 (Campbell and Shepard 1973); 51°23'N, 140°54'W, 17 March 1972 - 1 found dead on the ship, *Naess Pioneer* (Campbell and Shepard 1973); 48°31'N, 126°30'W, 28 April 1972 - 540 (Bourne and Dixon 1975); 51°00'N, 132°30'W, 7 June 1972 - 9 (Bourne and Dixon 1975).

Ship's officers aboard Ocean Weather Station Papa, still farther offshore at 50°N, 145°W, reported Mottled Petrels on only 4 occasions between 1958 and 1981. These records fall between 27 September and 10 October, just when birds might be expected to begin the southward migration to New Zealand (M.T. Myres pers. comm.).

REMARKS: The majority of records for the west coast of North America south of Alaska were of dead or dying individuals (Roberson 1980).

The Mottled Petrel was formerly referred to as the Scaled Petrel.

Figure 325. *Mottled Petrel found on MV CNAV* Endeavor *off the west coast of Vancouver Island (49°14'N, 127°01'W), 24 February 1971 (RBCM Photo 150; R. Wayne Campbell).*

Magnificent Frigatebird
Fregata magnificens Mathews

MAFR

RANGE: Breeds along the Pacific coast from Mexico to South America; locally in the Atlantic-Caribbean region, West Indies, and along the South American coast to southern Brazil; also off western Africa. Ranges at sea off the Pacific coast from northern California south to northern Peru. It is now a rare visitor in summer and autumn to southern California (McCaskie 1970).

STATUS: *Accidental.*

OCCURRENCE: During the past 15 years there have been at least 12 unconfirmed reports of very large, black or black-and-white birds with long narrow wings and deeply forked tails seen by commercial fishermen off the west coast of Vancouver Island. In 1979, there were 4 reports from July and August, but without adequate details. It is likely that these sightings were of Magnificent Frigatebirds, but as P. Harrison (1983) points out, "at sea, identification of frigatebirds is notoriously complex and represents, perhaps, the most difficult challenge in any seabird group." Observers are encouraged to record details, especially noting the distribution of white plumage on the immatures and females.

On 22 August 1981, an immature frigatebird was seen in Egeria Bay south of Cohoe Point, on Langara Island at the north-west corner of the Queen Charlotte Islands. The bird was watched for nearly 12 hours, sometimes within a range of 25 m, where it often sat on top of the trolling poles of fishing boats. The bird frequently fed on fish entrails that were discarded by fishermen. One, presumably the same bird, was photographed (RBCM Photo 656; Hunn and Mattocks 1982) on 25 August atop the mast of a fishing boat anchored at Cohoe Point (Fig. 326).

REMARKS: There are few records north of California. The Magnificent Frigatebird has been documented in Oregon on 18 and 19 February 1935 (Gabrielson and Jewett 1970) and 24 July 1979 (Roberson 1980) and in Washington on 1 July 1975 (McCabe, T.R. 1976). In south coastal Alaska unidentified frigatebirds have been reported during July 1957 and on 16 September 1969 (Isleib and Kessel 1973). Both records were considered hypothetical by the authors but the latter was accepted by the American Ornithologists' Union (1983). The only substantiated record is of a juvenile photographed in Belkofski Bay, Alaska Peninsula on 15 August 1985 (Gibson, D.D. 1986).

This species is commonly referred to as Man-o'-war-bird.

Figure 326. *Magnificent Frigatebird at Cohoe Point, 25 August 1981 (RBCM Photo 656; George Deagle).*

Least Bittern

Ixobrychus exilis (Gmelin)

LEBI

RANGE: Breeds in North America from southeastern Oregon, southern Manitoba, Ontario, and New Brunswick south to the West Indies and through Mexico. Winters from southern United States southward. Also occurs in Central and South America.

STATUS: *Casual* in summer.

OCCURRENCE: Two records. The Least Bittern has been recorded in summer, in the central southern interior and on the south mainland coast of British Columbia. On 30 July 1955, an adult was found alive on Twenty-sixth Street in Vernon. It was photographed, released in the marshes of nearby Swan Lake, and not seen again (Munro, J.A. 1955b). On 16 June 1974, an adult was photographed (RBCM Photo 352) in brackish willow marshes bordering the Point Grey Golf Course (Musqueam Flats) in Vancouver. The bird was not found on several subsequent searches in June.

REMARKS: The status of the Least Bittern in Canada has been reviewed by Sandilands and Campbell (1987).

Snowy Egret
Egretta thula (Molina)

SNEG

RANGE: Breeds from southeastern Oregon, southern Idaho, Oklahoma, and New Jersey south into Mexico, the West Indies, and Central America to Chile and Argentina. Post-breeding dispersal occurs north to southern Canada. Winters from southern United States southward.

STATUS: *Casual* in extreme southwestern British Columbia.

OCCURRENCE: Six records. The Snowy Egret was prematurely added to the list of British Columbia birds on the basis of 2 specimens taken at Burrard Inlet, Vancouver, in May 1879 (Fannin 1891). The species was included on all lists thereafter (e.g. Fannin 1898; Kermode 1904; American Ornithologists' Union 1910) until Brooks and Swarth (1925) published details that the specimens (RBCM 1592) were actually an eastern Asian species, the Intermediate Egret (*Egretta intermedia*). The origin of the birds was questionable and is discussed by Brooks (1923c).

All acceptable records are from southwestern portions of the province. A Snowy Egret was present from 23 to 25 May 1972 along Reichenbach Road, Pitt Meadows and was photographed (RBCM Photo 244) on the latter date (Campbell et al. 1974). Another was present at Esquimalt Lagoon, extreme southern Vancouver Island from 23 to 28 August 1972. The egret was photographed (RBCM Photo 239; Fig. 327) on 24 and 27 August (Tatum 1973).

On 17 April 1985 a single adult was observed at Serpentine Fen, Colebrook, and another, perhaps the same bird, was photographed (RBCM Photo 1096) on 11 May 1985 at Gibsons (Fig. 328), about 50 km to the northwest (Campbell 1985c; Mattocks 1985b). A single Snowy Egret was present at Cowichan Bay, southern Vancouver Island, on 18 and 19 November 1986 (Campbell 1987a). The most recent record is of a single bird at Hastings Flat (Saanich) from 23 to 27 May 1987 (Campbell 1987d).

REMARKS: There are 2 additional records we consider hypothetical. On 28 August 1946 Holdom (1948) recorded what he thought was an immature Snowy Egret at Crescent Beach on Boundary Bay. He later sent more details of the sighting to W.E. Godfrey at the National Museum of Canada (Holdom 1954) who agreed with the identification and included the species as a "sight record" in his list for British Columbia (Godfrey 1966). The other record, for which details are unfortunately lacking, was of a single bird seen at Serpentine Fen, Colebrook on 11 September 1976 (Shepard, M.G. 1977a).

The species was formerly placed in the genus *Leucophoyx*.

Figure 327. Snowy Egret at Esquimalt Lagoon, 27 August 1972 (RBCM Photo 239; Enid Lemon).

Figure 328. Snowy Egret at Gibsons, 11 May 1985 (RBCM Photo 1096; Andy Buhler).

Little Blue Heron
Egretta caerulea (Linnaeus)

RANGE: Breeds from southern California (since 1979), the southern Gulf states, and New England, and south through the West Indies, Central America, and much of South America. Post-breeding dispersal occurs north, irregularly, to the northern United States and southern Canada. Winters from southern Baja California, the Gulf coast, and coastal Virginia south throughout most of the breeding range.

STATUS: *Accidental.*

OCCURRENCE: The Little Blue Heron has increased in California during the past 2 decades (Unitt 1977) but still remains accidental in the Pacific Northwest. In British Columbia, an immature was seen frequently from 15 October to 10 November 1974 at Judson Lake, about 7 km southwest of Abbotsford. It was photographed (RBCM Photo 373) on 3 November (Fig. 329). The bird was not seen again until its final report on 5 January 1975 (Weber, W.C. and Hunn 1978).

REMARKS: The species was formerly placed in the genus *Florida*.

Figure 329. *Little Blue Heron at Judson Lake, 3 November 1974 (RBCM Photo 373; Ervio Sian).*

White-faced Ibis

Plegadis chihi (Vieillot)

WFIB

RANGE: Breeds from central California, eastern Oregon, southern Idaho, southern North Dakota, and Nebraska, and in coastal regions of Texas and Louisiana, south to Argentina and Chile. Winters from southern California, Baja California, and the Gulf coast of Texas and Louisiana south through the general breeding range in South America. Post-breeding wanderers occur north to southern Canada.

STATUS: *Casual* on the south coast; *casual* in spring in the southern interior.

OCCURRENCE: Six records. The status of the species in British Columbia in the 1800s is uncertain mainly because details concerning the records are obscure and incomplete. The earliest reference is provided by Fannin (1898) who mentions that 2 specimens had been taken, "... one on Saltspring Island, the other at the mouth of the Fraser River." Although specific details are lacking, Macoun and Macoun (1909) consider the species "a rare straggler in British Columbia." J.A. Munro and Cowan (1947) indicate that the records were "... not substantiated by specimens and there is nothing in the literature to indicate that Fannin or any other ornithologist examined these."

The first authentic record appears to be of a bird collected at Luckakuck Creek near Chilliwack in summer 1902 (Brooks 1917). The bird, an immature, was prepared as a full mount (RBCM 1587; Fig. 330). The date on the specimen label, however, is listed as November 1907. Over 60 years elapsed before the next occurrence. On 9 and 12 May 1968, 2 birds were seen together at Wasa Lake. One was photographed (RBCM Photo 257) on 12 May (Eastman 1974).

The next 2 occurrences, both from southern Vancouver Island, are well documented by written field descriptions. On 24 May 1982, an adult in summer plumage was seen in the marsh at Quicks Bottom, Saanich, at 0800 and again at 1030. At 0945 the same day, one was reported in Oak Bay, 11 km away. Although

observation periods were not continuous at either site, it seems apparent that 2 birds were present. On 20 July 1983, another adult was sighted at Cordova Spit, Central Saanich (Campbell 1983d). The bird was flushed from among a flock of gulls to a nearby slough were it was studied.

On 22 and 31 May 1985, a single bird was seen at Separation Lake, 5 km south of Kamloops (Campbell 1985c). The latest record is of a single bird that wintered at Hardy Bay, northeastern Vancouver Island in 1986/87. The bird arrived about 2 November 1986 and was seen daily, mostly in the vicinity of the Beaver Cove Trailer Park, until 8 May 1987. Numerous photographs (RBCM Photo 1148) were taken during its stay. When the ibis first arrived, its plumage was indistinguishable from that of a Glossy Ibis (*P. falcinellus*) but by mid-February the red eye and white facial border, characteristic of a breeding adult White-faced Ibis, were visible.

REMARKS: The arrival date for the Hardy Bay bird has been erroneously published as 27 November 1986 (Mattocks and Harrington-Tweit 1987) and 10 November 1986 (Campbell 1987a).

R.S. Palmer (1962) considers the White-faced Ibis and Glossy Ibis conspecific. Apparently, they breed sympatrically and therefore are considered separate species by the American Ornithologists' Union (1983).

See Pratt (1976) for problems concerning field identification of White-faced and Glossy ibises.

POSTSCRIPT: On 17 May 1988, 3 White-faced Ibises were found at Burges and James Gadsden Park west of Golden. Two of the birds were photographed (RBCM Photo 1216; Fig. 331) different copies of which have been published elsewhere (see Campbell 1988b; Zettergreen 1988). On 18 May only 1 bird was seen. It remained in the area until 20 May.

The status of the bird in British Columbia is elevated to *very rare*.

Figure 330. *White-faced Ibis collected at Luckakuck Creek, summer 1902 (RBCM 1587; Andrew Niemann).*

Figure 331. *White-faced Ibises at Burges and James Gadsden Park, 17 May 1988 (RBCM Photo 1216; Barry Zettergreen).*

Wood Stork

Mycteria americana Linnaeus

RANGE: Resident in western Mexico and southeastern United States south through most of Central and South America. Wanders north in the Pacific states to California and in the Atlantic states to Massachusetts.

STATUS: *Accidental.*

OCCURRENCE: A female Wood Stork was found alive at Telegraph Creek, northwestern British Columbia, on 15 September 1970. It died and was sent to the Royal British Columbia Museum (RBCM 11627; Fig 332). A photograph of the bird was published in a Victoria newspaper (Anonymous 1970).

REMARKS: The species was formerly known as Wood Ibis.

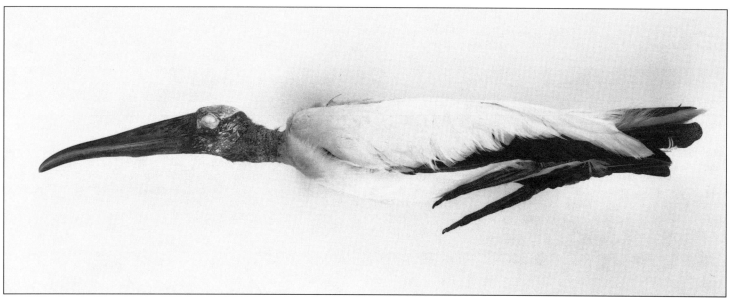

Figure 332. *Wood Stork that was found alive and subsequently died at Telegraph Creek, 15 September 1970 (RBCM 11627; Andrew Niemann).*

Fulvous Whistling-Duck

FWDU

Dendrocygna bicolor (Vieillot)

RANGE: Breeds locally in North America in the southern United States and Mexico. Wanders widely throughout the continent. Winters from southern United States southward. Also occurs in tropical America, Africa, and southern Asia.

STATUS: *Accidental.*

OCCURRENCE: Although we have several records on file, only one is fully documented. In September 1905, 5 Fulvous Whistling-Ducks were shot from a flock of 11 on the flats near Port Alberni, Vancouver Island (Macoun and Macoun 1909). One specimen, with the date 20 September 1905 (Munro, W.T. 1967), is in the Royal British Columbia Museum (RBCM 1561; Fig. 333).

REMARKS: Barnston (1861) casually mentions the occurrence of the species (without details) in British Columbia and later Fleming (1907) comments, also without specific evidence, that he "... shot one out of a pair of [Fulvous Whistling-Ducks] on the banks of the Columbia above Okanagan." The location is suspect even though the title of the paper, "The Fulvous Tree-Duck in British Columbia," suggests that the occurrence was in the province.

Another record, without details, is listed by T.H. Rogers (1963a). The entry states simply that "Even more unusual were a *Fulvous Tree Duck* near 100 Mile House, B.C. ... ." The final record was of an escapee. On 30 September 1984, an adult was found alive at Crescent Beach, on Boundary Bay, but died in captivity 4 hours later. The bird was wearing a band from which it was determined that it had been shipped from Maine, and escaped captivity in Surrey. The bird was donated to the Royal British Columbia Museum where it was prepared as a display mount.

See Bolen and Rylander (1983) for a discussion of the zoogeography, ecology, and anatomy of whistling-ducks.

The Fulvous Whistling-Duck was formerly known as the Fulvous Tree Duck.

Figure 333. *Fulvous Whistling-Duck collected near Port Alberni, 20 September 1905 (RBCM 1561; Andrew Niemann).*

Baikal Teal

BATE

Anas formosa Georgi

RANGE: Breeds in eastern Siberia. Winters from China, Korea, and Japan south to India and Burma.

STATUS: *Accidental.*

OCCURRENCE: A male was shot by a hunter in Ladner on 20 November 1957. It had been with a flock of Northern Pintails. The published date of the record as 20 December (Hatter, J. 1960; Godfrey 1986), may be an error, because the specimen label (UBC 8595; Fig. 334) reads 20 November.

There are at least 6 other winter records from the west coast of North America south of British Columbia (Roberson 1980). In western Alaska the Baikal Teal is considered a "casual migrant and summer visitant" and has been recorded from 23 May to 8 October (Kessel and Gibson 1978).

Figure 334. *Baikal Teal shot at Ladner, 20 November 1957 (UBC 8595; Andrew Niemann).*

Garganey

GARG

Anas querquedula Linnaeus

RANGE: Breeds across Eurasia and winters in west Africa, south Eurasia, and southeast Asia. In North America occurs rarely (but regularly) in migration in the western Aleutian Islands, Alaska.

STATUS: *Casual* on the south coast; *accidental* in the Okanagan valley.

OCCURRENCE: Four records. The first bird was observed near Sea and Iona islands from 14 to 31 May 1977 (Crowell and Nehls 1977b). It was photographed (RBCM Photo 464) on 14 May on a sewage pond at Iona Island (Macdonald 1978b). The second was seen at Iona Island from 8 to 12 June 1979 (Harrington-Tweit et al. 1979) and photographed (RBCM Photo 713) on 9 June (Fig. 335). The third was a juvenile (tertials and tertial coverts not yet replaced), shot by a hunter, at Port Alberni on 12 October 1980 (Spear et al. 1988). A wing, part of a Canadian hunter sample, showed smooth feather tips and no evidence of unusual wear as in a pen-reared bird. The fourth was photographed (RBCM Photo 916) on 23 May 1984 at Penticton; it was seen again on 24 May (Campbell 1984b; Rogers, T.H. 1984c).

REMARKS: It is unlikely that these birds represent escaped captives (see Spear et al. 1988). McCaskie in Macdonald (1978b) concludes that Garganeys seen in California are stragglers from Asia, rather than escapees. More convincing is the statement by Kessel and Gibson (1978) that the Garganey is a rare spring migrant (10 May to 21 June) and very rare fall migrant (mid-August to early October) on the outer Aleutian Islands.

Figure 335. Male Garganey at Iona Island, 9 June 1979 (RBCM Photo 713; Ervio Sian).

Common Eider

Somateria mollissima (Linnaeus)

COEI

RANGE: Breeds in northern North America and northern Eurasia. Winters in northern coastal waters of both continents; in western North America from the Bering Sea ice pack south to the Aleutians and Cook Inlet, Alaska.

STATUS: *Casual.*

OCCURRENCE: Two records. On 27 October 1934 (not 27 November 1934 as listed in J.A. Munro and Cowan 1947), a young female was collected (MVZ 99537) at Hardy Bay, northeastern Vancouver Island. On 31 October 1949, a "Pacific Eider [was] taken six miles east of Prince George, B.C. ... bears the tag number 565 and is 615 mm long and weighs six pounds" (Jobin 1952b). The identity of the specimen (NMC 47595) has recently been confirmed by H. Ouellet (pers. comm.).

REMARKS: The specimen (RBCM 10226) reported by J.A. Munro and Cowan (1947) from Masset has recently been identified as a King Eider. There are 3 additional records we consider hypothetical. A clutch of 5 eggs, collected on 13 June 1880 in "northern British Columbia, Canada," was discovered in the American Museum of Natural History (AMNH 379). Recently, W.E. Lanyon confirmed the identification and wrote "The collector's notes give bird seen as the basis for identification and 500 miles north of Victoria, B.C. as the locality." It is likely the eggs were collected from the vicinity of Glacier Bay, Alaska, where Common Eiders are known to breed (Wik and Streveler 1968).

Jobin (1952b) provides an inconclusive report:

During the fall of 1950 at Alkali Lake [Cariboo] ... noticed five eiders standing on the ice near a small opening in the centre of the lake. I tried to secure one or two of these birds for the record, but the ice was too thin to carry my weight. The next morning all the lake was frozen over and the eiders had disappeared.

Erskine and Stein (1964) also consider the report hypothetical.

J.D. Webster in correspondence with the Royal British Columbia Museum reported what he thought to be a Common Eider as follows:

... 22 September 1972. Place was a creek near milepost 80 on the Haines Road, in B.C. ... seemed to be a bit crippled because it wouldn't fly with other ducks, but swam away. Large size and shape of head indicated this species within the eider genus ... was unsure whether it was a female or an immature male ... suppose that it was an immature, probably from the Glacier Bay colony only 60 miles south ... .

There appear to be no well documented records south of British Columbia.

Steller's Eider

Polysticta stelleri (Pallas)

STEI

RANGE: Breeds in western and northern Alaska, as well as northeastern Asia. Winters regularly off Alaska and the Kamchatka Peninsula of northeastern Asia, and casually south to California.

STATUS: *Casual* on the coast; *accidental* in the extreme northwest interior.

OCCURRENCE: Four records. On 15 October 1948, a Steller's Eider was shot by a duck hunter, from among a flock of Lesser Scaup, at Masset Inlet, Queen Charlotte Islands (Racey 1950). The bird was an immature female (RBCM 10227). An adult male was photographed on 17 June 1970 (RBCM Photo 7) on Mittlenatch Island, in the Strait of Georgia, about 18 km southeast of Campbell River (Campbell 1971b; Fig. 337). The eider was roosting on intertidal rocks with 110 moulting Harlequin Ducks. A female was located on 13 February 1976 at the foot of Rothesay Avenue, Sidney, southern Vancouver Island, and was present until at least 27 March 1976. Colour and black-and-white photographs were obtained on 13 and 15 February (RBCM Photo 449; Fig. 336

Figure 336. Female Steller's Eider at Sidney, 13 February 1976 (RBCM Photo 449; Jack E. Williams).

Figure 337. Male Steller's Eider with Harlequin Ducks at Mitlenatch Island, 17 June 1970 (RBCM Photo 7; William Verbruggue).

Smew
Mergellus albellus (Linnaeus)

SMEW

RANGE: Breeds from Scandinavia east through northern Russia and Siberia to Kamchatka, south to southern Russia, and the vicinity of Sea of Okhotsk. Winters from Iceland, the British Isles, Scandinavia, Russia, and Kamchatka south to the vicinity of the Mediterranean Sea. Also winters in China, Korea, and Japan. In North America, Kessel and Gibson (1978) indicate that the Smew is currently a rare spring and autumn migrant and winter visitor on the outer Aleutian Islands.

STATUS: *Casual* on the south mainland coast.

OCCURRENCE: Three records. All records are listed in detail by W.C. Weber and Campbell (1978). A brief summary of these occurrences is as follows: Lost Lagoon, Vancouver, 14, 18, and 23 November 1970-1 adult male (Campbell et al. 1972a); Reifel Island 28 February to 21 March 1974-1 female or immature male (reported as a female by Crowell and Nehls 1974b); Reifel Island, 14 January to 30 March 1975-1 adult male (Fig. 338). The last 2 records are documented by photographs (RBCM Photos 345 and 395), copies of which were published in Roberson (1980).

Figure 338. *Male Smew at Reifel Island, 20 January 1975 (RBCM Photo 395; Ervio Sian).*

Hypothetical Species

The following 8 species of birds have been reported in various publications and for the following reasons the records are considered questionable.

1. The data on which the record is based are erroneous, cannot now be verified, were recorded by a single observer, have been rejected by a regional records committee, or are based on written or photographic evidence that is less than satisfactory.

2. The species' occurrence in the province is believed to be either through escape from captivity or human-aided other than from intentional introduction.

For another 5 species, we have detailed field notes on file but all are unpublished or have been reported by only a single observer. They include the Least Grebe *(Tachybaptus dominicus)*, Least Storm-Petrel *(Oceanodroma microsoma)*, Greater Flamingo *(Phoenicopterus ruber)*, Barnacle Goose *(Branta leucopsis)*, and Ruddy Shelduck *(Tadorna ferruginea)*.

Humboldt Penguin
Spheniscus humboldti Meyen

During June 1978, 1 or 2 penguins, probably this species, were independently reported from 3 locations off northern Vancouver Island. On 14 June, a commercial fisherman observed a single penguin about 15 m from his boat in Quatsino Sound (50°21'N, 127°59'W). The bird was "porpoising" in a northward direction. Lighthouse keepers on Egg Island (51°15'N, 127°50'W), northeast of the first sighting, were responsible for the second record. From 9 to 25, June they continually heard what sounded like a "mooing cow," and on 23 June the source was discovered: 2 penguins. The final record was of a single bird photographed on 20 June 1978 (RBCM Photo 550) off Mitlenatch Island (49°57'N, 125°00'W) at the northern end of the Strait of Georgia.

Many photographs (e.g. Anonymous 1978a) and articles (e.g. Burnes 1978; Curtin 1978) were published in regional newspapers. This resulted in an additional 2 sightings being reported. Beurling (1978) states:

> In 1944 I was in the navy and was making some installations close to Masset in the Queen Charlottes. One day as I was walking on the beach at Rose Spit I sighted a penguin standing erect on the sloping beach. A real beautiful bird [*sic*].
> ... I approached with caution. The penguin didn't make a move, just stood there like a statue. I extended my hand ... and stroked it gently ... the bird was about two feet high.

The other sighting was reported in correspondence, highlights of which are:

> ... Labour Day weekend 1975 ... Long Beach ... we got within 15 or 20 feet of ... a penguin ... waddling towards the water ... was about 2 or 2 1/2 feet tall ... when it got to the water it fell flat on its belly and starting swimming ...

On 27 August 1985, a Humboldt Penguin was observed off the Washington coast (S.M. Speich pers. comm.).

It is unlikely the penguins sighted in British Columbia were caged escapees or that they dispersed 10,000 km by swimming from their range off the Peruvian and Chilean coasts (Stonehouse 1968). Rather, the occurrences are considered to be the result of transport and release by fishermen (Anonymous 1978b).

Wedge-tailed Shearwater
Puffinus pacificus (Gmelin)

S.G. Jewett (1929) obtained a specimen of this species from a taxidermist in Ontario. The only data on the label was Vancouver, B.C. J.A. Munro and Cowan (1947) and Godfrey (1966) were unable to obtain additional information to suggest the specimen was actually taken in waters off the British Columbia coast.

Red-faced Cormorant
Phalacrocorax urile (Gmelin)

A specimen collected at Departure Bay, Vancouver Island on 7 April 1910 (NMC 4066; Taverner 1927) has subsequently been examined (Godfrey 1966) and determined to be a Double-crested Cormorant.

POSTSCRIPT: See Addenda.

Intermediate Egret
Egretta intermedia (Wagler)

A specimen was taken at Burrard Inlet (Vancouver) on 29 May 1879 (Macoun and Macoun 1909). The authority of the specimen has been questioned. J.A. Munro and Cowan (1947) suggest it was claimed on entirely hypothetical grounds (see Brooks 1923c) and that it was a substitution in the form of a purchased, dried skin which was subsequently mounted. However, Kermode (1923a, 1923b) stated that the specimen had "every appearance of having been mounted from a bird in the flesh."

Bean Goose
Anser fabalis (Latham)

A single bird was seen and photographed (RBCM Photo 1067) at Deadman Lake in the Okanagan valley from 14 to 26 April 1982. R.A. Cannings et al. (1987) states that it "... was apparently of the European subspecies and almost certainly an escapee."

The Bean Goose is considered a very rare but regular spring migrant in western and southwestern Alaska where it has been reported between 9 April and 20 June (Kessel and Gibson 1978; Roberson 1980).

Mandarin Duck
Aix galericulata Clark

There have been several unsuccessful attempts to introduce this species as free-flying birds to southern coastal areas. Only 2 introductions merit discussion.

In the late 1940s, at least 6 birds were released in Beacon Hill Park in Victoria. The birds survived until the late 1950s and were recorded on several annual Christmas Bird Counts (Clay 1950, 1957a; Guiguet 1952b). None has been introduced since.

Beginning in September 1983, up to 12 free-flying Mandarin Ducks have been reported in Stanley Park, Vancouver, and were listed on Christmas Bird Counts beginning in 1985 (Weber, W.C. and Kragh 1986, 1987). There have also been recent winter sightings from other localities near Vancouver such as Burnaby Lake, Richmond, and Tilbury Island. These birds disappear every summer and may be nesting somewhere nearby, but there are no positive breeding records, and the species cannot yet be considered established (W.C. Weber pers. comm.).

Falcated Teal
Anas falcata Georgi

On 15 April 1932, a full-plumaged male was reported to be on Swan Lake, 4.8 km north of Vernon. It was located during a search 2 days later (Brooks 1932). There is a strong possibility that the bird escaped from captivity and migrated north with wild birds. During the period 1928 to 1932, the Falcated Teal was the third most common live duck sold in markets around San Francisco (Swarth 1932). Brooks (1942) considers the record to be hypothetical as does J.A. Munro and Cowan (1947) and Godfrey (1966, 1986).

Spectacled Eider
Somateria fischeri (Brandt)

The only record comes from an observation by C.J. Guiguet. In his diary, *Field notes - local and interior - index, 1958-68* (RBCM collection), he states:

Sept. 22, 1962. Spectacled eider duck - south end James Island, in flight past boat - 60 to 70 feet - headed south-west towards Cordova Bay.

James Island is located in Haro Strait off the southern tip of Vancouver Island.

Godfrey (1966) later received additional information that the bird was "a male in full or near full plumage" but he decided to retain the hypothetical status of the record even though it had been published by Boggs and Boggs (1962a).

APPENDICES

APPENDIX 1

Migration Chronology

In the following table, dates are given for regular spring and/or autumn migrants in 3 coastal and 8 interior locations throughout the province. The data for composing the migration dates were obtained from literature as well as field notebooks of birders. Periods of records vary with area as follows: Victoria (1969-1985), Vancouver (1968-1986), Masset (1980-1986), Okanagan (1897-1986), Nakusp (1975-1986), Radium (1979-1986), Kamloops (1978-1986), Williams Lake (1958-1986), Prince George (1981-1986), Fort St. John (1980-1986), and Fort Nelson (1975-1986). Dates for peak movements (Fig. 339) are generally given as ranges. A single date indicates a calculated average for all records. Localities and dates were deleted if information was incomplete.

Each species generally falls into 1 of 3 categories: summer visitant, winter visitant, or passage migrant. Earliest arrival, latest departure and peak movement dates are given for each "season." A completed matrix for each category is as follows:

	SPRING			AUTUMN		
	Early Arrival	Late Departure	Peak Movement	Early Arrival	Late Departure	Peak Movement
Summer Visitant	X	—	X	—	X	X
Winter Visitant	—	X	X	X	—	X
Passage Migrant	X	X	X	X	X	X

Figure 339. Flock of migrating Greater White-fronted Geese over Langara Island, Queen Charlotte Islands, 29 April 1966 (R. Wayne Campbell).

	SPRING			AUTUMN		
	Early Arrival	Late Departure	Peak Movement	Early Arrival	Late Departure	Peak Movement
Red-throated Loon						
Victoria	—	27 Jun	Apr	—	—	Oct
Vancouver	—	7 Jun	27 Apr	15 Sep	—	25 Sep
Fort St. John	16 May	23 May	—	21 Aug	2 Oct	—
Pacific Loon						
Victoria	—	—	May-early Jun	—	—	—
Vancouver	—	8 Jun	11 May	11 Sep	—	27 Oct
Masset	2 Apr	—	—	Sep	—	—
Fort St. John	10 May	23 Jun	—	25 Sep	27 Oct	—
Common Loon						
Vancouver	—	—	27 Apr	—	—	25 Sep
Okanagan	—	—	19 Apr-1 May	—	—	10-22 Oct
Nakusp	3 Apr	—	25 Apr-10 May	5 Sep	22 Oct	10 Sep-20 Oct
Radium	1 Apr	—	15-17 Apr	—	3 Sep	—
Kamloops	3 Apr	—	15-25 Apr	—	30 Nov	—
Williams Lake	—	—	4-21 Apr	—	—	Sep-Oct
Prince George	23 Apr	—	—	—	1 Nov	—
Fort St. John	28 Apr	—	6-30 May	—	30 Oct	12-18 Oct
Fort Nelson	3 May	—	10-15 May	—	23 Oct	—
Yellow-billed Loon						
Victoria	—	13 May	—	29 Sep	—	—
Vancouver	—	7 May	—	26 Sep	—	—
Pied-billed Grebe						
Okanagan	late Mar	—	15 Apr	—	—	15 Sep-late Oct
Radium	—	—	18-25 Mar	—	19 Sep	—
Kamloops	25 Mar	—	—	5 Nov	—	—
Williams Lake	14 Mar	—	20 Mar-13 Apr	—	—	Nov
Fort St. John	6 May	—	—	—	26 Sep	—
Horned Grebe						
Victoria	—	—	early May	—	—	1-15 Sep
Vancouver	—	7 Jun	26 Apr	5 Aug	—	14 Sep
Okanagan	—	—	21 Apr-15 May	—	—	mid-Oct
Nakusp	27 Mar	—	13-20 Apr	—	—	—
Radium	30 Apr	—	—	—	20 Sep	—
Kamloops	5 Apr	—	25 Apr-15 May	—	30 Nov	5-20 Sep
Williams Lake	—	—	21-25 Apr	—	—	20 Sep-19 Oct
Fort St. John	25 Apr	—	6-20 May	—	4 Nov	10 Oct
Red-necked Grebe						
Victoria	—	—	1-15 May	—	—	10-25 Aug
Vancouver	—	—	27 Apr	—	—	15 Sep
Okanagan	28 Mar	—	23-25 Apr	—	—	27 Sep-28 Oct
Nakusp	12 Apr	—	20 Apr-10 May	—	21 Nov	—
Radium	25 Mar	—	25 Apr-9 May	—	22 Oct	—
Kamloops	5 Apr	—	8 Apr-10 May	—	15 Nov	15-30 Sep
Prince George	29 Apr	—	—	—	1 Nov	—
Fort St. John	27 Apr	—	5-15 May	—	4 Nov	20 Oct
Fort Nelson	12 May	—	—	—	8 Sep	—
Eared Grebe						
Victoria	—	5 Jun	early May	13 Aug	—	—
Vancouver	—	7 May	—	23 Aug	—	—
Okanagan	31 Mar	—	1-19 May	—	—	4 Nov
Kamloops	25 Apr	—	30 Apr	—	15 Sep	—
Williams Lake	—	—	19-25 Apr	—	—	—
Fort St. John	22 Apr	—	—	—	30 Oct	—

Migration Chronology

	SPRING			AUTUMN		
	Early Arrival	Late Departure	Peak Movement	Early Arrival	Late Departure	Peak Movement
Western Grebe						
Victoria	—	—	late Apr	—	—	mid-Sep
Vancouver	—	—	5 May	—	—	26 Sep
Okanagan	—	—	28 Apr-15 May	—	—	mid-Oct
Nakusp	12 Apr	—	6-18 May	—	3 Nov	—
Radium	10 May	—	10-15 May	—	29 Oct	1-17 Oct
Kamloops	28 Mar	—	5-20 May	—	30 Nov	1-20 Oct
Williams Lake	—	—	27 Apr-11 May	—	28 Nov	20 Sep-7 Nov
Prince George	—	—	—	4 Sep	27 Oct	—
Fort St. John	1 May	—	20-25 May	24 Oct	5 Nov	—
American White Pelican						
Okanagan	14 Mar	—	14 Apr-17 May	—	20 Nov	—
Kamloops	10 Apr	10 May	15-25 Apr	4 Sep	10 Sep	8 Sep
Williams Lake	—	—	18-24 Apr	—	—	Sep-early Oct
Brandt's Cormorant						
Victoria	—	—	late Apr	—	—	mid-Sep
Vancouver	—	24 May	4 Apr	26 Aug	—	—
American Bittern						
Okanagan	20 Apr	—	—	—	6 Nov	—
Radium	9 May	1 Jun	—	—	—	—
Kamloops	2 May	—	—	14 Oct	—	—
Williams Lake	—	—	15-29 May	—	—	Sep
Great Blue Heron						
Okanagan	—	—	21-30 Mar	—	—	—
Nakusp	19 Feb	—	—	—	10 Nov	—
Radium	10 Mar	—	—	—	16 Oct	—
Kamloops	1 Apr	—	10 Apr	—	30 Oct	25 Aug-20 Sep
Williams Lake	4 Jun	—	—	—	—	Sep
Prince George	—	—	—	30 Aug	27 Sep	—
Cattle Egret						
Victoria	—	30 Jan	—	23 Oct	—	mid-Nov-mid-Dec
Vancouver	—	12 Feb	—	4 Oct	—	13 Nov
Tundra Swan						
Victoria	—	16 Apr	—	25 Oct	—	—
Vancouver	—	5 May	15 Mar	14 Oct	—	13 Nov
Okanagan	—	—	8-15 Apr	—	—	21 Oct-3 Nov
Kamloops	—	26 May	20 Mar-10 Apr	6 Sep	—	15-30 Oct
Williams Lake	12 Mar	—	2-3 Apr	13 Oct	23 Nov	20 Oct-18 Nov
Fort St. John	3 Apr	—	21-28 Apr	20 Sep	26 Oct	5-14 Oct
Fort Nelson	26 Apr	12 May	—	—	—	early Sep
Trumpeter Swan						
Victoria	—	19 May	6-19 Apr	25 Oct	—	8-19 Nov
Vancouver	—	1 May	9 Mar	16 Oct	—	15 Nov
Masset	—	11 May	—	13 Oct	—	—
Okanagan	—	—	early Mar	—	—	—
Kamloops	20 Mar	—	—	28 Oct	25 Nov	—
Fort St. John	4 Apr	—	21-28 Apr	3 Oct	—	—
Greater White-fronted Goose						
Victoria	—	26 Jun	19-29 Apr	25 Aug	—	15-22 Sep
Vancouver	—	20 May	26 Apr	1 Sep	—	28 Sep
Masset	12 Apr	1 Jun	23 Apr-17 May	21 Sep	—	24 Sep
Kamloops	6 Mar	24 Apr	—	6 Sep	21 Oct	—
Fort St. John	13 Apr	—	15-25 Apr	2 Sep	21 Oct	2-9 Sep
Fort Nelson	28 Apr	13 May	—	—	—	—

Birds of British Columbia

	SPRING			AUTUMN		
	Early Arrival	Late Departure	Peak Movement	Early Arrival	Late Departure	Peak Movement
Snow Goose						
Victoria	—	11 Jun	25 Mar	1 Sep	—	10-18 Oct
Vancouver	—	3 Jun	18 Apr	13 Sep	—	18 Oct
Masset	5 Apr	10 Jun	—	29 Oct	—	—
Okanagan	10 Mar	—	3-10 May	—	24 Nov	—
Radium	2 May	14 May	—	—	29 Sep	—
Kamloops	11 Mar	—	24 Apr-15 May	21 Sep	24 Oct	—
Prince George	14 Apr	27 Apr	—	—	—	—
Fort St. John	16 Apr	6 May	—	—	—	—
Brant						
Victoria	11 Feb	30 Jun	4-28 Apr	—	—	—
Vancouver	—	—	6 Apr	—	—	—
Masset	—	—	mid-Apr	—	—	—
Canada Goose						
Vancouver	—	—	25 Apr	—	—	15 Oct
Masset	—	mid-Jun	mid-Mar-Apr	24 Jul	—	Oct
Okanagan	15 Mar	—	16-22 Apr	—	—	late Sep-mid-Nov
Nakusp	4 Mar	27 Mar	5-15 Apr	—	20 Nov	15-30 Sep
Radium	—	—	26 Mar-11 Apr	—	—	19-27 Aug
Kamloops	1 Mar	—	10-25 Mar	1 Sep	—	5 Sep-10 Oct
Williams Lake	1 Mar	24 Apr	17-18 Apr	16 Aug	10 Nov	Sep-Oct
Prince George	12 Mar	—	28 Mar	—	—	—
Fort St. John	18 Mar	—	10-25 Apr	16 Oct	11 Nov	23 Oct-5 Nov
Fort Nelson	19 Apr	9 May	—	—	—	—
Wood Duck						
Okanagan	17 Mar	—	12 Apr	—	26 Oct	late Sep-mid-Oct
Nakusp	5 Apr	—	—	—	11 Nov	—
Kamloops	30 Mar	20 May	10-15 May	—	13 Sep	—
Green-winged Teal						
Vancouver	—	—	19 Apr	—	—	8 Sep
Masset	—	—	11 Apr-2 May	12 Sep	—	—
Okanagan	—	—	3-23 Apr	10 Aug	—	15 Sep-15 Oct
Nakusp	6 Mar	—	5-20 Apr	10 Sep	18 Nov	5 Sep-10 Oct
Radium	7 Mar	—	21-30 Apr	13 Aug	—	15-24 Oct
Kamloops	4 Mar	—	5-25 Apr	1 Sep	—	—
Williams Lake	10 Mar	—	19 Mar-24 Apr	—	—	Sep
Prince George	23 Mar	—	4-6 Apr	4 Sep	1 Nov	—
Fort St. John	7 Apr	—	20-25 Apr	—	31 Oct	11-16 Sep
Fort Nelson	26 Apr	—	—	—	26 Oct	—
Mallard						
Vancouver	—	—	15 Apr	—	—	29 Sep
Masset	—	—	mid-Apr	—	—	—
Okanagan	20 Feb	—	—	late Aug	—	3-18 Nov
Radium	25 Mar	—	7-14 Apr	31 Aug	—	24 Sep-7 Oct
Kamloops	1 Mar	—	—	1 Sep	—	—
Williams Lake	—	—	19 Mar-10 Apr	—	—	Oct-Nov
Prince George	17 Mar	—	24 Mar	2 Sep	1 Nov	—
Fort St. John	21 Mar	—	10-15 Apr	—	18 Nov	—
Fort Nelson	24 Apr	—	7-11 May	—	—	1 Sep
Northern Pintail						
Vancouver	—	—	10 Apr	—	—	14 Sep
Masset	—	11 Jun	mid-Apr	11 Sep	—	—
Okanagan	22 Feb	—	mid-Apr	late Aug	—	—
Nakusp	18 Mar	—	1-15 Apr	1 Sep	27 Oct	—
Radium	15 Mar	30 Apr	25 Mar-2 Apr	31 Aug	—	18-26 Oct
Kamloops	25 Feb	—	15 Mar-5 Apr	1 Sep	—	—
Williams Lake	10 Mar	—	17 Mar-27 Apr	—	—	—
Prince George	28 Mar	—	—	—	—	—
Fort St. John	1 Apr	—	5-25 Apr	6 Oct	31 Oct	—
Fort Nelson	7 Apr	—	—	—	—	—

Migration Chronology

	SPRING			AUTUMN		
	Early Arrival	Late Departure	Peak Movement	Early Arrival	Late Departure	Peak Movement
Blue-winged Teal						
Victoria	19 Apr	—	mid-May	—	18 Nov	—
Vancouver	2 Apr	—	17 May	—	21 Nov	—
Masset	1 May	15 Jun	—	—	—	—
Okanagan	26 Mar	—	mid-May	—	—	late Aug
Nakusp	6 Mar	—	10-31 May	—	25 Sep	—
Radium	25 Apr	—	12-20 May	—	13 Sep	—
Kamloops	6 Apr	—	10-15 May	—	30 Sep	25 Aug-5 Sep
Williams Lake	29 Apr	—	1-22 May	—	—	—
Fort St. John	25 Apr	—	20-28 May	—	20 Oct	—
Fort Nelson	27 Apr	—	11 May	—	—	10 Sep
Cinnamon Teal						
Victoria	12 Mar	—	mid-Apr	—	15 Oct	—
Vancouver	28 Feb	—	30 Apr	—	24 Oct	—
Masset	25 Apr	—	25-29 Apr	—	—	—
Okanagan	17 Mar	—	late Apr-early May	—	—	—
Nakusp	14 Apr	—	—	—	—	—
Radium	25 Apr	—	—	—	—	—
Kamloops	6 Apr	—	20-25 May	—	1 Sep	25 Aug
Williams Lake	5 Apr	—	10 Apr-10 May	—	—	—
Fort St. John	2 May	11 May	—	—	—	—
Northern Shoveler						
Victoria	—	—	late Apr	—	—	Sep
Vancouver	—	—	12 Apr	—	—	6 Oct
Masset	27 Apr	—	early May	—	—	—
Okanagan	8 Apr	—	23 Apr-7 May	—	—	mid-Sep-mid-Oct
Nakusp	11 Apr	—	—	28 Aug	8 Oct	—
Radium	1 Apr	—	25 Apr-5 May	—	14 Oct	—
Kamloops	16 Mar	20 May	20 Apr-10 May	—	28 Nov	7-20 Sep
Williams Lake	—	—	1-27 Apr	—	—	—
Prince George	28 Mar	—	—	6 Sep	19 Oct	—
Fort St. John	16 Apr	—	May	—	31 Oct	—
Gadwall						
Victoria	—	14 May	late Apr	21 Aug	—	late Sep-early Oct
Vancouver	—	—	7 May	—	—	28 Sep
Okanagan	1 Apr	—	—	early Sep	—	—
Kamloops	15 Mar	—	1-10 May	—	28 Nov	10-15 Sep
Williams Lake	—	—	19-24 Apr	—	—	—
Fort St. John	21 Apr	—	21-26 May	—	24 Oct	—
Eurasian Wigeon						
Victoria	—	5 May	—	18 Sep	—	—
Vancouver	1 Apr	—	5 Apr	14 Sep	—	7 Nov
American Wigeon						
Victoria	—	—	Apr	—	—	late Sep
Vancouver	—	—	13 Apr	—	—	7 Oct
Okanagan	—	—	mid-late Apr	—	—	mid-Oct
Nakusp	20 Mar	—	5-25 Apr	—	27 Nov	Sep
Radium	21 Mar	—	25 Mar-10 Apr	—	27 Nov	18-31 Oct
Kamloops	1 Mar	—	15 Mar-20 Apr	—	—	Sep
Williams Lake	7 Mar	—	16 Mar-20 Apr	—	—	Oct-Nov
Prince George	28 Mar	—	—	2 Sep	1 Nov	—
Fort St. John	4 Apr	—	22 Apr-10 May	—	2 Nov	1-15 Oct
Fort Nelson	26 Apr	—	7-14 May	—	—	22 Sep
Canvasback						
Victoria	—	29 May	early Apr	23 Aug	—	mid-Oct
Vancouver	—	—	29 Mar	—	—	22 Oct
Masset	—	17 May	Mar-Apr	11 Nov	—	mid-Oct-mid-Nov
Okanagan	—	—	late Feb-early Mar	—	—	—
Radium	3 Apr	—	—	30 Aug	18 Oct	—
Kamloops	19 Feb	—	5 Mar-5 Apr	1 Sep	—	20 Oct-5 Nov
Williams Lake	11 Mar	—	15 Mar-25 Apr	—	—	—
Fort St. John	3 Mar	—	3-10 May	—	24 Oct	—

	SPRING			AUTUMN		
	Early Arrival	Late Departure	Peak Movement	Early Arrival	Late Departure	Peak Movement
Redhead						
Okanagan	—	—	Mar-Apr	early Sep	—	mid-Oct
Radium	15 Apr	—	18-30 Apr	7 Oct	—	18-25 Oct
Kamloops	4 Mar	—	15-25 Mar	5 Sep	20 Nov	20 Sep-10 Oct
Williams Lake	20 Mar	—	25 Mar-19 Apr	—	—	—
Fort St. John	22 Apr	—	—	8 Sep	30 Oct	—
Ring-necked Duck						
Victoria	—	—	late Apr	—	—	early Oct
Vancouver	—	—	9 Apr	—	—	21 Oct
Okanagan	late Mar	—	late Apr-early May	Sep	—	Oct
Nakusp	20 Mar	—	24 Apr-9 May	—	17 Nov	—
Radium	19 Mar	—	15-22 Apr	13 Sep	18 Oct	—
Kamloops	9 Mar	—	8-28 Apr	—	—	5 Sep-10 Oct
Williams Lake	14 Mar	—	24 Mar-20 Apr	—	—	Oct
Fort St. John	4 Apr	—	—	—	30 Oct	—
Fort Nelson	13 May	—	19 May-28 May	—	—	30 Jul
Tufted Duck						
Vancouver	—	7 Jun	20 Apr	27 Sep	—	23 Oct
Greater Scaup						
Victoria	—	—	Apr	—	—	late Sep
Vancouver	—	—	23 Apr	—	—	17 Oct
Okanagan	—	—	Mar	25 Sep	—	Nov
Kamloops	7 Mar	20 May	5-28 Apr	9 Oct	30 Nov	5 Oct-10 Nov
Williams Lake	—	—	20 Mar-1 Apr	—	—	—
Lesser Scaup						
Victoria	—	—	Apr	—	—	late Sep
Vancouver	—	—	28 Apr	—	—	—
Okanagan	—	—	late Apr	18 Sep	—	Oct-Nov
Kamloops	26 Feb	25 May	10 Apr-10 May	5 Sep	—	1-30 Nov
Williams Lake	—	—	20 Mar-20 Apr	—	—	—
Prince George	3 Apr	—	—	—	29 Oct	—
Fort St. John	7 Apr	—	6-18 May	—	5 Nov	—
Fort Nelson	27 Apr	28 May	13-28 May	—	29 Sep	—
Harlequin Duck						
Okanagan	1 Apr	—	—	—	21 Nov	—
Kamloops	2 May	—	2-10 May	—	—	—
Oldsquaw						
Victoria	—	—	Apr	—	—	Oct
Vancouver	—	—	1 Apr	—	—	22 Oct
Okanagan	19 Apr	—	late Apr-early May	30 Sep	—	—
Kamloops	28 Apr	22 May	—	—	—	—
Williams Lake	—	—	21 Apr-8 May	—	—	14 Oct-3 Nov
Fort St. John	24 Apr	30 May	2-14 May	8 Oct	2 Nov	—
Fort Nelson	11 May	25 May	—	—	—	—
Black Scoter						
Victoria	—	30 Jun	Apr	1 Sep	—	Oct
Vancouver	—	1 Jun	23 Apr	4 Sep	—	16 Oct
Surf Scoter						
Victoria	—	—	Apr	—	—	Sep
Vancouver	—	—	13 May	—	—	29 Sep
Okanagan	24 Apr	—	mid-May	29 Sep	—	Oct
Radium	11 May	16 May	—	—	—	—
Kamloops	6 May	—	8-12 May	21 Oct	1 Nov	—
Williams Lake	24 Mar	—	29 Apr-15 May	—	—	Oct
Prince George	4 May	—	—	5 Oct	—	—
Fort St. John	1 May	—	15-20 May	29 Sep	—	29 Sep-10 Oct

Migration Chronology

	SPRING			AUTUMN		
	Early Arrival	Late Departure	Peak Movement	Early Arrival	Late Departure	Peak Movement
White-winged Scoter						
Victoria	—	—	Apr	—	—	Aug
Okanagan	—	—	mid-May	—	—	—
Nakusp	7 May	1 Jun	—	—	—	—
Radium	13 May	6 Jun	—	13 Aug	—	—
Kamloops	28 Apr	5 Jul	8-12 May	21 Oct	1 Nov	—
Williams Lake	—	—	8 May	—	—	10-20 Sep
Prince George	4 May	—	—	13 Oct	1 Nov	—
Fort St. John	27 Apr	—	19-24 May	26 Sep	5 Nov	26 Sep-8 Oct
Fort Nelson	7 May	—	20-27 May	—	30 Sep	—
Common Goldeneye						
Victoria	—	—	Apr	—	—	early Nov
Vancouver	—	—	7 Apr	—	—	18 Nov
Okanagan	—	—	late Mar-early Apr	3 Oct	—	Nov
Nakusp	—	—	15 Mar-15 Apr	—	—	—
Radium	11 Mar	—	26 Mar-6 Apr	—	—	20-30 Sep
Kamloops	1 Mar	—	4 Mar-24 Apr	18 Aug	—	3-28 Nov
Williams Lake	2 Mar	—	15 Mar-20 Apr	—	—	1-26 Nov
Fort St. John	6 Mar	—	6-12 May	3 Oct	18 Nov	15-30 Oct
Fort Nelson	24 Apr	—	—	30 Aug	—	—
Barrow's Goldeneye						
Victoria	—	21 May	1-15 Apr	19 Sep	—	early Nov
Vancouver	—	—	16 Apr	—	—	1 Nov
Okanagan	30 Mar	—	late Apr-early May	—	—	late Sep-Oct
Radium	30 Mar	—	25 Apr-5 May	—	9 Oct	—
Kamloops	1 Mar	—	8 Apr-5 May	—	—	—
Williams Lake	9 Mar	—	18 Mar-19 Apr	—	—	Oct
Prince George	4 Apr	—	—	—	1 Nov	—
Fort St. John	16 Apr	—	—	—	4 Nov	1-15 Oct
Fort Nelson	5 May	—	18-22 May	—	30 Sep	—
Bufflehead						
Victoria	—	—	Apr	—	—	mid-Oct
Vancouver	—	—	25 Apr	—	—	3 Nov
Masset	—	28 May	mid-Apr	21 Sep	—	—
Okanagan	—	—	late Apr-early May	—	—	late Oct-early Nov
Nakusp	18 Mar	—	10-25 Apr	—	23 Nov	early Nov
Radium	28 Mar	—	22-30 Apr	—	—	20-26 Oct
Kamloops	26 Feb	—	25 Apr-10 May	—	—	20 Oct-10 Nov
Williams Lake	10 Mar	—	1-20 Apr	—	—	20 Oct-10 Nov
Prince George	2 Apr	—	—	—	1 Nov	—
Fort St. John	10 Apr	—	—	—	11 Nov	15-30 Oct
Fort Nelson	24 Apr	—	11-27 May	—	25 Sep	—
Hooded Merganser						
Vancouver	—	—	15 Apr	—	—	2 Nov
Masset	—	29 Apr	mid-Apr	21 Sep	—	—
Okanagan	—	—	—	—	—	late Nov-early Dec
Nakusp	8 Apr	—	—	—	11 Nov	—
Radium	28 Mar	—	—	—	9 Nov	14-20 Oct
Kamloops	1 Mar	—	20 May	20 Aug	1 Dec	10 Oct-10 Nov
Williams Lake	—	—	24 Mar-22 Apr	—	—	Nov
Fort St. John	17 Apr	—	—	—	4 Nov	—
Common Merganser						
Okanagan	—	—	Apr-early May	—	—	Nov-Dec
Radium	—	—	—	—	—	5-13 Nov
Kamloops	26 Feb	—	3 Mar-8 Apr	5 Sep	17 Dec	21 Oct
Williams Lake	—	—	9 Mar-22 Apr	—	—	Nov
Fort St. John	2 Mar	12 Apr	—	7 Oct	2 Nov	—

	SPRING			AUTUMN		
	Early Arrival	Late Departure	Peak Movement	Early Arrival	Late Departure	Peak Movement
Red-breasted Merganser						
Victoria	—	—	Apr	—	—	Oct
Vancouver	—	27 May	12 Apr	1 Sep	—	7 Oct
Okanagan	early Mar	—	early May	—	—	—
Radium	—	—	—	—	—	12-17 Oct
Kamloops	—	—	—	2 Nov	29 Dec	—
Williams Lake	—	—	14 Apr-13 May	—	—	Oct-Nov
Fort St. John	25 Apr	—	—	—	27 Oct	—
Ruddy Duck						
Victoria	—	12 Jun	Apr	2 Sep	—	early Oct
Vancouver	—	—	15 Apr	—	—	29 Oct
Okanagan	29 Feb	—	late Apr-early May	—	—	Sep-Oct
Kamloops	24 Feb	—	25 Apr-10 May	—	30 Nov	10-20 Sep
Williams Lake	7 Mar	—	31 Mar-27 Apr	—	—	—
Prince George	15 Apr	—	16-26 May	25 Sep	4 Nov	—
Fort St. John	15 Apr	—	—	16 Sep	4 Nov	—

APPENDIX 2

Summary of Christmas Bird Counts in British Columbia: 1957 through 1984

The following tables summarize by species, the Christmas Bird Count data for loons through waterfowl in British Columbia. Only official Christmas Bird Counts, as published in *Audubon Field Notes* and *American Birds* for the period 1957 through 1984 have been used. Highest provincial, interior, and coastal totals are the highest sums for all official counts in any one year in the province. "Count locality" refers to the most recent name under which that count has been published (e.g. Masset, Fig. 340). The time span of count activity for a particular location is shown under "Count years"; discontinuities can be determined by comparing "Count years" with "Total counts." "Frequency of occurrence" indicates the percentage of the counts in a locality on which a species has been recorded. The general abundance of the species over the count periods is shown by the range of values in the last 3 columns. The highest and lowest numbers recorded are given. An asterisk following a "High" number indicates that some caution is required in interpreting the data. Refer to the respective species account or to the note at the end of that species' entry in the table. The median has been chosen as an indicator of the "usual" value when the species does occur. It is the middle value of the data set and will lie closer to the low value when a species frequently occurs in small numbers and closer to the high value when a species rarely occurs in small numbers. In a symmetrically distributed data set the median is an unbiased and consistent estimate of the mean (Zar 1974). Counts of zero have not been used as the "Low" value but they can be determined using the values under "Frequency of occurrence" and "Total counts."

For example, there is about a 90% chance of seeing a Red-throated Loon on the Ladner Christmas Bird Count and the probability that this is an accurate estimate of the chance of seeing the bird is high because there is a long history of counts on which to base this estimate. Similarly, if you see the species you are likely to see about 30 birds, but more than 140 or less than 5 would be exceptional.

See Figure 177 for the location of official Christmas Bird Counts and Table 6 for the number of counts in each locality.

Figure 340. *Margo E. Hearne (left) and Peter J. Hamel counting birds at Delkatla Inlet during the Masset Christmas Bird Count, 15 December 1985 (David Phillips).*

Red-throated Loon

Highest provincial total: 433 (1984)
Highest interior total: Not recorded
Highest coastal total: 433 (1984)

Count locality	Count years	Total counts	Frequency of occurrence (%)	Range of total counts when species occurred		
				Low	Median	High
Coastal						
Campbell River	1972-1984	13	69	1	1	9
Comox	1961-1984	23	96	1	6	17
Deep Bay	1975-1984	10	80	1	6	11
Duncan	1970-1984	15	100	2	4	20
Kitimat	1974-1984	7	57	1	2	5
Ladner	1957-1984	26	92	5	34	140
Masset	1982-1984	3	100	1	1	1
Nanaimo	1963-1984	19	63	1	6	13
North Saanich	1960	1	100			9
Pender Islands	1964-1984	19	53	2	10	23
Pitt Meadows	1972-1984	13	15	1		1
Prince Rupert	1980-1984	5	100	2	7	18
Sayward	1973-1984	12	17	1		1
Skidegate Inlet	1982-1984	3	100	1	1	2
Sooke	1983-1984	2	100	14		49
Squamish	1980-1984	5	100	13	20	34
Sunshine Coast	1979-1984	6	67	1	1	2
Surrey	1960-1966	7	43	2	3	5
Vancouver	1957-1984	28	100	3	33	205
Victoria	1958-1984	27	100	4	15	147
White Rock	1971-1984	14	100	4	25	241

Pacific Loon

Highest provincial total: 3,232 (1977)
Highest interior total: 1 (1980,1981)
Highest coastal total: 3,232 (1977)

Count locality	Count years	Total counts	Frequency of occurrence (%)	Range of total counts when species occurred		
				Low	Median	High
Interior						
Oliver/Osoyoos	1979-1984	6	33	1		1
Coastal						
Bella Bella	1976	1	50			4
Campbell River	1972-1984	13	100	18	55	515
Comox	1961-1984	23	96	2	126	1,585
Deep Bay	1975-1984	10	100	13	376	466
Duncan	1970-1984	15	100	3	10	101
Hecate Strait	1980	1	100			30
Kitimat	1974-1984	7	29	3		3
Ladner	1957-1984	26	96	1	6	197
Masset	1982-1984	3	100	2	13	29
Nanaimo	1963-1984	19	84	2	16	71
North Saanich	1960	1	100			241
Pender Islands	1964-1984	19	89	15	374	1,626
Prince Rupert	1980-1984	5	100	1	8	11
Sayward	1973-1984	12	58	1	3	30
Skidegate Inlet	1982-1984	3	100	19	22	132
Sooke	1983-1984	2	100	30		65
Squamish	1980-1984	5	60	2	4	12
Sunshine Coast	1979-1984	6	33	2		5
Surrey	1960-1966	7	14			6
Vancouver	1957-1984	28	86	1	10	55
Victoria	1958-1984	27	96	5	37	267
White Rock	1971-1984	14	93	1	7	174

Common Loon

Highest provincial total: 916 (1983)
Highest interior total: 26 (1981)
Highest coastal total: 907 (1983)

Count locality	Count years	Total counts	Frequency of occurrence (%)	Range of total counts when species occurred		
				Low	Median	High
Interior						
Kamloops	1984	1	100			2
Kelowna	1981	1	100			4
Nakusp	1979-1984	6	17			2
Oliver/Osoyoos	1979-1984	6	83	1	5	10
Penticton	1974-1984	9	89	1	2	4
Revelstoke	1981-1984	4	25			2
Shuswap Lake	1972-1984	13	54	1	2	2
Vaseux Lake	1974-1984	11	55	1	1	2
Vernon	1975-1984	10	80	1	4	8
Yoho National Park	1975-1981	5	20			1
Coastal						
Bella Bella	1976	1	100			55
Campbell River	1972-1984	13	100	17	50	107
Comox	1961-1984	23	100	13	62	136
Deep Bay	1975-1984	10	100	50	85	113
Duncan	1970-1984	15	100	11	21	77
Hecate Strait	1980	1	100			5
Kitimat	1974-1984	7	57	1	3	5
Ladner	1957-1984	26	100	9	54	119
Masset	1982-1984	3	100	10	47	60
Nanaimo	1963-1984	19	100	3	21	82
North Saanich	1960	1	100			23
Pender Islands	1964-1984	19	95	2	10	62
Pitt Meadows	1972-1984	13	23	1	2	3
Port Alberni	1975	1	100			8
Prince Rupert	1980-1984	5	100	4	19	39
Sayward	1973-1984	12	50	1	2	3
Skidegate Inlet	1982-1984	3	100	38	44	63
Sooke	1983-1984	2	100	34		86
Squamish	1980-1984	5	100	9	12	22
Sunshine Coast	1979-1984	6	100	12	36	62
Surrey	1960-1966	7	100	4	7	18
Vancouver	1957-1984	28	100	6	40	110
Victoria	1958-1984	27	100	23	59	109
White Rock	1971-1984	14	100	24	48	87

Yellow-billed Loon

Highest provincial total: 8 (1983)
Highest interior total: 2 (1982,1983)
Highest coastal total: 6 (1983)

Count locality	Count years	Total counts	Frequency of occurrence (%)	Range of total counts when species occurred		
				Low	Median	High
Interior						
Oliver/Osoyoos	1979-1984	6	33	1		1
Vaseux Lake	1974-1984	11	18	1		1
Vernon	1975-1984	10	20	1		1
Coastal						
Deep Bay	1975-1984	10	20	1		1
Duncan	1970-1984	15	7			1
Ladner	1957-1984	26	23	1	1	1
Masset	1982-1984	3	33			3
Nanaimo	1963-1984	19	5			1
Pender Islands	1964-1984	19	5			2
Prince Rupert	1980-1984	5	20			2
Sooke	1983-1984	2	50			1
Squamish	1980-1984	5	20			1
Vancouver	1957-1984	28	4			2
Victoria	1958-1984	27	11	1	1	1
White Rock	1971-1984	14	29	1	1	1

Pied-billed Grebe

Highest provincial total: 318 (1983)
Highest interior total: 142 (1981)
Highest coastal total: 193 (1983)

Count locality	Count years	Total counts	Frequency of occurrence (%)	Range of total counts when species occurred		
				Low	Median	High
Interior						
Kelowna	1981	1	100			8
Lake Windermere	1979-1984	6	33	1		1
Oliver/Osoyoos	1979-1984	6	100	8	18	65
Penticton	1974-1984	9	100	2	5	31
Revelstoke	1981-1984	4	50	1		2
Shuswap Lake	1972-1984	13	15	2		3
Vaseux Lake	1974-1984	11	100	2	16	41
Vernon	1975-1984	10	90	2	12	26
Coastal						
Campbell River	1972-1984	13	23	1	1	1
Chilliwack	1972-1984	11	82	1	10	18
Comox	1961-1984	23	57	1	2	8
Deep Bay	1975-1984	10	20	1		1
Dewdney	1967	1	100			4
Duncan	1970-1984	15	100	1	4	10
Ladner	1957-1984	26	73	1	5	101
Nanaimo	1963-1984	19	89	1	4	18
Pender Islands	1964-1984	19	53	1	1	3
Pitt Meadows	1972-1984	13	92	1	3	12
Port Alberni	1975	1	100			3
Sooke	1983-1984	2	100	3		15
Squamish	1980-1984	5	80	1	2	2
Sunshine Coast	1979-1984	6	83	1	4	7
Surrey	1960-1966	7	28	1		1
Vancouver	1957-1984	28	96	1	7	35
Victoria	1958-1984	27	100	7	32	84
White Rock	1971-1984	14	64	1	3	6

Horned Grebe

Highest provincial total: 2,694 (1977)
Highest interior total: 287 (1980)
Highest coastal total: 2,655 (1977)

Count locality	Count years	Total counts	Frequency of occurrence (%)	Range of total counts when species occurred		
				Low	Median	High
Interior						
Fauquier	1984	1	100			27
Kelowna	1981	1	100			13
Nakusp	1979-1984	6	67	1	12	48
Oliver/Osoyoos	1979-1984	6	67	3	8	36
Penticton	1974-1984	9	100	14	65	90
Shuswap Lake	1972-1984	13	92	2	9	15
Vaseux Lake	1974-1984	11	82	1	5	77
Vernon	1975-1984	10	100	16	56	163
Coastal						
Bella Bella	1976	1	100			18
Campbell River	1972-1984	13	100	7	35	77
Chilliwack	1972-1984	11	45	1	2	5
Comox	1961-1984	23	100	10	76	158
Deep Bay	1975-1984	10	100	56	138	189
Dewdney	1967	1	100			1
Duncan	1970-1984	15	100	12	104	823
Kitimat	1974-1984	7	43	1	3	8
Ladner	1957-1984	26	100	8	90	293
Masset	1982-1984	3	100	5	8	10
Nanaimo	1963-1984	19	100	7	63	200
North Saanich	1960	1	100			246
Pender Islands	1964-1984	19	100	3	127	249
Pitt Meadows	1972-1984	13	85	1	3	57
Port Alberni	1975	1	100			9
Sayward	1973-1984	12	75	1	2	3
Skidegate Inlet	1982-1984	3	67	27		43
Sooke	1983-1984	2	100	68		139
Squamish	1980-1984	5	100	10	21	39
Sunshine Coast	1979-1984	6	100	26	44	58
Surrey	1960-1966	7	100	10	24	30
Vancouver	1957-1984	28	100	7	184	417
Victoria	1958-1984	27	100	15	519	1,153
White Rock	1971-1984	14	100	21	55	458

Red-necked Grebe

Highest provincial total: 1,020 (1983)
Highest interior total: 116 (1980)
Highest coastal total: 994 (1983)

Count locality	Count years	Total counts	Frequency of occurrence (%)	Range of total counts when species occurred		
				Low	Median	High
Interior						
Kelowna	1981	1	100			8
Nakusp	1979-1984	6	33	44		91*
Oliver/Osoyoos	1979-1984	6	83	2	5	12
Penticton	1974-1984	9	100	2	4	11
Shuswap Lake	1972-1984	13	54	1	2	10
Vaseux Lake	1974-1984	11	18	1		2
Vernon	1975-1984	10	90	1	6	21
Coastal						
Bella Bella	1976	1	100			6
Campbell River	1972-1984	13	100	2	25	76
Chilliwack	1972-1984	11	18	1		1
Comox	1961-1984	23	100	5	21	119
Deep Bay	1975-1984	10	100	9	22	74
Duncan	1970-1984	15	100	12	27	69
Kitimat	1974-1984	7	29	2		18
Ladner	1957-1984	26	96	1	12	227
Masset	1982-1984	3	100	19	44	45
Nanaimo	1963-1984	19	95	6	17	75
North Saanich	1960	1	100			38
Pender Islands	1964-1984	19	100	2	15	121
Pitt Meadows	1972-1984	13	8			1
Port Alberni	1975	1	100			2
Port Clements	1984	1	100			2
Prince Rupert	1980-1984	5	80	14	18	38
Sayward	1973-1984	12	42	1	3	4
Skidegate Inlet	1982-1984	3	100	67	88	101
Sooke	1983-1984	2	100	40		66
Squamish	1980-1984	5	100	5	20	25
Sunshine Coast	1979-1984	6	100	2	42	126
Surrey	1960-1966	7	100	1	2	13
Vancouver	1957-1984	28	100	4	43	119
Victoria	1958-1984	27	100	37	118	258
White Rock	1971-1984	14	100	2	23	73

Eared Grebe

Highest provincial total: 493 (1980)
Highest interior total: 18 (1981)
Highest coastal total: 490 (1980)

Count locality	Count years	Total counts	Frequency of occurrence (%)	Range of total counts when species occurred		
				Low	Median	High
Interior						
Kelowna	1981	1	100	1		14
Penticton	1974-1984	9	33	1	1	1
Shuswap Lake	1972-1984	13	15	1		2
Vernon	1975-1984	10	80	1	3	7
Coastal						
Campbell River	1972-1984	13	38	2	4	10
Chilliwack	1972-1984	11	9			1
Comox	1961-1984	23	52	1	4	12
Deep Bay	1975-1984	10	80	1	4	8
Duncan	1970-1984	15	87	1	2	10
Ladner	1957-1984	26	46	1	1	8
Nanaimo	1963-1984	19	68	1	5	18
North Saanich	1960	1	100			36
Pender Islands	1964-1984	19	53	1	4	461*
Sooke	1983-1984	2	50			1
Surrey	1960-1966	7	29	1		2
Vancouver	1957-1984	28	89	1	6	50
Victoria	1958-1984	27	96	1	33	123
White Rock	1971-1984	14	93	1	2	11

Christmas Bird Counts

Western Grebe

Highest provincial total: 24,967 (1977*)
Highest interior total: 89 (1983)
Highest coastal total: 24,963 (1977)

Count locality	Count years	Total counts	Frequency of occurrence (%)	Range of total counts when species occurred		
				Low	Median	High
Interior						
Kelowna	1981	1	100			7
Nakusp	1979-1984	6	33	1	3	
Oliver/Osoyoos	1979-1984	6	83	3	6	23
Penticton	1974-1984	9	78	1	5	25
Revelstoke	1981-1984	4	50	1		2
Shuswap Lake	1972-1984	13	23	1	3	41
Vaseux Lake	1974-1984	11	82	1	1	3
Vernon	1975-1984	10	100	1	8	76
Coastal						
Bella Bella	1976	1	100			62
Campbell River	1972-1984	13	77	2	14	364
Chilliwack	1972-1984	11	18	1		1
Comox	1961-1984	23	100	7	794	2,384
Deep Bay	1975-1984	10	100	600	4,023	15,174
Dewdney	1967	1	100			1
Duncan	1970-1984	15	100	121	3,415	7,215
Kitimat	1974-1984	7	14			16
Ladner	1957-1984	26	100	36	376	1,067
Masset	1982-1984	3	100	2	4	6
Nanaimo	1963-1984	19	95	22	306	2,000
North Saanich	1960	1	100			582
Pender Islands	1964-1984	19	100	6	188	1,356
Pitt Meadows	1972-1984	13	77	1	5	16
Port Alberni	1975	1	100			1,280
Prince Rupert	1980-1984	5	80	2	31	34
Sayward	1973-1984	12	17	2		2
Skidegate Inlet	1982-1984	3	100	13	140	227
Sooke	1983-1984	2	100	14		97
Squamish	1980-1984	5	100	87	331	925
Sunshine Coast	1979-1984	6	100	326	518	836
Surrey	1960-1966	7	100	2	13	34
Vancouver	1957-1984	28	100	491	4,917	15,450
Victoria	1958-1984	27	100	45	755	2,842
White Rock	1971-1984	14	100	14	38	380

Northern Fulmar

Highest provincial total: 1 (1964)
Highest interior total: Not recorded
Highest coastal total: 1 (1964)

Count locality	Count years	Total counts	Frequency of occurrence (%)	Range of total counts when species occurred		
				Low	Median	High
Coastal						
Victoria	1958-1984	27	4			1

Sooty Shearwater

Highest provincial total: 40 (1977)
Highest interior total: Not recorded
Highest coastal total: 40 (1977)

Count locality	Count years	Total counts	Frequency of occurrence (%)	Range of total counts when species occurred		
				Low	Median	High
Coastal						
Victoria	1958-1984	27	7	1		40*

Short-tailed Shearwater

Highest provincial total: 2 (1977)
Highest interior total: Not recorded
Highest coastal total: 2 (1977)

Count locality	Count years	Total counts	Frequency of occurrence (%)	Range of total counts when species occurred		
				Low	Median	High
Coastal						
Victoria	1958-1984	27	4			2*

Double-crested Cormorant

Highest provincial total: 1,807 (1983)
Highest interior total: Not recorded
Highest coastal total: 1,807 (1983)

Count locality	Count years	Total counts	Frequency of occurrence (%)	Range of total counts when species occurred		
				Low	Median	High
Coastal						
Bella Bella	1976	1	100			1
Campbell River	1972-1984	13	100	4	45	155
Comox	1961-1984	23	100	1	10	45
Deep Bay	1975-1984	10	100	27	45	260
Duncan	1970-1984	15	100	14	64	136
Hecate Strait	1980	1	100			2
Ladner	1957-1984	26	100	6	193	336
Masset	1982-1984	3	100	2	13	13
Nanaimo	1963-1984	19	100	2	43	146
North Saanich	1960	1	100			19
Pender Islands	1964-1984	19	95	9	65	135
Pitt Meadows	1972-1984	13	69	1	1	33
Port Alberni	1975	1	100			6
Prince Rupert	1980-1984	5	60	3	5	5
Sayward	1973-1984	12	75	1	2	20
Skidegate Inlet	1982-1984	3	100	4	9	13
Sooke	1983-1984	2	100	122		194
Squamish	1980-1984	5	100	5	17	33
Sunshine Coast	1979-1984	6	100	19	55	94
Surrey	1960-1966	7	43	1	1	1
Vancouver	1957-1984	28	100	51	230	379
Victoria	1958-1984	27	100	43	119	636
White Rock	1971-1984	14	100	20	43	101

Brandt's Cormorant

Highest provincial total: 4,986 (1979)
Highest interior total: Not recorded
Highest coastal total: 4,986 (1979)

Count locality	Count years	Total counts	Frequency of occurrence (%)	Range of total counts when species occurred		
				Low	Median	High
Coastal						
Bella Bella	1976	1	100			10
Campbell River	1972-1984	13	69	1	16	50
Comox	1961-1984	23	70	1	2	12
Deep Bay	1975-1984	10	100	2	12	45
Duncan	1970-1984	15	67	2	17	46
Hecate Strait	1980	1	100			17
Ladner	1957-1984	26	92	1	8	336
Masset	1982-1984	3	67	12		28
Nanaimo	1963-1984	19	95	1	29	2,262
North Saanich	1960	1	100			1
Pender Islands	1964-1984	19	95	1	438	3,667
Port Alberni	1975	1	100			5
Prince Rupert	1980-1984	5	20			7
Sayward	1973-1984	12	8			1
Skidegate Inlet	1982-1984	3	100	2	3	10
Sooke	1983-1984	2	100	141		1,219
Squamish	1980-1984	5	60	2	2	2
Sunshine Coast	1979-1984	6	67	1	3	4
Surrey	1960-1966	7	86	1	4	9
Vancouver	1957-1984	28	86	2	13	74
Victoria	1958-1984	27	96	2	141	1,664
White Rock	1971-1984	14	36	1	2	2

Pelagic Cormorant

Highest provincial total: 1,876 (1983)
Highest interior total: Not recorded
Highest coastal total: 1,876 (1983)

Count locality	Count years	Total counts	Frequency of occurrence (%)	Range of total counts when species occurred		
				Low	Median	High
Coastal						
Bella Bella	1976	1	100			5
Comox	1961-1984	23	100	12	71	219
Deep Bay	1975-1984	10	100	65	178	391
Duncan	1970-1984	15	100	2	9	43
Hecate Strait	1980	1	100			164
Kitimat	1974-1984	7	57	1	2	2
Ladner	1957-1984	26	96	3	34	81
Masset	1982-1984	3	100	40	123	164
Nanaimo	1963-1984	19	100	3	62	1,047
North Saanich	1960	1	100			183
Pender Islands	1964-1984	19	89	21	76	223
Port Alberni	1975	1	100			6
Prince Rupert	1980-1984	5	100	16	29	39
Sayward	1973-1984	12	75	1	6	13
Skidegate Inlet	1982-1984	3	100	73	214	300
Sooke	1983-1984	2	100	83		295
Squamish	1980-1984	5	100	7	11	42
Sunshine Coast	1979-1984	6	100	15	19	71
Vancouver	1957-1984	28	100	52	111	236
Victoria	1958-1984	27	100	92	434	2,345
White Rock	1971-1984	14	100	3	13	49

American Bittern

Highest provincial total: 13 (1984)
Highest interior total: Not recorded
Highest coastal total: 13 (1984)

Count locality	Count years	Total counts	Frequency of occurrence (%)	Range of total counts when species occurred		
				Low	Median	High
Coastal						
Duncan	1970-1984	15	20	1	1	1
Ladner	1957-1984	26	58	1	3	9
Nanaimo	1963-1984	19	26	1	1	2
Pitt Meadows	1972-1984	13	54	1	1	2
Vancouver	1957-1984	28	25	1	2	3
Victoria	1958-1984	27	4			1
White Rock	1971-1984	14	14	1		1

Great Blue Heron

Highest provincial total: 1,202 (1983)
Highest interior total: 72 (1981)
Highest coastal total: 1,132 (1983)

Count locality	Count years	Total counts	Frequency of occurrence (%)	Range of total counts when species occurred		
				Low	Median	High
Interior						
Cranbrook	1984	1	100			1
Kamloops	1984	1	100			2
Kelowna	1981	1	100			18
Lake Windermere	1979-1984	6	83	1	2	5
Nakusp	1979-1984	6	17			1
Oliver/Osoyoos	1979-1984	6	100	1	14	18
Penticton	1974-1984	9	78	1	2	10
Revelstoke	1981-1984	4	50	2		3
Shuswap Lake	1972-1984	13	46	1	1	5
Vaseux Lake	1974-1984	11	100	2	8	18
Vernon	1975-1984	10	100	4	7	29
Coastal						
Bella Bella	1976	1	100			11
Campbell River	1972-1984	13	100	12	25	63
Chilliwack	1972-1984	11	100	11	33	54
Comox	1961-1984	23	100	2	36	80
Deep Bay	1975-1984	10	100	3	17	24
Dewdney	1967	1	100			6
Duncan	1970-1984	15	100	18	56	132
Kitimat	1974-1984	7	71	1	1	4
Ladner	1957-1984	26	100	3	116	251
Masset	1982-1984	3	100	4	14	15
Nanaimo	1963-1984	19	100	1	18	74
North Saanich	1960	1	100			9
Pender Islands	1964-1984	19	100	1	11	27
Pitt Meadows	1972-1984	13	100	52	65	152
Port Alberni	1975	1	100			17
Prince Rupert	1980-1984	5	100	16	36	40
Sayward	1973-1984	12	100	1	4	8
Skidegate Inlet	1982-1984	3	100	8	10	15
Sooke	1983-1984	2	100	9		27
Squamish	1980-1984	5	100	13	18	26
Sunshine Coast	1979-1984	6	100	26	55	86
Surrey	1960-1966	7	86	1	10	11
Terrace	1963-1984	20	15	1	1	1
Vancouver	1957-1984	28	100	35	108	248
Victoria	1958-1984	27	100	10	52	152
White Rock	1971-1984	14	100	19	86	132

Great Egret

Highest provincial total: 1 (1978)
Highest interior total: Not recorded
Highest coastal total: 1 (1978)

Count locality	Count years	Total counts	Frequency of occurrence (%)	Range of total counts when species occurred		
				Low	Median	High
Coastal						
Vancouver	1957-1984	28	4			1

Cattle Egret

Highest provincial total: 4 (1979)
Highest interior total: Not recorded
Highest coastal total: 4 (1979)

Count locality	Count years	Total counts	Frequency of occurrence (%)	Range of total counts when species occurred		
				Low	Median	High
Coastal						
Duncan	1970-1984	15	7			1
Ladner	1957-1984	26	4			3
Masset	1982-1984	3	33			1
Pitt Meadows	1972-1984	13	8			1
Skidegate Inlet	1982-1984	3	33			1
Sunshine Coast	1979-1984	6	17			1
Vancouver	1957-1984	28	4			1
Victoria	1958-1984	27	7	1		2
White Rock	1971-1984	14	7			1

Green-backed Heron

Highest provincial total: 7 (1980)
Highest interior total: Not recorded
Highest coastal total: 7 (1980)

Count locality	Count years	Total counts	Frequency of occurrence (%)	Range of total counts when species occurred		
				Low	Median	High
Coastal						
Chilliwack	1972-1984	11	9			5
Comox	1961-1984	23	4			1
Duncan	1970-1984	15	67	1	1	2
Ladner	1957-1984	26	8	1		1
Pitt Meadows	1972-1984	13	8			1
Vancouver	1957-1984	28	11	1	1	1

Black-crowned Night-Heron

Highest provincial total: 1 (1983,1984)
Highest interior total: Not recorded
Highest coastal total: 1 (1983,1984)

Count locality	Count years	Total counts	Frequency of occurrence (%)	Range of total counts when species occurred		
				Low	Median	High
Coastal						
Ladner	1957-1984	26	8	1		1

Tundra Swan

Highest provincial total: 452 (1983)
Highest interior total: 441 (1983)
Highest coastal total: 122 (1974)

Count locality	Count years	Total counts	Frequency of occurrence (%)	Range of total counts when species occurred		
				Low	Median	High
Interior						
Kamloops	1984	1	100			81
Kelowna	1981	1	100			3
Oliver/Osoyoos	1979-1984	6	50	2	5	6
Revelstoke	1981-1984	4	25			9
Shuswap Lake	1972-1984	13	77	2	15	441
Vaseux Lake	1974-1984	11	55	5	11	19
Coastal						
Chilliwack	1972-1984	11	36	11	59	65
Comox	1961-1984	23	4			1
Duncan	1970-1984	15	60	1	1	7
Ladner	1957-1984	26	73	1	20	88
Nanaimo	1963-1984	19	16	1	2	4
Pitt Meadows	1972-1984	13	23	3	6	8
Squamish	1980-1984	5	20			1
Terrace	1963-1984	20	5			11
Vancouver	1957-1984	28	32	1	3	17
Victoria	1958-1984	27	19	1	1	41*
White Rock	1971-1984	14	7			1

Trumpeter Swan

Highest provincial total: 1,673 (1984)
Highest interior total: 13 (1983)
Highest coastal total: 1,662 (1984)

Count locality	Count years	Total counts	Frequency of occurrence (%)	Range of total counts when species occurred		
				Low	Median	High
Interior						
Oliver/Osoyoos	1979-1984	6	17			10
Shuswap Lake	1972-1984	13	23	1	2	13
Coastal						
Campbell River	1972-1984	13	92	2	20	58
Chilliwack	1972-1984	11	36	2	5	8
Comox	1961-1984	23	87	1	118	712
Deep Bay	1975-1984	10	100	8	36	221
Duncan	1970-1984	15	93	1	15	112
Kitimat	1974-1984	7	43	4	5	11
Ladner	1957-1984	26	46	1	51	132
Masset	1982-1984	3	100	9	16	26
Nanaimo	1963-1984	19	68	14	104	243
Pitt Meadows	1972-1984	13	54	6	42	154
Port Alberni	1975	1	100			178
Port Clements	1984	1	100			45
Sayward	1973-1984	12	100	32	75	98
Skidegate Inlet	1982-1984	3	33			3
Squamish	1980-1984	5	100	13	21	62
Terrace	1963-1984	20	45	1	8	31
Vancouver	1957-1984	28	18	1	5	18
Victoria	1958-1984	27	22	2	15	49
White Rock	1971-1984	14	7			1

Mute Swan

Highest provincial total: 186 (1983)
Highest interior total: 5 (1979,81)
Highest coastal total: 186 (1983)

Count locality	Count years	Total counts	Frequency of occurrence (%)	Range of total counts when species occurred		
				Low	Median	High
Interior						
Kelowna	1981	1	100			2
Oliver/Osoyoos	1979-1984	6	17			4
Penticton	1974-1984	9	33	2	2	3
Vaseux Lake	1974-1984	11	45	1	1	2
Vernon	1975-1984	10	10			1
Coastal						
Duncan	1970-1984	15	100	7	56	123
Ladner	1957-1984	26	8	1		2
Pender Islands	1964-1984	19	11	1		1
Sooke	1983-1984	2	100	1		4
Sunshine Coast	1979-1984	6	33	1		1
Vancouver	1957-1984	28	4			2
Victoria	1958-1984	27	70	16	33	77

Greater White-fronted Goose

Highest provincial total: 357 (1979)
Highest interior total: 1 (1978)
Highest coastal total: 357 (1979)

Count locality	Count years	Total counts	Frequency of occurrence (%)	Range of total counts when species occurred		
				Low	Median	High
Interior						
Vernon	1975-1984	10	10			1
Coastal						
Campbell River	1972-1984	13	23	1	1	2
Chilliwack	1972-1984	11	27	1	1	338
Comox	1961-1984	23	9	1		2
Duncan	1970-1984	15	47	1	4	8
Ladner	1957-1984	26	42	1	2	12
Nanaimo	1963-1984	19	16	1	1	10
North Saanich	1960	1	100			9
Pitt Meadows	1972-1984	13	8			1
Port Alberni	1975	1	100			1
Vancouver	1957-1984	28	36	1	1	3
Victoria	1958-1984	27	59	1	2	15
White Rock	1971-1984	14	7			3

Snow Goose

Highest provincial total: 15,103 (1978)
Highest interior total: 5 (1982)
Highest coastal total: 15,103 (1978)

Count locality	Count years	Total counts	Frequency of occurrence (%)	Range of total counts when species occurred Low	Median	High
Interior						
Kelowna	1981	1	100			2
Oliver/Osoyoos	1979-1984	6	17			5
Vernon	1975-1984	10	10			2
Coastal						
Chilliwack	1972-1984	11	9			1
Deep Bay	1975-1984	10	10			1
Ladner	1957-1984	26	81	13	3,019	15,101
Nanaimo	1963-1984	19	5			1
Pitt Meadows	1972-1984	13	15	3		50
Sunshine Coast	1979-1984	6	33	1		3
Vancouver	1957-1984	28	68	1	22	1,000
Victoria	1958-1984	27	37	1	1	4
White Rock	1971-1984	14	43	1	28	259

Emperor Goose

Highest provincial total: 1 (1977)
Highest interior total: Not recorded
Highest coastal total: 1 (1977)

Count locality	Count years	Total counts	Frequency of occurrence (%)	Range of total counts when species occurred Low	Median	High
Coastal						
Ladner	1957-1984	26	4			1

Brant

Highest provincial total: 600 (1960)
Highest interior total: Not recorded
Highest coastal total: 600 (1960)

Count locality	Count years	Total counts	Frequency of occurrence (%)	Range of total counts when species occurred Low	Median	High
Coastal						
Campbell River	1972-1984	13	8			1
Ladner	1957-1984	26	81	1	24	600
Nanaimo	1963-1984	19	5			3
Skidegate Inlet	1982-1984	3	100	89	129	283
Surrey	1960-1966	7	43	4	5	5
Vancouver	1957-1984	28	14	1	2	3
Victoria	1958-1984	27	37	1	6	13
White Rock	1971-1984	14	21	15	27	33

Christmas Bird Counts

Canada Goose

Highest provincial total: 11,307 (1981)
Highest interior total: 5,644 (1981)
Highest coastal total: 7,062 (1984)

Count locality	Count years	Total counts	Frequency of occurrence (%)	Range of total counts when species occurred		
				Low	Median	High
Interior						
Fauquier	1984	1	100			55
Kamloops	1984	1	100			337
Kelowna	1981	1	100			963
Lake Windermere	1979-1984	6	83	2	16	50
Nakusp	1979-1984	6	83	21	62	107
Oliver/Osoyoos	1979-1984	6	100	33	297	793
Penticton	1974-1984	9	100	218	725	866
Revelstoke	1981-1984	4	100	625	656	1,097
Shuswap Lake	1972-1984	13	100	9	121	362
Smithers	1977-1984	8	13			4
Vaseux Lake	1974-1984	11	100	4	234	501
Vernon	1975-1984	10	100	175	363	1,690
Coastal						
Campbell River	1972-1984	13	62	1	2	30
Chilliwack	1972-1984	11	91	19	424	743
Comox	1961-1984	23	52	2	7	41
Deep Bay	1975-1984	10	60	6	14	18
Dewdney	1967	1	100			1
Duncan	1970-1984	15	93	48	301	468
Kitimat	1974-1984	7	86	4	60	70
Ladner	1957-1984	26	77	1	466	1,731
Masset	1982-1984	3	100	596	680	830
Nanaimo	1963-1984	19	68	4	98	608
Pender Islands	1964-1984	19	32	1	50	1,168
Pitt Meadows	1972-1984	13	77	2	639	1,315
Port Alberni	1975	1	100			11
Port Clements	1984	1	100			230
Prince Rupert	1980-1984	5	60	10	44	50
Sayward	1973-1984	12	25	1	8	9
Skidegate Inlet	1982-1984	3	67	47		77
Sunshine Coast	1979-1984	6	100	1	28	49
Surrey	1960-1966	7	14			26
Terrace	1963-1984	20	25	9	24	139
Vancouver	1957-1984	28	100	8	242	1,721
Victoria	1958-1984	27	100	21	113	543
White Rock	1971-1984	14	86	2	403	1,454

Wood Duck

Highest provincial total: 270 (1979)
Highest interior total: 3 (1976, 1978)
Highest coastal total: 269 (1979)

Count locality	Count years	Total counts	Frequency of occurrence (%)	Range of total counts when species occurred		
				Low	Median	High
Interior						
Vaseux Lake	1974-1984	11	9			3
Vernon	1975-1984	10	50	1	2	3
Coastal						
Campbell River	1972-1984	13	8			9
Chilliwack	1972-1984	11	73	1	32	49
Duncan	1970-1984	15	100	3	32	71
Ladner	1957-1984	26	62	1	8	67
Nanaimo	1963-1984	19	53	1	8	24
Pitt Meadows	1972-1984	13	92	2	15	122
Sooke	1983-1984	2	50			2
Vancouver	1957-1984	28	96	2	51	101
Victoria	1958-1984	27	44	1	7	25
White Rock	1971-1984	14	36	3	19	80

Green-winged Teal

Highest provincial total: 16,641 (1981)
Highest interior total: 94 (1981)
Highest coastal total: 16,547 (1981)

Count locality	Count years	Total counts	Frequency of occurrence (%)	Range of total counts when species occurred		
				Low	Median	High
Interior						
Kamloops	1984	1	100			3
Kelowna	1981	1	100			18
Nakusp	1979-1984	6	17			11
Oliver/Osoyoos	1979-1984	6	67	2	6	7
Penticton	1974-1984	9	11			1
Shuswap Lake	1972-1984	13	15	3		10
Vaseux Lake	1974-1984	11	91	1	22	45
Vernon	1975-1984	10	90	3	13	33
Coastal						
Bella Bella	1976	1	100			1
Campbell River	1972-1984	13	85	1	14	44
Chilliwack	1972-1984	11	55	13	28	61
Comox	1961-1984	23	83	1	19	57
Deep Bay	1975-1984	10	80	3	15	98
Dewdney	1967	1	100			4
Duncan	1970-1984	15	100	58	256	796
Kitimat	1974-1984	7	71	1	5	25
Ladner	1957-1984	26	100	15	1,741	5,082
Masset	1982-1984	3	100	258	332	584
Nanaimo	1963-1984	19	95	3	38	230
North Saanich	1960	1	100			109
Pender Islands	1964-1984	19	37	2	3	11
Pitt Meadows	1972-1984	13	92	6	43	239
Port Alberni	1975	1	100			273
Port Clements	1984	1	100			91
Prince Rupert	1980-1984	5	40	12		24
Sayward	1973-1984	12	92	25	64	265
Skidegate Inlet	1982-1984	3	100	12	58	87
Sooke	1983-1984	2	100	20		69
Squamish	1980-1984	5	100	2	6	21
Sunshine Coast	1979-1984	6	83	1	5	12
Surrey	1960-1966	7	86	3	38	327
Terrace	1963-1984	20	15	3	4	12
Vancouver	1957-1984	28	100	4	958	3,513
Victoria	1958-1984	27	100	201	454	1,505
White Rock	1971-1984	14	100	5	632	8,842

Common Teal

Highest provincial total: 2 (1968)
Highest interior total: Not recorded
Highest coastal total: 2 (1968)

Count locality	Count years	Total counts	Frequency of occurrence (%)	Range of total counts when species occurred		
				Low	Median	High
Coastal						
Vancouver	1957-1984	28	11	1	1	2*

Note: Recently merged with Green-winged Teal (American Ornithologists' Union 1983)

American Black Duck

Highest provincial total: 12 (1981)
Highest interior total: 1 (1980)
Highest coastal total: 12 (1981)

Count locality	Count years	Total counts	Frequency of occurrence (%)	Range of total counts when species occurred		
				Low	Median	High
Interior						
Vaseux Lake	1974-1984	11	9			1
Coastal						
Chilliwack	1972-1984	11	27	1	1	4
Ladner	1957-1984	26	12	1	2	10
Vancouver	1957-1984	28	4			3
Victoria	1958-1984	27	11	1	1	2
White Rock	1971-1984	14	7			1

Mallard

Highest provincial total: 39,156 (1980)
Highest interior total: 7,501 (1983)
Highest coastal total: 33,850 (1981)

Count locality	Count years	Total counts	Frequency of occurrence (%)	Range of total counts when species occurred		
				Low	Median	High
Interior						
Cranbrook	1984	1	100			52
Fauquier	1984	1	100			116
Kamloops	1984	1	100			174
Kelowna	1981	1	100			552
Lake Windermere	1979-1984	6	100	10	171	283
Nakusp	1979-1984	6	100	84	119	168
Oliver/Osoyoos	1979-1984	6	100	130	390	1,832
Penticton	1974-1984	9	100	161	435	655
Quesnel	1981-1984	4	25			1
Revelstoke	1981-1984	4	100	8	223	761
Shuswap Lake	1972-1984	13	100	1	114	344
Smithers	1977-1984	8	25	1		5
Vaseux Lake	1974-1984	11	100	73	385	605
Vernon	1975-1984	10	100	1,088	2,537	5,200
Yoho National Park	1975-1984	5	80	2	5	12
Coastal						
Campbell River	1972-1984	13	100	9	93	159
Chilliwack	1972-1984	11	100	212	1,067	1,777
Comox	1961-1984	23	100	197	1,038	3,561
Deep Bay	1975-1984	10	100	103	250	516
Dewdney	1967	1	100			27
Duncan	1970-1984	15	100	562	1,514	2,663
Kitimat	1974-1984	7	100	6	82	275
Ladner	1957-1984	26	100	3	5,713	18,012
Masset	1982-1984	3	100	136	475	503
Nanaimo	1963-1984	19	100	4	311	822
North Saanich	1960	1	100			31
Pender Islands	1964-1984	19	89	8	45	200
Pitt Meadows	1972-1984	13	100	29	691	3,144
Port Alberni	1975	1	100			580
Port Clements	1984	1	100			184
Prince Rupert	1980-1984	5	100	17	20	74
Sayward	1973-1984	12	92	4	46	145
Skidegate Inlet	1982-1984	3	100	86	438	659
Sooke	1983-1984	2	100	141		238
Squamish	1980-1984	5	100	47	198	453
Sunshine Coast	1979-1984	6	100	161	276	339
Surrey	1960-1966	7	71	2	8	100
Terrace	1963-1984	20	20	1	24	373
Vancouver	1957-1984	28	100	706	3,186	4,640
Victoria	1958-1984	27	100	1,359	4,432	5,906
White Rock	1971-1984	14	100	55	1,192	2,421

Northern Pintail

Highest provincial total: 53,453 (1982)
Highest interior total: 58 (1976)
Highest coastal total: 53,440 (1982)

Count locality	Count years	Total counts	Frequency of occurrence (%)	Range of total counts when species occurred		
				Low	Median	High
Interior						
Lake Windermere	1979-1984	6	17			1
Oliver/Osoyoos	1979-1984	6	17			1
Penticton	1974-1984	9	11			1
Revelstoke	1981-1984	4	25			1
Shuswap Lake	1972-1984	13	15	1		2
Vaseux Lake	1974-1984	11	91	1	2	18
Vernon	1975-1984	10	60	1	8	40
Coastal						
Campbell River	1972-1984	13	46	1	4	18
Chilliwack	1972-1984	11	55	1	8	30
Comox	1961-1984	23	100	1	135	1,128
Deep Bay	1975-1984	10	90	2	31	216
Duncan	1970-1984	15	87	98	489	1,248
Kitimat	1974-1984	7	29	1		3
Ladner	1957-1984	26	100	1	7,898	48,981
Masset	1982-1984	3	100	43	174	228
Nanaimo	1963-1984	19	79	2	31	396
North Saanich	1960	1	100			60
Pender Islands	1964-1984	19	11	1		2
Pitt Meadows	1972-1984	13	92	2	22	357
Port Alberni	1975	1	100			197
Port Clements	1984	1	100			153
Prince Rupert	1980-1984	5	20			2
Sayward	1973-1984	12	100	7	59	233
Skidegate Inlet	1982-1984	3	67	40		106
Sooke	1983-1984	2	100	7		18
Squamish	1980-1984	5	100	1	10	33
Sunshine Coast	1979-1984	6	33	2		3
Surrey	1960-1966	7	100	66	113	436
Vancouver	1957-1984	28	100	77	534	3,652
Victoria	1958-1984	27	100	174	464	941
White Rock	1971-1984	14	100	44	2,199	13,011

Blue-winged Teal

Highest provincial total: 31 (1967)
Highest interior total: 7 (1982)
Highest coastal total: 31 (1967)

Count locality	Count years	Total counts	Frequency of occurrence (%)	Range of total counts when species occurred		
				Low	Median	High
Interior						
Kelowna	1981	1	100			4
Lake Windermere	1979-1984	6	17			4
Nakusp	1979-1984	6	33	2		3
Coastal						
Chilliwack	1972-1984	11	9			1
Comox	1961-1984	23	9	1		2
Duncan	1970-1984	15	7			1
Ladner	1958-1984	26	8	4		7
Nanaimo	1963-1984	19	5			30
Port Alberni	1975	1	100			2
Vancouver	1957-1984	28	11	1	2	3

Cinnamon Teal

Highest provincial total: 11 (1983)
Highest interior total: Not recorded
Highest coastal total: 11 (1983)

Count locality	Count years	Total counts	Frequency of occurrence (%)	Range of total counts when species occurred		
				Low	Median	High
Coastal						
Deep Bay	1975-1984	10	10			1
Ladner	1957-1984	26	12	2	8	8
Vancouver	1957-1984	28	4			3

Northern Shoveler

Highest provincial total: 1,930 (1978)
Highest interior total: 34 (1981)
Highest coastal total: 1,930 (1978)

Count locality	Count years	Total counts	Frequency of occurrence (%)	Range of total counts when species occurred		
				Low	Median	High
Interior						
Kelowna	1981	1	100			34
Vaseux Lake	1974-1984	11	9			1
Vernon	1975-1984	10	20	3		19
Coastal						
Campbell River	1972-1984	13	38	1	2	3
Chilliwack	1972-1984	11	55	1	3	24
Comox	1961-1984	23	70	1	3	12
Duncan	1970-1984	15	100	22	212	988
Ladner	1957-1984	26	88	1	69	340
Masset	1982-1984	3	67	4		25
Nanaimo	1963-1984	19	68	2	8	36
North Saanich	1960	1	100			1
Pender Islands	1964-1984	19	11	10		11
Pitt Meadows	1972-1984	13	62	1	6	35
Sayward	1973-1984	12	8			5
Sooke	1983-1984	2	100	1		3
Squamish	1980-1984	5	20			4
Surrey	1960-1966	7	14			1
Vancouver	1957-1984	28	96	2	52	657
Victoria	1958-1984	27	100	47	116	476
White Rock	1971-1984	14	71	1	10	17

Gadwall

Highest provincial total: 971 (1970)
Highest interior total: 364 (1981)
Highest coastal total: 971 (1970)

Count locality	Count years	Total counts	Frequency of occurrence (%)	Range of total counts when species occurred		
				Low	Median	High
Interior						
Kelowna	1981	1	100			48
Lake Windermere	1979-1984	6	17			1
Nakusp	1979-1984	6	17			1
Oliver/Osoyoos	1979-1984	6	83	5	11	35
Penticton	1974-1984	9	67	1	44	86
Shuswap Lake	1972-1984	13	38	1	4	6
Vaseux Lake	1974-1984	11	11	2	38	169
Vernon	1975-1984	10	100	6	36	99
Coastal						
Chilliwack	1972-1984	11	27	1	3	19
Comox	1961-1984	23	4			2
Deep Bay	1975-1984	10	20			2
Duncan	1970-1984	15	33	1	4	921
Ladner	1957-1984	26	65	1	24	132
Masset	1982-1984	3	100	3	5	8
Nanaimo	1963-1984	19	26	3	4	10
Pender Islands	1964-1984	19	4			1
Pitt Meadows	1972-1984	13	69	3	14	96
Port Clements	1984	1	100	1		2
Skidegate Inlet	1982-1984	3	67			12
Sooke	1983-1984	2	50			20
Squamish	1980-1984	5	20			3
Vancouver	1957-1984	28	79	11	134	382
Victoria	1958-1984	27	67	1	11	589
White Rock	1971-1984	14	71	1	2	12

Eurasian Wigeon

Highest provincial total: 71 (1984)
Highest interior total: Not recorded
Highest coastal total: 71 (1984)

Count locality	Count years	Total counts	Frequency of occurrence (%)	Range of total counts when species occurred		
				Low	Median	High
Coastal						
Campbell River	1972-1984	13	8			1
Comox	1961-1984	23	30	1	3	3
Deep Bay	1975-1984	10	30	1	1	2
Duncan	1970-1984	15	87	1	3	9
Ladner	1957-1984	26	58	1	4	20
Nanaimo	1963-1984	19	26	1	1	4
Pender Islands	1964-1984	19	16	1	1	2
Pitt Meadows	1972-1984	13	15	2		3
Port Alberni	1975	1	100			2
Port Clements	1984	1	100			3
Sayward	1973-1984	12	8			1
Skidegate Inlet	1982-1984	3	100	1	3	3
Sooke	1983-1984	2	100	3		4
Sunshine Coast	1979-1984	6	67	1	2	4
Vancouver	1957-1984	28	54	1	3	13
Victoria	1958-1984	27	81	1	8	21
White Rock	1971-1984	14	57	1	2	8

Christmas Bird Counts

American Wigeon

Highest provincial total: 60,867 (1982)
Highest interior total: 740 (1981)
Highest coastal total: 60,742 (1982)

Count locality	Count years	Total counts	Frequency of occurrence (%)	Range of total counts when species occurred		
				Low	Median	High
Interior						
Kelowna	1981	1	100			281
Kamloops	1984	1	100			21
Lake Windermere	1979-1984	6	33	1		2
Oliver/Osoyoos	1979-1984	6	100	2	14	108
Penticton	1974-1984	9	78	1	6	13
Revelstoke	1981-1984	4	75	1	2	13
Shuswap Lake	1972-1984	13	100	3	19	42
Vaseux Lake	1974-1984	11	100	12	53	242
Vernon	1975-1984	10	100	1	23	355
Coastal						
Campbell River	1972-1984	13	100	4	203	571
Chilliwack	1972-1984	11	100	13	70	311
Comox	1961-1984	23	100	147	1,008	3,213
Deep Bay	1975-1984	10	100	61	256	506
Dewdney	1967	1	100			52
Duncan	1970-1984	15	100	557	2,634	5,459
Kitimat	1974-1984	7	29	1		2
Ladner	1957-1984	26	100	6	11,616	42,726
Masset	1982-1984	3	100	1	18	53
Nanaimo	1963-1984	19	100	7	217	2,008
North Saanich	1960	1	100			723
Pender Islands	1964-1984	19	100	4	115	313
Pitt Meadows	1972-1984	13	100	28	210	906
Port Clements	1984	1	100			191
Prince Rupert	1980-1984	5	20			788
Sayward	1973-1984	12	100	1	57	242
Skidegate Inlet	1982-1984	3	100	64	69	194
Sooke	1983-1984	2	100	1,077		1,231
Squamish	1980-1984	5	80	2	9	26
Sunshine Coast	1979-1984	6	100	67	127	153
Surrey	1960-1966	7	57	2	5	5
Vancouver	1957-1984	28	100	144	2,455	9,437
Victoria	1958-1984	27	100	3,339	6,813	14,889
White Rock	1971-1984	14	100	5	2,724	8,164

Canvasback

Highest provincial total: 1,075 (1984)
Highest interior total: 402 (1976)
Highest coastal total: 998 (1984)

Count locality	Count years	Total counts	Frequency of occurrence (%)	Low	Median	High
Interior						
Kelowna	1981	1	100			4
Oliver/Osoyoos	1979-1984	6	67	1	4	16
Penticton	1974-1984	9	100	26	74	357
Revelstoke	1981-1984	4	25			3
Shuswap Lake	1972-1984	13	8			3
Vaseux Lake	1974-1984	11	55	7	15	36
Vernon	1975-1984	10	70	1	5	21
Coastal						
Campbell River	1972-1984	13	15	3		4
Chilliwack	1972-1984	11	36	3	5	6
Comox	1961-1984	23	70	2	5	31
Deep Bay	1975-1984	10	10			1
Dewdney	1967	1	100			3
Duncan	1970-1984	15	80	3	6	16
Kitimat	1974-1984	7	43	1	1	1
Ladner	1957-1984	26	77	2	40	753
Masset	1982-1984	3	100	1	2	2
Nanaimo	1963-1984	19	11	2		3
North Saanich	1960	1	100			14
Pitt Meadows	1972-1984	13	77	1	12	26
Port Alberni	1975	1	100			5
Port Clements	1984	1	100			1
Sayward	1973-1984	12	8			1
Sooke	1983-1984	2	50			6
Squamish	1980-1984	5	40	1		1
Sunshine Coast	1979-1984	6	17			1
Surrey	1960-1966	7	71	1	2	11
Vancouver	1957-1984	28	100	4	35	383
Victoria	1958-1984	27	100	25	57	232
White Rock	1971-1984	14	100	10	58	201

Redhead

Highest provincial total: 2,635 (1981)
Highest interior total: 2,626 (1981)
Highest coastal total: 36 (1983)

Count locality	Count years	Total counts	Frequency of occurrence (%)	Low	Median	High
Interior						
Kelowna	1981	1	100			36
Oliver/Osoyoos	1979-1984	6	50	3	7	41
Penticton	1974-1984	9	100	425	1,388	2,533
Revelstoke	1981-1984	4	25			9
Shuswap Lake	1972-1984	13	46	1	6	18
Vaseux Lake	1974-1984	11	45	2	10	28
Vernon	1975-1984	10	90	2	227	350
Coastal						
Chilliwack	1972-1984	11	9			2
Comox	1961-1984	23	4			12
Duncan	1970-1984	15	33	1	2	5
Ladner	1957-1984	26	42	1	2	16
Masset	1982-1984	3	67	1		1
Nanaimo	1963-1984	19	5			1
Pitt Meadows	1972-1984	13	46	1	12	17
Port Alberni	1975	1	100			7
Squamish	1980-1984	5	20			1
Vancouver	1957-1984	28	29	1	1	5
Victoria	1958-1984	27	30	1	4	8
White Rock	1971-1984	14	7			9

Ring-necked Duck

Highest provincial total: 697 (1984)
Highest interior total: 84 (1981)
Highest coastal total: 664 (1984)

Count locality	Count years	Total counts	Frequency of occurrence (%)	Range of total counts when species occurred		
				Low	Median	High
Interior						
Kelowna	1981	1	100			19
Nakusp	1979-1984	6	17			6
Oliver/Osoyoos	1979-1984	6	50	1	2	5
Penticton	1974-1984	9	78	1	4	10
Shuswap Lake	1972-1984	13	15	5		14
Vaseux Lake	1974-1984	11	100	21	35	78
Vernon	1975-1984	10	50	1	2	10
Coastal						
Campbell River	1972-1984	13	23	1	4	12
Chilliwack	1972-1984	11	91	1	17	63
Comox	1961-1984	23	26	1	8	17
Deep Bay	1975-1984	10	60	1	2	18
Dewdney	1967	1	100			1
Duncan	1970-1984	15	100	41	172	394
Kitimat	1974-1984	7	71	2	2	15
Ladner	1957-1984	26	38	1	4	31
Masset	1982-1984	3	33			21
Nanaimo	1963-1984	19	79	3	36	90
Pender Islands	1964-1984	19	89	2	24	74
Pitt Meadows	1972-1984	13	54	1	2	14
Port Alberni	1975	1	100			81
Prince Rupert	1980-1984	5	20			1
Sayward	1973-1984	12	25	2	4	5
Sooke	1983-1984	2	100	4		7
Squamish	1980-1984	5	60	3	8	8
Vancouver	1957-1984	28	86	1	3	13
Victoria	1958-1984	27	96	1	156	408
White Rock	1971-1984	14	43	1	2	10

Tufted Duck

Highest provincial total: 1 (1974, 1975, 1983)
Highest interior total: Not recorded
Highest coastal total: 1 (1974, 1975, 1983)

Count locality	Count years	Total counts	Frequency of occurrence (%)	Range of total counts when species occurred		
				Low	Median	High
Coastal						
Vancouver	1957-1984	28	7	1		1
Victoria	1958-1984	27	4			1

Greater Scaup

Highest provincial total: 17,737 (1980)
Highest interior total: 618 (1984)
Highest coastal total: 17,480 (1980)

Count locality	Count years	Total counts	Frequency of occurrence (%)	Range of total counts when species occurred		
				Low	Median	High
Interior						
Kamloops	1984	1	100			57
Oliver/Osoyoos	1979-1984	6	100	9	23	74
Penticton	1974-1984	9	100	8	61	345
Revelstoke	1981-1984	4	25			1
Shuswap Lake	1972-1984	13	69	8	67	182
Vaseux Lake	1974-1984	11	91	2	22	79
Vernon	1975-1984	10	80	4	25	45
Coastal						
Campbell River	1972-1984	13	100	52	162	364
Chilliwack	1972-1984	11	27	2	2	28
Comox	1961-1984	23	100	68	684	1,369
Deep Bay	1975-1984	10	100	822	1,283	1,599
Duncan	1970-1984	15	100	36	81	315
Kitimat	1974-1984	7	71	6	10	70
Ladner	1957-1984	26	100	19	483	3,003
Masset	1982-1984	3	100	24	65	82
Nanaimo	1963-1984	19	95	13	63	324
North Saanich	1960	1	100			425
Pender Islands	1964-1984	19	89	8	35	73
Pitt Meadows	1972-1984	13	100	2	114	377
Port Alberni	1975	1	100			496
Prince Rupert	1980-1984	5	60	140	207	469
Sayward	1973-1984	12	100	1	20	43
Skidegate Inlet	1982-1984	3	100	86	263	304
Sooke	1983-1984	2	100	82		109
Squamish	1980-1984	5	100	4	8	11
Sunshine Coast	1979-1984	6	100	20	47	53
Surrey	1960-1966	7	100	56	123	316
Vancouver	1957-1984	28	100	602	2,470	4,706
Victoria	1958-1984	27	96	26	1,235	3,139
White Rock	1971-1984	14	100	188	2,287	7,017

Lesser Scaup

Highest provincial total: 3,818 (1978)
Highest interior total: 425 (1984)
Highest coastal total: 3,785 (1978)

Count locality	Count years	Total counts	Frequency of occurrence (%)	Range of total counts when species occurred		
				Low	Median	High
Interior						
Kelowna	1981	1	100			10
Oliver/Osoyoos	1979-1984	6	67	1	3	6
Penticton	1974-1984	9	100	9	134	270
Revelstoke	1981-1984	4	25			12
Shuswap Lake	1972-1984	13	38	1	13	40
Vaseux Lake	1974-1984	11	55	7	24	34
Vernon	1975-1984	10	80	10	74	139
Coastal						
Campbell River	1972-1984	13	69	1	3	59
Chilliwack	1972-1984	11	64	2	5	30
Comox	1961-1984	23	70	1	21	259
Deep Bay	1975-1984	10	50	3	5	124
Duncan	1970-1984	15	100	9	381	1,080
Kitimat	1974-1984	7	14			1
Ladner	1957-1984	26	85	1	53	248
Nanaimo	1963-1984	19	100	1	43	234
North Saanich	1960	1	100			5
Pender Islands	1964-1984	19	47	1	4	13
Pitt Meadows	1972-1984	13	69	2	4	7
Port Alberni	1975	1	100			73
Prince Rupert	1980-1984	5	20			167
Sayward	1973-1984	12	8			6
Sooke	1983-1984	2	100	7		21
Squamish	1980-1984	5	60	2	5	9
Sunshine Coast	1979-1984	6	83	4	8	20
Surrey	1960-1966	7	14			4
Terrace	1963-1984	20	15	4	6	6
Vancouver	1957-1984	28	100	1	254	2,561
Victoria	1958-1984	27	96	2	95	1,012
White Rock	1971-1984	14	100	5	132	2,795

King Eider

Highest provincial total: 1 (1973, 1983, 1984)
Highest interior total: Not recorded
Highest coastal total: 1 (1973, 1983, 1984)

Count locality	Count years	Total counts	Frequency of occurrence (%)	Range of total counts when species occurred		
				Low	Median	High
Coastal						
Vancouver	1957-1984	28	11	1	1	1

Harlequin Duck

Highest provincial total: 1,895 (1982)
Highest interior total: 2 (1978, 1983)
Highest coastal total: 1,894 (1982)

Count locality	Count years	Total counts	Frequency of occurrence (%)	Range of total counts when species occurred		
				Low	Median	High
Interior						
Penticton	1974-1984	9	22	1		1
Vaseux Lake	1974-1984	11	36	1	1	2
Coastal						
Bella Bella	1976	1	100			6
Campbell River	1972-1984	13	92	20	105	204
Comox	1961-1984	23	100	13	203	385
Deep Bay	1975-1984	10	100	255	381	886
Duncan	1970-1984	15	13	1		3
Ladner	1957-1984	26	92	7	43	136
Masset	1982-1984	3	100	16	56	141
Nanaimo	1963-1984	19	95	6	39	72
North Saanich	1960	1	100			26
Pender Islands	1964-1984	19	79	9	37	91
Sayward	1973-1984	12	17	1		1
Skidegate Inlet	1982-1984	3	100	64	69	94
Sooke	1983-1984	2	100	7		49
Squamish	1980-1984	5	20			1
Sunshine Coast	1979-1984	6	100	14	56	76
Surrey	1960-1966	7	71	1	3	17
Vancouver	1957-1984	28	93	3	26	49
Victoria	1958-1984	27	100	82	220	417
White Rock	1971-1984	14	100	10	37	247

Oldsquaw

Highest provincial total: 1,959 (1980)
Highest interior total: 1 (1975)
Highest coastal total: 1,959 (1980)

Count locality	Count years	Total counts	Frequency of occurrence (%)	Range of total counts when species occurred		
				Low	Median	High
Interior						
Vaseux Lake	1974-1984	11	9			1
Coastal						
Campbell River	1972-1984	13	100	4	25	64
Comox	1961-1984	23	96	36	125	293
Deep Bay	1975-1984	10	100	5	45	164
Duncan	1970-1984	15	87	1	21	72
Hecate Strait	1980	1	100			303
Ladner	1957-1984	26	96	14	125	498
Masset	1982-1984	3	100	93	100	195
Nanaimo	1963-1984	19	68	1	9	55
North Saanich	1960	1	100			73
Pender Islands	1964-1984	19	79	1	11	96
Port Alberni	1975	1	100			1
Prince Rupert	1980-1984	5	80	1	12	19
Sayward	1973-1984	12	17	1		5
Skidegate Inlet	1982-1984	3	100	11	17	56
Sooke	1983-1984	2	100	11		32
Squamish	1980-1984	5	60	1	1	2
Sunshine Coast	1979-1984	6	83	6	24	75
Surrey	1960-1966	7	86	4	11	20
Vancouver	1957-1984	28	100	8	91	246
Victoria	1958-1984	27	100	48	225	783
White Rock	1971-1984	14	100	14	53	165

Christmas Bird Counts

Black Scoter

Highest provincial total: 3,537 (1976)
Highest interior total: Not recorded
Highest coastal total: 3,537 (1976)

Count locality	Count years	Total counts	Frequency of occurrence (%)	Range of total counts when species occurred		
				Low	Median	High
Coastal						
Bella Bella	1976	1	100			9
Campbell River	1972-1984	13	100	210	388	774
Comox	1961-1984	23	100	66	216	673
Deep Bay	1975-1984	10	100	287	661	1,095
Duncan	1970-1984	15	87	1	15	98
Hecate Strait	1980	1	100			2
Kitimat	1974-1984	7	14			1
Ladner	1957-1984	26	100	2	168	493
Masset	1982-1984	3	100	1	264	394
Nanaimo	1963-1984	19	95	5	35	280
North Saanich	1960	1	100			7
Pender Islands	1964-1984	19	47	1	10	12
Pitt Meadows	1972-1984	13	8			1
Prince Rupert	1980-1984	5	60	1	16	21
Skidegate Inlet	1982-1984	3	100	35	36	65
Sooke	1983-1984	2	100	5		9
Squamish	1980-1984	5	20			2
Sunshine Coast	1979-1984	6	100	69	88	256
Surrey	1960-1966	7	100	5	25	84
Vancouver	1957-1984	28	100	110	345	587
Victoria	1958-1984	27	81	1	9	216
White Rock	1971-1984	14	79	47	220	899

Surf Scoter

Highest provincial total: 13,843 (1983)
Highest interior total: 1 (1976)
Highest coastal total: 13,843 (1983)

Count locality	Count years	Total counts	Frequency of occurrence (%)	Range of total counts when species occurred		
				Low	Median	High
Interior						
Vernon	1975-1984	10	10			1
Coastal						
Bella Bella	1976	1	100			207
Campbell River	1972-1984	13	100	123	246	485
Comox	1961-1984	23	100	332	995	1,647
Deep Bay	1975-1984	10	100	776	1,136	1,835
Duncan	1970-1984	15	100	59	254	861
Hecate Strait	1980	1	100			1
Kitimat	1974-1984	7	29	50		400
Ladner	1957-1984	26	100	132	530	1,684
Masset	1982-1984	3	100	3	86	122
Nanaimo	1963-1984	19	100	16	260	1,943
North Saanich	1960	1	100			244
Pender Islands	1964-1984	19	100	29	99	657
Pitt Meadows	1972-1984	13	23	1	3	12
Prince Rupert	1980-1984	5	80	32	124	134
Sayward	1973-1984	12	17	8		8
Skidegate Inlet	1982-1984	3	100	106	143	594
Sooke	1983-1984	2	100	202		402
Squamish	1980-1984	5	100	2	7	35
Sunshine Coast	1979-1984	6	100	361	832	2,474
Surrey	1960-1966	7	100	6	126	312
Vancouver	1957-1984	28	100	1,196	2,968	5,562
Victoria	1958-1984	27	100	118	462	946
White Rock	1971-1984	14	100	292	921	4,280

White-winged Scoter

Highest provincial total: 5,018 (1977)
Highest interior total: Not recorded
Highest coastal total: 5,018 (1977)

Count locality	Count years	Total counts	Frequency of occurrence (%)	Range of total counts when species occurred		
				Low	Median	High
Coastal						
Bella Bella	1976	1	100			51
Campbell River	1972-1984	13	100	34	154	332
Comox	1961-1984	23	100	223	924	1,697
Deep Bay	1975-1984	10	100	960	1,482	2,029
Duncan	1970-1984	15	100	38	323	1,569
Hecate Strait	1980	1	100			68
Kitimat	1974-1984	7	29	1		3
Ladner	1957-1984	26	100	5	177	477
Masset	1982-1984	3	100	9	58	124
Nanaimo	1963-1984	19	100	7	52	292
North Saanich	1960	1	100			685
Pender Islands	1964-1984	19	100	1	23	179
Pitt Meadows	1972-1984	13	8			7
Port Alberni	1975	1	100			20
Prince Rupert	1980-1984	5	60	4	54	74
Sayward	1973-1984	12	8			2
Skidegate Inlet	1982-1984	3	100	29	169	333
Sooke	1983-1984	2	100	57		176
Sunshine Coast	1979-1984	6	100	20	69	169
Surrey	1960-1966	7	100	37	65	240
Vancouver	1957-1984	28	100	35	121	414
Victoria	1958-1984	27	100	71	310	834
White Rock	1971-1984	14	100	22	130	297

Common Goldeneye

Highest provincial total: 5,212 (1977)
Highest interior total: 647 (1982)
Highest coastal total: 5,076 (1977)

Count locality	Count years	Total counts	Frequency of occurrence (%)	Range of total counts when species occurred		
				Low	Median	High
Interior						
Cranbrook	1984	1	100			8
Fauquier	1984	1	100			4
Kamloops	1984	1	100			22
Kelowna	1981	1	100			17
Lake Windermere	1979-1984	6	100	26	91	94
Nakusp	1979-1984	6	100	6	21	34
Oliver/Osoyoos	1979-1984	6	100	14	44	77
Penticton	1974-1984	9	100	19	33	59
Revelstoke	1981-1984	4	100	18	40	77
Shuswap Lake	1972-1984	13	92	1	32	283
Vaseux Lake	1974-1984	11	100	12	76	156
Vernon	1975-1984	10	100	10	49	134
Coastal						
Bella Bella	1976	1	100			4
Campbell River	1972-1984	13	100	113	176	249
Chilliwack	1972-1984	11	100	32	96	168
Comox	1961-1984	23	100	14	386	789
Deep Bay	1975-1984	10	100	317	489	694
Dewdney	1967	1	100			24
Duncan	1970-1984	15	100	91	236	621
Hecate Strait	1980	1	100			17
Kitimat	1974-1984	7	100	27	260	400
Ladner	1957-1984	26	100	34	190	450
Masset	1982-1984	3	100	6	13	14
Nanaimo	1963-1984	19	100	65	121	192
North Saanich	1960	1	100			173
Pender Islands	1964-1984	19	100	14	89	172
Pitt Meadows	1972-1984	13	100	1	26	87
Port Alberni	1975	1	100			281
Prince Rupert	1980-1984	5	80	4	104	186
Sayward	1973-1984	12	67	1	5	10
Skidegate Inlet	1982-1984	3	100	41	125	155
Sooke	1983-1984	2	100	155		332
Squamish	1980-1984	5	100	44	86	268
Sunshine Coast	1979-1984	6	100	106	123	212
Surrey	1960-1966	7	100	11	38	68
Terrace	1963-1984	20	35	1	2	35
Vancouver	1957-1984	28	100	75	771	1,729
Victoria	1958-1984	27	100	143	305	495
White Rock	1971-1984	14	100	16	132	452

Barrow's Goldeneye

Highest provincial total: 4,890 (1984)
Highest interior total: 299 (1978)
Highest coastal total: 4,738 (1984)

Count locality	Count years	Total counts	Frequency of occurrence (%)	Range of total counts when species occurred		
				Low	Median	High
Interior						
Fauquier	1984	1	100			1
Kamloops	1984	1	100			24
Kelowna	1981	1	100			6
Lake Windermere	1979-1984	6	50	1	5	6
Nakusp	1979-1984	6	33	1		2
Oliver/Osoyoos	1979-1984	6	67	1	18	37
Penticton	1974-1984	9	100	1	5	12
Quesnel	1981-1984	4	75	5	8	10
Revelstoke	1981-1984	4	25			8
Shuswap Lake	1972-1984	13	100	5	43	138
Vaseux Lake	1974-1984	11	100	14	103	175
Vernon	1975-1984	10	60	3	26	40
Coastal						
Campbell River	1972-1984	13	92	1	5	12
Chilliwack	1972-1984	11	91	14	52	145
Comox	1961-1984	23	96	1	37	120
Deep Bay	1975-1984	10	100	6	47	71
Duncan	1970-1984	15	100	2	59	134
Kitimat	1974-1984	7	57	1	3	50
Ladner	1957-1984	26	77	1	15	87
Masset	1982-1984	3	67	1		2
Nanaimo	1963-1984	19	95	9	136	2,016
North Saanich	1960	1	100			5
Pender Islands	1964-1984	19	84	5	25	129
Pitt Meadows	1972-1984	13	85	1	25	59
Port Alberni	1975	1	100			2
Port Clements	1984	1	100			13
Prince Rupert	1980-1984	5	80	5	32	38
Skidegate Inlet	1982-1984	3	67	1		3
Sooke	1983-1984	2	100	43		48
Squamish	1980-1984	5	100	24	36	175
Sunshine Coast	1979-1984	6	100	250	454	814
Surrey	1960-1966	7	86	1	2	595
Terrace	1963-1984	20	25	2	4	47
Vancouver	1957-1984	28	96	272	1,701	3,388
Victoria	1958-1984	27	96	1	11	189
White Rock	1971-1984	14	100	7	17	50

Bufflehead

Highest provincial total: 7,207 (1983)
Highest interior total: 305 (1981)
Highest coastal total: 6,914 (1983)

Count locality	Count years	Total counts	Frequency of occurrence (%)	Range of total counts when species occurred		
				Low	Median	High
Interior						
Fauquier	1984	1	100			18
Kamloops	1984	1	100			2
Kelowna	1981	1	100			22
Lake Windermere	1979-1984	6	33	2		3
Nakusp	1979-1984	6	67	1	2	5
Oliver/Osoyoos	1979-1984	6	67	1	23	27
Penticton	1974-1984	9	100	18	49	90
Revelstoke	1981-1984	4	75	2	7	8
Shuswap Lake	1972-1984	13	77	1	4	14
Vaseux Lake	1974-1984	11	91	42	122	219
Vernon	1975-1984	10	100	26	36	120
Coastal						
Bella Bella	1976	1	100			96
Campbell River	1972-1984	13	100	131	247	724
Chilliwack	1972-1984	11	100	26	91	167
Comox	1961-1984	23	100	27	327	467
Deep Bay	1975-1984	10	100	322	460	633
Dewdney	1967	1	100			18
Duncan	1970-1984	15	100	173	326	1,107
Kitimat	1974-1984	7	100	2	22	61
Ladner	1957-1984	26	100	17	284	1,147
Masset	1982-1984	3	100	94	210	227
Nanaimo	1963-1984	19	100	59	140	304
North Saanich	1960	1	100			314
Pender Islands	1964-1984	19	100	9	251	674
Pitt Meadows	1972-1984	13	100	41	123	206
Port Alberni	1975	1	100			163
Port Clements	1984	1	100			37
Prince Rupert	1980-1984	5	60	33	42	48
Sayward	1973-1984	12	100	26	74	129
Skidegate Inlet	1982-1984	3	100	64	110	279
Sooke	1983-1984	2	100	642		698
Squamish	1980-1984	5	100	73	149	195
Sunshine Coast	1979-1984	6	100	84	118	194
Surrey	1960-1966	7	100	5	50	74
Terrace	1963-1984	20	30	1	4	54
Vancouver	1957-1984	28	100	178	389	595
Victoria	1958-1984	27	100	543	1,377	1,944
White Rock	1971-1984	14	100	66	194	481

Hooded Merganser

Highest provincial total: 900 (1984)
Highest interior total: 124 (1983)
Highest coastal total: 846 (1984)

Count locality	Count years	Total counts	Frequency of occurrence (%)	Range of total counts when species occurred		
				Low	Median	High
Interior						
Kelowna	1981	1	100			23
Oliver/Osoyoos	1979-1984	6	100	2	8	42
Penticton	1974-1984	9	100	6	16	48
Shuswap Lake	1972-1984	13	23	3	4	5
Smithers	1977-1984	8	13			2
Vaseux Lake	1974-1984	11	91	18	40	109
Vernon	1975-1984	10	100	7	18	39
Coastal						
Bella Bella	1976	1	100			9
Campbell River	1972-1984	13	100	4	12	28
Chilliwack	1972-1984	11	100	3	16	29
Comox	1961-1984	23	83	1	5	22
Deep Bay	1975-1984	10	100	2	10	28
Dewdney	1967	1	100			7
Duncan	1970-1984	15	100	9	31	58
Kitimat	1974-1984	7	29	2		7
Ladner	1957-1984	26	69	1	5	37
Masset	1982-1984	3	67	22		48
Nanaimo	1963-1984	19	79	2	9	40
North Saanich	1960	1	100			28
Pender Islands	1964-1984	19	95	4	67	112
Pitt Meadows	1972-1984	13	100	2	34	73
Port Alberni	1975	1	100			13
Prince Rupert	1980-1984	5	100	1	5	15
Sayward	1973-1984	12	67	1	2	9
Skidegate Inlet	1982-1984	3	67	1		2
Sooke	1983-1984	2	100	42		52
Squamish	1980-1984	5	80	1	3	7
Sunshine Coast	1979-1984	6	100	1	4	12
Terrace	1963-1984	20	25	1	2	6
Vancouver	1957-1984	28	100	3	27	93
Victoria	1958-1984	27	100	36	192	472
White Rock	1971-1984	14	86	1	6	33

Christmas Bird Counts

Common Merganser

Highest provincial total: 4,483 (1983)
Highest interior total: 668 (1983)
Highest coastal total: 3,815 (1983)

Count locality	Count years	Total counts	Frequency of occurrence (%)	Range of total counts when species occurred		
				Low	Median	High
Interior						
Cranbrook	1984	1	100			5
Fauquier	1984	1	100			1
Kamloops	1984	1	100			57
Kelowna	1981	1	100			6
Lake Windermere	1979-1984	6	100	4	9	21
Nakusp	1979-1984	6	67	1	1	2
Oliver/Osoyoos	1979-1984	6	100	26	65	139
Penticton	1974-1984	9	89	7	21	38
Revelstoke	1981-1984	4	100	1	7	40
Shuswap Lake	1972-1984	13	92	2	12	20
Smithers	1977-1984	8	38	1	2	4
Vaseux Lake	1974-1984	11	91	12	122	147
Vernon	1975-1984	10	100	11	49	530
Wells Gray	1984	1	100			1
Coastal						
Bella Bella	1976	1	100			21
Campbell River	1972-1984	13	100	34	90	1,219
Chilliwack	1972-1984	11	91	17	61	131
Comox	1961-1984	23	96	1	27	527
Deep Bay	1975-1984	10	100	29	74	150
Dewdney	1967	1	100			39
Duncan	1970-1984	15	100	142	893	1,536
Kitimat	1974-1984	7	86	2	4	6
Ladner	1957-1984	26	92	2	19	177
Masset	1982-1984	3	100	1	10	38
Nanaimo	1963-1984	19	95	6	72	138
North Saanich	1960	1	100			7
Pender Islands	1964-1984	19	89	1	89	350
Pitt Meadows	1972-1984	13	100	27	58	202
Port Alberni	1975	1	100			62
Prince Rupert	1980-1984	5	100	26	52	130
Sayward	1973-1984	12	100	2	10	25
Skidegate Inlet	1982-1984	3	100	9	28	29
Sooke	1983-1984	2	100	25		72
Squamish	1980-1984	5	100	57	78	197
Sunshine Coast	1979-1984	6	100	9	48	100
Surrey	1960-1966	7	29	2		2
Terrace	1963-1984	20	45	1	3	40
Vancouver	1957-1984	28	100	5	177	590
Victoria	1958-1984	27	100	52	397	1,602
White Rock	1971-1984	14	100	6	55	205

Red-breasted Merganser

Highest provincial total: 1,711 (1980)
Highest interior total: 16 (1982)
Highest coastal total: 1,706 (1980)

Count locality	Count years	Total counts	Frequency of occurrence (%)	Range of total counts when species occurred		
				Low	Median	High
Interior						
Kelowna	1981	1	100			1
Nakusp	1979-1984	6	33	1		2
Oliver/Osoyoos	1979-1984	6	83	1	2	10
Penticton	1974-1984	9	100	1	2	7
Shuswap Lake	1972-1984	13	8			3
Vaseux Lake	1974-1984	11	9			3
Vernon	1975-1984	10	30	1	5	7
Coastal						
Bella Bella	1976	1	100			5
Campbell River	1972-1984	13	100	20	50	84
Chilliwack	1972-1984	11	27	1	3	3
Comox	1961-1984	23	100	13	38	209
Deep Bay	1975-1984	10	100	14	53	76
Duncan	1970-1984	15	100	27	97	216
Hecate Strait	1980	1	100			2
Kitimat	1974-1984	7	29	2		4
Ladner	1957-1984	26	100	6	98	290
Masset	1982-1984	3	100	10	15	25
Nanaimo	1963-1984	19	100	14	51	89
North Saanich	1960	1	100			155
Pender Islands	1964-1984	19	95	4	79	403
Pitt Meadows	1972-1984	13	46	2	3	34
Prince Rupert	1980-1984	5	20			2
Sayward	1973-1984	12	33	3	7	155
Skidegate Inlet	1982-1984	3	100	11	18	46
Sooke	1983-1984	2	100	58		65
Squamish	1980-1984	5	100	9	22	74
Sunshine Coast	1979-1984	6	100	10	37	51
Surrey	1960-1966	7	71	2	7	26
Terrace	1963-1984	20	5			5
Vancouver	1957-1984	28	100	86	302	518
Victoria	1958-1984	27	100	94	224	338
White Rock	1971-1984	14	100	29	71	134

Ruddy Duck

Highest provincial total: 11,705 (1978)
Highest interior total: 42 (1979)
Highest coastal total: 11,689 (1978)

Count locality	Count years	Total counts	Frequency of occurrence (%)	Range of total counts when species occurred		
				Low	Median	High
Interior						
Penticton	1974-1984	9	100	3	12	19
Vaseux Lake	1974-1984	11	9			1
Vernon	1975-1984	10	50	1	5	42
Coastal						
Chilliwack	1972-1984	11	9			1
Comox	1961-1984	23	9	1		2
Duncan	1970-1984	15	93	7	51	587
Ladner	1957-1984	26	81	4	88	3,838
Nanaimo	1963-1984	19	63	1	8	19
North Saanich	1960	1	100			410
Pender Islands	1964-1984	19	11	1		6
Pitt Meadows	1972-1984	13	38	1	1	11
Squamish	1980-1984	5	20			3
Surrey	1960-1966	7	57	7	25	31
Vancouver	1957-1984	28	100	4	140	449
Victoria	1958-1984	27	100	1	57	429
White Rock	1971-1984	14	100	95	1,484	11,280

APPENDIX 3

Contributors

The following 4,629 people contributed information, mainly personal observations of birds, to this volume.

Abbey, E.
Abbey, J.
Ablitt, Sheila
Ackerman, Andy
Ackroyd, Gayle
Ackroyd, John
Acton, Tim
Adair, E.M.
Adalman, Steven
Adams, Barbara
Adams, Bob
Adams, Brenda
Adams, Elsie
Adams, Errol
Adams, J.
Adams, Kaye
Adams, Mark
Adams, Mike
Adams, W.
Adamson, Anne
Ainscough, H.M.
Aitchison, Cathy
Akerlund, W.
Aldcroft, David S.
Alderman, E.S.
Alderson, G.W.
Aldridge, Alex
Alexander, A.G.
Alexander, A.M.
Alexander, Linda
Alexander, M.E.
Alexander, T.R.
Alger, Dave
Allan, B.
Allan, Jean
Allen, Charles
Allen, Donald
Allen, Dorothy
Allen, Marty
Allen, Roy
Allies, Kelly
Allies, Wendy J.
Allies, Wilson F.
Allison, Barney
Almond, H.
Alton, R.R
Alway, J.H.
Ambridge, Dave
Amedro, Matt J.
Amos, Ralph
Amundsen, Adeline
Amys, Necia
Amys, Philip
Anderson, B.
Anderson, C.H.
Anderson, Dale
Anderson, Dix
Anderson, E.A.
Anderson, Errol M.
Anderson, F.
Anderson, Gail
Anderson, Gary
Anderson, Gerald

Anderson, Gladys
Anderson, J.S.
Anderson, J.W.
Anderson, Jerry
Anderson, John
Anderson, K.
Anderson, L.
Anderson, R.R.
Anderson, T.M.
Anderson, Tony L.
Anderson, Walter
Anderson, William A.
Anderson, William J.
Andre, Jean
Andrews, Betty
Andrews, N.
Angell, N.
Angermeyer, Katie
Angle, Edith
Angle, Neil
Angus, J.
Angus, Robert
Anker, B.
Ansell, Gerry
Ansell, Wendy
Antifeau, Ted
Antoniazzi, Cathy
Appleton, Frank
Arcese, Peter
Arlt, E.
Armstead, Carol
Armstead, Rex
Armstrong, Malcolm C.
Armstrong, Marie
Armstrong, P.
Armstrong, W.
Arnet, Dorothy
Arnet, Douglas
Arnet, Edward
Arnold, Genevieve
Arter, J.
Arvey, D.
Ashcroft, Greg
Asher, Dale
Asher, Richard C.
Ashmore, Margaret
Askevold, R.
Asplin, Heather
Assaly, Robin
Atkins, Allan
Atkins, M.
Atkinson, Chris
Atkinson, Knute
Atkinson, Pat
Atkinson, R.N.
Atkinson, R.W.
Auhold, Brad
Austin, Dorothy
Austin, June
Austring, Ruth
Axhorn, Denise
Axhorn, Peter
Ayers, Helen

Babcock, A.
Bach, Ernie
Bach, R.
Bachi, Albert
Bachi, Heidi
Backs, Mel
Backs, Rose
Bader, W.A.
Badgley, E.
Baechler, Marilyn
Bailey, Anne C.
Bailey, Norma
Bailey, Paul
Bailey, S.
Baillie, Steve
Bain, J.
Baine, Stan
Baird, Robin
Baker, Alan
Baker, Betty
Baker, Bob
Baker, D.
Baker, Eric
Baker, G.
Baker, Margaret
Baker, Phillip
Baker, Robert L.
Baker, Stanley W.F.
Baker, Teresa
Bakkom, W.
Baldwin, James
Ballard, John T.
Ballin, Peter
Bamford, Ted
Bampton, Chris
Bandy, P.J.
Banks, Douglas
Bantom, Audrey
Banwell, June
Barclay, Grace
Barclay, H.
Bard, Fred
Barker, I.
Barkley, William D.
Barkwill, W.
Barlow, Jon C.
Barnard, Anthony E.
Barnes, Helen
Barnes, Jack
Barnes, John
Barnes, Raymond
Barnes, Verna
Barnett, Henry
Barnett, Ian
Barnett, Jennifer M.
Barnett, Judy
Barr, Andy
Barr, Barry
Barr, Kenneth
Barr, R.A.
Barraclough, Dave
Barraclough, Edward
Barraclough, Mary

Barrard, Tony
Barrett, Grace
Bartholomew, K.
Bartkow, Virginia
Bartlett, Les
Barvis, Marg
Bashan, Berton
Bastaja, Dan S.
Bateman, Robert
Bates, Bob
Bates, Catherine
Bates, Ernie
Bates, Marjorie
Bates, T.H.
Bates, Tom
Bath, Fermine
Batt, Edna
Bauder, Kris
Bauer, H.E.
Baumbrough, Harold
Baumbrough, John
Baumbrough, June
Bavin, Helen
Bavin, Ryan
Bavington, B.
Bawtree, K.
Baylor, G.
Bazett, Stephen J.
Beacham, E. Derek
Beachem, Al
Beadle, David
Beak, Alice
Beals, Alice
Beam, B.
Beardmore, Roger
Beauchesne, Moira
Beaudet, Sheila
Beaulieu, Joanne
Beaulieu, Michelle
Beaumont, Art
Beaumont, Barbara
Beaven, N.
Bech, Paul
Bechett, K.R.
Bechler, Marilyn
Beck, J.E.
Beck, R.E.
Becker, Phyllis
Beckett, K. Ray
Beckner, D.
Beebe, Frank L.
Beedle, Mac
Begg, Barbara
Beise, Kathleen
Bekhuys, Timothy J.
Bell, Alistair
Bell, Barbara
Bell, Brian
Bell, Dick
Bell, Eileen
Bell, Ernie
Bell, Faith
Bell, Grace

Bell, H.M.
Bell, Hedley
Bell, Jacques
Bell, Karina
Bell, Katie
Bell, Kevin M.
Bell, W.
Bellevance, Anne
Bellis, Charles
Belsom, Betty
Belsom, June
Belsom, Sid
Belton, Desmond E.J.
Bendell, James F.
Bender, Fred
Beninger, P.
Benmore, B.
Bennett, Barry
Bennett, Bruce
Bennett, Gerry
Bennett, Herb
Bennett, Mary
Bennie, Fred
Bennie, Winnifred
Benoit, James
Benson, M.
Bentley, Caroline L.
Bentley, Mike
Benton, Bill
Benton, Fran
Benton, Julie
Benton, Marian
Benton, Roger
Benyon, E.
Bergen, M.
Berger, Alan
Bergerud, A.T.
Berry, Ron
Bertram, Douglas F.
Berukoff, P.
Best, Alan
Best, Ken
Best, Robin
Best, S.
Best, Ted
Bettison, L.J.
Betts, Mike
Bevan, Jan
Bewick, Mary
Beynon, Ed
Beynon, J.
Biel, Jim
Bigelow, E.
Bigelow, V.
Biggar, James
Biggin-Pound, J.
Bigley, Dick
Bijdemast, Edie
Billie, Tonio
Billings, Ray R.
Bilodau, B.
Bingham, Dan S.
Bingham, Peter
Bird, Fred
Bird, Jackie
Bird, W.
Birkel, Anne
Birkett, Wilma
Birney, C.E.
Bishop, Charlie
Bishop, James

Bishop, Jean
Bishop, L.
Black, Tom
Blackbourne, S.
Blais, Dan
Blake, Joe
Blanchard, Harriet
Bland, Trudy
Blankendaal, Cor
Blattner, Hans
Blaylock, S.G.
Bloem, Gerard
Blokker, P.F.
Blomgren, Bemgt
Blood, Donald A.
Bloom, F.C.
Blouw, Marjon
Blow, Barbara
Boag, D.A.
Boas, Charles
Boas, F.
Bode, Miles
Bodman, Geoff
Bogewold, Gwen
Boggs, Bob
Boggs, Elsie
Bolen, Loren
Bolton, Doris
Bomford, Charles
Bomford, H.
Bomford, Ted
Bonar, Richard L.
Boney, R.
Bonner, Vera
Boone, J.A.
Boot, Lance
Boot, Leslie
Booth, Barry
Booth, J.H.
Borrelly, Maurice
Bortnik, Shelly
Bosomworth, Myrna
Boston, R.E.
Boulton, G.
Bouman, Dan
Bourne, Jean
Bourne, Neil
Boutillier, Norma
Boux, J.
Bowden, Sheila
Bowden, Wallie
Bowe, L.
Bowen, Dan
Bowen, Edna
Bowers, Bonny
Bowers, David
Bowers, Deborah
Bowes, Stanley
Bowford, Ted
Bowling, Jack
Boyce, Kenneth C.
Boyd, W. Sean
Boye, J.C.
Boyle, Brad L.
Boyle, Larry
Bracewell, Dorothy
Bracewell, Vince
Brade, Robert
Bradford, Mike
Bradford, Sherry
Bradley, Arlene

Bradley, Dorothy M.
Bradley, M.
Bradley, Robert M.
Bradley, S.F.
Bradshaw, Jeff
Brand, Trudy
Brandie, G.
Brandon, Jean
Brandon, Jimmy
Brandt, Charles A.E.
Braun, Abe
Braun, Ralph
Bray, R.
Brayshaw, Chris
Breadon, James
Breault, Andre
Breen, Peter
Breitkreutz, A.R.
Brett, Roland J.
Brewer, David
Brewster, Bill
Brewster, N.
Briant, Pat
Briault, Peg
Bricknell, Peter
Briggs, Gwen
Briggs, Tom R.
Brigham, R. Mark
Britton, G.A.
Broadland, Ken R.
Broadley, Tom
Brock, Hugh
Brock, Lyle
Brodorson, Malfdan
Brokenshire, Betty
Bromley, Robert G.
Bronsch, Harold
Brook, M.
Brook, Nigel
Brook, S.
Brooke, Elizabeth
Brooke, Mavis
Brooke, Robert C.
Brooke, William
Brooks, A.A.
Brooks, Allan C.
Brooks, Betty J.
Brooks, D.
Brooks, E.S.
Brooks, J.A.
Brooks, Jocie M.
Brooks, Robert
Brooks, Vi
Broomfield, G.A.
Broomfield, J.F.
Brown, Andrew
Brown, Bedford B.
Brown, Bill
Brown, Bob
Brown, Debbie
Brown, Dennis
Brown, Dorothy
Brown, Doug
Brown, Eileen
Brown, G.L.
Brown, Gladys
Brown, Gordon
Brown, Janet
Brown, Margaret
Brown, Marian
Brown, Michael

Brown, Mildred
Brown, Paul
Brown, R.P.
Brown, Rory
Brown, Shawn
Brown, Susan J.
Brown, Thomas H.
Brown, Valerie
Brown, William M.
Browne-Clayton, Pat
Browning, R.W.
Brownlow, Harry
Brownsword, F.
Bruce, Dan
Bruce, Rosemary
Brucker, Maury
Brunham, C.
Brunham, G.
Brunt, Kim
Brunton, Daniel F.
Bruton, J.W.
Bryan, Anthea
Bryan, C.
Bryan, Jim
Bryden, Colleen
Bryden, Jim
Bryson, Greg
Buch, Nancy E.
Buchanan, Don
Buchanan, Melda
Buchanan, S.
Buck, E.
Buck, Jim
Buckingham, R.
Buckle, Evelyn
Buckle, Neil
Buckles, Jack
Budzinski, Luz
Buffam, Frank
Buhler, Andy
Buhler, Marilyn
Buhler, R.A.
Buker, Ian
Bull, John
Bull, P.
Bull, S.
Bullard, Collin
Bullen, Bev
Bullock, G.F.
Bultug, Helen
Bumpus, Ruth
Bunnell, Fred L.
Burbridge, Jim
Burbridge, Joan
Burger, Alan
Burgerjon, Joop
Burgerjon, Miep
Burgess, Joe
Burgess, Tom E.
Burgess, W.
Burne, C.S.
Burnett, Stella
Burnett, Terry
Burnette, Peter
Burns, Andrew
Burns, C.
Burns, J.E.
Burrell, Linda
Burroughs, A.O.
Burroughs, Betty
Burroughs, Bill

Contributors

Burroughs, May
Burton, Clyde H.
Busch, Fred
Bush, Dave
Bush, Gary
Bush, Gordon
Bushman, Ortrude
Bustard, David
Butler, Bruce
Butler, Elinor
Butler, Greg
Butler, Jim
Butler, Michelle
Butler, Richard
Butler, Robert W.
Butler, Sharon
Butt, Colin
Butters, Dan
Butterworth, David
Buys, Hans
Byatt, A.
Byatt, Steve
Bye, Dana
Bylie, Bill
Byrd, Vernon
Cachet, Klaus
Caldwell, Kit
Calef, George
Calladine, John
Callender, Graham
Callin, Elmer
Calvert, Gilbert
Calvert, Joy
Calvert, Lissa
Cameron, Arlene
Cameron, D.
Cameron, Fred
Cameron, I.
Cameron, Jim
Cameron, Mavis
Cameron, Sharon
Camfferman, Dean
Camp, Frank E.
Campbell, Barbara
Campbell, Barry
Campbell, Betty
Campbell, Carol
Campbell, D. Sean
Campbell, D. Wayne
Campbell, David
Campbell, Eileen C.
Campbell, J.V.
Campbell, Larry
Campbell, Lorne
Campbell, Lucile
Campbell, Marcile
Campbell, Mildred W.
Campbell, R. Wayne
Campbell, Robert L.
Campbell, Tessa N.
Camsell, M.
Cannings, E.J.
Cannings, Jean
Cannings, Richard J.
Cannings, Robert A.
Cannings, Stephen R.
Cannings, Sydney G.
Cannon, Violet E.
Cape, Barbara
Cape, Myrtle
Capes, Phil

Carpenter, L.
Caravetta, I.
Caravetta, Joe
Carcasson, Robert H.
Cardinal, K.
Cardwell, Sarah
Carefoot, T.H.
Carey, Betty
Carey, Neil
Carl, G. Clifford
Carl, Jennifer
Carl, Ruth
Carleton, J.
Carlisle, Susan
Carlson, Barbara E.
Carlson, Gary R.
Carlson, J.S.
Carmichael, Agnes
Carmody, Michael
Carper, Larry
Carr, Daniel
Carr, Elsie
Carr, Ian
Carr, Jan
Carruthers, Donald
Carson, Andy
Carson, Betty
Carson, Don
Carson, Kevin
Carson, Trudy
Carson, Walter
Carter, Bruce
Carter, Harry R.
Cartwright, Joan
Cartwright, John
Cartwright, Maureen
Caskey, Marlene
Casperson, Audrey
Casperson, R.
Casperson, Susan
Cassidy, Alice
Castagner, Lynn
Catchpole, Rob
Cathcart, M.
Catt, Danny
Cavenaugh, Brian
Cavers, Beth
Cawley, Nettie-Jean
Cehak, K.F.
Cerrenzia, Bob
Chaddock, Arnold
Chalmers, Graham
Chalmers, Hubert
Chalmers, Orville
Chambers, M.
Chan, Brian
Chandler, Art
Chandy, Rosalind
Chapman, Betty-Ann
Chapman, David P.
Chapman, F.
Chapman, Sharon
Charbonneau, Alan
Charbonneau, D.
Charles, Walter
Charlton, A.
Charters, D.
Chartier, A.
Chartier, B.
Chase, Dave
Chase, J.D.

Chatwin, R.
Cherney, Gordon
Chester, S.
Chesterfield, Norman
Child, Ken N.
Chisholm, B.R.
Christie, A.E.
Christie, H.C.
Christie, Norma
Christmas, M.J.
Chrysler, Judy
Chudyk, M.
Chudyk, W.
Chungranes, Vi
Church, Mike
Churchill, Betty
Churchill, Brian P.
Churchill, Bryon
Churchill, Harold
Chutter, Myke J.
Chutter, W.
Chwojka, Amy
Clague, Alexis
Clague, John
Clapham, Paul
Clapp, B.E.
Clapperton, D.
Clark, Alan M.
Clark, Colin
Clark, David
Clark, Frank C.
Clark, H.G.
Clark, Heather
Clark, Martin
Clark, Mary
Clark, Mike
Clark, Murray
Clarke, B.
Clarke, D.
Clarke, Edward
Clarke, I.
Clarke, M.
Clarke, Paul
Clarke, R.
Clarke, S.
Clarke, Vivian
Clarkson, Norman
Clarkson, Ron
Clarkson, Rosemary
Clayton, Gerry
Clayton, Margaret
Clegg, Dick
Clibbon, Brooke
Cline, Bev
Clough, A.
Clulow, George
Cnossen, Andy
Cnossen, Jenny
Coates, Dave
Cober, A.
Code, D.
Coderre, Elaine
Coe, Colin
Coffin, Ed
Cohen, Robin
Colby, C.H.
Colby, Gwen
Colby, Norris A.
Coldham, Frank
Coldwell, Barry
Cole, Joan

Collard, Paul
Collicut, Lorne
Colling, Richard
Collings, Brande
Collins, Henry A.
Collins, Jack M.
Collins, Mary
Collins, Peter
Collins, R.H.W.
Collins, Tom
Collinson, Shiela
Coltman, A.W.
Coltman, M.A.
Comer, John
Comfort, David
Como, G.
Condrashoff, S.F.
Congreve, W.M.
Conner, C.F.
Conti, Barbara
Conway, Kay
Cook, Ann
Cook, C.
Cook, F. Stanley
Cook, R.A.
Cook, Vernon
Cooke, F.
Coombes, Tom
Cooper, Albert
Cooper, Aziza
Cooper, Bunny
Cooper, Carrie
Cooper, Daphne
Cooper, Dave
Cooper, Dianne L.P.
Cooper, Dick
Cooper, Dorothy
Cooper, Dwane
Cooper, Heather
Cooper, Henry
Cooper, John K.
Cooper, John M.
Cooper, Louise
Cooper, Richard
Cooper, S.
Cooper, Walter
Coopland, Peter
Copeland, F.G.
Copping, Edna N.
Copping, Harold
Copping, R.P.
Corbet, Lew
Corbett, A.
Corbett, J.N.
Corderi, Merrilly
Corey, D.
Corey, James
Cormack, F.
Corman, J.
Cornall, F.A.
Corner, John
Cornish, Willa
Cornwall, Sonia
Corrance, Ian
Corrigan, Anne
Corry, M.
Cortez, Pascal
Cossentine, C.
Cossentine, E.R.
Costanzo, Brenda
Coste, S.

Côte, Serge
Cotton, Ray
Coulson, Evi
Coulson, Mel
Coulter, Annie
Coulter, Bob
Coulter, Eric
Coulter, Pat
Counsell, Eric
Counsell, Jean
Coutts, H.
Cowal, Doug
Cowan, Walt
Cowie, John T.
Cowley, Cliff
Cowlin, Charles
Cowlin, Sybil
Cox, Bryan
Cox, Les
Cox, Stephen
Cox, Terry
Coyle, R.L.
Crabbe, Joan
Crabtree, Tom
Crack, David T.
Craig, Gordon
Craig, Jean
Craig, Muriel
Craig, Noel
Crampton, Heather
Craven, Ruth
Crawford, Dosie
Crawford, Scott
Crichlow, E.
Crins, William J.
Critch, Marion
Critchlow, P.R.
Croft, Phil
Crook, Heather
Crook, W.D.
Cross, Janet
Cross, Mark
Crossman, E.
Crowe, Jim
Crowther, Marjorie
Crowthers, O.
Crystal, Bill
Cullen, L.
Cuming, Jean
Cumming, June
Cumming, Sue
Cunningham, Albert
Cunningham, Don
Cunningham, John
Cunningham, Marge
Cupp, Keith
Curran, Frances
Currie, H.H.
Currie, James
Curson, Jon
Curtain, Fred
Curtis, D.
Cuthbert, James
Cuthbert, Ross
Cutler, Herky
Dafoe, Eric
Dafoe, Peggy
Dahl, Kelly
Dahlke, Anna M.
Dale, Betty
Dale, Jack

Dale-Johnson, V.
Daloise, Richard
Daly, Carol
Daly, Eugene
Daly, Mark K.
Dance, Patti
Daniels, Wes
Danlock, Tye
Darby, Nancy
Darling, Jim
Darnall, Ruth A.
Darney, Judy
Darney, Mike
Dascon, D.
Dates, Steve
Daughty, Harry
Davenport, George
David, Art
Davidson, Albert R.
Davidson, Douglas
Davidson, Eleanor
Davidson, Gary S.
Davidson, Gordon
Davidson, Harry
Davidson, Marie
Davidson, Mary
Davidson, P.W.
Davidson, Peter J.
Davidson, Sarah
Davidson, Terry
Davies, A.R.
Davies, Bill
Davies, Brian
Davies, David
Davies, Doris
Davies, Dorothy
Davies, J.
Davies, Jennifer
Davies, K.
Davies, Lloyd
Davies, Rick G.
Davies, Roy
Davies, Thomas R.
Davis, D.G.
Davis, Ed
Davis, Edna
Davis, John
Davis, Lyndis
Davis, Margaret
Davis, Martin
Davis, S.K.
Dawdrey, Ernie
Dawe, George G.
Dawe, Jordan T.
Dawe, Karen E.
Dawe, Lynn R.
Dawe, Neil K.
Dawson, Jim
Dawson, John
Dawson, Rick
Day, Betty
Day, Colleen
Day, F.
De Burg, H.
De Jong, Westman M.M.
DeAngeles, Milo
DeBourdais, Lorraine
DeGeus, Nell
DeWitt, Art
DeWitt, Louis
Deagle, George

Deakin, D.
Deakin, Ronald
Dean, Anna
Dean, O.S.
Deanna, M.
Deas, Alec
Debent, Anne
de Boon, Arnold
de Boon, Frank
Decamp, Gwen
Decker, Dick
Demarchi, Raymond
Denis, David
Denison, R.A.
Dephyffer, John
Deptford, Vera
Dergthorson, F.
De Rousie, D.
Dery, E.
Desbrosse, Alain
Desrochers, Barbara
Devereux, Stan
Deveson, Bert
Dewitt, Larry
Diack, George
Diakow, Brent
Diakow, Joan
Diakow, Thor M.
Diakow, Wayne
Dibb, Allan
Dicer, Pam
Dick, Asher
Dick, Clarence
Dick, Gary M.
Dick, John
Dick, Pauline
Dickens, H.B.
Dickenson, Frances
Dickenson, George
Dickson, B.
Dickson, Doug
Dickson, Elaine
Dickson, J.
Dickson, Peter
Dickson, W.M.
Diduck, Dorothy
Diederichs, Ron
Diggle, Paul
Dilabio, Bruce
Dillabough, Cecil A.
Dillabough, Eileen D.
Din, Nasar A.
Dingman, Frank
Dingman, Helen
Dinsdale, Graham
Dinse, David
Dion, C.
Dionne, Suzie
Dirkson, Bob
Dirkson, Irene
Dirom, C.
Disney, John
Dites, G.
Dixon, J.
Dobson, Carrie
Dobson, David
Dobson, Donald
Dobson, Fred W.
Dobson, Ken
Dobson, Una
Dobson, Wendy K.

Dohan, Nancie J.
Dolan, Ethel
Donald, J.
Donald, Stephen
Donald, Tom
Donaldson, D.
Donaldson, Ed
Dooley, Brent
Dooley, Robert A.
Dorfer, M.
Dorst, Adrian
Dorst, Suzanne
Doubleday, Jody
Doubleday, Michael
Dougan, Harold
Dougan, Ida
Doughton, B.
Douglas, Aileen C.
Douglas, John
Douglas, Paul
Douglas, Quinn
Douglas, Sheila
Dow, Chris
Dow, Douglas D.
Dow, Margaret A.
Dowding, Bill
Dowling, D.B.
Downey, Phyl
Doyle, D.D.
Drabit, Aaron
Draper, Sid
Drent, Rudolf H.
Drew, Betty
Drew, Bill
Drew, Miles
Drewbrook, Robert
Drexel, Darrel
Drinnal, Warren
Drought, Brian
Duchastel, Andrea
Duchastel, Tom
Duffus, Al
Dumond, F.A.
Dumont, Floyd
Dunbar, David
Dunbar, Lu
Duncan, Adrian
Duncan, David
Duncan, Fred
Duncan, Lyn
Dundas, Bob
Dunham, C.
Dunlop, Florence
Dunn, J.
Dunn, Michael
Dunn, Pat
Dunn, Valerie
Dunning, Jesse
Dupilka, Allan
Dupilka, Becky
Durand, Chips
Durell, Linda
Durkee, Art
Dutton, Marilyn
Dwyer, D.
Dyck, E.
Dyer, Bob
Dyer, Michael
Eadie, John
Earl, Gordon T.
Eastman, Donald S.

Ebel, G.R.A.	Endicott, O.R.	Fink, J.	Foster, B.
Ebel, John	Endwick, Peter D.	Finlay, B.	Foster, Eric
Ebel, Roy	Eng, Marvin	Finley, Becky	Foster, G.G.
Eberts, Tony	England, Lindie	Finzel, J.E.	Foster, Ian
Eccles, Brian	England, Phillip	Fish, Gordon	Foster, J. Bristol
Eckman, R.	Englestonft, Chreistan	Fisher, D. Ross	Foster, Jack W.
Eddy, G.	Erasmus, G.	Fisher, Dean	Foster, M.
Eddy, Harold	Erasmus, J.	Fisher, J.G.	Foubister, M.
Eddy, Lorrie	Ericksen, J.R.	Fisher, Len	Foulser, Art
Eddy, Mike	Erickson, Harriette	Fisher, Martin	Fowle, D.
Eddy, Robbie	Erickson, Ron	Fisher, R.	Fowle, J.T.
Ede, H.	Erickson, Wayne	Fitch, John	Fowler, Fran
Eden, Don R.	Ernest, L.	Fitz-Gibbon, Joyce	Fowler, Scott
Edenshaw, Jaalen	Ernest, W.	Fitzpatrick, Erma	Fox, J.
Edenshaw, Jenny	Ernst, Rick	Fitzpatrick, Irmie	Fox, L.
Edgar, Joshua	Erskine, Anthony J.	Fitzpatrick, John	Fox, Rosemary
Edge, J.	Escott, Christopher J.	Fitzpatrick, Michael	Fox, S.D.
Edgell, Michael C.R.	Escott, Ralph W.	Fitzpatrick, Walter J.	Foxall, Roger
Edie, Alan	Eshleman, Valerie Ann	Flahaut, Martha	Fram, Roland
Edward, Anne	Esouloff, Lorna	Flaherty, Marg	Francis, Brian
Edwards, Barry	Esralson, Lloyd	Fleck, E.	Francis, G.
Edwards, Dan	Estock, Trudy	Flellow, Len	Frank, Floyd
Edwards, Eddie	Etzkorn, J.	Fleming, K.J.	Frank, P.
Edwards, Fred	Evans, Chuck	Fletcher, B.B.	Franken, John P.
Edwards, George	Evans, Darcy	Fletcher, Ross	Franklin, D.H.
Edwards, Glen	Evans, Dave	Fletcher, Russell	Franklin, June
Edwards, O.A.	Evans, Grant	Flett, J.A.	Franklin, R.
Edwards, R. Yorke	Evans, Jack	Fleury, Norman	Franko, G.
Edwards, Yvonne	Evans, Joan	Flowerdew, G.	Fraser, A.
Egely, Mary E.	Evans, Marie	Floyd, Randy	Fraser, Bill
Egg, C.W.	Evans, Theodore	Foessler, Lorraine	Fraser, David F.
Egger, K.	Evans, Tim	Fohr, Brian	Fraser, Douglas P.
Ehman, Gerry	Everette, Valene	Folbegg, Joyce	Fraser, Joan
Eisenmann, E.	Ewart, Anna	Fontaine, J.	Fraser, Kitsy
Eisser, Doug	Exworthy, R. June	Fontaine, L.	Fraser, M.A.
Eldridge, George	Faasse, Tambrey	Fontaine, Marlene	Fraser, Nancy
Eldridge, Ros	Faigin, Sybill	Fooks, A.	Fraser, Tom A.
Elias, Mel	Fair, Brent	Fooks, H.A.	Fraser, William
Ellames, Peggy	Fair, Joan	Foote, R.	Frazer, Evelyn
Ellingsen, Carl	Fairbairn, Steve	Foottit, Michael K.	Frazer, Frank
Ellingsen, David	Fairhurst, P.	Foottit, Robert G.	Frederick, Bruce G.
Elliot, D.W.	Fairley, J.	Forbes, Bob	Freebairn, Tom
Elliot, E.	Fairley, K.	Forbes, Joe	French, Brigitte
Elliot, J.A.	Fairweather, Noreen	Forbes, L. Scott	Freshwater, N.G.
Elliot, Jim	Fallis, Dave	Forbes, Robert	Frew, Gordon
Elliot, Peter	Fallis, Mary	Forbes, Susan	Frewin, M.
Elliot, Ritchie	Fallis, Mike	Forbes, Ted	Friberg, Sherrie
Elliott, Gillian H.	Falls, J. Bruce	Force, Michael	Fricke, Patricia
Elliott, John	Famer, H.	Ford, A.H.	Fried, S.
Elliott, Peter W.	Farley, Ted	Ford, Bruce S.	Friedli, E.
Ellis, Barbara	Farmer, Joanna	Ford, John	Friend, G.B.
Ellis, David V.	Farr, Anthea	Ford, Ron	Friesz, Ron
Ellis, David W.	Fawcett, Ian	Ford, Victor	Friis, Laura K.
Ellis, Rick	Fawcett, S.	Ford, William	Frisby, Alan
Ellis, Steve	Fedoruk, Alan	Foreman, Barbara	Froese, Dave
Ellis, W.C.	Fedoruk, Andrew	Forer, Barry	Froese, Susan
Ellison, Maurice	Feick, Jenny	Forman, Barry	Froimovitch, Mark J.
Elmore, D.T.	Feltner, Ben	Fornataro, Mark	Frost, Bud
Elphinstone, D.	Feltner, L.	Forrest, Margaret	Frost, D. Lorne
Elsasser, Doug	Fenwick, A.A.	Forrester, Shelly	Frost, M.L.
Elston, Alice L.	Ferrario, Giovanni	Forryan, Doreen	Fry, B.
Elston, Suzanne M.	Ferris, Jeanne	Forsman, Eric D.	Fry, Kathleen
Embleton, Nonie	Ferris, Ken	Forster, Mary	Fryer, Ralph
Embleton, Tony	Fieldgate, W.	Forster, Nancy	Fuhr, Brian L.
Emery, Chuck	Fields, Norman	Forsyth, Evelyn	Fuhrer, Hans
Emery, Robert	Filgate, Harry	Fortin, Shawn	Fujino, Ken K.
Emes, J.	Finch, Joanna	Forty, T.	Fulton, Murrey
Emmaneel, Klaus	Finch, Terry	Foskett, Ann	Funk, Phyllis
Emory, B.	Findlater, Jane	Foskett, Dudley	Furniss, O.C.
Emrich, Ralph W.	Findley, Finola	Foss, Ray	Fusco, L.
Enderwick, Peter	Finegan, Rory	Foster, A.	Futur, G.

Fyall, Gerrie
Fyles, J.
Fynn, Sonia
Gabreau, Martin
Gadsen, Ron
Gage, Kim
Gainer, Bob
Gak, Janice
Gak, Marc
Galbraith, Florence
Galbraith, J. Douglas
Gale, Alf
Galicz, George
Galliford, J.
Galloway, Phyllis
Galt, Betty
Gamble, Eleanor
Gammer, A.
Ganguin, Reiner
Gardiner, Mark
Gardner, Gerry
Gardner, Ivan
Gardner, Joe
Gardner, Penny
Gardner, W.E.
Gariett, C.
Garlick, Ella
Garneau, Larry
Garnier, Donald
Garnier, Hattie
Garrioch, Hans
Garrioch, Heather M.
Gaskin, Jeff
Gasser, Ellen
Gaston, Anthony J.
Gates, Bryan R.
Gates, Conrad
Gaunt, Sean
Gawn, Mark
Gaze, D.
Gebauer, Martin
Gee, Andrea
Geernaert, Karen
Geernaert, T.O.
Geeroms, Darryn
Gehlert, R.E.
Gehlin, Phil
Geist, V.
George, D.V.
George, H.E.
George, Val
Gerow, Dave
Gerow, Helen
Gibbard, Fern
Gibbard, H.J.
Gibbard, Les A.
Gibbard, P.
Gibbard, Robert T.
Gibbard, Violet
Gibbon, Robert
Gibbons, Bob
Gibbons, Jeanette
Gibbons, Terry
Gibbons, Tim
Gibbs, Andrew E.
Gibbs, Nicholas
Gibbs, Richard E.
Gibson, A.
Gibson, Carlen
Gibson, Daniel D.
Gibson, D.E.

Gibson, G.G.
Gibson, Ian
Gibson, Kenneth
Gibson, Kevin
Gibson, Pete
Gieson, Cyril
Gifford, Bruce
Gifford, Janet
Gilbert, Frank
Gilbert, Laura
Giles, Lorna
Gill, Cathy
Gill, Leslie
Gillard, Margaret
Gilles, A.S.
Gilles, Cathy
Gillespie, Grahame
Gillies, Barry
Gillingham, Michael
Gillis, W.M.
Gilmour, Bill
Giovanella, Carlo
Girard, Mark
Gissing, A.
Gladstone, B.
Glasgow, Nancy
Glazier, Bob
Glenny, Jim
Glide, Margaret
Glover, Bev
Gobbett, M.
Goble, Edie
Goble, Jim
Godau, Helmut
Goddard, Peter
Godfrey, Dudley
Godfrey, Monica
Godfrey, W. Earl
Godin, Tom
Godkin, Sharon
Godlien, Pat
Goff, A.
Goff, D.
Goff, H.
Gold, G.R.
Gold, P.
Goldberg, Kim
Golden, Linda
Golden, Sandy
Gonzales, B.
Good, Ed
Goodacre, Brian W.
Goodall, Kay
Goodwill, J.E. Victor
Goodwill, Margaret E.
Goodwin, Kent
Goodwin, Lance
Goodwin, Mark
Goodwin, Ruth
Goold, Joan
Goossen, J. Paul
Gorden, John
Gordon, Amelia
Gordon, Bruce
Gordon, Janette
Gordon, John
Gordon, K.
Gordon, Ruth
Gordon, Sheila
Gorman, Wyn
Gorog, K.

Gorsuch, C.V.
Gosling, A.G.
Gosling, Gordon D.
Goudie, Douglas M.
Gough, C.F.
Gould, Glen
Gould, Lenny
Gould, Lorne
Gould, T.C.
Goulet, Louise
Goward, Trevor
Goysuch, C.
Grabowski, Tony J.
Grady, Glen
Graenager, Earl
Graf, Ronald P.
Graham, David
Graham, Elaine
Graham, J. Douglas
Graham, Jim
Graham, Sheila
Graham, Walter
Granger, Ted
Grant, James
Grant, Peg
Grant, Robert
Grant-Duff, Adrian
Grass, Al
Grass, Jude F.
Gray, Alex
Gray, Chris
Gray, David
Gray, Dennis
Gray, Jim
Gray, N.
Gray, Ron
Gray, Tom
Greber, W.
Green, A.
Green, C. De B.
Green, Daphne
Green, David M.
Green, T.R.
Green, William
Greene, R.K.
Greener, Karl
Greenfield, Tony
Gregory, Ann
Gregory, M.S.
Gregory, Patrick T.
Gregson, Jack
Grenager, Earl
Grewer, D.
Grierson, John
Griffin, Mark
Griffin, R.V.
Griffiths, Pele
Grigg, Garry J.
Griggs, Tamar
Grinnel, Dick
Groenveld, Anna
Gronau, Christian W.
Gronau, Steffi G.
Gross, A.
Grossman, Eric
Grotage, Loyd
Grove, Sarah
Gruener, Karl
Grunberg, Helmut
Guernsey, Vera
Guest, Catherine

Guest, Harold
Guiguet, Charles J.
Guiguet, M.L.
Guiguet, Suzanne M.
Guillon, Frank E.
Guinet, Allan
Guinet, Frances
Guinet, Lynn
Guinet, Victor
Gully, P.
Gunther, Jack
Guppy, A.G.
Guppy, G.A.
Gurr, Ray
Gustafson, Barbara
Gustafson, Richard
Guthrie, David
Guthrie, Don
Guthrie, Jim
Gwilliam, John
Gyug, Les
Haas, Norma
Haavik, Andre
Haavik, Colleen
Haavik, Steven
Hack, F.W.
Hackett, John
Hackett, Kathy
Hackett, Shannon
Haddow, W.
Haegart, John
Haering, Penny
Hagen, Barry
Hagen, Betty
Hagen, Catherine
Hagen, Patricia
Haggart, Lee
Haggert, Leona
Hagmeier, E.M.
Hahn, Rick J.
Haig-Brown, Roderick
Halasz, Gabor
Hale, Hilda L.
Hales, D.
Halfnights, B.
Hall, Brian
Hall, D.
Hall, E.R.S.
Hall, J.
Hall, Ken
Hall, W.A.
Halladay, D. Raymond
Halliday, Erik
Halliday, R.L.
Halliday, Valerie
Halverson, Larry
Halz, Gabbro
Hamel, Peter J.
Hames, A.M.
Hames, Michael
Hamilton, Anthony N.
Hamilton, Daphne
Hamilton, Dulcie
Hamilton, John
Hamilton, K.
Hamilton, Marla
Hamilton, Richard
Hamilton, W.
Hammell, Terry
Hammill, Sally
Hammond, D.

Contributors

Hammond, Elsie
Hammond, Jo
Hammond, Vi
Hanceville, Dorothy
Handford, Paul
Handley, Catherine
Handley, L.
Hann, Paddy
Hannam, May
Hansen, J.
Hansen, Marilyn
Hansen, Ruth
Hansen, Stanley
Hansen, Vicky
Hanson, David
Hanson, Don
Hanson, L.
Hanson, Wayne G.
Hansvall, Erling
Hansvall, Louise
Haraldson, T.
Haras, Moreen
Haras, W.
Harcombe, Andrew P.
Harcombe, Rick
Hardie, David
Harding, Martha
Harding, Rob
Hardley, C.
Hards, Jennifer
Hardstaff, Lynn
Hardwick, S.
Hardy, Bill
Hardy, Chuck
Hardy, David
Hardy, Duncan
Hardy, G.A.
Hardy, Phyllis
Hardy, W.
Harestad, Alton S.
Hargrave, A. Nairn
Hark, F.W.
Harlock, F.
Harlow, Susan
Harman, Barry C.
Harms, W.
Harper, Charles
Harper, Don
Harper, Fred E.
Harper, John
Harper, Lynn
Harrington, R.F.
Harris, A.E.
Harris, B.J.
Harris, Brian S.
Harris, Chris
Harris, Christopher G.
Harris, Elizabeth
Harris, G.J.
Harris, Margaret
Harris, Nancy
Harris, P.
Harris, R.P.
Harris, Robert D.
Harris, Ron
Harris, Ross E.
Harrison, John
Harrison, Julian D.
Harrison, Linda
Harrison, William
Hart, A.M.

Hart, Carole
Hart, E.H.
Hart, F. Gordon
Hart, J.G.
Hart, J.S.
Hart, Kit
Hart, Lauren
Hart, Mark
Hart, Ted
Hartland, D.
Hartland, G.
Hartman, F.
Hartman, G.
Hartman, Harold
Hartman, Mary
Hartt, E.A.
Hartwick, E. Brian
Harvard, Peggy
Harvey, Merle
Harvey, Richard
Harvey, Virginnia
Harwell, W.
Haslam, Cathy
Hassell, Sharon
Hatfield, John
Hatler, David F.
Hatler, Mareca
Hatler, Mary Eta
Hatter, D.
Hatter, I.
Hatter, James
Haughan, Linda
Haun, Ariel
Hauser, Pearl
Haven, Stoner
Hawes, David B.
Hawes, David M.
Hawes, James
Hawes, Myrnal A.L.
Hawken, J.
Hawken, M.
Hawkey, G.
Hawkins, J.
Hawksley, Janet
Haworth, Kent
Hay, E.A.
Hay, Heather
Hay, Robert B.
Hayden, M.A.
Hayes, Eric
Hayes, Lauren
Hayes, Maryann
Hayes, Richard
Haylock, Cliff
Haylock, Linda
Hayman, Gus
Hayman, Tom
Haynes, Muriel
Hayton, B.
Hayton, M.
Hazelwood, Grant W.
Heakes, Todd
Healey, John
Healy, Michael
Hearn, David
Hearn, Dorothy
Hearn, Ed
Hearn, O.
Hearne, Georgina
Hearne, Margo E.
Heathman, R.L.

Hebert, Daryl
Hedley, A.F.
Heintz, Gretta
Helleiner, Fred
Helset, R.
Henderson, Bryan A.
Henderson, Martha
Henderson, Michael
Henderson, Nolan
Henderson, Nonie
Henderson, Otto
Henderson, Phil
Henderson, Valerie
Hendra, Isabel
Hendricks, Allan
Hendricks, Gus
Henkins, Harmon
Henn, Keith
Hennan, Ed G.
Hennig, Karla
Henning, E.E.
Henning, Mrs. E.E.
Henry, G.
Henry, John
Henry, Margaret
Henson, Colen
Henson, Gary
Henson, P.
Henson, Simon
Herbert, B.
Herbert, William S.
Herbison, B.
Heriot, Joan E.
Herr, G.R.
Hervieux, Margot
Herzig, R.J.
Hesse, Hilde
Hesse, Werner H.
Hetherington, Anne E.
Hett, M.
Hettis, Rob
Hewson, C.A.
Heybrock, Bill
Heyland, J.B.
Heywood, J.
Hickson, Cathie
Higginson, T.
Highe, Barbara
Highe, Donald
Hill, B.
Hill, Dorothy
Hill, L.
Hill, Mark
Hill, P.
Hill, Robert
Hill, Roy
Hillaby, Bruce
Hillard, R.W.
Hillier, George
Hilligan, D.
Hilligan, S.
Hillis, Nancy
Hilton, Jim
Hinckle, David
Hind-Smith, John
Hindson, Mr.
Hindson, Mrs.
Hines, Garfield
Hinton, J.L.
Hippen, H.
Hirschbolz, Heinz

Hirschbolz, Marlene
Hirst, Stanley
Hitchmough, John
Hlady, Debbie
Hoar, Carol
Hoar, N.J.
Hoar, Rick J.
Hoar, Robin
Hoar, W.
Hobeck, Erika
Hobson, Alan
Hobson, Cam
Hobson, J. Fred
Hobson, James
Hobson, Kerry
Hobson, Mark
Hobson, Marie
Hobson, Shirley
Hochachka, W.
Hocker, Pat
Hocking, Jack
Hocking, Jennifer H.
Hodgins, Betty
Hodson, C.
Hodson, Keith
Hoek, Jane
Hogarth, L.
Hogg, Edward
Hogg, Lori
Holden, D.
Holdom, Canon M.W.
Holland, David
Holland, M.
Holland, R.H.
Holland, Stephen
Hollands, Grant R.
Hollands, J.
Hollington, Jack
Hollington, Madge
Holloway, Lawrence
Holm, Margaret
Holman, John H.
Holman, M.
Holman, P.J.
Holmes, Brian
Holmes, George
Holmes, J.
Holmes, Ken
Holmes, Marc
Holmes, Norman
Holmes, Philip
Holms, Maureen
Holohan, Stewart
Holroyd, Geoff
Holsworth, W.N.
Holt, Beryl H.
Holt, John C.
Hood, Terry
Hook, R.
Hooke, J.
Hooper, Bob
Hooper, Daryl
Hooper, Gordon N.
Hooper, Gwennie
Hooper, Joan
Hooper, Mary
Hooper, Ronald
Hooper, Tracey D.
Hooper, Win
Hope, Herbert
Hopkins, Kay

Hopkins, Vera
Hopkinson, Bubsie
Hopp, Diane
Horn, Dorothy
Horn, J.C.
Horncastle, G.S.
Horne, L.
Horner, N.
Horvath, Otto
Horwood, Brenda
Horwood, Dennis
Hosford, Harold
Hosie, S.
Hosman, P.
Hotchkiss, C.T.
Houlhen, M.
House, H.B.
Houston, Bob
Houston, C.
Houston, G.F.
Houston, M.L.
Houston, R.
Howaldt, Jorg
Howard, B.
Howard, Maureen
Howard, R.G.
Howden, Patrick F.
Howe, Ann
Howe, N.I.
Howe, R.S.
Howe, Robert W.
Howell, Steven N.G.
Howes, Anne
Howie, Gordon
Howie, Richard R.
Howie, Thomas
Howland, E.R.
Howlett, Bruce
Howsam, Judy
Hoyer, G.A.
Hudson, Janet
Huett, Jim
Huett, Patsy
Huggard, Dave
Huggett, Colin
Hughes, Brenda
Hughes, Wm. M.
Hume, Alison
Humeniuk, Natalie
Humphries, Dianne
Hunley, W.
Hunn, Eugene
Hunt, Bob
Hunt, George
Hunt, Robert
Hunter, Bill
Hunter, Elizabeth
Hunter, Gary
Hunter, Joan
Hunter, John
Hunter, Paul
Hunter, Rodger
Hunter, T.
Huntington, Mary E.
Huppler-Poliak, Amy
Hurst, T.
Hustead, Eileen
Hustead, Jack
Hustead, Lynn
Hutchinson, Bob
Hutchinson, Neil

Huxley, Bill
Huxley, Mae
Hyatt, Ron
Hyde, A.S.
Hyde, Eric
Hyde, Frank
Hyde, George
Hyslop, Joyce
Ibera, Carlos
Iden, Bill
Iden, Margaret
Idu, Terry
Ikona, Katherina
Ikona, Richard
Ingles, Joan
Inglis, Rolli
Inkster, C.
Innes, Douglas W.
Innes, Marian
Innes, Martin
Ireland, John
Ireland, Teresa
Irons, Byron
Irvine, Bob
Irvine, Elsie
Irvine, Jean
Irving, Bruce K.
Irving, E. Bruce
Irving, Lyn
Irving, Peggy
Irwin, Alan
Irwin, Barbara
Irwin, Bob
Irwin, Jack
Irwin, Joel
Irwin, Kate
Irwin, Ki
Iverson, J.
Jack, Ian
Jacklin, Isabel
Jackson, Andrew
Jackson, Anne
Jackson, George
Jackson, J.
Jackson, Mary F.
Jacobs, A.E.
Jacobs, Karen
Jacobson, Tom
Jacobson, W.
Jacques, Art
Jacques, Tommy
Jakimchuk, R.D.
James, David
James, Eleanor E.
James, Jennie
James, Paul C.
James, Ross D.
James, Ted
James-Veitch, E.A.
Jamieson, Glen
Jamieson, Jean
Jamieson, Mrs. Glen
Jamison, Eric
Jamison, Margaret
Janelle, Yvan
Janes, Russell W.
Janyk, Barry
Janz, Douglas W.
Jaques, Tim
Jarvie, I.
Jay, K.

Jeal, Margaret
Jeal, Mary
Jean, Cheryl
Jeffrey, R.
Jellett, Jim
Jellicoe, Janice
Jenkerson, Douglas
Jenkins, Eric
Jenkins, Jane E.
Jenkins, Lynn J.
Jenkins, Mildred
Jenkins, Pam
Jenkins, Ron L.
Jenne, M.
Jennings, Gerald
Jennings, Iris
Jensen, B.A.
Jensen, Dale
Jensen, Eve
Jenson, Loraine
Jentsch, Carl
Jerema, Michael
Jerema, Richard S.
Jeroschewitz, Valerie
Jessop, P.
Johns, N.
Johnson, Albert
Johnson, Ann
Johnson, Daryl
Johnson, Donald A.
Johnson, Fran
Johnson, G.
Johnson, H.
Johnson, K.F.
Johnson, P.
Johnson, Sam
Johnson, Sigrid
Johnson, Stephen R.
Johnson, Terry
Johnson, Vern
Johnston, Aleda
Johnston, Dale
Johnston, David W.
Johnston, Dean
Johnston, Holly
Johnston, Jean
Johnston, Joan
Johnston, Larry
Johnston, Nancy
Johnston, Paul
Johnston, Richard
Johnston, Scott
Johnston, Stuart
Johnston, W.
Johnstone, Cecil
Joly, Stephen
Jones, Aaron
Jones, Ann
Jones, Dave
Jones, Don
Jones, Edgar T.
Jones, G.
Jones, Ian
Jones, Kate
Jones, Keith R.
Jones, Ken
Jones, Lindsay E.
Jones, Mike
Jones, Mildred
Jones, Peter
Jones, Robert D.

Jones, Ruth
Jones, Valerie
Jones, Wayne
Jones, William
Jorgensen, Mike
Joyce, Russ
Junck, Chris
Jury, Douglas
Jyrkkanen, Jorma
Kaiser, Dieter
Kaiser, Gary W.
Kaisner, George
Kalman, D.
Kalman, John
Kalmbach, Beverly
Kalmbach, Richard
Kantrim, Desi
Karger, Fritz
Karpuk, Allan
Karpuk, Betty
Karran, P.
Karst, Carl
Karup, Anthony
Karup, L.
Kashin, G.L.
Kautesk, Brian
Kay, A.T.
Kay, Ian
Keddie, Grant
Kedgh, Ruth
Keding, K.H.H.
Keith, Anthony
Keith, David
Keith, Mabel
Keith, Margaret
Keizer, Jasper
Kelleher, K.E.
Kellerhals, Heather
Kellerhals, Rolf
Kelley, Errol
Kelley, Janice
Kelly, Colleen
Kelly, Ethel
Kelly, Fran
Kelly, J.
Kelly, Mary
Kelly, Sean
Kelsey, Lee E.
Kembel, Vern
Kemmett, Dorothy
Kendall, Dean
Kendall, Frank
Kennah, J.
Kennedy, Archie
Kennedy, Bruce
Kennedy, D.M.
Kennedy, Ian D.
Kennedy, Kathryn
Kennedy, Ken
Kennedy, Kevin
Kennedy, Marilyn
Kennedy, R.
Kenner, Gail
Kenner, Rex
Kennett, Dorothy
Kenset, Sandra
Keogh, Ruth
Keranen, Eric
Kergin, A.J.
Kerr, Elspeth M.
Kerr, Frank

Contributors

Kerr, M.
Kerr, T.
Kershaw, M.
Kidd, J.I.
Kidder, E.L.
Kihm, Ruth
Killough, Harry
Kime, Doris
Kime, Frank
Kimpton, Jerry
Kindrachuk, Sonia
King, Avery
King, David G.
King, Derek
King, Don
King, Frances
King, Freeman
King, H.
King, James
King, Jean
King, Joan
King, Peter
King, Rod
King, Wayne
Kingswood, S.
Kinsey, Sandra
Kippin, Ethel
Kippin, J.W.C.
Kirbyson, John
Kirchner, Lothar
Kirkpatrick, F.
Kirkvold, Sherry
Kirschner, Ed
Kirschner, Ute
Kirychk, Walter
Kitson, Alan R.
Klassen, Barry
Klein, Kathy
Kline, C.R.
Kline, Kelly
Knapton, Richard W.
Knecht, Ernie
Knezevich, Gladys
Knezevich, John
Knight, Pat
Knight, Richard
Knowles, Anne
Knowles, David
Knowles, Ken
Knowles, Les
Knowles, Peter
Knowlson, Bill
Koch, Dorothy
Koch, Linda
Koechl, Rick
Koenig, D.F.
Kolstertan, A.
Konkin, Lorne
Kool, Richard
Koonts, Ralph
Koop, Frank
Kormski, Henry
Kormski, Mae
Koth, Edgar
Kowalczyk, L.W.
Kragh, Heather
Kragh, W. Douglas
Krahe, Rolf G.
Krebs, C.
Krebs, John R.
Kremsater, Laurie

Kremsater, Terry
Kribs, J.
Kroek, Jake
Kronlund, A.R.
Krown, Daronne
Krueger, Nancy
Krul, Jane
Kuipers, C.
Kuipers, S.
Kukan, Barbara
Kuntz, Christine
Kuschmin, A.M.
Kuyt, Ernie
Kyle, Brian
L'Ecuyer, Sylvia
Laberge, Frank
Lacey, E.
Lacey, M.
Lacey, P.
Lacon, H.R.
Ladbury, Joan
Laeser, Lynne
Lafave, L.D.
Lafontaine, J.D.
Laforme, George
Laforme, Margaret
Laishey, D.
Lalonde, Maurice
Lamb, Evelyn
Lamb, Helen
Lamb, J.
Lambert, Marilyn A.
Lambert, Phil
Lambert, Wendy
Lambin, Xavier
Lamond, Barry
Lamond, Bill
Lamont, Peter
Lamoureux, E.
Lancaster, R.
Lance, A.N.
Lanchester, Frank
Land, J.
Landry, Gaetan
Lane, Dale
Lane, David
Lane, L.P.
Lane, Les
Lang, Ken
Lang, Sylvia D.
Langdale-Smith, R.
Langer, Ann
Langevin, Arnica
Langevin, Kathy
Langevin, Marlene
Langin, H.
Langley, Lin
Lanko, Joyce
Lansdell, Jane
Lansdowne, Edith
Lansdowne, J. Fenwick
Larkey, J.
Laserre, L.
Lau, Alfred
Laub, Fred
Law, D.
Law, George
Law, Laird
Lawrason, M.G.
Lawrence, Alysoun
Lawrence, Arlene

Lawrence, David
Lawrence, Donald
Lawrence, Gary
Lawrence, Howard
Lawrence, Joanne
Lawrence, Kathleen
Lawrence, Susan
Lawrence, Theresa
Lawrenson, Lee
Laws, Ann
Lawson, Doreen
Lawson, E.H.
Lawson, John
Lawson, Steve
Lay, A.M.
Lay, Dan W.
Lay, R.
LeBaron, Ama
LeBaron, Robert
LeBourdais, Lorraine
Leach, Barry D.
Leadem, Carol
Leadem, Tim
Leaky, Mrs.
Leckie, C.P.
Leckie, Robert
Lecky, B.M.
Lee, Joyce
Lee, Martin C.
Lee, Tom
Lee, Wally
Lees, Sybil
Legate, Gail
Legg, K.
Legg, Peter
Lehman, Paul
Leighton, Douglas A.
Leinor, R.
LeJeune, John
Lellis, C.
Lemke, B.J.
Lemon, Enid K.
Lemon, Moira
Lenfesty, Jack
Lepin, Lynne
Leslie, Edna
Lester, Jody
Lester, Robert
Leveson-Gower, Heather
Levey, Don
Levey, Edith
Levy, E.
Lewall, B.C.
Lewall, Nel
Lewis, David E.
Lewis, J.M.
Lewis, J.P.
Lewis, Lee
Lewis, Moray
Liboiron, Sonia
Light, L.
Lightle, Bob
Lilcox, Joan
Lima, Steven
Lincoln, Arthur
Lincoln, Neville
Lincoln, Robert
Lindsay, G.
Lindstrom, Carl
Lindstrom, Dick
Lines, Mary

Lines, Molly
Lissel, H.
Lisson, R.A.
Little, Bill
Little, Bonnie
Little, Brian
Little, Bruce
Little, R.S.
Little, Robert W.
Littlejohn, David
Littler, Leona
Living, Len
Lloyd, Bob
Lloyd, E.
Lloyd, Helen
Lloyd, Kevin
Lloyd-Walters, J.G.
Loan, D.
Lockhart, D.
Lockhart, Roy
Lodge, Terry
Loewan, David
Lofroth, Eric C.
Loftus, Linda J.
Logan, Douglas B.
Logan, Vernon
Long, Ken
Long, W.S.
Lopatecki, L.
Lopatecki, M.
Lorimer, J.
Lothian, Betty
Lott, Joan
Lott, Tom
Louise, Mary
Love, R.
Lovett, Nancy
Low, Bill
Low, Dave
Lubbers, I.
Luck, Alan
Luck, Brian E.
Luckock, Brian
Lucuik, George
Lukinchuk, Al
Lunam, Betty
Lunam, Jim
Lundell, D.
Lunn, Jerry
Luscher, Robert E.
Luton, Tony
Lutz, Hope
Lutz, Larry
Luz, Fritz X.
Luz, Michael
Lynott, Mary
Lyon, Allan M.
Lyons, C.P.
MacAdam, G.
MacBean, Eric
MacColl, M.C.
MacColl, M.D.
MacDonald, Alan B.
MacDonald, Alex
MacDonald, Bruce A.
MacDonald, Carrie
MacDonald, Doris
MacDonald, Eloise
MacDonald, Greg
MacDonald, Heather
MacDonald, Ian

MacDonald, Lorne
MacDonald, Mary Louise
MacDonald, Murray
MacDonald, Ross G.
MacDonald, S.D.
MacDougall, S.
MacFarlane, Nathalie
MacFarlane, S.
MacGillivray, Alice
MacHutchon, Grant
MacIntosh, Jim
MacKay, D.
MacKay, J.R.
MacKay, Naomi
MacKay, Violet
MacKenzie, Hue
MacKenzie, Jo Ann
MacKenzie, Roddy
MacLeod, Adrian
MacNaughton, C.
MacNaughton, Nancy
MacPhee, Darcy
MacPherson, Bill
MacPherson, F.
MacPherson, Peggy
MacTavish, Bruce
Macartney, J.M.
Macartney, M.
Macher, Marlene
Mack, Eva
Mack, Jim W.
Mack, Mary
Mackay, Ronald H.
Mackenzie-Grieve, Margaret
Mackenzie-Grieve, Rob
Mackie, A.C.
Maclean, Neil
Madsen, Katy
Madsen, Kim
Magee, Elda
Mageorsen, F.
Maginnis, D.
Mahoney, Brian
Mahoney, N.A.
Maitland, Victoria
Major, Jack
Malins, Daphne
Mallet, Leo
Mallory, Enid
Mallory, Gord
Maloff, Diana
Malone, M.
Malyae, Jim
Manly, Betts
Mantle, P.
Manuwal, David A.
March, E.
Marchant, Chris
Marcus, Norman
Mark, David M.
Mark, Murray
Mark, Thomas C.
Marsh, V.
Marshall, Brian
Marshall, Chad
Marshall, Gordon
Marshall, Maureen
Marshall, Rick
Marshall, Sandy
Marshall, Sherwood B.
Marshall, Wayne

Marshall, Wendy
Marshall, William
Marsman, Peter
Martel, Paul
Martell, Andre
Martell, Arthur M.
Martell, Hugh
Martell, Sue
Marten, Malcolm
Martin, Dale
Martin, David
Martin, Elfreda
Martin, Evan
Martin, Gary
Martin, Joan
Martin, Karen
Martin, Malcolm
Martin, Nancy
Martin, Patrick W.
Martin, Peter
Martin, Rae
Marty, K.
Mason, Alfred
Mason, Byron
Mason, George
Mason, Gwen
Mason, Red
Mason, Robert
Massam, G.
Masters, Grant
Masters, Ruth
Mathews, E.C.
Mathews, Gary
Mathews, Herb
Mathews, Rosemary
Mattews, Dave
Matthews, F.
Matthews, W.H.
Mauer, Bud
Mauer, Freda
Maulton, Robert
Maurer, April
Maurer, Frank
Maurer, Mary C.
Maxey, M.
Maxie, Tom
Maxted, Diane
May, Doug
May, Jim
May, Nancy
May, Val
Mayall, June
Mayall, Ken
Maynard, A.H.
Maynard, Edith
Maynard, Ken
Maynes, Dennis
Mayo, Ron
McAlary, Eric
McAlary, F.
McAlary, Lois
McAllister, Nancy
McAllister, Pamela
McAllister, Pat
McAllister, Peter B.
McBain, Dona
McBryde, Trevor
McCall, Stephen
McCallion, Bonnie
McCallion, Russell
McCamant, T.

McCammon, B.M.
McCammon, James W.
McCann, Dorothy
McCann, Mike
McCarten, Michael
McCaskie, Guy
McCaughran, D.A.
McClarnon, J.
McClarnon, S.
McClellam, M.
McColl, Bill
McConnell, Steve D.
McCord, B.
McCord, D.
McCormick, J.
McCrory, Wayne
McCuaig, Georgina
McCurdy, Dave
McDaniel, Caroline
McDevitt, D.C.
McDiarmid, Ray
McDonald, D.
McDouglas, J.
McEachern, J.A.
McEallion, Bonnie
McFarland, David E.
McFarlane, Nancy
McFeat, Marjorie
McFeat, Mark
McFetridge, Jerry
McGavin, Rosemarie
McGibbon, Jane
McGill, Allan S.
McGillis, Joe
McGillivray, W. Bruce
McGinnis, Ed
McGowam, Mary
McGregor, Ian
McGregor, Jo
McGregor, K.
McGregor, Robert
McGrenere, Barbara
McGrenere, Mike
McGrenere, Rob
McGuingle, Terry
McHaffie-Gow, Bertha
McHughs, William M.
McIlwain, Rick
McInnes, G.R.
McInnes, J.D.
McInnis, Nelson
McIntosh, Audrey
McIntosh, Dave
McIntosh, John D.
McIntosh, Lorne D.
McIntosh, M.
McIntosh, W.
McIntyre, Betty
McIntyre, Mary
McIntyre, Walt
McIntyre, William E.
McIvor, Don
McKay, George M.
McKay, P.
McKay, R.H.
McKay, W.A.
McKee, Mike
McKelvey, Richard W.
McKenzie, A.
McKenzie, Dawson
McKerron, Alison

McKie, Mike
McKim, Christine S.
McKinnon, Audrey
McKinnon, Betty
McKinnon, Bill
McKinnon, Joe
McLardy, R.
McLaren, Art
McLaren, Bill
McLaren, Faith
McLaren, I.
McLaren, Karen
McLaren, Margaret
McLaren, Muriel
McLaren, Peter
McLaren, W.D.
McLaren, W.E.
McLary, Eric
McLaughlin, John
McLaughlin, Donna
McLaughlin, Ronald T.
McLaurin, Lee
McLean, A.
McLean, Carina
McLean, Leslie
McLeish, Isobel
McLennan, Ken P.
McLennon, Betty
McLeod, Alan
McLeod, April
McLeod, Erin
McLeod, Frances
McLeod, J.B.
McLintock, B.J.
McMackin, Edward
McMahon, John
McMehan, Fred
McMillan, Daryl
McMillan, Jack
McMillan, Jean
McMillan, Susan
McMullen, Kathy
McMullen, R.D.
McNab, Randy
McNall, Faye
McNall, Michael C.E.
McNaughton, Ernie
McNaughton, J.
McNaughton, Peter
McNeely, Dick
McNeil, I.G.
McNichol, Keith
McNicholl, G.
McNicholl, Martin K.
McPhee, Don
McPherson, Frances
McQuillan, Susan
McQuinn, Betty
McRay, Martha
McRuer, Sandy
McTaggart-Cowan, Ian
McTaggart-Cowan, Joyce
McTavish, Al
McTeer, Wilma
McWhirter, J.L.
McWilliams, Anita
Meadowcroft, Neil F.
Mechie, D.
Meiklejohn, Barbara
Meiklejohn, J.M.
Meiklejohn, Michael

Contributors

Meiklejohn, Teresa
Melbourne, M.C.
Melderis, Martin
Mellett, Mary
Mennel, B.
Mennel, Tuke
Menzies, Charles R.
Mercer, G.
Mercer, Joseph
Mercer, Marie
Mercer, Michael
Mercer, Robert
Mercereau, Lorne
Meredith, C.B.
Merideth-Jones, Winnifred
Merilees, William J.
Merkens, Markus
Merlies, Bob
Merriman, J.D.
Mesley, Victor
Meteer, A.
Meteer, W.A.
Meugens, Arthur L.
Meunier, Maurice
Meyer, Angie
Meyer, Bonnie
Meyer, G.
Meyer, H.
Meyer, Roger
Meyer, Ron
Meyers, Anika
Michael, Paige
Michael, Peter
Middlemass, A.D.
Middleton, H.
Miles, Doris
Miles, Jack
Miles, Keith
Millar, Steve
Miller, Bob
Miller, Doris
Miller, Dusty
Miller, George
Miller, Harold
Miller, Hettie
Miller, Joan
Miller, Josie
Miller, June
Miller, Kate
Miller, Linda
Miller, Lynn
Miller, M.
Miller, M.D.
Miller, Michael
Miller, Ruby
Miller, Stella
Miller, Steve
Milligan, D.
Milligan, Tony
Mills, A.
Mills, Eric L.
Mills, Marjorie
Mills, Maureen
Millward, Peter J.
Miln, H.
Milne, G.
Milne, R.
Milne, W.
Milnes, Lynne
Mitchell, George J.
Mitchell, J.

Mitchell, Marjorie
Mitchell, Nora
Mitchell, Paul
Mitchell, R.P.
Mitchell, Steve
Mitchell, W.
Mitchell-Banks, B.
Miyamoto, Susie
Mock, B.
Mock, Ralph
Mogensen, Faye
Mollet, L.
Mollet, M.
Molnar, Les
Molyneux, Betty
Monahan, Hugh
Moncton, P.M.
Mondey, Dave
Montador, Marian
Montague, P.
Monteith, W.B.
Montgomery, Gill
Montgomery, Pat
Moody, Anne I.
Moody, Ed
Moody, Robert
Mooney, Steve
Moore, Dwight D.
Moore, Huber
Moore, Keith
Moore, Lynn
Moore, Marion
Moore, R.A.
Moore, Richard
Moore, Trudy
Moores, Glen W.
Moores, Judith A.
Moorhead, Maeve
Morberg, Don
Mordy, J.P.B.
Morehen, C.W.
Morford, Bob
Morford, W.R.
Morgan, Barry
Morgan, Harold
Morgan, Jane
Morgan, Jeff
Morgan, Joan
Morgan, Ken
Morgan, M.P.
Morgan, Richard
Morganson, Faye
Morgenstern, Bruce
Morgenstern, Pearl
Morhan, Sue
Morin, Bill
Morley, Bill
Morley, Wayne
Morrell, Mike
Morris, Bill
Morris, G.
Morris, Mary C.
Morris, Mary J.
Morris, P.L.
Morris, William A.
Morrison, D.
Morrison, Jeff
Morrison, Karen
Morrison, Ken P.
Morrison, Terry
Morse, Ann

Morse, F.
Mortimer, John
Morton, Keith
Morton, Norma
Morton, Paul
Mosedale, M.
Mosedale, W.
Moss, L.
Moss, Patricia
Mossip, David
Mosveen, Norman
Mottishaw, B.
Mouat, I.
Mouat, S.
Mould, Alice
Mould, Frank
Moursey, Lee
Mowat, D.
Moyle, Diane
Moyle, Gail
Moyle, Ken
Moyls, B.
Muellers, Angela
Muffley, B.
Muir, Alexander
Muir, Allister
Muir, K.S.
Muirhead, Nancy
Muirhead, R.C.
Mullen, Karen
Mulligan, Pat
Mumford, Mary
Munn, A.
Munn, D.
Munn, R.
Munro, Beth
Munro, David A.
Munro, Deane
Munro, Edward
Munro, I.H.
Munro, Kathleen
Munro, Patricia
Munro, W.H.
Munro, William T.
Munson, T.
Murphy, Diane
Murphy, Pam
Murphy, Tim
Murr, Norman
Murray, Jim
Musfelt, V.
Myers, Helen
Myers, Roger
Myers, Shawn
Myers, Steve J.
Myres, Linda
Myres, M. Timothy
Nagel, R.A.
Nagorsen, David
Nairne, Charlie
Nancarrow, P.
Naomi, Anna
Napper, E.
Narod, Mary
Nash, Harry
Nash, Joyce
Nealis, Jonathan
Nealis, V.G.
Nebel, Isabel
Neiderlich, Wolf
Neilsen, Christian E.

Neilson, D.
Neilson, Winnifred
Neily, Wayne
Neish, Jim
Nelson, Erin
Nelson, Jim
Nelson, Judy
Nelson, Marge
Nelson, R. Wayne
Nelson, W. Lyon
Nero, Robert W.
Netbay, A.
Netting, Anthony
Neuls, Karl
Newall, Linda
Newberry, P.
Newell, David S.
Newell, Gail
Newell, George
Newell, Ted
Newman, J.
Newman, Roy
Newman, Wendy B.
Newson, Marion
Newson, Verna
Newton, Amy D.
Newton, Betty
Newton, E. Faye
Newton, Kevin S.
Newton, Kyla R.
Newton, M.I.
Newton, Rose
Newton, Sean
Nichol, R.H.
Nicholls, S.
Nichols, Alan
Nickel, Ellison
Nickel, Tom
Nicol, Adeline
Nicol, Karen
Nicolai, Brian
Nicholson, Cindy
Nielsen, C.E.
Nielsen, R.B.
Niemann, F.
Nishi, Geri
Nivison, C.
Nixon, Wendy
Nobel, D.
Noble, Leigh
Noble, Malcolm
Noble, R.W.
Noel, Doug
Noel, Phyllis
Noel, Russel
Nomme, K.
Norman, Alex
Norsworthy, Marge
North, Elizabeth
North, Ernie
North, Lois
Norton, Gloria
Nott, Phil R.
Nowosad, June
Nunwieler, Conrad
Nurmeste, Alan
Nuttall, J.K.
Nuttall, Pat
Nuttall, Brian
Nyberg, Brian
Nye, Doris F.

Nygren, Edward L.
Nygren, P.
Nyhof, Mark
O'Brian, Derek
O'Connor, David
O'Neil, Betty
O'Neill, Mike
O'Neill, Myrtle
O'Neill, W.R.
Oakley, Darryl
Oakley, Karen
Obana, J.
Oberg, Evelyn
Oberg, Nanny
Odear, Bob
Odion, D.
Odlum, D.G.
Odlum, Gordon C.
Ogilvie, H.
Ogilvie, Robert
Oguss, Emily
Ohanjanian, Penny
Oke, Dennis
Oko, Hilda
Oldaker, R. Frank
Oldfield, Mike
Oliphant, Bill
Oliver, Chris
Oliver, Joyce
Oliver, Lyle
Oliver, Marg
Oliver, Roy
Olmstead, J.
Olsen, Brent
Olsen, Carl
Olsen, H.I.
Olson, Daniel
Ommundson, P.
Orcut, Lowell
Orman, Linda
Orser, Ray
Osborn, Bill
Osborn, June
Osborne, C.
Osman, C.D.
Osmond-Jones, E.J.
Ostrom, Nancy
Otway, Bill
Ouellet, Henri
Overhoff, Nettie
Overstall, Richard
Pageot, Madeleine
Paget, John
Paget, Trine
Paille, Gerry
Paine, F.
Paine, Roger
Palfreyman, Gail
Palmateer, Calvor
Palmer, Greg
Palmer, Katherine
Palmer, Ken
Palmer, Mary
Palmer, Naida
Palmer, Ray
Palmer, Walter
Paquette, Maggie
Parham, H.J.
Parish, Pat
Parker, Bill
Parker, Delbert N.

Parker, Jess
Parkin, David
Parkin, Joan
Parkin, Tom W.
Parks, Lorraine
Parks, W.
Parlee, Richard
Parry, John
Parsons, Bob
Parsons, D.K.
Parsons, Evelyn
Parsons, L.
Parsons, Ron
Parsons, S.
Partington, Geoffrey W.
Paseika, Marilyn
Passmore, R.
Pastrick, Bobbie
Pastrick, Mary
Pastrick, Trudy
Paterson, Aurora
Paterson, Lyn
Paterson, Stan
Patey, W.
Patt, Diane
Patt, Roy
Patten, Ray
Pattenaude, Mary
Pattenden, B.
Patterson, Alec
Patterson, Ernie
Patterson, Gerry
Patterson, James
Patterson, Jane
Patterson, Joyce
Patterson, Lloyd
Patterson, Wilma
Pattinson, C.
Pattison, Lyn
Pattison, Stan
Paul, Anna
Paul, C.R.
Paul, Frank
Paul, Mary
Paul, W.A.B.
Paull, G.W.
Paulson, Dennis R.
Pavlick, Leon
Pawless, Irene I.
Payne, D.E.
Peach, Derek
Peake, Arthur
Peake, Fred
Pearce, David
Pearce, Ed
Pearce, Gordon
Pearce, Marguerite
Pearce, T.
Pearkes, Marg
Pearlstone, Paul
Pearse, Theed
Pearse, Tony
Pearson, A.M.
Pearson, G.A.
Pearson, Vi
Pearson, Winifred
Peatt, Alan D.
Peck, Jess
Peden, Alex E.
Pedersen, Vibeke
Pedley, David

Pedley, Lynne
Peers, Betty-Lou
Pegler, Moreen
Pelham, H.
Pelper, John A.
Pendergast, Bruce
Pendray, C.H.
Penker, Linden
Penker, Robin
Penker, Sandy
Penker, Wilfred
Perez, Mario
Perkins, Ann
Perkins, H.C.
Perreault, Henry
Perrin, David
Perrin, Jacob
Perrin, Janne
Perrin, Murielle
Perrin, Peter W.
Perrin, Roland
Perrin, Tim
Perrone, Mike
Perry, Audrey
Perry, Jim
Person, Everett
Petapiece, V.
Peters, Iris A.
Peters, Sheila
Peters, Vi
Peters, Wilbur
Petersen, Claus
Peterson, Bruce R.
Peterson, Dan
Peterson, Don
Peterson, Ernie
Peterson, Faye
Peterson, Gretchen
Peterson, Larry
Peterson, Les
Peterson, P.
Petley, Pat
Petrar, Brian J.
Petrar, Heidi
Peve, Armand
Peyton, Leonard J.
Phelps, Dave E.
Phillip, Connie
Phillip, John
Phillipedes, George
Phillips, Pat
Phillips, Roy W.
Phipps, Barbara
Phipps, Bill
Phyall, Doug
Pick, Paula
Pickens, Len C.
Pickens, Lola
Pickering, V.
Picman, Jaraslov
Piddington, Phyllis
Pielou, Chris
Pienze, J.
Pike, Gordon
Pike, P.C.
Pikula, Flo
Pilconis, Lorie
Pilkey, Ron
Pillsbury, R.W.
Pinch, Brian
Pinette, Tom

Pirnke, Mike
Pitt, Marg
Pitt, Rae
Pitt-Brook, David
Piuze, Jean
Plath, Tom
Platt, M.
Pleckaitis, Harold
Pletzer, Laurie
Plewes, Heather
Plowden-Wardlaw, J.
Po, Catherine
Pocklington, Bill
Poff, Carol
Poggenmiller, G.
Poile, Irene
Poirier, Evelyn
Pojar, Jim
Pojar, Rosamond
Polivka, Ivan
Poll, Dave
Pollard, Lynn
Pollock, Harold
Polsom, Jacob
Polson, John E.
Polson, Melissa
Pooley, R.H.
Pope, Arthur
Porcher, Alf
Port, Bert
Port, Sue
Porter, Bill
Porter, Julie
Porter, Marian
Porter, Steve
Postey, W.
Potsepp, Ted
Potts, E.
Potts, George
Potts, Marc
Poulsom, J.
Powell, David
Powell, Derek
Powell, Douglas
Powell, Joe L.
Powell, Joyce
Power, Damian
Power, M.
Power, Rosemary
Powers, Gerry
Poynter, G. Allen
Poynter, Helen
Pratt, F.C.
Pratt, T.
Pratt, W.J.
Precious, Norman
Prehara, Bea
Prentice, Jim
Preston, Al
Preston, John
Preston, Margaret
Preston, W.B.
Prestwich, T. Alex
Previer, Jim
Price, A.T.
Price, Maureen
Price, Michael
Price, Neil
Price, Richard
Prier, Jim
Prince, Shirley

Contributors

Prior, Roy
Pritchard, Bill
Pritchard, K.
Prokop, Randy
Proverbs, M.P.D.
Provo, Brian
Pryce, Colin
Pullman, K.
Puls, Judy
Punnett, Walter
Purches, Sandi
Purdy, Bob
Purdy, Jim
Purdy, Margaret
Purdy, Robert O.
Purssell, Norman
Purssell, W.
Quadvelieg, R.
Quayle, Jim
Quijano, Gina
Quirk, John
Quirk, Shirley
Rack, Kurt
Rack, Marilyn
Rae, William S.
Raible, L.
Raincock, M.
Rainville, Claire
Ralph, C.J.
Ralph, J.
Ramsay, B.
Ramsay, J.H.
Ramsay, Jamie
Ramsay, Leah
Ramsay, R.L.
Ramsay, Terri A.
Ramsdin, Bernice
Ramsey, Helen
Ramsey, Keith
Rankin, Cynthia
Rankin, Leo J.
Ransom, P.
Ransom, W.
Ranson, J. Philip
Rathbone, Phil
Rathbone, Sandy
Rathbone, Tony
Rattray, Jim
Rauch, F.
Ray, N.
Raymond, Gilbert
Raynor, C.
Read, Gloria
Realton, Clare
Realton, Jim
Redhead, Bob
Redhead, P.C.
Reed, Austin
Reed, Bob
Reed, Joyce Hagerbaumer
Reed, Ruth
Reedamon, Martin
Reeson, David
Reeve, Jeff
Reeve, Meredith
Regan, Howard
Reid, Chris
Reid, Clifford R.
Reid, Emerson
Reid, Ken
Reid, Lyle

Reid, Mary
Reid, Patrick
Reid, T.C.
Reider, C.
Reifel, George H.
Reimchen, Tom E.
Reimer, Al
Reiter, Jean
Reiter, John
Rekert, Gladys
Rekert, Harry
Rekert, Tony
Rempel, Dan
Rempel, Mary
Renfrey, G.
Renner, J.
Renouf, Ed M.
Rentmeester, Tony
Rephin, Steve E.
Retfalvi, Laszlo
Reusch, Randy
Reynolds, John
Reynolds, R.W.
Reynolds, Rob
Reynolds, Sheila
Rhama, Ann
Rhynas, K.
Rhynas, P.
Rice, Desmond
Rice, Louise
Richards, Dave
Richards, Keith
Richardson, Frank
Richmond, Mary
Richter, F.M.
Rick, Pamela
Ricker, William E.
Ridsdale, Doreen
Riedman, Martin
Riedman, Sophie
Riley, J.H.
Rissling, Jim P.
Ritcey, Clara
Ritcey, David
Ritcey, Ralph W.
Ritchie, Dave
Ritchie, M.
Ritz, C.W.
Ritz, W.
Roach, Anthony J.
Roberson, Don
Roberts, Ann
Roberts, Anna
Roberts, Dave
Roberts, Don
Roberts, G.
Roberts, Hanna
Roberts, Leila G.
Roberts, Naomi
Roberts, Phyllis
Roberts, Stan
Roberts, Syd
Roberts, William
Robertson, Betty
Robertson, Bob
Robertson, Brian
Robertson, Dorothy
Robertson, Fiona
Robertson, Ian
Robertson, J.F.
Robertson, Kelly

Robertson, L.
Robertson, R.M.
Robertson, Steven
Robertson, Strilan
Robertson, Terry
Robinson, Al
Robinson, Brian
Robinson, D.J.
Robinson, France
Robinson, G.
Robinson, Harold
Robinson, James I.
Robinson, Jack
Robinson, Joan
Robinson, Lois
Robinson, Ray
Robinson, Robin D.
Robinson, Ron
Robinson, Steve H.
Robinson, V.
Robinson, Wilma F.
Robitaille, Mary
Rocchini, R.
Roch, A.J.
Rock, Christopher
Rock, Kurt
Rock, Marilyn
Rockwell, Diane
Rockwell, I. Laurie
Roddick, M.
Rodgers, Ed
Rodgers, John
Rodway, Joy A.
Rodway, Michael S.
Roe, Earl
Roe, Elizabeth
Roe, Nicholas A.
Roe, Rick
Roemer, Hans
Rogan, M.L.
Roger, Benton
Rogers, B.W.
Rogers, Dale
Rogers, G.B.
Rogers, J.V.
Rogers, Jean
Rogers, Len
Rogers, Pat
Rogers, Paul
Rogers, Ray
Rogers, Ruth J.
Rogers, T.H.
Rogers, Victor
Rollins, Adrian
Rollins, Daphne P.
Rollins, P.
Rooklin, Lynda
Rose, Paul
Rosen, Carl
Ross, Alex
Ross, Barbara
Ross, D.A.
Ross, D.R.
Ross, F.
Ross, Gail
Ross, Graham
Ross, Joel
Ross, Lena
Ross, Martin
Ross, R.
Ross, Sandra

Rossiter, Doreen
Rote, Betty
Rottacher, B.
Routledge, Adele
Routledge, Dave
Routledge, Harold
Routledge, Maureen
Row, Earl
Roysum, Wayne
Ruckles, Phyllis A.
Ruckles, Gwen
Rudy, F.
Rungren, Peggy
Runyan, Bruce
Runyan, Craig
Rushton, Charles E.
Russell, Fraser
Russell, G.
Russell, Judy
Russell, L.S.
Russell, Noel
Russell, William
Russell, Yvonne
Rutherglen, Ted
Ryberg, Max
Ryder, Angie
Ryder, Dave
Ryder, Glen R.
Ryder, June
Ryder, P.
Ryder, R.A.
Ryder, Sue
Rye, Darrell
Ryff, Alan J.
Ryga, G.
Safir, Ann
Salal, J.
Salisbury, Dan
Samper, Cristian
Sampson, Phil
Sanders, Areta
Sanders, Jeffrey R.
Sanderson, Elaine
Sandwell, Robert
Sanford, Frank
Sanftleben, Peggy
Sargeant, L.E.
Sargeant, D.E.
Sarles, Jack G.
Sarles, John
Sarles, Rosamond
Sarlund, Barb
Sarlund, Lee
Sars, Karel
Sather, Mike
Satterfield, Joy
Satterfield, Ronald
Satterly, Jack
Sattman, R.
Saunders, Betty
Saunders, E.
Saunders, James
Saunders, Jane
Saunders, Jean
Saunders, Noel
Sauppe, Barry
Savale, Bill
Savard, Jean-Pierre L.
Sawade, Ron
Saxon, Greg
Scheer, Robert

Schell, Ed
Schick, W. Jack
Schmidt, Chris
Schmidt, Dennis
Schnider, Robert W.
Schoceten, Lorna
Schoceten, Madelen
Schoen, Ellen
Scholes, David
Schouten, Madelon
Schreck, J.M.
Schueler, Fred
Schultz, Zella M.
Schutz, Allan C.
Schutz, Phyllis
Schwab, B.
Schwab, Francis E.
Schwabl, Hubert
Scott, A.W.
Scott, Brian
Scott, Greg
Scott, Irving
Scott, Pat
Scott, W.E.
Scott-Mason, F.
Scott-Moncrieff, R.
Scotter, George
Screeton, Edward
Screeton, Roberta
Scruton, Andrew
Scruton, Colin
Scruton, David
Scruton, Joan
Seaborne, Jean
Seaborne, K.T.
Seabrook, Marie
Sealy, Spencer G.
Searing, Gary F.
Seaton, B.
Sedgewick, Barb
Sedgewick, Don
Seel, K.E.
Seggie, Mike
Seidel, D.C.
Sekhon, Kelly
Selby, R.C.
Self, Brian
Seliciki, Daphne
Selley, C.
Sendall, Bill
Sendall, Kelly
Seon, G.E.
Septer, Dirk
Sewell, Richard
Sewell, Roslyn
Sexsmith, Bob
Sexsmith, Sheila
Shaddick, Stan
Shamlock, Margaret
Shandler, B.
Shaneman, John
Shank, Howard
Shank, I.C.
Shank, M.
Sharp, Al
Sharp, Thelma
Shatwell, Alan
Shatwell, Rosemary
Shatwell, Una
Shaver, Gerry
Shaver, Jim

Shaw, Dorothy
Shaw, Eric
Shaw, Janice
Shaw, Rick
Shaw, Sandy
Shea, Josh
Shea, Judy
Sheard, C.
Shearer, B.
Shearman, S.
Shears, Ken
Sheehan, Brian R.
Sheehan, Michael W.
Sheer, B.
Shelford, J.C.
Shelford, Neil
Shenan, Frank
Shennon, F.
Shepard, Bettie
Shepard, Bob
Shepard, Chris D.
Shepard, J.
Shepard, Mark F.
Shepard, Michael G.
Shepard, Teresa E.
Shepard, V.
Shepherd, P.E.K.
Sheppard, R.F.
Sheppard, Stephen R.J.
Sheppy, J.
Shera, W.P.
Sherman, D.K.
Sherman, E.
Sherman, F.A.
Sherman, S.
Sherman, T.K.
Sherrif, Douglas
Sherrington, Peter
Shervill, Daniel
Sherwood, John
Shields, Joan
Shields, Ken
Shields, Tom
Shillaker, F.M.
Shinkawa, Anthony
Shireman, Tim
Short, Steve
Shorter, Harry
Shouldice, Wayne
Shriever, P.
Shunter, M.
Shutz, A.C.
Sian, Ervio
Siddle, Chris D.
Siddle, Sonja
Sieburth, H.G.
Sigsworth, Bill
Sigsworth, Jack
Sigsworth, Joan
Silver, D.
Silver, Rod
Silvey, Joe
Sim, Sybil
Simmon, Earl
Simmons, P.A.
Simmons, Stephen
Simon, David
Simon, Winnifred
Simonson, Tim
Simpson, Craig
Simpson, Don

Simpson, Fred A.
Simpson, George
Simpson, Ken
Simpson, L.
Simpson, Sam
Sims, J.
Sing, Edward C.
Sing, Kay
Sirk, George P.
Sirk, Lauren
Sirois, Jacques
Sironen, Sandra
Sismey, E.
Skapski, Kornel
Skapski, Viola
Skoba, Rosamond
Skoba, W. Fred
Skriletz, Jeff
Skwarok, Denise J.
Slack, Jack
Slack, Sharon
Slater, J.R.
Slater, M.E.
Slavens, R.D.
Sleeman, Ken
Slessor, Norman
Slingerland, Richard
Sloan, Bill
Sloan, Irene
Sloan, John
Slocom, M.
Slocombe, Jean
Slocombe, June
Slocombe, Linda
Slocombe, Scott
Sluggett, G.
Slupianek, B.
Smart, Gail
Smedley, C.
Smedley, Lydia
Smirl, Robert J.
Smith, Andrew
Smith, Arthur
Smith, Barney
Smith, Bernice
Smith, Beverly
Smith, Brad
Smith, Brian
Smith, Bruce
Smith, Cyril
Smith, D. Wayne
Smith, D.A.
Smith, D.J.
Smith, Daryl
Smith, Dave W.
Smith, Dean
Smith, Douglas H.
Smith, Elizabeth
Smith, Evan
Smith, Eve
Smith, George
Smith, Gertrude
Smith, Glen E.
Smith, Gordon
Smith, I.C.
Smith, Ian D.
Smith, James N.M.
Smith, Jason
Smith, Jeremy
Smith, Joseph
Smith, Karen M.

Smith, Karl
Smith, Kay
Smith, Larry
Smith, Lorraine C.
Smith, Norman
Smith, Nini
Smith, Pat
Smith, Raymond
Smith, Richard C.
Smith, Risa
Smith, Roger
Smith, Susan M.
Smith, T.G.
Smith, Terry
Smith, W.G.
Smither, J.J.
Smithson, Barry
Smyly, John
Smyly, Noreen
Smyth, Jonathan
Smythe, G.A.
Snee, Margaret E.
Snow, Derek
Snow, P.
Snyder, Andy
Snyder, Beth C.
Snye, Terry
Soadvent, Ralph
Soberg, D.
Solberg, H.A.
Solecki, D.
Soleckie, Daphne
Solf, J.D.
Solly, Grace
Somerford, M.
Somerville, Alison
Sopuck, Leonard
Sorapure, Peter
Sothcott, G.
Soules, Keith
Soulsby, Gladys
Sousby, H.W.S.
Soutar, D.
Souther, Barb
Souther, J.
Southerland, Grahame
Sowden, Margaret J.
Spalding, D.J.
Spalding, David A.E.
Spalding, H.
Spanier, T.
Sparks, Frank
Sparks, Tony
Sparling, D.B.
Spaulding, Anne
Spaulding, D.
Speechly, Win
Specht, Marlene
Speich, Steve M.
Spence, Chris
Spence, Doris
Spence, Gordon
Spenst, Del
Spenst, Sandy
Spicer, Chris
Spicer, Jean
Spiers, Carole
Spiers, L.T.
Spitman, Bernie
Spitman, Prue
Springett, B.

Stace-Smith, Tine
Stacey, Pam
Stachera, Stan
Stafford, B.
Stainer, B.
Stainer, John
Staines, G.
Stalker, W.J.
Stanley, Ann
Stanley, Denis
Stanley, Doris
Stanley, G.
Stanley, S.O.
Stark, J.P.
Steeds, Rita
Steel, D.
Steele, Billie
Steele, Doris W.
Steele, John
Steele, Rita
Steele, Tony
Steele, William
Steen, Ardell
Steeves, Jack
Steeves, John
Stein, David
Stein, R.C.
Steinke, Wally
Stelfox, H.A.
Stent, Peter
Stephen, J.A.
Stephenson, A.B.
Stephenson, J.
Stephenson, Marylee
Stepniewski, Andrew M.
Sterling, Tom
Stevens, Irene
Stevens, John
Stevens, Tom
Stevenson, B.
Stevenson, D.G.H.
Steward, G.E.
Stewart, Andy C.
Stewart, Ann
Stewart, Dave
Stewart, E. Ann
Stewart, Geoff E.
Stewart, Harold
Stewart, Lilian
Stewart, T.D.
Sties, Jack
Stinson, Jackie
Stirling, Andrew
Stirling, David
Stirling, Ian D.
Stirling, Ruth
Stiven, A.E.
Stockdale, T.D.
Stockman, William
Stocks, F.
Stone, Jack
Stoneberg, R.
Stoney, Frank
Stopne, Adrianne
Storey, Katherine
Straight, L.
Straith, Bob
Straley, Gerald
Stratton, M.B.
Stream, Lee
Street, Hazel

Street, Janet
Street, Jim
Strickland, Al
Strickland, William
Strikwerda, Fred
Stroctman, Anita
Strom, G.
Strube, Becky
Stuart-Stubbs, Basil
Stubbe, Eileen F.
Stubley, Ken
Stuible, Shirley
Stushnoff, Brian G.
Sugden, Ben A.
Sugden, J.
Sugden, L.
Suggitt, B.
Suggitt, L.
Sullivan, B.
Sullivan, R.D.
Sullivan, Sibohan
Sullivan, Terry
Summers, J.D.
Summers, Kenneth R.
Summerville, Valeri
Sunderland, Graham
Sundquist, Lance
Sundstrom, J.
Sundstrom, V.
Surkan, David
Suterbach, Bob
Sutherland, Bob
Sutherland, Doreen
Suttill, D.E.H.
Suttill, Dennis L.
Suttill, Kaye
Sutton, Britt
Sutton, Derek
Sutton, Dorothy
Sutton, Kathy
Sutton, William
Svoboda, Emily
Svoboda, John Jr.
Swanson, Harold
Swindle, Pat
Switzer, Bob
Switzer, Jim
Symon, Margaret
Symons, P.E.K.
Symons, P.W.
T'Amboline, D.
Tabak, John
Tagles, Robin
Tainter, S.L.
Tait, Doreen
Tait, J.D.
Tait, Mary
Takacs, J.
Takishita, Faith
Tamasi, J.
Tamke, Vern
Tansky, J.E.
Tarr, Hugh
Tarr, Tom
Tate, Mary Ann
Tatum, Jeremy B.
Taylor, B.W.
Taylor, Bill
Taylor, Carrie
Taylor, Clark
Taylor, Cynthia

Taylor, Darwin
Taylor, Dudley
Taylor, M. Elizabeth
Taylor, Ernie W.
Taylor, Gary
Taylor, George
Taylor, Gwen
Taylor, Jim
Taylor, John D.
Taylor, John S.
Taylor, Keith G.
Taylor, Ken
Taylor, Leah
Taylor, Lucinda
Taylor, Marty
Taylor, Mary
Taylor, Petty
Taylor, Philip S.
Taylor, Roger
Taylor, Ron
Taylor, Ruth
Taylor, Sid
Taylor, Simon
Taylor, Stirling
Taylor, Traff
Taylor, W.L.
Teal, Aileen
Teichroe, Peter
Telosky, B.M.
Telosky, Howard A.
Templemann, D.
Tennant, Walt
Teske, Irene
Thacker, B.M.
Thacker, George
Thacker, T.L.
Thatcher, D.J.
Thomas, Vincent
Thompson, Al
Thompson, Anne
Thompson, Antony B.
Thompson, David
Thompson, Diana
Thompson, Gary
Thompson, George
Thompson, Jean
Thompson, John
Thompson, Ken
Thompson, Marlene
Thompson, Peter
Thompson, Ron D.
Thomsen, Kurt
Thomson, Brenda
Thomson, Chuck
Thomson, David
Thomson, George
Thomson, Glen
Thomson, H.
Thomson, John
Thomson, Robert
Thorgeirson, Jack
Thornber, R.
Thornburgh, J.
Thorne, B.
Thorne, Debby
Thorne, E.
Thorne, Frank
Thorne, G.
Thorne, Walter
Thornton, Ed
Thornton, Meredith

Ticard, E.G.
Tidmus, Rene
Tiernan, John
Till, Madeline
Timmins, Moira
Tingley, S.
Tinney, Art
Tinney, Jean
Tipper, G.K.
Tisdale, Rod
Tivel, Tracey
Tnasky, A.
Todd, Jack
Todd, Terese
Toft, Lowes
Toftdahl, Kjeld
Tomlinson, Mike
Tompa, Frank
Tonge, Peter
Tonge, Win
Toochin, John
Toochin, Mike
Tootell, Barbara
Tootell, Bert
Tosh, B.
Touzeau, K.
Tow, P.H.
Towers, Ruth
Traicheff, George
Trefry, Colin
Trefry, Sharon
Tremblay, Ellen
Trembley, Wayne
Tremewen, Charles
Trenholme, Neil S.
Trent, Robert
Trevitt, John
Trotter, Brenda
Trotter, Charles A.
Tsang, Larry
Tucker, G.W.
Tuffy, B.
Tull, C. Eric
Tuomaala, Eileen
Turcotte, Jean-Pierre
Turcotte, Yves
Turnbull, A.D.
Turnbull, Douglas
Turnbull, G.J.
Turnbull, Rochelle
Turnbull, W.G.
Turner, Charles
Turner, Frank
Turner, Margaret
Turney, Laurence
Tutt, Jim
Tyson, Danny
Udvardy, Miklos D.F.
Uliet, Bob
Underhill, J.E.
Upshall, Muriel
Upton, Ross
Urban, Judy
Usher, Robyn
Vaida, Tom
Vaillancourt, Andre
Valenda, Lon J.
Valentin, W.J.
Vallee, Anne
Van Blaricom, E.W.
Van Damme, Linda

Van De Vlassaker, J.
Van Den Berg, Duanne
Van Den Berg, Kees
Van Der Gulick, L.
Van Der Gulick, R.
Van Der Pol, Hank
Van Der Raay, Brigitta M.
Van Driel, Lenard
Van Drimmelen, Ben
Van Egmond, John
Van Herwaarden, Tina
Van Kerkoerle, Anneke
Van Kerkoerle, Peter
Van Meecuven,
Van Meel, Rosie
Van Oosdam, Jay
Van Strien, Jack
Van Tets, Gerard F.
Van Thienen, F.J.
Van Tighem, Kevin J.
Van Tine, Leo
Vance, Horace R.
Vandenburg, K.
Vanderburg, D.
Vandergucht, Matthew
Vanderlinde, Jost
Vanderpol, Hank
Vanhove, John
Vanson, John
Varger, Fritz
Vaudry, A.
Veale, David
Vedova, Dan
Venables, E.P.
Verbeek, Nicolaas A.M.
Verbrugge, William
Vereeken, Irene
Verner, J.
Vicker, Sue
Vickers, A.
Vickery, Keith
Vickery, Sue
Viken, Aubrey J.
Villenueve, Claudette
Vipond, Clare
Visentin, Paul
Vogel, Bill
Vold, Cecily
Von Sacken, Angela
Von Shuckmann, Sylvia
Voous, Karel H.
Vooys, J.
Vulgaris, Sam
Vyse, Alan
Vyse, Frances
Vyse, Rachel
Waddell, E.
Waddell, James B.
Wade, Carson
Wade, Keith
Wadsworth, Gordon
Wahl, Terrence R.
Waibler, Stephen F.
Wainwright, Margaret
Wainwright, Mary
Waite, Jean
Waite, Leon
Waite, Ronald
Wakefield, K. Stuart
Wakelam, Richard
Wakelam, William

Walburger, Bill
Waldon, A.G.
Waldon, Robert
Walens, Stanley
Walker, Andrew
Walker, Bruce
Walker, Frank
Walker, H.D.
Walker, Ian
Walker, J.
Walker, M.D.
Walker, Ronald P.
Walker-Taylor, Gwen
Walkley, Doug
Wallace, Brenda
Wallace, Jane
Wallace, Kurt
Wallach, Elizabeth
Wallden, John
Waller, Lillian
Walsh, Bob
Walsh, D.
Walsh, J.
Walsh, L.
Walton, C.
Walton, E.M.
Walton, John
Walton, Kenneth
Walton, Marge
Walton, Mark
Walton, Robert
Wampler, Ed
Wanderer, J.
Ward, Goldpan
Ward, Greg
Ward, H.
Ward, John G.
Ward, L.W.
Ward, Peter R.B.
Ward, Rick
Ward, S.C.
Ward-Harris, E.D.
Ward-Harris, Jane
Warde, Martha
Ware, Marie
Wareing, Jane
Warham, Bill
Warham, Mildred
Warhurton, S.
Warkentin, W.
Warren, H.O.
Warren, Keith
Warren, Morgan
Warren, W.H.
Waterhouse, Louise
Waterhouse, Michaela J.
Waterman, A.
Waterman, Flora
Waterman, K.
Waters, G.Ross
Watkins, Al
Watkins, Gord
Watmough, D.
Watson, G.D.
Watson, Jane
Watson, Lorraine
Watson, Margaret
Watson, Peg
Watson, Philip R.
Watt, Alison M.E.
Watts, Brad F.

Watts, Emily
Watts, Marilyn
Watts, Sid
Wayne, Margaret
Webb, A.
Webb, Dick
Webb, J.
Webb, Keith
Webb, Richard C.
Webb, Robert
Webb, Scott
Webb, Suzanne
Webber, Bernard
Webber, Christine
Webber, Christopher
Webber, Jeremy
Weber, K.
Weber, Robin A.
Weber, Wayne C.
Weber, Wendy
Webster, B.
Webster, J. Dan
Webster, Marg
Weeden, Don
Weeden, Linda
Weeden, R.B.
Wege, Rita
Weiler, O.J.
Weins, Andy
Weir, F.B.
Weismiller, Dianne
Weismiller, Teresa
Welch, Dave
Welch, R.
Welland, R.
Wellborn, Jean
Wellborn, Roy
Wells, G.
Wellwood, Ron
Weninger, Margery
Wershler, Deborah
Wershler, Peter
Wershler, Roy M.
Wessel, J.C.O.
West, Al
West, Mark
West, Nancy
West, Rick
Westcott, D.
Westerborg, Betty
Westhaver, Stan
Westheuser, H.
Westman, M. Marja de J.
Weston, Danny
Weston, Inez
Weston, Jim
Weston, Tom
Wetmore, Stephen P.
Wetmore, T.
Whalen, Paul
Whebell, Yvonne M.
Whellams, Neil
Whipps, Olga
White, Al
White, Andy
White, Betty
White, D.L.
White, Eric R.
White, Graham
White, John
White, Ken

White, Mildred V.
White, P.
White, Sheila
White, Ted
Whiteaves, J.F.
Whitecross, Wally
Whitehead, Phil E.
Whitehead, George
Whitelaw, D.W.
Whitelaw, Virginia R.
Whitfield, Judy
Whiting, David
Whitley, Wendy
Whitman, D.
Whitman, S.D.
Whitney, Alan G.
Whitney, Irene E.
Whitney, R.
Whittaker, Andrew
Whittaker, Jean
Whittaker, Michael
Whittington, Bruce
Whittington, Margaret
Whittington, Mary
Whyte, C.
Whyte, M.
Whyte, Peter
Wick, A.L.
Widdowson, T.
Wideski, Tony
Wiebe, Karen L.
Wier, Josette
Wieringa, D.
Wieringa, L.
Wiggins, Ira L.
Wiggs, A.J.
Wight, G.
Wigmore, Ruth
Wilcox, Vi
Wilding-Davies, Michelle
Wilding-Davies, Peter
Wilford, Kathy
Wilkes, Brian
Wilkes, Myrtle
Wilkes, Ralph
Wilkie, Dale
Wilkie, R.
Wilkinson, Doug
Wilkinson, George
Wilkinson, Henry
Wilkinson, Margaret
Wilkowski, Joe
Will, John
William, Jean
Williams, Anthony
Williams, Donna R.
Williams, Dorothy
Williams, Eldred
Williams, Geoff
Williams, George
Williams, Jack E.
Williams, Joan E.
Williams, Kerry
Williams, Laidlaw
Williams, Laurel
Williams, Margaret
Williams, Mark
Williams, Marlene
Williams, Murray
Williams, Nancy
Williams, P. Ray

Contributors

Williams, P.H.
Williams, Raechelle
Williams, Ray
Williams, Robert
Williams, Ronald
Williams, Sarah
Williams, Seiriol
Williamson, Susan
Willies, Gordon
Willies, Karen
Willies, Peter
Willis, Karen
Willis, Les
Willox, Mavis E.
Wilson, Anthony
Wilson, Bill
Wilson, Dan
Wilson, Daryll
Wilson, Don
Wilson, Douglas J.
Wilson, Eilbeck B.
Wilson, Eunice
Wilson, Heather
Wilson, Jim A.
Wilson, Jim C.
Wilson, Kerry
Wilson, Mary
Wilson, Robert
Wilson, Roslyn
Wilson, Ruby
Wilson, S.E.
Wilson, V.
Wilson, W.G.
Winchester, Neville
Winson, J.W.
Winstone, Mary
Wintemute, Ben P.
Winterbottom, J.M.
Wise, Betty
Wishlow, Bill
Wisnia, Lynn
Wisselink, A.
Withers, Lois
Witte, Marion
Wittrin, Martin P.
Wolfe, Michael
Wolterson-Strauss, Anna J.
Wong, Kent
Wood, Anne
Wood, C. Edward
Wood, Chauncey
Wood, Daryl
Wood, Douglas
Wood, E.D.
Wood, F.H.
Wood, J.
Wood, Peter
Wood, R.
Wood, Sarah
Woodcock, Don
Woodcock, Joe
Woodcock, Mike
Woods, G.
Woods, John G.
Woods, Marcia E.
Woods, Susan M.
Woodworth, Freda
Woodworth, John
Wooldridge, Chris E.
Wooldridge, Donald R.
Woolgar, David

Woolgar, Pam
Wootton, A.
Workman, Bob
Wrenshall, Anne
Wright, Dan
Wright, Eileen
Wright, G.W.
Wright, James
Wright, Ken
Wright, Lois
Wright, Richard T.
Wrigley, Bill
Wydman, Roy
Wye, Doris
Wylie, Bill
Wysong, Dennis
Yak, John
Yardley, C.
Yaunk, Hans
Yellowlees, Jean
Yellowlees, Lou A.
Yellowlees, Mary
Yellowlees, Robin
Yewchan, Karl
Yorke, Paul
Youds, J.
Younger, Dave
Youngson, Danny
Youngson, Margie
Youwe, A..
Zamluk, Joan
Zeck, Hal
Zeeman, T.
Zeral, Martin
Zettergreen, Barry
Zielinski, Anne
Zieroth, Dale
Zimmerman, Ella
Zinkan, Betty
Zinkan, Ted
Zolinski, Ed
Zoyetz, Cynthia
Zroback, Bill
Zroback, Ki
Zurowski, Tim
Zwickel, Fred C.

REFERENCES CITED

REFERENCES CITED

Originally the nonpasserine component of *Birds of British Columbia* was prepared as one volume with two parts, both relying on a common bibliography. During the editorial phase, however, each book evolved as a self contained volume, primarily for the convenience of the reader. Due to time constraints in the publication process we chose to include the entire list of references with each volume knowing that repetition occurs.

Citations of unpublished material contain a reference to the two-volume *A Bibliography of British Columbia Ornithology* (Campbell et al. 1979b, 1988). Copies of the papers cited in that publication are on file at the Royal British Columbia Museum.

Ainley, D.G. 1976. The occurrence of seabirds in the coastal region of California. Western Birds 7:33-68.

_____. 1980. Geographic variation in Leach's Storm-Petrel. Auk 97:837-853.

Ainley, D.G. and T.J. Lewis. 1974. The history of Farallon Island marine bird populations, 1854-1972. Condor 76:432-446.

Ainley, D.G. and B. Manolis. 1979. Occurrence and distribution of the Mottled Petrel. Western Birds 10:113-123.

Aitchison, N.W. 1972. The Pigeon Guillemot, *Cepphus columba*: breeding biology and brood size. B.Sc. Thesis, University of British Columbia, Vancouver. 25 pp.

Alcorn, G.D. 1958. Nesting of the Caspian Tern in Gray's Harbor, Washington. Murrelet 39:19-20.

_____. 1959. Puffins on the south Gray's Harbor beaches. Murrelet 40:21.

Aldrich, J.W. and H. Friedmann. 1943. A revision of the Ruffed Grouse. Condor 45:85-103.

Allen, A.A. 1928. Downy Woodpecker story. Bird-Lore 30:415-424.

Allen, J.N. 1980. The ecology and behavior of the Long-billed Curlew in southeast Washington. Wildlife Monographs 73:1-67.

Amaral, M.J. 1977. A comparative breeding biology of the Tufted and Horned Puffin in the Barren Islands, Alaska. M.S. Thesis, University of Washington, Seattle. 98 pp.

American Ornithologists' Union. 1895. Check-list of North American birds, 2nd edition. E.W. Wheeler Press, New York. 372 pp.

_____. 1910. Check-list of North American birds, 3rd edition. American Ornithologists' Union, New York. 430 pp.

_____. 1931. Check-list of North American birds, 4th edition. Lancaster, Pennsylvania. 526 pp.

_____. 1957. Check-list of North American birds, 5th edition. Lord Baltimore Press, Inc., Baltimore, Maryland. 691 pp.

_____. 1973. Thirty-second supplement to the American Ornithologists' Union Check-list of North American birds. Auk 90:411-419.

_____. 1983. Check-list of North American birds, 6th edition. Allen Press, Inc., Lawrence, Kansas. 877 pp.

_____. 1984. Report of meeting of the committee on classification and nomenclature. Auk 101:348.

_____. 1985. Thirty-fifth supplement to the American Ornithologists' Union Check-list of North American birds. Auk 102:680-686.

_____. 1987. Thirty-sixth supplement to the American Ornithologists' Union Check-list of North American birds. Auk 104:591-596.

_____. 1989. Thirty-seventh supplement to the American Ornithological' Union Check-list of North American birds. Auk 106:532-538.

Ammann, G.A. 1957. The prairie grouse of Michigan. Michigan Department of Conservation Technical Bulletin, Lansing.

Anderson, C.M., D.G. Roseneau, B.J. Walton, and P. Bente. 1988. New evidence of a peregrine migration on the west coast of North America. Pages 507-516 *in* T.J. Cade, J.H. Enderson, C.G. Thelander, and C.M. White (editors). Peregrine Falcon populations - their management and recovery. The Peregrine Fund, Inc., Boise, Idaho.

Anderson, D.R. and C.J. Henny. 1972. Population ecology of the Mallard: I. A review of previous studies and the distribution and migration from breeding areas. United States Department of the Interior, Fish and Wildlife Service Resource Publication 105, Washington, D.C. 166 pp.

Anderson, D.R., P.A. Skaptason, K.G. Fahey, and C.J. Henny. 1974. Population ecology of the Mallard: III. Bibliography of published research and management findings. United States Department of the Interior, Fish and Wildlife Service Resource Publication 119, Washington, D.C. 46 pp.

Anderson, D.W. and I.T. Anderson. 1976. Distribution and status of Brown Pelicans in the California current. American Birds 30:3-12.

Anderson, E. 1967a. Commensal feeding of gull and peregrine. Blue Jay 25:72.

_____. 1967b. The intermediates are busy birders. Vancouver Natural History Society News 135:9-10.

Anderson, E.A. 1972. Unusual behavior of a male Mute Swan. Federation of British Columbia Naturalists Newsletter 10:4.

Anderson, E.M. 1914. Report on birds collected and observed during April, May and June 1913 in the Okanagan Valley, from Okanagan Landing south to Osoyoos Lake. Pages G7-G16 *in* Report of the Provincial Museum of Natural History for the year 1913, Victoria, British Columbia.

_____. 1915. Report of E.M.Anderson on Atlin expedition, 1914. Pages F7-F17 *in* Report of the Provincial Museum of Natural History for the year 1914, Victoria, British Columbia.

Anderson, M. 1976. Ecology of Long-tailed Jaegers. Journal of Animal Ecology 45:537-559.

Anderson, R.R. 1976. Summary of all-time highest counts of individuals for Canada. American Birds 30:645-648.

_____. 1977. Summary of highest counts of individuals for Canada. American Birds 31:916-918.

_____. 1978. Summary of highest counts of individuals for Canada. American Birds 32:931-933.

_____. 1979. Summary of highest counts of individuals for Canada. American Birds 33:708-709.

_____. 1980. Summary of highest counts of individuals for Canada. American Birds 34:708-710.

_____. 1981. Summary of highest counts of individuals for Canada. American Birds 35:763-765.

_____. 1982. Summary of highest counts of individuals for Canada. American Birds 36:784-786.

_____. 1983. Summary of highest counts of individuals for Canada. American Birds 37:797-799.

Annas, R.M. and R. Coupe (editors). 1979. Biogeoclimatic zones and subzones of the Cariboo forest region, British Columbia Ministry of Forests, Victoria. 103 pp.

Anonymous. 1922. Ornithology. Page 11 *in* Provincial Museum of Natural History Report for the year 1921, Victoria, British Columbia.

_____. 1947. Bird note. Victoria Naturalist 4:20.

_____. 1951. Hawk Owl (*Surnia ulula*). Victoria Naturalist 8:9.

_____. 1958. We get Sage Grouse from Oregon. Wildlife Review 2:30.

_____. 1970. Rare Bird ... short life. Daily Colonist, 23 September, Victoria, British Columbia.

_____. 1972. Little Gull rare sight. Victoria Daily Colonist, 2 November, p. 48.

_____. 1978a. Chilean Willy? Campbell River Upper Islander Newspaper, 6 September.

_____. 1978b. A rare catch. Victoria Times Newspaper, 7 November.

_____. 1984. North American management plan for Trumpeter Swans (draft of July 1984). United States Fish and Wildlife Service, Washington, D.C. and Canadian Wildlife Service, Ottawa, Ontario. 62 pp.

_____. 1985. Gazetteer of Canada-British Columbia. Canada Department of Energy, Mines, and Resources, Surveys and Mapping Branch, Ottawa, Ontario. 281 pp.

_____. 1986. The North American Trumpeter Swan survey-1985. United States Fish and Wildlife Service - Migratory Bird Management Office report. Portland, Oregon. 9 pp.

_____. 1987. Creston Valley Wildlife Management Area Annual Newsletter, 1986-1987. Creston, British Columbia. 6 pp.

_____. 1987a. Goshawk banding results (1980-1986). Western Foundation for Raptor Conservation News 1:6-8.

_____. 1988. Lazy Osprey fathers fail to bring home the goods. Simon Fraser Week 40(11):2.

Anthony A.W. 1896. The Black-vented Shearwater (*Puffinus opisthomelas*). Auk 13:222-228.

Anthony, R. 1970. Ecology and reproduction of California Quail in southeastern Washington. Condor 72:276-287.

Anthony, R.G., R.L. Knight, G.T. Allen, B.R. McClelland, and J.J. Hodges. 1982. Habitat use by nesting and roosting Bald Eagles in the Pacific Northwest. Transactions of the North American Wildlife and Natural Resources Conference 47:332-342.

Antifeau, T. 1977. Carpenter Lake folio inventory: wildlife and range condition, summer 1977. British Columbia Fish and Wildlife Branch Unpublished Report, Kamloops. 134 pp. (Bibliography 2170).

Anweiler, G. 1960. The Boreal Owl influx. Blue Jay 10:61-63.

Appelby, R.H., S.C. Madge, and K. Mullarney. 1986. Identification of divers in immature and winter plumages. British Birds 79:365-391.

Arbib, R. 1975. The blue list for 1976. American Birds 29:1067-1072.

_____. 1979. The blue list for 1980. American Birds 33:830-835.

Armstrong, D.P. 1986. Some aspects of the economics of territoriality in North American hummingbirds. M.Sc. Thesis, University of British Columbia, Vancouver. 108 pp.

_____. 1987. Economics of breeding territoriality in male Calliope Hummingbirds. Auk 104:242-253.

Ashmole, N.P. 1963. The regulation of numbers of tropical oceanic birds. Ibis 103:458-473.

_____. 1971. Seabird ecology and the marine environment. Pages 223-286 *in* D.S.Farner and J.R. King (editors). Avian Biology, Volume 1. Academic Press, New York.

Atkinson, R.N. 1963. Flammulated Owl nesting in British Columbia. Canadian Field-Naturalist 77:59-60.

Austin, J.E. and L.H. Frederickson. 1986. Moult of female Lesser Scaup immediately following breeding. Auk 103:293-298.

Bailey, A.M. 1927. Notes on the birds of southeastern Alaska. Auk 44:1-23.

_____. 1948. Birds of arctic Alaska. Colorado Museum of Natural History Popular Series No. 8:1-317.

Bailey, P.F. 1977. The breeding biology of the Black Tern (*Chlidonias niger surinamensis* Gmelin). M.Sc. Thesis, University of Wisconsin, Oshkosh. 67 pp.

Bailey, R.G. 1980. Descriptions of the ecoregions of the United States. United States Department of Agriculture Miscellaneous Publications No.1391, Washington, D.C. 77 pp.

_____. 1983. Delineation of ecosystem regions. Environmental Management 7:365-373.

Bailey, R.G. and H.C. Hogg. 1986. A world ecoregions map for resource reporting. Environmental Conservation 13:195-202.

Baillie, J.L. 1963. Three bird immigrants from the Old World. Transactions of the Royal Canadian Institute 34:95-105.

_____. 1969. In memoriam: James Alexander Munro. Auk 86:624-630.

Baird, S. 1858a. Birds. *in* Reports of explorations and surveys to ascertain the most practicable and economical route for a railroad from the Mississippi River to the Pacific Ocean. Volume 2, Part 2. Washington, D.C.

Baird, S.F. 1858b. Reports of explorations and surveys for a railroad route to the Pacific ocean. Volume 9 (Part 2):1-1005.

Baldridge, A. and J.B. Crowell. 1966. The fall migration - northern Pacific coast region. Audubon Field Notes 20:81-86.

Baldwin, P.H. and N.K. Zaczkowski. 1963. Breeding biology of the Vaux Swift. Condor 65:400-406.

Balmer, A. 1935. Some new state records at Westport, Washington. Murrelet 16:16.

Baltosser, W.H. 1987. Age, species, and sex determination of four North American hummingbirds. North American Bird Bander 12:151-166.

Baltz, D.M. and G.V. Morejohn. 1977. Food habits and niche overlap of seabirds wintering on Monterey Bay, California. Auk 94:526-543.

Bang, B.G. 1966. The olfactory apparatus of tubenosed birds. Acta Anatomica 65:391-415.

Banko, W.E. 1960. The Trumpeter Swan: its history, habits and populations in the United States. North American Fauna No. 63, Washington, D.C. 214 pp.

Banks, R.C. 1986. Subspecies of the Glaucous Gull, *Larus hyperboreus* (Aves: Charadriiformes). Proceedings of the Biological Society of Washington 99:149-159.

_____. 1988. Geographic variation in the Yellow-billed Cuckoo. Condor 90:473-477.

Banks, R.C. and N.K. Johnson. 1961. A review of North American hybrid hummingbirds. Condor 63:3-28.

Barkley, W.D. 1966. Shuswap Lake nature house - 1966 season report. British Columbia Parks Branch Unpublished Report, Victoria. 15 pp. (Bibliography 2197).

Barnard, A.E. 1973. Occurrence of Black Brant moulting in Boundary Bay, British Columbia. Murrelet 54:12-13.

Barnston, G. 1861. Recollections of the swans and geese of Hudson Bay. Canadian Naturalist and Geologist 6:334.

Barry, T.W. 1968. Observations on natural mortality and native use of eider ducks along the Beaufort Sea coast. Canadian Field-Naturalist 82:140-144.

Barth, E.K. 1968. The circumpolar systematics of *Larus argentatus* and *Larus fuscus* with special reference to the Norwegian populations. Nytt Magasin Zoologi 15:1-50.

Bartle, J.A. 1968. Observations on the breeding habits of Pycroft's Petrel. Notornis 15:70-99.

Bartonek, J.C. and D.D. Gibson. 1972. Summer distribution of pelagic birds in Bristol Bay, Alaska. Condor 74:416-422.

Bauer, R.D. 1979. Historical and status report of the Tule White-fronted Goose. Pages 44-55 *in* R.L. Jarvis and J.C. Bartonek (editors). Management and Biology of Pacific Flyway Geese. A symposium sponsored by the Northwest Section, The Wildlife Society, 16 February 1979, Portland, Oregon. Oregon State University Book Store, Inc., Corvallis.

Beardslee, C.S. and H.D. Mitchell. 1965. Birds of the Niagara Frontier Region. Bulletin of the Buffalo Society of Natural Science 22:1-478.

Beckett, R. 1971. European Grey Partridge (*Perdix perdix* L.). Victoria Naturalist 28:34-35.

Beebe, F.L. 1959. A nesting record of a Black Swift. Murrelet 40:9-10.

_____. 1960. The marine peregrines of the northwest Pacific coast. Condor 62:145-189.

_____. 1965. The known status of the Peregrine Falcon in British Columbia. Pages 53-60 *in* J.J. Hickey (editor). Peregrine Falcon populations: their biology and decline. University of Wisconsin Press, Madison.

_____. 1974. Field studies of the Falconiformes of British Columbia. British Columbia Provincial Museum Occasional Paper No.17, Victoria. 163 pp.

Behle, W.H. and W.A. Goates. 1957. Breeding biology of the California Gull. Condor 59:235-246.

Bell, K.M. 1973. Birds of Tahsis, Vancouver Island (September, 1967 to July, 1973). British Columbia Provincial Museum Unpublished Report, Victoria. 5 pp. (Bibliography 2210).

_____. 1975. Fall flocking and migration. British Columbia Parks Branch Unpublished Report, Victoria. 9 pp. (Bibliography 2211).

Bellrose, F.C. 1955. Housing for Wood Ducks. Illinois Natural History Survey Circular 45, Urbana. 48 pp.

_____. 1976. Ducks, geese, and swans of North America. Stackpole Books, Harrisburg, Pennsylvania. 540 pp.

Belton, D. 1973. Park naturalists' report, Manning Provincial Park. British Columbia Parks Branch Unpublished Report, Victoria. 33 pp. (Bibliography 2223).

Bendell, J.F. 1955. Age, breeding behavior and migration of sooty grouse, *Dendragapus obscurus fuliginosus* (Ridgway). Transactions of the North American Wildlife Conference 20:367-381.

Bendell, J.F. and F.C. Zwickel. 1984. A survey of the biology, ecology, abundance, and distribution of the Blue Grouse (Genus *Dendragapus*). Pages 163-192 *in* P.J. Hudson and T.W.I. Lovel (editors). Third International Grouse Symposium, York University, Toronto, Ontario.

Bendire, C.E. 1882. Malheur Lake, Oregon. Ornithologist and Oologist 7:137-138.

Bengtson, S.-A. 1966. Field studies on the Harlequin Duck in Iceland. Wildfowl Trust Annual Report 17:79-94.

Bennie, W. 1979. Common Loon's nest with three eggs. Federation of British Columbia Naturalists Newsletter 17(4):4.

Bent, A.C. 1919. Life histories of North American diving birds. United States National Museum Bulletin No.107, Washington, D.C. 239 pp.

_____. 1922. Life histories of North American petrels, pelicans and their allies. United States National Museum Bulletin No.121, Washington, D.C. 343 pp.

_____. 1923. Life histories of North American wildfowl. Part 1. United States National Museum Bulletin No. 126, Washington, D.C. 244 pp.

_____. 1925. Life histories of North American wildfowl. Part 2. United States National Museum Bulletin No.130, Washington, D.C. 314 pp.

_____. 1926. Life histories of North American marsh birds. United States National Museum Bulletin No. 135, Washington, D.C. 392 pp.

_____.1927. Life histories of North American shorebirds. Part 1. United States National Museum Bulletin No.142, Washington, D.C. 420 pp.

_____. 1932. Life histories of North American gallinaceous birds. United States National Museum Bulletin No. 162, Washington, D.C. 490 pp.

_____. 1938. Life histories of North American birds of prey. Orders Falconiformes and Strigiformes. United States National Museum Bulletin No. 170, Washington, D.C. 482 pp.

_____. 1939. Life histories of North American Woodpeckers. United States National Museum Bulletin No. 174, Washington, D.C. 334 pp.

_____. 1940. Life histories of North American cuckoos, goatsuckers, hummingbirds, and their allies. United States National Museum Bulletin No. 176, Washington, D.C. 506 pp.

Bergerud, A.T. and H.D. Hemus. 1975. An experimental study of the behavior of Blue Grouse (*Dendragapus obscurus*). 1. Differences between the founders from three populations. Canadian Journal of Zoology 53:1222-1237.

Bertram, D.F. 1988. The provisioning of nestlings by parent Rhinoceros Auklets (*Cerorhinca monocerata*). M.Sc. Thesis, Simon Fraser University, Burnaby, British Columbia. 100 pp.

Bertram, D.F. and G.W. Kaiser, 1988. Monitoring growth and diet of nesting Rhinoceros Auklets to guage prey availability. Canadian Wildlife Service Technical Report Series No. 48, Delta, British Columbia, 45 pp.

Beurling, G. 1978. On patting a penguin. Vancouver Sun Newspaper, 19 August.

Bicknell, F.T. 1914. California Brown Pelican in British Columbia. Condor 16:92.

Binford, L.C. and J.V. Remsen. 1974. Identification of the Yellow-billed Loon (*Gavia adamsii*). Western Birds 5:111-126.

Binford, L.C., B.G. Elliott, and S.W. Singer. 1975. Discovery of a nest and the downy young of the Marbled Murrelet. Wilson Bulletin 87:303-319.

Binkley, C.S. and R.S. Miller. 1983. Population characteristics of the Whooping Crane, *Grus americanus*. Canadian Journal of Zoology 61:2768-2776.

Birkhead, M.E. and C.M. Perrens. 1986. The Mute Swan. Christopher Helm Publishers Ltd., London, England. 157 pp.

Bishop, L.B. 1905. The Gray Sea Eagle (*Haliaeetus albicilla*) in British Columbia. Auk 22:79-80.

_____. 1930. An Ancient Murrelet in the inside passage. Murrelet 11:19.

Blake, E.R. 1977. Manual of Neotropical birds (Volume 1). University of Chicago Press, Chicago, Illinois. 674 pp.

Blakiston, T.W. 1861-1862. On birds collected and observed in the interior of British North America. Ibis, October, 1861, pp. 314-320; January, 1862, pp. 3-10.

_____. 1863. On the birds of the interior of British North America. Ibis, January, pp. 39-87; April, pp. 121-155.

Bledsoe, A.H. and D. Sibley. 1985. Patterns of vagrancy of Ross' Gull. American Birds 39:219-227.

Blockstein, D.E. and H.B. Tordoff. 1985. Gone forever - a contemporary look at the extinction of the Passenger Pigeon. American Birds 39:845-851.

Blokpoel, H., P.J. Blancher, and P.M. Fetterolf. 1985. On the plumage of nesting Ring-billed Gulls of different ages. Journal of Field Ornithology 56:113-124.

Blomquist, S. 1983. Bibliography of the Genus *Phalaropus*. Ottenby Bird Observatory, Degerhamn, Sweden. 27 pp.

Blood, D.A. 1976. Migratory bird use of the Ladysmith-Chemainus area, winter 1974-75. Canadian Wildlife Service Unpublished Report, Delta, British Columbia. 64 pp. (Bibliography 2282).

Blood, D.A. and G.W. Smith. 1967. Report on the status of waterfowl hunting in the Tofino area. British Columbia Fish and Wildlife Branch Unpublished Report, Nanaimo. 9 pp.

Bock, C.E. 1970. The ecology and behavior of the Lewis' Woodpecker (*Asyndesmus lewisi*). University of California Publications in Zoology 92:1-100.

Boersma, P.D. 1986. Body temperature, torpor, and growth in chicks of Fork-tailed Storm-Petrels (*Oceanodroma furcata*). Physiological Zoology 59:10-19.

Boersma, P.D., N.T. Wheelwright, M.K. Nerini, and E.S. Wheelwright. 1980. The breeding biology of the Fork-tailed Storm-Petrel (*Oceanodroma furcata*). Auk 97:268-282.

Boggs, B. and E. Boggs. 1960. The winter season - northern Pacific coast region. Audubon Field Notes 14:334-336.

_____. and _____. 1961a. The winter season - northern Pacific coast region. Audubon Field Notes 15:352-353.

_____. and _____. 1961b. The spring migration - northern Pacific coast region. Audubon Field Notes 15:433-434.

_____. and _____. 1961c. The nesting season - northern Pacific coast region. Audubon Field Notes 15:487-489.

_____. and _____. 1962a. The fall migration - northern Pacific coast region. Audubon Field Notes 16:67-69.

_____. and _____. 1962b. The winter season - northern Pacific coast region. Audubon Field Notes 16:357-359.

_____. and _____. 1962c. The spring migration - northern Pacific coast region. Audubon Field Notes 16:440-442.

_____. and _____. 1962d. The nesting season - northern Pacific coast region. Audubon Field Notes 16:500-502.

_____. and _____. 1963a. The fall migration - northern Pacific coast region. Audubon Field Notes 17:58-61.

_____. and _____. 1963b. The winter season - northern Pacific coast region. Audubon Field Notes 17:351-353.

_____. and _____. 1963c. The nesting season - northern Pacific coast region. Audubon Field Notes 17:478-480.

_____. and _____. 1964. Sight record of Short-tailed Albatross. Murrelet 45:48.

Boise, C.M. 1977. Breeding biology of the Lesser Sandhill Crane *Grus canadensis* (L.) on the Yukon-Kuskokwim Delta. M.S. Thesis, University of Alaska, Fairbanks. 74 pp.

Bolen, E.G. and M.K. Rylander. 1983. Whistling-ducks: Zoogeography, ecology, anatomy. Special Publications The Museum Texas Tech University No.20, Lubbock, Texas. 67pp.

Bonar, R.L. 1978a. Summary of terrestrial biology program - Revelstoke project - first annual report March, 1977 - March, 1978. British Columbia Hydro and Power Authority Unpublished Report, Vancouver. 11 pp. (Bibliography 2312).

_____. 1978b. Summary of terrestrial biology program - Revelstoke project - 2nd annual report , 1978. British Columbia Hydro and Power Authority Unpublished Report, Vancouver. 118 pp. (Bibliography 2313).

Bourne, W.R.P. and T.J. Dixon. 1975. Observations of seabirds 1970-1972. Sea Swallow 24:65-88.

Boxall, P. 1980. Ecology of wintering Snowy Owls. M.Sc. Thesis, University of Calgary, Calgary, Alberta. 213 pp.

Boyd, H. and L.S. Maltby. 1979. The Brant of the western Queen Elizabeth Islands, N.W.T. Pages 5-21 *in* R.L. Jarvis and J.C. Bartonek (editors). Management and Biology of Pacific Flyway Geese. Oregon State University Book Stores, Corvallis.

Bradley, D.M. 1959. Birds and mammals seen at the V.N.H.S. camp, Cosen's Bay, Kalamalka Lake, north Okanagan, July 4-14, 1958. Bulletin of the Vancouver Natural History Society 108:3-4.

Branson, N.J.B.A., E.D. Ponting, and C.D.T. Minton. 1978. Turnstone migration in Britain and Europe. Bird Study 25:181-187.

Braun, C.E. 1969. Population dynamics, habitat and movements of white-tailed ptarmigan in Colorado. Ph.D. Thesis, Colorado State University, Fort Collins. 189 pp.

_____. 1980. Alpine bird communities of western North America: implications for management and research. Pages 280-291 *in* R.M. DeGraff and M.G. Tilghman (compilers). Workshop Proceedings, Management of western forests and grasslands for non-game birds. United States Department of Agriculture, Forest Service General Technical Report INT-86.

_____. 1984. Biological investigations of White-tailed Ptarmigan in Colorado, U.S.A. - A review. Pages 131-147 *in* P.J. Hudson and T.W.I. Lovel (editors). Third International Grouse Symposium, World Pheasant Association, York University, Toronto, Ontario.

Braun, C.E., J.H. Enderson, C.J. Henny, H. Meng, and A.G. Nye. 1977. Conservation committee report on falconry: effects on raptor populations and management in North America. Wilson Bulletin 89:360-369.

Breault, A.M. 1988. Productivity and distribution of Great Blue Heron colonies in the Strait of Georgia. Canadian Wildlife Service Unpublished Report, Delta, British Columbia. 59 pp.

Breault, A.M., K.M. Cheng, and J-P.L. Savard. 1988. Distribution and abundance of Eared Grebes (*Podiceps nigricollis*) in British Columbia. Canadian Wildlife Service Technical Report Series No.51, Delta, British Columbia. 87 pp.

Breckenridge, W.J. 1935. An ecological study of some Minnesota Marsh Hawks. Condor 37:268-276.

_____. 1956. Nesting study of Wood Ducks. Journal of Wildlife Management 20:16-21.

Briggs, K.T. and E.W. Chu. 1986. Sooty Shearwaters off California: distribution, abundance, and habitat use. Condor 88:355-364.

Brigham, R.M. 1989. Roost and nest sites of Common Nighthawks: are gravel roots important? Condor 91:722-724.

Brisbin, I.L. 1968. The Passenger Pigeon: a study in the ecology of extinction. Modern Game Breeding 4:13-20.

British Columbia Ministry of Forests. 1988. Biogeoclimatic zones of British Columbia 1988. British Columbia Ministry of Forests, Victoria. Map.

Britton, D. 1980. Identification of Sharp-tailed Sandpipers. British Birds 73:333-345.

Brooke, R.K. 1978. The *Catharacta* Skuas (Aves: Laridae) occurring in south African waters. Durban Museum Novitates 11:295-308.

Brooks, A. 1900. Notes on some of the birds of British Columbia. Auk 17:104-107.

_____. 1901. Notes on the winter birds of the Cariboo district, B.C. Ottawa Naturalist 15:152-154.

_____. 1903. Notes on the birds of the Cariboo district, British Columbia. Auk 20:277-284.

_____. 1909a. Some notes on the birds of Okanagan, British Columbia. Auk 26:60-63.

_____. 1909b. Three records for British Columbia. Auk 26:313-314.

_____. 1912. Some British Columbia records. Auk 29:252-253.

_____. 1917. Birds of the Chilliwack district, B.C. Auk 34:28-50.

_____. 1918. Brief notes on the prevalence of certain birds in British Columbia. Canadian Field-Naturalist 31:139-141.

_____. 1920. Notes on the Limicolae of southern British Columbia. Condor 22:26-32.

_____. 1921. A twelve month with the shorebirds. Condor 23:151-156.

_____. 1923a. Notes on the birds of Porcher Island, B.C. Auk 40:217-224.

_____. 1923b. Some recent records for British Columbia. Auk 40:700-701.

_____. 1923c. A comment on the alleged occurrence of *Mesophoyx intermedia* in North America. Condor 25:180-181.

_____. 1926. Scarcity of the Marbled Murrelet. Murrelet 7:39.

_____. 1927. Notes on Swarth's report on a collection of birds and mammals from the Atlin region. Condor 29:112-114.

_____. 1928. Does the Marbled Murrelet nest inland? Murrelet 9:68.

_____. 1930. In memoriam: Charles de Blois Green. Condor 32:9-11.

_____. 1932. The occurrence of the Falcated Duck (*Eunetta falcata*) in Okanagan, British Columbia. Murrelet 13:92.

_____. 1937. Pacific Golden Plover and Curlew Sandpiper on the Pacific Coast of North America. Condor 39:176-177.

_____. 1942. Additions to the distributional list of the birds of British Columbia. Condor 44:33-34.

Brooks, A. and H.S. Swarth. 1925. A distributional list of the birds of British Columbia. Pacific Coast Avifauna No.17, Berkeley, California. 158 pp.

Brown, B. 1985. Sidney man loses old-gull friend. Victoria Times-Colonist, 24 August:A1-A2.

Brown, P.W. 1977. Breeding biology of the White-winged Scoter (*Melanitta fusca*). M.Sc. Thesis, Iowa State University, Ames. 46 pp.

Browne, P.W.P. 1958. The field identification of Baird's and Semipalmated Sandpipers. British Birds 51:81.

Browning, M.R. 1977. Interbreeding members of the *Sphyrapicus varius* group (Aves: Picidae) in Oregon. Bulletin of the Southern California Academy of Science 76:38-41.

Bruce, A.M., R.J. Anderson, and G.T. Allen. 1982. Observations of Golden Eagles nesting in western Washington. Raptor Research 16:132-134.

Brunton, D.F. and T. Pratt. 1986. Sightings of a Black-throated Sparrow, *Amphispiza bilineata*, and a Black Vulture, *Coragyps atratus atratus*, in British Columbia. Canadian Field-Naturalist 100:256-257.

Brunton, D.F., S. Andrews, and D.G. Paton. 1979. Nesting of the Calliope Hummingbird in Kananaskis Provincial Park, Alberta. Canadian Field-Naturalist 93:449-451.

Buchanan, J.B. 1988a. Migration and winter populations of Greater Yellowlegs, *Tringa melanoleuca*, in western Washington. Canadian Field-Naturalist 102: 611-616.

_____. 1988b. North American Merlin populations: an analysis using Christmas Bird Count data. American Birds 42:1178-1180.

Buffam, F. 1966. Wickaninnish Provincial Park summer report 1966. British Columbia Parks Branch Unpublished Report, Victoria. 14 pp. (Bibliography 2389).

Bull, J. 1963. On leg color in immature jaegers. Linnaean Newsletter 17: April.

_____. 1974. Birds of New York state. Doubleday/Natural History Press, Garden City, New York. 655 pp.

Bump, G., R.B. Darrow, F.C. Edminster, and W.F. Grissey. 1947. The Ruffed Grouse - life history, propagation, management. New York State Conservation Department, Buffalo. 915 pp.

Bunn, D.S., A.B. Warburton and R.D.S. Wilson. 1982. The Barn Owl. Buteo Books, Vermillion, South Dakota. 264 pp.

Bunnell, F.L. and R.G. Williams. 1980. Subspecies and diversity - The spice of life or prophet of doom. Pages 246-259 *in* R. Stace-Smith, L. Johns, and P. Joslin (editors). Proceedings of the Symposium on Threatened and Endangered Species and Habitats in British Columbia and the Yukon. British Columbia Ministry of Environment, Victoria.

Bunnell, F.L., D. Dunbar, L. Koza, and G. Ryder. 1981. Effects of disturbance on the productivity and numbers of White Pelicans in British Columbia - observations and models. Colonial Waterbirds 4:2-11.

Bunni, M.K. 1959. The Killdeer, *Charadrius v. vociferus* Linnaeus, in the breeding season: ecology, behaviour, and the development of homoiothermism. PhD. Thesis, University of Michigan, Ann Arbor.

Burgess, T.E. 1970. Foods and habitat of four Anatinids wintering on the Fraser delta tidal marshes. M.Sc. Thesis, University of British Columbia, Vancouver. 124 pp.

Burn, D.M. and J.R. Mather. 1974. The White-billed Diver in Britain. British Birds 67:258-296.

Burnes, J. 1978. Penguins seen around north end of island. Vancouver Sun Newspaper, 12 August.

Burns, F.L. 1915. Comparative periods of deposition and incubation of some North American birds. Wilson Bulletin 27:275-286.

Burr, I.W. 1967. King Eider (*Somateria spectabilis*) in the San Juans. Murrelet 48:7.

Burton, B.A. 1977. Some aspects of the ecology of Lesser Snow Geese wintering on the Fraser River estuary. M.Sc. Thesis, University of British Columbia, Vancouver. 173 pp.

Burton, J. and R. McNeil. 1976. Age determination of six species of North American shorebirds. Bird-Banding 47:201-209.

Butler, J.R. and G.D. Fenton. 1986. Bird watchers at Point Pelee National Park, Canada: their characteristics and activities, with special consideration to their social and resource impacts. Paper presented at First National Symposium on Social Science in Resource Management, Oregon State University, Corvallis, May 12-16.

Butler, R.W. 1973. Mitlenatch Island Nature Park - 1973 summer report. British Columbia Parks Branch Unpublished Report. Victoria. 41 pp. (Bibliography 2408).

_____. 1989. Breeding ecology and population trends of the Great Blue Heron *Ardea herodias fannini*, in the Strait of Georgia, British Columbia. Pages 112-117 *in* K. Vermeer and R.W. Butler (editors). The ecology and status of marine and shoreline birds in the Strait of Georgia, British Columbia. Canadian Wildlife Service Special Publication, Ottawa, Ontario.

Butler, R.W. and S. Butler. 1976. Naturalists' summer report, Mitlenatch Island (May 19-August 30, 1976). British Columbia Parks Branch Unpublished Report, Victoria. 9 pp. (Bibliography 2409).

Butler, R.W. and R.W. Campbell. 1987. The birds of the Fraser River delta: populations, ecology, and international significance. Canadian Wildlife Service Occasional Paper No.65, Ottawa, Ontario. 73 pp.

Butler, R.W. and J.W. Kirbyson. 1979. Oyster predation by the Black Oystercatcher in British Columbia. Condor 81:433-435.

Butler, R.W. and J.-P.L. Savard. 1985. Monitoring of the spring migration of waterbirds throughout British Columbia: a pilot study. Canadian Wildlife Service Unpublished Report, Delta, British Columbia. 13 pp.

Butler, R.W., N.A.M. Verbeek, and R.G. Foottit. 1980. Mortality and dispersal of the Glaucous-winged Gulls of southern British Columbia. Canadian Field-Naturalist 94:315-320.

Butler, R.W., B.G. Stushnoff, and E. McMackin. 1986. The birds of the Creston valley and southeastern British Columbia. Canadian Wildlife Service Occasional Paper No. 58, Ottawa, Ontario. 37 pp.

Butler, R.W., G.W. Kaiser, and G.E.J. Smith. 1987. Migration chronology, length of stay, sex ratio, and weight of Western Sandpipers (*Calidris mauri*) on the south coast of British Columbia. Journal of Field Ornithology 58:103-111.

Byrd, G.V., D.D. Gibson, and D.L. Johnson. 1974. The birds of Adak Island, Alaska. Condor 76:288-300.

Cade, T.J. 1955. Variation of the Common Rough-legged Hawk in North America. Condor 57:313-346.

_____. 1960. Ecology of the peregrine and Gyrfalcon population in Alaska. University of California Publications in Zoology 63:151-290.

Calder, J.A. and R.L. Taylor. 1968. Flora of the Queen Charlotte Islands, Part 1. Systematics of the vascular plants. Canada Department of Agriculture Research Branch Agriculture Monograph 4(1), Ottawa. 659 pp.

Calder, W.A. 1971. Temperature relationships and nesting of Calliope Hummingbird. Condor 73:314-321.

_____.1974. The thermal and radiant environment of a winter hummingbird nest . Condor 76: 268-273.

Call, M.W. 1978. Nesting habitats and surveying techniques for common western raptors. United States Department of the Interior Bureau of Land Management Technical Note TN-316, Washington, D.C. 115 pp.

Callin, E. 1962. Winter bird counts. Blue Jay 20:38.

Campbell, E.C. and R.W. Campbell. 1983. Status report on the Common Barn-Owl (*Tyto alba*) in Canada - 1982. Committee on the Status of Endangered Wildlife in Canada Report, Canadian Nature Federation, Ottawa, Ontario. 71 pp. (Bibliography 2428).

_____. and _____. 1984. Status report on the Spotted Owl (*Strix occidentalis caurina*) in Canada - 1983. Committee on the Status of Endangered Wildlife in Canada Report, Canadian Nature Federation, Ottawa, Ontario. 62 pp. (Bibliography 2429).

Campbell R.W. 1965. Mitlenatch Island Nature Park, December 19-22, 1965. British Columbia Parks Branch Unpublished Report, Victoria. 8 pp. (Bibliography 2501).

_____. 1966. On Black Oystercatchers "catching" oysters. Victoria Naturalist 23:26.

_____. 1967. Common Teals wintering in southwestern British Columbia. Murrelet 48:27.

_____. 1968a. Notes on a twenty-year-old Glaucous-winged Gull. Bird-Banding 39:226-227.

_____. 1968b. Status of breeding Herring Gulls at Bridge Lake, British Columbia, from 1933 to 1963. Canadian Field-Naturalist 82:217-219.

_____. 1968c. Two records of the Ruddy Duck nesting at Vancouver, British Columbia. Canadian Field-Naturalist 82:220-221.

_____. 1968d. Long-tailed Jaegers sighted at Vancouver, British Columbia. Murrelet 49:6.

_____. 1968e. Occurrence and nesting of the Black Oystercatcher near Vancouver, British Columbia. Murrelet 49:11.

_____. 1968f. A sight record of the Emperor Goose at White Rock, British Columbia. Murrelet 49:14.

_____. 1968g. Alexandrian rat predation on Ancient Murrelet eggs. Murrelet 49:38.

_____. 1968h. Capturing Ancient Murrelets by night-lighting. Blue Jay 26:90-91.

_____. 1969a. Spring bird observations on Langara Island, British Columbia. Blue Jay 27:155-159.

_____. 1969b. Occurrence and nesting of Wilson's Phalaropes at Vancouver, British Columbia. Condor 71:434.

_____. 1970a. The Sabine's Gull in southwestern British Columbia. Canadian Field-Naturalist 84:310-311.

_____. 1970b. Occurrence and nesting of Black Terns in southwestern British Columbia. Condor 72:500.

_____. 1970c. The White Pelican in southwestern British Columbia. Murrelet 51:18-19.

_____. 1970d. Recent information on nesting colonies of Mew Gulls on Kennedy Lake, Vancouver Island, British Columbia. Syesis 3:5-14.

_____. 1971a. First Canadian specimen of New Zealand Shearwater. Canadian Field-Naturalist 85:329-330.

_____. 1971b. Steller's Eider photographed near Campbell River, British Columbia. Canadian Field-Naturalist 85:330-331.

_____. 1971c. Status of the Caspian Tern in British Columbia. Syesis 4:185-189.

_____. 1972a. Coastal records of the Long-billed Curlew for British Columbia. Canadian Field-Naturalist 86:167-168.

_____. 1972b. Summary of selected winter bird counts in British Columbia. Vancouver Natural History Society Discovery 1:2-5.

_____. 1972c. The American Avocet (*Recurvirostra americana*) in British Columbia. Syesis 5:173-178.

_____. 1972d. The Green Heron in British Columbia. Syesis 5:235-247.

_____. 1973a. The seventy-third Christmas bird count - Vancouver, B.C. American Birds 27:182-183.

_____. 1973b. Coastal records of the Barred Owl for British Columbia. Murrelet 54:25.

_____. 1974. British Columbia roadside raptor census - southern British Columbia, September 11-15, 1973. British Columbia Provincial Museum Unpublished Report, Victoria. 5 pp. (Bibliography 2435).

_____. 1975a. Longevity record of a Glaucous-winged Gull. Bird-Banding 46:166.

_____. 1975b. Seabird colonies in Skidegate Inlet, Queen Charlotte Islands, British Columbia. Syesis 8:355-361.

_____. 1975c. Marginal habitat used by Glaucous-winged Gulls for nesting. Syesis 8:393.

_____. 1976a. Sea-bird colonies of Vancouver Island area. British Columbia Provincial Museum, Victoria. Map. (Bibliography 1989).

_____. 1976b. Sea-birds breeding on the Canadian West Coast. Pages 39-65 in H. Hosford (editor). Selected papers from the Fifth Annual Conference of the Canadian Nature Federation, Victoria, British Columbia, June 12/16, 1975. Canadian Nature Federation Special Publication No.5 and British Columbia Museum Heritage Record No. 1.

_____. 1977a. Checklist of British Columbia birds (to June 1977). British Columbia Provincial Museum, Victoria. Leaflet. (Bibliography 1990).

_____. 1977b. Use of man-made structures as nest sites by Pigeon Guillemots. Canadian Field-Naturalist 91:193-194.

_____. 1977c. Seabird colonies in Masset and Juskatla Inlets, Queen Charlotte Islands, British Columbia. British Columbia Provincial Museum Unpublished Report, Victoria. 5 pp. (Bibliography 1771).

_____. 1978a. British Columbia roadside raptor census, Vancouver to Smithers, May 17-18, 1978. British Columbia Provincial Museum Unpublished Report, Victoria. 9 pp. (Bibliography 2436).

_____. 1978b. Census of Herring, California and Ring-billed gulls nesting on Whiskey Island, Okanagan Lake. British Columbia Provincial Museum Unpublished Report, Victoria. 3 pp. (Bibliography 2438).

_____. 1978c. Assessment of Boundary Lake as a provincial ecological reserve for breeding marsh birds. British Columbia Museum Unpublished Report, Victoria. 5 pp. (Bibliography 2440).

_____. 1978d. Census of waterbirds nesting at Cecil Lake, British Columbia. British Columbia Provincial Museum Unpublished Report, Victoria. 10 pp. (Bibliography 2441).

_____. 1979. Proposal for an ecological reserve at "McQueen's Slough", Dawson Creek area, British Columbia. British Columbia Provincial Museum Unpublished Report, Victoria. 6 pp.

_____. 1980. Charlie Guiguet retires. B.C. Naturalist 18(1):7.

_____. 1981. Spring migrants observed 16-21 May 1981 at Atlin British Columbia. British Columbia Provincial Museum Unpublished Report, Victoria. 7 pp. (Bibliography 2447).

_____. 1981a. List of species and subspecies of British Columbia birds (through September 1981). British Columbia Provincial Museum Unpublished Report Victoria. 19 pp. (Bibliography 2448).

_____. 1982a. Wildlife atlases progress report. B.C. Naturalist 20(2):8-10.

_____. 1982b. Wildlife atlases progress report - spring 1982. B.C. Naturalist 20(3):6-8.

_____. 1982c. Wildlife atlases progress report - summer 1982. B.C. Naturalist 20(4):5-7.

_____. 1983a. Wildlife atlases progress report. B.C. Naturalist 21(1):4-5.

_____. 1983b. Wildlife atlases progress report - winter 1982-83. B.C. Naturalist 21(2):4-5.

_____. 1983c. Wildlife atlases progress report - spring-summer 1983. B.C. Naturalist 21(3):4-6.

_____. 1983d. Wildlife atlases progress report - fall 1983. B.C. Naturalist 21(4):4-6.

_____. 1983e. Feeding ecology of the Common Barn-Owl in North America. M.Sc. Thesis, University of Washington, Seattle. 87 pp.

_____. 1983f. Census of Double-crested and Pelagic cormorants breeding on Chain Islets Ecological Reserve - August 1983. British Columbia Provincial Museum Unpublished Report Victoria. 7 pp (Bibliography 2456).

_____. 1984a. Wildlife atlases progress report - winter 1983-1984. B.C. Naturalist 22(2):6-7.

_____. 1984b. Wildlife atlases progress report - fall 1984. B.C. Naturalist 22(4):6-7, 19.

_____. 1984c. Checklist of British Columbia birds (to May 1984). British Columbia Provincial Museum, Victoria. Leaflet. (Bibliography 2458).

_____. 1985a. Wildlife atlases progress report - winter 1984-1985. B.C. Naturalist 23(1):6-7.

_____. 1985b. Wildlife atlases progress report - spring 1985. B.C. Naturalist 23(2):6-7.

_____. 1985c. Wildlife atlases progress report - summer 1985. B.C. Naturalist 23(3):6-7.

_____. 1985d. Wildlife atlases progress report - fall 1985. B.C. Naturalist 23(4):6-9.

_____. 1985e. Census of birds nesting on Ellis Island, Fraser Lake, British Columbia, in 1985. British Columbia Provincial Museum Unpublished Report, Victoria. 2 pp.

_____. 1985f. First record of the Eurasian Kestrel for Canada. Condor 87:294.

_____. 1986a. Wildlife atlases progress report - spring 1986. B.C. Naturalist 24(2):6-7.

_____. 1986b. Violet Gibbard retires as nest program coordinator. B.C. Naturalist 24(2):7.

_____. 1986c. Wildlife atlases progress report - summer 1986. B.C. Naturalist 24(3):6-7.

_____. 1986d. Wildlife atlases progress report - autumn 1986. B.C. Naturalist 24(4):6-7.

_____. 1986e. Birds and mammals observed during a cruise of Moresby Island, Queen Charlotte Islands, 11-20 May 1986. British Columbia Provincial Museum Unpublished Report, Victoria. 10 pp.

_____. 1986f. Birds and mammals observed during a cruise of Moresby Island, Queen Charlotte Islands, 9-19 June 1986. British Columbia Provincial Museum Unpublished Report, Victoria. 16 pp.

_____. 1986g. List of British Columbia birds. Pages 9-29 *in* Higher vertebrates of British Columbia. British Columbia Provincial Museum, Victoria.

_____. 1987a. British Columbia wildlife - winter report 1986-87. B.C. Naturalist 25(1):6-7.

_____. 1987b. Birds and mammals observed during a cruise of Moresby Island, Queen Charlotte Islands, 9-18 May 1987. British Columbia Provincial Museum Unpublished Report, Victoria. 9 pp.

_____. 1987c. British Columbia wildlife - spring report 1987. B.C. Naturalist 25(2):6-7.

_____. 1987d. British Columbia wildlife - summer report 1987. B.C. Naturalist 25(3):6-7.

_____. 1987e. British Columbia wildlife - autumn report 1987. B.C. Naturalist 25(4):6-7.

_____. 1988a. British Columbia wildlife - winter report 1987-88. B.C. Naturalist 26(1):6-7.

_____. 1988b. British Columbia wildlife - spring report 1988. B.C. Naturalist 26(2):6-7.

_____. 1988c. British Columbia wildlife - summer report 1988. B.C. Naturalist 26(4):6-7.

_____. 1988d. Checklist of British Columbia birds (to June 1988). Royal British Columbia Museum, Victoria.

_____. 1989a. British Columbia wildlife - autumn report 1988. B.C. Naturalist 27(1):6-7.

_____. 1989b. Checklist of British Columbia birds (to June 1989). Federation of British Columbia Naturalists, Vancouver. Leaflet.

_____. 1989c. British Columbia wildlife - winter report 1988-1989. B.C. Naturalist 27(2):6-7.

_____. 1989d. British Columbia wildlife - spring report 1989. B.C. Naturalist 27(3): 6-8.

Campbell, R.W. and W.J. Anderson. 1972. Black-necked Stilt, new for British Columbia. Canadian Field-Naturalist 86:296.

Campbell, R.W. and R.G. Foottit. 1972. The Franklin's Gull in British Columbia. Syesis 5:99-106.

Campbell, R.W. and H.M. Garrioch. 1978a. Report on the Herring Gull colony on Ellis Island, Fraser Lake, British Columbia. British Columbia Provincial Museum Unpublished Report, Victoria. 9 pp. (Bibliography 1950).

_____. and _____. 1978b. Waterbirds nesting on south Westwick Lake, British Columbia - June, 1978. British Columbia Provincial Museum Unpublished Report, Victoria. 8 pp. (Bibliography 2481).

_____. and _____. 1979. Sea-bird colonies of the Queen Charlotte Islands. British Columbia Provincial Museum, Victoria. Map. (Bibliography 2482).

Campbell, R.W. and V. Gibbard. 1973. British Columbia nest records scheme - eighteenth annual report, 1972. Federation of British Columbia Naturalists Newsletter 11(1):3-5.

_____. and _____. 1981. British Columbia nest record scheme 1979/80. B.C. Naturalist 19(2):7-10.

_____. and _____. 1984. B.C. nest records scheme - twentieth annual report - 1983. B.C. Naturalist 22:9-11.

_____. and _____. 1986. British Columbia nest records scheme - thirtieth annual report - 1985. B.C. Naturalist 24(1):14, 16-17.

Campbell, R.W. and P.T. Gregory. 1976. The Buff-breasted Sandpiper in British Columbia, with notes on its migration in North America. Syesis 9:123-130.

Campbell, R.W. and A.P. Harcombe. 1985. Wildlife habitat handbooks for British Columbia: standard taxonomic list and codes of amphibians, reptiles, birds, and mammals. British Columbia Ministry of Forest Wildlife Habitat Research WHR-20, British Columbia Ministry of Environment Wildlife Report R-11, Victoria. 86 pp.

Campbell R.W. and H. Hosford. 1979. Attracting and feeding birds in British Columbia. British Columbia Provincial Museum Methods Manual No. 7, Victoria. 31 pp.

Campbell, R.W. and K. Kennedy. 1965. An annotated list of birds of Mitlenatch Island, June 23-August 27, 1965. British Columbia Parks Branch Unpublished Report, Victoria. 13 pp. (Bibliography 2492).

_____. and _____. 1966. Mitlenatch Island Nature Park summer report, 1966. British Columbia Parks Branch Unpublished Report, Victoria. 172 pp. (Bibliography 2493).

Campbell, R.W. and R.E. Luscher. 1972. Semi-palmated Plover breeding at Vancouver, British Columbia. Murrelet 53:11-12.

Campbell, R.W. and M.D. MacColl. 1978. Winter foods of Snowy Owls in southwestern British Columbia. Journal of Wildlife Management 42:190-192.

Campbell, R.W. and M.C.E. McNall. 1982. Field report of the Provincial Museum expedition to the vicinity of Kotcho Lake, northeastern British Columbia, June 11-July 9, 1982. British Columbia Provincial Museum Unpublished Report, Victoria. 307 pp. (Bibliography 2495).

Campbell, R.W. and A.L. Meugens. 1971. The summer birds of Richter Pass, British Columbia. Syesis 4:93-123.

Campbell, R.W. and M.G. Shepard. 1971. Summary of spring and fall pelagic birding trips from Tofino, British Columbia. Vancouver Natural History Society Discovery 150:13-16.

_____. and _____. 1972. Summary of 1971 offshore birding trips. Vancouver Natural History Society Discovery 1:7-8.

_____. and _____. 1973. Laysan Albatross, Scaled Petrel, Parakeet Auklet: additions to the list of Canadian birds. Canadian Field-Naturalist 87:179-180.

Campbell, R.W. and D. Stirling. 1968a. Notes on the vertebrate fauna associated with a Brandt's Cormorant colony in British Columbia. Murrelet 49:7-9.

_____. and _____. 1968b. Notes on the natural history of Cleland Island, British Columbia, with emphasis on the breeding bird fauna. Pages 25-43 in Provincial Museum of Natural History and Anthropology Report for the Year 1967, Victoria, British Columbia.

_____. and _____. 1971. A photoduplicate file for British Columbia vertebrate records. Syesis 4:217-222.

Campbell, R.W. and K.R. Summers. In press. Vertebrates of the Brooks Peninsula, British Columbia. Royal British Columbia Museum Heritage Record.

Campbell, R.W. and B.M. Van Der Raay. 1981. Winter distribution and population dynamics of Bald Eagles in south-western mainland British Columbia. British Columbia Provincial Museum Unpublished Report, Victoria. 29 pp. (Bibliography 2498).

Campbell, R.W. and W.C. Weber. 1976. Occurrence and status of the Tufted Duck in British Columbia. Syesis 9:25-30.

_____. and _____. 1977. The Cattle Egret in British Columbia. Canadian Field-Naturalist 91:87-88.

Campbell, R.W., M.G. Shepard, and R.H. Drent. 1972a. Status of birds in the Vancouver area in 1970. Syesis 5:137-167.

Campbell, R.W., M.G. Shepard, and W.C. Weber. 1972b. Vancouver birds in 1971. Vancouver Natural History Society Special Publication, Vancouver, British Columbia. 88 pp.

Campbell, R.W., M.G. Shepard, B.A. Macdonald, and W.C. Weber. 1974. Vancouver birds in 1972. Vancouver Natural History Society Special Publication, Vancouver, British Columbia. 96 pp.

Campbell, R.W., J.G. Ward, and M.G. Shepard. 1975. A new Common Murre colony in British Columbia. Canadian Field-Naturalist 89:244-248.

Campbell, R.W., M.A. Paul, M.S. Rodway, and H.R. Carter. 1977. Tree-nesting Peregrine Falcons in British Columbia. Condor 79:500-501.

Campbell, R.W., H.R. Carter, and S.G. Sealy. 1979a. Nesting of Horned Puffins in British Columbia. Canadian Field-Naturalist 93:84-86.

Campbell, R.W., H.R. Carter, C.D. Shepard, and C.J. Guiguet. 1979b. A bibliography of British Columbia ornithology: volume 1. British Columbia Provincial Museum Heritage Record No. 7, Victoria. 185 pp.

Campbell, R.W., R.J. Cannings, S.G. Cannings, and R.A. Cannings. 1979c. A proposal for an ecological reserve at Rock Lake, Becher's Prairie, British Columbia. British Columbia, Provincial Museum Unpublished Report, Victoria. 9 pp. (Bibliography 2474).

Campbell, R.W., J.M. Cooper, and M.C.E. McNall. 1983. Field report of the Provincial Museum expedition in the vicinity of Haines Triangle, northwestern British Columbia, May 27-July 4, 1983. British Columbia Provincial Museum Unpublished Report, Victoria. 351 pp. (Bibliography 2477).

Campbell, R.W., E.D. Forsman, and B.M. Van Der Raay. 1984. An annotated bibliography of literature on the Spotted Owl. British Columbia Ministry of Forests Land Management Report No. 24, Victoria. 115 pp.

Campbell, R.W., B.M. Van Der Raay, I. Robertson, and B.J. Petrar. 1985. Spring and summer distribution, status, and nesting ecology of the Arctic Loon, *Gavia arctica*, in interior British Columbia. Canadian Field-Naturalist 99:337-342.

Campbell, R.W., D.A. Manuwal, and A.S. Harestad. 1987. Food habits of the Common Barn-Owl in British Columbia. Canadian Journal of Zoology 65:578-586.

Campbell, R.W., T.D. Hooper, and N.K. Dawe. 1988. A bibliography of British Columbia ornithology: volume 2. Royal British Columbia Museum Heritage Record No.19 , Victoria. 591 pp.

Canada Department of Fisheries and Environment. 1978. Groundfish and herring resources. Canada Department of Fisheries and Environment Protection Service Map No.4, Ottawa, Ontario.

Canaris, A.G. 1950. Sight record of American Egret in eastern Washington. Murrelet 31:46.

Canning, D.J. and S.G. Herman. 1983. Gadwall breeding range expansion into western Washington. Murrelet 64:27-31.

Cannings, R.A. 1974. Another record of the Flammulated Owl in Canada. Canadian Field-Naturalist 88:234-235.

_____. 1975a. Natural history report: Cape Scott Park. British Columbia Parks Branch Unpublished Report, Victoria. 80 pp. (Bibliography 2552).

_____. 1975b. The Parasitic Jaeger in the British Columbia interior. Syesis 8:395-396.

Cannings, R.A., R.J. Cannings, and S.G. Cannings. 1987. Birds of the Okanagan Valley, British Columbia. Royal British Columbia Museum, Victoria. 420 pp.

Cannings, R.J. 1973. Shuswap birds, 1973 - annotated list. British Columbia Parks Branch Unpublished Report, Victoria. 15 pp. (Bibliography 2528).

_____. 1987. The breeding biology of Northern Saw-whet Owls in southern British Columbia. Pages 193-198 in R.W. Nero, R.J. Clark, R.J. Knapton, and R.H. Hamre (editors). Biology and Conservation of Northern Forest Owls: Symposium Proceedings. 1987 Feb. 3-7; Winnipeg, Manitoba. United States Department of Agriculture, Forest Service General Technical Report RM-142, Fort Collins Colorado. 309 pp.

_____. 1989. A Common Black-headed Gull: second Vancouver record. Vancouver Natural History Society Discovery 18: 14-15.

Cannings, R.J., B. Fredericks, and A. Stepniewski. 1974. Year-end hike: 1974 - Tonquin area - Mt. Robson Park. British Columbia Parks Branch Unpublished Report, Victoria. 5 pp. (Bibliography 2542).

Cannings, R.J., S.R. Cannings, J.M. Cannings, and G.P. Sirk. 1978. Successful breeding of the Flammulated Owl in British Columbia. Murrelet 59:74-75.

Cannings, S.G. 1973. Mount Robson vertebrate report, 1973. British Columbia Parks Branch Unpublied Report, Victoria. 18 pp. (Bibliography 2558).

_____. 1974. South Okanagan bird report - summer 1974. British Columbia Parks Branch Unpublished Report, Victoria. 27 pp. (Bibliography 2559).

Cannings, S.R. 1972. Some bird records from the Okanagan valley. Vancouver Natural History Society Discovery 1:37.

Carey, A.B. 1985. A summary of the scientific basis for Spotted Owl management. Pages 100-114 in R.J. Gutierrez and A.B. Carey (editors). Ecology and management of the Spotted Owl in the Pacific Northwest. United States Department of Agriculture, Forest Service General Technical Report PNW-185, Portland, Oregon.

Carl, G.C. 1942. Another record of the King Eider in British Columbia. Murrelet 23:62.

_____. 1959. In memoriam - James Alexander Munro. Murrelet 40:17-18.

Carl, G.C. and C.J. Guiguet. 1972. Alien animals in British Columbia. British Columbia Provincial Museum Handbook No.14, Victoria. 103 pp.

Carl, G.C. and G.A. Hardy. 1945. Flora and fauna of the Paradise Mine area, British Columbia. Pages 13-38 in Provincial Museum of Natural History and Anthropology Report for the year 1944, Victoria, British Columbia.

Carl, G.C., C.J. Guiguet, and G.H. Hardy. 1951. Biology of the Scott Island Group, British Columbia. Pages B21-B63 in Provincial Museum of Natural History and Anthropology Report for the year 1950, Victoria, British Columbia.

_____, _____, and _____. 1952. A natural history survey of the Manning Park area, British Columbia. British Columbia Provincial Museum Occasional Paper No.9, Victoria. 130 pp.

Carson, T. and J. Howsam. 1978. A study of waterfowl in relation to spawning herring at Ganges Harbour and Captain's Passage, British Columbia. British Columbia Provincial Museum Unpublished Report, Victoria. 39 pp. (Bibliography 1925).

Carter, B.C. 1958. The American Goldeneye in central New Brunswick. Canadian Wildlife Service Wildlife Management Bulletin (Series 2) No.9, Ottawa, Ontario. 47 pp.

Carter, H.R. 1984. At-sea biology of the Marbled Murrelet (*Brachyramphus marmoratus*) in Barkley Sound, British Columbia. M.Sc. Thesis, University of Manitoba, Winnipeg. 143 pp.

Carter, H.R., and S.G. Sealy. 1984. Marbled Murrelet (*Brachyramphus marmoratus*) mortality and a gill-net fishery in Barkley Sound, British Columbia. Pages 212-220 in D.N. Nettleship, G.A. Sanger and P.F. Springer (editors). Marine birds: their feeding ecology and commercial fisheries relationships. Canadian Wildlife Service Special Publication. Ottawa, Ontario.

_____. and _____. 1986. Year-round use of coastal lakes by Marbled Murrelets. Condor 88:473-477.

_____. and _____. 1987. Inland records of downy young and fledgling Marbled Murrelets in North America. Murrelet 68:58-63.

Carter, H.R., K.A. Hobson, and S.G. Sealy. 1984. Colony-site selection by Pelagic Cormorants (*Phalacrocorax pelagicus*) in Barkley Sound, British Columbia. Colonial Waterbirds 7:25-34.

Caspell, B., A. Danvers, J. Hutchinson, P. Ostrander, D. Pringle, and D. Udey. 1979. Field report of fall migration of waterbirds in the Columbia Valley, 1979. Canadian Wildlife Service Unpublished Report, Delta, British Columbia. 28 pp.

Cassidy, A.L.E.V. 1983. Winter ecology of Bald Eagles at Qualicum River estuary, British Columbia. B.Sc. Thesis, University of Victoria, Victoria, British Columbia. 34 pp.

Catling, P.M. 1972. A study of the Boreal Owl in southern Ontario, with particular reference to the irruption of 1968-69. Canadian Field-Naturalist 86:223-232.

Centennial Wildlife Society of British Columbia. 1987. Our Wildlife Heritage: 100 Years of Wildlife Management. Centennial Wildlife Society of British Columbia, Victoria, 192 pp.

Chamberlain, M. 1887. Catalogue of Canadian birds with notes on the distribution of the species. St. John, New Brunswick. 143 pp.

Chamberlain, M.L. 1977. Observations on Red-necked Grebe nesting in Michigan. Wilson Bulletin 89:32-46.

Chaniot, G.E. 1966. Another California specimen of *Pluvialis dominica fulva*. Condor 68:212.

Chapman, B.-A., J.P. Goossen, and I. Ohanjanian. 1985. Occurrences of Black-necked Stilts, *Himantopus mexicanus*, in Western Canada. Canadian Field-Naturalist 99:254-257.

Chapman, F.M. 1890. On a collection of birds made by Mr. Clark P. Streator in British Columbia, with field notes by the collector. Bulletin of the American Museum of Natural History 3:123-158.

Chapman, J.A., C.J. Henny, and H.M. Wight. 1969. The status, population dynamics, and harvest of the Dusky Canada Goose. Wildlife Monographs 18:1-48.

Chapman, J.D. 1952. The climate of British Columbia. Paper presented to the Fifth British Columbia Natural Resources Conference, University of British Columbia, Vancouver, February 27th, 1952. 47 pp.

Chapman-Mosher, B.-A. 1986. Factors influencing reproductive success and nesting strategies in Black Terns. M.Sc. Thesis, Simon Fraser University, Burnaby, British Columbia. 154 pp.

Chilton, G. and S.G. Sealy. 1987. Species roles in mixed-species feeding flocks of seabirds. Journal of Field Ornithology 58:456-463.

Choate, T.S. 1963. Habitat and population dynamics of White-tailed Ptarmigan in Montana. Journal of Wildlife Management 27:684-699.

Christensen, G.C. 1970. The Chukar Partridge - Its introduction, life history, and management. Nevada Department of Fish and Game Biological Bulletin No. 4, Reno. 82 pp.

Christman, M.J. 1969. Bird sightings in Kootenay National Park. Parks Canada Unpublished Report, Radium Hotsprings, British Columbia. 14 pp. (Bibliography 2591).

_____. 1970. Occurrence of birds on the Vermilion Pass burn, Kootenay National Park. Parks Canada Unpublished Report, Radium Hotsprings, British Columbia. 51 pp. (Bibliography 2592).

Chu, E.W. 1984. Sooty Shearwaters off California: diet and energy gain. Pages 64-71 in D.N. Nettleship, G.A. Sanger and P.F. Springer (editors). Marine birds: their feeding ecology and commercial fisheries relationships. Proceedings of the Pacific Seabird Group Symposium, Seattle, Washington, 6-8 January 1982. Canadian Wildlife Service Special Publication. Ottawa, Ontario.

Clague, J.J. 1981. Late quaternary geology and geochronology of British Columbia. Part 2: summary and discussion of radio-carbon-dated quaternary history. Geological Survey of Canada Paper 80-35, Ottawa, Ontario. 41pp.

Clark, R.J. 1970. A field study of the Short-eared Owl (*Asio flammeus* Pontoppidan) in North America. Ph.D. Thesis, Cornell University, Ithaca, New York. 209 pp.

Clark, R.J., D.G. Smith and L.H. Kelso. 1978. Working bibliography of owls of the world. National Wildlife Federation Scientific and Technical Series No.1, Washington, D.C. 319 pp.

Clark, W.S. 1983. The field identification of North American eagles. American Birds 37:822-826.

Clay, J.O. 1946. Western Willet seen at Victoria, British Columbia. Murrelet 27:13.

_____. 1947. Note on a hummingbird. Victoria Naturalist 3:105.

_____. 1950. Christmas bird count. Victoria Naturalist 6:88-89.

_____. 1955. Christmas bird census, 1954 - Victoria, British Columbia. Canadian Field-Naturalist 69:58.

_____. 1955a. Birds seen out of season. Victoria Naturalist 11:100-101.

_____. 1957a. Christmas bird census, 1956 - Victoria, British Columbia. Canadian Field-Naturalist 71:28.

_____. 1957b. Some interesting birds. Victoria Naturalist 14:73-75.

Coffey, B.B. 1948. Post-juvenal migration of herons. Bird-Banding 19:1-5.

Cogswell, H.L. 1977. Water birds of California. University of California Press, Berkeley. 399 pp.

Collins, C.T. and R.E. Landry. 1977. Artificial nest burrows for Burrowing Owls. North American Bird-Bander 2:151-154.

Conant, B. 1988. Alaska productivity surveys of geese, swans and Brant - 1987. United States Fish and Wildlife Service Report, Juneau, Alaska. 26 pp.

Connors, P.G. 1983. Taxonomy, distribution, and evolution of golden plovers (*Pluvialis dominica* and *Pluvialis fulva*). Auk 100:607-620.

Conover, M.R. and G.G. Chasko. 1985. Nuisance Canada Goose problems in the eastern United States. Wildlife Society Bulletin 13:228-233.

Cook, F.R. and D. Muir. 1984. The Committee on the Status of Endangered Wildlife in Canada (COSEWIC): history and progress. Canadian Field-Naturalist 98:63-70.

Cook, F.S. 1947. Notes on some fall and winter birds of the Queen Charlotte Islands, British Columbia. Canadian Field-Naturalist 61:131-133.

Cooke, W.W. 1915. Distribution and migration of North American gulls and their allies. United States Department of Agriculture Bulletin No. 292, Washington, D.C. 70 pp.

Cooper, J.G. 1860. Report upon the birds collected on the survey. Land birds. Chapter 1. United States Pacific Rail Road Exploration and Survey 12 (Book 2. Zoology) 3:140-226.

Cooper, J.K. 1969. First breeding record of the White-headed Woodpecker for Canada. Canadian Field-Naturalist 83:276-277.

Cooper, J.M. 1983. Recent occurrences of the American Avocet in British Columbia. Murrelet 64:47-48.

Cooper, J.M. 1987. Notes on the vertebrates of Delkatla Inlet, Queen Charlotte Islands, 2 May-15 August 1987. Royal British Columbia Museum Unpublished Report, Victoria. 185 pp.

Cooper, J.M. and M. Adams. 1979. The birds and mammals of Kwadacha Wilderness Park, August 13-September 8, 1979. British Columbia Provincial Museum Unpublished Report, Victoria. 10 pp. (Bibliography 2687).

Cooper, J.M. and D.L.P. Cooper. 1983. A second report on the summer vertebrates of the Fern Lake area of Kwadacha Wilderness Park. British Columbia Provincial Museum Unpublished Report, Victoria. 7 pp. (Bibliography 2688).

Corkran, C.C. 1988. Status and potential for breeding of the Common Loon in the Pacific Northwest. Pages 107-116; in P.I.V. Strong (editor). Papers from the 1987 Conference on Common Loon Research and Management. North American Loon Fund, Meredith, New Hampshire.

Cottam, C., J.J. Lynch and A.L. Nelson. 1944. Food habits and management of American sea brant. Journal of Wildlife Management 8:36-56.

Council of Biology Editors, Committee on Form and Style. 1972. CBE style manual. Third edition. American Institute of Biological Sciences, Washington, D.C. 297 pp.

Cowan, I.McT. 1939. The vertebrate fauna of the Peace River district of British Columbia. British Columbia Provincial Museum Occasional Paper No.1, Victoria. 102 pp.

_____. 1939a. The White-tailed Ptarmigan of Vancouver Island. Condor 41:82-83.

_____. 1940. Bird records from British Columbia. Murrelet 21:69-70.

_____. 1940a. Winter occurrence of summer birds on Vancouver Island, British Columbia. Condor 42:213-214.

_____. 1942a. Food habits of the Barn Owl in British Columbia. Murrelet 23:48-53.

_____. 1942b. Economic status of the pheasant on the cultivated lands of the Okanagan Valley, B.C. Pages 49-62 *in* Annual Report of the British Columbia Provincial Game Commission for 1942, Victoria.

_____. 1955. The Whooping Crane. Bulletin of the Vancouver Natural History Society 95:2-3.

_____. 1987. Science and the conservation of wildlife in British Columbia. Pages 85-106 *in* Our Wildlife Heritage: 100 years of Wildlife Management. The Centennial Wildlife Society of British Columbia, Victoria. 192 pp.

Cowan, I.McT. and C.J. Guiguet. 1965. The mammals of British Columbia. British Columbia Provincial Museum Handbook No. 11, Victoria. 414 pp.

Cowan, I.McT. and J.A. Munro. 1944. Birds and mammals of Revelstoke National Park. Canadian Alpine Journal 29:100-121; 237-256.

Cramp, S. (editor). 1983. Handbook of the birds of Europe, the Middle East and North Africa: The birds of the western Palearctic, Volume III - waders to gulls. Oxford University Press, Oxford, England. 913 pp.

Craven, S.R. 1981. The Canada Goose (*Branta canadensis*) - an annotated bibliography. United States Department of the Interior, Fish and Wildlife Service Special Scientific Report - Wildlife No.231, Washington, D.C. 66 pp.

Cringan, A.T. 1957. Notes on the biology of the Red-necked Grebe in western Ontario. Canadian Field-Naturalist 71:72-73.

Crispens, C.G. 1960. Quails and partridges of North America - a bibliography. University of Washington Press, Seattle. 125 pp.

Crockett, A.B. and H.H. Hadow. 1975. Nest site selection by Williamson and Red-naped sapsuckers. Condor 77:365-368.

Cronau, J.P., R.G.M. Goede, and E. Nieboer. 1986. A new character for age determination in the Bar-tailed Godwit *Limosa lapponica*. Ringing and Migration 7:135-138.

Crowell, J.B. and H.B. Nehls. 1966a. The fall migration - northern Pacific coast region. Audubon Field Notes 20:449-453.

_____. and _____. 1966b. The spring migration - northern Pacific coast region. Audubon Field Notes 20:539-542.

_____. and _____. 1966c. The nesting season - northern Pacific coast region. Audubon Field Notes 20:591-595.

_____. and _____. 1967a. The winter season - northern Pacific coast region. Audubon Field Notes 21:448-452.

_____. and _____. 1967b. The spring migration - northern Pacific coast region. Audubon Field Notes 21:532-535.

_____. and _____. 1967c. The nesting season - northern Pacific coast region. Audubon Field Notes 21:596-600.

_____. and _____. 1968a. The fall migration - northern Pacific coast region. Audubon Field Notes 22:78-83.

_____. and _____. 1968b. The winter season - northern Pacific coast region. Audubon Field Notes 22:468-472.

_____. and _____. 1968c. The spring migration - northern Pacific coast region. Audubon Field Notes 22:567-571.

_____. and _____. 1968d. The nesting season - northern Pacific coast region. Audubon Field Notes 22:638-642.

_____. and _____. 1969a. The winter season - northern Pacific coast region. Audubon Field Notes 23:508-513.

_____. and _____. 1969b. The spring migration - northern Pacific coast region. Audubon Field Notes 23:615-619.

_____. and _____. 1969c. The nesting season - northern Pacific coast region. Audubon Field Notes 23:684-688.

_____. and _____. 1970a. The fall migration - northern Pacific coast region. Audubon Field Notes 24:82-88.

_____. and _____. 1970b. The winter season - northern Pacific coast region. Audubon Field Notes 24:530-533.

_____. and _____. 1970c. The spring migration - northern Pacific coast region. Audubon Field Notes 24:635-638.

_____. and _____. 1970d. The nesting season - northern Pacific coast region. Audubon Field Notes 24:708-711.

_____. and _____. 1971a. The winter season - northern Pacific coast region. Audubon Field Notes 25:614-619.

_____. and _____. 1971b. The spring migration - northern Pacific coast region. Audubon Field Notes 25:787-793.

_____. and _____. 1972a. The fall migration - northern Pacific coast region. American Birds 26:107-111.

_____. and _____. 1972b. The winter season - northern Pacific coast region. American Birds 26:644-648.

_____. and _____. 1972c. The nesting season - northern Pacific coast region. American Birds 26:893-897.

_____. and _____. 1972d. The spring migration - northern Pacific coast region. American Birds 26:797-801.

_____. and _____. 1973a. The fall migration - northern Pacific coast region. American Birds 27:105-110.

_____. and _____. 1973b. The winter season - northern Pacific coast region. American Birds 27:652-656.

_____. and _____. 1973c. The spring migration - northern Pacific coast region. American Birds 27:809-812.

_____. and _____. 1973d. The nesting season - northern Pacific coast region. American Birds 27:908-911.

_____. and _____. 1974a. The fall migration - northern Pacific coast region. American Birds 28:93-98.

_____. and _____. 1974b. The winter season - northern Pacific coast region. American Birds 28:679-684.

_____. and _____. 1974c. The spring migration - northern Pacific coast region. American Birds 28:840-845.

_____. and _____. 1974d. The nesting season - northern Pacific coast region. American Birds 28:938-943.

_____. and _____. 1975a. The fall migration - northern Pacific coast region. American Birds 29:105-112.

_____. and _____. 1975b. The spring migration - northern Pacific coast region. American Birds 29:897-902.

_____. and _____. 1976. The winter season - northern Pacific coast region. American Birds 30:755-760.

_____. and _____. 1977a. The fall migration - northern Pacific coast region. American Birds 31:212-216.

_____. and _____. 1977b. Spring migration - northern Pacific coast region. American Birds 31:1037-1041.

Crowley, J.M. 1967. Biogeography. Canadian Geographer 11:312-326.

Cumming, R.A. 1924. Pectoral Sandpiper eating seeds. Migrant 2:15. (Bibliography 1936).

_____. 1926. Vancouver notes. Migrant 3:43-44. (Bibliography 1944).

_____. 1931. Some birds observed in the Queen Charlotte Islands, British Columbia. Murrelet 11:15-17.

_____. 1932. Birds of the Vancouver district, British Columbia. Murrelet 13:1-15.

_____. 1935. Rock Ptarmigan at Vancouver, British Columbia. Murrelet 16:39.

Curtin, F. 1978. Rare penguins sighted off Vancouver Island. Vancouver Province Newspaper, 16 August.

Cushing, J.E. 1941. Notes on the feeding habits of two species of hawks. Condor 43:70-71.

Cuthbert, J.T. 1972. Port Hardy airport eagle study - final report for period October 28-December 3, 1972. L.G.L. Ltd. Environmental Research Associates Unpublished Report, Toronto, Ontario. 67 pp. (Bibliography 2751).

Dane, C.W. 1966. Some aspects of breeding biology of the Blue-winged Teal. Auk 83:389-402.

Darcus, S.J. 1927. Discovery of the nest of the Marbled Murrelet (*Brachyramphus marmoratus*) in the Queen Charlotte Islands, British Columbia. Canadian Field-Naturalist 41:197-199.

_____. 1930. Notes on birds of the northern part of the Queen Charlotte Islands in 1927. Canadian Field-Naturalist 44:45-49.

_____. 1930a. Status of Canada Geese on the Vaseux Lake bird sanctuary, British Columbia. Canadian Field-Naturalist 44:21-22.

_____. 1935. Christmas bird census, 1934 - Summerland, Okanagan Lake, British Columbia. Canadian Field-Naturalist 49:44.

Darwin, L.H. 1916. First and second annual reports of the chief game warden to the governor of the state of Washington, June 12, 1913 to February 28, 1915. Olympia, Washington. 58 pp.

_____. 1918. Third and fourth reports of the state game warden to the governor of the state of Washington, March 1, 1915 to February 28, 1917. Olympia, Washington. 78 pp.

Davidson, A.R. 1963. An annotated list of the birds of southern Vancouver Island. Victoria Natural History Society Mimeo Report, Victoria, British Columbia. 23 pp. (Bibliography 306).

_____. 1965. Victoria Natural History Society bird report - 1964. Victoria Natural History Society Mimeo Report, Victoria, British Columbia. 12 pp. (Bibliography 1249).

_____. 1966. Annotated list of birds of southern Vancouver Island. Victoria Natural History Society, Victoria, British Columbia. 23 pp. (Bibliography 306).

_____. 1979. Unusual sighting in the Comox valley. Victoria Naturalist 35:77.

Davies, R.G. 1973. Demography and behaviour of Ruffed Grouse in British Columbia. M.Sc. Thesis, University of Victoria, Victoria, British Columbia. 86 pp.

_____. 1978. Status of swans wintering on Vancouver Island between 1971 and 1977. British Columbia Fish and Wildlife Branch Unpublished Report, Nanaimo. 16 pp.

_____. 1981a. Swan survey of region 1 - February 1981. British Columbia Fish and Wildlife Branch Unpublished Report, Victoria. 8 pp. (Bibliography 2776).

_____. 1981b. Abundance and distribution of Mute Swans on Vancouver Island, British Columbia. British Columbia Fish and Wildlife Branch Unpublished Report, Victoria. 7 pp. (Bibliography 2777).

_____. 1981c. Status of swans wintering on Vancouver Island between 1971 and 1977. Pages 86-90 *in* Proceedings and Papers of the Sixth Trumpeter Swan Society Conference, Anchorage, Alaska, September 7-11, 1978. (Bibliography 2778).

Davis, T.A., M.F. Platter-Reiger, and R.A. Ackerman. 1984. Incubation water loss by Pied-billed Grebe eggs: adaptation to a hot, wet nest. Physiological Zoology 57:384-391.

Dawe, N.K. 1971. Nature interpretation report on Wasa, Moyie, and Jimsmith Provincial Parks, British Columbia. British Columbia Parks Branch Unpublished Report, Victoria. 97 pp. (Bibliography 1172).

_____. 1972. Franklin's Gull sighted in southeastern British Columbia. Vancouver Natural History Society Discovery 1:6.

_____. 1973. Sighting of a Bar-tailed Godwit at the George C. Reifel Waterfowl Refuge. Vancouver Natural History Society Discovery 1:110-111.

_____. 1976. Flora and fauna of the Marshall-Stevenson Wildlife area. Canadian Wildlife Service Report, Delta, British Columbia. 201 pp. (Bibliography 1862).

_____. 1980. Flora and fauna of the Marshall-Stevenson Unit, Qualicum National Wildlife Area (update to June 1979). Canadian Wildlife Service Report, Qualicum Beach, British Columbia. 149 pp. (Bibliography 2788).

Dawe, N.K. and B. Davies. 1975. A nesting study of Canada geese on the George C. Reifel Migratory Bird Sanctuary, British Columbia. Syesis 8:1-7.

Dawe, N.K. and L.E. Jones. 1986. Vegetation of the Koksilah Marsh, Cowichan estuary: a pre-restoration study, July 1985. Canadian Wildlife Service Technical Report Series No.9, Delta, British Columbia. 30 pp.

Dawe, N.K. and S.D. Lang. 1980. Flora and fauna of the Nanoose Unit, Qualicum National Wildlife Area. Canadian Wildlife Service Unpublished Report. Qualicum Beach, British Columbia. 117 pp. (Bibliography 2791).

Dawe, N.K. and J.D. McIntosh. 1987. Changes in vegetation following dyke removal on the Englishman River estuary (1979-1986). Research Note. Northwest Environmental Journal 3:150-151.

Dawe, N.K. and E.L. Nygren. 1989. Vancouver Island Brant: 1989 survey. B.C. Naturalist 27(3):18-19.

Dawe, N.K., W.S. Boyd, and D.E.C. Trethewey. 1987. Vegetation of man-made marshes on the Campbell River estuary: a five year study. Research Note. Northwest Environmental Journal 3:151-152.

Day, R.H., K.L. Oakley, and D.R. Barnard. 1983. Nest sites and eggs of Kittlitz's and Marbled murrelets. Condor 85:265-273.

Degner, M.A. 1988. Song, vegetation, and sound production in Blue Grouse. M.Sc. Thesis, University of Alberta, Edmonton. 140 pp.

de Goutiere, J. 1968. The pathless way. J.J. Douglas Ltd., Vancouver, British Columbia. 194 pp.

Delacour, J. 1954. The waterfowl of the world (Volume 1). Country Life Limited, London, England. 284 pp.

_____. 1956. The waterfowl of the world (Volume 2). Country Life Limited, London, England. 232 pp.

Demarchi, D.A. 1987. Defining British Columbia's regional ecosystem. Pages 57-68 in Bits and Pieces Symposium. Federation of British Columbia Naturalists, Vancouver, November 20-21, 1987.

_____. 1988a. A regional wildlife ecosystem classification for British Columbia. Pages 11-19 in H.A. Stelfox and G.R. Ironside (compilers). Land/Wildlife integration workshop No. 3, Mount Ste.-Marie, Quebec, 16-19 September 1985. Ecological Land Classification Series No. 22, Canadian Wildlife Service, Ottawa, Ontario. 215 pp.

_____. 1988b. Ecoregions of British Columbia. British Columbia Ministry of Environment and Parks, Wildlife Branch, Victoria. Map.

Demarchi, D.A. and E.C. Lea. 1987. Biophysical habitat classification in British Columbia: an interdisciplinary approach to ecosystem evaluation. Symposium on Land Classification based on Vegetation, Applications for Resource Management, Moscow, Idaho, 17-19 November 1987.

Demarchi, R.A. 1962. A study of the Chukar partridge in the Thompson valley of south-central British Columbia. B.Sc. Thesis, University of British Columbia, Vancouver. 61 pp. (Bibliography 2806).

Demarchi, R.A. and W.G. Smith. 1967. Spring and fall waterfowl surveys in the Columbia River marshes of the East Kootenay. British Columbia Fish and Wildlife Unpublished Report, Victoria. 44 pp. (Bibliography 2805).

Demaree, S.R. 1970. Nest-building, incubation period, and fledging in the Black-chinned Hummingbird. Wilson Bulletin 82:225.

Denson, E.P. 1964. Comparison of waterfowl hunting techniques at Humboldt Bay, California. Journal of Wildlife Management 28:103-119.

De Smet, K.D. 1982. Status of the Red-necked Grebe *(Podiceps grisegena)* in Canada. Committee on the Status of Endangered Wildlife in Canada Report, c/o Canadian Nature Federation, Ottawa, Ontario. 103 pp. (Bibliography 2809).

_____. 1983. Breeding ecology and productivity of Red-necked Grebes in Turtle Mountain Provincial Park, Manitoba. M.Sc. Thesis, University of North Dakota, Bismarck. 100 pp.

_____. 1986. A status report on the Golden Eagle *(Aquila chrysaetos)* in Canada. Committee on the Status of Endangered Wildlife in Canada, c/o Canadian Nature Federation, Ottawa, Ontario.

_____. 1987. First nesting record and status of the Clark's Grebe in Canada. Blue Jay 45:101-105.

Deusing, M. 1939. Nesting habits of the Pied-billed Grebe. Auk 56:367-373.

Devillers, P. 1970. Identification and distribution in California of the *Sphyrapicus varius* group of sapsuckers. California Birds 1:47-76.

_____. 1977. The skuas of the North American Pacific coast. Auk 94:417-429.

Dickinson, J.C. 1953. Report on the McCabe collection of British Columbia birds. Bulletin of the Museum of Comparative Zoology 100:123-209.

Dixon, K.R. and T.C. Juelson. 1987. The political economy of the Spotted Owl. Ecology 68:772-776.

Dobkin, D.S., J.A. Holmes, and B.A. Wilcox. 1986. Traditional nest-site use by White-throated Swifts. Condor 88:252-253.

Douglas, A. 1984. An evaluation of wintering raptors in the lower mainland of British Columbia. British Columbia Institute of Technology Unpublished Report, Burnaby. 60 pp.

Douglas, S.D. and T.E. Reimchen. 1988a. Habitat characteristics and population estimate of breeding Red-throated Loons, *Gavia stellata*, on the Queen Charlotte Islands, British Columbia. Canadian Field-Naturalist 102: 679-684.

_____. and _____. 1988b. Reproductive phenology and early survivorship in Red-throated Loons, *Gavia stellata*. Canadian Field-Naturalist 102: 701-704.

Dow, D.D. and W.H. Hesse. 1969. British Columbia record of Skua in terrestrial habitat. Canadian Field-Naturalist 83:402.

Dow, J.S. 1943. A study of nesting Canada geese in Honey Lake Valley, California. California Fish and Game 29:3-18.

Drent, R.H. 1961. On the supposed nesting of the Rhinoceros Auklet near Metlakahtla, Alaska. Auk 78:257-258.

_____. 1965. Breeding biology of the Pigeon Guillemot, *Cepphus columba*. Ardea 53:99-160.

Drent, R.H. and C.J. Guiguet. 1961. A catalogue of British Columbia sea-bird colonies. British Columbia Provincial Museum Occasional Paper No. 12, Victoria. 173 pp.

Drent, R. and J. Ward. 1970. Report on the sightings of wing-tagged Glaucous-winged Gulls, 1969/70. Vancouver Natural History Society Discovery 149:8-10.

Drent, R., G.R. van Tets, F. Tompa and K.Vermeer. 1964. The breeding birds of Mandarte Island, British Columbia. Canadian Field-Naturalist 78:208-263.

Drent, R.H., V. Gibbard, and W. Smith. 1971. British Columbia nest records scheme - 16th annual report, 1970. Federation of British Columbia Naturalists Newsletter 9(1):3-5.

_____, _____, and _____. 1972. British Columbia nest records scheme - 17th annual report, 1971. Federation of British Columbia Naturalists Newsletter 10(1):3-5.

Drewien, R.C. and E.C. Bizeau. 1974. Status and distribution of Greater Sandhill Cranes in the Rocky Mountains. Journal of Wildlife Management 38:720-742.

Drury, W.H. 1961. The breeding biology of shorebirds on Bylot Island, Northwest Territories, Canada. Auk 78:176-219.

Ducks Unlimited Canada. 1983. Annotated checklist of birds for the vicinity of eight Ducks Unlimited projects in the Cariboo-Chilcotin region of British Columbia. Ducks Unlimited (Canada) Unpublished Report, Kamloops, British Columbia. 29 pp. (Bibliography 2837).

Dunbar, D.L. 1984. The breeding ecology and management of White Pelicans at Stum Lake, British Columbia. British Columbia Fish and Wildlife Report R-6, Victoria. 85 pp.

Dunn, E.H. and C.D. MacInnes. 1987. Geographic variation in clutch size and body size of Canada Geese. Journal of Field Ornithology 58:355-371.

Dunn, J. 1978. The races of the Yellow-bellied Sapsucker. Birding 10:142-149.

Duvall, A.J. 1946. An early record of the Passenger Pigeon for British Columbia. Auk 63:598.

Dwight, J. 1925. The gulls (Laridae) of the world: their plumages, moults, variations, relationships and distribution. Bulletin of the American Museum of Natural History 52:63-401.

Dzubin, A. 1959. Growth and plumage development of wild-trapped juvenile Canvasback (*Aythya valisineria*). Journal of Wildlife Management 23:279-290.

_____. 1965. A study of migrating Ross' Geese in western Saskatchewan. Condor 67:511-534.

_____. 1979. Recent increase of blue geese in western North America. Pages 141-175 *in* R.L. Jarvis and J.C. Bartonek (editors). Management and Biology of Pacific Flyway Geese. United States Fish and Wildlife Service, Portland, Oregon.

Dzubin, A., H.W. Miller and G.V. Schildman. 1964. White-fronts. Pages 135-143 *in* J.P. Linduska (editor). Waterfowl Tomorrow. United States Government Printing Office, Washington, D.C.

Ealey, D.M. 1986. Tim Myres: recipient of the 11th Loran L. Goulden Memorial award. Alberta Naturalist 16:25-29.

Eamer, J. 1985. Winter habitat for dabbling ducks on southeastern Vancouver Island, British Columbia. M.Sc. Thesis, University of British Columbia, Vancouver. 103 pp.

Eastman, D.S. 1974. White-faced Ibis photographed in British Columbia. Canadian Field-Naturalist 88:354.

Ebel, G.R.A. 1973a. Band-tailed Pigeon in the northern interior of British Columbia. Murrelet 54:36-37.

_____. 1973b. Nechako River bird sanctuary - some thoughts and recommendations. Canadian Wildlife Service Unpublished Report, Delta, British Columbia. 76 pp. (Bibliography 2861).

Edgell, M.C.R. 1984. Trans-hemispheric movements of Holarctic Anatidae: the Eurasian Wigeon (*Anas penelope* L.) in North America. Journal of Biogeography 11:27-39.

Edson, J.M. 1935. Some records supplementary to the distributional checklist of the birds of the state of Washington. Murrelet 16:11-14.

Edwards, R.Y. 1949. A faunal investigation of E.C. Manning Park. British Columbia Parks Branch Unpublished Report, Victoria. 89 pp. (Bibliography 1396).

_____. 1953. Barrow's Goldeneye using crow nests in British Columbia. Wilson Bulletin 65:197-198.

_____. 1965. Birds seen in Active Pass, British Columbia. Pages EE19-EE22 in Provincial Museum of Natural History and Anthropology Report for the Year 1964, Victoria, British Columbia.

_____. 1968. Notes on gulls of southwestern British Columbia. Syesis 1:199-202.

Edwards, R.Y. and R.W. Ritcey. 1967. The birds of Wells Gray Park, British Columbia. British Columbia Parks Branch, Victoria. 37 pp. (Bibliography 1025).

Einarsen, A.S. 1965. Black Brant - sea goose of the Pacific coast. University of Washington Press, Seattle. 142 pp.

Elliott, J.E., R.W. Butler, R.J. Norstrom, and P.E.Whitehead. 1988. Levels of polychlorinated dibenzodioxins and polychlorinated dibenzofurans in eggs of Great Blue Herons (*Ardea herodias*) in British Columbia, 1983-87; possible impacts on reproductive success. Canadian Wildlife Service Progress Notes No. 176, Ottawa, Ontario. 7 pp.

Ellison, L.N. 1971. Territoriality in Alaskan Spruce Grouse. Auk 88:652-664.

Ellison, M. and W. Merilees. 1980. Winter Harlequins in the west Kootenay. Vancouver Natural History Society Discovery 9:17-18.

Emms, S.K. and K.H. Morgan. 1989. The breeding biology and distribution of the Pigeon Guillemot (*Cepphus columba*) in the Strait of Georgia. Pages 100-106 *in* Vermeer, K. and R.W. Butler (editors). The ecology and status of marine and shoreline birds in the Strait of Georgia, British Columbia. Canadian Wildlife Service Special Publication, Ottawa, Ontario.

Enderson, J.H. 1964. A study of the Prairie Falcon in the central Rocky Mountain region. Auk 81:332-352.

Ennis, T. 1969. Field characters of immature Little Gulls and Kittiwakes. British Birds 62:234-237.

Environment Canada. 1979. Canada's resource lands. Map Folio No.4, Environment Canada Lands Directorate, Ottawa. 232 pp.

Erasmus, G. and J. Erasmus. 1972. Mitlenatch Island Nature Park - summer 1972. British Columbia Parks Branch Unpublished Report, Victoria. 44 pp. (Bibliography 2883).

Erickson, R.C. 1948. Life history and ecology of the Canvas-back, *Nyroca valisinera* (Wilson), in south-eastern Oregon. Ph.D. Thesis, Iowa State College, Ames. 324 pp.

Erskine, A.J. 1959. A joint clutch of Barrow's Goldeneye and Bufflehead eggs. Canadian Field-Naturalist 73:131.

_____. 1960. Three sight records of unusual birds in the Vancouver, British Columbia area. Murrelet 41:9.

_____. 1962. Some new data on introgression in flickers from British Columbia. Canadian Field-Naturalist 76:82-87.

_____. 1964. Bird migration during April in southern British Columbia. Murrelet 45:15-22.

_____. 1968. Birds observed in north-central Alberta, summer 1964. Blue Jay 26:24-31.

_____. 1971. Growth and annual cycles in weights, plumages, and reproductive organs of Goosanders in eastern Canada. Ibis 113:42-58.

_____. 1971a. Nest record card program in Canada. Canadian Field-Naturalist 85:3-11.

_____. 1972. Buffleheads. Canadian Wildlife Service Monograph Series No.4, Ottawa, Ontario. 240 pp.

_____. 1978. Durability of tree holes used by Buffleheads. Canadian Field-Naturalist 92:94-95.

Erskine, A.J. and G.S. Davidson. 1976. Birds in the Fort Nelson lowlands of northeastern British Columbia. Syesis 9:1-11.

Erskine, A.J. and R.C. Stein. 1964. A re-evaluation of the avifauna of the Cariboo parklands. Pages 18-35 *in* Provincial Museum Natural History and Anthropology Report for the year 1963, Victoria, British Columbia.

Evans, D.L. 1982. Status reports on twelve raptors. United States Department of the Interior Fish and Wildlife Service Special Scientific Report - Wildlife No. 238, Washington, D.C. 68 pp.

Everett, W.T. 1988. Biology of the Black-vented Shearwater. Western Birds 19:89-104.

Fannin, J. 1891. Check-list British Columbia birds. British Columbia Provincial Museum, Victoria. 49 pp.

_____. 1895. The Emperor Goose in British Columbia. Auk 12:76.

_____. 1898. A preliminary catalogue of the collections of natural history and ethnology of the Provincial Museum, Victoria, British Columbia. British Columbia Provincial Museum, Victoria. 196 pp.

Farley, A.L. 1979. Atlas of British Columbia. University of British Columbia Press, Vancouver. 135 pp.

Farr, A. 1977. Observations of Sharp-tailed Grouse (*Pedioecetes phasianellus*) in the East Kootenay. British Columbia Fish and Wildlife Branch Unpublished Report, Cranbrook. 12 pp. (Bibliography 2903).

_____. 1987. Managing habitat for Bald Eagles in the Fraser valley of British Columbia: 1986-1987 observations. British Columbia Ministry of Environment and Parks Unpublished Report, Victoria. 40 pp.

Farr, A.C.M. and D.L. Dunbar. 1987. British Columbia's 1987 midwinter Bald Eagle survey. British Columbia Ministry of Environment and Parks Unpublished Report, Surrey. 23 pp.

_____. and _____. 1988. British Columbia's 1988 midwinter Bald Eagle survey. British Columbia Ministry of Environment, Surrey. 33 pp.

Farrand, John. 1977. What to look for: Eskimo and Little curlews compared. American Birds 31:137-138.

Feinstein, B. 1958. Xantus' Murrelet (*Endomychura hypoleuca scrippsi*) from the State of Washington. Auk 75:90-91.

Ferris, R.W. 1940. Eight years of banding of Western Gulls. Condor 42: 189-197

Findholt, S. and C.H. Trost. 1981. White Pelicans nesting in Idaho. Murrelet 62:19-20.

Finnegan, R.P. 1972. Pheasant counts on the Saanich Peninsula, 1966-1972. British Columbia Fish and Wildlife Branch Unpublished Report, Victoria. 75 pp. (Bibliography 2909)

Fisher, H.I. 1966. Airplane - albatross collisions on Midway Atoll. Conder 68:229-242.

Fisher, J. 1952. The Fulmar. Collins, St. James Place, London. 496 pp.

Fitch, H.S., F. Swenson, and D.F. Tillotson. 1946. Behavior and food habits of the Red-tailed Hawk. Condor 48:205-237.

Fitz-Gibbon, J. 1977. Wasa Lake Park - fauna records, 1977. British Columbia Parks Branch Unpublished Report, Victoria. 43 pp. (Bibliography 2914).

Fitzner, J.N. 1978. The ecology and behavior of the Long-billed Curlew (*Numenius americanus*) in southeastern Washington. PhD. Thesis, Washington State University, Pullman.

Fitzner, R.E. 1978. Behavioral ecology of the Swainson's Hawk (*Buteo swainsoni*) in southeastern Washington. Ph.D. Thesis, Washington State University, Pullman. 194 pp.

Fix, D. 1984. The spring migration-northern Pacific coast region. American Birds 38:948-952.

Flahaut, M.R. 1949. Spring migration - north Pacific coast region. Audubon Field Notes 3:220-222.

_____. 1950a. Fall migration - north Pacific coast region. Audubon Field Notes 4:30-32.

_____. 1950b. Winter season - north Pacific coast region. Audubon Field Notes 4:216-218.

_____. 1953a. The fall migration - north Pacific coast region. Audubon Field Notes 7:31-33.

_____. 1953b. The winter season - north Pacific coast region. Audubon Field Notes 7:230-231.

_____. 1953c. The spring migration - north Pacific coast region. Audubon Field Notes 7:287-288.

_____. 1953d. The spring migration - north Pacific coast region. Audubon Field Notes 7:322-324.

Flahaut, M.R. and Z.M.Schultz. 1954a. The fall migration - north Pacific coast region. Audubon Field Notes 8:36-38.

_____. and _____. 1954b. The spring migration - north Pacific coast region. Audubon Field Notes 8:324-326.

_____. and _____. 1955. The fall migration - north Pacific coast region. Audubon Field Notes 9:47-50.

_____. and _____. 1956. The fall migration - north Pacific coast region. Audubon Field Notes 10:47-50.

Fleming, J.H. 1907. The Fulvous Tree-Duck in British Columbia. Ottawa Naturalist 20:213.

Flint, V.E., R.L. Boehme, Y.V. Kostin, and A.A. Kuznepsov. 1984. A field guide to the birds of the USSR. Princeton University Press, New Jersey. 353 pp.

Flook, D.R. and L.S. Forbes. 1983. Ospreys and water management at Creston, British Columbia. Pages 281-286 *in* D.M. Bird (editor). Biology and Management of Bald Eagles and Ospreys. Proceedings of First International Symposium on Bald Eagles and Ospreys, Montreal, 28-29 October 1981. (Bibliography 2961).

Foottit, R. 1968. Summer report for 1968 - Mitlenatch Island Nature Park. British Columbia Parks Branch Unpublished Report, Victoria. 33 pp. (Bibliography 2962).

_____. 1969. Summer report for 1969 - Mitlenatch Island Nature Park. British Columbia Parks Branch Unpublished Report, Victoria. 25 pp. (Bibliography 2963).

_____. 1970. Summer report for 1970 - Mitlenatch Island Nature Park. British Columbia Parks Branch Unpublished Report, Victoria. 18 pp. (Bibliography 1910).

Forbes, L.S. 1984. The nesting ecology of the Western Grebe in British Columbia. Canadian Wildlife Service Report, Delta, British Columbia. 20 pp.

_____. 1985a. Nesting of Eared Grebes at Duck Lake, near Creston, British Columbia. Murrelet 66:20-21.

_____. 1985b. The feeding ecology of Western Grebes breeding at Duck Lake, British Columbia. M.Sc. Thesis, University of Manitoba, Winnipeg. 72 pp.

_____. 1988. Western Grebe nesting in British Columbia. Murrelet 69:28-33.

Forbes, L.S., K. Simpson, J.P. Kelsall, and D.R. Flook. 1985a. Great Blue Heron colonies in British Columbia. Canadian Wildlife Service Manuscript Report, Delta, British Columbia. 78 pp.

_____, _____, _____, and _____. 1985b. Reproductive success of Great Blue Herons in British Columbia. Canadian Journal of Zoology 63:1110-1113.

Force, M.P. and P.W. Mattocks. 1986. The winter season - northern Pacific coast region. American Birds 40:316-321.

Forsell, D.J. and P.J. Gould. 1980. Distribution and abundance of seabirds wintering in the Kodiak area of Alaska. United States Fish and Wildlife Service Unpublished Report, Anchorage, Alaska. 83 pp.

_____. and _____. 1981. Distribution and abundance of marine birds and mammals wintering in the Kodiak area of Alaska. United States Fish and Wildlife Service Report FWS/OBS-81-13, Washington, D.C. 72 pp.

Forsman, E.D. 1983. Methods and materials for locating and studying Spotted Owls. Pacific Northwest Forest and Range Experiment Station General Technical Report PNW-162, Portland, Oregon. 8 pp.

Forsman, E.D. and B. Booth. 1986. A survey of the Spotted Owl in the Skagit River region of British Columbia. British Columbia Wildlife Branch Unpublished Report, Surrey. 17 pp.

Forsman, E.D. and D. Dunbar. 1985. A survey of the Spotted Owl in British Columbia. British Columbia Wildlife Branch Unpublished Report, Surrey. 21 pp.

Forsman, E.D., E.C. Meslow, and M.J. Strub. 1977. Spotted Owl abundance in young versus old-growth forests, Oregon. Wildlife Society Bulletin 5:43-47.

Forsman, E.D., E.C. Meslow, and H.M. Wight. 1984. Distribution and biology of the Spotted Owl in Oregon. Wildlife Monographs 87:1-64.

Foster, B. 1974. A study of fall pheasant population dynamics on Westham Island, B.C. University of British Columbia Faculty of Forestry Unpublished Report, Vancouver. 16 pp. (Bibliography 2978).

Fox, G.A. 1971. Recent changes in reproductive success of the Pigeon Hawk. Journal of Wildlife Management 35:122-128.

Fraser, D.F. 1984. An annotated list of the birds of the Elk and Flathead drainages. Environmental Services Westar Mining Unpublished Report, Sparwood, British Columbia. 110 pp. (Bibliography 2989).

Fredrickson, L.H. 1967. Some aspects of reproductive behavior of American Coots (*Fulica americana*). Ph.D. Thesis, Iowa State University, Ames 113 pp.

Friedmann, H. 1943. A new race of Sharp-tailed Grouse. Journal of the Washington Academy of Science 33:189-191.

Frost, D.L. 1972. A recent nest record of a Pygmy Owl. Vancouver Natural History Society Discovery 1:35-36.

Fry, K. 1980. Aspects of the wintering ecology of the Dunlin (*Calidris alpina*) on the Fraser River delta. Canadian Wildlife Service Unpublished Report, Delta, British Columbia. 45 pp. (Bibliography 2997).

Fujimaki, Y. 1986. Seabird colonies on Hokkaido Island. Pages 152-165 *in* N. Litvinenko (editor). Seabirds of the Far East (Morskie ptitsy dalnego vostoka). Unedited translation number LSM-7-00912. Environment Canada, Ottawa.

Fuller, R.W. 1953. Studies in the life history and ecology of the American Pintail, *Anas acuta tzitzihoa* (Vieillot) in Utah. M.S. Thesis, Utah State Agricultural College, Logan.

Furness, R.W. 1987. The Skuas. T. and A.D. Poser Ltd. Calton, England. 363 pp.

Furrer, R.K. 1974. First spring sight record of the Yellow Rail for the Pacific Northwest. Murrelet 55:25-26.

Fyfe, R. and S.M. Teeple. 1968. 1968 field survey of colony fish-eating birds in the Kootenay River valley of British Columbia. Canadian Wildlife Service Manuscript Report No. 2051, Edmonton, Alberta. 16 pp.

Fyfe, R.W., R.W. Riseborough, and W. Walker. 1976. Pollutant effects on the reproduction of the Prairie Falcons and Merlins of the Canadian prairies. Canadian Field-Naturalist 90:346-355.

Gabrielson, I.N. and S.G. Jewett. 1940. Birds of Oregon. Oregon State College Monographs Studies in Zoology No.2, Corvallis, Oregon. 650 pp.

_____. and _____. 1970. Birds of the Pacific Northwest. Dover Publications, New York. 650 pp.

Gabrielson, I.N. and F.C. Lincoln. 1959. The birds of Alaska. The Stackpole Company, Harrisburg, Pennsylvania. 922 pp.

Gaines, D. 1974. Review of the status of the Yellow-billed Cuckoo in California: Sacramento Valley populations. Condor 76:204-209.

Garber, D.P. and J.R. Koplin. 1972. Prolonged and bisexual incubation by California Ospreys. Condor 74:201-202.

Gass, C.L. 1974. Feeding territoriality in postbreeding migratory Rufous Hummingbirds. Ph.D. Thesis, University of Oregon, Eugene. 138pp.

_____. 1978. Rufous Hummingbird feeding territoriality in a suboptimal habitat. Canadian Journal of Zoology 56:1535-1539.

_____. 1979. Territory regulation, tenure, and migration in Rufous Hummingbirds. Canadian Journal of Zoology 57:914-923.

Gass, C.L., G. Angehr, and J. Centa. 1976. Regulation of food supply by feeding territoriality in the Rufous Hummingbird. Canadian Journal of Zoology 54:2046-2054.

Gaston, A.J. and R. Decker. 1985. Interbreeding of Thayer's Gull, *Larus thayeri*, and Kumlien's Gull, *Larus glaucoides kumlieni*, on Southampton Island, Northwest Territories. Canadian Field-Naturalist 99:257-259.

Gaston, A.J. and D.N. Nettleship. 1981. The Thick-billed Murres of Prince Leopold Island. Canadian Wildlife Service Monograph Series No. 6, Ottawa,Ontario. 350 pp.

Gaston, A.J. and D.G. Noble. 1985. Studies on Ancient Murrelets at Reef Island, 1985. Canadian Wildlife Service Unpublished Report, Ottawa, Ontario. 46 pp.

Gaston, A.J. and D.W. Powell. 1989. Natural incubation, egg neglect, and hatchability in the Ancient Murrelet. Auk 106:433-438.

Gaston, A.J., I.L. Jones, D.G. Noble, and S.A. Smith. 1988. Orientation of Ancient Murrelet, *Synthliboramphus antiquus*, chicks during passage from the burrow to the sea. Animal Behaviour 36:300-303.

Gauthier, G. 1985. A functional analysis of territorial behaviour in breeding Bufflehead. Ph.D. Thesis, University of British Columbia, Vancouver. 165 pp.

Gehrman, K.H. 1951. An ecological study of the Lesser Scaup Duck (*Aythya affinis* Eyton) at West Medical Lake, Spokane County, Washington. M.S. Thesis, Washington State College, Pullman. 94 pp.

Geist, O.W. 1939. Sea birds found far inland in Alaska. Condor 41:68-70.

George, D.V. 1980. Hummingbird! B.C. Naturalist 18 (2 and 3):16.

Gerrard, J.M. 1983. A review of the current status of Bald Eagles in North America. Pages 5-21 *in* D.M. Bird (editor). Biology and Management of Bald Eagles and Ospreys. Proceedings of First International Symposium on Bald Eagles and Ospreys, Montreal, 28-29 October 1981. Harpell Press. Ste. Anne de Bellevue, Quebec.

Gerson, H. 1987. The status of the Black Tern (*Chlidonias niger*) in Canada. Committee on the Status of Endangered Wildlife in Canada, c/o Ontario Ministry of Natural Resources, Toronto, Ontario. 54 pp.

Gerstenberg, R.H. 1979. Habitat utilization by wintering and migrating shorebirds on Humboldt Bay, California. Studies in Avian Biology 2:33-40.

Gibson, D.D. 1981. Migrant birds at Shemya Island, Aleutian Islands, Alaska. Condor 83:65-77.

_____. 1986. The autumn migration - Alaska region. American Birds 40:155-156.

Gibson, D.D. and N.D. Hogg. 1982. Direct recovery in Alaska of California-banded Cattle Egret. American Birds 36:335.

Gibson, D.D. and B. Kessel. 1989. Geographic variation in the Marbled Godwit and description of an Alaskan subspecies. Condor 91:436-443.

Gibson, F. 1971. The breeding biology of the American Avocet (*Recurvirostra americana*) in central Oregon. Condor 73:444-454.

Gibson, G.G. 1965. The taxonomy and biology of Splendidofilari-ine nematodes of the Tetraonidae of British Columbia. Ph.D. Thesis, University of British Columbia, Vancouver. 241 pp.

Gilkey, A.K., W.D. Loomis, B.M. Breckenridge, and C.H. Richardson. 1944. The incubation period of the Great Horned Owl. Auk 60:272-273.

Gill, R. and P.D.Jorgenson. 1979. A preliminary assessment of timing and migration of shorebirds along the northcentral Alaska peninsula. Studies in Avian Biology 2:113-123.

Gill, R.E. 1977. Breeding avifauna of the south San Francisco Bay estuary. Western Birds. 8:1-12.

Gill, R.E. and L.R. Mewaldt. 1983. Pacific coast Caspian Terns: dynamics of an expanding population. Auk 100:369-381.

Gill, R.E., C.M. Handel, and L.A. Shelton. 1983. Memorial to a Black Turnstone: an exemplar of breeding and wintering site fidelity. North American Bird Bander 8:98-101.

Girard, G.L. 1939. Notes on the life history of the Shoveler. Transactions of the North American Wildlife Conference 4:364-371.

_____. 1941. The Mallard: its management in western Montana. Journal of Wildlife Management 5:223-259.

Gissing, A. 1959. Black-billed Cuckoo in British Columbia. Murrelet 40:12.

Glendenning, R. 1921. Notes on the fauna and flora of Mt. McLean, B.C. Proceedings of the Entomological Society of British Columbia 18:39-44.

Godfrey, W.E. 1947. A new Long-eared Owl. Canadian Field-Naturalist 61:196-197.

_____. 1952. Birds of the Lesser Slave Lake - Peace River areas, Alberta. National Museum of Canada Bulletin 126:142-175.

_____. 1954. Birds of Prince Edward Island. Pages 155-213 *in* National Museum of Canada Bulletin No. 132. Ottawa, Ontario.

_____. 1955. Additionial notes on birds of the east Kootenay, British Columbia. National Museum of Canada Bulletin 136:89-94.

_____. 1958. Birds of Cape Breton Island, Nova Scotia. Canadian Field-Naturalist 73:7-27.

_____. 1966. The birds of Canada. National Museum of Canada Bulletin 203, Ottawa, Ontario. 428 pp.

_____. 1967. Some winter aspects of the Great Gray Owl. Canadian Field-Naturalist 81:99-101.

_____. 1970. Canada's endangered birds. Canadian Field-Naturalist 84:24-26.

_____. 1986. The birds of Canada, revised edition. National Museums of Canada, Ottawa, Ontario. 595 pp.

Goggans, R. 1986. Habitat use by Flammulated Owls in northeastern Oregon. M.Sc. Thesis, Oregon State University, Corvallis. 54 pp.

Goldman, L.J. 1936. Observations concerning waterfowl in Canada, with special reference to migratory species, May 19 to August 10, 1936. Canadian Wildlife Service Unpublished Report, Delta, British Columbia. 46 pp. (Bibliography 3033).

_____. 1940. Migratory waterfowl - British Columbia (May 25, 1940 to August 26, 1940). United States Fish and Wildlife Service Unpublished Report. California. 35 pp. (Bibliography 3034).

Gollop, J.B. and W.H. Marshall. 1954. A guide for aging duck broods in the field. Mississippi Flyway Council Technical Section Report, Jackson. 14 pp.

Golovkin, A.N. 1984. Seabirds nesting in the USSR: The status and protection of populations. Pages 473-486 *in* Croxall, J.P., P.G.H. Evans, and R.W. Schreiber (editors). Status and conservation of the world's seabirds. International Council for Bird Preservation Technical Publication No. 2. Cambridge, England.

Goodwill, M.E. and J.E.V. Goodwill. 1988. Terek Sandpiper in British Columbia, Canada. American Birds 42:177.

Goodwin, D. 1967. Pigeons and doves of the world. The British Museum (Natural History), London, England. 446 pp.

Goossen, J.P., R.W. Butler, B. Stushnoff, and D. Stirling. 1982. Distribution and breeding status of Forster's Tern, *Sterna forsteri*, in British Columbia. Canadian Field-Naturalist 96:345-346.

Gosselin, M. and N. David. 1975. Field identification of Thayer's Gull *Larus thayeri* in eastern North America. American Birds 29:1059-1066.

Gould, E. 1981. Ralph Edwards of Lonesome Lake. Hancock House Publishers Ltd. North Vancouver, British Columbia. 293 pp.

Gould, P.J., D.J. Forsell and C.J. Lensink. 1982. Pelagic distribution and abundance of seabirds in the Gulf of Alaska and the eastern Bering Seas. United States Fish and Wildlife Service Report FWS/OBS-82/48, Washington, D.C. 264 pp.

Goward, T. 1976. Addendum to the birds of Wells Gray Park - an annotated list. British Columbia Parks Branch Unpublished Report, Victoria. 8 pp. (Bibliography 3050).

Graf, R.P. 1978. The ecology of the Ring-necked Pheasant, *Phasianus colchicus*, on Westham Island, B.C. B.Sc. Thesis, University of British Columbia, Vancouver. 101 pp.

Grant, J. 1951. Christmas bird census, 1950 - Vernon, British Columbia. Canadian Field Naturalist 65:74-75.

_____. 1956. Christmas bird census for 1955, Vernon, British Columbia. Canadian Field-Naturalist 70:90-91.

_____. 1959. A summer record of the Great Gray Owl in southern British Columbia. Canadian Field-Naturalist 73:173.

_____. 1966a. A Black Swift nest in British Columbia. Canadian Field-Naturalist 80:60-61.

_____. 1966b. The Barred Owl in British Columbia. Murrelet 47:39-45.

_____. 1966c. The Red-headed Woodpecker near Vernon, British Columbia. Murrelet 47:45.

_____. 1975. Observations. North Okanagan Naturalists Club Newspacket 2:5-6 (Bibliography 3057).

Grant, K.A. and V. Grant. 1968. The hummingbirds and their flowers. Columbia University Press, New York. 115 pp.

Grant, P.J. 1979. Field identification of west Palearctic gulls. British Birds 72:142-182.

_____. 1981. Identification of Semipalmated Sandpiper. British Birds 74:505-509.

_____. 1982. Gulls - a guide to identification. Buteo Books, Vermillion, South Dakota. 280 pp.

Grant, P.J. and R.E. Scott. 1969. Field identification of juvenile Common, Arctic, and Roseate Terns. British Birds 62:297-299.

Grass, A. 1968. A Stilt Sandpiper sight record for British Columbia. Murrelet 49:28.

_____. 1971. Wells Gray Park naturalist's report. British Columbia Parks Branch Unpublished Report, Victoria. 45 pp. (Bibliography 1175).

Grass, A. and J. Grass. 1978. Squamish eagle count. Federation of British Columbia Naturalists Newsletter 16:9-10.

Greel, G.J. 1974. Sharp-tailed Sandpiper with flesh-coloured legs and feet. British Birds 67:211.

Green, C. deB. 1916. Note on the distribution and nesting-habits of *Falco peregrinus pealei* Ridgway. Ibis (Series 10) 4:473-476.

Green, D. and R.W. Campbell. 1984. The amphibians of British Columbia. British Columbia Provincial Museum Handbook No. 45, Victoria. 101 pp.

Greenwood, J.G. 1984. Migration of Dunlin *Calidris alpina*: a worldwide overview. Ringing and Migration 5:35-39._____. 1986. Geographical variation and taxonomy of the Dunlin *Calidris alpina* (L.). Bulletin of the British Ornithological Club 106:43-56.

Gregory, P.T. and R.W. Campbell. 1984. The reptiles of British Columbia. British Columbia Provincial Museum Handbook No. 44, Victoria, 103 pp.

Greyell, R. 1966. Report on wildlife survey, Creston flats, summer 1966. Canadian Wildlife Service Unpublished Report, Delta, British Columbia. 28 pp. (Bibliography 3080).

Grieb, J.R. 1970. The shortgrass prairie Canada Goose population. Wildlife Monographs 22:1-49.

Griffith, D.E. 1973. Notes on the birds of Summit Lake Pass, British Columbia. Vancouver Natural History Society Discovery. 2:45-51.

Grinnell, J. 1913. Two new races of the Pygmy Owl from the Pacific coast. Auk 30:222-224.

Gross, A.O. 1923. The Black-crowned Night Heron (*Nycticorax nycticorax naevius*) of Sandy Neck. Auk. 40:1-30.

_____. 1935. The life history cycle of the Leach's Petrel (*Oceanodroma leucorhoa*) on the outer sea islands of the Bay of Fundy. Auk 52:382-399.

_____. 1947. Cyclic invasions of the Snowy Owl and the migration of 1945-46. Auk 64:589-601.

Groves, S. 1982. Aspects of foraging in Black Oystercatchers (Aves: *Haematopodidae*). Ph.D. Thesis, University of British Columbia, Vancouver. 123 pp.

_____. 1984. Chick growth, sibling rivalry, and chick production in American Black Oystercatchers. Auk 101:525-531.

Grub, T.C. 1972. Smell and foraging in shearwaters and petrels. Nature 237:404-405.

Gruchy, C.G., A.A.R. Dykes and R.H. Bowen. 1972. The Short-tailed Albatross recorded at Ocean Station Papa, North Pacific Ocean, with notes on other birds. Canadian Field-Naturalist 86:285-287.

Grunberg, H. 1982. The spring migration - northwestern Canada region. American Birds 36:873-874.

_____. 1983a. The winter season - northwestern Canada region. American Birds 37:318-320.

_____. 1983b. The spring migration - northwestern Canada region. American Birds 37:890-891.

_____. 1983c. The autumn migration - northwestern Canada region. American Birds 37:201-202.

_____. 1984a. The autumn migration - northwestern Canada region. American Birds 38:223-224.

_____. 1984b. The winter season - northwestern Canada region. American Birds 38:336-337.

_____. 1984c. The spring migration - northwestern Canada region. American Birds 38:935-936.

_____. 1984d. The nesting season - northwestern Canada region. American Birds 38:1040-1041.

_____. 1985a. The autumn migration - northwestern Canada region. American Birds 38:77-78.

_____. 1985b. The winter season - northwestern Canada region. American Birds 39:187-189.

_____. 1985c. The spring season - northwestern Canada region. American Birds 39:326-327.

_____. 1985d. The nesting season - northwestern Canada region. American Birds 39:937-938.

_____. 1986. The autumn migration - northwestern Canada region. American Birds 40:141-142.

Guiguet, C.J. 1949. Kennicott's Screech Owl on British Columbia coastal islands. Canadian Field-Naturalist 63:206-207.

_____. 1950a. Notes on Common Murres nesting in British Columbia. Murrelet 31:12-13.

_____. 1950b. Saw-whet Owl at Victoria. Victoria Naturalist 7:55-56.

_____. 1952a. Report on the Francois-Ootsa Lake area visited in June, 1951. Pages B15-B18 *in* Provincial Museum of Natural History and Anthropology Report for the Year 1951, Victoria, British Columbia.

_____. 1952b. Christmas bird census, 1951 - Victoria, British Columbia. Canadian Field-Naturalist 66:56.

_____. 1953a. An ecological study of Goose Island, British Columbia, with special reference to mammals and birds. British Columbia Provincial Museum Occasional Paper No.10, Victoria. 78 pp.

_____. 1953b. Asiatic Chukar Partridge released on B.C. mainland. Victoria. Daily Colonist. Page 2.

_____. 1953c. Mountain Quail on Island shy and retiring species. Daily Colonist Newspaper, 22 November:2.

_____. 1954. The birds of British Columbia: (1) The woodpeckers, (2) The crows and their allies. British Columbia Provincial Museum Handbook No. 6, Victoria. 51 pp.

_____. 1955a. The birds of British Columbia: (3) The shorebirds. British Columbia Provincial Museum Handbook No. 8, Victoria. 54 pp.

_____. 1955b. The birds of British Columbia: (4) Upland game birds. British Columbia Provincial Museum Handbook No. 10, Victoria. 47 pp.

_____. 1956. Enigma of the Pacific. Audubon Magazine 58:164-167, 174.

_____. 1957. The birds of British Columbia: (5) Gulls, terns, jaegers and skua. British Columbia Provincial Museum Handbook No. 13, Victoria. 42pp.

_____. 1958. The birds of British Columbia: (6) Waterfowl. British Columbia Provincial Museum Handbook No. 15, Victoria. 84 pp.

_____. 1959. Anna's Hummingbird (*Calypte anna*) at Victoria, British Columbia. Murrelet 40:13.

_____. 1960a. The Golden Plover (*Pluvialis dominica*) nesting in British Columbia. Page 40 *in* Provincial Museum of Natural History and Anthropology Report for the Year 1959, Victoria, British Columbia.

_____. 1960b. The birds of British Columbia: (7) Owls. British Columbia Provincial Museum Handbook No. 18, Victoria. 62 pp.

_____. 1964. The birds of British Columbia: (8) Chickadees, thrushes, kinglets, pipits, waxwings, and shrikes. British Columbia Provincial Museum Handbook No. 22, Victoria. 66 pp.

_____. 1971. A list of sea bird nesting sites in Barkley Sound, British Columbia. Syesis 4:253-259.

_____. 1972. The birds of British Columbia: (9) Diving birds and tube-nosed swimmers. British Columbia Provincial Museum Handbook No. 29, Victoria. 104 pp.

_____. 1978. The birds of British Columbia: (10) Goatsuckers, swifts, hummingbirds, and swallows. British Columbia Provincial Museum Handbook No. 37, Victoria. 58 pp.

_____. 1983. The birds of British Columbia: (11) Sparrows and finches. British Columbia Provincial Museum Handbook No. 42, Victoria. 122 pp.

Guillon, G.W. 1951. The frontal shield of the American Coot. Wilson Bulletin 63:157-166.

Gunn, W.W.H. 1972. Bald Eagles at Port Hardy airport: Interim Report No. 2, for the period November 1-21, 1972. LGL Limited Report, Toronto, Ontario. 3 pp. (Bibliography 3116).

Gutierrez, R.J. and A.B. Carey (editors). 1985. Ecology and management of the Spotted Owl in the Pacific Northwest. United States Department of Agriculture, Forest Service General Technical Report PNW-185 Portland, Oregon. 119 pp.

Guzman, J.R. 1981. The wintering of Sooty and Short-tailed shearwaters (Genus *Puffinus*) in the north Pacific. Ph.D. Thesis. University of Calgary, Calgary, Alberta. 510 pp.

Guzman, J.R. and M.T. Myres. 1983. The occurrence of shearwaters (*Puffinus* spp.) off the west coast of Canada. Canadian Journal of Zoology 61:2064-2077.

Hackman, C.D. and C.J. Henny. 1971. Hawk migration over White Marsh, Maryland. Chesapeake Science 12:137-141.

Hadow, H.H. 1973. Winter ecology of migrant and resident Lewis' Woodpeckers in southeastern Colorado. Condor 75:210-224.

_____. 1976. Growth and development of nesting Downy Woodpeckers. North American Bird Bander 1:155-164.

Hagar, D.C. 1957. Nesting populations of Red-tailed Hawks and Horned Owls in central New York. Wilson Bulletin 69:263-272.

Hagar, J.A. 1966. Nesting of the Hudsonian Godwit at Churchill, Manitoba. Living Bird 5:5-43.

Hagenstein, W. 1928. Miscellaneous observations from Washington and British Columbia. Murrelet 9:69.

Haig, B. 1980. In the footsteps of Thomas Blakiston: 1858. Historic Trails Society of Alberta, Lethbridge. 57 pp.

Haig, S. 1985. The status of the Piping Plover in Canada. Committee on the Status of Endangered Wildlife in Canada, c/o Canadian Nature Federation, Ottawa, Ontario 23 pp.

Hamel, P. 1983. The eighty-third Audubon Christmas bird count - Masset, B.C. American Birds 37:441-442.

Hamilton, R.C. 1975. Comparative behavior of the American Avocet and the Black-necked Stilt (Recurvirostridae). American Ornithologists' Union Ornithological Monographs No. 17, Lawrence, Kansas.

Hammond, M.C. and C.J. Henry. 1949. Success of Marsh Hawk nests in North Dakota. Auk 66:271-274.

Hancock, D.A. 1963. The abundance of wintering waterfowl in the Victoria, B.C. area. B.Sc. Thesis, Victoria College [University of Victoria], Victoria, British Columbia. 40 pp. (Bibliography 3143).

_____. 1964. Breeding record for Bufflehead west of the coast range in British Columbia. Canadian Field-Naturalist 78:64-65.

_____. 1970. New Rhinoceros Auklet colony for British Columbia. Condor 72:491.

Hannon, S.J. 1982. Female aggression, breeding density, and monogamy in Willow Ptarmigan. Ph.D. Thesis, University of British Columbia, Vancouver. 118 pp.

_____. 1983. Spacing and breeding density of Willow Ptarmigan in response to an experimental alteration of sex ratio. Journal of Animal Ecology 52:807-820.

Hannon, S.J. and J.N.M. Smith. 1984. Factors influencing age-related reproductive success in the Willow Ptarmigan. Auk 101:848-854.

Hannon, S.J., K. Martin, and J.O. Schieck. 1988. Timing of reproduction in two populations of Willow Ptarmigan in northern Canada. Auk 105:330-338.

Hansen, H.A. 1962. Canada geese of coastal Alaska. Transactions of the North American Wildlife Conference 27:301-319.

Hansen, H.A. and V.C. Nelson. 1957. Brant of the Bering Sea, migration, and mortality. Transactions of the North American Wildlife and Natural Resources Conference 22:237-254.

_____. and _____. 1964. Honkers large and small. Pages 109-124 *in* J.P. Linduska (editor). Waterfowl Tomorrow. United States Department of the Interior Fish and Wildlife Service, Washington, D.C.

Hansen, H.A., P.E.K. Shepherd, J.G. King, and W.T. Troyer. 1971. The Trumpeter Swan in Alaska. Wildlife Monographs No. 26:1-83.

Hanson, W.C. 1971. The 1966-67 Snowy Owl incursion in southeastern Washington and the Pacific northwest. Condor 73:114-116.

Hanson, W.C. and R.L. Browning. 1959. Hanford Reservation nesting geese. Journal of Wildlife Management 23:129-137.

Hardy, G.A. 1927. Report on a collecting trip to Garibaldi Park, B.C. Pages 15-26 *in* Report of the Provincial Museum of Natural History for the Year 1926, Victoria, British Columbia.

_____. 1957. Notes on the flora and fauna of Blenkinsop Lake area on southern Vancouver Island, British Columbia. Pages 25-66 *in* Provincial Museum of Natural History and Anthropology Report for the Year 1956, Victoria, British Columbia.

Hare, F.K. and M.K. Thomas. 1974. Climate Canada. Wiley Publishers of Canada Limited, Toronto, Ontario. 256 pp.

Harrington, B.A. 1983. The migration of the Red Knot. Oceanus 26:44-48.

Harrington, B.A. and R.I.G. Morrison. 1979. Semipalmated Sandpiper migration in North America. Studies in Avian Biology 2:83-100.

Harrington-Tweit, B. and P.W. Mattocks. 1984. The nesting season - northern Pacific coast region. American Birds 38:1054-1056.

_____. and _____. 1985. The nesting season - northern Pacific coast region. American Birds 39:953-956.

Harrington-Tweit, B., P.W. Mattocks, and E.S. Hunn. 1978. Nesting season - northern Pacific coast region. American Birds 32:1199-1203.

_____, _____, and _____. 1979. Nesting season - northern Pacific coast region. American Birds 33:890-893.

_____, _____, and _____. 1980. The nesting season - northern Pacific coast region. American Birds 34:922-925.

_____, _____, and _____. 1981. Nesting season - northern Pacific coast region. American Birds 35:970-973.

Harris, C. 1987. Black-chinned Hummingbird - first Vancouver record. Vancouver Natural History Society Discovery 16:126.

Harris, H. 1941. The annals of *Gymnogyps* to 1900. Condor 43:3-55.

Harris, M.P. 1964. Aspects of the breeding biology of the gulls *Larus argentatus*, *L. fuscus* and *L. marinus*. Ibis 106:432-456.

_____. 1969. The biology of storm petrels in the Galapagos Islands. Proceedings of the California Academy of Science 37:95-166.

Harris, R.D. 1971. Further evidence of tree nesting in the Marbled Murrelet. Canadian Field-Naturalist 85:67-68.

Harris, R.D. and E.J. O'Neil. 1967. Biological investigations, Duck Lake Creston, B.C. Canadian Wildlife Service Unpublished Report, Delta, British Columbia. 10 pp. (Bibliography 3166).

Harris, S.W. 1974. Status, chronology, and ecology of nesting storm petrels in northwestern California. Condor 76:249-261.

Harrison, C. 1978. A field guide to the nests, eggs, and nestlings of North American birds. Collins, Glasgow. 416 pp.

_____. 1979. Short-tailed Albatross. Oceans 12:24.

Harrison, C.S., M.B. Naughton, and S.I. Fefer, 1984. The status and conservation of seabirds in the Hawaiian Archipelago and Johnston Atoll. Pages 513-526 *in* Croxall, J.P., P.G.H. Evans, and R.W. Schreiber (editors). The status and conservation of the world's seabirds. International Council for Bird Preservation Technical Publication No. 2, Cambridge, England.

Harrison, G.H. 1979. Bird watching: the fastest growing family fun is an industry. Science Digest 86:74-80.

Harrison, P. 1983. Seabirds: an identification guide. Houghton Mifflin Company, Boston. 448 pp.

Hart, F.G. 1978. A January letter from Green Island lighthouse. Vancouver Natural History Society Discovery 7:30-32.

_____. 1978a. Green Island in summer. Vancouver Natural History Society Discovery 7:73-75.

Hart, J.L. 1973. Pacific fishes of Canada. Fisheries Research Board of Canada Bulletin No. 180, Ottawa, Ontario. 740 pp.

Hartwick, E.B. 1973. Foraging strategy of the Black Oystercatcher. Ph.D. Thesis, University of British Columbia, Vancouver. 138 pp.

_____. 1974. Breeding ecology of the Black Oystercatcher (*Haematopus bachmani* Audubon). Syesis 7:83-92.

Hartwick, E.B. and W. Blaylock. 1979. Winter ecology of a Black Oystercatcher population. Studies in Avian Biology 2:207-215.

Harwell, M. 1946. Vancouver Island bird list (June 2-6, 1946). Victoria Naturalist 3:54-57.

Hasbrouck, E.M. 1944. Apparent status of the European Widgeon in North America. Auk 61:93-104.

Hasegawa, H. 1978. The Laysan Albatross breeding in the Ogasawara Islands. Pacific Seabird Group Bulletin 5:16-17.

_____. 1982. The breeding status of the Short-tailed Albatross *Diomedea albatrus*, on Torishima, 1979/80-1980/81. Journal of the Yamashina Institute of Ornithology 14:16-24.

_____. 1984. Status and conservation of seabirds in Japan, with special attention to the Short-tailed Albatross. Pages 487-500 *in* Corxall, J.P., P.G.H. Evans, and R.W. Schreiber (editors). The status and conservation of the world's seabirds. International Council for Bird Preservation Technical Publication No. 2. Cambridge, England.

Hasegawa, H. and A.R. DeGange. 1982. The Short-tailed Albatross, *Diomedea albatrus*, its status, distribution, and natural history. American Birds 36:806-814.

Hatfield, J.P. 1979. Canada Goose production on Vaseux Lake. Canadian Wildlife Service Unpublished Report, Delta, British Columbia. 3 pp.

Hatler, D.F. 1973. An analysis of use, by waterfowl, of tideflats in southern Clayoquot Sound, British Columbia. Canadian Wildlife Service Unpublished Report, Edmonton, Alberta. 134 pp. (Bibliography 997).

_____. 1983. Concerns for ungulate collision mortality along new surface route - Rogers Pass project report. MacLaren Plansearch Corporation Unpublished Report, Vancouver, British Columbia. 109 pp. (Bibliography 3181).

Hatler, D.F., R.W. Campbell and A. Dorst. 1973. Birds of Pacific Rim National Park, British Columbia. Canadian Wildlife Service Unpublished Report, Edmonton, Alberta. 383 pp. (Bibliography 1147).

_____, _____, and _____ 1978. Birds of Pacific Rim National Park. British Columbia Provincial Museum Occasional Paper No.20, Victoria. 194 pp.

Hatter, I. and D. Bustard. 1975. A survey of an Ancient Murrelet colony on Lyell Island, Queen Charlotte Islands, British Columbia. British Columbia Fish and Wildlife Branch Unpublished Report, Smithers. 25 pp.

Hatter, I. and L. Stordeur. 1978. An inventory of Canada Geese and seabirds nesting in Juskatla, Masset, Skidegate, and Long inlets, Queen Charlotte Islands, British Columbia: British Columbia Fish and Wildlife Report, Victoria. 44 pp. (Bibliography 1896).

Hatter, J. 1955. Blue Grouse. British Columbia Fish and Wildlife Branch Unpublished Report, Victoria. 3 pp.

_____. 1960. Baikal Teal in British Columbia. Condor 62:480.

Hawkins, A.S. 1970. Honkers move to the city. Pages 120-130 *in* H.H. Hilland and F.B. Lee (editors). Home grown honkers. United States Department of the Interior, Fish and Wildlife Service, Washington, D.C. 154 pp.

Hay, R.B. 1976. An environmental study on the Kitimat region with special reference to the Kitimat River estuary. Canadian Wildlife Service Unpublished Report, Delta, British Columbia. 85 pp. (Bibliography 1204).

Hayman, P., J. Marchant, and T. Prater. 1986. Shorebirds: an identification guide to the waders of the world. Houghton Mifflin Company, Boston, Massachusetts. 412 pp.

Hays, H. 1973. Polyandry in the Spotted Sandpiper. Living Bird 11:43-57.

Hazelwood, W.G. 1973. Cape Scott Park - a preliminary look at its wildlife values, October 25-28. British Columbia Parks Branch Unpublished Report, Victoria. 11 pp. (Bibliography 3186).

_____. 1976a. Tweedsmuir Park initial wildlife and fisheries inventory (Area C and D). British Columbia Parks Branch Unpublished Report, Victoria. 116 pp. (Bibliography 1202).

_____. 1976b. Kwadacha Park 1976. British Columbia Parks Branch Unpublished Report, Victoria. 19 pp. (Bibliography 3191).

_____. 1976c. Atsutla Range report. British Columbia Parks Branch Unpublished Report, Victoria. 12 pp. (Bibliography 3194).

_____. 1979. Tatlatui Park summer trip report - August 2 and 3, 1979. British Columbia Parks Branch Unpublished Report. 6 pp. (Bibliography 3202).

Headley, P.C. 1967. Ecology of the Emperor Goose. Report of the Alaska Cooperative Wildlife Unit, University of Alaska College, Fairbanks. 106 pp.

Hearne, M. and J.M. Cooper. 1987. Aleutian Tern (*Sterna aleutica*), a new bird for Canada. Canadian Field-Naturalist 101:589-590.

Heath, H. 1915. Birds observed on Forrester Island, Alaska, during the summer of 1913. Condor 17:20-41.

Hegner, R.W. 1906. Life of the Redtail. Bird-Lore 8:151-157.

Hekstra, G.P. 1982. Description of twenty-four new subspecies of American *Otus*. Bulletin Zoologisch Museum Universiteit Van Amsterdam 9:49-63.

Henderson, B.A. 1972. The control and organization of parental feeding and its relationships to the food supply for the Glaucous-winged Gull *Larus glaucescens*. M.Sc. Thesis, University of British Columbia, Vancouver. 94 pp.

Hennan, E. 1977. Wildlife observations - Chilcotin Lake, 1977. Ducks Unlimited (Canada) Unpublished Report, Williams Lake, British Columbia. 37 pp. (Bibliography 1913).

_____. 1975. Columbia River marshes, British Columbia waterfowl habitat assessment. Ducks Unlimited (Canada) Special Report No. 7104, Kamloops, British Columbia. 48 pp. (Bibliography 3208).

_____. 1979. Upper Dean River project - waterfowl habitat assessment. Ducks Unlimited (Canada) Unpublished Report, Kamloops, British Columbia. 51 pp. (Bibliography 3209).

Henny, C.J. 1983. Distribution and abundance of nesting Ospreys in the United States. Pages 175-186 *in* D.M.Bird (editor). Biology and Management of Bald Eagles and Ospreys. Proceedings First International Symposium on Bald Eagles and Ospreys, Montreal, 28-29 October 1981. Harpell Press. Ste Anne de Bellevue, Quebec.

_____. 1986. Osprey (*Pandion haliaetus*): Section 4.3.1, United States Army Corps of Engineers Wildlife Resources Management Manual, Technical Report EL-86-5, prepared by the United States Fish and Wildlife Service, Corvallis, Oregon, for the United States Army Engineer Waterways Experiment Station, Vicksburg, Mississippi.

Henny, C.J. and N.E. Holgersen. 1974. Range expansion and population increase of the Gadwall in eastern North America. Wildfowl 25:95-101.

Henny, C.J. and H.M. Wight. 1969. An endangered osprey population: estimates of mortality and production. Auk 86:188-198.

_____. and _____. 1972. Population ecology and environmental pollution: Red-tailed and Cooper's hawks. Pages 229-250 *in* Population ecology of migratory birds. United States Fish and Wildlife Service Wildlife Resource Report No. 2, Washington, D.C. 278 pp.

Henshaw, H.W. 1881. On *Podiceps occidentalis* and *P. clarkii*. Bulletin Nuttall Ornithological Club 6:211-216.

Herrick, F.H. 1932. Daily life of the American eagle: early phase. Auk 49:307-323.

Herzog, P.W. 1977. Summer habitat use by White-tailed Ptarmigan in southwestern Alberta. Canadian Field-Naturalist 91:367-371.

_____. 1980. Winter habitat use by White-tailed Ptarmigan in southwestern Alberta. Canadian Field-Natralist 94:159-162.

Hesse, W. and H. Hesse. 1961. Sight record of the downy young Semipalmated Plover in the Chilcotin of British Columbia. Murrelet 42:3.

Hetherington, A.E., I.E. Teske, D.G. Milne, A. Von Sacken, and S. Myers. 1987. Spotted Owl and old-growth habitat survey, 1987. British Columbia Conservation Foundation Report, Langley. 91 pp.

Hilden, O. 1971. Occurrence, migration, and colour phases of the Arctic Skua (*Stercorarius parasiticus*) in Finland. Annales Zoologica Fennici 8:223-230.

Hilden, O. and S. Vuolanto. 1972. Breeding biology of the Red-necked Phalarope *Phalaropus lobatus* in Finland, Ornis Fennica 49:57-85.

Hills, G.A., D.A. Love, and D.S. Lacate. 1973. Developing a better environment: ecological land-use planning in Ontario. Ontario Economic Council, Toronto. 182 pp.

Hines, J.E. 1986. Social organization, movements, and home ranges of Blue Grouse in fall and winter. Wilson Bulletin 98:419-432.

Hirsch, K.V., D.A. Woodby, and L.B. Astheimer. 1981. Growth of a nestling Marbled Murrelet. Condor 83:264-265.

Hirst, S.M. and C.A. Easthope. 1981. Use of agricultural lands by waterfowl in southwestern British Columbia. Journal of Wildlife Management 45:454-462.

Hobson, K.A. and J.C. Driver. 1989. Archaeological evidence for the use of the Strait of Georgia by marine birds. Pages 168-173 *in* K. Vermeer and R.W. Butler (editors). The ecology and status of marine and shoreline birds in the Strait of Georgia, British Columbia. Canadian Wildlife Service Special Publication, Ottawa, Ontario.

Hobson, K.A. and S.G. Sealy. 1986. Use of diurnal roosting sites by Pelagic Cormorants in Barkley Sound, British Columbia. Murrelet 67:65-74.

Hobson, K.A. and D. Wilson. 1985. Colony establishment by Pelagic Cormorants on man-made structures in southwest coastal British Columbia. Murrelet 66:84-86.

Hobson, M. 1976. Naturalist's summer report - Miracle Beach Park, 1976. British Columbia Parks Branch Unpublished Report, Victoria. 23 pp. (Bibliography 3237).

Hochbaum, H.A. 1944. The Canvasback on a prairie marsh. North American Wildlife Institute, Washington, D.C. 201 pp.

Hodges, J.I., J.G. King and R. Davies. 1983. Bald Eagle breeding population survey of coastal British Columbia. Abstract only. Page 321 *in* D.M. Bird (editor). Biology and Management of Bald Eagles and Ospreys. Proceedings First International Symposium on Bald Eagles and Ospreys, Montreal, 28-29 October 1981. Harpell Press, Ste Anne de Bellevue, Quebec.

Hodges, J.I., E.L. Boeker, and A.J. Hansen. 1987. Movements of radio-tagged Bald Eagles, *Haliaeetus leucocephalus*, in and from southeastern Alaska. Canadian Field-Naturalist 101:136-140.

Hodson, K. 1980. Peregrine Falcons in British Columbia. Pages 85-87 *in* R. Stace-Smith, L. Johns, and P. Joslin (editors). Threatened and Endangered Species and Habitats in British Columbia and the Yukon. British Columbia Ministry of Environment, Victoria.

Hoffman, R. 1924. Breeding of the ancient murrelet in Washington. Condor 26:191.

Hoffman, R.W. and C.E. Braun. 1975. Migration of a wintering population of White-tailed Ptarmigan in Colorado. Journal of Wildlife Management 39:485-490.

Hoffman, W., W.P. Elliot, and J.M. Scott. 1975. The occurrence and status of the Horned Puffin in the western United States. Western Birds 6:87-94.

Hoffman, W., J.A. Wiens, and J.M. Scott. 1978. Hybridization between gulls (*Larus glaucescens and L. occidentalis*) in the Pacific Northwest. Auk 95:441-458.

Hohn, E.O. 1966. Ringing (banding) and recoveries of phalaropes, a summary of presently available information. Bird-Banding 37:197-200.

Holdom, M.W. 1943. Christmas bird census, 1942 - Crescent Beach, British Columbia. Canadian Field-Naturalist 57:57.

_____. 1945. Christmas bird census, 1944 - Crescent, British Columbia. Canadian Field-Naturalist 59:37-38.

_____. 1947. Christmas bird census, 1946 - Crescent, British Columbia. Canadian Field-Naturalist 61:66.

_____. 1948. Immature Snowy Egret (?) (*Leucophoyx thula*) at Crescent, B.C. Canadian Field-Naturalist 62:125.

_____. 1952. Glimpses of bird life in Surrey. The Surrey Leader, Cloverdale, British Columbia. 10 pp.

_____. 1954. Random bird notes. Surrey Leader, Cloverdale, British Columbia. 22 pp.

_____. 1962. Sixty-second Christmas bird count - Surrey Municipality, B.C. Audubon Field Notes 16:90.

Holland, S.S. 1964. Landforms of British Columbia: a physiograhic outline. British Columbia Department of Mines and Petroleum Resources Bulletin No. 48, Victoria. 138 pp.

Holmes, R.T. 1966. Breeding ecology and annual cycle adaptations of the Red backed Sandpiper (*Calidris alpina*) in northern Alaska. Condor 68:3-46.

Holmes, R.T. and F.A. Pitelka. 1964. Breeding behavior and taxonomic relationships of the Curlew Sandpiper. Auk 81:362-379.

Holroyd, G.L. and P.L. Jalkotzy. 1986. The breeding strategy of the Black Swift. Poster presented at the International Ornithological Congress, 22-28 June 1986, Ottawa, Ontario, Canada.

Honacki, J.H., K.E. Kinman, and J.W. Koeppl (editors). 1982. Mammal species of the world - a taxonomic and geographic reference. Association of Systematics Collections, Lawrence, Kansas.

Hooper, D.C. 1951. Waterfowl nesting at Minto Lakes, Alaska. Proceedings of the 2nd Alaskan Science Conference: 318-321.

Hooper, T.D. 1988. Habitat, reproductive parameters, and nest-site tenacity of urban-nesting Glaucous-winged Gulls at Victoria, British Columbia. Murrelet 69:10-14.

Hooper, T.D. and M. Nyhof. 1986. Food habits of the Long-eared Owl in south-central British Columbia. Murrelet 67:28-30.

Hooper, T.D. and K. Sars. 1986. An analysis of census methods and population trends for the Ring-necked Pheasant (*Phasianus colchicus*) on the Saanich Peninsula, Vancouver Island. British Columbia Ministry of Environment Wildlife Branch Unpublished Report, Victoria. 24 pp.

Horak, G.J. 1964. A comparative study of Virginia and Sora rails with emphasis on foods. M.S. Thesis, Iowa State University, Ames. 73 pp.

Horvath, O. 1963. Contributions to nesting ecology of forest birds. M.S.F. Thesis, University of British Columbia, Vancouver. 181 pp.

_____. 1964. Seasonal differences in Rufous Hummingbird nest height and their relation to nest climate. Ecology 45:235-241.

Hosford, H. 1975. Stray feathers - Daphne: early bird got carrots. Victoria Times Newspaper, 19 April.

Hoskins, H., M.W. Richards, and J.T.R. Sharrock. 1979. Best recent black-and-white bird photographs. British Birds 72:580-589.

Houston, C.S. 1963. R.F. Oldaker, the man who reads gull bands with a telescope. Blue Jay 21:53-57.

_____. 1977. Movements of Saskatchewan-banded California Gulls. Bird-Banding 48:158-161.

Houston, C.S. and P.W. Brown. 1983. Recoveries of Saskatchewan banded White-winged Scoters (*Melanitta fusca*). Canadian Field-Naturalist 97:454-455.

Hout, J.L. 1967. Contribution toward a bibliography on Brant. United States Department of the Interior Fish and Wildlife Service Special Scientific Report - Wildlife No. 103, Washington, D.C. 15 pp.

Howard, R.P. 1975. Breeding ecology of the Ferruginous Hawk in northern Utah and southern Idaho. M.S. Thesis, Utah State University, Logan. 60 pp.

Howe, M.A. 1975. Behavioural aspects of the pair bond in Wilson's Phalarope. Wilson Bulletin 87:248-270.

Howell, T.R. 1952. Natural history and differentiation in the Yellow-bellied Sapsucker. Condor 54:237-282.

_____. 1953. Racial and sexual differences in migration in *Sphyrapicus varius*. Auk 70:118-126.

Howie, R.R. 1975. The fall migration at Golden, B.C. and adjacent areas of the Rocky Mountain cordillera 1975. British Columbia Provincial Museum Unpublished Report, Victoria. 30 pp. (Bibliography 3272).

_____. 1980. The Burrowing Owl in British Columbia. Pages 88-95 in R. Stace-Smith, L. Johns and P. Joslin (editors). Threatened and Endangered Species and Habitats in British Columbia and the Yukon. British Columbia Ministry of Environment, Victoria.

_____. 1987. Status report on the Flammulated Owl (*Otus flammeolus*) in Canada - 1986. Committee on the Status of Endangered Wildlife in Canada Unpublished Report, c/o Canadian Nature Federation, Ottawa, Ontario. 58 pp.

Howie, R.R. and R. Ritcey. 1987. Distribution, habitat selection, and densities of Flammulated Owls in British Columbia. Pages 249-254 in R.W. Nero, R.J. Clark, R.J. Knapton, and R.H. Hamre (editors). Biology and Conservation of Northern Forest Owls: Symposium Proceedings. 1987 Feb. 3-7; Winnipeg, Manitoba. United States Department of Agriculture Forest Service General Technical Report RM-142, Fort Collins, Colorado.

Hoyt, J.S.Y. 1944. Preliminary notes on the development of nesting Pileated Woodpeckers. Auk 61:376-384.

Hoyt, S.F. 1957. The ecology of the Pileated Woodpecker. Ecology 38:246-256.

Hubbs, C.L. and G.A. Bartholomew. 1951. Persistence of a rare colour aberration in the Heermann Gull. Condor 53:221-227.

Hudson, G.E. and C.F. Yocom. 1954. A distributional list of the birds of southeastern Washington. Research Studies, State University of Washington 22:25.

Hughes, W.M. 1956. Observations of our less common birds. Vancouver Natural History Society News 105:4-6.

_____. 1961. Green Heron in southwestern British Columbia. Canadian Field-Naturalist 75:169-170.

_____. 1963. Sight record of the Tufted Duck at Vancouver, British Columbia. Canadian Field-Naturalist 77:62-63.

Huhtala, K., E. Korpimakl, and E. Pulliainen. 1987. Foraging activity and growth of nestlings in the Hawk Owl: adaptive strategies under northern conditions. Pages 152-156 in R.W. Nero, R.J. Clark, R.J. Knapton, and R.H. Hamre (editors). Biology and Conservation of Northern Forest Owls: Symposium Proceedings. 1987 Feb.3-7; Winnipeg, Manitoba. United States Department of Agriculture Forest Service General Technical Report RM-142, Fort Collins, Colorado.

Hume, S. 1988. Neighbors feud over peacocks. Times-Colonist 25 February, p. B1.

Hunn, E.S. and P.W. Mattocks. 1981a. Fall migration - northern Pacific coast region. American Birds 35:216-219.

_____. and _____. 1981b. The spring migration - northern Pacific coast region. American Birds 35:854-857.

_____. and _____. 1982. Fall migration - northern Pacific coast region. American Birds 36:208-211.

_____. and _____. 1983a. Fall migration - northern Pacific coast region. American Birds 37:214-218.

_____. and _____. 1983b. The spring migration - northern Pacific coast region. American Birds 37:903-906.

_____. and _____. 1984. The autumn migration - northern Pacific coast region. American Birds 38:236-240.

_____. and _____. 1985. The autumn migration - northern Pacific coast region. American Birds 39:92-96.

_____. and _____. 1986. The autumn migration - northern Pacific coast region. American Birds 40:321-324.

Inkster, C. 1971. Sibling competition in the Double-crested Cormorant (*Phalacrocorax auritus*). B.Sc. Thesis. Simon Fraser University, Burnaby, British Columbia. 60pp.

International Union for Conservation of Nature and Natural Resources. 1969. Red data book, Volume 2, *Aves*. American Peregrine Falcon. Sheet B/35/Falcon/Per/Ana.

Irving, E.B. 1953. Birds at Carmanah Point. Victoria Naturalist 10:19-22; 28-31.

Isleib, M.E. and B. Kessel. 1973. Birds of the North Gulf coast - Prince William Sound region, Alaska. Biological Papers of the University of Alaska No.14, Fairbanks. 149 pp.

Jackson, J.A. 1983. Nesting phenology, nest site selection, and reproductive success of Black and Turkey vultures. Pages 245-271 in S.R. Wilbur and J.A. Jackson (editors). Vulture biology and management. University of California Press, Berkeley.

Jacobson, T. 1974. Birds of Kamloops country. Published by the author, Kamloops, British Columbia. 34 pp. (Bibliography 1751).

James, R. 1980. Snowy Owl food in different habitats in the Toronto region. Ontario Field Biologist 34:11-16.

Jeffrey, R. and G. Kaiser. 1979. The Snow Goose flock of the Fraser and Skagit deltas. Pages 266-279 *in* R.L. Jarvis and J.C. Bartonek (editors). Management and Biology of Pacific Flyway Geese. A symposium sponsored by the Northwest Section, The Wildlife Society, 16 February 1979, Portland, Oregon. Oregon State University Book Store, Inc., Corvallis.

Jehl, J.R. 1968. Relationships in the Charadrii (shorebirds): a taxonomic study based on color patterns of the downy young. San Diego Society of Natural History Memoir No.3, San Diego, California.

_____. 1973a. Late autumn observations of pelagic birds off southern California. Western Birds 4:45-52.

_____. 1973b. Breeding biology and systematic relationships of the Stilt Sandpiper. Wilson Bulletin 85:115-147.

_____. 1979. The autumnal migration of Baird's Sandpiper. Studies in Avian Biology 2:55-68.

_____. 1982. The biology and taxonomy of Townsend's Shearwater. Le Gerfaut 72:121-135.

_____. 1985. Hybridization and evolution of oystercatchers on the Pacific coast of Baja California. Ornithological Monographs 6:484-504.

_____. 1987. Geographic variation and evolution in the California Gull (*Larus californicus*). Auk 104:421-428.

Jehl, J.R. and B.A. Smith. 1970. Birds of the Churchill region, Manitoba. Manitoba Museum of Man and Nature Special Publication No.1, Winnipeg. 87 pp.

Jehl, J.R., and P.K. Yochem. 1986. Movements of Eared Grebes indicated by banding recoveries. Journal of Field Ornithology 57:208-212.

Jenkins, J.A. 1969. A note on the local distribution of Buller's Shearwaters. Notornis 16:220.

_____. 1974. Local distribution and feeding habits of Buller's Shearwater (*Puffinus bulleri*). Notornis 21:109-120.

Jerema, R.S. 1973. Birds of Port Coquitlam. Published by City of Port Coquitlam, British Columbia. 59 pp. (Bibliography 811).

Jewett, S.A., W.A. Taylor, W.T. Shaw, and J.W. Aldrich. 1953. Birds of Washington state. University of Washington Press, Seattle. 767 pp.

Jewett, S.G. 1929. The Wedge-tailed Shearwater off the coast of Vancouver Island, British Columbia. Auk 46:224.

_____. 1942. Bird notes from southeastern Alaska. Murrelet 23:67-75.

Jobin, L. 1952a. Some uncommon birds collected in the Cariboo parkland area of British Columbia. Murrelet 33:9.

_____. 1952b. Records of *Somateria mollisima V-nigra* on the mainland of British Columbia. Murrelet 33:12.

_____. 1952c. Records of the Burrowing Owl and Long-eared Owl in the Cariboo, British Columbia, Canada. Murrelet 33:43.

_____. 1955. Notes on the Black Swift and Vaux Swift at their nesting sites in central British Columbia. Canadian Field-Naturalist 69:131-132.

Johns, J.E. 1969. Field studies of Wilson's Phalarope. Auk 86:660-670.

Johnsgard, P.A. 1965. Handbook of waterfowl behavior. Cornell University Press, Ithaca, New York. 378 pp.

_____. 1968. Waterfowl: their biology and natural history. University of Nebraska Press, Lincoln.

_____. 1973. Grouse and quails of North America. University of Nebraska Press, Lincoln. 553 pp.

_____. 1981. The plovers, sandpipers, and snipes of the world. University of Nebraska Press, Lincoln. 493 pp.

_____. 1983. The hummingbirds of North America. Smithsonian Institution Press, Washington, D.C. 303 pp.

_____. 1983a. The grouse of the world. University of Nebraska Press, Lincoln.

Johnson, D.H. and R.E. Stewart. 1983. Racial composition of migrant populations of Sandhill Cranes in the northern plains states. Wilson Bulletin 85:148-162.

Johnson, D.H., D.E. Timm, and P.F. Springer. 1979. Morphological characteristics of Canada geese in the Pacific flyway. Pages 56-76 *in* R.J. Jarvis and J.C. Bartonek (editors). Management and Biology of Pacific Flyway Geese. A symposium sponsored by the Northwest Section, The Wildlife Society, 16 February 1979, Portland, Oregon. Oregon State University Book Stores, Inc., Corvallis.

Johnson, N.K. and C.B. Johnson. 1985. Speciation in sapsuckers (*Sphyrapicus*): II. Sympatry, hybridization, and mate preference in S. *ruber daggetti* and *S. nuchalis*. Auk 102:1-15.

Johnson, R. and J.J. Dinsmore. 1986. Habitat use by breeding Virginia Rails and Soras. Journal of Wildlife Management 50:387-392.

Johnston, D.W. 1955. The Glaucous Gull in western North America south of its breeding range. Condor 57:202-207.

_____. 1961. Timing of annual molt in the Glaucous Gulls of northern Alaska. Condor 63:474-478.

Johnston, S. and H.R. Carter. 1985. Cavity-nesting Marbled Murrelets. Wilson Bulletin 97:1-3.

Johnston, W.G. and C. McEwen. 1986a. The winter season - northwestern Canada region. American Birds 40:303-304.

_____. and _____. 1986b. The nesting season - northwestern Canada region. American Birds 40:1228-1229.

Johnstone, S.T. 1970. Waterfowl eggs. Aviculture Magazine 76: 52-55.

Johnstone, W.B. 1949. An annotated list of the birds of the east Kootenay, British Columbia. British Columbia Provincial Museum Occasional Paper No.7, Victoria. 87pp.

_____. 1964. Two interior British Columbia records for the Ancient Murrelet. Canadian Field-Naturalist 78:199-200.

Jones, E.T. 1985. BC/Yukon bird observations - summer, 1984. Alberta Naturalist 15:72-73.

_____. 1987. Observations of the Northern Hawk Owl in Alberta. Pages 149-151 *in* R.W. Nero, R.J. Clark, R.J. Knapton, and R.H. Hamre (editors). Biology and conservation of Northern Forest Owls: Symposium Proceedings. 1987. Feb. 3-7; Winnipeg, Manitoba. United States Department of Agriculture Forest Service General Technical Report RM-142, Fort Collins, Colorado.

Jones, I.L. 1985. The structure and function of vocalizations and related behavior of the Ancient Murrelet *Synthliborhamphus antiquus*. M.Sc. Thesis. University of Toronto, Ontario. 178pp.

Jones, I.L. and J.B. Falls. 1987. Colony departure of family groups of Ancient Murrelets. Condor 89:940-943.

_____. and _____. 1989. The vocal repertoire of the Ancient Murrelet. Condor 91: 699-710.

Jones, I.L., J.B. Falls, and A.J. Gaston. 1987a. Vocal recognition between parents and young of Ancient Murrelets, *Synthliboramphus antiquus* (Aves:Alcidae). Animal Behaviour 35:1405-1415.

_____, _____, and _____. 1987b. Colony departure of family groups of Ancient Murrelets. Condor 89:940-943.

Jones, J.K., D.C. Carter, H.H. Genoways, R.S. Hoffman, D.W. Rice, and C. Jones. 1986. Revised checklist of North American mammals north of Mexico, 1986. Occasional Papers The Museum Texas Tech University No.107, Lubbock. 22 pp.

Jones, R.D. 1973. A method for appraisal of annual reproductive success in the Black Brant population. M.S. Thesis, University of Alaska, Fairbanks. 117 pp.

Jones, S. 1981. Habitat management series for unique or endangered species. Report No.17. The accipiters - Goshawk, Cooper's Hawk, Sharp-shinned hawk. United States Department of the Interior, Bureau of Land Management Technical Note 335, Denver, Colorado. 51 pp.

Kaiser, G. and M. Lemon. 1987. Protecting our seabird colonies. Vancouver Natural History Society Discovery 16:77-80.

Kaiser, G.W., R.W. McKelvey, and D.W. Smith. 1978. A preliminary report on the first set of aerial surveys to be conducted through a full annual cycle in the Columbia valley between the Libby Reservoir and Golden, British Columbia (1976-1977). Canadian Wildlife Service Unpublished Report, Delta, British Columbia. 54 pp. (Bibliography 3354).

Kaiser, G.W., D. Bertram, and D. Powell. 1984. A band recovery for the Rhinoceros Auklet. Murrelet 65:57.

Kautesk, B.M. 1985a. A possible sighting of the Little Curlew. Vancouver Natural History Society Discovery 14:12-13.

_____. 1985b. "Caribbean Coots" in British Columbia? Vancouver Natural History Society Discovery 14:49-51.

Kautesk, B.M., R.E. Scott, D.S. Aldcroft, and J. Ireland. 1983. Temminck's Stint at Vancouver, British Columbia. American Birds 37:347-349.

Keen, J.H. 1910. Bird migration in northern British Columbia. Ottawa Naturalist 24:116-117.

Keisker, D.G. 1986. Nest tree selection by primary cavity nesting birds in south-central British Columbia. M.Sc. Thesis, Simon Fraser University, Burnaby, British Columbia. 71 pp.

Keith, L.B. 1963. Wildlife's ten-year cycle. University of Wisconsin Press, Madison. 201 pp.

Kelleher, K.E. 1963. A study of the hole-nesting avifauna of southwestern British Columbia. M.Sc. Thesis, University of British Columbia, Vancouver. 169 pp.

Kellert, S.R. 1985. Birdwatching in American society. Leisure Sciences 7:343-360.

Kelso, J.E.H. 1924. The Osprey or fish hawk on Arrow Lake. Migrant 2:17 (Bibliography 1937).

_____. 1926. Birds of Arrow Lakes, Kootenay District, British Columbia. Ibis 2:689-723.

Kempton, R.M. 1927. Notes on the home life of the Turkey Vulture. Wilson Bulletin 39:142-145.

Kendrew, W.G. and D. Kerr. 1955. The climate of British Columbia and the Yukon Territory. Queens Printer, Ottawa, Ontario. 222 pp.

Kennedy, A.J., F.J. van Thienen, and R.M. McKelvey. 1982. Winter foods of Snowy Owls on the southern coast of British Columbia. Vancouver Natural History Society Discovery 11:119-121.

Kennedy, K. and B. Foottit. 1967. Summer report for 1967 - Mitlenatch Island Nature Park. British Columbia Parks Branch Unpublished Report, Victoria. 27 pp. (Bibliography 3372).

Kenyon, K.W. 1937. Two sea-bird records for southern California. Condor 39:257-258.

Kermode, F. 1904. Catalogue of British Columbia birds. British Columbia Provincial Museum, Victoria. 69 pp. (Bibliography 1003).

_____. 1923a. Notes on the occurrence of the Plumed Egret (*Mesophoyx intermedia*) in British Columbia. Canadian Field-Naturalist 37:64-65.

_____. 1923b. Notes on the Plumed Egret (*Mesophoyx intermedia*) in British Columbia. Murrelet 4:3-5.

_____. 1933. California Brown Pelican seen at Victoria, British Columbia. Murrelet 14:15.

Kermode, F. and E.M. Anderson. 1914. Report on birds collected and observed during September, 1913 on Atlin Lake, from Atlin to the south end of the lake. Pages G19-G21 *in* Annual Report of the British Columbia Provincial Museum of Natural History for the year 1913, Victoria.

Kessel, B. 1984. Migration of Sandhill Cranes, *Grus canadensis*, in east-central Alaska, with routes through Alaska and western Canada. Canadian Field-Naturalist 98:279-292.

_____. 1986. Yellow-bellied Sapsucker, *Sphyrapicus varius*, in Alaska. Journal of Field Ornithology 57:42-47.

Kessel, B. and D.D. Gibson. 1978. Status and distribution of Alaskan birds. Studies in Avian Biology No. 1:1-100.

Kevan, C.L. 1970. An ecological study of Red-necked Grebes on Astotin Lake, Alberta. M.Sc. Thesis, University of Alberta, Edmonton.

Kieser, J.A. and F.T.H. Smith. 1982. Field identification of the Pectoral Sandpiper *Calidris melanotos*. Australian Bird Watcher 9:137-146.

Kiff, L. 1981. Eggs of the Marbled Murrelet. Wilson Bulletin 93:400-403.

Kilham, L. 1962. Reproductive behavior of Downy Woodpeckers. Condor 64:126-133.

King, D.G. 1973. First records of nesting by Marsh Hawks on Vancouver Island. Canadian Field-Naturalist 87:470.

King, J.G. and B. Conant. 1981. The 1980 census of Trumpeter Swans on Alaska nesting habitats. American Birds 35: 789-793.

King, J.G. and G.A. Sanger. 1979. Oil vulnerability index for marine-oriented birds. Pages 227-239 *in* J.C. Bartonek and D.N. Nettleship (editors). Conservation of marine birds of northern North America. United States Fish and Wildlife Service Wildlife Research Report No. 11, Washington, D.C. 319 pp.

King, W.B. 1967. Sea-birds of the Tropical Pacific Ocean: preliminary Smithsonian identification manual. United States National Museum, Washington, D.C.

_____ (compiler). 1981. Endangered birds of the world - The ICB bird red data book. Smithsonian Institution Press, Washington, D.C.

_____. 1984. Incidental mortality of seabirds in gillnets in the North Pacific. Pages 709-716 *in* J.P. Croxall, P.G.H. Evans and R.W. Schreiber (editors). Status and conservation of the world's seabirds. International Council for Bird Preservation Technical Publication No. 2. Cambridge, England.

King, W.B., R.G.B. Brown and G.A. Sanger. 1979. Mortality to marine birds through commercial fishing. Pages 195-200 *in* J.C. Bartonek and D.N. Nettleship (editors). Conservation of marine birds of northern North America. United States Department of the Interior Fish and Wildlife Service Wildlife Research Report 11, Washington, D.C. 319 pp.

Kitchen, D.W. and G.S. Hunt. 1969. Brood habitat of the Hooded Merganser. Journal of Wildlife Management 33:605-609.

Knorr, O.N. 1961. The geographical and ecological distribution of the Black Swift in Colorado. Wilson Bulletin 73:155-170.

Kortright, F.H. 1942. The ducks, geese, and swans of North America. Stackpole Co., Harrisburg, Pennsylvania and Wildlife Management Institute, Washington, D.C. 476 pp.

Kozlik, F.M., A.W. Miller, and W.C. Rienecker. 1959. Color-marking white geese for determining migration routes. California Fish and Game 45:69-82.

Kragh, W.D. 1982. The Cattle Egret in the Fraser Delta area, British Columbia. Murrelet 63:86-89.

Kragh, W.D., B.M. Kautesk, J. Ireland, and E. Sian. 1986. Far Eastern Curlew in Canada. American Birds. 40:13-15.

Krajina, V.J. 1959. Bioclimatic zones in British Columbia. University of British Columbia Botanical Series No. 1, Vancouver. 47 pp.

_____. 1965. Biogeoclimatic zones and biogeocoenoses of British Columbia. Ecology of Western North America 1:1-17.

_____. 1969. Ecology of forest trees in British Columbia. Ecology of western North America. 2:1-146.

Kramer, G.W., L.R. Raven, and S.W. Harris. 1979. Populations, hunting mortality, and habitat use of Black Brant at San Quintin Bay, Baja California, Mexico. Pages 242-254 *in* R.L. Jarvis and J.C. Bartonek (editors). Management and Biology of Pacific flyway Geese. A symposium sponsored by the Northwest Section, The Wildlife Society, 16 February 1979, Portland, Oregon. Oregon State University Book Stores, Inc., Corvallis.

Krohn, W.B. and E.G. Bizeau. 1979. Molt migration of the Rocky Mountain population of the western Canada Goose. Pages 130-140 *in* R.L. Jarvis and J.C. Bartonek (editors). Management and Biology of Pacific Flyway Geese. A symposium sponsored by the Northwest Section, The Wildlife Society, 16 February 1979, Portland, Oregon. Oregon State University Book Stores, Inc., Corvallis.

Kurata, Y. 1978. Breeding record of the Laysan Albatross (*Diomedea immutabilis*) on the Ogasawara Islands (a preliminary report). Miscellaneous Report Yamashina Institute of Ornithology 10:185-187.

Kuroda, N. 1960. Analysis of seabird distribution in the northwest Pacific Ocean. Pacific Science 14:55-67.

_____. 1962. On the melanic phase of the McCormick Great Skua. Miscellaneous Reports of the Yamashina Institute for Ornithology 3:212-217.

Kuroda, N. and a Special Committee of the Ornithological Society of Japan. 1958. A hand-list of the Japanese birds, fourth edition. Tokyo Ornithological Society of Japan.

Kuzyakin, A.P. 1963. On the biology of the Long-billed [Marbled] Murrelet. Ornitologiya 6:315-320 (translation in Van Tyne Memorial Library, University of Michigan, Ann Arbor).

Lack, D. 1967. Interrelationships in breeding adaptations as shown by marine birds. Proceedings of the 14th International Ornithological Congress:3-42.

Laing, H.M. 1932. White Pelican on Vancouver Island. Canadian Field-Naturalist 46:190.

_____. 1934. Some Vancouver Island bird notes. Canadian-Field Naturalist 48:37-38.

_____. 1935. Some Vancouver Island bird notes. Canadian Field-Naturalist 49:56-57.

_____. 1937. Birds of River's Inlet region, B.C. - summer 1937. National Museum of Canada Unpublished Report, Ottawa, Ontario. 117 pp. (Bibliography 3397).

_____. 1942. Birds of the coast of central British Columbia. Condor 44:175-181.

_____. 1956. Nesting of Golden Eagle on Vancouver Island. Canadian Field-Naturalist 70:95-96.

_____. 1979. Allan Brooks: Artist-Naturalist. British Columbia Provincial Museum, Victoria. 234 pp.

Lane, R.K. 1962. A Short-tailed Albatross off British Columbia. Canadian Field-Naturalist 76:178-179.

Larrison, E.J. and K.G. Sonnenberg. 1968. Washington birds - their location and identification. Seattle Audubon Society, Seattle, Washington. 258 pp.

Lauro, A.J. and B.J. Spencer. 1980. A method for separating juvenal and first-winter Ring-billed Gulls (*Larus delawarensis*) and Common Gulls (*Larus canus*). American Birds 34:111-117.

Laymon S.A. and M.D. Halterman. 1987. Can the western subspecies of the Yellow-billed Cuckoo be saved from extinction? Western Birds 18:19-25.

Leach, B.A. 1970. A "Slimbridge" in British Columbia. Wildfowl 21:112-114.

_____. 1972. The waterfowl of the Fraser delta, British Columbia. Wildfowl 23:45-54.

_____. 1982. Waterfowl on a Pacific estuary: a natural history of man and waterfowl on the lower Fraser River. British Columbia Provincial Museum Special Publication No. 5, Victoria. 211 pp.

Lee, P.L. 1985. History and current status of Spotted Owl (*Strix occidentalis*) habitat management in the Pacific Northweest region, USDA, Forest Service. Pages 5-9 *in* R.J. Gutierrez and A.B. Carey (editors). Ecology and management of the Spotted Owl in the Pacific Northwest. United States Department of Agriculture, Forest Service General Technical Report PNW-185, Portland Oregon.

Lees, J. 1946. All the year breeding of the Rock Dove. British Birds 39:136-141.

Le Franc, M.N., and W.S. Clark. 1983. Working bibliography of the Golden Eagle and the genus *Aquila*. National Wildlife Federation Scientific and Technical Series No. 7, Washington, D.C. 222 pp.

Lehman, P. 1980. The identification of the Thayer's Gull in the field. Birding 12:198-210.

Leinonen, A. 1978. Hawk Owl breeding biology and behaviour at nest. Lintumies 13:13-18.

Lemon, E.K. 1958. Bird watching at Drumadoon, 1957. Victoria Naturalist 14:93-94.

Lemon, M. and M. Rodway. 1983. Survey of breeding population of Ancient Murrelets of Lyell Island, in 1982. Canadian Wildlife Service Technical Report, Delta, British Columbia. 22 pp.

_____. and _____. 1985a. Survey of breeding population of Ancient Murrelets and Cassin's Auklets on Hippa Island, 1983. Canadian Wildlife Service Technical Report, Delta, British Columbia. 45 pp.

_____. and _____. 1985b. Census of Ancient Murrelets and Cassin's Auklets nesting on Ramsay Island, B.C. in 1984. Canadian Wildlife Service Technical Report, Delta, British Columbia. 49 pp.

Lemon, M., M. Rodway and A. Vallee. 1983. Census of Tufted Puffins breeding on Triangle Island, in 1982. Canadian Wildlife Service Technical Report, Delta, British Columbia. 22 pp.

Lensink, C.C. 1984. The status and conservation of seabirds in Alaska. Pages 13-28 *in* Croxall, J.P., P.G.H. Evans and R.W. Schreiber (editors). The satus and conservation of the world's seabirds. International Council for Bird Preservation Technical Publication No. 2. Cambridge, England.

Lensink, C.J. 1954. Waterfowl breeding ground survey, Ft. Yukon Flats, Alaska. Progress Report Federal Aid Project W-3-R-9, Alaska Game Commission, Juneau.

_____. 1964. Distribution of recoveries from bandings of ducklings. United States Fish and Wildlife Service Special Scientific Report - Wildlife No. 89, Washington, D.C. 146 pp.

_____. 1969. The distribution recoveries from White-fronted geese (*Anser albifrons frontalis*) banded in North America. United States Bureau of Sport Fisheries and Wildlife Unpublished Report, Bethel, Alaska. 63 pp.

Leopold, A.S. and R.H. Smith. 1953. Numbers and winter distribution of Pacific Black Brant in North America. California Fish and Game 39:95-101.Leschner, L.L. 1976. The breeding biology of the Rhinoceros Auklet on Destruction Island. M.Sc. Thesis. University of Washington, Seattle. 77 pp.

Lewin, V. 1963. Reproduction and development of young in a population of California Quail. Condor 65:249-278.

_____. 1965. The introduction and present status of California Quail in the Okanagan valley of British Columbia. Condor 67:61-66.

Lewis, H.F. 1929. The natural history of the Double-crested Cormorant (*Phalacrocorax auritus auritus* (Lesson)). Ru-Mi-Lou Books, Ottawa, Ontario. 94 pp.

Lewis, R.A. 1984. Non-territorial adult males and breeding densities of Blue Grouse. Wilson Bulletin 96:723-725.

Lewis, R.A. and F.C. Zwickel. 1980. Removal and replacement of male Blue Grouse on persistent and transient territorial sites. Canadian Journal of Zoology 58:1417-1423.

LGL Limited. 1974. Use of the Morice, Nanika, and Entiako River drainage systems by migrating waterbirds; October 1974. Canadian Wildlife Service Unpublished Report, Delta, British Columbia. 38 pp. (Bibliography 3439).

L'Hyver, M-A. 1985. Intraspecific variability in nesting phenology, clutch size, and egg size in the Black Oystercatcher *Haematopus bachmani*. M.Sc. Thesis, University of Victoria, Victoria, British Columbia. 224 pp.

Lies, M.F. and W.H. Behle. 1966. Status of the White Pelican in the United States and Canada through 1964. Condor 68: 279-292.

Lincer, J.L., W.S. Clark, and M.N. LeFranc. 1979. Working bibliography of the Bald Eagle. National Wildlife Federation Scientific and Technical Series No .2, Washington, D.C. 219 pp.

Lincoln, R.C. 1986. Burrowing Owl recovery plan. B.C. Naturalist 24:20.

Lindvall, M.L. and J.B. Low. 1982. Nesting ecology and production of Western Grebes at Bear River Migratory Bird Refuge, Utah. Condor 84:66-70.

Littlefield, C.D. and S.P. Thompson. 1979. Distribution and status of the central valley population of greater Sandhill Cranes. Pages 113-120 *in* J.C. Lewis (editor). Proceedings 1978 Crane Workshop. Colorado State University Printing Service, Fort Collins, Colorado.

_____. and _____. 1981. History and status of the Franklin's Gull on Malheur National Wildlife Refuge, Oregon. Great Basin Naturalist 41:440-444.

_____. and _____. 1982. The Pacific coast population of lesser Sandhill Cranes in the contiguous United States. Pages 288-294 *in* J.C. Lewis (editor). Proceedings 1981 Crane Workshop. National Audubon Society, Tavernier, Florida.

Loomis, L.M. 1918. Expedition of the California Academy of Sciences to the Galapagos Islands, 1905-1906 - A review of the albatrosses, petrels, and diving petrels. Proceedings of the California Academy of Sciences 2:1-187.

Lord, J.K. 1866. The naturalist in Vancouver Island and British Columbia (Volume 2). London, Richard Bentley. 375 pp.

Lovvorn, J.R. and C.M. Kirkpatrick. 1981. Roosting behavior and habitat of migrant greater Sandhill Cranes. Journal of Wildlife Management 45:842-857.

Low, J.B. 1941. Nesting of the Ruddy Duck in Iowa. Auk 58: 506-517.

_____. 1945. Ecology and management of the Redhead, *Nyroca americana*, in Iowa. Ecological Monograph 15:35-69.

Lumsden, H.G. 1984. The pre-settlement breeding distribution of Trumpeter Swans (*Cygnus buccinator*) and Tundra Swans (*C. columbianus*) in eastern Canada. Canadian Field-Naturalist 98:415-424.Luttich, S.N., L.B. Keith, and J.D. Stephenson. 1971. Population dynamics of the Red-tailed Hawk (*Buteo jamaicensis*) at Rochester, Alberta. Auk 88:75-87.

Lynch, J.J. and J.F. Voelzer. 1974. 1973 productivity and mortality among geese, swans, and brant wintering in North America. United States Fish and Wildlife Service Unpublished Report, Albuquerque, New Mexico. 43 pp.

Lyons, J.R. 1982. Nonconsumptive wildlife-associated recreation in the U.S.: identifying the other constituency. Pages 667-685 *in* Transactions of the 47th North American and Natural Resources Conference, Portland, Oregon, March 28, 1982.

Macdonald, B.A. 1978a. Curlew Sandpiper at Iona Island. Vancouver Natural History Society Discovery 6:89-90.

_____. 1978b. Sighting of a Garganey at Iona Island. Vancouver Natural History Society Discovery 7:18-19.

MacDonald, S.D. 1968. The courtship and territorial behaviour of Franklin's race of Spruce Grouse. Living Bird 7:5-25.

Mace, P.M. 1983. Bird predation on juvenile salmonids in the Big Qualicum estuary, Vancouver Island. Canadian Technical Report of Fisheries and Aquatic Sciences No. 1176, Vancouver, British Columbia.

MacFarlane, R. and C. Mair. 1908. Notes on the mammals and birds of northern Canada. Pages 1-494 *in* A narrative of the Athabasca and Peace River Treaty Expedition of 1899. William Briggs, Toronto, Ontario.

Mackay, R.H. 1950. British Columbia Trumpeter Swan census, winter 1949-50. Canadian Wildlife Service Report CWSC 448, Ottawa, Ontario. 5 pp. (Bibliography 3459).

_____. 1957. Movements of Trumpeter Swans shown by band returns and observations. Condor 59:339.

Mackenzie-Grieve, R.C. and J.B. Tatum. 1974. Costa's Hummingbird, a new bird for Canada. Canadian Field-Naturalist 88:91-92.

Mackie, R. 1985. Hamilton Mack Laing: Hunter-Naturalist. Sono Nis Press, Victoria, British Columbia. 234 pp.

Mackie, R.J. and H.K. Buechner. 1963. The reproductive cycle of the Chukar. Journal of Wildlife Management 27:246-260.

MacLean, S.F. and R.T. Holmes. 1971. Bill lengths, wintering areas, and taxonomy of North American Dunlins, *Calidris alpina*. Auk 88:893-901.

Macoun, J. 1900. Catalogue of Canadian birds. Part 1. Waterbirds, gallinaceous birds, and pigeons. Geological Survey of Canada, 213 pp.

Macoun, J. and J.M. Macoun. 1909. Catalogue of Canadian birds. Canada Department of Mines Geological Survey Branch, Ottawa, Ontario. 761pp.

Macpherson, A.H. 1961. Observations on Canadian arctic *Larus* gulls, and on the taxonomy of *L. thayeri* Brooks. Arctic Institute of North America Technical Paper 7:1-40.

Maguire, W.S. 1950. Christmas bird census, 1949 - New Westminster, British Columbia. Canadian Field-Naturalist 64:81.

Maher, W.J. 1974. Ecology of Pomarine, Parasitic, and Long-tailed jaegers in northern Alaska. Pacific Coast Avifauna No. 37, Los Angeles, California. 148 pp.

Mailliard, J. 1932. Birds and mammals from the Kootenay valley, southeastern British Columbia. Proceedings of the California Academy of Science 20:269-290.

Manuwal, D.A. 1972. The population ecology of Cassin's Auklet on southeast Farallon Island, California. Ph.D. Thesis, University of California, Los Angeles. 298 pp.

_____. 1974a. The natural history of Cassin's Auklet (*Ptychoramphus aleuticus*). Condor 76:421-431.

_____. 1974b. Effects of territoriality on breeding in a population of Cassin's Auklet. Ecology 55:1399-1406.

_____. 1978. Criteria for aging Cassin's Auklet. Bird-Banding 49:157-161.

_____. 1979. Reproductive commitment and success of Cassin's Auklet. Condor 81:111-121.

Manuwal, D.A. and R.W. Campbell. 1979. Status and distribution of breeding seabirds of southeastern Alaska, British Columbia and Washington. Pages 73-91 *in* J.S. Bartonek and D. Nettleship (editors). Conservation of marine birds of northern North America. United States Fish and Wildlife Service, Wildlife Research Report No. 11, Washington, D.C.

Manuwal, D.A., P.W. Mattocks, and K.O. Richter. 1979. First Arctic Tern colony in the contiguous western United States. American Birds 33:144-145.

March, G.L. 1971. The biology of the Band-tailed Pigeon (*Columba fasciata*) in British Columbia. Ph.D. Thesis, Simon Fraser University, Burnaby, British Columbia. 97 pp.

March, G.L. and R.M.F.S. Sadleir. 1972. Studies on the Band-tailed Pigeon (*Columba fasciata*) in British Columbia. II. Food resource and mineral-gravelling activity. Syesis 5:279-284.

Mark, D.M. 1974. Preliminary results of some Great Blue Heron (*Ardea herodias*) studies in the Vancouver checklist area. Vancouver Natural History Society Discovery 3:38-45.

_____. 1976. An inventory of Great Blue Heron (*Ardea herodias*) nesting colonies in British Columbia. Northwest Science 50:32-41.

_____. 1981. Thayer's Gulls from western Christmas bird counts: a cautionary note. American Birds 35:898-900.

Marsh, R.D. 1988. Macroclimatic regions of British Columbia. Pages 22-32 *in* H.A. Stelfox and G.R. Ironside *(compilers)*. Land/wildlife integration workshop No. 3, Mount Ste.-Marie, Quebec, 16-19 September 1985. Ecological Land Classification Series No. 22, Canadian Wildlife Service, Ottawa, Ontario. 215 pp.

Marshall, D.B. 1987. Status of the Marbled Murrelet with special emphasis on the Oregon population. Audubon Society of Portland Unpublished Report, Portland, Oregon. 46 pp.

Marshall, J.T. 1967. Parallel variation in north and middle American screech owls. Western Foundation Vertebrate Zoology Monograph No.1, Los Angeles, California. 72 pp.

_____. 1988. Status of the Marbled Murrelet in North America: with special emphasis on populations in California, Oregon, and Washington. United States Department of the Interior Fish and Wildlife Service Biological Report 88(30), Washington, D.C. 19 pp.

Marti, C.D., P.W. Wagner, and K.W. Denne. 1979. Nest boxes for the management of Barn Owls. Wildlife Society Bulletin 7:145-148.

Martin, P.W. 1942. Notes on some pelagic birds on the coast of British Columbia. Condor 44:27-29.

_____. 1955. Chukar partridge - summary of stocking, 1950-1955. British Columbia Fish and Wildlife Branch Unpublished Report, Kamloops. 7pp. (Bibliography 4339 - erroneously listed as authored by E.W. Taylor).

_____. 1978. A winter inventory of the shoreline and marine oriented birds and mammals of Chatham Sound. British Columbia Fish and Wildlife Branch Unpublished Report, Victoria. 47 pp. (Bibliography 3521).

Martin, P.W. and M.T. Myres. 1969. Observations on the distribution and migration of some seabirds off the outer coasts of British Columbia and Washington State, 1946-1949. Syesis 2:241-256.

Mathews, W.H. (compiler). 1986. Physiographic map of the Canadian Cordillera. Map 1701A, Geological Survey of Canada, Surveys and Mapping Branch, Ottawa, Ontario.

Mattocks, P.W. 1984. The winter season - northern Pacific coast region. American Birds 38:349-351.

_____. 1985a. The winter season - northern Pacific coast region. American Birds 39:201-204.

_____. 1985b. The spring season - northern Pacific coast region. American Birds 39:340-344.

_____. 1986a. The spring migration - northern Pacific coast region. American Birds 40:514-518.

_____. 1986b. The nesting season - northern Pacific coast region. American Birds 40(5):1244-1248.

Mattocks, P.W. and B. Harrington-Tweit. 1987. The autumn migration - northern Pacific coast region. American Birds 41:132-136.

Mattocks, P.W. and B. Harrington-Tweit. 1987a. The spring migration - northern Pacific Coast region. American Birds 41:478-482.

Mattocks, P.W. and E.S. Hunn. 1978. The spring season - northern Pacific coast region. American Birds 32:1045-1049.

_____. and _____. 1980. The autumn migration - northern Pacific coast region. American Birds 34:191-194.

_____. and _____. 1981. The winter season - northern Pacific coast region. American Birds 35:328-331.

_____. and _____. 1982. Spring migration - northern Pacific coast region. American Birds 36:886-888.

_____. and _____. 1983a. Spring migration - northern Pacific coast region. American Birds 37:903-906.

_____. and _____. 1983b. The nesting season - northern Pacific coast region. American Birds 37:1019-1022.

Mattocks, P.W., E.S. Hunn, and T.R. Wahl. 1976. A checklist of the birds of Washington state, with recent changes annotated. Western Birds 7:1-24.

Mattocks, P.W., B. Harrington-Tweit, and E.Hunn. 1983. The nesting season - northern Pacific coast region. American Birds 37:1019-1022.

Mayr, E. and L.L. Short. 1970. Species taxa of North American birds. Publications of the Nuttall Ornithological Club 9:1-127.

McAllister, N.M. 1958. Courtship, hostile behaviour, nest establishment, and egg laying in the Eared Grebe (*Podiceps caspicus*). Auk 75:290-311.

_____. 1963. Ontogeny of behaviour in five species of grebes. Ph.D. dissertation, University of British Columbia, Vancouver. 135 pp.

_____. N.M. 1980. Avian fauna from the Yuquot excavation. Pages 103-174 *in* W.J. Folan and J. Dewhirst (editors). The Yuquot project, volume 2. History and Archaeology 43. Parks Canada, Ottawa, Ontario.

McCabe, R.A. and A.S. Hawkins. 1946. The Hungarian Partridge in Wisconsin. American Midland Naturalist 36:1-75.

McCabe, T.R. 1976. First record of a Magnificent Frigatebird in inland Pacific Northwest. Murrelet 57:43-44.

McCabe, T.T. and I. McT. Cowan. 1945. *Peromyscus maniculatus macrorhinus* and the problem of insularity. Transactions of the Royal Canadian Institute 1945:117-215.

McCaskie, R.G. 1965. The Cattle Egret reaches the west coast of the United States. Condor 67:89.

_____. 1968. A Broad-winged Hawk in California. Condor 70:93.

_____. 1969. The fall migration - southern Pacific coast region. Audubon Field Notes 23:106-112.

_____. 1970. The occurrence of four species of Pelecaniformes in the southwestern United States. California Birds 1:117.

_____. 1973. A second look at the exotic waterfowl. Birding 5:45-47.

_____. 1979. The nesting season - southern Pacific coast region. American Birds 33:396-398.

_____. 1985. The winter season - southern Pacific coast region. American Birds 39:101-105.

McCourt, K.H. 1969. Dispersion and dispersal of female and juvenile Franklin's Grouse in lodgepole pine forest in southwestern Alberta. M.Sc. Thesis, University of Alberta, Edmonton. 137 pp.

McEwan, C. and W.G. Johnston. 1986. The spring migration - northwestern Canada region. American Birds 40:497-498.

_____. and _____. 1987. The autumn migration - northwestern Canada region. American Birds 41:116-118.

McEwan, E.H. and K. Fry. 1984. Food habits of wintering Dunlin (*Calidris alpina*). Canadian Wildlife Service Unpublished Report, Delta, British Columbia. 10 pp.

_____. and _____. 1986a. Activity budgets of Dunlin (*Calidris alpina*) overwintering in British Columbia. Canadian Wildlife Service Unpublished Report, Delta, British Columbia.

_____. and _____. 1986b. Foraging tactics of Dunlin (*Calidris alpina*). Canadian Wildlife Service Unpublished Report, Delta, British Columbia.

McEwan, E.H. and D.K. Gordon. 1985. Benthic invertebrates of Boundary Bay and Roberts Bank, British Columbia. Canadian Wildlife Service Unpublished Report, Delta, British Columbia. 18 pp.

McEwan, E.H. and P.M. Whitehead. 1984. Seasonal changes in body weight and composition of Dunlin (*Calidris alpina*). Canadian Journal of Zoology 62:154-156.

McFetridge, J. and J. Kirbyson. 1978. Mitlenatch interpretation report - 1978. British Columbia Parks Branch Unpublished Report, Victoria. 43 pp. (Bibliography 3546).

McGilvrey, F.B. 1966. Nesting of Hooded Mergansers on the Patuxent Wildlife Research Center, Laurel, Maryland. Auk 83:477-479.

McKay, W.A. 1957. This area could become fine game bird district past records show. Grand Forks Gazette, Grand Forks, British Columbia.

McKelvey, R.W. 1976. Fall aerial survey of marine birds and mammals off the British Columbia coast. Canadian Wildlife Service Unpublished Report, Delta, British Columbia. 8 pp. (Bibliography 3552).

_____. 1981a. Surveys of water birds in the Boudreau Lakes area, northeastern British Columbia. Canadian Wildlife Service Unpublished Report, Delta, British Columbia. 25 pp.

_____. 1981b. Some aspects of the winter feeding ecology of Trumpeter Swans at Port Alberni and Comox Harbour, British Columbia. M.Sc. Thesis, Simon Fraser University, Burnaby, British Columbia. 117 pp.

_____. 1986. The status of Trumpeter Swans in British Columbia and the Yukon, summer 1985. Canadian Wildlife Service Technical Report Series No. 8, Delta, British Columbia. 30 pp.

McKelvey, R.W. and C. Burton. 1983. A possible migration route for Trumpeter Swans (*Cygnus buccinator*) in British Columbia. Canadian Wildlife Service Progress Notes 138, Ottawa, Ontario. 4 pp.

McKelvey, R.W. and N.A.M. Verbeek. 1988. Habitat use, behaviour and management of Trumpeter Swans, *Cygnus buccinator*, wintering at Comox, British Columbia. Canadian Field-Naturalist 102:434-441.

McKelvey, R.W., I. Robertson, and P.E. Whitehead. 1978. The effect of non-petroleum oil spills on wintering birds near Vancouver, British Columbia. Canadian Wildlife Service Unpublished Report, Delta, British Columbia. 8 pp. (Bibliography 3560)

McKelvey, R.W., K.J. McCormick, and L.J. Shandruk. 1988. The status of Trumpeter Swans, *Cygnus buccinator*, in western Canada. Canadian Field-Naturalist 102:495-499.

McKinnon, D.T. and F.C. Zwickel. 1988. Length of incubation period of Blue Grouse. Murrelet 69:73-75.

McKnight, D.E. 1974. Dry-land nesting by Redheads and Ruddy Ducks. Journal of Wildlife Management 38:112-119.

McLandress, M.R. 1979. Status of Ross' Geese in California. Pages 255-265 *in* R.L. Jarvis and J.C. Bartonek (editors). Management and Biology of Pacific Flyway Geese. A symposium sponsored by the Northwest Section, The Wildlife Society, 16 February 1979, Portland, Oregon. Oregon State University Book Stores, Inc., Corvallis.

McLardy, R. 1983. The eighty-third Audubon Christmas Count - Pender Islands, B.C. American Birds 37:442-443.

McLaren, P.L. and M.A. McLaren. 1973. A sight record of the Ferruginous Hawk in British Columbia. Blue Jay 31:59.

McMannama, Z.V. 1951. Growth in the Glaucous-winged Gull, *Larus glaucescens*. M.Sc. Thesis, University of Washington, Seattle. 60 pp.

McMillan, W.J., A. Panteleyev, and T. Hoy. 1987. Mineral deposits in British Columbia: a review of their tectonic settings. Pages 1-18 *in* I.C. Elliott and B.W. Smee (editors). Proceedings of Exploration in the North American Cordillera. Association of Exploration Geochemists, May 12-14, 1986, Vancouver, British Columbia.

McNicholl, M.K. 1975. Sight record of White-throated Swift on Vancouver Island. Western Birds 6:10.

_____. 1988. Common Loon distribution and conservation problems in Canada. Pages 196-214 *in* P.I.V. Strong (editor). Papers from the 1987 Conference on Common Loon Research and Management. North American Loon Fund, Meredith, New Hampshire.

McNulty, F. 1966. The Whooping Crane: the bird that defies extinction. Clark, Irwin and Co., Ltd., Toronto. 190 pp.

Meehan, R.H. and R.J. Ritchie. 1982. Habitat requirements of Boreal and Hawk owls in interior Alaska. Pages 188-196 *in* W.N. Ladd and P.F. Schempf (editors). Proceedings of a Symposium and Workshop on Raptor Management and Biology in Alaska and Western Canada, February 17-20, 1981, Anchorage, Alaska. United States Department of the Interior, Fish and Wildlife Service Anchorage, Alaska.

Meidinger, D. (compiler). 1987. Recommended vernacular names for common plants of British Columbia. British Columbia Ministry of Forests and Lands, Research Branch, Victoria. 64 pp.

Mellen, T.K. 1987. Home range and habitat use of Pileated Woodpeckers, western Oregon. M.S. Thesis, Oregon State University, Corvallis. 96 pp.

Melville, D.S. 1984. Seabirds of China and the surrounding seas. Pages 501-511 *in* J.P. Croxell, P.G.H. Evans, and R.G. Schreiber (editors). Status and conservation of the world's seabirds. International Council for Bird Preservation Technical Publication No. 2, Cambridge, England.

Melvin, S.M. and S.A. Temple. 1982. Migration ecology of Sandhill Cranes: a review. Pages 73-87 *in* J.C. Lewis (editor). Proceedings 1981 Crane Workshop. National Audubon Society, Tavernier, Florida.

Mendall, H.L. 1958. The Ring-necked Duck in the northeast. University of Maine Bulletin No. 60, Orono. 317 pp.

Meng, H.K. 1951. The Cooper's Hawk. Ph.D. Thesis, Cornell University, Ithaca, New York. 216 pp.

Menzies, A. 1792. Menzies' Journal of Vancouver's voyage, April to October, 1792. *In* C.F. Newcombe (editor). Archives of British Columbia Memoir No. 5, Victoira, 1923. 171 pp.

Merilees, W.J. 1971. Observations of Turkeys in British Columbia. Blue Jay 29:25-27.

_____. 1974a. Ring-billed and California gull nesting colony in south central British Columbia. Canadian Field-Naturalist 88:484-485.

_____. 1974b. A Glaucous-winged Gull mated to a Herring Gull on Okanagan Lake, British Columbia. Canadian Field-Naturalist 88:485-486.

Merilees, W.J. and M. McNall. 1981. Cattle Egret update. Vancouver Natural History Society Discovery 10:18-20.

Merriam, C.H. 1890. Results of a biological survey of the San Francisco mountain region and desert of the Little Colorado in Arizona. North American Fauna No. 3:1-135.

Mershon, W.B. 1907. The Passenger Pigeon. Outing Publishing Company, New York.

Metras, L. 1986. Migratory birds killed in Canada during the 1985 season. Canadian Wildlife Service Progress Notes No. 166, Ottawa, Ontario. 42 pp.

Meugens, A.L. 1945. A trip to Bare Island. Victoria Naturalist 2:75-76.

Meugens, A.L. and J.K. Cooper. 1962. Notes on the bird fauna of the Richter Pass area. British Columbia Provincial Museum Unpublished Report, Victoria. 14 pp. (Bibliography 1999).

Middleton, H. 1949. Christmas bird census, 1948 - Vancouver, British Columbia. Canadian Field-Naturalist 63:65-66.

Miller, H.W., A. Dzubin, and J.T. Sweet. 1968. Distribution and mortality of Saskatchewan-banded White-fronted Geese. Transactions of the 33rd North American Wildlife and Natural Resources Conference: 101-118.

Mills, E.L. 1960a. Bird observations in the Queen Charlotte Islands, British Columbia. Canadian Field-Naturalist 74:156-158.

_____. 1960b. Heermann's Gull in Barkley Sound, Vancouver Island. Canadian Field-Naturalist 74:162.

Millsap, B.A. 1986. Status of wintering Bald Eagles in the conterminous 48 states. Wildlife Society Bulletin 14:433-440.

Mindell, D.P. 1983. Harlan's hawk (*Buteo jamaicensis harlani*): a valid subspecies. Auk 100:161-169.

Mitchell, G.J. 1959. Bird observations at Tahsis Inlet, Vancouver Island, British Columbia. Canadian Field-Naturalist 73:6-13.

Mitchell, W.R. and R.E. Green. 1981. Identification and interpretation of ecosystems of the western Kamloops forest region. Volume 1. British Columbia Ministry of Forests Unpublished Report, Victoria.

Modafferi, R.D. 1975. Aspects of morphology in female Rock Ptarmigan (*Lagopus mutus*) during ovarian recrudescence. Ph.D. Thesis, University of Alaska, Fairbanks.

Moffit, J. 1939. Ninth annual Black Sea Brant census in California. California Fish and Game 25:335-342.

Moisan, G., R.I. Smith, and R.K. Martinson. 1967. The Green-winged Teal: its distribution, migration and population dynamics. United States Fish and Wildlife Service Special Scientific Report-Wildlife No. 100, Washington, D.C. 248 pp.

Monaghan, P. and N. Duncan. 1979. Plumage variation of known-age Herring Gulls. British Birds 72:100-103.

Monroe, B.L. 1973. Summary of all-time highest counts of individuals for Canada and the U.S. American Birds 27:541-547.

_____. 1974. Summary of highest counts of individuals for Canada and the U.S. American Birds 28:568-576.

_____. 1976. Summary of highest counts of individuals for Canada and the U.S. American Birds 30:637-641.

_____. 1977. Summary of highest counts of individuals for Canada and the U.S. American Birds 31:910-915.

_____. 1978. Summary of highest counts of individuals for Canada and the U.S. American Birds 32:924-930.

_____. 1979. Summary of highest counts of individuals for Canada and the U.S. American Birds 33:703-707.

_____. 1981. Summary of highest counts of individuals for Canada and the U.S. American Birds 35:758-762.

_____. 1982. Summary of highest counts of individuals for Canada and the U.S. American Birds 36:779-783.

_____. 1983. Summary of highest counts of individuals for Canada and the U.S. American Birds 37:793-796.

_____. 1984. Summary of highest counts of individuals for Canada and the U.S. American Birds 38:837-839.

_____. 1985a. Summary of highest counts of individuals for Canada and the U.S. American Birds 39:826-831.

_____. 1985b. Summary of highest counts of individuals for Canada and the U.S. American Birds 39:832-834.

Morrison, K.P. 1969. Mourning Dove ecology in south-central British Columbia. M.Sc. Thesis, Colorado State University, Fort Collins. 116 pp.

Morse, D.H. 1970. Ecological aspects of some mixed species foraging flocks of birds. Ecological Monographs 40:119-168.

Morse, T.E., J.L. Jakabosky, and V.P. McCrow. 1969. Some aspects of the breeding biology of the Hooded Merganser. Journal of Wildlife Management 33:596-604.

Mousely, H. 1938. A study of the home life of the eastern Belted Kingfisher. Wilson Bulletin 50:3-12.

_____. 1939. Home life of the American Bittern. Wilson Bulletin 51:83-85.

Moyle, J.B., F.B. Lee, R.L. Jessen, N.J. Ordal, R.I. Benson, J.P. Lindmeier, R.E. Farmes, and M.M. Nelson. 1964. Ducks and land use in Minnesota. Minnesota Department of Conservation Technical Bulletin No. 8, Minneapolis. 140 pp.

Mueller, H.C. and D.D. Berger. 1967. Some observations and comments on the periodic invasion of Goshawks. Auk 84:183-191.

Mueller, H.C., D.D. Berger, and G. Allez. 1976. Age and sex variation in the size of Goshawks. Bird-Banding 47:310-318.

_____, _____, and _____. 1979a. Age and sex differences in size of Sharp-shinned Hawks. Bird-Banding 50:34-44.

_____, _____, and _____. 1979b. The identification of North American accipiters. American Birds 33:236-240.

_____, _____, and _____. 1981. Age, sex, and seasonal differences in size of Cooper's Hawks. Journal of Field Ornithology 52:112-126.

Mulholland, R. 1985. Habitat suitability index models: Lesser Scaup (wintering), United States Fish and Wildlife Service Biological Report 82 (10.91), Washington, D.C. 15 pp.

Munro, D. and K. Munro. 1987. Western Grebe a rare attraction. Salmon Arm Observer Newspaper, 6 May: 8.

Munro, D.A. 1947. A preliminary study of the waterfowl of Burnaby Lake, British Columbia. B.A. Thesis. University of British Columbia, Vancouver. 66 pp.

_____. 1952. Ornithological investigations in British Columbia, 1950 and 1951. University of British Columbia Department of Zoology Unpublished Report, Vancouver. 122 pp. (Bibliography 3640).

_____. 1953. Observations of Canada Geese in British Columbia and western Alberta in 1952. University of British Columbia Department of Zoology Unpublished Report, Vancouver. 33 pp. (Bibliography 3641).

_____. 1954. Notes on the Western Grebe in British Columbia. Auk 71:333.

Munro, J.A. 1917. Report on field work in Okanagan and Shuswap districts, 1916. Pages Q12-Q18 *in* Annual Report of the Provincial Museum of Natural History for 1916, Victoria, British Columbia.

_____. 1918. Notes on some British Columbia birds. Auk 35:234-235.

_____. 1919. Notes on some birds of the Okanagan valley, British Columbia. Auk 36:64-74.

_____. 1921. British Columbia bird notes, 1920-1. Murrelet 2:15-17.

_____. 1923. A preliminary report on the relation of various ducks and gulls to the propagation of sockeye salmon at Henderson Lake, Vancouver Island, British Columbia. Canadian Field-Naturalist 37:81-83; 107-116.

_____. 1925. The European Gray Partridge in the Okanagan valley, British Columbia. Canadian Field-Naturalist 29:163-164.

_____. 1925a. Further notes from southern Vancouver Island, Canadian Field-Naturalist 39:156-158.

_____. 1925b. Some observations on Bare Island, B.C. Murrelet 6:55-57.

_____. 1927. Christmas bird census returns, 1926 - Okanagan Landing, British Columbia. Canadian Field-Naturalist 41:15.

_____. 1928. Horned owl migration in British Columbia. Auk 45:99.

_____. 1929a. A further note on the Horned Owl and Goshawk migration in British Columbia. Auk 46:387-388.

_____. 1929b. Status of sea birds on Bare Island, British Columbia, 1927. Canadian Field-Naturalist 43:167.

_____. 1935a. Recent records from British Columbia. Condor 37:178-179.

_____. 1935b. Bird life at Horse Lake, British Columbia. Condor 37:185-193.

_____. 1935c. Nesting colonies of the Herring Gull in British Columbia. Condor 37:214-215.

_____. 1935d. Glaucous Gull on the British Columbia coast. Condor 37:255-256.

_____. 1935e. Report of J.A. Munro, Okanagan Landing, B.C., summarizing activities for the month of March, 1935. Canadian Wildlife Service Unpublished Report, Delta, British Columbia. 33 pp. (Bibliography 3651).

_____. 1935f. Barrow's Goldeneye nesting in marmot's burrow. Condor 37:82-83.

_____. 1936a. A wader migration at Tlell, Queen Charlotte Islands, British Columbia. Condor 38:230-234.

_____. 1936b. Behaviour of White-fronted Goose at Tl-ell, Queen Charlotte Islands, B.C. Wilson Bulletin 48:137.

_____. 1936c. Water-fowl conditions in the Okanagan valley, April, May and June, 1936. Canadian Wildlife Service Unpublished Report, Delta, British Columbia. 6 pp. (Bibliography 3652).

_____. 1937. Nesting colonies of the Double-crested Cormorant in British Columbia. Pages K26-K30 *in* Annual report of the British Columbia Provincial Museum of Natural History for the year 1936, Victoria.

_____. 1938. Studies of waterfowl in the Cariboo region, British Columbia,1937-38. Canadian Wildlife Service Unpublished Report, Delta, British Columbia. 47 pp. (Bibliography 3657).

_____. 1939a. Studies of waterfowl in British Columbia - Barrow's Golden-eye, American Golden-eye. Transactions of the Royal Canadian Institute 22:259-318.

_____. 1939b. Nesting of the Western Grebe in British Columbia. Pages K16-K17 *in* Report of the Provincial Museum of Natural History for the year 1938, Victoria, British Columbia.

_____. 1939c. Waterfowl observations in the Okanagan district -October, 1939. Canadian Wildlife Service Unpublished Report, Delta, British Columbia. 4pp. (Bibliography 3661).

_____. 1939d. Waterfowl observations in the Okanagan district, British Columbia, November, 1939. Canadian Wildlife Service Unpublished Report, Delta, British Columbia. 3pp. (Bibliography 3662).

_____. 1939e. Food of ducks and coots at Swan Lake, British Columbia. Canadian Journal of Research D17: 178-186.

_____. 1939f. Studies of waterfowl in British Columbia 1938 (December) - 1939 covering parts of southern Vancouver Isand, Okanagan, Kamloops, Nicola and Cariboo. Canadian Wildlife Service Unpublished Report, Ottawa, Ontario.

_____. 1939g. Studies of waterfowl in British Columbia 1938 (December)-1939 covering parts of southern Vancouver Island, Okanagan, Kamloops, Nicola and Cariboo. Canadian Wildlife Service Unpublished Report, Ottawa, Ontario. 116 pp. (Bibliography 3658).

_____. 1941a. Studies of waterfowl in British Columbia - Greater Scaup Duck, Lesser Scaup Duck. Canadian Journal of Research D19:113-138.

_____. 1941b. The grebes: studies of waterfowl in British Columbia. British Columbia Provincial Museum Occasional Paper No.3, Victoria. 71 pp.

_____. 1942a. Studies of waterfowl in British Columbia - Bufflehead. Canadian Journal of Research D20:133-160.

_____. 1942b. Observations of waterfowl in British Columbia - September, October, November, 1942. Canadian Wildlife Service Unpublished Report, Delta, British Columbia. 15 pp. (Bibliography 3667).

_____. 1943. Studies of waterfowl in British Columbia - Mallard. Canadian Journal of Research D21:223-260.

_____. 1944. Studies of waterfowl in British Columbia. Canadian Wildlife Service Unpublished Report, Ottawa, Ontario. 8 pp. (Bibliography 3669).

_____. 1945a. Birds of the Cariboo parklands. Canadian Journal of Research D23:17-103.

_____. 1945b. Observations of waterfowl in southern British Columbia, 1944. Canadian Wildlife Service Unpublished Report, Ottawa, Ontario. 16pp. (Bibliography 3670).

_____. 1945c. Observations of the loon in the Cariboo Parklands, British Columbia. Auk 62:38-49.

_____. 1946. Birds and mammals of the Vanderhoof region, British Columbia, with comments on other resources. Canadian Wildlife Service Unpublished Report, Ottawa, Ontario. 161 pp.

_____. 1947a. Observations of birds and mammals in central British Columbia. British Columbia Provincial Museum Occasional Paper No. 6, Victoria. 165 pp.

_____. 1947b. A preliminary report on the Duck Lake area, British Columbia. Canadian Wildlife Service Unpublished Report, Delta, British Columbia. 19 pp. (Bibliography 3672).

_____. 1949. Studies of waterfowl in British Columbia - Green-winged Teal. Canadian Journal of Research D 27:149-178.

_____. 1949a. The birds and mammals of the Vanderhoof region, B.C. American Midland Naturalist 41:3-138.

_____. 1950. The birds and mammals of the Creston region, British Columbia. British Columbia Provincial Museum Occasional Paper No.8, Victoria. 90 pp.

_____. 1955a. Additional observations of birds and mammals in the Vanderhoof region, British Columbia. American Midland Naturalist 52:56-60.

_____. 1955b. A record of the Least Bittern in British Columbia. Murrelet 36:44.

_____. 1955c. The birds of the Cariboo parklands: a supplement. Pages 79-85 *in* Provincial Museum of Natural History and Anthropology Report for the year 1954, Victoria, British Columbia.

_____. 1958a. The birds and mammals of the Creston region, British Columbia: a supplement. Pages C65-C82 *in* British Columbia Provincial Museum of Natural History and Anthropology Report for the year 1957, Victoria, British Columbia.

_____. 1958b. The status of nesting waterfowl in the Cariboo parklands, British Columbia, in 1958. Canadian Wildlife Service Unpublished Report, Delta, British Columbia. 67 pp.

Munro, J.A. and W.A. Clemens. 1931. Waterfowl in relation to the spawning of herring in British Columbia. Bulletin of the Biological Board of Canada No. 17:1-46.

_____. and _____. 1937. The American Merganser in British Columbia and its relation to the fish population. Biological Board of Canada Bulletin No. 55, Ottawa, Ontario. 50 pp.

Munro, J.A. and I. Mc T. Cowan. 1947. A review of the bird fauna of British Columbia. British Columbia Provincial Museum Special Publication No. 2, Victoria. 285 pp.

Munro, W.T. 1967. Occurrence of the Fulvous Tree Duck in Canada. Canadian Field-Naturalist 81:151-152.

_____. 1979a. Preliminary Canada Goose management plan for British Columbia. British Columbia Fish and Wildlife Branch Report, Victoria. 15 pp. (Bibliography 3681).

_____. 1979b. Preliminary Brant management plan for British Columbia. British Columbia Ministry of Environment Fish and Wildlife Branch Report, Victoria. 18 pp. (Bibliography 3683).

Munro, W.T. and R.W. Campbell. 1979. Programs and authorities of the province of British Columbia related to marine bird conservation. Pages 247-250 *in* J.C. Bartonek and D.N. Nettleship (editors). Conservation of marine birds of northern North America. United States Department of the Interior Fish and Wildlife Service Wildlife Research Report No. 11, Washington, D.C.

Munro, W.T. and S.T. Goodchild. 1981. Preliminary duck management plan for British Columbia. British Columbia Ministry of Environment Unpublished Report, Victoria. 23 pp.

Munro, W.T. and R. McKelvey. 1983. Cooperative waterfowl management plan for British Columbia. British Columbia Ministry of Environment Unpublished Manuscript. Victoria. 29 pp.

Munro, W.T. and B. van Drimmelen. 1988. Status of peregrines in the Queen Charlotte Islands, British Columbia. Pages 69-72 *in* T.J. Cade, J.H. Enderson, C.G. Thelander, and C.M. White (editors). Peregrine Falcon populations - their management and recovery. The Peregrine Fund, Inc. Boise, Idaho.

Munyer, E.A. 1965. Inland wanderings of the Ancient Murrelet. Wilson Bulletin 77:235-242.

Murphy, D. 1984. Burrowing Owl project (1984). British Columbia Wildlife Branch Unpublished Report, Kamloops. 24 pp.

Myres, M.T. 1957. Clutch size and laying dates in Cliff Swallow colonies. Condor 59:311-316.

_____. 1986. Thomas W. Blakiston, Charles Waterton and John George Brown, and their interconnected associations with Waterton Lakes National Park, Alberta. Alberta Naturalist 16:29-31.

Myres, M.T., and S.R. Cannings. 1971. A Canada Goose migration through the southern interior of British Columbia. Pages 23-34 *in* Studies of Bird Hazards to Aircraft. Canadian Wildlife Service Report Series No.14, Ottawa, Ontario.

Myres, M.T. and J.R. Guzman. 1976-1977. Ecology and behaviour of southern hemisphere shearwater (genus *Puffinus*) and other seabirds, when over the Outer Continental Shelf of the Bering Sea and Gulf of Alaska during the northern summer. Environmental Assessment of the Alaskan Continental Shelf, Principal Investigator's Reports, for the year ending March 1977, Vol.3, Pages 179-191. United States Department of Commerce, National Oceanic and Atmospheric Administration, and United States Department of the Interior, Bureau of Land Management, Boulder, Colorado.

Myres, M.T., I.McT. Cowan and M.D.F. Udvardy. 1957. The British Columbia nest records scheme. Condor 59:308-310.

Nagy, A.C. 1977. Population trend indices based on 40 years of autumn counts at Hawk Mountain Sanctuary in north-eastern Pennsylvania. Pages 243-253 *in* R.D. Chancellor (editor). World Conference on Birds of Prey (1975). Report of Proceedings of the International Council for Bird Preservation. Cambridge, England.

National Audubon Society. 1983. The Audubon Society Master Guide to Birding. Volumes 1 and 2. Alfred A. Knopf, New York. 845 pp.

National Geographic Society. 1983. Field Guide to the birds of North America. National Geographic Society, Washington, D.C. 464 pp.

Neff, J.A. 1947. Habits, food, and economic status of the Band-tailed Pigeon. United States Fish and Wildlife Service North American Fauna No.58, Washington, D.C. 76 pp.

Nelson, B. 1979. Seabirds: their biology and ecology. A & W Publishers Inc., New York. 224 pp.

Nelson, R.W. 1970. Some aspects of the breeding behavior of peregrines on Langara Island, British Columbia. M.Sc. Thesis, University of Calgary, Alberta. 306 pp.

_____. 1977. Behavioral ecology of coastal peregrine (*Falco peregrinus pealei*). Ph.D. Thesis, University of Calgary, Alberta. 490 pp.

Nelson, R.W. and M.T. Myres. 1976. Declines in populations of Peregrine Falcons and their seabird prey at Langara Island, British Columbia. Condor 78:281-293.

Nelson, U.C. and H.A. Hansen. 1959. The cackling goose - its migration and management. Transactions of the North America Wildlife Conference 24:174-187.

Nero, R.W. 1969. The status of the Great Gray Owl in Manitoba, with special reference to the 1968-69 influx. Blue Jay 27: 191-209.

_____. 1980. The Great Gray Owl - phantom of the northern forest. Smithsonian Institution Press, Washington, D.C. 167 pp.

Nettleship, D.N. 1973. Breeding ecology of turnstones *Arenaria interpres* at Hazen Camp, Ellesmere Island, N.W.T. Ibis 115:202-217.

_____. 1976. Census techniques for seabirds of arctic eastern Canada. Canadian Wildlife Service Occasional Paper No. 25, Ottawa, Ontario. 33 pp.

Newton, I. 1979. Population ecology of raptors. Buteo Books, Vermillion, South Dakota. 339 pp.

Nichols, J.T. 1927. Tubinares off the north-west coast. Auk 44:326-327.

Noble, M.D. 1972. Blue geese observation in British Columbia. Murrelet 53:13.

Nuechterlein, G.L. 1981. Courtship behavior and reproductive isolation between Western Grebe color morphs. Auk 98: 335-349.

O'Brien, D. 1974. Manning Park avifauna report - summer 1974. British Columbia Parks Branch Unpublished Report, Victoria. 12 pp. (Bibliography 3790).

O'Brien, D. and K.M. Bell. 1975. The avifauna of Bowron Lake Provincial Park - report for summer 1975. British Columbia Parks Branch Unpublished Report, Victoria. 22 pp. (Bibliography 3791).

Odlum, G.C. 1952. Banding at the Triple Island lightstation. News from the Bird-Banders 27:34.

O'Donald, P. 1983. The Arctic Skua: a study of the ecology and evolution of a seabird. Cambridge University Press, London, England 324 pp.

Oeming, A.F. 1955a. A preliminary study of the Great Gray Owl (*Scotiaptex nebulosa nebulosa* Forster) in Alberta with observations on some other species of owls. M.Sc. Thesis, University of Alberta, Edmonton.

_____. 1955b. In quest of the rare Great Gray Owl. Canadian Geographical Journal 73:236-243.

Ogden, V.T. 1973. Nesting density and reproductive success of the Prairie Falcon in southwesern Idaho. M.S. Thesis, University of Idaho, Moscow. 43 pp.

Ogi, H. 1984. Seabird mortality incidental to the Japanese salmon gill-net fishery. Pages 717-722 *in* J.P. Croxall, P.G.H. Evans and R.W. Schreiber (editors). Status and conservation of the world's seabirds. International Council for Bird Preservation Technical Report No. 2. Cambridge, England.

Ohanjanian, I.A. 1986a. Effects of a man-made dyke on the reproductive behavior and nesting success of Red-necked Grebes. M.Sc. thesis, Simon Fraser University, Burnaby. 83 pp.

_____. 1986b. The Long-billed Curlew in the east Kootenay - status report and enhancement schedule for Skookumchuck Prairie. British Columbia Wildlife Branch Unpublished Report, Cranbrook. 12 pp.

Oldaker, R.F. 1960. Band reading by telescope. News from the Bird-Banders 35:39-42.

_____. 1961. Survey of the California Gull. Western Bird Bander 36:26-30.

_____. 1963a. Unusual nest site of the Glaucous-winged Gull. Canadian Field-Naturalist 77:65-66.

_____. 1963b. Sight records of banded California Gulls. Western Bird Bander 38:7-10.

Oliphant, L.W. 1985, North American Merlin breeding survey. Raptor Research 19:37-41.

Oliphant, L.W. and E. Haug. 1985. Productivity, population density and rate of increase of an expanding Merlin population. Raptor Research 19:56-59.

Oliphant, L.W. and W.J.P. Thompson. 1978. Recent breeding success of Richardson's Merlin in Saskatchewan. Raptor Research 12: 35-39.

Olson, S.T. and W.H. Marshall. 1952. The Common Loon in Minnesota. Minnesota Museum of Natural History Occasional Papers No. 5, Minneapolis 77 pp.

Orcutt, L. 1967. Intermediate naturalists are busy birders. Vancouver Natural History Society News 134:5-8.

Orians, G. and F. Kuhlman. 1956. The Red-tailed Hawk and Great Horned Owl populations in Wisconsin. Condor 58:371-385.

Oring, L.W. 1966. Breeding biology and molts of the Gadwall, *Anas strepera* Linnaeus. Ph.D. Thesis, University of Oklahoma, Norman. 103 pp.

_____. 1968. Growth, molts, and plumages of the Gadwall. Auk 85:355-380.

_____. 1969. Summer biology of the Gadwall of Delta, Manitoba. Wilson Bulletin 81:44-54.

_____. 1973. Solitary Sandpiper early reproductive behavior. Auk 90:652-663.

Oring, L.W. and S.J. Maxon. 1978. Instances of simultaneous polyandry by a Spotted Sandpiper (*Actitis macularia*). Ibis 120:349-353.

Osgood, W.H. 1901. Natural History of the Queen Charlotte Islands, British Columbia - the Cook Inlet region Alaska. United States Department of Agriculture, Division of Biological Survey, North American Fauna 21:1-87.

Osmond-Jones, E.J., M. Sather, W.G. Hazelwood and B. Ford. 1977. Spatsizi and Tatlatui wilderness parks: an inventory of wildlife, fisheries, and recreational values in a northern wilderness park. British Columbia Parks Branch, Victoria. 292 pp.

Ouelet, H. 1987. Profile of a pioneer: P.A. Taverner. American Birds 41:20-25.

Owen, D.F. 1963a. Variation in North American screech owls and their sub-species concept. Systematic Zoology 12:8-14.

Pacific Flyway Study Committee. 1982. Pacific flyway management plan for the Pacific flyway population of lesser sandhill cranes. Pacific Flyway Council, c/o United States Fish and Wildlife Service, Portland, Oregon. 19 pp.

Pacific Flyway Study Committee. 1982a. Pacific flyway management plan for the Central Valley population of greater sandhill cranes. Pacific Flyway Council, c/o United States Fish and Wildlife Service, Portland, Oregon.

Page, G., B. Fearis and R.M. Jurek. 1972. Age and sex composition of Western Sandpipers on Bolinas Lagoon. California Birds 3:79-86.

Page, R. and A.T. Bergerud. 1979. The caribou calf mortality study-1979: a progress report. University of Victoria Department of Biology Unpublished Report, Victoria, British Columbia. 65 pp. (Bibliography 3808).

Palmer, D.A. 1986. Habitat selection, movements, and activity of Boreal and Saw-whet Owls. M.Sc. Thesis, Colorado State University, Fort Collins. 101 pp.

Palmer, R.S. (editor). 1962. Handbook of North American birds: Volume 1. Loons through Flamingos. Yale University Press, New Haven, Connecticut. 567 pp.

_____. 1967. Buff-breasted Sandpiper. Pages 212-214 *in* G.P. Stout (editor). The shorebirds of North America. Viking Press, New York.

_____. 1976a. Handbook of North American birds. Volume 2. Waterfowl (Part 1). Yale University Press, New Haven, Connecticut. 521 pp.

_____. 1976b. Handbook of North American birds. Volume 3. Waterfowl concluded. Yale University Press, New Haven, Connecticut. 560 pp.

_____. 1988a. Handbook of North American birds: Volume 4. Diurnal Raptors (Part 1). Yale University Press, New Haven, Connecticut. 433 pp.

_____. 1988b. Handbook of North American Birds: Volume 5. Diurnal Raptors (Part 2). Yale University Press, New Haven, Connecticut. 465 pp.

Parham, H.J. 1937. A nature lover in British Columbia. H.F. and G. Witherby Ltd., London. 292 pp.

Parkham, C.H. 1950. Two uncommon birds from Westport, Washington. Murrelet 31:46.

Parkin, D.T. and J.M. McMeeking. 1985. The increase of Canada Geese in Nottinghamshire from 1980. Bird Study 32:132-140.

Parmelee, D.F. and S.D. MacDonald. 1960. The birds of west-central Ellesmere Island and adjacent areas. National Museum of Canada Bulletin No. 169, Ottawa, Ontario. 103 pp.

Parmelee, D.F., D.W. Greiner, and W.D. Graul. 1968. Summer schedule and breeding biology of the White-rumped Sandpiper in the central Canadian Arctic. Wilson Bulletin 80:1-29.

Patch, C.A. 1922. A biological reconnaisance on Graham Island of the Queen Charlotte group. Canadian Field-Naturalist 36:101-105, 133-136.

Patten, S.M. 1974. Breeding ecology of the Glaucous-winged Gull (*Larus glaucescens*) in Glacier Bay, Alaska. M.Sc. Thesis, University of Washington, Seattle. 78 pp.

Patten, S. and A.R. Weisbrod. 1974. Sympatry and interbreeding of Herring and Glaucous-winged Gulls in southeastern Alaska. Condor 76:343-344.

Paul, W.A.B. 1959. The birds of Kleena Kleene, Chilcotin district, British Columbia, 1947-1958. Canadian Field-Naturalist 73:83-93.

_____. 1964. Birds of Kleena Kleene, Chilcotin district, British Columbia, 1959-1962. Canadian Field-Naturalist 78:13-16.

Paulson, D.R. 1986. Identification of juvenile tattlers, and a Gray-tailed Tattler record from Washington. Western Birds 17:33-36.

Payne, R.B. 1965. The molt of breeding Cassin Auklets. Condor 67:220-228.

Payne, R.B. and L.L. Master. 1983. Breeding of a mixed pair of white-shielded and red-shielded American Coots in Michigan. Wilson Bulletin 95:467-469.

Payne, R.B. and C.J. Risley. 1976. Systematics and evolutionary relationships among the herons. University of Michigan Museum of Zoology Miscellaneous Publication No. 150, Ann Arbor.

Peakall, D.B. 1965. The status of the Ruff in North America. Wilson Bulletin 77:294-296.

Pearse, T. 1923. Banding Glaucous-winged Gulls with other notes on a colony in southern British Columbia. Canadian Field-Naturalist 37:132-135.

_____. 1926. Notes on the birds seen on a trip off the east coast of Vancouver Island, June 1924. Migrant 3:37-39.

_____. 1931. The Burrowing Owl on Vancouver Island, British Columbia. Murrelet 12:81-82.

_____. 1935. Red Phalaropes on Vancouver Island. Murrelet 16:16-17.

_____. 1936. A record of the Passenger Pigeon in B.C. Auk 53:446-447.

_____. 1946. Nesting of the Western Gull off the coast of Vancouver Island, British Columbia, and possible hybridization with the Glaucous-winged Gull. Murrelet 27:39-40.

_____. 1947. Abnormal plumage of Glaucous-winged Gulls. Murrelet 28:39-40.

_____. 1948. The 1948 spring migration at Comox, B.C. Canadian Field-Naturalist 5:29-32.

_____. 1953. Franklin Gull on the Pacific coast of British Columbia. Condor 54:219.

_____. 1956. Changes in breeding populations of pelagic birds in the Gulf of Georgia, B.C. Murrelet 37:22-23.

_____. 1960. Christmas bird census, 1959-1960 - Comox, British Columbia. Canadian Field-Naturalist 74:44.

_____. 1963. Results from banding Glaucous-winged Gulls in the northern Gulf of Georgia, B.C., from 1922 to 1949. Bird-Banding 34:30-36.

_____. 1968. Birds of the early explorers in the northern Pacific. Published by the author, The Close, Comox, British Columbia. 275 pp.

Pearson, T.G. 1919. Turkey Vulture. Bird-Lore 21:319-322.

Peck, G.K. and R.D. James. 1983. Breeding birds of Ontario - nidiology and distribution - Volume 1: Nonpasserines. Royal Ontario Museum Life Sciences Miscellaneous Publication, Toronto, Ontario. 321 pp.

Pendergast, B.A. 1969. Nutrition of Spruce Grouse of the Swan Hills, Alberta. M.Sc. Thesis, University of Alberta, Edmonton. 73 pp.

Pendergast, B.A. and D.A. Boag. 1971. Maintenance and breeding of Spruce Grouse in captivity. Journal of Wildlife Management 35:177-179.

Penland, S.T. 1976. The natural history and current status of the Caspian Tern (*Hydroprogne caspia*) in Washington state. M.S. Thesis, University of Puget Sound, Tacoma, Washington.

_____. 1981. Natural history of the Caspian Tern in Gray's Harbor, Washington. Murrelet 62:66-72.

Pennant, T. 1785. Arctic Zoology, Volume 2, Class 2, Birds. London, England.

Penner, D.F. 1976. Peace River sites C and E environmental impact studies: wildlife resources. Renewable Resources Consulting Services Report, Edmonton, Alberta. 307 pp.

Peters, F.L. and successors. 1931-1979. Check-list of birds of the world. Volumes 1-10, 12-15. Museum of Comparative Zoology, Cambridge, Massachusetts.

Peters, J.L. 1931. Check-list of birds of the world. Volume 1. Harvard University Press, Cambridge, Massachusetts. 345 pp.

_____. 1934. Check-list of birds of the world. Volume 2. Harvard University Press, Cambridge, Massachusetts. 401 pp.

Peterson, B. and G. Gauthier. 1985. Nest site use by cavity-nesting birds of the Cariboo parkland, British Columbia. Wilson Bulletin 97:319-331.

Peterson, R.T. 1961. Bird's-eye view. Audubon 63:73.

Phillips, A.R. 1975. Semipalmated Sandpiper: identification, migrations, summer, and winter ranges. American Birds 29:799-806.

Phillips, J.C. 1928. Wild birds introduced or transplanted in North America. United States Department Agriculture Bulletin 61, Washington, D.C. 63 pp.

Phillips, J.H. 1963. The pelagic distribution of the Sooty Shearwater, *Procellaria grisea*. Ibis 105:340-353.

Pierce, D.J. and T.R. Simons. 1986. The influence of human disturbance on Tufted Puffin breeding success. Auk 103:214-216.

Pitelka, F.A. 1942. Territoriality and related problems in North American hummingbirds. Condor 44:189-204.

_____. 1950. Geographic variation and the species problem in the genus *Limnodromus*. University of California Publications in Zoology 50:1-108.

Pitman, R.L. and M.R. Graybill. 1985. Horned Puffin sightings in the eastern Pacific. Western Birds 16:99-102.

Pitman, R., M. Newcomer, J. Butler, J. Cotton, and G. Friedrichsen. 1983. A Crested Auklet from Baja California. Western Birds 14:47-48.

Pojar, J. 1980. Threatened forest ecosystems of British Columbia. Pages 28-39 *in* R. Stace-Smith, L. Johns, and P. Joslin (editors). Proceedings of the Symposium on Threatened and Endangered Species and Habitats in British Columbia and the Yukon. British Columbia Ministry of Environment, Victoria.

_____. 1983. Forest ecology. Pages 221-318 *in* S.B. Watts (editor). Forestry Handbook for British Columbia, 4th edition. University of British Columbia Faculty of Forestry, Vancouver.

Pojar, J., K. Klinka, and D.V. Meidinger. 1987. Biogeoclimatic classification in British Columbia. Forestry Ecology and Management 22:119-154.

Poll, D.M., M.M. Porter, G.L. Holroyd, R.M. Wershler, and L.W. Gyug. 1984. Ecological land classification of Kootenay National Park. Volume II. Wildlife resource. Canadian Wildlife Service, Edmonton. 260 pp.

Poole, F. 1966. Birds of the North Pacific. Sea Swallow 18:71-74.

Portenko, L. 1944. New subspecies of birds from Wrangel Island. C.R. (Doklady) Academy of Sciences U.R.S.S. 43:225-228.

Porter, J.M. 1980. The dynamics of seabird multispecies flocks in Barkley Sound, British Columbia. M.Sc. Thesis, University of Manitoba, Winnipeg. 135 pp.

Porter, J.M. and S.G. Sealy. 1981. Dynamics of seabird multispecies feeding flocks: chronology of flocking in Barkley Sound, British Columbia, in 1979. Colonial Waterbirds 4:104-113.

Porter, R.D., M.A. Jenkins, and A.L. Gaski. 1987. Working bibliography of the Peregrine Falcon. National Wildlife Federation Scientific and Technical Series No. 9, Washington, D.C. 185 pp.

Pospahala, R.S., D.R. Anderson, and C.J. Henny. 1974. Population ecology of the Mallard: II. Breeding habitat conditions, size of the breeding populations, and production indices. United States Department of the Interior Fish and Wildlife Service Resource Publication 115, Washington, D.C. 73 pp.

Poston, H.J. 1974. Home range and breeding biology of the Shoveler. Canadian Wildlife Service Report Series No. 25, Ottawa, Ontario. 49 pp.

Potapov, R.L. 1985. Fauna of the USSR: birds. Volume III. Order Galliformes, Family Tetraonidae. Science Institute, Leningrad (In Russian).

Poynter, G.A. 1958. Bird notes. Victoria Naturalist 15:5-6.

_____. 1959. Discovery Island birds. Victoria Naturalist 16:37.

_____. 1960. A report on the birds of the lower Vancouver Island region for the year of 1959. Victoria Natural History Society Mimeo, Victoria. 27 pp. (Bibliography 308).

_____. 1972. British Columbia record of Snowy Plover. Vancouver Natural History Society Discovery 1:69-70.

_____. 1976. Glaucous-winged Gulls - unusual nesting sites. Vancouver Natural History Society Discovery 5:8-10.

Pratt, H.D. 1976. Field identification of White-faced and Glossy ibises. Birding 8:1-5.

Preble, E.A. 1922. Roderick Ross Macfarlane, 1833-1920. Auk 37:203-210.

Preece, W.H.A. 1925a. An Ivory Gull, *Pagophila alba* Gunn., observed at Victoria. British Columbia. Canadian Field-Naturalist 39:172-173.

_____. 1925b. January bird notes from Mount Tolmie, Victoria, British Columbia. Canadian Field-Naturalist 39:175-176.

Prose, B.L. 1985. Habitat suitability index models: Belted Kingfisher. United States Department of the Interior Fish and Wildlife Service Biological Report 82(10.87), Washington, D.C. 22 pp.

Pullianen, E. and K. Loisa. 1977. Breeding biology and food of the Great Gray Owl, *Strix nebulosa*, in northeastern Finnish Forest Lapland. Aquilo Serie. Zoologica 17:23-33.

Purdy, M.A. 1985. Parental behaviour and role differentiation in the Black Oystercatcher *Haematopus bachmani*. M.Sc. Thesis, University of Victoria, Victoria, British Columbia. 239 pp.

Purdy, R.M. 1978. The effect of radiant energy on the energy and activity budgets of the Rufous Hummingbird (*Selasphorus rufus*). B.Sc. Thesis, University of British Columbia, Vancouver. 104 pp.

Pyle, R. and J. Sarles. 1958. Glaucous-winged Gull banding sponsored by Pacific International Chapter, summer, 1958. News from the Bird-Banders 33:36-37.

Quinlan, S.E. 1979. Breeding biology of storm-petrels at Wooded Islands, Alaska. M.Sc. Thesis. University of Alaska, Fairbanks. 206 pp.

Racey, K. 1921. Notes on the Northwest coast Heron in Stanley Park, Vancouver, B.C. Canadian Field-Naturalist 35:118-119.

_____. 1926. Notes on the birds observed in the Alta Lake region, British Columbia. Auk 43:319-325.

_____. 1933. White Pelican (*Pelecanus erythrorhynchos*) in British Columbia. Auk 50:205.

_____. 1944. Extension of range of the Northern Spotted Owl (*Strix occidentalis caurina*). Canadian Field-Naturalist 58:104.

_____. 1945. Bird nesting notes from western British Columbia. Murrelet 26:38,46.

_____. 1946. Nesting of the Black Oystercatcher in B.C. Victoria Naturalist 2:138.

_____. 1947. Pallas' Murre in British Columbia. Canadian Field-Naturalist 61:116.

_____. 1948. Birds of the Alta Lake region, British Columbia. Auk 63:383-401.

_____. 1950. The Steller Eider in British Columbia. Canadian Field-Naturalist 64:51.

Rand, A.L. 1944. Birds of the Alaska Highway in British Columbia. Canadian Field-Naturalist 58:111-125.

Ransom, W.H. 1938. Yellow Rail (*Coturnicops noveboracensis*) recorded in the State of Washington. Murrelet 19:16.

Ratti, J.T. 1979. Reproductive separation and isolating mechanisms between sympatric dark- and light-phase Western Grebes. Auk 96:573-586.

_____. 1981. Identification and distribution of Clark's Grebe. Western Birds. 12:41-46.

Ratti, J.T. and D.E. Timm. 1979. Migratory behavior of Vancouver Canada geese: recovery rate bias. Pages 208 to 212 *in* R.L. Jarvis and J.C. Bartonek (editors). Management and Biology of Pacific Flyway Geese. A symposium sponsored by the Northwest Section, The Wildlife Society, 16 February 1979, Portland, Oregon. Oregon State University Book Stores, Inc., Corvallis.

Rawls, C.K. 1949. An investigation of the life history of the White-winged Scoter (*Melanitta fusca deglandi*). M.Sc. Thesis, University of Minnesota, Rochester. 128 pp.

Redfield, J.A. 1973. Variations in weight of Blue Grouse (*Dendragapus obscurus*). Condor 75:312-321.

Redmond, R.L. 1986. Egg size and laying date of Long-billed Curlews *Numenius americanus*: implications for female reproductive tactics. Oikos 46:330-338.

Redmond, R.L. and D.A. Jenni. 1982. Natal philopatry and breeding area fidelity of Long-billed Curlews (*Numenius americanus*): patterns and evolutionary consequences. Behavioural Ecology and Sociobiology 10:277-279.

_____. and _____. 1986. Population ecology of the Long-billed Curlew (*Numenius americanus*) in western Idaho. Auk 103:755-767.

Reese, J.G. 1975. Productivity and management of feral Mute Swans in Chesapeake Bay. Journal of Wildlife Management 39:280-286.

Reid, T.C. 1975. Liard River Hotsprings Park - natural history observations (autumn, 1974 and winter, spring, summer - 1975). British Columbia Parks Branch Unpublished Report, Victoria. 117 pp. (Bibliography 3893).

Reimchen, T.E. and S. Douglas. 1980. Observations of loons (*Gavia immer* and *G. stellata*) at a bog lake on the Queen Charlotte Islands. Canadian Field-Naturalist 94:398-404.

_____. and _____. 1984. Feeding schedule and daily food consumption in Red-throated Loons (*Gavia stellata*) over the prefledging period. Auk 101:593-599.

_____. and _____. 1985. Differential contribution of the sexes of prefledged young in Red-throated Loons. Auk 102:198-201.

Remsen, J.V. and L.C. Binford. 1975. Status of the Yellow-billed Loon (*Gavia adamsii*) in the western United States and Mexico. Western Birds 6:7-20.

Reynolds, R.T. 1983. Management of western coniferous forest habitat for nesting accipiter hawks. United States Department of Agriculture, Forest Service, General Technical Report RM-102, Fort Collins, Colorado. 7 pp.

Reynolds, R.T. and B.D. Linkhart. 1987a. Fidelity to territory and mate in Flammulated Owls. Pages 234-238 *in* R.W. Nero, R.J. Clark, R.J. Knapton, and R.H. Hamre (editors). Biology and Conservation of Northern Forest Owls: Symposium Proceedings. 1987 Feb. 3-7; Winnipeg, Manitoba. United States Department of Agriculture Forest Service General Technical Report RM-142, Fort Collins, Colorado.

_____. and _____. 1987b. The nesting biology of Flammulated Owls in Colorado. Pages 239-248 *in* R.W. Nero, R.J. Clark, R.J. Knapton, and R.H. Hamre (editors). Biology and Conservation of Northern Forest Owls: Symposium Proceedings. 1987 Feb. 3-7; Winnipeg, Manitoba. United States Department of Agriculture Forest Service General Technical Report RM-142, Fort Collins, Colorado.

Reynolds, R.T. and H.M. Wight. 1978. Distribution, density, and productivity of accipiter hawks breeding in Oregon. Wilson Bulletin 90:182-196.

Rhoads, S.N. 1891. The wild pigeon (*Ectopistes migratorius*) on the Pacific Coast. Auk 8:310-312.

_____. 1893a. The birds observed in British Columbia and Washington during spring and summer, 1892. Proceedings of the Academy of Natural Sciences of Philadelphia 45:21-65.

_____. 1893b. Notes on certain Washington and British Columbia birds. Auk 10:16-24.

Rice, D.W. 1959. Birds and aircraft on Midway Island - 1957-58 investigations. United States Department of the Interior, Fish and Wildlife Service Special Scientific Report - Wildlife No. 44, Washington, D.C. 49 pp.

Rice, D.W. and K.W. Kenyon. 1962. Breeding distribution, history, and populations of north Pacific albatrosses. Auk 79:365-386.

Richardson, F. 1961. Breeding biology of the Rhinoceros Auklet on Protection Islands, Washington. Condor 63:456-473.

_____. 1970. A North American record of the Bristle-thighed Curlew outside Alaska. Auk 87:815.

_____. 1971. Birds of Grant Bay and Browning Inlet, northwest Vancouver Island, British Columiba: a years phenology. Murrelet 52:29-40.

Richdale, L.E. 1963. Biology of the Sooty Shearwater, *Puffinus griseus*. Proceedings of the Zoological Society of London 141:1-117.

Ricker, W.E. 1937. Christmas bird census, 1936. Vedder Crossing, British Columbia, December 28, 1936. Canadian Field-Naturalist 51:27.

Rieck, C.A. 1962. A Common Egret in western Washington. Murrelet 43:52.

Riley, J.H. 1912. Birds collected or observed on the expedition of the Alpine Club of Canada to Jasper Park, Yellowhead Pass and Mount Robson region. Canadian Alpine Journal 1912:47-75.

Riske, M. 1976. Environmental and human impacts of grebes breeding in central Alberta. Ph.D. Thesis, University of Calgary, Calgary, Alberta.

Ritcey, R.W. 1953. Winter wildlife report - Wells Gray Park, 1952-1953. British Columbia Forest Service, Unpublished Report, Victoria. 56 pp. (Bibliography 3919).

_____. 1956. Report on Tweedsmuir reconnaisance - summer 1956. British Columbia Forest Service, Parks and Recreation Division Unpublished Report, Victoria. 55 pp. (Bibliography 3920).

_____. 1985. Progress Report - Thompson owls. British Columbia Wildlife Branch Unpublished Report, Kamloops. 6 pp.

Ritcey, R.W. and N.A.M. Verbeek. 1961. An annotated list of birds, Bowron Lake Park, 1961. British Columbia Provincial Park Unpublished Report, Victoria. 12 pp. (Bibliography 920).

Ritter, L.V. 1983. Growth, development, and behavior of nestling Turkey Vultures in central California. Pages 287-303 *in* S.R. Wilbur and J.A. Jackson (editors). Vulture biology and management. University of California Press, Berkeley.

Robbins, C.S. 1974. A history of North American hawkwatching. Pages 29-40 *in* Proceedings of the 1974 North American Hawk Migration Conference. Syracuse, New York, 18-21 April. 165 pp.

Roberson, D. 1980. Rare birds of the west coast of North America. Woodcock Publications, Pacific Grove, California. 496 pp.

Roberts, A. 1973. Birds of the Cariboo. Williams Lake Field Naturalists Club, Williams Lake. 11 pp. (Bibliography 1108).

Roberts, H.A. 1963. Aspects of the life history and food habits of Rock and Willow ptarmigan. M.Sc. Thesis, University of Alaska, Fairbanks. 108 pp.

Robertson, I. 1971. The influence of brood-size on reproductive success in two species of cormorant, *Phalacrocorax auritus* and *P. pelagicus*, and its relation to the problem of clutch-size. M.Sc. Thesis, University of British Columbia, Vancouver. 47 pp.

_____. 1974. An inventory of seabirds occurring along the west coast of Canada. Part II: the shoreline and inlet zone. Canadian Wildlife Service Unpublished Report, Delta, British Columbia. 64 pp. (Bibliography 3935).

_____. 1974a. The food of nesting Double-crested and Pelagic cormorants at Mandarte Island, British Columbia, with notes on feeding ecology. Condor 76:346-348.

Robinson, W.F. 1974. The greater Sandhill Cranes of the Pitt Polder. Issued by the author, Pitt Meadows, British Columbia. 24 pp. (Bibliography 1238)

Rodway, M.S. 1988. British Columbia Seabird Colony Inventory: Report No. 3-Census of Glaucous-winged Gulls, Pelagic Cormorants, Black Oystercatchers, and Pigeon Guillemots in the Queen Charlotte Islands, 1986. Canadian Wildlife Service Technical Report Series No. 43, Delta, British Columbia. 95 pp.

_____. 1989a. Distribution and abundance of waterbirds in Barkley Sound and the Long Beach/Tofino/Grice Bay area in spring 1989 following the Nestucca oil spill. Canadian Wildlife Service Technical Report Series No. 76, Delta, British Columbia.

_____. 1990. Status report on the Marbled Murrelet (*Brachyramphus marmoratus*) in Canada - 1990. Committee on the Status of Endangered Wildlife in Canada Report, Canadian Nature Federation, Ottawa, Ontario. 58 pp.

_____. In press. Status and conservation of breeding seabirds in British Columbia. Submitted to J.P. Croxall (editor). Status and conservation of the world's seabirds. International Council for Bird Preservation, Cambridge, England.

Rodway, M.S. and R.W. Campbell. 1977. Natural history theme study of marine bird and mammal habitats in the Gulf Islands, British Columbia. Parks Canada Unpublished Report, Ottawa, Ontario. 107 pp. (Bibliography 1900).

Rodway, M.S., N. Hillis, and L. Langley. 1983. Nesting population of Ancient Murrelets on Langara Island, British Columbia. Canadian Wildlfie Service Seabird Colony Report No. 1, Delta, British Columbia. 47 pp.

Rodway, M.S., M.J.F. Lemon, and G.W. Kaiser. 1988. British Columbia colony inventory: Report No. 1 - east coast Moresby Island. Canadian Wildlife Service, Technical Report Series No. 50 Delta, British Columbia. 276 pp.

_____, _____, and_____. 1989. British Columbia Seabirds Colony Inventory: Report No. 2 west coast Moresby Island. Canadian Wildlife Service Technical Report Series No. 65, Delta, British Columbia.

Rodway, M.S., R.W. Campbell, and M.J.F. Lemon. (In prep.) Breeding, seabirds of British Columbia: history, populations, and international significance. Environment Canada, Canadian Wildlife Service.

Rodway, M.S., M.J.F. Lemon, J.-P. Savard, and R. McKelvey. (In Press). Nestucca oil spill: Impact assessment on avian populations and habitat. Canadian Wildlife Service Technical Report No. 68, Delta, British Columbia. 48 pp.

Rogers, J.P. 1962. The ecological effects of drought on reproduction of the Lesser Scaup, *Aythya affinis* (Eyton). Ph.D. Thesis, University of Missouri, Columbia. 99 pp.

Rogers, T.H. 1963a. Fall migration - northern Rocky Mountain-Intermountain region. Audubon Field Notes 17:51-53.

_____. 1963b. The nesting season - northern Rocky Mountain-Intermountain region. Audubon Field Notes 17:472-474.

_____. 1964a. The fall migration - northern Rocky Mountain-Intermountain region. Audubon Field Notes 18:57-60.

_____. 1966a. The fall migration - northern Rocky Mountain-Intermountain region. Audubon Field Notes 20:72-76.

_____. 1966b. The winter season - northern Rocky Mountain-Intermountain region. Audubon Field Notes 20:442-445.

_____. 1968a. The spring migration - northern Rocky Mountain-Intermountain region. Audubon Field Notes 22:557-560.

_____. 1968b. The nesting season - northern Rocky Mountain-Intermountain region. Audubon Field Notes 22:628-632.

_____. 1969. The winter season - northern Rocky Mountain-Intermountain region. Audubon Field Notes 23:498-503.

_____. 1970a. The fall migration - northern Rocky Mountain-Intermountain region. Audubon Field Notes 24:70-74.

_____. 1970b. The winter season - northern Rocky Mountain-Intermountain region. Audubon Field Notes 24:521-524.

_____. 1970c. The spring migration - northern Rocky Mountain-Intermountain region. Audubon Field Notes 24:625-628.

_____. 1970d. The nesting season - northern Rocky Mountain-Intermountain region. Audubon Field Notes 24:699-702.

_____. 1971a. The fall migration - northern Rocky Mountain-Intermountain region. American Birds 25:80-84.

_____. 1971b. The winter season - northern Rocky Mountain-Intermountain region. American Birds 25:603-606.

_____. 1972. The fall migration - northern Rocky Mountain-Intermountain region. American Birds 26:88-92.

_____. 1973a. The fall migration - northern Rocky Mountain-Intermountain region. American Birds 27:85-91.

_____. 1973b. The winter season - northern Rocky Mountain-Intermountain region. American Birds 27:639-643.

_____. 1973c. The spring migration - northern Rocky Mountain-Intermountain region. American Birds 27:796-799.

_____. 1974a. The fall migration - northern Rocky Mountain-Intermountain region. American Birds 28:78-83.

_____. 1974b. The winter season - northern Rocky Mountain-Intermountain region. American Birds 28:665-668.

_____. 1974c. The spring migration - northern Rocky Mountain-Intermountain region. American Birds 28:828-832.

_____. 1981. The autumn migration - northern Rocky Mountain-Intermountain region. American Birds 35:205-208.

_____. 1983a. The autumn migration - northern Rocky Mountain-Intermountain region. American Birds 37:202-204.

_____. 1983b. The winter season - northern Rocky Mountain-Intermountain region. American Birds 37:320-322.

_____. 1983c. The spring season - northern Rocky Mountain-Intermountain region. American Birds 37:892-894.

_____. 1983d. The nesting season - northern Rocky Mountain-Intermountain region. American Birds 37:1007-1009.

_____. 1984a. The autumn migration - northern Rocky Mountain-Intermountain region. American Birds 38:224-227.

_____. 1984b. The winter season - northern Rocky Mountain-Intermountain region. American Birds 38:337-340.

_____. 1984c. The spring migration - northern Rocky Mountain-Intermountain region. American Birds 38:936-939.

_____. 1984d. The nesting season - northern Rocky Mountain-Intermountain region. American Birds 38:1041-1044.

_____. 1985a. The autumn migration - northern Rocky Mountain-Intermountain region. American Birds 39:78-81.

_____. 1985b. The winter season - northern Rocky Mountain-Intermountain region. American Birds 39:189-191.

_____. 1985c. The spring season - northern Rocky Mountain-Intermountain region. American Birds 39:327-329.

_____. 1985d. The nesting season - northern Rocky Mountain-Intermountain region. American Birds 39:938-941.

_____. 1986a. The autumn migration - northern Rocky Mountain-Intermountain region. American Birds 40:142-145.

_____. 1986b. The winter season - northern Rocky Mountain-Intermountain region. American Birds 40:304-306.

_____. 1986c. The spring migration - northern Rocky Mountain-Intermountain region. American Birds 40:498-502.

_____. 1986d. The nesting season - northern Rocky Mountain-Intermountain region. American Birds 40:1229-1232.

_____. 1987. The autumn migration - northern Rocky Mountain-Intermountain region. American Birds 41:118-121.

Rohwer, S., D.F. Martin and G.G. Benson. 1979. Breeding of the Black-necked Stilt in Washington. Murrelet 60:67-61.

Rowan, W. 1925. On the wintering of *Perdix perdix* in Alberta, 1924-25. Canadian Field-Naturalist 39:114-115.

_____. 1927. Details of the release of the Hungarian Partridge (*Perdix perdix*) in central Alberta. Canadian Field-Naturalist 41:98-101.

_____. 1938. The Hungarian Partridge on the Canadian prairie. Outdoor America 3:6-7.

Rowe, J.S. 1984. Understanding forest landscapes: what you conceive is what you get. Leslie L. Schaffer Lectureship in Forest Science, University of British Columbia, Vancouver. 13 pp.

Runyan, B. 1971. Bowron Lake Park natural history report, 1971. British Columbia Parks Branch Unpublished Report, Victoria. 51 pp. (Bibliography 4043).

Runyan, C.S. 1978. Pitt wildlife management area wildlife inventory report. British Columbia Fish and Wildlife Branch Unpublished Report, Vancouver. 102 pp. (Bibliography 1192).

_____. 1987. Location and density of nests of the Red-tailed Hawk, *Buteo jamaicensis*, in Richmond, British Columbia. Canadian Field-Naturalist 101:415-418.

Ryder, G.R. 1972. Pelican park - naturalist report for 1971. British Columbia Parks Branch Unpublished Report, Victoria. 91 pp. (Bibliography 1295).

_____. 1973. Report on White Pelican Provincial Park, 1973. British Columbia Parks Branch Unpublished Report, Victoria. 122 pp. (Bibliography 1134).

_____. 1986. Rare sighting of Barred Owl recorded at park. Langley Advance, 19 July :20.

Rydzewski, W. 1956. The nomadic movements and migrations of the European Common Heron (*Ardea cinerea*). Ardea 44:71-253.

Rye, D. 1952. Factors affecting orchard pheasant populations in the Okanagan valley of British Columbia, with special reference to orchard insecticides. M.A. Thesis, University of British Columbia, Vancouver. 67 pp.

Salomonsen, F. 1950. The birds of Greenland. Parts 1-3. Ejnar Munksgaard, Copenhagen. 607 pp.

Salt, W.R. and J.R. Salt. 1976. The birds of Alberta. Hurtig Publishers, Edmonton, Alberta. 498 pp.

Salt, W.R. and A.L. Wilk. 1966. The birds of Alberta (Second Edition). Queen's Printer, Edmonton. 511 pp.

Salvin, O. 1883. A list of birds collected by Captain A.H. Markham on the west coast of America. Pages 419-432 *in* Proceedings of the Zoological Society of London.

Salwasser, H. 1987. Spotted Owls: turning a battleground into a blueprint. Ecology 68:776-779.

Sandilands, A.P. and C.A. Campbell. 1987. Status report on the Least Bittern *Ixobrychus exilis* in Canada. Committee on the Status of Endangered Wildlife in Canada Report, c/o Canadian Nature Federation, Toronto, Ontario. 29 pp.

Sanford, F.J. 1974. Gulls nesting on Water Street - 1972-73. Vancouver Natural History Society Discovery 2:119-120.

Sanger, G.A. 1964. A possible sight record of a Short-tailed Albatross. Murrelet 45:47.

_____. 1970. The seasonal distribution of some seabirds off Washington and Oregon, with notes on their ecology and behavior. Condor 72:339-357.

_____. 1972a. The recent pelagic status of the Short-tailed Albatross (*Diomedea albatrus*). Biological Conservation 4:189-193.

_____. 1972b. Checklist of bird observations from the Eastern North Pacific Ocean. Murrelet 53:16-21.

_____. 1973a. Pelagic records of Glaucous-winged and Herring gulls in the north Pacific Ocean. Auk 90:384-393.

_____. 1973b. New northern record for Xantus' Murrelet. Condor 75:253.

_____. 1974a. Pelagic studies of seabirds in the central and eastern North Pacific Ocean: III Black-footed Albatross (*Diomedea nigripes*). Smithsonian Contributions to Zoology 158:96-128.

_____. 1974b. Pelagic studies of seabirds in the central and eastern North Pacific Ocean: IV Laysan Albatross (*Diomedea immutabilis*). Smithsonian Contributions to Zoology 158:129-153.

Sarles, J. and R. Sarles. 1983. Golden Eagle on the 1955 Vancouver Christmas bird count. Vancouver Natural History Society Discovery 11(4):D.

Saunders, W.E. 1902. Canadian hummingbirds. Ottawa Naturalist 16:97-103.

Sauppe, B. 1980. Hawk migration observed from Cypress Provincial Park: fall 1979. Vancouver Natural History Society Discovery 8:75.

Sauppe, B., B.A. Macdonald, and D.M. Mark. 1978. First Canadian and third North American record of the Spoon-billed Sandpiper (*Eurynorhynchos pygmeus*). American Birds 32:1062-1064.

Savard, J.-P.L. 1978. Aerial surveys in Dixon Entrance, Hecate Strait and Chatham Sound (February 13, 15 and 16, 1978). Canadian Wildlife Service Unpublished Report, Delta, British Columbia. 27 pp. (Bibliography 4078).

_____. 1979. Marine birds of Dixon Entrance, Hecate Strait and Chatham Sound during fall 1977 and winter 1978 (number, species composition and distribution). Canadian Wildlife Service Technical Report, Delta, British Columbia. 106 pp.

_____. 1981. Molting ducks in the coastal waters of British Columbia - a progress report. Canadian Wildlife Service Unpublished Report, Delta, British Columbia. 21 pp. (Bibliography 4085).

_____. 1982. Intra- and inter-specific competition between Barrow's Goldeneye (*Bucephala islandica*) and Bufflehead (*Bucephala albeola*). Canadian Journal of Zoology 60:3439-3446.

_____. 1984. Territorial behaviour of Common Goldeneye, Barrow's Goldeneye and Bufflehead in areas of sympatry. Ornis Scandinavica 15:211-216.

_____. 1985a. Evidence of long-term pair bonds *in* Barrow's Goldeneye (*Bucephala islandica*). Auk 102:389-391.

_____. 1985b. Conservation of Barrow's Goldeneye (*Bucephala islandica*) - use of nest boxes. Pages 45-51 *in* B. Shautz and H. Shautz (editors). Proceedings of the eighth annual North American Bluebird Society Conference, Calgary, Alberta.

_____. 1986. Territorial behavior, nesting success, and brood survival in Barrow's Goldeneye and its congeners. Ph.D. Thesis, University of British Columbia, Vancouver. 219 pp.

_____. 1987. A summary of current knowledge on the distribution and abundance of moulting seaducks in the coastal waters of British Columbia. Canadian Wildlife Service Technial Report Series No. 45, Delta, British Columbia. 81 pp.

_____. 1987a. Status report on Barrow's Goldeneye. Canadian Wildlife Service Technical Report Series No. 23, Delta, British Columbia. 57 pp.

_____. In press. Causes and functions of brood amalgamation in Barrow's Goldeneye and Bufflehead. Canadian Journal of Zoology.

Savard, J.-P.L. and G.W. Kaiser. 1982. Reconnaissance of marine birds on the northwest coast of British Columbia during March and May. Canadian Wildlife Service Unpublished Report, Delta, British Columbia. 37 pp. (Bibliography 4087).

Savile, D.B.O. 1972. Evidence of tree nesting by the Marbled Murrelet in the Queen Charlotte Islands. Canadian Field-Naturalist 86:389-390.

Schaffner, F.C. 1986. Trends in Elegant Tern and northern anchovy populations in California. Condor 88:347-354.

Schlatter, R.P. 1984. The status and conservation of seabirds in Chile. Pages 261-269 *in* Croxall, J.P., P.G.H. Evans, and R.W. Schreiber (editors). The status and conservation of the world's seabirds. International Council for Bird Preservation Technical Publications No. 2, Cambridge, England.

Schmidt, V. 1964. Late nesting of a Gray Partridge. Blue Jay 22:149.

Schmutz, J.K. 1977. Relationships between three species of the genus *Buteo* (Aves) coexisting in the prairie-parkland ecotone of southeastern Alberta. M.S. Thesis, University of Alberta, Calgary. 126 pp.

Schnider, B., D. Beacham, and T. Stevens. 1971. Shuswap Lake nature house annual report (1971). British Columbia Parks Branch Unpublished Report, Victoria. 15 pp. (Bibliography 4089).

Schorger, A.W. 1955. The Passenger Pigeon, its natural history, and extinction. University of Wisconsin Press, Madison. 424 pp.

Schouten, M. 1979. The seventy-ninth Audubon Christmas Bird count - White Rock, B.C. American Birds 33:381.

Schreiber, R.W. and R.L. DeLong. 1969. Brown Pelican status in California. Audubon Field Notes 23:57-59.

Schreiber, R.W. and R.W. Risebrough. 1972. Studies of the Brown Pelican. I. Status of Brown Pelican populations in the United States. Wilson Bulletin 84:119-135.

Schultz, Z.M. 1958. The spring migration - northern Pacific coast region. Audubon Field Notes 12:377-379.

_____. 1970. The occurrence of the Yellow-billed Loon in Washington. Murrelet 51:23.

Scott, D.M., C.D. Ankney, and C.H. Jarosch. 1976. Sapsucker hybridization in British Columbia: changes in 25 years. Condor 78:253-257.

Scott, G. 1973. Avifauna of the Vermillion Pass burn. B.Sc. Thesis, University of Calgary, Alberta. 60 pp. (Bibliography 1155).

Scott, G.A. 1963. First nesting of the Little Gull (*Larus minutus*) in Ontario and the New World. Auk 80:548-549.

Scott, J.M. 1971. Interbreeding of the Glaucous-winged Gull and Western Gull in the Pacific Northwest. California Birds 2:129-133.

Scott, J.M., J. Butler, W.G. Pearcy, and G.A. Bertrand. 1971. Occurrence of the Xantus' Murrelet off the Oregon coast. Condor 73:254.

Scott, J.M., W. Hoffman, and C.F. Zeillemaker. 1974. Range expansion and activity patterns in Rhinoceros Auklets. Western Birds 5:13-20.

Scudder, G.G.E. 1980. The Osoyoos-arid biotic area. Pages 49-55 *in* R. Stace-Smith, L. Johns, and P. Joslin (editors). Proceedings of the Symposium on Threatened and Endangered Species and Habitats in British Columbia and the Yukon. British Columbia Ministry of Environment, Victoria.

Sealy, S.G. 1967. Notes on the breeding biology of the Marsh Hawk in Alberta and Saskatchewan. Blue Jay 25:63-69.

_____. 1972. Adaptive differences in breeding biology in the marine bird family Alcidae. Ph.D. Thesis, University of Michigan, Ann Arbor. 283 pp.

_____. 1973a. Interspecific feeding assemblages of marine birds off British Columbia. Auk 90:796-802.

_____. 1973b. Breeding biology of the Horned Puffin on St. Lawrence Island, Bering Sea, with zoo-geographical notes on the North Pacific puffins. Pacific Science 27:99-119.

_____. 1974. Breeding phenology and clutch size in the Marbled Murrelet. Auk 91:10-23.

_____. 1975a. Egg size in murrelets. Condor 77:500-501.

_____. 1975b. Aspects of the breeding biology of the Marbled Murrelet in British Columbia. Bird-Banding 46:141-154.

_____. 1975c. Feeding ecology of the Ancient and Marbled murrelets near Langara Island, British Columbia. Canadian Journal of Zoology 53:418-433.

_____. 1976. Biology of nesting Ancient Murrelets. Condor 78:294-306.

_____. 1984. Interruptions extend incubation by Ancient Murrelets, Crested Auklets, and Least Auklets. Murrelet 65:53-56.

Sealy, S.G. and R.W. Campbell. 1979. Post-hatching movements of young Ancient Murrelets. Western Birds 10:25-30.

Sealy, S.G. and H.R. Carter. 1984. At-sea distribution and nesting habitat of the Marbled Murrelet in British Columbia: problems in the conservation of a solitarily nesting seabird. Pages 737-756 in J.P. Croxall, P.G.H. Evans, and R.W. Schreiber (editors). Status and conservation of the world's seabirds. International Council for Bird Preservation Technical Publication No. 2. Cambridge, England.

Sealy, S.G. and N. Gessler. 1988. A specimen of the Long-eared Owl from the Queen Charlotte Islands. Murrelet 69:27-28.

Sealy, S.G. and R.W. Nelson. 1973. The occurrences and status of Horned Puffin in British Columbia. Syesis 6:51-55.

Sealy, S.G., H.R. Carter, and D. Allison. 1982. Occurrences of the Asiatic Marbled Murrelet [*Brachyramphus marmoratus perdix* (Pallas)] in North America. Auk 99: 778-781.

Seel, K.E. 1965. The birds of Kootenay National Park (First Report 1965) - field studies. Parks Canada Unpublished Report, Radium Hot Springs, British Columbia. 41 pp. (Bibliography 4123).

Senner, S.E. and E.F. Martinez. 1982. A review of Western Sandpiper migration in interior North America. Southwest Naturalist 27:149-159.

Senner, S.E., G.C. West, and D.W. Norton. 1981. The spring migration of Western Sandpipers and Dunlins in southcentral Alaska: numbers, timing, and sex ratio. Journal of Field Ornithology 52:271-284.

Serventy, D.L. 1957. The banding programme on *Puffinus tenuirostris* (Temminck): I. First Report. Commonwealth Scientific and Industrial Research Organization Wildlife Research 2:51-59.

_____. 1961. The banding programme on *Puffinus tenuirostris* (Temminck). I. Second Report. Commonwealth Scientific and Industrial Research Organization Wildlife Research 6:42-55.

_____. 1967. Aspects of the population ecology of the Short-tailed Shearwater *Puffinus tenuirostris*. Proceedings of the 14th International Ornithological Congress: 165-190.

Serventy, D.L., V. Serventy, and J. Warham. 1971. The handbook of Australian sea-birds. A.H. & A.W. Reed, Sydney, Australia. 254 pp.

Servheen, C.W. and W. English. 1979. Movements of rehabilitated Bald Eagles and proposed seasonal movement patterns of Bald Eagles in the Pacific Northwest. Raptor Research 13:79-88.

Shepard, M.G. 1974. British Columbia birds - winter season, 1973-1974. Vancouver Natural History Society Discovery 3:4-11.

_____. 1975a. British Columbia birds - spring and summer, 1974. Vancouver Natural History Society Discovery 3:32-38.

_____. 1975b. British Columbia birds - spring 1975. Vancouver Natural History Society Discovery 4:41-44.

_____. 1975c. British Columbia birds - July to September, 1975. Vancouver Natural History Society Discovery 4:67-69.

_____. 1975d. British Columbia birds - October to December, 1975. Vancouver Natural History Society Discovery 5:10-13.

_____. 1976a. Notes on the Laysan Albatross, New Zealand Shearwater, and Skua in the north Pacific Ocean. Murrelet 57:48-49.

_____. 1976b. British Columbia birds - October to December, 1975. Vancouver Natural History Society Discovery 5:10-13.

_____. 1976c. British Columbia birds - April to June, 1976. Vancouver Natural History Society Discovery 5:48-50.

_____. 1977a. British Columbia birds - July to September, 1976. Vancouver Natural History Society Discovery 5:65-67.

_____. 1977b. British Columbia birds - October to December, 1976. Vancouver Natural History Society Discovery 6:18-20.

_____. 1978. Pelagic birding trips - fall 1977. Vancouver Natural History Society Discovery 6:90-91.

Shepard, T. 1977. Naturalist's summer report, Lakelse Lake Park. British Columbia Parks Branch Unpublished Report, Victoria. 29 pp. (Bibliography 4144).

Sherman, A. 1910. At the sign of the Northern Flicker. Wilson Bulletin 22:135-171.

Sherman, A.R. 1911. Nest life of the Screech Owl. Auk 28:155-168.

_____. 1913. Nest life of the Sparrow Hawk. Auk 30:406-418.

Short, L.L. 1969. Taxonomic aspects of avian hybridization. Auk 86:84-105.

Shuntov, V.P. 1964. Transequatorial migrations of the Short-tailed Shearwater *Puffinus tenuirostris* (Temminck). Zoologichesky Zhurnal 43:36-48.

_____. 1974. Sea birds and the biological structure of the oceans. Translated from Russian by I. Allardt for United States Department of the Interior, Bureau of Sports Fisheries and Wildlife, Washington, D.C. 565 pp.

_____. 1986. Seabirds in the Sea of Okohotrk. In N.M. Litvinenko (editor), Seabirds of the Far East: Collection of scientific papers. USSR Academy of Sciences, Vladivostok (Translation for Environment Canada, Ottawa).

Siddle, C. 1981. Potential effects of the activities of the Scurry-Rainbow oil company on the avifauna of the south end of Charlie Lake. British Columbia Fish and Wildlife Branch Unpublished Report, Fort St. John. 12 pp. (Bibliography 4158).

_____. 1982. The status of birds in the Peace River area of British Columbia. British Columbia Provincial Museum Unpublished Report, Victoria. 319pp. (Bibliography 4159).

_____. 1984. Raptor mortality on northeastern British Columbia trapline. Blue Jay 42:184.

_____. 1986. The phenology of the Hudsonian Godwit in northeastern British Columbia, British Columbia Provincial Museum Unpublished Report, Victoria. 6 pp.

Siemens, A.H. 1968. The process of settlement in the lower Fraser valley - in its provincial context. Pages 27-50 in A.H.Siemens (editor). Lower Fraser valley: evolution of a cultural landscape. B.C. Geographical Series No.9, Tantalus Research Limited, Vancouver.

Silovsky, G.D. 1969. Distribution and mortality of Pacific coast Band-tailed Pigeons. M.S. Thesis, Oregon State University, Corvallis. 70 pp.

Simberloff, D. 1987. The Spotted Owl fracas: mixing academic, applied, and political ecology. Ecology 68:766-772.

Simons, T.R. 1979. Behavior and attendance patterns of the Fork-tailed Storm-Petrel. M.Sc. Thesis, University of Washington, Seattle. 35 pp.

_____. 1980. Discovery of a ground-nesting Marbled Murrelet. Condor 82:1-9.

_____. 1981. Behavior and attendance patterns of the Fork-tailed Storm-Petrel. Auk 98:145-158.

Simpson, G.B. 1925. Christmas bird censuses, 1924 - Lake Cowichan, V.I., British Columbia. Canadian Field-Naturalist 39:21.

_____. 1926. Christmas bird census from Lake Cowichan, B.C. Canadian Field-Naturalist 40:10.

_____. 1927. Christmas bird census at Lake Cowichan, B.C. Canadian Field-Naturalist 41:10.

Sirk, G. 1968. Summer and fall visitants to Vancouver. Vancouver Natural History Society News 137:6-7.

_____. 1972. Summer report for Monck Park, 1972. British Columbia Parks Branch Unpublished Report, Victoria. 11 pp. (Bibliography 4166).

Sirk, G. and L. Sirk. 1971. Mitlenatch Island Nature Park - annual report, 1971. British Columbia Parks Branch Unpublished Report, Victoria. 12 pp. (Bibliography 4168).

Sirk, G.P., R.J. Cannings, and M.G. Shepard. 1973. Shuswap Lake Park annual report, - 1973. British Columbia Parks Branch Unpublished Report, Victoria. 66 pp. (Bibliography 4169).

Skeel, M.A. 1983. Nesting success, density, philopatry, and nest site selection of the Whimbrel (*Numenius phaeopus*) in different habitats. Canadian Journal of Zoology 61:218-255.

Sladen, W.J.L. 1966. Additions to the avifauna of the Pribilof Islands, Alaska, including five species new to North America. Auk 83:130-135.

_____. 1973. A continental study of Whistling Swans using neck collars. Wildfowl 24:8-14.

Sladen, W.J. and A.A. Kistchinski. 1977. Some results from circumpolar marking programs on northern swans and snow geese. XIII International Congress of Game Biologists, Atlanta, Georgia. 631 pp.

Sloan, N.G. 1982. Status of breeding colonies of White Pelicans in the United States through 1979. American Birds 36:250-254.

Smith, C.C. 1963. First breeding record of the Spotted Owl in British Columbia. Condor 65:440.

Smith, D.A. 1970. Observations on nesting Hawk Owls at Mer Bleu, near Ottawa, Canada. Canadian Field-Naturalist 84:377-383.

Smith, D.G. and J.R.Murphy. 1973. Breeding ecology of raptors in the eastern Great Basin of Utah. Brigham Young University Science Bulletin Biological Series 18:1-76.

Smith, I.D. 1972. Status of the Nimpkish goose transplant program: Oct. 30, 1972. British Columbia Fish and Wildlife Branch Unpublished Report, Nanaimo. 4 pp. (Bibliography 4197).

_____. 1973. Report on the Nimpkish Valley goose transplant program: May 1, 1973. British Columbia Fish and Wildlife Branch, Victoria. 10 pp. (Bibliography 4198).

Smith, I.D. and D.A. Blood. 1972. Native swans wintering on Vancouver Island over the period 1969-71. Canadian Field-Naturalist 86:213-216.

Smith, I.D., D. Hatler, W. Munro, and K. Hodson. 1976. Queen Charlotte Islands, British Columbia *in* R.W. Fyfe, S.A.Temple, and T.J. Cade (editors). The 1976 North American Peregrine Falcon Survey. Canadian Field-Naturalist 90:228-273.

Smith, K.M., N.J. Anderson, and K.I. Beamish. 1973. Nature west coast: a study of plants, insects, birds, mammals and marine life as seen in Lighthouse Park. Discovery Press, Vancouver, British Columbia. 283 pp.

Smith, N.G. 1966. Evolution of some arctic gulls (*Larus*): an experimental study of isolating mechanisms. Ornithological Monographs 4:1-99.

Smith, R.H. and G.H. Jensen. 1970. Black Brant on the mainland coast of Mexico. Transactions of the 35th North American Wildlife and Natural Resources Conference: 227-241.

Smith, S.M. 1965. Seasonal changes in the survival of the Black-capped Chickadee. M.Sc. Thesis, University of British Columbia, Vancouver. 31 pp.

Smith, W.G. 1952. The food habits of a population of Black Turnstones, Aleutian Sandpipers, and Surf-Birds wintering in southern British Columbia. B.A. Thesis, University of British Columbia, Vancouver. 51pp.

Snow, C. 1973. Habitat management series for unique or endangered species: the Golden Eagle. United States Department of the Interior, Bureau of Land Management Report No.7, Washington, D.C. 52 pp.

_____. 1974. Habitat management series for unique or endangered species Report No.9: Gyrfalcon *Falco rusticolus* L. United States Department of the Interior, Bureau of Land Management Technical Note 241, Denver, Colorado. 14 pp.

Snyder, L.L. 1935. A study of the Sharp-tailed Grouse. Contributions of the Royal Ontario Museum of Zoology No. 6, Toronto, Ontario. 66 pp.

Snyder, N.F.R., H.A. Snyder, J.C. Lincer, and R.T. Reynolds. 1973. Organochlorines, heavy metals, and the biology of North American accipiters. Bioscience 23:300-305.

Soikkeli, M. 1967. Breeding cycle and population dynamics of the Dunlin (*Calidris alpina schinzii*) in Finland. Annales Zoologica Fennici 4:158-198.

Somerville, A.J. 1985. Advantages to late breeding in Ruddy Ducks. M.Sc. Thesis. University of British Columbia, Vancouver. 107 pp.

Soper, J.D. 1949. Birds observed in the Grande Prairie - Peace River region of northwestern Alberta, Canada. Auk 66:233-257.

Sordahl, T.A. 1978. First record of the Curlew Sandpiper (*Calidris ferruginea*) in Utah, with comments on its occurrence in North America. American Birds 32:1065-1068.

Southern, H.N. 1943. The two phases of *Stercorarius parasiticus* (Linnaeus). Ibis 85:443-485.

Sowls, A.L., S.A. Hatch, and C.J. Lensink. 1978. Catalogue of Alaskan seabird colonies. United States Fish and Wildlife Service FWS/OBS-78/78, Washington, D.C. 249 pp.

Sowls, A.L., A.R. DeGange, R. Nelson, J.W. Lester, and G.S. Lester. 1980. Catalogue of California seabird colonies. United States Department of the Interior, Fish and Wildlife Service Biological Services Program FWS/OBS 37/80.

Spalding, D. 1966. Are pheasants a plague? Wildlife Review 3:4-6.

Spalding, D.J. and R.P .Stoneberg. 1981. A history of the pheasant in the Okanagan region of southern British Columbia. British Columbia Ministry of Environment and Parks Wildlife Report No. R-4, Victoria. 64 pp.

Sparling, D.B. and R. Sparling. 1974. The Bar-tailed Godwit. Victoria Naturalist 30:80.

Spear, L.B., M.J. Lewis, M.T. Myres, and R.L. Pyle. 1988. The recent occurrence of Garganey in North America and the Hawaiian Islands. American Birds 42:385-392.

Speich, S. and D.A. Manuwal. 1974. Gular pouch development and population structure of Cassin's Auklet. Auk 91:291-306.

Speich, S.M. and T.R. Wahl. 1989. Catalogue of Washington seabird colonies, United States Department of the Interior Fish and Wildlife Service Biological Report, Series 88(6), Washington, D.C.

References Cited

Spencer, H.E. 1953. The Cinnamon Teal, *Anas cyanoptera* (Vieillot): its life history, ecology, and management. M.S. Thesis, Utah State University, Logan. 184 pp.

Spitzer, P.R., A.F. Poole, and M. Scheibel. 1983. Initial population recovery of breeding Ospreys in the region between New York city and Boston. Pages 231 - 241 *in* D.M. Bird (editor). Biology and Management of Bald Eagles and Ospreys. Proceeding First International Symposium on Bald Eagles and Ospreys, Montreal, 28-29 October 1981. Harpell Press, Ste. Anne de Bellevue, Quebec.

Spofford, W. 1969. Problems of the Golden Eagle in North America. Pages 345-347 *in* J. Hickey (editor). Peregrine Falcon populations; their biology and decline. University of Wisconsin Press, Madison.

Springer, P.R., G.V. Byrd, and D.W. Woolington. 1978. Reestablishing Aleutian Canada Geese. Pages 331-338 *in* S.A. Temple (editor). Endangered Birds. University of Wisconsin Press, Madison.

Sprot, G.D. 1936. A tree-nesting colony of White-crested Cormorants in Trincomali Channel, British Columbia. Condor 38:247-248.

Stallcup, R.W. 1976. Pelagic birds on Monterey Bay, California. Western Birds 7:113-136.

Stalmaster, M.V. and J.A. Gessaman. 1984. Ecological energetics and foraging behavior of overwintering Bald Eagles. Ecological Monographs 54:407-428.

Stalmaster, M.V. and J.R. Newman. 1978. Behavioral responses of wintering Bald Eagles to human activity. Journal of Wildlife Management 42:506-513.

Stanwell-Fletcher, J.F. and T.C. Stanwell-Fletcher. 1940. Naturalists in the wilds of British Columbia. Scientific Monthly 50:1-44.

_____. and _____. 1943. Some accounts of the flora and fauna of the Driftwood Valley region of northcentral British Columbia. British Columbia Provincial Museum Occasional Paper No. 4, Victoria. 97pp.

Steenhof, K. and J.M. Brown. 1978. Management of wintering Bald Eagles. United States Department of the Interior, Fish and Wildlife Service Biological Services Program FWS/OBS-78/79, Washington, D.C. 59 pp.

Sterling, J. and T.F. Campbell. 1985. The autumn migration - middle Pacific coast region. American Birds 39:96-101.

Stevens, T. 1969. Bird report for the Shuswap Lake region (prepared September 1969). British Columbia Parks Branch Unpublished Report, Victoria. 6 pp. (Bibliography 4261).

Stevens, T. and D. Belton. 1969. Annual report for the Shuswap Lake nature house - 1969. British Columbia Parks Branch Unpublished Report, Victoria. 19 pp. (Bibliography 4262).

Stevens, T., A. Grass, and G. Sirk. 1970. Shuswap Lake nature house annual report - 1970. British Columbia Parks Branch Unpublished Report, Victoria. 23 pp. (Bibliography 4260).

Stevenson, H.M. 1975. Identification of difficult birds. Part 3. Semi-palmated Sandpipers and Western Sandpipers. Florida Field Naturalist 3:39-44.

Stewart, P.A. 1985. Need for new direction in research on Black and Turkey Vultures in the USA. Vulture News 13:8-12.

Stewart, R.M. 1927. Marbled Murrelet taken at Harrison Lake, British Columbia. Murrelet 8:16.

Stiles, F.G. 1970. Food supply and the annual cycle of the Anna Hummingbird. Ph.D. Thesis, University of California, Los Angeles. 239 pp.

_____. 1971. On the field identification of California hummingbirds. California Birds 2:41-54.

Stirling, D. 1960a. Sight records of unusual birds in the Victoria area for 1959. Murrelet 41:10-11.

_____. 1960b. Bird life at Esquimalt Lagoon. Victoria Naturalist 16:61.

_____. 1961. Summer birds of Miracle Beach. British Columbia Parks Branch Unpublished Report, Victoria. 14 pp. (Bibliography 4278).

_____. 1962. Some bird notes from Vancouver Island - 1961. Victoria Natural History Society Mimeo, Victoria, British Columbia. 9 pp. (Bibliography 309).

_____. 1964. Western Grebe colony at Shuswap Lake re-visited. Murrelet 45:8-9.

_____. 1965a. Two new heron records for Vancouver Island. Murrelet 46:15.

_____. 1965b. A sight record of Emperor Goose at Victoria, British Columbia. Murrelet 46:36.

_____. 1966a. First nesting record of Brandt's Cormorant in Canadian waters. Victoria Naturalist 23:1-2.

_____. 1966b. Bird report (Victoria) number four - 1965. Victoria Natural History Society Mimeo, Victoria. 6 pp. (Bibliography 310).

_____. 1967. Ross' Gull *Rhodostethia rosea*, rarest of accidental stragglers. Victoria Naturalist 23:49-50.

_____. 1970. A sight record of the Barred Owl on Vancouver Island. Murrelet 51:19.

_____. 1971. Notes on birds of Mount Robson Provincial Park, 1970. Blue Jay 29:66-72.

_____. 1972a. More Franklin's Gulls in southeastern British Columbia. Vancouver Natural History Society Discovery 1:37.

_____. 1972b. Birds of Vancouver Island for birdwatchers. Published by the author, Victoria. 27 pp. (Bibliography 307).

_____. 1986. Mountain Quail returns? B.C. Naturalist 24:5.

Stirling, D. and R. Buffam. 1966. The first breeding record of Brandt's Cormorant in Canada. Canadian Field-Naturalist 80:117-118.

Stockman, B. 1972. The Pitt waterfowl study. Canadian Wildlife Service Unpublished Report, Delta, British Columbia. 84 pp. (Bibliography 4283).

Stoneberg, R.P. 1967. A preliminary study of the breeding biology of the Spruce Grouse in northwestern Montana. M.Sc. Thesis, University of Montana, Missoula.

Stonehouse, B. 1968. Penguins. Golden Press, New York. 96 pp.

Storer, R.W. 1952. A comparison of variation, behavior and evolution in the sea bird genera *Uria* and *Cepphus*. University of California Publications in Zoology 52:121-222.

Storer, R.W. and G.L. Nuechterlein. 1985. An analysis of plumage and morphological characters of the two color phases of the Western Grebe *(Aechmophorus)*. Auk 102:102-119.

Stotts, V.D. and C.J. Henny. 1975. The age at first flight for young American Ospreys. Wilson Bulletin 87:277-278.

Stresemann, E. and D. Amadon. 1979. Order Falconiformes. Pages 271-425 *in* E. Mayr and G.W. Cottrell (editors). Check-list of birds of the world. Museum of Comparative Zoology, Cambridge, Massachusetts.

Strong, P.I.V., J.A. Bissonette, and R. Souza. 1986. A case of brood mixing by Common Loons. Wilson Bulletin 98:478-479.

Stutz, S.S. 1965. Size of Common Merganser broods. Murrelet 46:47-48.

Sugden, L.G. 1963. Barrow's Goldeneye using crow nests. Condor 65:330.

Sullivan, T. 1985. A survey of Christie Islet Migratory Bird Sanctuary, B.C. Canadian Wildlife Service Unpublished Report, Delta, British Columbia. 8 pp.

Summers, K.R. 1974. Seabirds breeding along the east coast of Moresby Island, Queen Charlotte Islands, British Columbia. Syesis 7:1-12.

Summers, K.R. and R.H. Drent. 1979. Breeding biology and twinning experiments of Rhinoceros Auklet on Cleland Island, British Columbia. Murrelet 60:16-22.

Sutton, G.M. and D.F. Parmelee. 1955. Breeding of the Semipalmated Plover on Baffin Island. Bird-Banding 26:137-147.

Sutton, G.M. and J.B. Semple. 1941. An egg of the Marbled Murrelet. Auk 58:580-581.

Swarth, H.S. 1912. Report on a collection of birds and mammals from Vancouver Island. University of California Publications in Zoology 10:1-124.

_____. 1922. Birds and mammals of the Stikine River region of northern British Columbia and southeastern Alaska. University of California Publications in Zoology 24:125-314.

_____. 1924. Birds and mammals of the Skeena River region of northern British Columbia. University of California Publications in Zoology 24:315-394.

_____. 1926. Report on a collection of birds and mammals from the Atlin region, northern British Columbia. University of California Publications in Zoology 30:51-62.

_____. 1932. Status of the Baikal Teal in California. Condor 34:259.

_____. 1936. A list of the birds of the Atlin region, British Columbia. Proceedings of the California Academy of Sciences 23:35-58.

Swenson, J.E. 1983. Is the northern interior Bald Eagle population in North America increasing? Pages 23-34 in D.M. Bird (editor). Biology and Management of Bald Eagles and Ospreys. Proceedings of First International Symposium on Bald Eagles and Ospreys, Montreal, 28-29 October 1981. Harpell Press, Ste. Anne de Bellevue, Quebec.

Swift, P. 1975. Annotated list of birds of Goldstream Park, spring 1975. British Columbia Parks Branch Unpublished Report, Victoria. 5 pp. (Bibliography 4311).

Sykes, P.W. 1975. Caribbean Coot collected in southern Florida. Florida Field Naturalist 3:25-27.

Syroechkovskiy, Ye.V. and K.Ye. Litvin. 1986. Investigation of the migration of the Snow Geese of Wrangel Island by the method of individual marking. Pages 1-17 in V.Ye. Sokolov and I.N. Dobrinina (editors). The Ringing and Marking of Birds in the U.S.S.R. 1979-1982. Moscow: "Nauka":5-20. (Translation by M.A. Bousfield, Department of Zoology, University of Alberta, Edmonton).

Szuba, K.J. and J.F. Bendell. 1983. Population densities and habitats of Spruce Grouse in Ontario. Pages 199-213 in Proceedings of a conference held at Thunder Bay, Ontario, August, 1982. Association of Canadian Universities for Northern Studies, Ottawa.

Tacha, T.C., P.A. Vohs, and G.C. Iverson. 1984. Migration routes of Sandhill Cranes from mid-continental North America. Journal of Wildlife Management 48:1028-1033.

Tait, E.M. 1929. Christmas bird census, 1928 - Summerland, Okanagan Lake, British Columbia. Canadian Field-Naturalist 43:34.

_____. 1932. Black-crowned Night Heron in Okanagan Valley, British Columbia. Canadian Field-Naturalist 46:190.

_____. 1949. Nesting of the Pacific Harlequin Duck in vicinity of Penticton, B.C. Canadian Field-Naturalist 63:43.

Tamm, S. 1985. Breeding territory quality and agnostic behavior: effects of energy availability and intruder pressure in hummingbirds. Behavioral Ecology Sociobiology 16:203-207.

_____. 1986. Behavioural energetics: acquisition and use of energy by hummingbirds. Ph.D. Thesis, University of Stockholm, Sweden.

Tate, J. 1981. The blue list for 1981. American Birds 35:3-10.

_____. 1986. The blue list for 1986. American Birds 40:227-236.

Tate, J. and D.J. Tate. 1982. The blue list for 1982. American Birds 36:126-135.

Tatum J.B. (editor). 1970. Experimental annual bird report for southern Vancouver Island 1969. Victoria Natural History Society Mimeo, Victoria. 34 pp.

_____. (editor). 1971. Bird report for southern Vancouver Island (1970). Victoria Natural History Society, Victoria, British Columbia. 64 pp.

_____. (editor). 1972. Annual bird report - 1971 - for southern Vancouver Island. Victoria Natural History Society, Victoria, British Columbia. 66 pp.

_____. 1972a. A Canadian ornithological records committee. Canadian Field-Naturalist 86:181.

_____. (editor). 1973. Annual bird report - 1972 - for southern Vancouver Island. Victoria Natural History Society, Victoria, British Columbia. 80 pp.

_____. 1980. The effect of the Coriolis force on the flight of a bird. Auk 97:99-117.

Taverner, P.A. 1918. Summer birds of Alert Bay, British Columbia. Condor 20:183-186.

_____. 1919. The summer birds of Hazelton, British Columbia. Condor 21:80-86.

_____. 1919a. Birds of Eastern Canada. Canada Department of Mines Memoir 104, Number 3, Biological Series, Ottawa, Ontario. 297 pp.

_____. 1926. Birds of Western Canada. Canada Department of Mines Museum Bulletin Number 41, Ottawa, Ontario. 380 pp.

_____. 1927. Some recent Canadian records. Auk 44:217-218.

_____. 1929. A study of the Canadian races of Rock Ptarmigan (*Lagopus rupestris*). Pages 28-38 in National Museum of Canada Annual Report for 1928, Ottawa, Ontario.

_____. 1936. Taxonomic comments on Red-tailed Hawk. Condor 38:66-71.

_____. 1940. Variation in the American Goshawk. Condor 42:157-160.

_____. 1942. The distribution and migration of the Hudsonian Curlew. Wilson Bulletin 54:3-11.

Taylor, A.L. and E.D. Forsman. 1976. Recent range extensions of the Barred Owl in western North America, including the first records for Oregon. Condor 78:560-561.

Taylor, E.W. 1950. A study of factors affecting reproduction and survival of the Ring-necked Pheasant in the lower Fraser River valley of British Columbia. M.A. Thesis, University of British Columbia, Vancouver. 116 pp.

_____. 1959. Reports of E.W. Taylor - 1954 to 1959. British Columbia Fish and Wildlife Branch Unpublished Report, Vancouver. 27 pp. (Bibliography 4344).

_____. 1962. A report on the Ringneck Pheasant population of the district municipality of Salmon Arm and the Salmon River valley. British Columbia Fish and Wildlife Branch Unpublished Report, Victoria. 23pp.

Taylor, R.L. and B. MacBryde. 1977. Vascular plants of British Columbia: a descriptive resource inventory. University of British Columbia Botanical Garden Technical Bulletin No. 4, Vancouver. 754 pp.

Telosky, H.A. 1977. Ruby-throated Hummingbird reported on north-eastern Vancouver Island. Vancouver Natural History Society Discovery 6:57-60.

Temple, S.A. 1972. Systematics and evolution of the North American Merlins. Auk 89:325-338.

Terres, J.K. 1980. The Audubon Society encyclopedia of North American birds. Alfred Knopf, New York. 1110 pp.

Thacker, B.M. and T.L. Thacker. 1923. Extracts from note-book for Little Mountain, Hope, B.C. - Year, 1922. Migrant 1:20-21 (Bibliography 1929).

Thacker, T.L. 1923. Bird notes made at Vaseux Lake, south Okanagan, British Columbia. Canadian Field-Naturalist 37:66-69.

_____. 1948. Sight record of Red-bellied Hawk at Hope, British Columbia. Murrelet 29:50.

Thompson, B.H. 1933. History and present status of the breeding colonies of the White Pelican (*Pelecanus erythrorhynchos*) in the United States. United States Department of Interior National Park Service Occasional Paper No. 1, Washington, D.C. 82 pp.

Thompson, D.Q. 1951. Notes on distribution of north Pacific albatrosses. Auk 68:227-235.

Thompson, M.C. 1974. Migratory patterns of Ruddy Turnstone in the central Pacific region. Living Bird 12:5-23.

Thompson, M.C. and R.L. DeLong. 1969. Birds new to North America and the Pribilof Islands, Alaska. Auk 86:744-749,

Thomson, A.L. (editor). 1964. A new dictionary of birds. McGraw-Hill Book Company, New York. 928 pp.

Thomson, D. 1974. Naturalist program at Black Tusk 1974. British Columbia Parks Branch Unpublished Report, Victoria. 17 pp. (Bibliography 4360).

Thomson, R.E. 1981. Oceanography of the British Columbia coast. Canadian Special Publication of Fisheries and Aquatic Sciences 56. Canada Department Fisheries and Oceans, Ottawa. 291 pp.

Thoresen, A.C. 1964. Breeding behavior of the Cassin Auklet. Condor 66:456-476.

Thoresen, A.C. and E.S. Booth. 1958. Breeding activities of the Pigeon Guillemot *Cepphus columba columba* (Pallas). Walla Walla College Publications in Biological Science No. 23, Walla Walla, Washington. 36 pp.

Tierney, R. 1974. Bowron Lake Provincial Park - bird report 1974. British Columbia Parks Branch Unpublished Report, Victoria. 14 pp. (Bibliography 4364).

Tilgham, N.G. 1980. The Black Tern survey, 1979. Passenger Pigeon 42:1-8.

Timm, D.E. and C.P. Dau. 1979. Productivity, mortality, distribution, and population status of Pacific White-fronted Geese. Pages 280-298 *in* R.L. Jarvis and J.C. Bartonek (editors). Management and Biology of Pacific Flyway Geese. A symposium sponsored by the Northwest Section, The Wildlife Society, 16 February 1979, Portland, Oregon. Oregon State University Book Stores, Inc., Corvallis.

Timm, D.E., M.L. Wege, and D.S. Gilmer. 1982. Current status and management challenges for Tule White-fronted Geese. Transactions of the North American Wildlife and Natural Resources Conference 47:453-463.

Tisdale, E.W. and A. McLean. 1957. The Douglas fir zone of southern British Columbia. Ecological Monographs 27:247-266.

Trapp, J.L., M.A. Robus, G.J. Tans, and M.A. Tans. 1981. First breeding record of the Sora and American Coot in Alaska - with comments on drought displacement. American Birds 35:901-902.

Trauger, D.L., A. Dzubin, and J.P. Ryder. 1971. White geese intermediate between Ross' Geese and Lesser Snow Geese. Auk 88:856-875.

Trethewey, R.B. and J.M. Cooper. 1975. Wood Duck project final report, 1972-1975. Pitt Waterfowl Management Association Unpublished Report, Pitt Meadows, British Columbia. 9 pp. (Bibliography 4381).

Trimble, S.A. 1975. Habitat management series for unique or endangered species Report No. 15: Merlin (*Falco columbarius*), United States Department of Interior, Bureau of Land Management Technical Note, Denver, Colorado.

Tuck, G. 1978. A field guide to the seabirds of Britain and the world. Collins, London, England.

Tuck, L.M. 1960. The murres: their distribution, populations and biology - a study of the genus *Uria*. Queens Printer, Ottawa, Ontario. 260 pp.

_____. 1972. The snipes. Canadian Wildlife Service Monograph Series No. 5, Ottawa, Ontario. 429 pp.

Tull, C.E. 1979. Raptor nest sites along segments 2-6, Shakwak highway British Columbia - Yukon, May to June, 1979. LGL Limited Unpublished Report, Edmonton, Alberta. 66 pp. (Bibliography 4389).

Turner, I.G. 1970. A daily record of Trumpeter Swans at Lonesome Lake, British Columbia (October to March, 1969-1970). Canadian Wildlife Service Unpublished Report, Delta. 47 pp. (Bibliography 4391).

Turner, J. 1971. Trumpeter Swans - Lonesome Lake, B.C. - winter 1970-71. Canadian Wildlife Service Unpublished Report, Delta, British Columbia. 68 pp.

Tyler, W.M. 1937. *Cathartes aura septentrionalis* Wied. Turkey Vulture. Pages 12-28 *in* A.C. Bent (editor). Life histories of North American birds of prey. United States National Museum Bulletin No. 167, Washington, D.C.

Udvardy, M.D.F. 1954. Summer movements of Black Swifts in relation to weather conditions. Condor 56:261-267.

Ulke, T. 1923. Birds observed in Yoho Park, B.C. in August 1922. Canadian Field-Naturalist 37:54-55.

United States Department of the Interior. 1982. 1980 national survey of fishing, hunting, and wildlife associated recreation. United States Department of the Interior Fish and Wildlife Service, Washington, D.C. 152 pp.

_____. 1988. Catalogue of Alaskan seabird colonies - computer data base. United States Department of Interior, Fish and Wildlife Service, Anchorage, Alaska.

United States Fish and Wildlife Service. 1973. Threatened wildlife of the United States. United States Fish and Wildlife Resource Publication 114, Washington, D.C. 289 pp.

Unitt, P. 1976. Occurrence and migration of the Long-tailed Jaeger in North America. Pacific Seabird Group Bulletin 3:31 (Abstract).

_____. 1977. The Little Blue Heron in California. Western Birds 8:151-154.

_____. 1984. The birds of San Diego county. San Diego Society of Natural History Memoir 13, San Diego, California. 276 pp.

Vallee, A. and R.J. Cannings. 1983. Nesting of the Thick-billed Murre, *Uria lomvia*, in British Columbia. Canadian Field-Naturalist 97:450-451.

Vance, H. 1970. Seventieth Christmas bird count - Terrace, B.C. Audubon Field Notes 24:125.

van Drimmelen, B. 1973. An analysis of the 1972 Pitt Polder Wood Duck nesting project. British Columbia Fish and Wildlife Branch Unpublished Report, Surrey. 19 pp. (Bibliography 4417).

_____. 1986. 1986 Queen Charlotte Islands Peale's Peregrine Falcon inventory. British Columbia Ministry of Environment Unpublished Report, Smithers.

van Drimmelen, B. and S.A. Sullivan. 1976. Report on the 1975 falcon survey in south-central B.C. (May 20 to July 23). British Columbia Fish and Wildlife Branch Unpublished Report, Victoria. 35 pp. (Bibliography 1897).

van Tets, G.F. 1959. A comparative study of the reproductive behaviour and natural history of three sympatric species of cormorants (*Phalacrocorax auritus*, *P. penicillatus*, and *P. pelagicus*) at Mandarte Island, B.C. M.A. Thesis, University of British Columbia, Vancouver. 86 pp.

_____. 1963. A report on the seabird colony at Mitlenatch Island. British Columbia Parks Branch Unpublished Report, Victoria. 133 pp. (Bibliography 1912).

_____. 1968. Seasonal fluctuations in the mortality rates of three northern-and three southern-hemisphere gulls. Commonwealth Scientific and Industrial Research Organization Wildlife Research 13:1-9.

van Tighem, K.J. 1977. The avifauna of Kootenay National Park. Parks Canada Unpublished Report, Radium Hotsprings, British Columbia. 151 pp. (Bibliography 4431).

van Tighem, K.J. and L.W. Gyug. 1983. Ecological land classification of Mount Revelstoke and Glacier National Parks, British Columbia. Volume II - Wildlife Resource. Canadian Wildlife Service and Parks Canada Report, Edmonton, Alberta. 254 pp.

Varoujean, D.H. and W.A. Williams. 1986. Nest locations and nesting habitat of the Marbled Murrelet (*Brachyramphus marmoratus*) in coastal Oregon. United States Department of the Interior, Fish and Wildlife Service Interim Report, Portland, Oregon. 33 pp.

Vaurie, C.A. 1959. The birds of the Palearctic fauna: Order Passeriformes. H.F. & G. Witherby, London, England. 762 pp.

_____. 1965. The birds of the Palearctic fauna: Non-passeriformes. H.F. & G. Witherby Limited, London, England 763 pp.

Veit, R. and L. Jonsson. 1984. Field identification of smaller sandpipers within the genus *Calidris*. American Birds 38:853-876.

Venables, E.P. 1909. The Burrowing Owl. Ottawa Naturalist 22:261.

Verbeek, N.A.M. 1966. Wanderings of the Ancient Murrelet: some additional comments. Condor 68:510-511.

_____. 1979. Timing of primary molt and egg-laying in Glaucous-winged Gulls. Wilson Bulletin 91:420-425.

_____. 1986. Aspects of the breeding biology of an expanded population of Glaucous-winged Gulls in British Columbia. Journal of Field Ornithology 57:22-33.

Vermeer, K. 1963. The breeding ecology of the Glaucous-winged Gull (*Larus glaucescens*) on Mandarte Island, B.C. British Columbia Provincial Museum Occasional Paper No. 13, Victoria. 104 pp.

_____. 1968. Ecological aspects of ducks nesting in high densities among larids. Wilson Bulletin 80:78-83.

_____. 1970. Breeding biology of California and Ring-billed Gulls. Canadian Wildlife Service Report Series No. 12, Ottawa, Ontario. 52 pp.

_____. 1971. The pelican - protection or extinction. Canadian Audubon 33:103-104.

_____. 1977. Comparison of White Pelican recoveries from colonies east and west of the Canadian Rocky Mountains. Murrelet 58:79-82.

_____. 1978. Extensive reproductive failure of Rhinoceros Auklets and Tufted Puffins. Ibis 120:112.

_____. 1979. Nesting requirements, food and breeding distribution of Rhinoceros Auklets, *Cerorhinca monocerata*, and Tufted Puffins, *Lunda cirrhata*. Ardea 67:101-110.

_____. 1980. The importance of timing and type of prey to reproductive success of Rhinoceros Auklets *Cerorhinca monocerata*. Ibis 122:343-350.

_____. 1981. The importance of plankton to Cassin's Auklets during breeding. Journal of Plankton Research 3:315-329.

_____. 1982. Foods and distribution of three *Bucephala* species in British Columbia waters. Wildfowl 33:22-30.

_____. 1983. Marine bird populations in the Strait of Georgia: comparison with the west coast of Vancouver Island. Canadian Technical Report of Hydrography and Ocean Sciences No. 19, Sydney, British Columbia. 18 pp.

Vermeer, K. and L. Cullen. 1979. Growth of Rhinoceros Auklets-and Tufted Puffins, Triangle Island, British Columbia. Ardea 67:22-27.

_____. and _____. 1982. Growth comparison of a plankton-and a fish-feeding alcid. Murrelet 63:34-39.

Vermeer, K. and D. Devito. 1986. The nesting biology of Mew Gulls (*Larus canus*) on Kennedy Lake, British Columbia, Canada: comparison with Mew Gulls in northern Europe. Colonial Waterbirds 9:95-103.

_____. and _____. 1989. Population trends of nesting Glaucous-winged Gulls in the Strait of Georgia. Pages 89-93 *in* Vermeer, K. and R.W. Butler (editors). The ecology and status of marine and shoreline birds in the Strait of Georgia, British Columbia. Canadian Wildlife Service Special Publication, Ottawa, Ontario.

Vermeer, K. and M. Lemon. 1986. Nesting habits and habitats of Ancient Murrelets and Cassin's Auklets in the Queen Charlotte Islands, British Columbia. Murrelet 67:33-44.

Vermeer, K. and C.D. Levings. 1977. Populations, biomass and food habits of ducks on the Fraser Delta intertidal area, British Columbia. Wildfowl 28:49-60.

Vermeer, K. and L. Rankin. 1984. Population trends in nesting Double-crested Cormorants and Pelagic Cormorants in Canada. Murrelet 65:1-9.

Vermeer, K. and R. Vermeer. 1975. Oil threat to birds on the Canadian west coast. Canadian Field-Naturalist 89:278-298.

Vermeer, K., R.F. Oldaker, M.D.F. Udvardy, and K. Kelleher. 1963. Aberrant Glaucous-winged Gulls. Condor 65:332-333.

Vermeer, K., D.A. Manuwal and D.S. Bingham. 1976. Seabirds and pinnipeds of Sartine Island, Scott Island group, British Columbia. Murrelet 57:14-16.

Vermeer, K., K.R. Summers, and D.S. Bingham. 1976. Birds observed at Triangle Island, British Columbia, 1974 and 1975. Murrelet 57:35-42.

Vermeer, K., L. Cullen, and M. Porter. 1979a. A provisional explanation of the reproductive failure of Tufted Puffins (*Lunda cirrhata*) on Triangle Island, British Columbia. Ibis 121:348-354.

Vermeer, K., R. Vermeer, K.R. Summers, and R.R. Billings. 1979b. Numbers and habitat selection of Cassin's Auklets breeding on Triangle Island, British Columbia. Auk 96:143-151.

Vermeer, K., D. Power and G.E.J. Smith. 1988. Habitat selection and nesting biology of roof-nesting Glaucous-winged Gulls. Colonial Waterbirds II:109-201.

Vermeer, K., K. Morgan, and J. Smith. 1989. Population trends and nesting habitat of Double-crested and Pelagic cormorants in the Strait of Georgia. Pages 94-99 *in* Vermeer, K. and R.W. Butler (editors). The ecology and status of marine and shoreline birds in the Strait of Georgia, British Columbia. Canadian Wildlife Service Special Publication, Ottawa, Ontario.

Vesall, D.B. 1940. Notes on nesting habits of the American Bittern. Wilson Bulletin. 52:207-208.

Vickery, P.D., and R.P. Yunick. 1979. The 1978-1979 Great Gray Owl incursion across northeastern North America. American Birds 33:242-244.

Voous, K.H. 1973. List of recent holarctic bird species. Non-passerines. Ibis 115:612-638.

Vyatkin, P.S. 1986. Nesting cadastres of colonial birds in the Kamchatka regon. *In* N.M. Litvienko (editor). Seabirds of the Far East: collection of scientific papers. USSR Academy of Sciences, Vladivostok (Translation for Environment Canada).

Wade, C. 1977. The birds of Yoho National Park. Parks Canada Unpublished Report, Ottawa, Ontario. 799 pp. (Bibliography 1994).

References Cited

Wahl, T.R. 1970. A Short-tailed Albatross record for Washington state. California Birds 1:113-114.

_____. 1972. Glaucous-winged Gull nesting at Lake Whatcom, Bellingham, Washington. Murrelet 53:51.

_____. 1975. Seabirds in Washington's offshore zone. Western Birds 6:117-134.

_____. 1985. The distribution of Buller's Shearwater, (*Puffinus bulleri*) in the North Pacific Ocean. Notornis 32:109-117.

Wahl, T.R., S.M. Speich, D.A. Manuwal, K.V. Hirsch, and C. Miller. 1981. Marine bird populations of the Strait of Juan de Fuca, Strait of Georgia, and adjacent waters in 1978 and 1979. Interagency Energy-Environment Research and Development Program Report, EPA-600/7-81-156. NOAA, Marine Ecosystems Analysis Program, Seattle, Washington. 391 pp.

Wakefield, K.S. 1987. Greylegs - a most uncommon bird. Vancouver Natural History Society. Discovery 16:47-48.

Walkinshaw, L.H. 1935. The incubation period of the Sora Rail. Wilson Bulletin 47:79-80.

_____. 1937. The Virginia Rail in Michigan. Auk 54:464-475.

_____. 1940. Summer life of the Sora Rail. Auk 57:153-168.

_____. 1949. The Sandhill Cranes. Cranbrook Institute of Science Bulletin No. 29, Bloomfield Hills, Michigan. 202 pp.

_____. 1981. The Sandhill Cranes. *in* Lewis, J.C. and H. Masatomi (editors). Crane Research Around the World. Proceedings of the International Crane Symposium at Sapporo, Japan in 1980 and papers from the World Working Group on Cranes, ICBP. International Crane Foundation, Baraboo, Wisconsin.

Wallace, D.I.M. 1974. Field identification of small species of the genus *Calidris*. British Birds 67:1-17.

_____. 1979. Review of British records of Semipalmated Sandpipers and claimed Red-necked Stints. British Birds 72:264-274.

Wallace, G.J. 1948. The Barn Owl in Michigan. Michigan State College Agriculture Experiment Station 208:1-61.

Wallace, W.M. 1961. Scaled Petrel in Oregon. Condor 63:417.

Walsh, T. 1988. Identifying Pacific loons - some old and new problems. Birding 20:12-28.

Ward, J.G. 1973. Reproductive success, food supply, and the evolution of clutch-size in the Glaucous-winged Gull. Ph.D. Thesis, University of British Columbia, Vancouver. 119 pp.

Ward, P.R.B. 1973. Further record of Snowy Plover in B.C. Vancouver Natural History Society Discovery 2:80-81.

Warren, C.L. and P.C. Rump. 1981. The urbanization of rural land in Canada: 1966-1971 and 1971-1976. Land Use in Canada Series No. 20, Environment Canada, Ottawa, Ontario. 283 pp.

Warren, W.H. 1970. Mute Swans in Victoria. Victoria Naturalist 27:11.

Watanuki, Y., M. Aotsuka and T. Terasawa. 1986. Status of seabirds breeding on Teuri Island. Tori 34:146-150.

Watson, A. 1956. The annual cycle of Rock Ptarmigan. Ph.D. Thesis, Aberdeen University, Aberdeen, Scotland. 333 pp.

Watson, D. 1977. The Hen Harrier. T. and A.D. Poyser Ltd., Berkharnsted, Hertfordshire, England. 307 pp.

Watson, G.E. 1962. Sympatry in Palearctic *Alectoris* partridges. Evolution 16:11-19.

Webb, R. 1952. Annotated bird list for Wells Gray Park, 1952. British Columbia Parks Branch Unpublished Report, Victoria. 41 pp. (Bibliography 4492).

Weber, J.W. and R.E. Fitzner. 1986. Nesting of the Glaucous-winged Gull east of the Washington Cascades. American Birds 40:567-569.

Weber, W.C. 1975. Occurrence and possible breeding of the White-throated Swift at Spence's Bridge, British Columbia. Murrelet 56:10-11.

_____. 1980. A proposed list of rare and endangered bird species for British Columbia. Pages 160-182 *in* R. Stace-Smith, L. Johns and, P. Joslin (editors). Proceedings of the Symposium on Threatened and Endangered Species and Habitats in British Columbia and the Yukon. British Columbia Ministry of Environment, Victoria.

_____. 1982. Vancouver bird records committee: first annual report. Vancouver Natural History Society Discovery 11:110-115.

_____. 1985. Vancouver bird records committee report for 1982. Vancouver Natural History Society Discovery 12:51-55.

Weber, W.C. and R.W. Campbell. 1978. Occurrence of the Smew in British Columbia, with comments on other North American Records. American Birds 32:1059-1061.

Weber, W.C. and S.R. Cannings. 1976. The White-headed Woodpecker (*Dendrocopos albolarvatus*) in British Columbia. Syesis 9:215-220.

Weber, W.C. and E.S. Hunn. 1978. First record of the Little Blue Heron for British Columbia and Washington. Western Birds 9:33-34.

Weber, W.C. and W.D. Kragh. 1986. The 86th Christmas bird count - British Columbia. American Birds 40:644-645.

_____. and _____. 1987. The 87th Christmas bird count - British Columbia. American Birds 41:647-665.

Weber, W.J. 1972. A new world for the Cattle Egret. Natural History 81:56-63.

Webster, J.D. 1969. Thirty-third breeding bird census - white spruce forest. Audubon Field Notes 23:717.

Wedgewood, I.A. 1978. The status of the Burrowing Owl in Canada. Committee on the Status of Endangered Wildlife in Canada Report. Canadian Wildlife Service, Ottawa, Ontario. 82 pp.

Weeden, R.B. 1959a. The ecology and distribution of ptarmigan wintering in North America. Ph.D. Thesis, University of British Columbia, Vancouver. 247 pp.

_____. 1959b. A new breeding record for the Wandering Tattler in Alaska. Auk 76:230-232.

_____. 1960. The birds of Chilkat Pass, British Columbia. Canadian Field-Naturalist 74:119-129.

_____. 1963. Management of ptarmigan in North America. Journal of Wildlife Management 27:673-683.

_____. 1965a. Further notes on Wandering Tattlers in central Alaska. Condor 67:87-89.

_____. 1965b. Breeding density, reproductive success, and mortality of Rock Ptarmigan at Eagle Creek, Alaska, from 1960-1964. Transactions of the North American Wildlife Conference 30:336-348.

Wehle, D.H.S. 1980. The breeding biology of the puffin: Tufted Puffin (*Lunda cirrhata*), Horned Puffin (*Fratercula corniculata*), Common Puffin (*F. arctica*), and Rhinoceros Auklet (*Cerorhinca monocerata*). Ph.D. Thesis, University of Alaska, Fairbanks.

_____. 1983. The food, feeding, and development of young Tufted and Horned Puffins in Alaska. Condor 85:427-442.

Weller, M.W. 1957. Growth, weight, and plumages of the Redhead, *Aythya americana*. Wilson Bulletin 69:5-38.

_____. 1959. Parasitic egg laying in the Redhead (*Aythya americana*) and other north American Anatidae. Ecological Monographs 29:333-365.

_____. 1964. Distribution and migration of the Redhead. Journal of Wildlife Management 28:64-103.

Wells, A.N. 1954. Green heron at Chilliwack, British Columbia. Murrelet 35:50.

Wenzel, B.M. 1980. Chemoreception in seabirds. Pages 41-67 *in* Burger, J., B.L. Olla and H.E. Winn (editors). Behavior of marine animals. Vol. 4. Plenum, New York.

Weseloh, D.V. 1981. Presidents of FAN - the first ten years: M.T. Myres - President 1970/71. Alberta Naturalist 1:71-74.

Westerborg, B.J. and D. Stirling. 1963. Twenty-seventh breeding bird census - disturbed second-growth coast forest. Audubon Field Notes 17:500-501.

Westerskov, K. 1956. Age determination and dating nesting events in the Willow Ptarmigan. Journal of Wildlife Management 20:274-279.

_____. 1965. Winter ecology of the partridge *(Perdix perdix)* in the Canadian prairie. Proceedings of the New Zealand Ecological Society 12:23-30.

_____. 1966. Winter food and feeding habits of the partridge *(Perdix perdix)* in the Canadian prairie. Canadian Journal of Zoology 44:303-322.

Weston, J.B. 1968. Nesting ecology of the Ferruginous Hawk *(Buteo regalis)*. M.S. Thesis, Brigham Young University, Provo, Utah. 40 pp.

Wetmore, A. 1926. Food and economic relations of North American grebes. United States Department of Agriculture Bulletin 1196, Washington, D.C.

Wetmore, S.P., R.A. Keller, and G.E.J. Smith. 1985. Effects of logging on bird populations in British Columbia as determined by a modified point-count method. Canadian Field-Naturalist 99:224-233.

Whelton, B.D. 1989. Distribution of the Boreal Owl in eastern Washington and Oregon. Condor 91:712-716.

White, C.M. 1968. Diagnosis and relationships of the North American tundra-inhabiting Peregrine Falcons. Auk 85:179-191.

White, C.M. and D.A. Boyce. 1988. An overview of Peregrine Falcon subspecies. Pages 789-810 *in* T.J. Cade, J.H. Enderson, C.G. Thelander, and C.M. White (editors). Peregrine Falcon populations - their management and recovery. The Peregrine Fund, Inc., Boise, Idaho.

Whitelaw, V.R. 1977. The Anna's Hummingbird in British Columbia. Vancouver Natural History Society Discovery 6:53-56.

Whittaker, S. 1987. Wild Turkeys thriving in new Kootenay home. Kootenay Advertiser, 11 May 1987, p. 4.

Wik, D. and G. Streveler. 1968. Birds of Glacier Bay National Monument. Updated Edition. United States National Park Service. 80 pp.

Wiken, E. 1986. Terrestrial ecozones of Canada. Environment Canada Ecological Land Classification Series No. 19, Ottawa, Ontario. 26 pp.

Wilbur, S.R. 1978. Turkey Vulture eggshell thinning in California, Florida, and Texas. Wilson Bulletin 90:642-643.

_____. 1983. The status of vultures in the western hemisphere. Pages 113-123 *in* S.R. Wilbur and J.A. Jackson (editors). Vulture biology and management. University of California Press, Berkeley.

Wilbur, S.R. and J. A. Jackson (editors). 1983. Vulture biology and management. University of California Press, Berkeley. 550 pp.

Wilbur, S.R. and C.F. Yocom. 1972. Unusual geese in the Pacific coast states. Murrelet 52:16-19.

Wilds, C. and M. Newton. 1983. The identification of dowitchers. Birding 15:151-166.

Willett, G. 1915. Summer birds of Forrester Island, Alaska. Auk 32:295-305.

Willey, C.H. 1968. The ecology, distribution and abundance of the Mute Swan *(Cygnus olor)* in Rhode Island. M.S. Thesis, University of Rhode Island, Kingston. 93 pp.

Williams, J.H. 1978. Fort D'Epinette: a description of faunal remains from an early fur trade site in northern British Columbia. M.A. Thesis, Simon Fraser University, Burnaby, British Columbia.

Williams, M. 1964. Importation of game birds into British Columbia. British Columbia Fish and Wildlife Branch Unpublished Report, Victoria. 9 pp (Bibliography 4584).

Williams, M.Y. 1933a. Biological notes, covering parts of the Peace, Liard, Mackenzie and Great Bear River basins. Canadian Field-Naturalist 47:23-31.

_____. 1933b. Fauna of the former Dominion Peace River block, British Columbia. Pages 14-22 *in* Provincial Museum of Natural History and Anthropology for the year 1932, Victoria, British Columbia.

Williams, M.Y. and G.J. Spencer. 1942. The Flammulated Screech Owl at Kamloops. Canadian Field-Naturalist 56:138.

Williamson, F.S.L. and L.J. Peyton. 1963. Interbreeding of Glaucous-winged and Herring Gulls in the Cook Inlet region, Alaska. Condor 65:24-65.

Williamson, F.S.L. and M.A. Smith. 1964. The distribution and breeding status of the Hudsonian Godwit in Alaska. Condor 66:41-50.

Wilson, D. 1977. Wintering raptors in northern Pitt Meadows, B.C.: their distribution and significance. British Columbia Institute of Technology Unpublished Report, Burnaby. 46 pp. (Bibliography 4594).

Wilson, D.J. 1989. Avocets on the B.C. coast: first breeding record. Vancouver Natural History Society Discovery 18:95-97.

Wilson, M.C., E. Wilson, and L. Wilson. 1972. Ornithological notes from Columbia Lake, British Columbia. Syesis 5:63-65.

Wilson, U.W. 1977. A study of the biology of the Rhinoceros Auklet on Protection Island, Washington. M.Sc. Thesis, University of Washington, Seattle. 98 pp.

_____. 1986. Artificial Rhinoceros Auklet burrows: a useful tool for management and research. Journal of Field Ornithology 57:295-299.

Wilson, U.W. and D.A. Manuwal. 1986. Breeding biology of the Rhinoceros Auklet in Washington. Condor. 88:143-155.

Wilson-Jacobs, R. and E.C. Meslow. 1984. Distribution, abundance, and nesting characteristics of Snowy Plovers on the Oregon Coast. Northwest Science 58:40-48.

Winter, G.R. 1968. Agricultural development in the lower Fraser River valley. Pages 101-115 *in* A.H. Siemens (editor). Lower Fraser valley: evolution of a cultural landscape. B.C. Geographical Series No. 9, Tantalus Research Limited, Vancouver.

Winter, J. and D. Erickson. 1977. The fall migration - middle Pacific Coast region. American Birds 31:216-221.

Witherby, H.F., F.C.R. Jourdain, N.F. Ticehurst, and B.W. Tucker. 1943. The handbook of British birds. H.F. and G. Witherby Ltd., London, England.

Wohl, K.D. 1975. Sightings of New Zealand shearwaters in the northern Gulf of Alaska. Canadian Field-Naturalist 89:320-321.

Wood, C. 1976. First record of the Black-headed Gull for British Columbia. Syesis 9:361.

Wood, C.C. 1984. Foraging behaviour of Common Mergansers *(Mergus merganser)* and their dispersion in relation to the availability of juvenile Pacific salmon. Ph.D. Thesis, University of British Columbia, Vancouver.

_____. 1986. Dispersion of Common Merganser *(Mergus merganser)* breeding pairs in relation to the availability of juvenile Pacific salmon in Vancouver Island streams. Canadian Journal of Zoology 64:756-765.

Wood, K. 1964. Holidays at Invermere. Lake Windermere - Valley Echo, August 27, 1964.

Woodbury, A.M. and H. Knight. 1951. Results of the Pacific gull color-banding project. Condor 53:57-77.

Woods, J.G. 1979. Who gives a hoot. Revelstoke Review, November 28, 1979: p. 9. (Bibliography 4612).

Woolington, D.W., P.F. Springer, and D.R. Yparraguirre. 1979. Migration and wintering distribution of Aleutian Canada Geese. Pages 299-309 *in* R.L. Jarvis and J.C. Bartonek (editors). Biology and Management of Pacific Flyway Geese. A symposium sponsored by the Northwest Section, The Wildlife Society, 16 February 1979, Portland, Oregon. Oregon State University Book Stores, Inc., Corvallis.

Wyatt, B. 1963. A Short-tailed Albatross sighted off the Oregon Coast. Condor 65:163.

Wylde, M.A. 1923. Ornithological Notes: Quail. Migrant 2:44.

Yesner, D.R. 1976. Aleutian Island albatrosses: a population history. Auk 93:263-280.

Yocom, C.F. 1943. The Hungarian partridge, *Perdix perdix* Linn., in the Palouse Region, Washington. Ecological Monographs 13:167-202.

_____. 1956. The Sage Hen in Washington State. Auk 73:540-550.

Young, C.J. 1930. A study of the Rhinoceros Auklet and other birds in British Columbia, 1929. Pages F16-F19 *in* British Columbia Provincial Museum of Natural History Annual Report for 1929, Victoria.

Zar, J.H. 1974. Biostatistical Analysis. Prentice-Hall Inc., Englewood Cliffe, New Jersey. 620 pp.

Zettergreen, B. 1988. Rare bird sighting. The Golden Times, 8 June 1988: p. 8.

Zimmerman, D.A. 1973. Range expansion of Anna's Hummingbird. American Birds 27:827-835.

Zwickel, F.C. 1967. Early behaviour in young Blue Grouse. Murrelet 48:2-7.

Zwickel, F.C. and J.F. Bendell. 1967. Early mortality and the regulation of numbers in Blue Grouse. Canadian Journal of Zoology 45:817-851.

_____. and _____. 1985. Blue Grouse - effects on, and influences of, a changing forest. Forestry Chronicle 1985:185-188.

Zwickel, F.C. and A.N. Lance. 1965. Renesting in Blue Grouse. Journal of Wildlife Management 29:202-204.

The following species, an addition to the provincial list, was recorded after 31 December 1987, the cutoff date for this volume.

Red-faced Cormorant

RFCO

Phalacrocorax urile (Gmelin)

RANGE: Breeds in the Bering Sea and adjacent waters including the Aleutian Islands and coast of southern Alaska, west in the North Pacific Ocean to the Commander Islands and off Japan. Winters generally throughout the breeding range.

STATUS: *Accidental.*

OCCURRENCE: On 10 and 11 April 1988, a bird in breeding plumage was observed in Masset Sound off Haida, Queen Charlotte Islands. That constitutes the first record for Canada (Campbell 1988c), and removes the species from the Hypothetical list. Detailed field notes and photographs (RBCM Photo 1246; Fig. 341) document its occurrence.

On 14 April 1988, a bird in breeding plumage was reported off Campbell River (R. MacIntosh pers. comm.). MacIntosh presented the record as hypothetical but suggested that Red-faced Cormorants may wander into British Columbia infrequently.

Figure 341. Red-faced Cormorant at Masset Sound, 11 April 1988. Note the large, white flank patches (RBCM Photo 1246; Peter J. Hamel).

INDEX

Index

ABOUT THE AUTHORS

R. Wayne Campbell was born in Edmonton, Alberta, in 1942. His fields of interest include zoogeography, feeding ecology of raptors, marine bird populations, and conservation of birds. He graduated from the University of Victoria in 1976 and received his M.Sc. degree from the University of Washington in 1983.

After high school, he worked as a seasonal naturalist with the British Columbia Parks Branch and in 1969 joined the staff at the University of British Columbia as Curator of the Cowan Vertebrate Museum in the Department of Zoology. Over the next 4 years he established the Photo-Records File, a system to document the occurrence of rare vertebrates in the province, and took over administrative responsibilities for the British Columbia Nest Records Scheme, which he continues today. He also became very active in the executives of several conservation organizations including the British Columbia Waterfowl Society and the Vancouver Natural History Society.

In 1973 he moved to the Royal British Columbia Museum as Curator of Ornithology, a position he holds today. Over the next 15 years he conducted wildlife inventories of remote areas of the province including the first complete census of breeding seabird colonies. In addition, he amassed an enormous provincial vertebrate data base which includes details for 1.5 million specimen and sight records, 200,000 breeding records, and hard copies of nearly 10,000 published and unpublished articles on reptiles, amphibians, birds, and mammals.

R. Wayne Campbell has written over 300 scientific and popular articles, government reports, and books on higher vertebrates. He has served as British Columbia coordinator for the North American Breeding Bird Survey since 1976, and as a select member of the national ornithology group for the Committee on the Status of Endangered Wildlife in Canada since 1980. He belongs to 24 professional and natural history organizations and is a Life Member and Elected Member of the American Ornithologists' Union, Life Member of the Cooper Ornithological Society, and Honourary Life Member of the Vancouver Natural History Society.

He has received numerous honours and awards for lecturing, writing, and conservation activities, and in 1989 received the "Award of Excellence in Biology" from the Association of Professional Biologists of British Columbia.

Neil K. Dawe was born in New Westminster, British Columbia, in 1943. After graduation from high school, his interest turned to the world of finance, and banking became his vocation for the next 7 years. In 1970, he returned to the University of British Columbia where his interest in natural history was inspired by the enthusiasm and encouragement of Wayne Campbell. That interest grew into a career in habitat management and a commitment to the wildlife of the province.

In 1971, he worked as a seasonal naturalist for the British Columbia Parks Branch. Later that year he became Chief Naturalist at the George C. Reifel Bird Sanctuary where he developed interpretation and education programs for the British Columbia Waterfowl Society until 1975. Since 1975 he has worked for the Canadian Wildlife Service managing their wildlife areas, migratory bird sanctuaries, and working to protect migratory bird habitats on Vancouver Island.

Neil K. Dawe is a member of a number of professional, conservation, and scientific organizations including the Association of Professional Biologists of British Columbia, the Society of Wetland Scientists, and the Pacific Estuarine Research Society. He has served as first regional Vice-President of the Federation of British Columbia Naturalists for Vancouver Island and on the executive of the Vancouver Natural History Society, and has helped organize Christmas Bird Counts, raptor counts, and Brant surveys. He has also taught birding courses at regional colleges and public schools in British Columbia.

His research interests include garter snake ecology, the breeding biology of the Barn Swallow, and the enhancement and rehabilitation of migratory bird habitats, with emphasis on estuarine wetlands.

He has written over 30 popular and scientific papers and reports, and has recently co-authored a popular children's bird book.

Ian McTaggart-Cowan, born in Edinburgh, Scotland in 1910, is a career biologist with special concentration on the systematics, biology, and conservation of birds and mammals. He graduated from the University of British Columbia in 1932 and earned a Ph.D. degree from the University of California in 1935. He has

been awarded D.Sc. degrees by the University of British Columbia and the University of Victoria, LL.D. degrees by the University of Alberta and Simon Fraser University, and a Doctor of Environmental Studies degree by the University of Waterloo.

He was the biologist at the Provincial Museum in Victoria from 1935 until 1940 when he joined the Faculty of the University of British Columbia. During 35 years there he established and taught courses in vertebrate zoology, undertook research in ornithology and mammalogy and guided the research of some 100 graduate students. In the ensuing years his studies took him to 6 continents and resulted in more than 260 publications, 110 television programs, and 12 teaching films.

His public service related to vertebrate zoology and conservation includes 7 years on the National Research Council of Canada where he was the first Chairman of the Advisory Committee on Wildlife Research. He also served as Chairman of the Environmental Council of Canada, the Habitat Enhancement Committee of the Province of British Columbia, the Board of Governors of the Arctic Institute of North America, and Vice-President of the International Union for the Conservation of Nature and Natural Resources. In addition, he was a member of the Select Committee on National Parks for the United States Secretary of the Interior and the Nature Trust of British Columbia.

Ian McTaggart-Cowan has received numerous honours, including: Officer of the Order of Canada, Fellow of the Royal Society of Canada, Leopold Medal of the Wildlife Society, Fry Medal of the Canadian Society of Zoologists, Einarsen Award in Conservation by the Northwest Section of the Wildlife Society, and the J. Dewey Soper Award by the Alberta Society of Professional Biologists.

John M. Cooper was born in New Westminster, British Columbia in 1956. His early interest in birds and the natural world was stimulated by his parents, Jack and Louise Cooper. Each spring, for nearly 2 decades, the Cooper family travelled throughout British Columbia and Alberta, often with close friends Lorne Frost and Glen Ryder, in search of birds and their nests. John's passion for birds, wilderness, and environmental issues, was born from those experiences.

He studied zoology at the University of British Columbia, graduating in 1978, and worked as a biological consultant for several years. In 1981, he joined the Royal British Columbia Museum and has since participated in many museum expeditions to inventory vertebrates in unknown and remote areas of the province. He is now a graduate student in the Biology Department at the University of Victoria and is studying the breeding biology of Least Sandpipers on the Queen Charlotte Islands.

He is a member of several scientific and conservation organizations including the Association of Professional Biologists of British Columbia, and has directed fund-raising activities for Ducks Unlimited Canada to aid their wetland preservation program in British Columbia.

He has written several articles and reports on birds in British Columbia.

Gary W. Kaiser was born in Sussex, England in 1944. During his high school years, as a member of the Macoun Field Club, he regularly visited the National Museum of Canada where he became a dedicated amateur coleopterist. He obtained a B.Sc. from Carleton University in Ottawa, Ontario in 1966, and a M.Sc. 5 years later. During that same period he assisted with research on scarab beetles in Colombia and Ecuador.

In 1968, ornithology first played a role in his career with a temporary position studying bird hazards to aircraft. Later the same year, he joined the Canadian Wildlife Service and assisted with duck-hunter surveys, breeding waterfowl surveys on the Prairies and in northern Ontario, and studies involving waterfowl banding. In 1974, he moved to the British Columbia office of the Canadian Wildlife Service and began work on waterfowl surveys of the Chilcotin-Cariboo region. During the next 15 years he participated in aerial surveys of waterfowl along the coast and in the Rocky Mountain Trench. He also organized shorebird banding programs on the Fraser River delta and breeding seabird surveys along the British Columbia coast.

He has maintained a keen interest in tropical ecology. Much of his free time is spent with shorebird banding projects, wildlife surveys, and teaching wildlife management workshops in the Philippines, Borneo, Colombia, and Peru.

His bibliography contains 20 scientific papers and internal government reports.

Michael C.E. McNall, born in Wingham, Ontario in 1951, spent much of his early life hunting, fishing, and studying nature. He obtained a diploma in Wildlife Management from Sir Sandford Fleming College, Ontario in 1971. After graduation, he joined the Ornithology Department of the Royal Ontario Museum and spent the next 3 years on field expeditions in the West Indies, British Isles, Holland, Iceland, and throughout North America.

While at the Royal Ontario Museum, he was encouraged by artist Terry Shortt to carry out his own research. In 1975 and 1976, with guidance and support from Henri Ouellet and Stewart Mac-Donald of the National Museum of Canada, he carried out a behavioural study of Parasitic and Long-tailed jaegers on Southampton Island and Bathurst Island in the Canadian arctic.

After his arctic experience, Michael moved to Victoria and in 1980 joined the staff of the Royal British Columbia Museum. Since that time he has travelled throughout remote areas of the province collecting data for these books.

He is an accomplished photographer and wooden decoy carver.

LIBRARY

	DATE DUE		